CAMPING

FRANCE 2015

Selection 2015

2,300 selected camping sites including:
2,000 with chalets, gîtes and mobile homes
1,200 with campervan facilities

*D*ear Reader,

The Michelin Camping Guide is perfect for all those who love the great outdoors and enjoy spending their leisure time in a tent, caravan, campervan, chalet or mobile home. We have selected the best campsites in France with our usual care, listing those with the best facilities in the most pleasant surroundings.

Using the traditional Michelin classification method, this guide provides you with an easy, speedy reference for assessing the category of each site: 1 to 5 tents (see pages 8–9).

The guide is updated each year, so consult the latest edition for the most up-to-date information and pricing.

Here are a few tips on how to use the guide

→ To select a campsite

The guide covers all 22 regions of France – see the map and list of regions on pages 4–5. Each region has been colour-coded so that you can find your way around the guide easily: the band at the top of the page matches the colour used in the map. Once you have selected a region, turn to the detailed map at the start of that region's section. It shows all the localities that have at least one campsite. The localities with campsites and their descriptions are listed alphabetically within each region section.

→ To find a specific locality

Refer to the index on page 514, where all the places are listed in alphabetical order.

→ To make a selection based on specific criteria

See the list of campsites on pages 26–33 for an at-a-glance summary of selected facilities available at sites, listed region by region.

→ For a detailed description of each individual site

The essential information and brief description given for each site are supplemented by symbols, which provide a wealth of additional information and detail. See pages 10–12 for the key to the symbols used in both the campsite entries and the maps.

→ Glossary of French terms

For a list of useful words, turn to the Glossary on page 14 for a translation of common terms.

→ Descriptions of the sites start on page 34

For more information on visiting particular towns or regions, consult the relevant regional Michelin Green Guide. We also recommend you use the appropriate Michelin regional map to locate your selected campsite, to calculate distances and to work out the best route.

→ To get the most out of this giude, read pages 6–12 carefully.

© Jharela / Folotia.com

We welcome your feedback on our listed campsites.

Please email us at:
campingfrance@tp.michelin.com

Many thanks in advance!

Practical information for each location with cross reference to Michelin maps

Michelin classification of selected sites

Services and leisure facilities available

Brief description of the site and its capacity

Peak season rates

For key to the symbols, see pages 10 to 12

CENTRE

LORRIS

45260 – Michelin map **318** M4 – pop. 2 941 – alt. 126
▶ Paris 132 – Gien 27 – Montargis 23 – Orléans 55

⚠ L'Étang des Bois

✆ 02 38 92 32 00. www.canal-orleans.fr

Address : 6km west along the D 88, follow the signs for Châteauneuf-sur-Loire, near the lake at Les Bois

Opening times : from beginning April to end Sept.

3 ha (150 pitches) grassy

Tariff : (2014 Price) ✝ 3.80€ ⇌ 国 6.20€ – (g) (10A) 4.65€
Rental rates : (2014 Price) (from beginning April to end Sept.) – 4 ㎝. Per night from 52 to 67€ – Per week from 320 to 435€
A wooded setting in a pleasant location.

Surroundings : ▱ ♀♀
Leisure activities : ▦ ♫
Facilities : ⇌ ⚲ ♈ ♈ 圖
Nearby : ✗ 国 ≈ (beach) ⬅ ⚞

Longitude : 2.44454
Latitude : 47.87393

LUÇAY-LE-MÂLE

36360 – Michelin map **323** E4 – pop. 1 496 – alt. 160
▶ Paris 240 – Le Blanc 73 – Blois 60 – Châteauroux 43

⚠ Municipal la Foulquetière

✆ 02 54 40 43 31. www.lucaylemale.fr

Address : La Foulquetière (3.8km southwest along the D 960, follow the signs for Loches, D 13, follow the signs for Ecueillé to the left and take the road to the right)

Opening times : from beginning April to mid Oct.

1.5 ha (30 pitches) flat and relatively flat, grassy

Tariff : (2014 Price) ✝ 2€ ⇌ 国 2.50€ – (g) (6A) 1.50€
Rental rates : Permanent ⚞ – 3 ㎝ – 2 gîtes. Per night from 90€ – Per week from 270 to 338€
㊂ borne 3€
80m from a small lake that is very popular with anglers.

Surroundings : ▱ ♀
Leisure activities : ⬅
Facilities : ♿ ⇌ 圀 ㎒ ⚲ 圖
Nearby : ♈ ✗ ⚲ ✗ ♫ ≈ (beach) ⬅ pedalos

Longitude : 1.40417
Latitude : 47.1109

LUNERY

18400 – Michelin map **323** J5 – pop. 1 449 – alt. 150
▶ Paris 256 – Bourges 23 – Châteauroux 51 – Issoudun 28

⚠ Intercommunal de Lunery

✆ 02 48 68 07 38. www.cc-fercher.fr

Address : 6 rue de l'Abreuvoir (in the town, near the church)

Opening times : from mid April to mid Sept.

0.5 ha (37 pitches) flat, grassy

Tariff : (2014 Price) 12€ ✝✝ ⇌ 国 (g) (10A) – Extra per person 3€
Near the remains of an old windmill, near the Cher river.

Surroundings : ⚶ ▱ ♀♀
Leisure activities : ▦ ⬅
Facilities : ♿ ⚮ ㎝ 圖
Nearby : ♈ ✗ ⚲

Longitude : 2.27038
Latitude : 46.93658

MARCILLY-SUR-VIENNE

300 – Michelin map **317** M6 – pop. 559 – alt. 60
Paris 280 – Azay-le-Rideau 32 – Chinon 30 – Châtellerault 29

Intercommunal la Croix de la Motte

02 47 65 20 38. www.cc-saintemauredetouraine.fr

dress : 1.2km north along the D 18, follow the signs for L'Ile-
uchard and take turning to the right

ha (61 pitches) flat, grassy

ntals : ⚑ – 2 ▣ – 1 tent lodge.

uated in pleasant, shaded surroundings near the Vienne
er.

urroundings : ⌧ ▭ ♀
eisure activities : ⛵↗ ⤳
acilities : ♿ ⛽ ♨ ▣

Directions to campsite

G	Longitude : 0.54337
P	Latitude : 47.05075
S	

GPS

MENNETOU-SUR-CHER

320 – Michelin map **318** I8 – pop. 878 – alt. 100
Paris 209 – Bourges 56 – Romorantin-Lanthenay 18 – Selles-sur-
er 27

Municipal Val Rose

02 54 98 11 02. mairie.mennetou@wanadoo.fr

dress : rue de Val Rose (south of the town, to the right after the
dge over the canal, 100m from the Cher river)

ening times : from mid May to mid Sept.

ha (50 pitches) flat, grassy

riff : (2014 Price) ⛺ 2€↝ ▣ 3€ – ⚡ (6A) 2.50€

borne 2€ – ⬤▣8€

urroundings : ▭ ♀
eisure activities : ⛵↗
acilities : ♿ ⛽ ⛺
earby : ✂ ⚒ ⤳ ♦

Address of campsite

G	Longitude : 1.86173
P	Latitude : 47.26937
S	

*To make the best possible use of this guide, please read
pages 2–15 carefully.*

Sani-station (borne) and fee (see page 12)

MESLAND

150 – Michelin map **318** D6 – pop. 547 – alt. 79
Paris 205 – Amboise 19 – Blois 23 – Château-Renault 20

Yelloh! Village Le Parc du Val de Loire ⚹⚹

02 54 70 27 18. www.parcduvaldeloire.com

dress : 155 route de Fleuray (located 1.5km west)

ening times : from mid April to mid Sept.

ha (300 pitches)

riff : 18€ ⛺⛺ ↝ ▣ ⚡ (10A) – Extra per person 6€

ntal rates : (from mid April to mid Sept.) ⚑ – 150 ▣ –
⬤ – 4 tent lodges. Per night from 39 to 141€ – Per week
om 273 to 987€

a wooded setting opposite a vineyard.

urroundings : ⌧ ▭♀♀
eisure activities : ⛵✂ ⛲ ⛰↗⚙% ✂
✄▦⚒⛵
acilities : ♿ ⛽ ⛺⚒⛵⛄ ▣ ⛲⛺

Rental options and rates

G	Longitude : 1.10477
P	Latitude : 47.51001
S	

The Michelin Camping Guide selection lists the best sites in each 'comfort' category:

��‍ ⚏⚏ Extremely comfortable, equipped to a very high standard

⚏⚏ ⚏⚏ Very comfortable, equipped to a high standard

⚏⚏ ⚏⚏ Comfortable and well equipped

⚏⚏ ⚏⚏ Reasonably comfortable

⚏⚏ ⚏⚏ Satisfactory

Exceptional campsites in each category are awarded an additional rating:

⚏⚏...⚏⚏ Particularly pleasant setting, good quality and range of services available.

How the selection works:

• Campsites are ranked according to their location, facilities, etc., and are awarded a number of tent symbols – see above.

• In order for the guide to remain wholly objective, the selection is made on an entirely independent basis. There is no charge for being selected for the guide.

• The Michelin classification (⚏⚏ … ⚏) is totally independent of the official star classification system awarded by the local prefecture or other official organisation.

• All practical information and classifications are revised and updated annually so that the information is as reliable and up to date as possible. Some information or pricing may have changed since the guide went to press. We recommend you check the price list online in advance or at the entrance to the campsite and enquire about possible restrictions.

• Our inspectors make regular visits to campsites; our readers' comments are also a valuable source of information, and regular follow-up visits are undertaken.

24 campsites have been classified ⚏⚏ / ⚏⚏ and 89 ⚏⚏ / ⚏⚏ in 2015. This selection can be found below and on the opposite page.

⚏⚏ 2015

BERNY-RIVIÈRE	La Croix du Vieux Pont	DOL-DE-BRETAGNE	Les Castels Domaine des Ormes
CANET-PLAGE	Yelloh! Village Le Brasilia	GHISONACCIA	Arinella-Bianca
CARNAC	Les Castels La Grande Métairie	PIERREFITTE-SUR-SAULDRE	Les Alicourts

⚏⚏ 2015

BIRON	FranceLoc Le Moulinal	PYLA-SUR-MER	Yelloh! Village Panorama du Pyla
CANET-DE-SALARS	Les Castels Le Caussanel	QUIMPER	Les Castels L'Orangerie de Lanniron
CARANTEC	Yelloh! Village Les Mouettes	RAMATUELLE	Le Kon Tiki
CHASSIERS	Sunêlia Domaine Les Ranchisses	RUOMS	Sunêlia Aluna Vacances
DIENNÉ	DéfiPlanet au Domaine de Dienné	ST-CAST-LE-GUILDO	Les Castels Le Château de la Galinée
GHISONACCIA	Homair Vacances Marina d'Erba Rossa	ST-CRÉPIN-ET-CARLUCET	Les Peneyrals
GRANVILLE	Les Castels Le Château de Lez-Eaux	ST-JULIEN-DES-LANDES	Les Castels La Garangeoire
GRIMAUD	Les Prairies de la Mer	ST-JUST-LUZAC	Les Castels Sequoia Parc
HOURTIN-PLAGE	Club Airotel La Côte d'Argent	ST-LÉON-SUR-VÉZÈRE	Le Paradis
LACANAU-OCÉAN	Yelloh! Village Les Grands Pins	SAMPZON	Yelloh! Village Soleil Vivarais
LONGEVILLE-SUR-MER	MS Vacances Les Brunelles	SARLAT-LA-CANÉDA	La Palombière
MONTCLAR	Yelloh! Village Domaine d'Arnauteille	SOMMIÈRES	Les Castels Le Domaine de Massereau
MUROL	Sunêlia La Ribeyre		
NOYAL-MUZILLAC	Moulin de Cadillac	VALLON-PONT-D'ARC	Les Castels L'Ardéchois
PERROS-GUIREC	Yelloh! Village Le Ranolien	VIAS-PLAGE	Yelloh! Village Club Farret

⛰⛰⛰⛰ 2015

AGAY	Esterel Caravaning	MESSANGES	Club Airotel Le Vieux Port
ARGELÈS-GAZOST	Sunêlia Les Trois vallées	RAMATUELLE	Yelloh! Village Les Tournels
ARGELÈS-SUR-MER	La Sirène et l'Hippocampe	ROQUEBRUNE-SUR-ARGENS	Domaine de la Bergerie
BADEN	Mané Guernehué	ST-ALBAN	Sunêlia Le Ranc Davaine
BÉNODET	Sunêlia L'Escale St-Gilles	ST-AVIT-DE-VIALARD	Les Castels St-Avit Loisirs
BISCARROSSE	Club Airotel Domaine de la Rive	ST-BREVIN-LES-PINS	Sunêlia Le Fief
FRÉJUS	La Baume - La Palmeraie	ST-RAPHAËL	Les Castels Douce Quiétude
LABENNE-OCÉAN	Yelloh! Village le Sylvamar	SÉRIGNAN	Yelloh! Village Le Sérignan Plage
LECTOURE	Yelloh! Village Le Lac des 3 Vallées	VALRAS-PLAGE	Domaine de La Yole

⛰⛰⛰ 2015

AIGUES-MORTES	Yelloh! Village La Petite Camargue	MARSEILLAN-PLAGE	Les Méditerranées - Beach Club Nouvelle Floride
ARGELÈS-SUR-MER	Le Front de Mer	MÉZOS	Club Airotel Le Village de Sen Yan
ARGELÈS-SUR-MER	Le Soleil	MIMIZAN-PLAGE	Club Airotel Marina-Landes
ARZANO	Les Castels Ty Nadan	LA PALMYRE	Village Siblu Bonne Anse Plage
AVRILLÉ	FranceLoc Le Domaine des Forges	PORNIC	Club Airotel La Boutinardière
BELVÈS	FranceLoc Les Hauts de Ratebout	PORTIRAGNES-PLAGE	Les Sablons
BÉNODET	Le Letty	RUOMS	Domaine de Chaussy
BIDART	Les Castels Le Ruisseau des Pyrénées	RUOMS	Yelloh! Village La Plaine
BIDART	Yelloh! Village Ilbarritz	ST-AYGULF	L'Étoile d'Argens
BISCARROSSE	Mayotte Vacances	ST-CYPRIEN-PLAGE	Cala Gogo
BONIFACIO	Pertamina Village - U-Farniente	STE-CATHERINE-DE-FIERBOIS	Les Castels Parc de Fierbois
BORMES-LES-MIMOSAS	Le Camp du Domaine	ST-HILAIRE-DE-RIEZ	Les Biches
CARNAC-PLAGE	Les Menhirs	ST-JEAN-DE-LUZ	Club Airotel Itsas Mendi
CASTELLANE	Les Castels Le Domaine du Verdon	ST-JEAN-DE-MONTS	Les Amiaux
CHAMBON-SUR-LAC	Yelloh! Village Le Pré Bas	ST-JEAN-DE-MONTS	Le Bois Joly
COL-ST-JEAN	Yelloh! Village L'Étoile des Neiges	SARLAT-LA-CANÉDA	Les Castels Le Moulin du Roch
CONTIS-PLAGE	Yelloh! Village Lou Seurrots	SÉRIGNAN-PLAGE	Yelloh! Village Aloha
CORCIEUX	Yelloh! Village Le Domaine des Bans	SOUSTONS	Sunêlia Village Vacances Framissima Nature
DOUCIER	Le Domaine de Chalain	TALMONT-ST-HILAIRE	Yelloh! Village Le Littoral
FOUESNANT	Sunêlia L'Atlantique	TORREILLES	Sunêlia Les Tropiques
FRÉJUS	Sunêlia Holiday Green	TORREILLES	Mar I Sol
GHISONACCIA	Sunêlia Perla Di Mare	VARENNES-SUR-LOIRE	Les Castels Domaine de la Brèche
GIEN	Kawan Village Les Bois du Bardelet	VIAS	Sunêlia Le Domaine de la Dragonnière
ÎLE DE RÉ	Sunêlia Interlude	VIELLE-ST-GIRONS	Sunêlia Le Col Vert
ÎLE DE RÉ	L'Océan	VINSOBRES	Franceloc Le Sagittaire
ÎLE D'OLÉRON	Club Airotel Les Gros Joncs	VITRAC	Domaine Soleil Plage
LACANAU-OCÉAN	Club Airotel L'Océan	VOGÜÉ	Domaine du Cros d'Auzon
LARNAS	FranceLoc Le Domaine d'Imbours	VOLONNE	Sunêlia L'Hippocampe
LIT-ET-MIXE	Tohapi Les Vignes		
LES MATHES	La Pinède		
MARIGNY	Les Castels La Pergola		

You can find a particular village or town in the index on page 514.

CAMPSITES

Michelin classification

ᗧᗧᗧ ᗧᗧᗧ	Extremely comfortable, equipped to a very high standard
ᗧᗧ ᗧᗧ	Very comfortable, equipped to a high standard
ᗧᗧ ᗧᗧ	Comfortable and well equipped
ᗧ ᗧ	Reasonably comfortable
ᗧ ᗧ	Satisfactory

• **Campsites are ranked according to their location, facilities, etc., within each category and are awarded a number of tent symbols – see page 8.**

• **Michelin classification (ᗧᗧᗧ ... ᗧ) is totally independent of the official star classification system awarded by the local prefecture or other official organisation.**

Opening times

Permanent — Site open all year round

Special features

❄ Winter caravan sites: these sites are specially equipped for a winter holiday in the mountains. Facilities generally include central heating, electricity and drying rooms for clothes and equipment.

👥 Child-friendly sites, including washing facilities for young children, playgrounds and activities monitored by professionals

Exceptional in its category

ᗧᗧᗧ ... ᗧ — Particularly pleasant setting, quality and range of services available.

🦢🦢 — Tranquil, isolated site – quiet site, particularly at night

≪≪ — Exceptional view – Interesting or panoramic view

General information

Access	Direction from the city centre
✆	Telephone
⊶	24 hour security: a warden usually lives on site and can be contacted during reception hours, although this does not mean round-the-clock surveillance outside normal hours
⊶	Day security only
🐕	No dogs (if dogs are permitted, a current vaccination certificate is required)
P	Cars must be parked away from pitches
⛺	Reservations not accepted
🚫	Credit cards not accepted
✓	Chèque-vacances (French holiday vouchers) not accepted
cc	Chèque-vacances accepted

Site information

3 ha	Area available in hectares (1ha = 2.47 acres)
60 ha/3 ha for camping	Total area of the property/total area available for camping
90 pitches	Number of pitches
⊏⊐	Marked-off pitches
♀ ♀♀ ♀♀♀	Shade: fair amount of shade to well shaded
⚓	Waterside location with swimming area

Facilities

▥	Heating facilities
♿	Facilities for the disabled
👶	Baby changing facilities
⚱ 🚰	Each bay is equipped with water/drainage
▣	Washing machines, laundry
🛒 🛍	Supermarket – Grocery
🍲	Takeaway meals
📶	Internet or Wifi point

Facilities for campervans

🚐	Services for campervans
sani-station 4 €	Type of service points and rates (see page 12)
3 ▣ 15.50 €	Number of pitches equipped for campervans/daily rate per pitch
8 to 13 € [⚡]	Daily charge for this special price (with or without electricity)
🐾	Special FFCC price for campervans at site (Fédération Française de Camping et Caravaning)

Sports and leisure facilities

⛆	Bar (serving alcohol)
✗	Eating places (restaurant, snack-bar, etc)
⌂	Common room or games room
☺	Miscellaneous activities (sports, culture, leisure)
🏃	Children's club
⅃⚡	Exercise room or gym
⌇s	Sauna
🛝	Playground
🚲	Cycle hire
✗ 🔲	Tennis courts: open air/indoor
m	Minigolf
🏊 🏊	Swimming pool: indoor/open air
≋	Bathing allowed (or supervised bathing)
🛝	Waterslide
🐟	Fishing
🛶	Canoeing
⚓	Sailing (school or centre)
⚓	Mooring pontoon (river mooring)
🐎	Pony trekking or riding

• The majority of outdoor leisure facilities are only open in season and during peak periods; opening times are not necessarily the same as those of the site and some facilities are only available during the summer season.

Nearby	The guide only features facilities that are in the vicinity of the campsite (500 m)

Charges in euros

Daily charge:

🚶 5 €	per person
🚗 2 €	per vehicle
▣ 7.50 €	per pitch (tent/caravan)
[⚡] 2.50 € (4A)	for electricity (calculated by number of ampere units)

Inclusive rates:

25 € 🚶🚶 🚗	pitch for 2 people
▣ [⚡] (10A)	including vehicle and electricity

• The prices listed were supplied by the campsite owners in Autumn 2014 (if prices were not available, those from the previous year are given). The fees should be regarded as basic charges and may fluctuate with inflation.

• Listings shown in light type **(i.e. not bold) indicate that not all revised charges have been provided by the owners.**

• Additional charges may apply for some facilities (e.g., swimming pool, tennis courts), as well as for long stays.

• Special rates may apply for children – ask owner for details.

Rentals

12	🚐	Number of mobile homes
20	🏠	Number of chalets
6	🛏	Number of rooms to rent
Per night 30 to 50€		Minimum/maximum rates per night
Per week 300 to 800€		Minimum/maximum rates per week

LOCALITY INFORMATION

23700	Postcode
343 B8	Michelin map reference
Rennes 47	Distance in kilometres
1 050 pop.	Population
alt. 675	Altitude (in metres)
⚓	Spa
1200/1900m	Altitude (in metres) of resort/ highest point reached by lifts

• **Should you have grounds for complaint during your stay at a campsite about your reservation, the prices, standards of hygiene or facilities available, we recommend that you first try to resolve the problem with the proprietor or with the person responsible.**

• **If you are unable to resolve the disagreement, and if you are sure that you are within your rights, you could take the matter up with the relevant prefecture of the department.**

• **We welcome all suggestions and comments, whether in criticism or praise, relating to the campsites recommended in our guide. However, we must stress that we have neither the facilities nor the authority to deal with complaints between campers and proprietors.**

A sani-station, known in French as a 'borne', can be one of several proprietary commercial makes or a local, home-made 'artisanale' device. In return for a payment of a few euros or using a 'jeton', a pre-paid token, you receive fresh water, mains electricity and access to rubbish bins, plus grey and black waste disposal.

borne	sani-station
borne artisanale	local sani-station
borne eurorelais, flot bleu, raclet, Urbaco	different types of commercial sani-station
borne autre	other type of sani-station

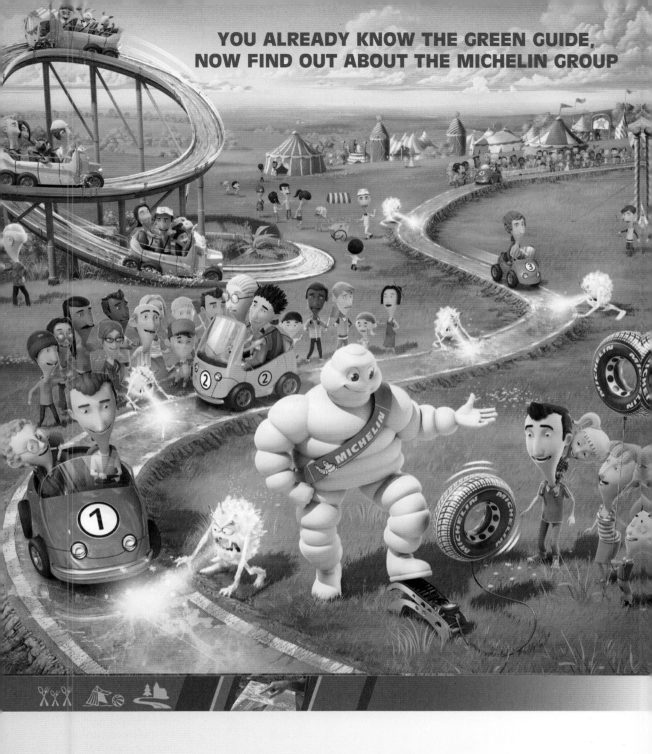

YOU ALREADY KNOW THE GREEN GUIDE,
NOW FIND OUT ABOUT THE MICHELIN GROUP

A better way forward

accès difficile	difficult access
accès direct à	direct access to…
accidenté	uneven, hilly
adhésion	membership
aire (de repos)	rest area
après-midi	afternoon
arrêt	stop (traffic instruction)
Ascension	Feast of the Ascension
assurance obligatoire	insurance cover compulsory
août	August
automne	autumn
avenue (av.)	avenue
avril	April
baie	bay
bain	bath
base de loisirs	leisure and activity park/ centre
bois, boisé	wood, wooded
bord	shore, riverbank
au bord de la mer	by the sea
borne	sani-station (see page 12)
boucher	butcher
boulanger	baker
boulevard (bd.)	boulevard.
au bourg	in town/in the village
cadre agréable	attractive setting
cadre sauvage	natural setting
carrefour	crossroads
cases réfrigérées	refrigerated food storage facilities
cedez le passage	give way (on roads)
centre équestre	equestrian centre
chambre d'hôte	guesthouse, B&B
château	castle
chemin	path
conseillé	advised
cotisation obligatoire	membership charge obligatory
en cours d'aménagement	rebuilding work in progress
croisement difficile	difficult access
crêperie	pancake restaurant/stall
décembre (déc.)	December
déjeuner	lunch
derrière	behind
dimanche	Sunday
dîner	dinner
douche	shower
à droite	on/to the right
église	church
embouteillage	traffic jam

emplacement (empl.)	pitch
entrée	way in, entrance
entrée fleurie	attractive floral entrance/ reception area
essence	petrol, gas
étang	lake, pool
été	summer
falaise	cliff
famille	family
fermé	closed
feu rouge	traffic lights
février (fév.)	February
forêt	forest
garage	parking
garage pour caravans	covered parking for caravans
garderie (d'enfants)	(children's) crèche
gare routière	bus/coach station
gare (S.N.C.F.)	railway station
à gauche	on/to the left
gazole	diesel
goudronné	surfaced road
GPL	LPG
gratuit	free, no charge
gravier	gravel
gravillons	fine gravel
hammam	Turkish-style steam bath with plunge pools
herbeux	grassy
hiver	winter
hors saison	out of season
île, îlot	island
incliné	sloping
indispensable	essential
interdit	forbidden, prohibited
intersection	junction
janvier (janv.)	January
jeudi	Thursday
jour	day
juillet (juil.)	July
juin	June
lac	lake
lande	heath/moorland
licence obligatoire	camping licence/ international camping carnet compulsory
au lieu-dit	in the small locality of/at the place known as
lundi	Monday

mai	May	priorité à droite	priority to right (give way to traffic from right, traffic joining roundabouts has priority, traffic on minor roads has right-of-way onto major roads, sign: black cross inside red triangle)
mairie	town hall		
marché	market		
mardi	Tuesday		
mars	March		
matin	morning		
mer	sea		
mercredi	Wednesday		
mineurs non accompagnés non admis	under 18s must be accompanied by an adult	à proximité	nearby
montagne	mountain	quartier	quarter, district, area
Noël	Christmas	Rameaux	Palm Sunday
non clos	open site (landscape)	réservé	reserved, booked
novembre (nov.)	November	rive droite, gauche	right, left bank
nuit	night	rivière	river
à la nuitée	per night, on a nightly basis	rocailleux	stony, rocky, rugged
		rocheux	rocky
octobre (oct.)	October	rond-point	roundabout
ouvert	open	route (rte)	road
ouverture prévue	opening scheduled	rue (r.)	street
		ruisseau	stream
en panne	broken down	sablonneux	sandy
Pâques	Easter	saison (tourist)	tourist season
parcours de santé	fitness trail	samedi	Saturday
passage non admis	no touring pitches	avec sanitaires	with sanitary facilities
péage	toll	schéma	local map
pelouse	lawn	semaine	week
pente	sloping/slope	à la semaine	per week, on a weekly basis
Pentecôte	Whitsun	septembre (sept.)	September
personne (pers.)	person	soir	evening
petit-déjeuner	breakfast	sortie	way out, exit
pierreux	stony	sous-bois	undergrowth
piéton	pedestrian	(face) à la station	(opposite) at the filling station
pinède	pine trees, pine wood	supplémentaire (suppl.)	extra
place (pl.)	square		
places limitées pour le passage	limited number of touring pitches	en terrasses	terraced
plage	beach	toboggan aquatique	water slide
plan d'eau	stretch of water, artificial lake	torrent	torrent (river/stream)
		Toussaint	All Saints' Day (1 Nov)
plat	flat	tout compris	all inclusive
pneu	tyre	tout droit	straight ahead
pont	bridge		
port	port, harbour	unleaded	sans plomb
prairie	grassland, lawn		
pré	meadow	vacances scolaires	school holidays
près de	near	vallonné	undulating
presqu'île	peninsula	vendredi	Friday
prévu	projected	verger	fruit trees, orchard
printemps	spring	vers	in the direction of/towards
en priorité	as a priority	Voie Verte	green trail
		voir	see

SPA FACILITIES ON THE CAMPSITES

Spas are back in fashion! And outdoor campsites are only too keen to ride the crest of this wave of enthusiasm for relaxation and health by expanding their range of services to include spa treatments. More and more tourists are attracted to the idea of spending a few hours on holiday in a spa, especially in the resort where they are actually staying.

But what do we really mean when we talk about spa facilities? The term 'spa' covers any kind of treatment with hot water (20–34°C) involving hydro massage, such as jacuzzi and whirlpool bathing. Often these are combined with other treatments using dry or wet steam (saunas and hammams), as well as massage and body sculpting massage.

Hot water and water vapour have many benefits: relaxing the muscles, stimulating blood circulation, eliminating toxins and dead skin, and dilating the pores. It is an excellent way to treat rheumatic and skin conditions and helps reduce stress.

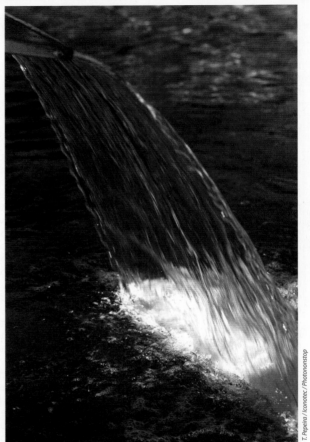

© T. Pepeira / Iconotec / Photononstop

On campsites, spa centres – areas specifically dedicated to providing these treatments – are not medical facilities as such, but they are run by healthcare professionals. Nor are they open access, as the amenities provided generally have to be paid for.

© Image Source G / Photononstop

Particular attention is given to the decor of such centres, often utilising a Greco-Roman or contemporary type design, special lighting effects, background music and an array of aromas: everything is designed to make you feel completely relaxed. We have carefully chosen campsites with the finest spa facilities (see the names and detailed descriptions of the selected campsites), where you will find jacuzzis, saunas, hammams and massages. What a great way to relax!

Club Airotel Domaine de la Rive

AWWA

AQUITAINE
Biscarrosse (40)
See page 55

This holiday village is located on the shores of a lake (Cazaux-Sanguinet) and has direct access to the beach. It offers accommodation in chalets tucked away in the pine forest with wooden terraces that provide a sense of warmth and (something important to hardcore campers) space. But the real plus point of this place is Aquarive Park, with its slides, banana boats and other colourful attractions, which children will love, whilst for adults there is a wave pool and the more adventurous can safely learn water sports (such as sailing, water skiing, racing between buoys) at La Rive Watersports.

Village Vacances Port Lalande

AW

AQUITAINE
Castelmoron-sur-Lot (47)
See page 58

Port Lalande is a small harbour built on the banks of the Lot. Located in a huge area of greenery, this resort offers accommodation in extremely comfortable air-conditioned chalets with terraces and outdoor garden lounges. You can safely leave children aged 6 to 10 in the care of childminders to supervise their activities (including paddling) while you explore the area, swim in the outdoor pool or head for the spa facility, one of the best features of the place, offering sauna, hammam and massages. It has all you need to eliminate toxins or stress.

Mayotte Vacances

AWA

AQUITAINE
Biscarrosse (40)
See page 55

This feels like a tropical island! The Indian Ocean my be a long way from the Atlantic, but you could quite easily believe that's where you are once you arrive here, right down to the lovely mobile homes and tented lodges in bright colours. As well as all the usual amenities of a luxury campsite (including 450 square metres of shops), Mayotte Vacances offers a large area for aquatic activities, complete with lagoon pool, water slides and paddling pools, gym, spa, restaurant, sports facilities for beach volleyball, basketball and mini-golf, four children's clubs (grouped according to age), cabaret evenings and even a beauty salon. You almost never need to set foot outside the place!

Yelloh! Village Le Sylvamar

AWWA

AQUITAINE
Labenne-Océan (40)
See page 65

If you head to the heart of the pine forest, you'll discover Le Sylvamar hidden away. Located in the Labenne-Océan district, this resort on the Landes coast offers a wide variety of camping accommodation from simple pitches to Palombière, beautiful cabins built in the trees. Comfortable cottages and chalets are also available. Then you are spoiled for choice in terms of sports; you can enjoy a huge area for aquatic activities and two heated pools. And for those who want to explore the country, Spain and the Pyrenees are virtually next door.

Yelloh! Village Les Grands Pins

AQUITAINE
Lacanau-Océan (33)
See page 66

Just a few yards from the beach, this camp-site is a great holiday village, with the typical hilly terrain and shady pine trees that are common to the Landes. It has first-class amenities too, of course. These include partially covered swimming pools and a small shopping centre for everything you might need during your stay, not to mention the comfortable mobile homes located on the main site itself. Some have a tall wooden design that blends in with the surroundings and wooden decor reminiscent of the pine trees. Finally, part of the place is closed off to motor vehicles, in order to protect the environment and for the comfort of holidaymakers, especially those with children.

Sunêlia Village Vacances Le Framissima Nature

AQUITAINE
Soustons (40)
See page 87

This resort is unusual in that it was built only recently. Just a few years ago it was simply a stretch of Landes pine forest. Then the Fram Group, travel specialists, decided to open their first site here, building wooden mobile homes and tented lodges with large covered terraces and all the latest facilities on the beach, in the shade of the pine trees. To blend in with the natural environment, the buildings are made of Landes pinewood and the pool is drained naturally into the surrounding greenery. In addition to its spa facilities, this new holiday resort benefits from being close to Lake Soustons and the sea.

Club Airotel Le Vieux Port

AQUITAINE
Messanges (40)
See page 69

A short walk from the ocean and the large sandy Landes beaches, Le Vieux Port has a landscape lined with trees. You can even ignore the Atlantic if you like, since the aquatic area of the campsite has several pools, a paddling pool and slides for children, both younger (from aged 3) and older (from aged 10). Other attractions include an equestrian centre, activities and sports facilities. Relax and recharge your batteries at this lovely spot while all the family has fun.

Yelloh! Village Le Pré Bas

AUVERGNE
Chambon-sur-Lac (63)
See page 97

These camping facilities lie on the shore of Lake Chambon, which is overlooked by an enormous mountain range. High hedges, mostly flat or slightly inclined, surround the buildings, offering some privacy. The floral spaces are well laid out and you can swim in the lake or in one of two heated pools, complete with four slides. There is entertainment galore, plus a play area for children and fitness facilities for adults. Walkers or sports enthusiasts into hiking, biking or climbing will love the clean air in the vast surrounding open space.

Mané Guernehué

▲▲▲

BRITTANY
Baden (56)
See page 117

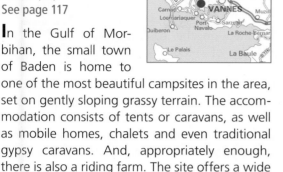

In the Gulf of Morbihan, the small town of Baden is home to one of the most beautiful campsites in the area, set on gently sloping grassy terrain. The accommodation consists of tents or caravans, as well as mobile homes, chalets and even traditional gypsy caravans. And, appropriately enough, there is also a riding farm. The site offers a wide selection of activities and entertainment, including a partially covered aquatic area with slides. For those who prefer to relax while on holiday, new facilities include a jacuzzi, sauna, hammam and gym, with massages and facials also available. It's a great place in which to unwind.

Yelloh! Village Les Pins

▲▲

BRITTANY
Erquy (22)
See page 125

This is like a small town among pine trees, but one equipped with plenty of space and gentle undulations that divide into areas offering good shade. A small swimming pool, ideal for doing lengths, is there to welcome you, along with a massive aquatic area with waterfalls and slides, all centrally located. Stay in one of the chalets with a living area of 37 square metres and let your little ones check out the kids club while you enjoy the spa, gym or tennis courts. A perfect place to enjoy a relaxing holiday *en famille*.

Sunêlia L'Escale St-Gilles

▲▲▲

BRITTANY
Bénodet (29)
See page 118

L'Escale St Gilles is ideally located right on the coast. There is a magnificent first class spa centre on site, a large heated and partially covered aquatic area and beautiful beaches with straw huts providing shade. It remains open on some evenings in season to the great delight of those who enjoy slides and other water games. On other nights you can enjoy cabaret entertainment, quizzes and karaoke. Whether you bring your own equipment (tents/caravans) or choose to stay in one of the very comfortable mobile homes, you will be on a clearly marked pitch covering at least 100 square metres.

Sunêlia L'Atlantique

▲▲

BRITTANY
Fouesnant (29)
See page 127

The Atlantic is exactly the right name for this campsite. A stone's throw from the sea, this holiday village has some 150 mobile homes with facilities for families but also has 100 pitches on which to put up your tents or park your caravan in the shade of large trees. The water park complex is particularly impressive with several different pools with marine themes, complete with lighthouses, coconut palms, waterfalls and cliffs. The indoor pool takes up the baton on rainy days. The spa is ultra modern and there to be enjoyed by all those wanting to enjoy its facilities.

Yelloh! Village Le Ranolien

ᗰᗰᗰ

BRITTANY
Perros-Guirec (22)
See page 135

There is plenty of variety at Le Ranolien. The campsite has pitches for tents or caravans and boasts outdoor mobile homes, atmospheric gypsy caravans and top quality chalets. The latter are equipped with a 1.8-metre bed, two flat screen TVs, hi-fi system and dishwasher. Le Ranolien is also a holiday club with many activities, sports during the day, entertainment or cultural events in the evening, plus superb facilities for health and relaxation treatments: spa, hammam, sauna, massage. It has a unique location in the heart of a protected natural site. What more could one want?

Arinella-Bianca

ᗰᗰᗰ

CORSICA
Ghisonaccia (20)
See page 199

Located on the east coast of Corsica, known as the 'Isle of Beauty', Ghisonaccia is a small resort offering several campsites but Arinella Bianca stands out because of the quality of its services and its great location. It is right next to the sandy beach, and the vegetation, including palm trees, eucalyptus and oleander, make this a particularly pleasant resort. Many of the available activities revolve around water: sea fishing or in the small inland lake, outdoor fitness facilities and an indoor spa, a sailing club and, for fun, buoy-to-buoy racing! There are plenty of things to do in the evening as well and sometimes it may even be your turn to take to the stage!

Les Alicourts

ᗰᗰᗰᗰ

CENTRE
Pierrefitte-sur-Sauldre (41)
See page 181

You'll never be bored at Les Alicourts. The resort offers plenty of aquatic activities, with four swimming pools (including one wave pool), a lavish spa area and a 6-hectare lake for swimming and canoeing. You'll be spoilt for choice between relaxation (spa) and sports (fishing, golf, mini-golf, skate park, fitness facilities), and your children will be kept amused with organized activities throughout the day. Every type of accommodation is available: spacious pitches for tents and caravans, chalets, cottages, tree houses, and – the latest arrival – 'explorer' and 'safari' lodges.

Yelloh! Village Mer et Soleil

ᗰᗰᗰ

LANGUEDOC-ROUSSILLON
Agde (34)
See page 226

Between the Rhone and the Mediterranean, this 8-hectare landscaped environment with its flat grassy or sandy terrain features mobile homes, chalets, furnished tents and simple pitches. Leisure activities involving water are a key feature at this site, with the sea just a kilometre away, an excellent aquatic area with an upstairs restaurant and, best of all for spa lovers, wonderful facilities over 650 square metres in size. In this haven of relaxation choose from such delightful options as 'Bitter Orange and Poppy', 'Volcanic Escape' or even 'Provençal Relaxation'. After treating yourself to a treatment, you will be ready for the evening activities that await.

L'Arche

ᗰᗰ

LANGUEDOC-ROUSSILLON
Anduze (30)
See page 227

This seaside campsite seems a million miles from any urban or industrial setting. A charming and friendly welcome lends it a family atmosphere. Located at the foot of the Cevennes, it is the perfect place for a vacation in the countryside on a quiet site designed for relaxation. There isn't a great variety of properties to rent. Camping facilities predominate. Pleasant shady pitches overlook the river and the small sandy beach with rocks lying a little further on. The site's amenities include a pleasant indoor pool, while the hammam, sauna and jacuzzi complement the outdoor pool and water slides.

Albirondack Park

ᗰᗰ

MIDI-PYRÉNÉES
Albi (81)
See page 288

Located near the historic city of Albi, a designated UNESCO World Heritage site, this campsite is in a hilly, shady location and provides pitches for tents, caravans and motor homes as well as chalets, mobile homes and even treehouses for the more adventurous. After a day of sightseeing or simply relaxing, you will find an on-site pool with a lovely terrace, a new indoor spa offering sauna, hammam and jacuzzi, and finally, for lunch or for dinner, a high quality restaurant with American-style interior.

Sunêlia
Les Tropiques

ᗰᗰ

LANGUEDOC-ROUSSILLON
Torreilles-Plage (66)
See page 256

This 8-hectare site with its lush vegetation is an established resort with pitches under palm trees and mobile homes of various sizes, some of which have been adapted to accommodate disabled persons. Naturally, there is an aquatic area with several pools, one of which has a waterslide (with four tracks). Children and younger guests are catered for too and enjoy the giant inflatable giraffe. Adults can enjoy the numerous sports on offer (tennis, petanque, archery, etc.) and can take advantage of the spa facilities, which are open 7 days a week during the summer season.

Village Vacances Le Domaine du Pré

PAYS-DE-LA-LOIRE
La Chapelle-Hermier (85)
See page 364

Situated beside Lake Jaunay, Domaine du Pré offers a concept of outdoor tourism that combines ecology, health and leisure. There are 82 chalets spread over 12 hectares of natural beauty, wholly dedicated to your relaxation and well-being. As well as enjoyable amenities such as an indoor pool and a heated lake for swimming, the resort has a fitness centre where massages, chromotherapy, colonic irrigation and rebirth relaxation are all available. The activities offered vary according to the season, but all revolve around similar themes combining nature and health.

Sunêlia Interlude

POITOU-CHARENTES
Le Bois-Plage-en-Ré (17)
See page 410

This really is Ile de Ré at its best. The huge campsite is set on slightly hilly terrain with dry vegetation reminiscent of that of the south of France. Its irregularly shaped plots seem to accentuate the feeling of an untamed landscape. Mobile homes clad in dark wood on terraces blend into the landscape perfectly. Some pitches for tents and caravans are also available. The site has excellent amenities including a brasserie, a restaurant, a supermarket and a beautiful pool. In summer the atmosphere buzzes with all the events and activities taking place throughout the day.

Sunêlia Le Fief

PAYS-DE-LA-LOIRE
St-Brévin-les-Pins (44)
See page 381

This village resort lies on the Côte de Jade between the sea and the forest. It covers a large flat grassy area. In addition to traditional camping facilities, high quality mobile homes are also available. A dozen camp organizers ensure a lively atmosphere with colourful theme nights during which even children get to take part in musical extravaganzas. The area set aside for children is large and very well equipped. There is a 500-square metre aquatic area with rapids, lagoons and waterfalls, along with a wide variety of sports facilities, including archery and beach volleyball. And for those seeking tranquility and health, there is no better place to relax than the spa area with its jacuzzi and sauna.

L'Océan

POITOU-CHARENTES
La Couarde-sur-Mer (17)
See page 410

Although it was affected by Cyclone Xynthia, this campsite has made a spirited recovery. The management used the opportunity to refurbish and renew the rental accommodation and equipment to the latest standards. The result is a consistent, well-run site, with disabled access, offering a vast array of mobile homes, including an exclusive village made up of mobile homes with three bedrooms, superb bathrooms and a luxurious exclusive aquatic area with a large swimming pool under palm trees. The sports facilities include a multi-purpose sports ground, tennis courts and mini-golf. And for those who like fishing, there is a small pond containing eels, bream and bass.

DéfiPlanet au Domaine de Dienné

POITOU-CHARENTES
Dienné (86)
See page 408

In this beautiful area of 47-hectares you can choose between a small campsite, with all the modern comforts, in an environmentally friendly setting, and a range of unusual accommodation: prefab cube shelters (*carré d'étoiles*), gypsy caravans, cabins and treehouses or yurts, etc. All the activities are organized with health in mind: there's a variety of sports, an equestrian centre, water aerobics, fitness trails, walking and biking. There are also zip wires, a climbing tower and fishing. If you just want to relax, you can use the jacuzzi and hammam. Finally, the restaurant offers 'designer menus' (for losing weight or to help with cardiovascular problems) prepared by a doctor and a Michelin-starred chef.

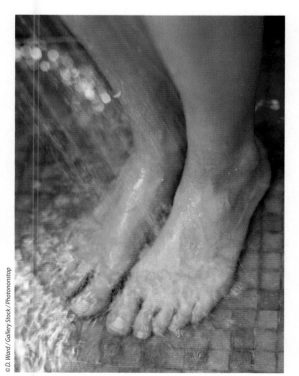

© D. Ward / Gallery Stock / Photononstop

Club Airotel Les Gros Joncs

POITOU-CHARENTES
St-Georges-d'Oléron (17)
See page 413

Backing onto the dunes that are lapped by the ocean, this campsite occupies a pleasant location with direct access to the beach via beautiful shady wild trails – a village hidden in the forest. The accommodation consists of mobile homes and cottages, five of which are accessible to people with reduced mobility. The site facilities offer disabled access, including to the pool. The amenities are also first rate, with a grocery store, a restaurant offering fine cuisine and a swimming pool, not to mention the spa with its counter-current pool and whirlpool. Most of all, it offers a charming and professional welcome.

Esterel Caravaning

PROVENCE-ALPES-
CÔTE-D'AZUR
Agay (83)
See page 428

At the heart of the Esterel massif, this is a very comfortable place to stay. The beautiful living space around which it is organized offers all the amenities you could ever want: a large grocery store, shop, excellent restaurant, bar with a cosy atmosphere and spa centre. The aquatic area may not be eye-catching, but it is fully equipped with covered swimming pools and paddling pools. There are other activities and a sports ground plus a ranch. You can stay in a mobile home or on one of the pitches in the hilly section of the site, shaded by pines. There are various clubs and activities to suit all ages and tastes, along with entertainment in the evenings.

Yelloh! Village L'Étoile des Neiges

PROVENCE-ALPES-
CÔTE-D'AZUR
Col Saint-Jean (04140)
See page 437

Perched 1,300 metres above sea level, this family campsite is open in both winter and summer. Lying on a gentle green slope in the foothills of the Dormillouse massif, it has a panoramic outdoor pool, an indoor leisure pool and a beautiful indoor spa facility, including sauna, hammam and fitness suite. Most of the site consists of accommodation, offering a wide range of mobile homes and some beautiful cottages sheltered by pines. You can ski here in winter, using the nearby ski lifts.

Domaine de la Bergerie

PROVENCE-ALPES-
CÔTE-D'AZUR
Roquebrune-sur-Argens
(83)
See page 452

This site is located in a wonderful 60-hectare wooded park and its rental mobile homes are sparsely dotted around the entire complex, among cork oaks, shady pines and mimosa trees. Traditional camping pitches are situated in the lower section. Activities take place in the heart of the site and active holidaymakers will enjoy the water park, keep-fit and spa facilities, sports grounds, large open-air 600-seat amphitheatre for evening shows, clubs for kids, teenagers and adults and a disco. There are lovely places to relax and to eat.

Les Prairies de la Mer

PROVENCE-ALPES-
CÔTE-D'AZUR
Grimaud (83)
See page 443

This site is notable for its direct access to a sandy beach and stunning views of St Tropez and its gulf. In addition to a standard range of accommodation and traditional campsite pitches, it also offers original accommodation in the shape of exotic wood-clad huts (*fares*). Some of these form an unusual village with small wooden bridges, water points, internal gardens and communal areas for relaxation. Other (very popular) huts line the beach and offer a unique view of the Gulf of St Tropez. Naturally, the site also possesses all the amenities you would expect, including spa facilities and leisure activities to suit all ages.

Yelloh! Village Au Joyeux Réveil

RHÔNE-ALPES
Autrans (38)
See page 467

Nestling in a peaceful valley of the Vercors mountains, this small campsite is 1,050 metres above sea level. It is run by Christine and Franck, and is a very family friendly. Just a short distance from the village of Autrans, the site offers a nice relaxing pool area, including three heated pools, one indoor pool for the more delicate and three small slides. The pitches, which boast thick grass, are quite spacious and provide some shade. Towards the rear of the site are tastefully furnished mobile homes. In summer, a lively team organizes entertainment and fun activities for children.

Sunêlia Domaine Les Ranchisses

RHÔNE-ALPES
Chassiers (07)
See page 474

The sound of cicadas, vines, olive trees… this stunning location is in the southern part of the Regional Natural Park of Monts d'Ardèche. At the entrance stands a restored Cévennes farmhouse, now home to the reception and restaurant. The extensive range of facilities and activities include a superb pool with a variety of slides, a wellness suite (offering massages and other treatments), a fitness club, a skate park and canoeing. The well-shaded and compact camping pitches are next to the river, while further up, on the other side of the road, another part of the site consists of cottages and modern accommodation, in the form of stylish 'Taos' mobile homes.

© L. Invernizzi Tettoni / Tips / Photononstop

Sunêlia Aluna Vacances

RHÔNE-ALPES
Ruoms (07)
See page 495

White oaks, vines and scrubland surround this family campsite, which has not been over-expanded. Part of the site consists of comfortable rental cottages, some of which are accessible to disabled persons, while the rest is, of course, dedicated to traditional camping pitches. The large pool facilities, featuring an artificial 'island', offer waterslides, waterfalls, a swimming area, a paddling pool and a solarium. And there's plenty to do at night too! There is a café-theatre, where cabaret and musicals and other entertainment are organized, as well as discos on some evenings.

Sunêlia Le Ranc Davaine

RHÔNE-ALPES
St-Alban-Auriolles (07)
See page 497

This village set in the scrubland really does offer all the shops and facilities you could ever need, including internet access. On the vast site, there is a choice of accommodation in chalets and cottages of varying sizes, all with private terraces, or on a shaded campsite. Most importantly, it has extensive aquatic facilities including a swimming area with two separate pools, waterfalls, a paddling pool, a whirlpool bath and a spa centre. There are clubs for younger children and of course, evening entertainment with shows, games and a disco.

Key

On the following pages you will find a region-by-region summary of localities with at least one site with the following facilities:

BRITTANY	Name of the region
Carnac	Name of the locality
🛶	Locality with at least one quiet and peaceful campsite
P	Town with at least one campsite open all year round
👥	Locality with at least one campsite suitable for families: child-friendly site including washing facilities for young children, playgrounds and activities monitored by professionals
🏊	Locality with at least one campsite with a water park
B	Locality with at least one selected site with a spa centre
🎭	Locality with at least one campsite offering entertainment/organized activities (sports, culture, leisure)

• For more details on specific sites, refer to the individual campsite entries

	Page	🐌	Permanent	👥	⛷	Spa centre	♨
Éclaron	190			👥			♨
Ervy-le-Châtel	190	🐌					
Giffaumont-Champaubert	191	🐌					♨
Langres	191	🐌		👥			
Mesnil-Saint-Père	191	🐌		👥			
Signy-l'Abbaye	192	🐌					
Thonnance-les-Moulins	192			👥			♨
CORSICA							
Aléria	195			👥			♨
Bonifacio	195	🐌		👥			♨
Calvi	197			👥			
Casaglione	198	🐌					
Castellare-di-Casinca	198	🐌		👥			♨
Centuri	198	🐌					
Corte	198	🐌					
Ghisonaccia	199			👥	⛷	B	♨
Lumio	199	🐌					
Piana	200	🐌					
Pinarellu	200	🐌					
Porto	200	🐌		👥		B	
Sagone	203			👥			♨
Sainte-Lucie-de-Porto-Vecchio	203			👥			
Solenzara	203	🐌		👥			♨
Tiuccia	203	🐌					
FRANCHE-COMTÉ							
Bonnal	207			👥			♨
Champagnole	208			👥			♨
Châtillon	208	🐌		👥			
Clairvaux-les-Lacs	208			👥			♨
Dole	208						♨
Doucier	209			👥			♨
Foncine-le-Haut	209	🐌					
Huanne-Montmartin	209						♨
Lachapelle-sous-Rougemont	210	🐌					
Lons-le-Saunier	210						♨
Maisod	211						♨
Malbuisson	211			👥			♨
Marigny	211			👥			♨
Ornans	212			👥			
Ounans	212			👥			♨
Uxelles	214	🐌					♨
Vesoul	215		P				♨
ÎLE-DE-FRANCE							
Boulancourt	219	🐌	P				
Champigny-sur-Marne	219		P				
Louan	220						♨
Paris	220		P				
Pommeuse	221			👥			♨
Rambouillet	221			👥			
Touquin	221	🐌					
Tournan-en-Brie	221		P				
Versailles	222	🐌					
Villiers-sur-Orge	222		P				

	Page	🐌	Permanent	👥	⛷	Spa centre	♨
LANGUEDOC-ROUSSILLON							
Agde	226	🐌		👥		B	♨
Aigues-Mortes	227			👥			
Alet-les-Bains	227		P				
Allègre-les-Fumades	227			👥			♨
Anduze	227	🐌		👥		B	♨
Argelès-sur-Mer	228			👥		B	♨
Balaruc-les-Bains	231			👥			
Le Barcarès	231		P	👥			♨
Barjac	232	🐌					
Belcaire	233		P				
Blavignac	233	🐌					
Boisset-et-Gaujac	233			👥			♨
Boisson	233			👥			♨
Le Bosc	234					B	
Brissac	234			👥			♨
Canet-Plage	235		P	👥			♨
Carcassonne	236			👥			
Casteil	236	🐌					
Castries	237	🐌					
Celles	237	🐌					
Cendras	237						♨
Clermont-l'Hérault	238		P				
Connaux	238		P				
Crespian	238			👥			
Égat	238	🐌					
Err	239	🐌	P				
Estavar	239	🐌		👥			
Florac	239			👥			
Font-Romeu	242			👥			♨
Formiguères	240	🐌					
Frontignan Plage	240			👥			♨
Gallargues-le-Montueux	240			👥		B	♨
Goudargues	241			👥			
La Grande-Motte	241			👥			
Le Grau-du-Roi	242			👥			♨
Lanuéjols	242	🐌					
Laroque-des-Albères	243	🐌					
Lattes	243		P				
Laurens	243			👥			♨
Marseillan-Plage	243	🐌		👥		B	♨
Marvejols	244		P				
Massillargues-Attuech	244			👥			
Matemale	244	🐌	P				
Mende	245	🐌	P				
Meyrueis	245	🐌	P				♨
Montclar	246	🐌		👥		B	♨
Narbonne	246			👥			♨
Naussac	246	🐌					
Palavas-les-Flots	247			👥			♨
Port-Camargue	247	🐌		👥			♨
Portiragnes-Plage	248			👥			♨
Quillan	249					B	
Remoulins	249			👥			♨
Rocles	249	🐌					
Le Rozier	250			👥			

ALSACE

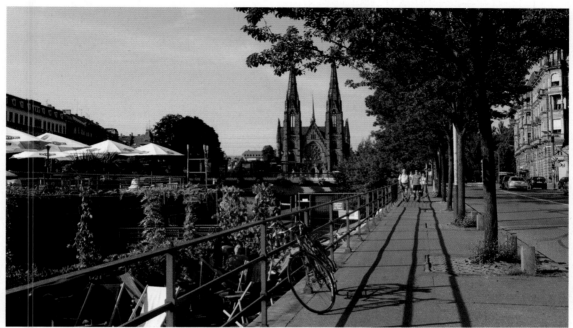

R. Mattes / hemis.fr

Alsace is perhaps the most romantic of France's regions, a place of fairy-tale castles, gentle vine-clad hills and picturesque villages perched on rocky outcrops or nestling in lush, green valleys. From Colmar's 'Little Venice' with its flower-decked balconies, famous storks (the region's iconic emblem) and wonderful Unterlinden Museum, to the spectacular lights and tempting delights of Strasbourg's Christmas market, via the atmospheric half-timbered houses, reflected in the meandering River Ill, Alsace radiates an inviting warmth that even the winter temperatures cannot chill. The region is known for its wonderful scenery, traditional cuisine, local produce and excellent wine. Head to a brasserie and enjoy a regional beer in a lively atmosphere or relax in a local *winstub* (wine lounge), tucking into a steaming dish of *choucroute* (sauerkraut with smoked pork) and a generous slice of *Kugelhopf* cake, all washed down with a glass of fruity Sylvaner or Riesling. Alsace has something for everyone.

Legend:
- Locality with campsite
- Locality with campsite and rental option
- Vannes — Locality with campsite and campervan area
- Moyaux — Locality with at least one pleasant campsite
- Motorway service area for campervans

DEUTSCHLAND

St-Avold

MOSELLE

Sarreguemines

Wissembourg

Lauterbourg

Oberbronn

A 65

A 4

Haguenau

D 1063

Château-Salins

Seille

Sarrebourg

Saverne

A 4

A 35

RHIN

ET-MOSELLE

Lunéville

N 4

Sarre

BAS-RHIN

Wasselonne

A 5

Meurthe

N 59

Dabo

STRASBOURG

nières

Molsheim

Celles-s-Plaine

Obernai

A 35

Moselle

Bassemberg

le Hohwald

Dambach-la-Ville

Rhinau

Rombach-le-Franc

Lièpvre

la Chapelle-devant-Bruyères

Corcieux

Anould

Gemaingoutte

N 59

Sélestat

HAUT-KOENIGSBOURG

Herpelmont

D 415

Ribeauvillé

Xonrupt-Longemer

Kaysersberg

le Tholy

Turckheim

D 417

Wihr-au-Val

COLMAR

Gérardmer

Munster

Éguisheim

Biesheim

emiremont

Saulxures-s-Moselotte

Mittlach

Ste-Croix-en-Plaine

es-Bains

la Bresse

Ranspach

N 83

Kruth

Geishouse

Guebwiller

A 35

d'Ajol

N 66

Bussang

Issenheim

HAUT-RHIN

BATTENHEIM

Fresse-s-M.

Moosch

Wattwiller

St-Maurice-s-M.

Thann

Cernay

Mélisey

Fresse

Masevaux

N 66

A 36

MULHOUSE

Champagney

Guewenheim

Heimsbrunn

A 5

N 19

Lachapelle-s/s-Rougemont

Burnhaupt-le-Haut

D 438

A 36

LA PORTE D'ALSACE

Altkirch

A 35

BASEL

sexel

BELFORT

A 3

SAÔNE

Montbéliard

Seppois-le-Bas

SUISSE

Mandeure

A 36

artin

Doubs

St-Hippolyte

BASSEMBERG

67220 – Michelin map **315** H7 – pop. 268 – alt. 280
▶ Paris 432 – Barr 21 – St-Dié 35 – Sélestat 19

⚠ Campéole Le Giessen

✆ 03 88 58 98 14, www.camping-vosges.net

Address : route de Villé (take northeastern exit on the D 39; beside the Giessen river)

Opening times : from beginning April to mid Sept.

4 ha (79 pitches) flat, grassy

Tariff : (2014 Price) 27.50€ ✦✦ ⇔ 🔲 ⚡ (6A) –

Extra per person 6.90€ – Reservation fee 15€

Rental rates : (2014 Price) (from beginning April to mid Sept.) ⚐ (1 mobile home) – 8 🚐 – 5 🛖 – 8 canvas bungalows. Per night from 35 to 119€ – Per week from 245 to 833€ – Reservation fee 25€

A pretty site near a water park.

Surroundings : ◁ ⌂
Leisure activities : ⛾ 🎲 daytime ⬅ 🚲
Facilities : 🚿 ⌀ ▥ 🗑 🍴 🚱 refrigerators
Nearby : ✂ 🏓 🎱 ⚓ 🎿

G P S Longitude : 7.28911
Latitude : 48.33602

BIESHEIM

68600 – Michelin map **315** J8 – pop. 2 398 – alt. 189
▶ Paris 520 – Strasbourg 85 – Freiburg-im-Breisgau 37 – Basel 68

⚠ Tohapi L'Île du Rhin

✆ 03 89 72 57 95, www.village-center.fr

Address : tourist area of l'Île du Rhin (5km east along the N 415, follow the signs for Fribourg)

Opening times : from end April to mid Sept.

3 ha (220 pitches)

Tariff : 18€ ✦✦ ⇔ 🔲 ⚡ (6A) – Extra per person 7€ – Reservation fee 10€

Rental rates : (from end April to mid Sept.) – 26 🚐. Per night from 31 to 102€ – Per week from 217 to 714€ – Reservation fee 10€

🚐 borne 3€

A pleasant site and setting between the Rhine and the Canal d'Alsace, on the Franco–German border.

Surroundings : ♀
Leisure activities : ✗ 🎱 🎲 daytime 🚲
Facilities : 🚿 ⌀ 🚱 🍴 launderette ⬆ 🚱
Nearby : 🎱 🎿 water skiing

G P S Longitude : 7.57278
Latitude : 48.02746

BURNHAUPT-LE-HAUT

68520 – Michelin map **315** G10 – pop. 1 596 – alt. 300
▶ Paris 454 – Altkirch 16 – Belfort 32 – Mulhouse 17

⚠ Les Castors

✆ 03 89 48 78 58, www.camping-les-castors.fr

Address : 4 route de Guewenheim (2.5km northwest along the D 466)

Opening times : from mid March to mid Oct.

2.5 ha (135 pitches) flat, grassy

Tariff : ✦ 3.50€ ⇔ 2.30€ 🔲 4.50€ – ⚡ (10A) 3.30€

Rental rates : Permanent – 2 🚐. Per night from 60 to 80€ – Per week from 360 to 440€

🚐 borne 4€ – 2 🔲 15.40€

In a rural setting beside a river and a lake. Extensive green spaces.

Surroundings : ♀
Leisure activities : ⛾ ✗ ⬅ ⚓ 🚱
Facilities : 🚿 ⌀ ▥ 🚱 🍴 launderette

G P S Longitude : 7.12383
Latitude : 47.77455

CERNAY

68700 – Michelin map **315** H10 – pop. 11 288 – alt. 275
▶ Paris 461 – Altkirch 26 – Belfort 39 – Colmar 37

⚠ Les Cigognes

✆ 03 89 75 56 97, www.camping-les-cigognes.com

Address : 16 rue René Guibert (take the exit following signs for Belfort then take a right turn after the bridge; beside the Thur river)

Opening times : from beginning April to end Sept.

3.5 ha (138 pitches) flat, grassy

Tariff : (2014 Price) 17.80€ ✦✦ ⇔ 🔲 ⚡ (6A) –

Extra per person 4.70€ – Reservation fee 5€

Rental rates : (2014 Price) (from beginning April to end Sept.) ⚐ 4 🚐. Per night from 45 to 75€ – Per week from 260 to 460€ – Reservation fee 15€

🚐 borne 5€

Pretty, green pitches within the town.

Surroundings : ♀
Leisure activities : 🎱
Facilities : 🚿 ⌀ ▥ 🚱 🍴 🗑
Nearby : ✂ 🏓 🎱 (open air in season)

G P S Longitude : 7.16876
Latitude : 47.80519

This guide is not intended as a list of all the camping sites in France; its aim is to provide a selection of the best sites in each category.

COLMAR

68000 – Michelin map **315** I8 – pop. 67 214 – alt. 194
▶ Paris 450 – Basel 68 – Freiburg 51 – Nancy 140

⚠ Indigo L'Ill

© Camping Indigo

✆ 03 89 41 15 94, www.campingdelill.fr

Address : situated 2km east along the N 415, follow the signs for Fribourg; beside the Ill river

Opening times : from end March to beginning Jan

2.2 ha (150 pitches)

Tariff : (2014 Price) 21.10€ ✦✦ ⇔ 🔲 ⚡ (10A) – Extra per person 4.50€ – Reservation fee 22€

Rental rates : (2014 Price) (from end March to beginning Jan) 8 🚐 – 10 tent lodges. Per night from 40 to 97€ – Per week from 196 to 577€ – Reservation fee 22€

🚐 borne 7€ – 40 🔲 16.10€

A shaded site on the peaceful banks of the Ill river.

Surroundings : ♀♀
Leisure activities : ⛾ ✗ 🎱 ⬅ 🚱
Facilities : 🚿 ⌀ ▥ 🍴 🗑 ⬆ 🚱

G P S Longitude : 7.38676
Latitude : 48.07838

DAMBACH-LA-VILLE

67650 – Michelin map **315** I7 – pop. 1 946 – alt. 210
▶ Paris 443 – Barr 17 – Obernai 24 – Saverne 61

⚠ L'Ours

☎ 03 88 92 46 09, camping-de-l-ours@orange.fr

Address : 2 rue du stade (1.2km east along the D 210, follow the signs for Ebersheim and take road to the left)

1.8 ha (120 pitches) flat, grassy

A shaded setting in the heart of the countryside with a very attractive view of Mount Honeck.

Surroundings : ≤ ♀
Facilities : ৬ ⊶ ⚲ 🗑
Nearby : 🏊 🛶 ✕ 🎣

| **G P S** | Longitude : 7.44324 Latitude : 48.32274 |

ÉGUISHEIM

68420 – Michelin map **315** H8 – pop. 1 622 – alt. 210
▶ Paris 452 – Belfort 68 – Colmar 7 – Gérardmer 52

⚠ Des Trois Châteaux

☎ 03 89 23 19 39, www.eguisheimcamping.fr

Address : 10 rue du Bassin (to the west)

Opening times : from beginning April to beginning Nov.

2 ha (133 pitches)

Tariff : 17.80€ ✦✦ 🚐 🗐 ⚡ (8A) – Extra per person 4€ – Reservation fee 10€

Rental rates : (from beginning April to beginning Nov.) 20 🛖. Per night from 40 to 110€ – Per week from 280 to 616€ – Reservation fee 10€

The sanitary facilities are a little jaded, but a pleasant location near a vineyard and the beautiful village of Eguisheim.

Surroundings : 🌳 ≤ ♀
Facilities : ৬ ⊶ 🚻 🗑

| **G P S** | Longitude : 7.29909 Latitude : 48.04274 |

GEISHOUSE

68690 – Michelin map **315** G9 – pop. 484 – alt. 730
▶ Paris 467 – Belfort 53 – Bussang 23 – Colmar 55

⚠ Au Relais du Grand Ballon

☎ 03 89 82 30 47, www.aurelaisdugrandballon.com – limited spaces for one-night stay

Address : 17 Grand-Rue (southern exit)

Opening times : Permanent

0.3 ha (24 pitches) flat, grassy

Tariff : 19.80€ ✦✦ 🚐 🗐 ⚡ (10A) – Extra per person 4.80€

Rental rates : Permanent – 4 🏠. Per night from 57€ – Per week from 300 to 380€

A small, pretty site in the heart of the mountains; a family atmosphere with a very busy restaurant.

Surroundings : 🌳 ⛺ ♀
Leisure activities : ⛴ ✕ 🎠 🏊
Facilities : ৬ ⊶ 🚻 ♨ launderette

| **G P S** | Longitude : 7.05852 Latitude : 47.88056 |

GUEWENHEIM

68116 – Michelin map **315** G10 – pop. 1 256 – alt. 323
▶ Paris 458 – Altkirch 23 – Belfort 36 – Mulhouse 21

⛰ La Doller

☎ 03 89 82 56 90, www.campingdoller.com

Address : rue du Commandant Charpy (located 1km north along the D 34, follow the signs for Thann and take the road to the right; beside the Doller river)

0.8 ha (40 pitches) flat, grassy

Rentals : 6 🛖.

A family atmosphere in a green setting with flowers; a lovely dining room.

Surroundings : 🌳 ♀
Leisure activities : ⛴ 🎠 🏊 ⛷
Facilities : ৬ ⊶ 🚻 ♨ ⚲ 🍳 🗑
Nearby : ✕ 🚴

| **G P S** | Longitude : 7.09827 Latitude : 47.75597 |

HEIMSBRUNN

68990 – Michelin map **315** H10 – pop. 1 453 – alt. 280
▶ Paris 456 – Altkirch 14 – Basel 50 – Belfort 34

⚠ Parc la Chaumière

☎ 03 89 81 93 43, www.camping-lachaumiere.com – limited spaces for one-night stay

Address : 62 rue de Galfingue (take the southern exit along the D 19, follow the signs for Altkirch)

Opening times : Permanent

1 ha (53 pitches)

Tariff : (2014 Price) 14.64€ ✦✦ 🚐 🗐 ⚡ (10A) – Extra per person 3.60€

Rental rates : (2014 Price) Permanent – 4 🛖. Per week from 120 to 500€

🚐 borne 4€ – 6 🗐 14.50€ – 🚐 ⚡ 12.50€

A nice family atmosphere, in a pleasant setting among trees and shrubs.

Surroundings : 🌳 ⛺ ♀
Leisure activities : 🎠 🏊 (small swimming pool)
Facilities : ⊶ 🚻 ♨ 🌳

| **G P S** | Longitude : 7.22477 Latitude : 47.72242 |

LE HOHWALD

67140 – Michelin map **315** H6 – pop. 496 – alt. 570 – Winter sports : 600/1100 m
▶ Paris 430 – Lunéville 89 – Molsheim 33 – St-Dié 46

⚠ Municipal

☎ 03 88 08 03 90, lecamping.herrenhaus@orange.fr – alt. 615

Address : 28 rue du Herrenhaus (take the western exit along the D 425, follow the signs for Villé)

Opening times : from mid June to mid Sept.

2 ha (100 pitches) very uneven, terraced, fine gravel, flat, grassy

Tariff : (2014 Price) ✦ 3.75€ 🚐 1.80€ 🗐 2.20€ – ⚡ (6A) 2.10€

A pleasant setting in the heart of the mountains, among pines, spruces and beech trees.

Surroundings : ♀
Leisure activities : 🎠 🏊 sports trail
Facilities : 🚻 🗑

| **G P S** | Longitude : 7.32328 Latitude : 48.4063 |

ISSENHEIM

68500 – Michelin map **315** H9 – pop. 3 418 – alt. 245
▣ Paris 487 – Strasbourg 98 – Colmar 24 – Mulhouse 22

⚠ Le Florival

𝒫 03 89 74 20 47, www.camping-leflorival.com

Address : route de Soultz (2.5km southeast along the D 430, follow the signs for Mulhouse and take D 5 to the left, follow the signs for Issenheim)

Opening times : from mid April to mid Oct.

3,5 ha (73 pitches)

Tariff : (2014 Price) 17,40€ ★★ ⊸ 🗉 🔌 (10A)

Extra per person 3,90€

Rental rates : (2014 Price) (from mid April to mid Nov.) ⅍ (2 chalets) ⅏ – 20 🏠. Per night from 52 to 88€ – Per week from 270 to 584€

In a pleasant setting at the edge of the woods. There's a swimming area with an Olympic-size pool nearby.

Surroundings : ⋖ 🗀
Leisure activities : 🖼 🚣 🛝
Facilities : 🕭 ⊶ 🕌 🕌 ♨ 🍴 launderette
Nearby : 🔲 🔧 🔧
GPS Longitude : 7.23879
Latitude : 47.90014

KAYSERSBERG

68240 – Michelin map **315** H8 – pop. 2 721 – alt. 242
▣ Paris 438 – Colmar 12 – Gérardmer 46 – Guebwiller 35

🏔 Municipal

𝒫 03 89 47 14 47, www.camping-kaysersberg.fr ⅏ (from beginning April to end June)

Address : rue des Acacias (take northwestern exit along the N 415, follow the signs for St-Dié and take a right turn)

Opening times : from beginning April to end Sept.

1.6 ha (115 pitches) flat, grassy

Tariff : (2014 Price) 18,60€ ★★ ⊸ 🗉 🔌 (13A) – Extra per person 4,63€

A charming site beside the La Weiss river.

Surroundings : ⋖ ♀
Leisure activities : 🖼 🚣 🍴
Facilities : ⊶ ♨ 🚿 🚽 🍴 launderette
GPS Longitude : 7.25404
Latitude : 48.14887

KRUTH

68820 – Michelin map **315** F9 – pop. 1 029 – alt. 498
▣ Paris 453 – Colmar 63 – Épinal 68 – Gérardmer 31

🏔 Le Schlossberg

𝒫 03 89 82 26 76, www.schlossberg.fr

Address : rue du Bourbaach (2.3km northwest along the D 13b, follow the signs for La Bresse and take turning to the left)

Opening times : from beginning April to beginning Oct.

5.2 ha (200 pitches)

Tariff : 22€ ★★ ⊸ 🗉 🔌 (6A) – Extra per person 1,50€ – Reservation fee 10€

Rental rates : (from beginning Dec. to beginning Oct.) – 9 🏠. Per night from 48 to 86€ – Per week from 335 to 599€ – Reservation fee 10€

🚐 8 🗉 15€

A pleasant location in the heart of the Parc des Ballons, close to the lovely Lac de Kruth. Cycle path at the entrance.

Surroundings : ⅍ ⋖ ♀
Leisure activities : 🍴 🚣
Facilities : 🕭 ⊶ 🆑 ♨ 🍴 launderette

LAUTERBOURG

67630 – Michelin map **315** N3 – pop. 2 266 – alt. 115
▣ Paris 519 – Haguenau 40 – Karlsruhe 22 – Strasbourg 63

🏔 Municipal des Mouettes

𝒫 03 88 54 68 60, camping-lauterbourg@wanadoo.fr – limited spaces for one-night stay ⅍

Address : located 1.5km southwest along the D 3 and take road to the left, 100m from a small lake (direct access)

2.7 ha (136 pitches) flat, grassy

🚐 borne – 6 🗉

The site boasts extensive green spaces beside a large leisure and activity park.

Leisure activities : 🍴 🍽
Facilities : 🕭 ⊶ 🕌 🕌 🍴
Nearby : 🚣 🏊 🔧 ♨
GPS Longitude : 8.1654
Latitude : 48.9708

LIEPVRE

68660 – Michelin map **315** H7 – pop. 1 751 – alt. 272
▣ Paris 428 – Colmar 35 – Ribeauvillé 27 – St-Dié-des-Vosges 31

🏔 Haut-Koenigsbourg

𝒫 03 89 58 43 20, www.liepvre.fr/camping

Address : route de La Vancelle (900m east along the C 1 follow the signs for la Vancelle)

Opening times : from mid March to mid Oct.

1 ha (56 pitches)

Tariff : 15.70€ ★★ ⊸ 🗉 🔌 (8A) – Extra per person 4€

Rental rates : (from mid March to mid Oct.) ⅍ – 6 🏠. Per night from 60 to 95€ – Per week from 310 to 480€

The entrance is marked by a centuries-old sequoia; absolute peace in the middle of the countryside.

Surroundings : ⅍ ⋖ ♀
Leisure activities : 🖼 🚣
Facilities : 🕭 ⊶ 🕌 🗉
GPS Longitude : 7.2903
Latitude : 48.27303

MASEVAUX

68290 – Michelin map **315** F10 – pop. 3 278 – alt. 425
▣ Paris 440 – Altkirch 32 – Belfort 24 – Colmar 57

⚠ Le Masevaux

𝒫 03 89 82 42 29, www.camping-masevaux.com

Address : 3 rue du Stade (beside the Doller river)

Opening times : from mid March to end Oct.

3.5 ha (133 pitches) flat, grassy

Tariff : (2014 Price) ★ 3.70€ ⊸ 🗉 3.70€ – 🔌 (6A) 3.60€

A pleasant wooded setting with flowers. Numerous walking trails begin at the site.

Surroundings : ♀♀
Leisure activities : 🍴 🖼 🚣 🏊
Facilities : 🕭 ⊶ ✍ 🕌 ♨ 🍴 launderette
Nearby : 🛒 🍽 🔲 🔧
GPS Longitude : 6.99093
Latitude : 47.77833

MITTLACH

68380 – Michelin map **315** G8 – pop. 323 – alt. 550
▶ Paris 467 – Colmar 28 – Gérardmer 42 – Guebwiller 44

⚠ Municipal Langenwasen

✆ 0389776377, www.mittlach.fr – alt. 620

Address : chemin du Camping (3km southwest; beside a stream)

Opening times : from mid April to mid Oct.

3 ha (77 pitches) terrace, flat and relatively flat, gravelled, grassy

Tariff : (2014 Price) ⚹ 3.65€ ⇔ 1.20€ ▣ 1.55€ – ⅏ (10A) 6.20€

A wooded site at the bottom of a peaceful valley.

Surroundings : ⇕ ⇐ ⌂ ♀	G	Longitude : 7.01867
Leisure activities : ⌂ ⚒	P	Latitude : 47.98289
Facilities : ⚙ (July-Aug.) ▣	S	

MOOSCH

68690 – Michelin map **315** G9 – pop. 1 764 – alt. 390
▶ Paris 463 – Colmar 51 – Gérardmer 42 – Mulhouse 28

⚠ La Mine d'Argent

✆ 0389823066, www.camping-la-mine-argent.com – limited spaces for one-night stay

Address : rue de la Mine d'Argent (located 1.5km southwest along the r. de la Mairie; beside a stream)

Opening times : from mid April to mid Oct.

2 ha (75 pitches)

Tariff f : (2014 Price) ⚹ 3,95€ ⇔ ▣ 3.95€ – ⅏ (10A) 5.60€

Rental rates : (2014 Price) (from mid April to mid Oct.) – 4 ⚏. Per night from 40 to 120€ – Per week from 220 to 400€

⚏ borne

Situated on a lush, green, undulating site in the mountains.

Surroundings : ⇕ ⇐ ♀	G	Longitude : 7.03054
Leisure activities : ⌂ ⚒	P	Latitude : 47.85102
Facilities : ⚙ ⚑ launderette	S	

MULHOUSE

68100 – Michelin map **315** I10 – pop. 111 156 – alt. 240
▶ Paris 465 – Basel 34 – Belfort 43 – Besançon 130

⚠ L'Ill

✆ 0389062066, www.camping-de-lill.com

Address : 1 rue Pierre de Coubertin (to the southwest, along the A 36, take the exit for Dornach)

Opening times : from beginning April to end Sept.

5 ha (193 pitches) flat, grassy

Tariff f : (2014 Price) 20,10€ ⚹⚹ ⇔ ▣ ⅏ (10A) – Extra per person 5.30€ – Reservation fee 5€

Rental rates : (2014 Price) (from beginning April to end Sept.) ⚒ – 8 ⚏ – 15 ⚑. Per night from 70 to 90€ – Per week from 330 to 560€ – Reservation fee 15€

⚏ borne 5€ – 11 ▣ 20,10€

In a wooded setting beside a river and the Euro cycle route 6.

Surroundings : ♀♀	G	Longitude : 7.32283
Leisure activities : ⌂ ⚒	P	Latitude : 47.73424
Facilities : ⚙ ⚑ ⚏ ⚑ ▣ ⚎	S	
Nearby : ⚑ ⚎ skating rink, mountain biking		

MUNSTER

68140 – Michelin map **315** G8 – pop. 4 889 – alt. 400
▶ Paris 458 – Colmar 19 – Gérardmer 34 – Guebwiller 40

⚠ Tohapi Le Parc de la Fecht

✆ 0825002030, www.village-center.fr

Address : route de Gunsbach (located 1km east along the D 10, follow the signs for Turckheim)

Opening times : from beginning June to end Aug.

4 ha (192 pitches) flat, grassy

Tariff : (2014 Price) 13€ ⚹⚹ ⇔ ▣ ⅏ (6A) – Extra per person 7€ Reservation fee 27€

Rental rates : (2014 Price) (from beginning June to end Aug.) 30 ⚏. Per night from 33 to 129€ – Per week from 231 to 903€ Reservation fee 27€

A wooded site beside the Fecht river but the sanitary facilities have seen better days.

Surroundings : ♀♀	G	Longitude : 7.15102
Leisure activities : ⌂ ⚒ ⚒ ⚲	P	Latitude : 48.04316
Facilities : ⚙ ⚏ ▣ ⚑ ▣	S	
Nearby : ⚒		

OBERBRONN

67110 – Michelin map **315** J3 – pop. 1 543 – alt. 260 – ⚐
▶ Paris 460 – Bitche 25 – Haguenau 24 – Saverne 36

⚠⚠ Flower L'Oasis

✆ 0388097196, www.oasis-alsace.com

Address : 3 rue du Frohret (located 1.5km south along the D 28, follow the signs for Ingwiller and take the road to the left)

Opening times : from end March to beginning Nov.

2.5 ha (139 pitches)

Tariff : 24€ ⚹⚹ ⇔ ▣ ⅏ (6A) – Extra per person 5€ – Reservation fee 15€

Rental rates : (from end March to beginning Nov.) ⚿ (2 chalets) 28 ⚏ – 11 huts, 1 gite d'etape (lodge). Per week from 210 to 670€ – Reservation fee 15€

⚏ borne 9€

On the edge of a forest, with a magnificent view over the mountain and the village of Oberbronn.

Surroundings : ⇕ ⇐	G	Longitude : 7.60347
Leisure activities : ⚑ ✗ ⌂ ⚒ ⚒ ⚒ ⚒ sports trail, spa centre	P	Latitude : 48.9286
Facilities : ⚿ ⚙ ▣ ⚑ ⚑ ▣ ⚎	S	
Nearby : ⚑		

OBERNAI

67210 – Michelin map **315** I6 – pop. 10 803 – alt. 185
▶ Paris 488 – Colmar 50 – Erstein 15 – Molsheim 12

⚠⚠ Municipal le Vallon de l'Ehn

✆ 0388953848, www.obernai.fr

Address : 1 rue de Berlin (take the western exit along the D 426, follow the signs for Ottrott, for caravans, recommended route via the bypass (rocade) south of the town)

Opening times : from mid March to mid Jan

3 ha (150 pitches) flat and relatively flat, grassy

Tariff : 20.46€ ⚹⚹ ⇔ ▣ ⅏ (16A) – Extra per person 4.50€

borne 2€ – 30 回 20,46€
A restful site with a pretty view of Mont Sainte-Odile.

Surroundings : ≤ ♀
Leisure activities : 🛶 ⚓ m
Facilities : & o–🗑 🛖 🏕 ♨ 🚰 launderette
Nearby : ✗ 🏓 🛶 🐎

GPS Longitude : 7.46715
Latitude : 48.46505

RANSPACH

68470 – Michelin map **315** G9 – pop. 852 – alt. 430
▶ Paris 459 – Belfort 54 – Bussang 15 – Gérardmer 38

⛰ Flower Les Bouleaux

☏ 0389826470, www.alsace-camping.com
Address : 8 rue des Bouleaux (south of the town along the N 66)
Opening times : Permanent
1.75 ha (75 pitches) flat, grassy
Tariff : 27€ ✿✿ ⇋ 回 ⚡ (6A) – Extra per person 6€ – Reservation fee 10€
Rental rates : Permanent ⚷ (2 chalets) – 25 🏠. Per night from 50 to 110€ – Per week from 250 to 770€ – Reservation fee 10€
borne 4€ – 5 回 27€
An extensive, attractive green site in the shade of birch trees, but the sanitary facilities are rather jaded.

Surroundings : ≤ ♀
Leisure activities : 🍴 ✗ 🛶 ⚓ 🚲 ♨ 🛶
Facilities : & o–🗑 🏕 🚰 launderette

GPS Longitude : 7.01037
Latitude : 47.88084

RHINAU

67860 – Michelin map **315** K7 – pop. 2 698 – alt. 158
▶ Paris 525 – Marckolsheim 26 – Molsheim 38 – Obernai 28

⛰ Ferme des Tuileries

☏ 0388746045, www.fermedestuileries.com ✾
Address : 1 rue des Tuileries (take the northwestern exit, follow the signs for Benfeld)
Opening times : from beginning April to end Sept.
4 ha (150 pitches) flat, grassy
Tariff : (2014 Price) ✿ 4€ ⇋ 4€ 回 – ⚡ (6A) 3.20€
Rental rates : (2014 Price) (from beginning April to end Dec.) ✾ 5 🏠. Per night from 50 to 85€ – Per week from 350 to 600€
A well-equipped site scattered with fruit trees, next to a lake.

Surroundings : 🌲 ♀
Leisure activities : ✗ 🛖 ⛵ ⚓ 🚲 ✗ ♨ 🛶 ≋ (lake) 🏊 🎣
Facilities : o–🗑 🏕 🚰 launderette 🔧

GPS Longitude : 7.6986
Latitude : 48.32224

Key to rentals symbols:

12 🚐	*Number of mobile homes*
20 🏠	*Number of chalets*
6 🛏	*Number of rooms to rent*
Per night 30–50€	*Minimum/maximum rate per night*
Per week 300–1,000€	*Minimum/maximum rate per week*

RIBEAUVILLÉ

68150 – Michelin map **315** H7 – pop. 4 798 – alt. 240
▶ Paris 439 – Colmar 16 – Gérardmer 56 – Mulhouse 60

⛰ Municipal Pierre-de-Coubertin

☏ 0389736671, http://camping-alsace.com/camping-pierre-coubertin-ribeauville – 🏬
Address : 23 rue de Landau (take the eastern exit along the D 106 then take the turning to the left)
Opening times : from mid March to mid Nov.
3.5 ha (208 pitches) flat, grassy
Tariff : ✿ 4.20€ ⇋ 回 5.20€ – ⚡ (16A) 3.70€
borne – 18 回
There's a pretty view of mountains, vineyards and a château.

Surroundings : 🌲 ≤ ♀
Leisure activities : 🛶 ⚓ ✗
Facilities : & o–🗑 🏕 🚰 ⚡ 回 🛶
Nearby : 🏓 🛶 🏊

GPS Longitude : 7.336
Latitude : 48.195

ROMBACH-LE-FRANC

68660 – Michelin map **315** H7 – pop. 877 – alt. 290
▶ Paris 431 – Colmar 38 – Ribeauvillé 30 – St-Dié 34

⛰ Municipal les Bouleaux

☏ 0389584156, www.valdargent.com/camping-rombach-les-bouleaux.htm – access difficult for caravans
Address : route de la Hingrie (located 1.5km to the northwest)
Opening times : from mid April to mid Oct.
1.3 ha (38 pitches)
Tariff : (2014 Price) ✿ 2.55€ ⇋ 1.90€ 回 1.90€ – ⚡ (13A) 2.45€
Rental rates : (2014 Price) Permanent ✾ – 5 🏠. Per week from 270 to 400€
Situated in a valley surrounded by pines and crossed by a stream.

Surroundings : 🌲 ♀
Leisure activities : 🛶 ⚓
Facilities : & 🏕 🚰 launderette

GPS Longitude : 7.2402
Latitude : 48.2877

STE-CROIX-EN-PLAINE

68127 – Michelin map **315** I8 – pop. 2 661 – alt. 192
▶ Paris 471 – Belfort 78 – Colmar 10 – Freiburg-im-Breisgau 49

⛰ Clair Vacances

☏ 0389492728, www.clairvacances.com ✾
Address : route de Herrlisheim (On the D1)
Opening times : from mid April to mid Oct.
4 ha (145 pitches) flat, grassy
Tariff : 28€ ✿✿ ⇋ 回 ⚡ (16A) – Extra per person 7.50€ – Reservation fee 10€
Rental rates : (from mid April to beginning Oct.) ✾ – 12 🚐. Per night from 48 to 94€ – Per week from 332 to 862€ – Reservation fee 10€
10 回 28€
Attractive trees and shrubs; a peaceful site with plenty of charm.

Surroundings : 🔲
Leisure activities : 🛶 ⚓ 🛶
Facilities : & o–🗑 🏕 🚰 launderette

GPS Longitude : 7.35289
Latitude : 48.01454

SAVERNE

67700 – Michelin map **315** I4 – pop. 12 046 – alt. 200
▶ Paris 450 – Lunéville 88 – St-Avold 89 – Sarreguemines 65

⛰ Seasonova Les Portes d'Alsace

✆ 03 88 91 35 65, www.camping-lesportesdalsace.com

Address : 40 rue du Père Libermann (1.3km southwest along the D 171)

Opening times : from beginning April to beginning Nov.

2.1 ha (145 pitches)

Tariff : (2014 Price) 26€ ★★ ⇔ 🔲 – Extra per person 6€ – Reservation fee 12€

Rental rates : (2014 Price) Permanent 🚫 – 10 🚐. Per week from 300 to 790€ – Reservation fee 15€

🚐 borne 3€ – 15 🔲 10€ – 🔋 10€

A small rural oasis in an urban environment; a peaceful and well-appointed site.

Surroundings : ⩽ ♀
Leisure activities : 🖼 🏊 🔲 (open air in season)
Facilities : ♿ ⚷ 🅲 ⦀ ♨ 🍴 launderette
Nearby : 🍴 🐎 🔲

GPS	Longitude : 7.35539
	Latitude : 48.73095

SÉLESTAT

67600 – Michelin map **315** I7 – pop. 19 332 – alt. 170
▶ Paris 441 – Colmar 24 – Gérardmer 65 – St-Dié 44

⚠ Municipal les Cigognes

✆ 03 88 92 03 98, www.selestat-haut-koenigsbourg.com

Address : 1 rue de la 1ère Division France Libre

Opening times : from beginning April to mid Oct. from mid Nov. to end Dec.

0.7 ha (48 pitches) flat, grassy

Tariff : (2014 Price) 17,65€ ★★ ⇔ 🔲 (10A) Extra per person 4.50€

🚐 borne 5.60€ – 20 🔲 17.65€

A charming site 5 minutes from the town centre.

Surroundings : ♀
Leisure activities : 🏊
Facilities : ⚷ ⦀ 🍴 🖼
Nearby : 🍴 🔲 🏊

GPS	Longitude : 7.44828
	Latitude : 48.25444

SEPPOIS-LE-BAS

68580 – Michelin map **315** H11 – pop. 1 164 – alt. 390
▶ Paris 454 – Altkirch 13 – Basel 42 – Belfort 38

⛰ Tohapi Les Lupins

✆ 03 89 25 65 37, www.village-center.com

Address : 1 rue de la Gare (take the northeastern exit along the D 172, follow the signs for Altkirch)

Opening times : from mid May to mid Sept.

3.5 ha (158 pitches)

Tariff : (2014 Price) 15€ ★★ ⇔ 🔲 (16A) – Extra per person 5€ – Reservation fee 10€

Rental rates : (2014 Price) (from mid May to mid Sept.) Ⓟ 10 🚐. Per night from 25 to 110€ – Per week from 175 to 798€ Reservation fee 10€

🚐 6 🔲 15€ – 🔋 15€

A leafy, green site with the reception in an the old station building.

Surroundings : 🏞 ♀
Leisure activities : 🖼 🔲 🏊 🛥
Facilities : ♿ ⚷ ⦀ ♨ 🍴 launderette
Nearby : 🍴

GPS	Longitude : 7.17893
	Latitude : 47.53956

TURCKHEIM

68230 – Michelin map **315** H8 – pop. 3 747 – alt. 225
▶ Paris 471 – Colmar 7 – Gérardmer 47 – Munster 14

⛰ Le Médiéval

✆ 03 89 27 02 00, www.camping-turckheim.com

Address : quai de la Gare (to the west of the town, behind the stadium – access via the road between the level crossing and the bridge)

Opening times : from beginning April to beginning Nov.

2.5 ha (117 pitches) flat, grassy

Tariff : 18.20€ ★★ ⇔ 🔲 (16A) – Extra per person 4.35€

Reservation fee 10€

Rental rates : (from beginning April to beginning Nov.) – 6 🚐. Per night from 42 to 145€ – Per week from 308 to 676€ – Reservation fee 10€

🚐 30 🔲 14.20€

Situated beside a small canal and near the Fecht river.

Surroundings : 🌳 ♀
Leisure activities : 🖼
Facilities : ♿ ⚷ ⦀ 🍴 launderette
Nearby : 🍴

GPS	Longitude : 7.27144
	Latitude : 48.08463

*The classification (1 to 5 tents, **black** or **red**) that we award to selected sites in this guide is our own system. It should not be confused with the classification (1 to 5 stars) of official organisations.*

WASSELONNE

67310 – Michelin map **315** I5 – pop. 5 562 – alt. 220
▶ Paris 464 – Haguenau 42 – Molsheim 15 – Saverne 15

⛰ Municipal

✆ 03 88 87 00 08, www.camping-wasselonne.com

Address : rue des Sapins (located 1km west along the D 224, follow the signs for Wangenbourg)

Opening times : from mid April to mid Oct.

1.5 ha (100 pitches)

Tariff : (2014 Price) ★ 8,82€ ⇔ – (10A) 3,50€

Rental rates : (2014 Price) (from beginning March to end Nov.) ♿ (1 chalet) – 12 🚐. Per night from 50 to 80€ – Per week from 310 to 500€

🚐 borne 2€

A pretty, green site within the grounds of a leisure centre.

Surroundings : ⩽ ♀
Leisure activities : 🏊 🔲
Facilities : ⚷ 🍴 launderette 🏊
Nearby : 🍴 🍴 🔲

GPS	Longitude : 7.44869
	Latitude : 48.63691

WATTWILLER

68700 – Michelin map **315** H10 – pop. 1 734 – alt. 356
▶ Paris 478 – Strasbourg 116 – Freiburg-im-Breisgau 81 – Basel 56

⛰ Les Sources ♣♣

℘ 03 89 75 44 94, www.campinglessources.com

Address : route des Crêtes

Opening times : from beginning April to end Sept.

15 ha (200 pitches)

Tariff : 33 € ♣♣ ⟺ 🅴 ⚡ (6A) – Extra per person 7 € – Reservation fee 10 €

Rental rates : (from beginning April to end Oct.) – 50 ⟫ 20 🏠. Per night from 35 to 125 € – Per week from 210 to 850 € – Reservation fee 20 €

⟲ borne 5 € – 10 🅴 10 € – ⬥ ⚡14 €

A pleasant wooded site, but the infrastructure and sanitary facilities are getting old.

Surroundings : ⬡ ⟳ ♨
Leisure activities : 🍴 ✗ ⟫ ☺daytime 🏃
⚓ 🎾 🎣 ☒ 🏊
Facilities : ♿ ☛ ⌂ ⚑ launderette ⟚ ⟐
Nearby : 🐎

Longitude : 7.16736
Latitude : 47.83675

WIHR-AU-VAL

68230 – Michelin map **315** H8 – pop. 1 237 – alt. 330
▶ Paris 463 – Colmar 14 – Gérardmer 38 – Guebwiller 35

⛺ La Route Verte

℘ 03 89 71 10 10, www.camping-routeverte.com

Address : 13 rue de la Gare (take the southern exit along the D 43, follow the signs for Soultzbach-les-Bains)

Opening times : from end April to end Sept.

1,2 ha (55 pitches) flat and relatively flat, grassy

Tariff : ♣ 3,15 €⟺ 🅴 4 € – ⚡ (10A) 6,45 €
⟲ borne 5 € – ⬥ 9 €

A small, lovely family-orientated site in the heart of a charming village surrounded by vineyards.

Surroundings : ⬡ ♀
Leisure activities : ⚓
Facilities : ♿ ☛ ⌂ ⚑ 🖪
Nearby : 🍴 ✗

Longitude : 7.20513
Latitude : 48.05159

AQUITAINE

H. Lenain / hemis.fr

Welcome to Aquitaine, home to prehistoric remains, fortified towns and a mosaic of landscapes, as distinctive and welcoming as the hospitality and humour of its locals. A quick stop to buy *confit d'oie* (confit of goose) could lead to an invitation to look around the farm! Aquitaine has dense forests, imposing mountains and sweeping beaches; it is home to picturesque villages, bustling cities, large estates and imposing châteaux. No stay would be complete without visiting at least one of the renowned vineyards of Bordeaux. Then head over to the 'Silver Coast', with its many surfers, rugby fans and bullfighters, all raised on *gâteau Basque*, a cake made with almond flour, and *piment d'Espelette*, a rather spicy pepper. This rugged, sunlit land between the Pyrenees and the Atlantic remains fiercely proud of its identity. Spend a little time in a sleepy Basque village and you will soon discover the region's traditional colours of red, white and green proudly displayed.

AGEN

47000 – Michelin map **336** F4 – pop. 33 920 – alt. 50
▶ Paris 662 – Auch 74 – Bordeaux 141 – Pau 159

🏕 Le Moulin de Mellet

📞 05 53 87 50 89. www.camping-moulin-mellet.com

Address : at St Hilaire de Lusignan, route de Prayssas (head 8km northwest along the D 813 and take a right turn along the D 107)

Opening times : from beginning April to mid Oct.

5 ha/3.5 for camping (48 pitches) flat, grassy, stream, small lake

Tariff : (2014 Price) 23.80€ 🏃🏃 🚐 🔲 🔌 (10A) –
Extra per person 6.45€

Rental rates : (2014 Price) (from beginning April to mid Oct.) –
2 🚐 – 6 🏠. Per night from 55 to 130€ – Per week from 55 to 230€

🚐 15 🔲 23.80€

Surroundings : 🌿 🞉
Leisure activities : 🎭 🛶 🏊 🎣
Facilities : 🚿 🕳 🏕 🍴 🔥
Nearby : paintballing

GPS	Longitude : 0.54188
	Latitude : 44.2436

AINHOA

64250 – Michelin map **342** C3 – pop. 672 – alt. 130
▶ Paris 791 – Bayonne 28 – Biarritz 29 – Cambo-les-Bains 11

🏕 Xokoan

📞 05 59 29 90 26. www.camping-xokoan.com

Address : at Dancharia (head 2.5km southwest then take the left turn before the customs post, (border with Spain)

Opening times : Permanent

0.6 ha (30 pitches)

Tariff : 20€ 🏃🏃 🚐 🔲 🔌 (10A) – Extra per person 6€

Rental rates : Permanent – 2 🚐 – 6 🛏. Per night from 90€ –
Per week from 420€

🚐 borne 6€ – 8 🔲 16.50€

Situated alongside a stream that marks the border between France and Spain.

Surroundings : 🌿 🞉
Leisure activities : 🍴 ✖ 🖼
Facilities : 🚿 🕳 🏛 🔥 🍴 launderette 🛒
Nearby : 🛒

GPS	Longitude : -1.50369
	Latitude : 43.29139

🏕 Harazpy

📞 05 59 29 89 38. www.camping-harazpy.com – 🏕

Address : Gastelu-Gaïna district (to the northwest of the town, behind the church)

Opening times : from beginning April to end Oct.

1 ha (25 pitches)

Tariff : 20€ 🏃🏃 🚐 🔲 🔌 (10A) – Extra per person 6€

🚐 6 🔲 16.50€

A delightful and tranquil meadow setting with a view of typical Basque countryside.

Surroundings : 🌿 ≤ 🞉
Leisure activities : 🖼
Facilities : 🚿 🕳 🍴 launderette

GPS	Longitude : -1.50172
	Latitude : 43.3089

AIRE-SUR-L'ADOUR

40800 – Michelin map **335** J12 – pop. 6 275 – alt. 80
▶ Paris 722 – Auch 84 – Condom 68 – Dax 77

🏕 Les Ombrages de l'Adour

📞 05 58 71 75 10. www.camping-adour-landes.com

Address : rue des Graviers (located near the bridge, behind the arenas; beside the Adour river)

Opening times : from April to Oct.

2 ha (100 pitches) flat, grassy

Tariff : (2014 Price) 🏃 4.20€ 🚐 2€ 🔲 5€ – 🔌 (10A) 3.15€

Rental rates : (2014 Price) (from mid April to end Oct.) – 8 🚐 –
2 canvas bungalows. Per night from 45 to 69€ – Per week from 200 to 405€

🚐 borne

Situated near the town centre.

Surroundings : 🌿 🞉
Leisure activities : 🛶 🏊 ⛵
Facilities : 🕳 🍴 launderette
Nearby : 🏊

GPS	Longitude : -0.25793
	Latitude : 43.70257

ALLES-SUR-DORDOGNE

24480 – Michelin map **329** G6 – pop. 344 – alt. 70
▶ Paris 534 – Bergerac 36 – Le Bugue 12 – Les Eyzies-de-Tayac 22

🏔 Port de Limeuil

📞 05 53 63 29 76. www.leportdelimeuil.com

Address : 3km northeast on the D 51e, near the bridge at Limeuil, where the Dordogne and the Vézère rivers meet

Opening times : from beginning May to end Sept.

7 ha/4 for camping (90 pitches)

Tariff : 33.90€ 🏃🏃 🚐 🔲 🔌 (10A) – Extra per person 7.50€ –
Reservation fee 15€

Rental rates : (2014 Price) (from end April to end Sept.) – 13 🚐 –
1 gîte. Per week from 175 to 990€ – Reservation fee 15€

🚐 borne – 14 🔲

Surroundings : 🌿 🞉 🛁
Leisure activities : 🍴 🎭 🛶 🚲 ✂ 🏊 ⛵
Facilities : 🚿 🕳 🏕 🔥 🍴 launderette 🛒 🛁
Nearby : ✖ 🐎

GPS	Longitude : 0.88599
	Latitude : 44.87969

ANGLET

64600 – Michelin map **342** C2 – pop. 37 661 – alt. 20
▶ Paris 773 – Bordeaux 187 – Pamplona 108 – Donostia-San Sebastián 51

🏔 Le Parme

📞 05 59 23 03 00. www.campingdeparme.com

Address : 2 allée Etchecopar (near the flying club)

Opening times : from mid April to beginning Nov.

3.5 ha (187 pitches)

Tariff : (2014 Price) 18.50€ 🏃🏃 🚐 🔲 🔌 (10A) –
Extra per person 6.30€ – Reservation fee 15€

Rental rates : (2014 Price) (from mid April to beginning Nov.) –
60 🚐 – 30 🏠. Per night from 46 to 135€ – Per week from 322 to 945€ – Reservation fee 15€

🚐 6 🔲 25€

A range of rental options of differing levels of comfort. Choose the pitches away from the road.

Surroundings : 🖙 ♧♧
Leisure activities : ♟ ✕ 🚐 🖫 ⚡ 🛶 🏊 multi-sports ground
Facilities : ﺁ �o━ ♣ ♈ launderette ♨ ♣

GPS Longitude : -1.53238
Latitude : 43.4643

ANGOISSE

24270 – Michelin map **329** H3 – pop. 610 – alt. 345
▶ Paris 445 – Bordeaux 180 – Périgueux 51 – Limoges 53

⚠ Rouffiac en Périgord

🖉 05 53 52 68 79. www.semitour.com – traditional camp. spaces also available

Address : at the leisure centre of Rouffiac (4km southeast along the D 80, follow the signs for Payzac, 150m from a small lake, direct access)

Opening times : from mid June to mid Sept.

54 ha/6 for camping (40 pitches)

Tariff : ♣ 5.50€ ⟵ 🖃 8.40€ ⚡ (16A)

Rental rates : (from mid April to end Oct.) – 2 🚐 – 35 🏠. Per night from 83 to 165€ – Per week from 220 to 670€
🖭 borne – 10 🖃 5.50€

Organised cultural and sporting holidays based around the sailing centre.

Surroundings : 🖏 🖙 ♧♧
Leisure activities : ♟ 🚐
Facilities : ﺁ o━ 🖮 ♈ 🖳
Nearby : 🚲 ✗ 🏊 (beach) ♪ 🐎 forest trail

GPS Longitude : 1.16648
Latitude : 45.41449

ANTONNE-ET-TRIGONANT

24420 – Michelin map **329** F4 – pop. 1 203 – alt. 106
▶ Paris 484 – Bordeaux 139 – Périgueux 10 – Limoges 91

⚠ Au Fil de l'Eau

🖉 05 53 06 17 88. www.campingaufildeleau.com

Address : in Antonne, 6 allées des Platanes (take the northeastern exit and follow the signs for Escoire to the right; beside the island, on the D 6)

Opening times : from mid April to mid Sept.

1.5 ha (50 pitches)

Tariff : 25€ ♣♣ ⟵ 🖃 ⚡ (6A) – Extra per person 6€
Rental rates : (from mid April to mid Sept.) – 10 🚐 – 4 canvas bungalows. Per night from 250 to 700€

Surroundings : ♧♧
Leisure activities : ⚡ 🛶 🖳 🚣
Facilities : ﺁ o━ ♈ 🖳

GPS Longitude : 0.83754
Latitude : 45.213

These symbols are used for a campsite that is exceptional in its category:

🏔....⚠ Particularly pleasant setting, quality and range of services available

🖏🖏 Tranquil, isolated site – quiet site, particularly at night

≪≪ Exceptional view – interesting or panoramic view

ARAMITS

64570 – Michelin map **342** H4 – pop. 677 – alt. 293
▶ Paris 829 – Mauléon-Licharre 27 – Oloron-Ste-Marie 15 – Pau 49

⚠ Barétous-Pyrénées

🖉 05 59 34 12 21. www.camping-pyrenees.com

Address : Ripaude district (take the western exit along the D 918, follow the signs for Mauléon-Licharre; beside the Vert de Barlanes , river)

Opening times : from beginning April to mid Oct.

2 ha (61 pitches) flat, grassy

Tariff : (2014 Price) 28.40€ ♣♣ ⟵ 🖃 ⚡ (10A) – Extra per person 6.50€ – Reservation fee 15€

Rental rates : (2014 Price) (from mid Dec. to mid Oct.) ﺁ (chalet) – 10 🚐 – 11 🏠 – 3 canvas bungalows. Per night from 42 to 87€ – Per week from 240 to 605€ – Reservation fee 18€

Very comfortable wooden chalets (hotel service available on request).

Surroundings : 🖙 ♧♧
Leisure activities : ♟ ✕ 🚐 ≋ jacuzzi ⚡ 🚲 🛶
Facilities : ﺁ o━ 🖮 ♈ launderette ♣

GPS Longitude : -0.73243
Latitude : 43.12135

This guide is updated regularly, so buy your new copy every year!

ARÈS

33740 – Michelin map **335** E6 – pop. 5 548 – alt. 6
▶ Paris 627 – Arcachon 47 – Bordeaux 48

⚠ Les Goélands

🖉 05 56 82 55 64. www.goelands.com

Address : 64 avenue de la Libération (1.7km southeast, near lakes and 500m from the quayside)

10 ha/6 for camping (400 pitches)

Rentals : 16 🚐.

Surroundings : 🖏 🖙 ♧♧
Leisure activities : ♟ ✕ 🖫 ⚡ 🛶 🚲 🏊 🎣 multi-sports ground
Facilities : ﺁ o━ 🖮 ♈ launderette ♨ ♣
Nearby : 🏊 (pond) ♪ ♪

GPS Longitude : -1.11979
Latitude : 44.75747

⚠ Sites et Paysages La Cigale

🖉 05 56 60 22 59. www.camping-lacigale-ares.com – limited spaces for one-night stay

Address : 53 rue du Général de Gaulle (take the northern exit)

Opening times : from end April to beginning Oct.

2.4 ha (75 pitches)

Tariff : 37.50€ ♣♣ ⟵ 🖃 ⚡ (10A) – Extra per person 8€ – Reservation fee 18€

Rental rates : (from mid April to beginning Nov.) – 6 🏠 – 3 tent lodges. Per night from 43 to 130€ – Per week from 300 to 910€ Reservation fee 20€
🖭 borne – 🖱 🖮 19€

Surroundings : 🖏 🖙 ♧♧
Leisure activities : ♟ ✕ 🚐 ⚡ 🛶
Facilities : ﺁ o━ ♈ launderette ♣

GPS Longitude : -1.14188
Latitude : 44.77287

⛰ Les Abberts

📞 05 56 60 26 80. www.lesabberts.com

Address : 17 rue des Abberts (take the northern exit then take the turning to the left)

Opening times : from beginning June to mid Sept.

2 ha (125 pitches)

Tariff : 35.50€ ✶✶ 🚗 🔲 🔌 (6A) – Extra per person 9.50€ – Reservation fee 19€

Rental rates : (from mid April to end Sept.) 🚲 – 30 🏚 – 1 🏡. Per night from 55 to 75€ – Per week from 250 to 975€ Reservation fee 19€

Surroundings : 🌊 99	G	Longitude : -1.1444
Leisure activities : 🍴✖ 🏠 🛶 🚲 🛝 ⛷	P	Latitude : 44.77163
Facilities : 🚿 ⊶ 🚽 launderette 🚮	S	

⚠ Pasteur

📞 05 56 60 33 33. www.atlantic-vacances.com – limited spaces for one-night stay

Address : 1 rue du Pilote (take the southeastern exit, 300m from the quayside)

Opening times : from mid March to end Oct.

1 ha (50 pitches)

Tariff : ✶ 5€ 🚗 🔲 25€ – 🔌 (6A) 4.50€ – Reservation fee 17€

Rental rates : (from mid March to end Oct.) – 16 🏚 – 14 🏡. Per night from 45 to 100€ – Per week from 280 to 740€ – Reservation fee 17€

🚐 borne 11€ – 15 🔲 15.50€ – 💧 11€

Surroundings : 🌊 99	G	Longitude : -1.13681
Leisure activities : 🛶 🚲 🛝 (small swimming pool)	P	Latitude : 44.76174
Facilities : 🚿 ⊶ 🚽 🔲	S	

ATUR

24750 – Michelin map **329** F5 – pop. 1 744 – alt. 224
▶ Paris 499 – Bordeaux 134 – Périgueux 6 – Brive-la-Gaillarde 83

⛰ Iris Parc Le Grand Dague ♣♟

📞 05 53 04 21 01, www.irisparc.com – limited spaces for one-night stay 🚲 (from end April to end Sept.)

Address : route du Grand Dague (3km southeast following signs for St-Laurent-sur-Manoire – if on southern diversion coming from Brive or Limoges: take the road towards Bergerac and take the road to the right)

Opening times : from end April to end Sept.

22 ha/12 for camping (382 pitches)

Tariff : (2014 Price) 37€ ✶✶ 🚗 🔲 🔌 (6A) – Extra per person 7.50€ Reservation fee 20€

Rental rates : (2014 Price) (from end April to end Sept.) 🚿 (1 mobile home) 🅿 – 278 🏚 – 92 tent lodges. Per night from 21 to 149€ – Per week from 105 to 1,043€ – Reservation fee 20€

🚐 borne 2€

A well-equipped indoor children's play area.

Surroundings : 🌊 🔲 99	G	Longitude : 0.77656
Leisure activities : 🍴✖ 🏠 🕹 🏓 🛶 🛝 🛝 🛝 paintballing	P	Latitude : 45.14816
Facilities : 🚿 ⊶ 🔲 🏛 🚽 🚮 launderette 🚮	S	

40200 – Michelin map **335** D9 – pop. 935 – alt. 10
▶ Paris 689 – Bordeaux 103 – Mont-de-Marsan 79 – La Teste 59

⛰ Tohapi Aurilandes ♣♟

📞 08 25 00 20 30. www.village-center.fr

Address : 1001 Promenade de l'Étang (located 1km to the northeast, near the lake)

Opening times : from beginning April to end Sept.

6 ha (440 pitches)

Tariff : (2014 Price) 22€ ✶✶ 🚗 🔲 🔌 (6A) – Extra per person 7€ – Reservation fee 10€

Rental rates : (2014 Price) (from beginning April to end Aug.) – 18 🏚. Per night from 28 to 133€ – Per week from 196 to 931€ Reservation fee 10€

Surroundings : 🌊 99 ⛰		
Leisure activities : 🏠 🕹 🏓 🛶 🏊 jacuzzi 🛶 🚲 🛝 ⛵ multi-sports ground	G	Longitude : -1.20314
Facilities : 🚿 ⊶ 🚽 🚽 launderette 🚮 🚮	P	Latitude : 44.22306
Nearby : 🐎 ⚓	S	

Using the traditional Michelin classification method, the guide provides you with an easy, speedy reference for assessing the category of each site: 1 to 5 tents (see page 10).

40140 – Michelin map **335** D12 – pop. 575 – alt. 9
▶ Paris 730 – Bayonne 54 – Dax 25 – Mimizan 79

⛰ FranceLoc La Paillotte ♣♟

📞 05 58 48 12 12. www.paillotte.com 🚲

Address : 66 route des Campings (located 1.5km southwest; beside the Lac de Soustons)

Opening times : from mid April to late Sept.

7 ha (310 pitches)

Tariff : (2014 Price) 40.50€ ✶✶ 🚗 🔲 🔌 (10A) – Extra per person 7€ Reservation fee 27€

Rental rates : (2014 Price) (from beginning April to end Sept.) 🚲 – 205 🏚 – 50 🏡. Per night from 30 to 191€ – Per week from 210 to 1,337€ – Reservation fee 27€

An exotically decorated but pretty chalet village with a large water park, beside the lake.

Surroundings : 🌊 ⟨ 🔲 99 ⛰		
Leisure activities : 🍴✖ 🏠 🕹 🏓 ⛷ 🕹 🛝 🛝 🛶 ⛵	G	Longitude : -1.30875
Facilities : 🚿 ⊶ 🚽 🔲 🚽 launderette 🚮 🚮	P	Latitude : 43.78731
Nearby : 🚲 🚭 🎿 💧 pedalos	S	

⛰ Azur Rivage

📞 05 58 48 30 72. www.campingazurivage.com

Address : 720 route des Campings (situated 2km to the south, 100m from the lake at Soustons)

Opening times : from beginning June to mid Sept.

6.5 ha (250 pitches)

Tariff : (2014 Price) 32.80€ ✶✶ 🚗 🔲 🔌 (10A) – Extra per person 7.30€ – Reservation fee 17€

Rental rates : (2014 Price) (from mid April to mid Sept.) – 62 🚐. Per night from 40 to 61€ – Per week from 555 to 995€ – Reservation fee 17€

Surroundings : ♨️
Leisure activities : 🏇 🏊 🛶 multi-sports ground
Facilities : 🚿 ⛽ (July-Aug.) 🏕 🚲 📺 🛝 🎣 refrigerated food storage facilities
Nearby : 🚴 🍴 🎯 🚣 pedalos

GPS Longitude : -1.23047
Latitude : 43.78477

BADEFOLS-SUR-DORDOGNE

24150 – Michelin map **329** F6 – pop. 211 – alt. 42
▶ Paris 542 – Bergerac 27 – Périgueux 54 – Sarlat-la-Canéda 47

▲▲▲ Club Airotel Les Bö Bains

📞 0553735252. www.bo-bains.com – limited spaces for one-night stay

Address : route de Bergerac (take the western exit, along the D 29; beside the Dordogne)

Opening times : from beginning April to end Sept.

5 ha (97 pitches)

Tariff : (2014 Price) 33€ 🚻 🚗 📺 💧 (9A) – Extra per person 9€ – Reservation fee 25€

Rental rates : (2014 Price) (from beginning April to end Sept.) 🚿 (1 mobile home) – 40 🚐 – 34 🏠. Per night from 50 to 80€ – Per week from 250 to 999€ – Reservation fee 25€

Surroundings : ⬅️ 🏕 ♨️
Leisure activities : 🍴 🍴 🛋️ 🌙 nighttime 🎯
🏇 🚲 🏊 🛶 🎣
Facilities : 🚿 ⛽ 🏕 🍴 launderette 🎣
Nearby : 🍴

GPS Longitude : 0.78541
Latitude : 44.84155

LA BASTIDE-CLAIRENCE

64240 – Michelin map **342** E4 – pop. 984 – alt. 50
▶ Paris 767 – Bayonne 26 – Hasparren 9 – Peyrehorade 29

▲▲▲ Village Vacances Les Collines Iduki

(rental of apartments and maisonnettes only)

📞 0559702081, www.location-vacances-paysbasque.com

Address : Pont de Port

Opening times : Permanent

2.5 ha very uneven, terraced

Rental rates : 🚿 (1 apartment) – 6 🏠 – 30 apartments. Per night from 65 to 214€ – Per week from 324 to 1,759€

Pretty Basque buildings and a good-quality restaurant.

Surroundings : 🌲 ⬅️ ♨️
Leisure activities : ✖️ 🛋️ 🏇 🏊
Facilities : 🚿 ⛽ 🅿️ 🏕 🍴 launderette
Nearby : 🍴

GPS Longitude : -1.25742
Latitude : 43.43324

*For more information on visiting particular towns or regions, consult the relevant regional **MICHELIN Green Guide**. We also recommend you use the appropriate Michelin regional map to locate your selected campsite, to calculate distances and to work out the best route.*

BAUDREIX

64800 – Michelin map **342** K3 – pop. 537 – alt. 245
▶ Paris 791 – Argelès-Gazost 39 – Lourdes 26 – Oloron-Ste-Marie 48

▲▲▲ Les Ôkiri

📞 0559929773. www.lesokiri.com 🚫 (from beginning July to end Aug.)

Address : avenue du Lac (at the leisure and activity park)

Opening times : from beginning April to end Sept.

20 ha/2 for camping (60 pitches) flat, grassy

Tariff : 🚹 10€ 🚗 – 💧 (6A) 10€ – Reservation fee 10€

Rental rates : Permanent 🚫 🅿️ – 10 🚐 – 24 🏠 – 5 canvas bungalows. Per night from 62 to 100€ – Per week from 240 to 715€ Reservation fee 10€

A large boating centre; wooden chalets of a basic standard, mobile homes both with/without sanitary facilities and a campsite with about 50 pitches.

Surroundings : 🌲 🛋️ ♨️ ⛰️
Leisure activities : 🍴 ✖️ 🏇 🚲 🚣 (beach) 🛶 🎣 pedalos 🚫 multi-sports ground
Facilities : 🚿 ⛽ (July-Aug.) 📺🍴 launderette 🎣

GPS Longitude : -0.26124
Latitude : 43.20439

BEAUVILLE

47470 – Michelin map **336** H4 – pop. 584 – alt. 208
▶ Paris 641 – Agen 26 – Moissac 32 – Montaigu-de-Quercy 16

▲ Les 2 Lacs

📞 0553954541, www.les2lacs.info

Address : Vallon de Gerbal (900m southeast along the D 122, follow the signs for Bourg de Visa)

Opening times : from beginning April to end Oct.

22 ha/2.5 for camping (80 pitches)

Tariff : 🚹 5.60€ 🚗 📺 10.15€ – 💧 (6A) 2.95€ – Reservation fee 25€

Rental rates : (from beginning April to end Oct.) – 2 🚐 – 1 🏠 – 7 canvas bungalows. Per night from 30 to 100€ – Per week from 167 to 700€ – Reservation fee 25€

There's a snack bar terrace beside the lake.

Surroundings : 🌲 🛋️ ♨️
Leisure activities : 🍴 ✖️ 🏇 🚫 🚣 🎣 boats to hire 🚫
Facilities : 🚿 ⛽ 🍴 launderette

GPS Longitude : 0.88819
Latitude : 44.27142

BÉLUS

40300 – Michelin map **335** E13 – pop. 605 – alt. 135
▶ Paris 749 – Bayonne 37 – Dax 18 – Orthez 36

▲ La Comtesse

📞 0558576907. www.campinglacomtesse.com

Address : in Claquin (2.5km northwest along the D 75 and take turning to the right)

6 ha (115 pitches) flat, grassy

Rentals : 15 🚐.

In a pleasant grove of poplar trees, beside a lake.

Surroundings : 🌲 🛋️ ♨️
Leisure activities : 🍴 ✖️ 🛋️ 🎯 🚫 🏊 🛶 🎣
Facilities : 🚿 ⛽ 🏕 🍴 launderette 🎣

GPS Longitude : -1.13075
Latitude : 43.60364

BELVÈS

24170 – Michelin map **329** H7 – pop. 1 432 – alt. 175
▶ Paris 553 – Bergerac 52 – Le Bugue 24 – Les Eyzies-de-Tayac 25

FranceLoc Les Hauts de Ratebout

☏ 05 53 29 02 10. www.camping-hauts-ratebout.fr

Address : Ste-Foy-de-Belvès, Ratebout (7km southeast along the D 710, follow the signs for Fumel, D 54 and take turning to the left)

Opening times : from end April to beginning Sept.

12 ha/6 for camping (200 pitches) terraced, flat and relatively flat, grassy

Tariff : (2014 Price) 43€ ♦♦ ⇆ 🔲 (10A) – Extra per person 7€ – Reservation fee 27€

Rental rates : (2014 Price) (from end April to beginning Sept.) – 4 caravans – 162 ⛺ – 11 tent lodges – 5 gîtes. Per night from 39 to 158€ – Per week from 154 to 1,260€ – Reservation fee 27€

A pretty, renovated Périgord farmhouse with a top-quality children's play area.

Surroundings :
Leisure activities :
Facilities : launderette

G P S Longitude : 1.04529
Latitude : 44.74151

RCN Le Moulin de la Pique

☏ 05 53 29 01 15. www.rcn.fr

Address : Moulin de la Pique (3km southeast along the D 710, follow the signs for Fumel; near the Nauze river, a lake and a millpond)

Opening times : from end April to end Sept.

15 ha/6 for camping (200 pitches)

Tariff : 54.25€ ♦♦ ⇆ 🔲 (10A) – Extra per person 6.75€ – Reservation fee 19.95€

Rental rates : (from end April to end Sept.) – 61 ⛺ – 3 apartments – 5 tent lodges. Per night from 36 to 193€ – Reservation fee 19.95€

⛽ borne 16€

Based around a pretty 18th-century mill and its outbuildings.

Surroundings :
Leisure activities :
Facilities : launderette

G P S Longitude : 1.01371
Latitude : 44.7305

Flower Les Nauves

☏ 05 53 29 12 64. www.lesnauves.com

Address : Le Bos Rouge (4.5km southwest along the D 53, follow the signs for Monpazier and turn left following the signs for Larzac)

Opening times : from beginning April to end Sept.

40 ha/5 for camping (100 pitches) relatively flat to hilly, grassy

Tariff : 27€ ♦♦ ⇆ 🔲 (6A) – Extra per person 4€ – Reservation fee 15€

Rental rates : (from beginning April to end Sept.) – 32 ⛺ – 4 🏠 – 3 canvas bungalows – 8 tent lodges. Per night from 30 to 120€ – Per week from 150 to 840€ – Reservation fee 15€

Surroundings :
Leisure activities : farm or petting farm
Facilities :
Nearby :

G P S Longitude : 0.98184
Latitude : 44.75497

BEYNAC-ET-CAZENAC

24220 – Michelin map **329** H6 – pop. 522 – alt. 75
▶ Paris 537 – Bergerac 62 – Brive-la-Gaillade 63 – Fumel 60

Le Capeyrou

☏ 05 53 29 54 95. www.campinglecapeyrou.com

Address : route de Sarlat (take the eastern exit, along the D 57; beside the Dordogne river)

Opening times : from end April to end Sept.

4.5 ha (120 pitches) flat, grassy

Tariff : (2014 Price) ♦ 6.75€ ⇆ 🔲 10.90€ – (10A) 4.45€ – Reservation fee 10€

Rental rates : (2014 Price) (from end April to end Sept.) – 4 tent lodges. Per week from 290 to 670€ – Reservation fee 10€

Surroundings : ≤ Château de Beynac
Leisure activities :
Facilities : launderette
Nearby :

G P S Longitude : 1.14843
Latitude : 44.83828

Michelin classification:

▲▲▲▲	*Extremely comfortable, equipped to a very high standard*
▲▲▲	*Very comfortable, equipped to a high standard*
▲▲	*Comfortable and well equipped*
▲▲	*Reasonably comfortable*
▲	*Satisfactory*

BIARRITZ

64200 – Michelin map **342** C4 – pop. 25 397 – alt. 19
▶ Paris 772 – Bayonne 9 – Bordeaux 190 – Pau 122

Club Airotel Biarritz-Camping

☏ 05 59 23 00 12. www.biarritz.camping.fr

Address : 28 rue Harcet

3 ha (170 pitches) terraced, relatively flat, flat, grassy

Rentals : 72 ⛺ – 14 canvas bungalows.

Situated 300m from the Cité de l'Océan (maritime museum) and 700m from the beach. There's a bus for the town.

Surroundings :
Leisure activities : jacuzzi
Facilities : launderette
Nearby :

G P S Longitude : -1.56685
Latitude : 43.46199

The prices listed were supplied by the campsite owners in 2014 (if prices were not available, those from the previous year are given). The fees should be regarded as basic charges and may fluctuate with inflation.

BIAS

40170 – Michelin map **335** D10 – pop. 736 – alt. 41
▶ Paris 706 – Castets 33 – Mimizan 7 – Morcenx 30

⚠ Municipal Le Tatiou ♣♣

Municipal Le Tatiou

☎ 0558090476. www.campingletatiou.
com

Address : route de Lespecier (situated 2km west)

Opening times : from beginning April to end Sept.

10 ha (501 pitches)

Tariff : (2014 Price) 23€ ♣♣ 🚗 🔲 🔲 (6A) – Extra per person 6€ – Reservation fee 20€

Rental rates : (2014 Price) (from beginning April to end Sept.) – 6 🛏 – 5 canvas bungalows. Per night from 20 to 95€ – Per week from 120 to 640€ – Reservation fee 20€

Surroundings : 🌳 🎯🎯
Leisure activities : 🍽 ✗ 🏠 🏊 🚣 🚴 ⛳
🎣 🎣
Facilities : 🔥 🚿 🔥 ⚙ launderette 🧺 🛁
refrigerated food storage facilities

Longitude : -1.24029
Latitude : 44.14531

BIDART

64210 – Michelin map **342** C2 – pop. 6 117 – alt. 40
▶ Paris 783 – Bordeaux 196 – Pau 119 – Bayonne 13

⚠ Les Castels Le Ruisseau des Pyrénées ♣♣

Le Ruisseau des Pyrénées

(rental of mobile homes, chalets and canvas bungalows only)

☎ 0559419450. www.camping-le-ruisseau.fr – traditional camp. spaces also available

Address : rue Burruntz (situated 2km east; beside the Ouhabia river and a stream – divided into two separate areas)

Opening times : from mid April to end Sept.

15 ha/7 for camping (440 pitches) terraced, flat, grassy

Rental rates : 🔥 (1 mobile home) – 200 🛏 – 200 🏠 – 3 cabins in the trees – 4 canvas bungalows – 4 tent lodges. Per night from 42 to 200€ – Per week from 294 to 1,400€ – Reservation fee 20€

🚐 borne – 14 🔲 22€

Divided into two sections, with lots of green space for relaxation or leisure activities and two water parks, one partially indoor and 'zen'-style, and one with waterslides.

Surroundings : 🌳 🎯🎯
Leisure activities : 🍽 ✗ 🏠 ⚙ 🏊 🚴 🎣
hammam, jacuzzi 🚴 🎣 ⛳ 🎣 🎣 🎣 🎣
fitness trail, farm or petting farm,
multi-sports ground
Facilities : 🔥 🚿 ⚙ launderette 🧺 🛁
Nearby : 🐎

Longitude : -1.56835
Latitude : 43.43704

To visit a town or region, use the MICHELIN Green Guides.

⚠ Yelloh! Village Ilbarritz ♣♣

☎ 0559230029. www.camping-ilbarritz.com

Address : avenue de Biarritz (situated 2km to the north)

Opening times : from end March to beginning Oct.

6 ha (374 pitches) terraced, flat and relatively flat, grassy, sandy

Tariff : 57€ ♣♣ 🚗 🔲 🔲 (10A) – Extra per person 9€

Rental rates : (from end March to beginning Oct.) 🔥 (1 mobile home) – 166 🛏 – 24 🏠. Per night from 39 to 249€ – Per week from 299 to 1,743€

The spacious entrance is attractive, with pretty buildings in the Basque style.

Surroundings : 🖵 🎯🎯
Leisure activities : 🍽 ✗ 🏠 ⚙ 🎣 jacuzzi
🚴 🎣 🏊 🎣 surfing, multi-sports ground
Facilities : 🔥 🚿 🔥 ⚙ launderette 🧺 🛁
refrigerated food storage facilities
Nearby : 🎣 disco

Longitude : -1.57374
Latitude : 43.45315

⚠ Sunêlia Berrua ♣♣

☎ 0559549666. www.berrua.com

Address : rue Berrua (500m east, follow the signs for Arbonne)

Opening times : from beginning April to end Sept.

5 ha (261 pitches) terraced, relatively flat, grassy

Tariff : 47.90€ ♣♣ 🚗 🔲 🔲 (10A) – Extra per person 8.40€ – Reservation fee 36€

Rental rates : (from beginning April to end Sept.) – 146 🛏 – 10 🏠 – 2 tent lodges. Per night from 40 to 236€ – Per week from 280 to 1,652€ – Reservation fee 36€

🚐 borne 4€

A well-maintained site with flowers; some luxurious rental options.

Surroundings : 🖵 🎯🎯
Leisure activities : 🍽 ✗ 🏠 ⚙ 🎣 hammam
🚴 🎣 ⛳ 🎣 🏊 🎣 multi-sports ground
Facilities : 🔥 🚿 🔲 ⚙ launderette 🧺 🛁
Nearby : surfing

Longitude : -1.58176
Latitude : 43.43824

⚠ Club Airotel Oyam ♣♣

☎ 0559549161. www.camping-oyam.com

Address : chemin Oyhamburua (located 1km east along the follow the signs for Arbonne then take the turning to the right)

Opening times : from mid April to end Sept.

7 ha (350 pitches)

Tariff : (2014 Price) 44.30€ ♣♣ 🚗 🔲 🔲 (6A)

Extra per person 7.90€ – Reservation fee 20€

Rental rates : (2014 Price) (from mid April to end Sept.) 🔥 (1 mobile home) – 102 🛏 – 18 🏠 – 14 apartments – 5 tipis – 10 canvas bungalows – 28 tent lodges. Per night from 48 to 152€ – Per week from 224 to 1,064€ – Reservation fee 20€

🚐 borne – 11 🔲 38€

Many and varied rental options; some attractive pitches for tents and caravans beside a water park surrounded by vegetation.

Surroundings : 🖵 🎯🎯
Leisure activities : 🍽 ✗ 🏠 🏊 🚴 🎣 🏊
multi-sports ground
Facilities : 🔥 🚿 ⚙ launderette 🛁

Longitude : -1.58278
Latitude : 43.43501

▲▲▲ Ur-Onea ♦▲

GOYA

✆ 0559265361, www.uronea.com

Address : rue de la Chapelle (300m east, 500m from the beach)

Opening times : from beginning April to end Sept.

5 ha (269 pitches) terraced, relatively flat, grassy, sandy

Tariff : 43€ ♦♦ ⇔ 🅴 ⚡ (10A) – Extra per person 7.50€ – Reservation fee 25€

Rental rates : (from beginning April to end Sept.) ⚡ – 51 🚐 – 5 🏠. Per night from 40 to 145€ – Per week from 260 to 1,005€ Reservation fee 35€

🚐 12 🅴 46€

Surroundings : 👍
Leisure activities : ♟ ✕ 🏠 🏃 ⛵ 🔲 🏊 multi-sports ground
Facilities : ♿ ⛽ 🛁 ♨ 🚰 ☂ 🧺 launderette ♨ refrigerated food storage facilities

G P S Longitude : -1.59035 Latitude : 43.43416

▲▲▲ Pavillon Royal

✆ 0559230054. www.pavillon-royal.com ⚡

Address : avenue du Prince de Galles (situated 2km to the north; beside the beach)

Opening times : from mid May to end Sept.

5 ha (303 pitches) terraced, flat, grassy

Tariff : 59€ ♦♦ ⇔ 🅴 ⚡ (10A) – Extra per person 14€ – Reservation fee 25€

Rental rates : (from mid May to end Sept.) ⚡ – 3 🏠 – 1 studio – 1 apartment. Per week from 482 to 1,085€ – Reservation fee 25€

In a secluded location near a golf course, château and the ocean.

Surroundings : ⛵ ⛱ 🏖 ⛰
Leisure activities : ♟ ✕ 🏠 ☕ daytime 🎯 ⛵ 🏊 beauty treatments, surfing
Facilities : ♿ ⛽ 🅿 🛁 ☂ 🚰 🧺 launderette ♨ ♨
Nearby : 🌙 nighttime 🕺 disco

G P S Longitude : -1.57642 Latitude : 43.45469

▲▲▲ Flower Harrobia ♦▲

✆ 0559265471, www.harrobia.fr

Address : rue Maurice Pierre (1.2km to the south, 400m from the beach)

Opening times : from mid June to end Sept.

3 ha (145 pitches)

Rentals : 135 🚐 – 2 🏠 – 5 apartments.

Near the railway line, a mobile home park with just under 10 pitches for tents and caravans.

Surroundings : 👍
Leisure activities : ♟ ✕ 🏠 🏃 ⛵ 🏊
Facilities : ♿ ⛽ 🛁 🚰 launderette

G P S Longitude : -1.59903 Latitude : 43.42773

BIGANOS

33380 – Michelin map **335** F7 – pop. 9 464 – alt. 16
▶ Paris 629 – Andernos-les-Bains 15 – Arcachon 27 – Bordeaux 47

▲▲▲ Le Marache

✆ 0557706119. www.marachevacances.com

Address : 25 rue Gambetta (take the northern exit along the D 3, follow the signs for Audenge and take turning to the right)

2 ha (115 pitches)

Rentals : 35 🚐 – 6 🏠.

Surroundings : 🌳 👍
Leisure activities : ♟ ✕ 🏠 🏊 multi-sports ground
Facilities : ♿ ⛽ 🛁 ♨ 🚰 ☂

G P S Longitude : -0.97943 Latitude : 44.65081

The guide covers all 22 regions of France – see the map and list of regions on pages 4–5.

BIRON

24540 – Michelin map **329** G8 – pop. 182 – alt. 200
▶ Paris 583 – Beaumont 25 – Bergerac 46 – Fumel 20

▲▲▲ FranceLoc Le Moulinal ♦▲

✆ 0553408460. www.campings-franceloc.fr – limited spaces for one-night stay

Address : Étang du Moulinal (4km to the south, follow the signs for Lacapelle-Biron then continue 2km following signs for Villeréal to the right)

Opening times : from beginning April to mid Sept.

10 ha/5 for camping (300 pitches)

Tariff : (2014 Price) 38€ ♦♦ ⇔ 🅴 ⚡ (10A) – Extra per person 7.50€ Reservation fee 27€

Rental rates : (2014 Price) (from beginning April to mid Sept.) – 260 🚐 – 20 🏠. Per night from 50 to 170€ – Per week from 175 to 1,200€ – Reservation fee 27€

Pleasant location beside a lake, great variety of luxuriant foliage.

Surroundings : ⛵ ⛱ 👍
Leisure activities : ♟ ✕ 🏠 ☕ 🏃 ⛵ 🚴 ✂ ⛱ 🔲 🏊 🏖 (beach) 🎣 🦆 🐝 multi-sports ground, entertainment room
Facilities : ♿ ⛽ 🛁 ☂ 🚰 🧺 launderette ♨ ♨

G P S Longitude : 0.87116 Latitude : 44.60031

▲▲▲ Village Vacances Castelwood (rental of chalets only)

✆ 0553579608. www.castelwood.fr

Address : Bois du Château-Les Fargues (located 1km south along the D 54, follow the signs for Lacapelle-Biron)

Opening times : Permanent

1 ha

Rental rates : ♿ (1 chalet) – 15 🏠. Per night from 48 to 119€ Per week from 271 to 833€

Luxury chalets nestling in the Périgord Pourpre (Purple Périgord) forest.

Surroundings : ⛵ 🌲
Leisure activities : 🏊
Facilities : ⛽ ▦ 🚰 🛁

G P S Longitude : 0.87701 Latitude : 44.62495

BISCARROSSE

40600 – Michelin map **335** E8 – pop. 12 163 – alt. 22

▶ Paris 656 – Arcachon 40 – Bayonne 128 – Bordeaux 74

🛆🛆🛆 Club Airotel Domaine de la Rive 🚹🚹

📞 05 58 78 12 33. www.larive.fr

Address : route de Bordeaux (8km northeast along the D 652, follow the signs for Sanguinet, then continue 2.2km along the turning to the left, beside the Étang de Cazaux (lake)

Opening times : from beginning April to end Aug.

15 ha (800 pitches)

Tariff : 59 € ✶✶ 🚐 🗉 🔌 (10A) – Extra per person 11 € – Reservation fee 30 €

Rental rates : (from beginning April to end Aug.) ♿ (1 mobile home) – 260 🛏 – 30 🏠. Per night from 82 to 315 € – Per week from 574 to 2,205 € – Reservation fee 30 €

🛱 borne

An attractive swimming area, partially covered.

Surroundings : 🌊 ⛳️ ▲
Leisure activities : 🍸 ✗ 🎱 🎣 🏕 🎠 🏊 hammam jacuzzi 🏄 🚴 ✂️ 🎰 🎮 🎳 🎿 (beach) 💧 water skiing, multi-sports ground, spa centre, entertainment room, skate park
Facilities : ♿ 🚿 🆑 🐕 🚰 🍴 launderette 🍽 refrigerated food storage facilities

G P S Longitude : -1.1299
Latitude : 44.46022

🛆🛆🛆 Mayotte Vacances 🚹🚹

📞 05 58 78 00 00. www.mayottevacances.com

Address : 368 chemin des Roseaux (6km north following signs for Sanguinet then turn left at Goubern and continue for 2.5km; 150m from the Étang de Cazaux (lake, direct access)

Opening times : from beginning April to end Sept.

15 ha (714 pitches)

Tariff : 55 € ✶✶ 🚐 🗉 🔌 (16A) – Extra per person 9.50 € – Reservation fee 30 €

Rental rates : (from beginning April to end Sept.) – 275 🛏 – 21 tent lodges. Per night from 28 to 299 € – Per week from 196 to 2,093 € – Reservation fee 30 €

Surroundings : 🌊 ⛳️ ▲
Leisure activities : 🍸 ✗ 🎱 🎣 🏕 🎠 🏊 hammam, jacuzzi 🏄 🚴 ✂️ 🎰 🎳 🎿 💧 fitness trail, multi-sports ground, spa centre, entertainment room
Facilities : ♿ 🚿 🐕 🚰 🍴 launderette 🍽 refrigerated food storage facilities

G P S Longitude : -1.1538
Latitude : 44.43488

🛆🛆🛆 Les Écureuils 🚹🚹

📞 05 58 09 80 00. www.ecureuils.fr – limited spaces for one-night stay

Address : 646 chemin de Navarrosse (4.2km north following signs for Sanguinet and turn left towards Navarrosse; 400m from the Étang de Cazaux (lake)

Opening times : from beginning April to end Sept.

6 ha (183 pitches)

Tariff : (2014 Price) 50 € ✶✶ 🚐 🗉 🔌 (10A) – Extra per person 8 € Reservation fee 32 €

Rental rates : (2014 Price) (from beginning April to end Sept.) 🏚 3 🛏 – 2 🏠 – 1 tent lodge. Per night from 43 to 158 € – Per week from 300 to 1,100 € – Reservation fee 32 €

Pretty shrubs and flowers.

Surroundings : 🌊 🌳 💧
Leisure activities : 🍸 ✗ 🎱 🏕 jacuzzi 🏄 🚴 ✂️ 🎳 🎿 (beach) 🦆
Facilities : ♿ 🚿 🆑 🐕 🍴 launderette 🍽
Nearby : 🐎 💧

G P S Longitude : -1.16765
Latitude : 44.42947

🛆🛆🛆 Bimbo

📞 05 58 09 82 33. www.campingbimbo.fr (limited spaces for one-night stay)

Address : 176 chemin de Bimbo (3.5km north following signs for Sanguinet and turn left towards Navarrosse)

Opening times : from beginning April to end Sept.

6 ha (177 pitches)

Tariff : 50 € ✶✶ 🚐 🗉 🔌 (6A) – Extra per person 8 € – Reservation fee 25 €

Rental rates : (from beginning April to mid Nov.) – 35 🛏 – 12 🏠 – 5 tent lodges. Per night from 27 to 168 € – Per week from 185 to 1,177 € – Reservation fee 25 €

🛱 borne

Surroundings : 🌊 🌳 ⛳️
Leisure activities : 🍸 ✗ 🎱 🏕 🏄 🚴 ✂️ 🎿 multi-sports ground
Facilities : ♿ 🚿 🐕 🍴 launderette 🍽 refrigerated food storage facilities
Nearby : 🎣

G P S Longitude : -1.16137
Latitude : 44.42588

🛆🛆 Village Vacances La Fontaine de Nava

(rental of mobile homes only)

📞 05 58 09 83 11, www.lesfontainesdenava.com

Address : chemin de Bimbo, Navarrosse (3.5km north following signs for Sanguinet then follow the signs for Navarrosse)

12 ha/7 for camping

Rentals : 🏚 – 35 🛏.

Surroundings : 🌊 🌳
Leisure activities : 🍸 ✗ 🎱 🎳 🎿 multi-sports ground
Facilities : 🚿 🍴 🆑

G P S Longitude : -1.16763
Latitude : 44.39439

There are several different types of sani-station ('borne' in French) – sanitation points providing fresh water and disposal points for grey water. See page 12 for further details.

Routes nationales are main roads and their identifying numbers begin with N or RN. Routes départementales are generally quieter roads and begin with D or DN.

⛺ Campéole de Navarrosse ♣♦

Campéole de Navarrosse

📞 0558098432. www.camping-navarrose.com

Address : 712 chemin de Navarrosse (5km to the north, follow the signs for Sanguinet and turn left towards Navarrosse; beside the Étang de Cazaux (lake)

Opening times : from beginning April to end Sept.

9 ha (500 pitches)

Tariff : (2014 Price) 31.52€ ♦♦ ⬛ 🔲 [½] (10A) – Extra per person 10.10€ – Reservation fee 25€

Rental rates : (2014 Price) (from beginning April to end Sept.) ♿ (1 mobile home) – 45 🚐 – 11 🏠 – 139 canvas bungalows. Per night from 22 to 180€ – Per week from 144 to 1,260€ – Reservation fee 25€

🚰 borne

Surroundings : ⛱ 🏊 ⚠

Leisure activities : 🍴 🍽 🎮 🏓 🚣 🛶

Facilities : ♿ ⚿ 🚿 ᴪ launderette 🧺

Nearby : 🛒 🚲 🎣 ⚓

BISCARROSSE-PLAGE

40600 – Michelin map **335** E8

▶ Paris 669 – Bordeaux 91 – Mont-de-Marsan 100

⛰ Campéole le Vivier

📞 0558782576. www.camping-biscarosse.info

Address : 681 rue du Tit (north of the resort, 700m from the beach)

17 ha (830 pitches)

Rentals : ♿ (1 mobile home) – 74 🚐 – 20 🏠 – 186 canvas bungalows.

Surroundings : 🏊
Leisure activities : 🍴 🎮 🏓 🚣 🚲 🛶 multi-sports ground, entertainment room
Facilities : ♿ ⚿ ᴪ launderette 🧺 refrigerated food storage facilities
Nearby : 🏊

GPS Longitude : -1.24056
Latitude : 44.45938

The pitches of many campsites are marked out with low hedges of attractive bushes and shrubs.

BLASIMON

33540 – Michelin map **335** K6 – pop. 866 – alt. 80

▶ Paris 607 – Bordeaux 47 – Mérignac 63 – Pessac 60

⛰ Le Lac

📞 0556715962. http://www.gironde.fr/jcms/c_5115/les-domaines-d-hostens-et-blasimon

Address : Domaine departemental Volny Favory (at the leisure and activity park)

Opening times : from mid April to end Oct.

50 ha/0.5 (39 pitches) flat, grassy

Tariff : (2014 Price) ♦ 3€ ⬛ 🔲 12.50€ – [½] (1A) 3€

Rental rates : (from beginning June to end Sept.) – 9 🚐. Per night from 35 to 50€ – Per week from 200 to 300€

🚰 7 🔲 15€

Surroundings : 🏊 🚣 ⚠
Leisure activities : 🎮
Facilities : ♿ ⚿ 🚿 ✏
At the leisure/activities centre : 🍴 🧺 🚣 🍽 🏖 (beach) 🛶

BORDEAUX

33000 – Michelin map **335** H5 – pop. 236 725 – alt. 4

▶ Paris 572 – Mont-de-Marsan 138 – Bayonne 191 – Arcachon 72

⛰ International de Bordeaux Lac

📞 0557877060. www.camping-bordeaux.com

Address : at Bordeaux Lac, Bruges, Bvld Jacques Chaban-Delmas – take exit 5 from the bypass: Parc des expositions

Opening times : Permanent

13 ha/6 for camping (340 pitches) flat, grassy

Tariff : 32€ ♦♦ ⬛ 🔲 [½] (10A) – Extra per person 9€

Rental rates : Permanent ♿ (1 mobile home) – 231 🚐 – 9 🏠. Per night from 39 to 240€ – Per week from 273 to 1,680€

🚰 borne

The site is beside several small but pretty lakes.

Surroundings : 🏊
Leisure activities : 🍴 🧺 🚣 🚲 🛷
Facilities : ♿ ⚿ 🚿 🧺 🛒 ᴪ launderette 🏊 🧺
Nearby : 🛶 🎣

GPS Longitude : -0.5827
Latitude : 44.89759

*For more information on visiting particular towns or regions, consult the relevant regional **MICHELIN Green Guide**. We also recommend you use the appropriate Michelin regional map to locate your selected campsite, to calculate distances and to work out the best route.*

BRANTÔME

24310 – Michelin map **329** E3 – pop. 2 140 – alt. 104

▶ Paris 470 – Angoulême 58 – Limoges 83 – Nontron 23

⛰ Brantôme Peyrelevade

📞 0553057524. www.camping-dordogne.net

Address : avenue André Maurois (located 1km east along the D 78; beside the Dronne river)

Opening times : from beginning May to end Sept.

5 ha (170 pitches) flat, grassy

Tariff : (2014 Price) 25€ ♦♦ ⬛ 🔲 [½] (10A) – Extra per person 5€ Reservation fee 10€

Rental rates : (2014 Price) (from beginning May to end Sept.) – 22 🚐 – 5 tent lodges. Per night from 23 to 90€ – Per week from 195 to 620€ – Reservation fee 10€

🚰 10 🔲 21€

Surroundings : 🏊 🚣 🏊
Leisure activities : 🍴 🚣 🍽 🛷 🏖 (beach) 🛶
Facilities : ♿ ⚿ 🚿 🧺 ᴪ launderette

GPS Longitude : 0.66043
Latitude : 45.36107

LE BUGUE

24260 – Michelin map **329** G6 – pop. 2 800 – alt. 62
▶ Paris 522 – Bergerac 47 – Brive-la-Gaillarde 72 – Cahors 86

Vagues-Océanes La Linotte ♣♦

📞 02 51 28 28 38. www.vagues-oceanes.com – limited spaces for one-night stay

Address : route de Rouffignac (3.5km northeast along the D 710 following the signs for Périgueux and turn right onto D 32)

Opening times : from beginning April to end Sept.

13 ha/2.5 for camping (120 pitches) terraced, flat and relatively flat, grassy

Tariff : (2014 Price) 40€ ♣♦ ⬛ 🔲 ⚡ (10A) – Extra per person 8€ Reservation fee 26€

Rental rates : (from beginning April to end Sept.) – 2 caravans – 99 🚐 – 7 🏠. Per night from 36 to 163€ – Per week from 252 to 1,141€ – Reservation fee 26€

🚰 borne 4.50€

A very undulating site with few pitches for tents and caravans.

Surroundings : 🏞 ⬲ 🏕 ♒
Leisure activities : ⛲ 🏛 🏃 jacuzzi ⛵ ╔
🏊 ⛷ multi-sports ground
Facilities : ♿ ⚬ 🏠 🍴 launderette 🐾

GPS	Longitude : 0.93659
	Latitude : 44.93386

Les Trois Caupain

📞 05 53 07 24 60. www.camping-des-trois-caupain.com

Address : allée Paul-Jean Souriau

Opening times : from beginning April to end Oct.

4 ha (160 pitches) flat, grassy

Tariff : 24.20€ ♣♦ ⬛ 🔲 ⚡ (16A) – Extra per person 5.50€ – Reservation fee 5€

Rental rates : (from beginning April to end Oct.) – 42 🚐. Per night from 35 to 66€ – Per week from 159 to 700€ – Reservation fee 15€

🚰 borne 5€ – 25 🔲 9.90€ – 🚐 9.90€

Surroundings : 🏞 ♒
Leisure activities : ✗ 🏊 🚣 multi-sports ground
Facilities : ♿ ⚬ 🏠 🏕 🍴 launderette 🐾
Nearby : 🐟 large aquarium

GPS	Longitude : 0.93178
	Latitude : 44.90916

LE BUISSON-DE-CADOUIN

24480 – Michelin map **329** G6 – pop. 2 143 – alt. 63
▶ Paris 532 – Bergerac 38 – Périgueux 52 – Sarlat-la-Canéda 36

Domaine de Fromengal ♣♦

📞 05 53 63 11 55. www.domaine-fromengal.com

Address : La Combe de Cussac (6.5km southwest along the D 29, follow the signs for Lalinde, turn left onto D 29, follow the signs for Cadouin and take the road to the right)

22 ha/3 for camping (90 pitches) adjacent wood

Rentals : 26 🚐 – 21 🏠 – 4 canvas bungalows.

Surroundings : 🏞 🏕 ♒
Leisure activities : ✗ 🏛 🏃 ⛵ 🚲 🍴
🏊 ⛷
Facilities : ♿ ⚬ ▦ 🏠 🏕 🍴 launderette
🏊 🐾

GPS	Longitude : 0.86006
	Latitude : 44.82292

*We value your opinion and welcome your feedback.
Do email us at campingfrance@tp.michelin.com*

BUNUS

64120 – Michelin map **342** F3 – pop. 147 – alt. 186
▶ Paris 820 – Bayonne 61 – Hasparren 38 – Mauléon-Licharre 22

Inxauseta

📞 05 59 37 81 49. www.inxauseta.fr

Address : In the village, near the church

Opening times : from mid June to mid Sept.

0.8 ha (40 pitches) relatively flat

Tariff : ♦ 4.60€ ⬛ 🔲 4.60€ – ⚡ (5A) 3.10€

Lovely sitting rooms in an old renovated Basque house where exhibitions are held (paintings, etc.).

Surroundings : 🏞 ⬲ ♒
Leisure activities : 🏛
Facilities : ♿ ⚬ 🏕 🍴

GPS	Longitude : -1.06794
	Latitude : 43.20974

The information in the guide may have changed since going to press.

CAMBO-LES-BAINS

64250 – Michelin map **342** D2 – pop. 6 466 – alt. 67 – ♨
▶ Paris 783 – Bayonne 20 – Biarritz 21 – Pau 115

Bixta Eder

📞 05 59 29 94 23. www.campingbixtaeder.com

Address : 52 avenue d'Espagne (1.3km southwest along the D 918, follow the signs for St-Jean-de-Luz)

Opening times : from mid April to mid Oct.

1 ha (90 pitches) relatively flat, flat, grassy, gravelled

Tariff : 20€ ♣♦ ⬛ 🔲 ⚡ (10A) – Extra per person 4.50€ – Reservation fee 15€

Rental rates : (from mid March to mid Nov.) – 19 🚐 – 3 🏠. Per night from 38 to 50€ – Per week from 240 to 635€ Reservation fee 15€

A pleasant, small site with some well-appointed mobile homes.

Surroundings : 🏕 ♒
Leisure activities : 🏛
Facilities : ♿ 🏠 🍴 launderette 🐾
Nearby : ✗ 🚣

GPS	Longitude : -1.41448
	Latitude : 43.35567

CAMPAGNE

24260 – Michelin map **329** G6 – pop. 367 – alt. 60
▶ Paris 542 – Bergerac 51 – Belvès 19 – Les Eyzies-de-Tayac 7

Le Val de la Marquise ♣♦

📞 05 53 54 74 10. www.levaldelamarquise.com

Address : Le Moulin (500m east along the D 35, follow the signs for St-Cyprien)

Opening times : from beginning April to end Sept.

4 ha (104 pitches)

Tariff : 27.30€ ♣♦ ⬛ 🔲 ⚡ (16A) – Extra per person 6.40€

Rental rates : (from beginning April to end Sept.) 🚣 – 18 🚐 – 8 🏠. Per night from 36 to 122€ – Per week from 203 to 854€ Reservation fee 20€

🚰 borne 12.90€

Surroundings : 🏕 ♒
Leisure activities : ✗ 🏛 🏃 ⛵ 🏊 🚣
Facilities : ♿ ⚬ ▦ 🏠 🍴 launderette 🐾

GPS	Longitude : 0.9743
	Latitude : 44.90637

CARSAC-AILLAC

24200 – Michelin map **329** I6 – pop. 1 479 – alt. 80
▶ Paris 536 – Brive-la-Gaillarde 59 – Gourdon 18 – Sarlat-la-Canéda 9

⚠ Le Plein Air des Bories

☏ 05 53 28 15 67. www.camping-desbories.com

Address : Les Bories (1.3km south along the D 703, follow the signs for Vitrac and take road to the left; beside the Dordogne river)

Opening times : from mid April to mid Sept.

3.5 ha (110 pitches)

Tariff : (2014 Price) 27.60€ ✶✶ 🚗 ▣ ⚡ (6A)

Extra per person 6.50€ – Reservation fee 15€

Rental rates : (2014 Price) (from mid April to mid Sept.) – 41 🛏 – 8 canvas bungalows. Per night from 30 to 78€ – Per week from 180 to 730€ – Reservation fee 15€

Surroundings : ⟋ 🗀 ♒
Leisure activities : 🎯 ⚆ 🏊 (open air in season) 🎣 🚴
Facilities : ⚐ ⚲ 🍴 ▣

GPS Longitude : 1.2684
Latitude : 44.83299

⚠ Le Rocher de la Cave

☏ 05 53 28 14 26. www.rocherdelacave.com

Address : La Pommarède (1.7km south along the D 703, follow the signs for Vitrac and take road to the left; beside the Dordogne)

Opening times : from beginning May to end Sept.

5 ha (150 pitches) flat, grassy

Tariff : (2014 Price) ✶ 6.70€ 🚗 ▣ 8.60€ – ⚡ (16A) 4€

Rental rates : (2014 Price) (from beginning May to end Sept.) – 23 🛏 – 12 canvas bungalows – 5 tent lodges. Per night from 25 to 100€ – Per week from 180 to 700€

🚐 borne

Surroundings : ⟋ ♒
Leisure activities : 🍷 ⚆ 🏊 🎣 🚴
Facilities : ⚐ ⚲ 🍴 launderette ⚇

GPS Longitude : 1.26719
Latitude : 44.82977

CASTELJALOUX

47700 – Michelin map **336** C4 – pop. 4 773 – alt. 52
▶ Paris 674 – Agen 55 – Langon 55 – Marmande 23

� Village Vacances Castel Chalets

(rental of chalets only)

☏ 05 53 93 07 45. www.castel-chalets.com

Address : route de Mont de Marsan, at the lake Clarens (2.5km southwest along the D 933, follow the signs for Mont-de-Marsan)

Opening times : Permanent

4 ha

Rental rates : ⚐ (1 chalet) – 25 🛏. Per night from 90 to 155€ – Per week from 275 to 720€

🚐 borne 10€ – 10 ▣ 15€

A small chalet village beside the lake, opposite the very well-equipped leisure and activity park.

Surroundings : ⟋ ≤ ♒ ⛰
Leisure activities : 🎯 ⚆ 🎣
Facilities : ⚲ ▥ 🍴
Nearby : 🍷 ✕ 🚲 🎿 ⚡ 🐎 forest trail

CASTELMORON-SUR-LOT

47260 – Michelin map **336** E3 – pop. 1 755 – alt. 49
▶ Paris 600 – Agen 33 – Bergerac 63 – Marmande 35

⚠ Village Vacances Port-Lalande

(rental of chalets only)

☏ 04 68 37 65 65. www.grandbleu.fr

Address : located 1.5km southeast

Opening times : from beginning April to beginning Oct..

4 ha flat, grassy
Rental rates : ⚐ (1 chalet) 🅿 – 60 🛏. Per night from 65 to 85€ – Per week from 196 to 917€

Beside the Lot river and a marina.

Surroundings : ⟋ ≤ ♢
Leisure activities : 🎮 ▣ 🏊 🏌 ⛵ hammam 🏊 🎣 spa centre
Facilities : ▥ 🍴 launderette
Nearby : ⚓

GPS Longitude : 0.50661
Latitude : 44.38803

Some campsites benefit from proximity to a municipal leisure centre.

CASTELNAUD-LA-CHAPELLE

24250 – Michelin map **329** H7 – pop. 477 – alt. 140
▶ Paris 539 – Le Bugue 29 – Les Eyzies-de-Tayac 27 – Gourdon 25

⚠ Flower Lou Castel

☏ 05 53 29 89 24. www.loucastel.com

Address : Prente Garde (take the southern exit along the D 57 then continue 3.4km along the road to the château, for caravans, access is strongly recommended via Pont-de-Cause and the D 50, follow the signs for Veyrines-de-Domme)

5.5 ha/2.5 for camping (110 pitches) adjacent wood

Rentals : 50 🛏 – 10 🛏.

Situated in a pleasant oak grove.

Surroundings : ⟋ 🗀 ♒♒
Leisure activities : 🎯 ⚆ 🏊 🎿 multi-sports ground
Facilities : ⚐ ⚲ 🍴 ⚇ 🍴 launderette

GPS Longitude : 1.13182
Latitude : 44.79746

⚠ Maisonneuve

☏ 05 53 29 51 29. www.campingmaisonneuve.com

Address : chemin de Maisonneuve (located 1km southeast along the D 57 and take road to the left; beside the Céou river)

Opening times : from beginning April to end Oct.

6 ha/3 for camping (140 pitches)

Tariff : (2014 Price) ✶ 7.20€ 🚗 ▣ 9€ – ⚡ (10A) 4.30€ – Reservation fee 15€

Rental rates : (2014 Price) (from beginning April to end Oct.) 🎿 (from beginning July to end Aug.) – 10 🛏 – 3 cabins in the trees – 2 tent lodges – 2 gîtes. Per night from 56 to 80€ – Per week from 290 to 850€ – Reservation fee 15€

🚐 borne

Based around an old renovated farmhouse and surrounded by flowers.

Surroundings : ≤ 🗀 ♒♒
Leisure activities : 🍷 ✕ 🎯 ⚆ 🏇 🏊 ⚽ 🎣
Facilities : ⚐ ⚲ ▥ 🍴 launderette ⚇

GPS Longitude : 1.15822
Latitude : 44.80482

CASTELS

24220 – Michelin map **329** H6 – pop. 647 – alt. 50
▶ Paris 551 – Bordeaux 181 – Montauban 145 – Brive-la-Gaillarde 73

🔺 Village Vacances La Noyeraie (rental of chalets only)

🖉 05 53 31 24 43. www.chaletlanoyeraie.fr

Address : Le Grelat (located 1km southeast along the D 703, follow the signs for Sarlat)

1.5 ha flat, grassy
Rentals : ⌖ 🅿 – 19 ⌂.

Surroundings : 🛶🛶
Leisure activities : 🖼 ⚓ 🏊 (open air in season)
Facilities : ⊶ 🎰 launderette

GPS Longitude : 1.08071
Latitude : 44.85004

CASTETS

40260 – Michelin map **335** E11 – pop. 1 945 – alt. 48
▶ Paris 710 – Dax 21 – Mimizan 40 – Mont-de-Marsan 61

🔺 Municipal Le Galan

🖉 05 58 89 43 52. www.camping-legalan.com

Address : 73 rue du Stade (located 1km east along the D 42, follow the signs for Taller and take turning to the right)

4 ha (181 pitches) flat and relatively flat, grassy, sandy
Rentals : 8 ⌻ – 5 ⌂ – 1 cabin.

Pilgrims on their way to Santiago de Compostella are welcome to stay in a small wooden cabin.

Surroundings : 🛶 🛶
Leisure activities : 🖼 ⚓ 🏊
Facilities : ⚓ ⊶ 🚿 🍽 🎰 launderette
Nearby : 🎿 fitness trail

GPS Longitude : -1.13754
Latitude : 43.88059

CASTILLON LA BATAILLE

33350 – Michelin map **335** K5 – pop. 3 203 – alt. 17
▶ Paris 549 – Bergerac 46 – Libourne 18 – Montpon-Ménestérol 27

🔺 Municipal La Pelouse

🖉 05 57 40 04 22. www.castillonlabataille.fr

Address : 2 prom. Dubourdieu (east of the town; beside the Dordogne river)

Opening times : from mid May to mid Oct.

0.5 ha (38 pitches) flat, grassy
Tariff : (2014 Price) 15€ ✶✶ 🚗 🔋 (15A) – Extra per person 5€

Surroundings : 🛶 🛶
Leisure activities : 🏊
Facilities : ⚓ ⊶ 🚿 🍽 🎰

GPS Longitude : -0.03569
Latitude : 44.85337

CÉNAC-ET-ST-JULIEN

24250 – Michelin map **329** I7 – pop. 1 218 – alt. 70
▶ Paris 537 – Le Bugue 34 – Gourdon 20 – Sarlat-la-Canéda 12

⛰ Le Pech de Caumont

🖉 05 53 28 21 63. www.pech-de-caumont.com

Address : situated 2km to the south

Opening times : from beginning April to end Sept.

2.2 ha (100 pitches)
Tariff : ⌖ 5.60€ 🚗 🔋 7.20€ – (16A) 3.60€ – Reservation fee 12.50€

Rental rates : (from beginning April to end Sept.) ⌖ – 20 ⌻ – 6 ⌂. Per night from 34 to 53€ – Per week from 200 to 670€ – Reservation fee 12.50€

Looking out over the Dordogne valley, opposite the village of Domme.

Surroundings : 🛶 ⚮ 🛶🛶
Leisure activities : 🍽 🖼 ⚓ 🏊
Facilities : ⚓ ⊶ 🚿 🍽 🎰 ⌕

GPS Longitude : 1.20908
Latitude : 44.78654

LA CHAPELLE-AUBAREIL

24290 – Michelin map **329** I5 – pop. 471 – alt. 230
▶ Paris 515 – Brive-la-Gaillarde 40 – Les Eyzies-de-Tayac 21 Montignac 9

⛰ La Fage

🖉 05 53 50 76 50, www.camping-lafage.com

Address : La Fage (1.2km northwest following signs for St-Amand-de-Coly, head towards D 704 and take road to the left)

Opening times : from mid April to mid Oct.

5 ha (60 pitches)
Tariff : (2014 Price) 29€ ✶✶ 🚗 🔋 (10A) – Extra per person 6.50€ Reservation fee 10€

Rental rates : (2014 Price) (from mid April to mid Oct.) – 25 ⌻ – 6 ⌂. Per night from 35 to 118€ – Per week from 209 to 830€ Reservation fee 10€

Surroundings : 🛶 🛶🛶
Leisure activities : ✕ 🖼 ⚓ 🏊
Facilities : ⚓ ⊶ 🔧 🍽 🎰 launderette ⌕

GPS Longitude : 1.1882
Latitude : 45.01745

CONTIS-PLAGE

40170 – Michelin map **335** D10
▶ Paris 714 – Bayonne 87 – Castets 32 – Dax 52

⛰⛰ Yelloh! Village Lous Seurrots ♠♠

🖉 05 58 42 85 82. www.lous-seurrots.com

Address : 606 avenue de l'Océan (take the southeastern exit along the D 41, near the Courant de Contis (small river), 700m from the beach)

Opening times : from end March to end Sept.

14 ha (610 pitches) undulating, flat and relatively flat, grassy, sandy
Tariff : 49€ ✶✶ 🚗 🔋 (16A) – Extra per person 8€

Rental rates : (from end March to end Sept.) ⚓ (1 chalet) – 239 ⌻ – 101 ⌂ – 20 canvas bungalows. Per night from 30 to 217€ – Per week from 210 to 1,519€

Surroundings : 🛶 🛶
Leisure activities : 🍽 ✕ 🖼 🎭 (open-air theatre) ⚓ 🚲 🎯 🎿 🏊 multi-sports ground
Facilities : ⚓ ⊶ 🎰 🚿 🍽 launderette 🗄 ⌕ refrigerated food storage facilities
Nearby : 🐎 🏄 surfing

GPS Longitude : -1.31685
Latitude : 44.08878

These symbols are used for a campsite that is exceptional in its category :

⛰⛰...⛰ *Particularly pleasant setting, quality and range of services available*

🛶🛶 *Tranquil, isolated site – quiet site, particularly at night*

⚮⚮ *Exceptional view – interesting or panoramic view*

COURBIAC

47370 – Michelin map **336** I3 – pop. 110 – alt. 145
▶ Paris 623 – Bordeaux 172 – Agen 46 – Montauban 59

⚲ Le Pouchou

✆ 05 53 40 72 68, www.camping-le-pouchou.com

Address : head 1.8km west following signs for Tournon-d'Agenais, take road to the left

Opening times : from beginning March to end Nov.

15 ha/2 for camping (30 pitches)

Tariff : 19.30€ ★★ ⇔ 国 ⑭ (4A) – Extra per person 4.75€
Rental rates : Permanent ᴳ (1 chalet) – 1 ⛺ – 8 ⛺. Per night from 55 to 100€ – Per week from 248 to 648€
⛽ borne – 3 国 10.55€ – ⛽ 13€

A pleasant setting among undulating hills, beside a small lake.

Surroundings :	⚲ ← ⚲	
Leisure activities : ⛵ 🏠 🚲 ⚓ ⚓ walking trails		**G P S** Longitude : 1.02293 Latitude : 44.37854
Facilities : ᴳ ⚬ ⚬ ⚬ ⚓ 🍴 launderette		

COUX-ET-BIGAROQUE

24220 – Michelin map **329** G7 – pop. 993 – alt. 85
▶ Paris 548 – Bergerac 44 – Le Bugue 14 – Les Eyzies-de-Tayac 17

⚲ Les Valades

✆ 05 53 29 14 27. http://www.lesvalades.com

Address : Les Valades (4km northwest along the D 703, follow the signs for Les Eyzies then take left turning)

Opening times : from beginning April to end Sept.

11 ha (85 pitches) small lake, natural setting among trees and bushes

Tariff : 30€ ★★ ⇔ 国 ⑭ (10A) – Extra per person 7€ – Reservation fee 15€
Rental rates : (from beginning April to end Sept.) ᴳ (1 chalet) – 6 ⛺ – 19 ⛺ – 2 tent lodges. Per week from 230 to 890€ Reservation fee 15€

Surroundings : ⚲ ← ⚲ ⚲	
Leisure activities : ✗ 🏠 ⚓ 🚲 ⚓ ☀ (beach) ⚓ 🐎	**G P S** Longitude : 0.96367 Latitude : 44.8599
Facilities : ᴳ ⚬ ⚬ – 10 individual sanitary facilities (🚿 ⚬ 🚽 wc) ⚓ 🍴 launderette ⚓	

COUZE-ET-ST-FRONT

24150 – Michelin map **329** F7 – pop. 775 – alt. 45
▶ Paris 544 – Bergerac 21 – Lalinde 4 – Mussidan 46

⚲ Les Moulins

✆ 06 89 85 76 24. www.campingdesmoulins.com – limited spaces for one-night stay

Address : Les Maury Bas (take the southeastern exit along the D 660, follow the signs for Beaumont and take a right turn, near the sports field; beside the Couze river)

Opening times : Permanent

2.5 ha (50 pitches)

Tariff : 32€ ★★ ⇔ 国 ⑭ (10A) – Extra per person 9€ – Reservation fee 10€

Rental rates : Permanent – 10 ⛺. Per night from 50 to 80€ – Per week from 220 to 620€ – Reservation fee 10€
⛽ borne 6€ – 8 国 12€ – ⛽ ⑭ 12€

In a green setting perched on a rocky spur opposite the village.

Surroundings : ← ⚲ ⚲	
Leisure activities : ⛵ 🏠 ⚓ 🚲 ⚓ ⚓ ⚓	**G P S** Longitude : 0.70448 Latitude : 44.82646
Facilities : ᴳ ⚬ 国 🍴 launderette	

DAGLAN

24250 – Michelin map **329** I7 – pop. 555 – alt. 101
▶ Paris 547 – Cahors 48 – Fumel 40 – Gourdon 18

⚲ La Peyrugue

✆ 05 53 28 40 26. www.peyrugue.com

Address : La Peyrugue (located 1.5km north along the D 57, follow the signs for St-Cybranet, 150m from the Céou river)

Opening times : from beginning April to end Sept.

5 ha/2.5 for camping (85 pitches)

Tariff : ★ 7.80€ ⇔ 国 11.50€ – ⑭ (10A) 4.20€ – Reservation fee 10€
Rental rates : (from beginning April to end Sept.) ᴳ (2 chalets) – 3 ⛺ – 10 ⛺ – 2 canvas bungalows – 1 gîte. Per night from 30 to 120€ – Per week from 210 to 840€ – Reservation fee 10€

Surroundings : ⚲ ⚲ ⚲	
Leisure activities : ⛵ 🏠 ⚓ ⚓	**G P S** Longitude : 1.18798 Latitude : 44.75267
Facilities : ᴳ ⚬ ⚓ 🍴 launderette ⚓	

DAX

40100 – Michelin map **335** E12 – pop. 21 003 – alt. 12 – ⚕
▶ Paris 727 – Bayonne 54 – Biarritz 61 – Bordeaux 144

⚲ Les Chênes ⚐⚐

✆ 05 58 90 05 53. www.camping-les-chenes.fr

Address : allée du Bois de Boulogne (1.8km west of the town centre, in the Bois de Boulogne, 200m from the Adour river)

Opening times : from mid March to beginning Nov.

5 ha (230 pitches)

Tariff : (2014 Price) 20.30€ ★★ ⇔ 国 ⑭ (10A) – Extra per person 6€ Reservation fee 7.50€
Rental rates : (2014 Price) (from mid March to beginning Nov.) – 34 ⛺ – 20 ⛺. Per night from 43 to 89€ – Per week from 301 to 621€ – Reservation fee 7.50€
⛽ borne 6€

In a pleasant wood near a lake.

Surroundings : ⚲ ⚲ ⚲	
Leisure activities : 🏠 ⚓ ⚓ 🚲 ⚓	**G P S** Longitude : -1.07174 Latitude : 43.71138
Facilities : ᴳ ⚬ 🚿 ⚓ ⚓ 🍴 launderette ⚓	
Nearby : ⛵ ✗ ⚓ 🐎	

⚲ Le Bascat

✆ 05 58 56 16 68. www.campinglebascat.com

Address : rue de Jouandin (2.8km west from the town centre through the Bois de Boulogne, access from the Vieux Pont (left bank) and the avenue running along the banks of the Adour)

Opening times : from beginning March to beginning Nov.

3.5 ha (160 pitches) terraced, flat, grassy, gravelled

Tariff : 19€ ★★ ⇔ 国 ⑭ (6A) – Extra per person 4.50 € – Reservation fee 5€

Rental rates : (from mid March to beginning Nov.) – 41 🚍. Per night from 45 to 65€ – Per week from 299 to 375€ – Reservation fee 5 €

🚰 borne 12€ – 10 📦 12€ – 💧12€

Surroundings : 🌳 ♨
Leisure activities : 🛶
Facilities : ♿ ⚡ 🚻 🧺 ♨ 🚰 launderette ☕

For more information on visiting particular towns or regions, consult the relevant regional MICHELIN Green Guide. We also recommend you use the appropriate Michelin regional map to locate your selected campsite, to calculate distances and to work out the best route.

DOMME

24250 – Michelin map **329** I7 – pop. 989 – alt. 250
▶ Paris 538 – Cahors 51 – Fumel 50 – Gourdon 20

🏔 Village Vacances Les Ventoulines

(rental of chalets only)

📞 0553283629. www.gites-dordogne-sarlat.fr

Address : Les Ventoulines (3.6km to the southeast)

Opening times : Permanent

3 ha

Rental rates :(2014 Price) 🅿 – 6 🚍 – 18 🏠. Per night from 80 to 100€ – Per week from 450 to 640€

Surroundings : 🌳 ♨♨
Leisure activities : 🛶 🚣 📺 🎿
Facilities : ♿ ⚡ 🚻 🧺 launderette

🏔 Perpetuum 👥

📞 0553283518. www.campingleperpetuum.com

Address : head 2km south along the D 50 and take road to the right; beside the Dordogne river

Opening times : from beginning May to mid Oct.

4.5 ha (120 pitches) flat, grassy

Tariff : 🧍 7.90€ – 🚗 3€ 📦 7.90€ – 🔌 (10A) 5€ – Reservation fee 92€
Rental rates : (from beginning May to end Sept.) 🏕 – 30 🚍. Per week from 240 to 850€ – Reservation fee 12€

🚰 borne 15€

Surroundings : 🌳 🚤 ♨♨
Leisure activities : ✕ 🛶 🏹 🚣 🎿 ⛵ 🏊 multi-sports ground entertainment room
Facilities : ♿ ⚡ 🚽 ♨ 🧺 launderette ☕

🏔 Village Vacances de la Combe (rental of chalets only)

📞 0631405341, www.sarlat-gites-dordogne.com

Address : Le Pradal (located 1.5km southeast)

Opening times : from beginning April to mid Nov.

2 ha terraced, flat, grassy

Rental rates : ♿ (1 chalet) 🅿 –12 🏠. Per night from 65 to 75€ – Per week from 350 to 825€ – Reservation fee 18€

Surroundings : 🌳 ♨♨
Leisure activities : 🛶 🎿
Facilities : ⚡ 🚽 🚻 ♨ 📺

🏔 Le Bosquet

📞 0553283739. www.lebosquet.com

Address : La Rivière (900m south of Vitrac-Port, along the D 46)

Opening times : from mid April to end Sept.

1.5 ha (60 pitches)

Tariff : 21.50€ 🧍🧍 🚗 📦 🔌 (10A) – Extra per person 5.20€

Reservation fee 8€

Rental rates : (from mid April to end Sept.) – 21 🚍. Per night from 36 to 65€ – Per week from 230 to 680€ – Reservation fee 8€

🚰 borne – 💧9€

Surroundings : 🌳 ⬅ ☁ ♨♨
Leisure activities : ✕ 🛶 🚣 🎿
Facilities : ♿ ⚡ ♨ 🧺 📺 ☕

🏔 Le Moulin de Caudon

📞 0553310369. www.campingdordogne.com

Address : Caudon (6km northeast along the D 46e and the D 50,follow the signs for Groléjac; near the Dordogne – recommended route for caravans via Vitrac-Port)

Opening times : Permanent

2 ha (60 pitches) flat, grassy

Tariff : 🧍 4€ – 🚗 4€ 📦 3.30€ – 🔌 (10A) 3.30€
Rental rates : Permanent 🏕 – 4 🚍. Per week from 210 to 500€

🚰 borne – 💧🔌14€

Surroundings : ☁ ♨♨
Leisure activities : 🛶 🚣
Facilities : ♿ ⚡ (season) ♨ 🚻 📺
Nearby : 🏊

EYMET

24500 – Michelin map **329** D8 – pop. 2 563 – alt. 54
▶ Paris 560 – Bergerac 24 – Castillonnès 19 – Duras 22

🏔 Le Château

📞 0553238028. www.eymetcamping.com

Address : rue de la Sole (behind the château; beside the Dropt river)

Opening times : from end April to end Sept.

1.5 ha (66 pitches) flat, grassy, adjacent public garden

Tariff : 15€ 🧍🧍 🚗 📦 🔌 (10A) – Extra per person 4€

A pleasant location by the river, the municipal park and the ramparts.

Surroundings : 🌳 ☁ ♨♨
Leisure activities : 🚲 🛶
Facilities : ♿ ⚡ 🚲 🧺 ♨ 📺

Key to rentals symbols:

12 🚍	*Number of mobile homes*
20 🏠	*Number of chalets*
6 🛏	*Number of rooms to rent*
Per night 30–50€	*Minimum/maximum rate per night*
Per week 300–1,000€	*Minimum/maximum rate per week*

GPS Longitude : -1.07043 Latitude : 43.70617
GPS Longitude : 1.22588 Latitude : 44.84048
GPS Longitude : 1.22065 Latitude : 44.81542
GPS Longitude : 1.22243 Latitude : 44.8161
GPS Longitude : 1.22555 Latitude : 44.82185
GPS Longitude : 1.24466 Latitude : 44.82061
GPS Longitude : 0.39584 Latitude : 44.66925

LES EYZIES-DE-TAYAC

24620 – Michelin map **329** H6 – pop. 839 – alt. 70
▶ Paris 536 – Brive-la-Gaillarde 62 – Fumel 62 – Lalinde 35

⚠ Vacances Directes Le Mas 👥

(rental of mobile homes and chalets only)

📞 0825 133 400. www.campinglemas.com

Address : 7 km east along the D 47 follow the signs for Sarlat-la-Canéda then continue 2.5km following signs for Sireuil to the left

5 ha

Surroundings : 🌳 � ♨
Leisure activities : 🍷 🍴 (farm-inn) 🧗 🏄
🏓 🏊 🛶
Facilities : ⚿ 🚿 launderette 🧺

GPS Longitude : 1.0849
Latitude : 44.93675

⚠ La Rivière

📞 05 53 06 97 14. www.lariviereleseyzies.com

Address : 3 route du Sorcier (located 1km northwest along the D 47, follow the signs for Périgueux and take the turning to the left after the bridge, 200m from the Vézère)

Opening times : from mid April to mid Oct.

7 ha/3 for camping (120 pitches) flat, grassy

Tariff : (2014 Price) 🚶 6.99€ 🚗 📷 10.54€ – (½) (10A) 4.80€
Reservation fee 4€

Rental rates : (2014 Price) (from mid April to mid Oct.) – 13 🏠 – 6 🛏 – 1 tent lodge. Per night from 37 to 100€ – Per week from 169 to 948€ – Reservation fee 4€

🚐 borne 4.50€ – 20 📷 14€ – 🔌 (½)14€

Surroundings : �   ♨
Leisure activities : 🍷 🍴 🏄 🏊 🛶
Facilities : ⚿ 🚿 🍴 🏊 🛶 🚿
launderette 🧺

GPS Longitude : 1.00582
Latitude : 44.93732

⚠ La Ferme du Pelou

📞 05 53 06 98 17. www.lafermedupelou.com

Address : Le Pelou (4km northeast along the D 706, follow the signs for Montignac then take the turning to the right)

Opening times : from mid March to mid Nov.

1 ha (65 pitches)

Tariff : 15.60€ 🚶🚶 🚗 📷 (½) (10A) –
Extra per person 4.20€

Rental rates : (from mid March to mid Nov.) – 2 🏠. Per night from 40 to 68€ – Per week from 315 to 480€

🚐 borne
A farm campsite.

Surroundings : 🚲 � ♨
Leisure activities : 🖼 🛶
Facilities : ⚿ 🚿 launderette
Nearby : 🐎

GPS Longitude : 1.04472
Latitude : 44.95527

La Ferme du Pelou

*The classification (1 to 5 tents, **black** or red) that we award to selected sites in this guide is our own system. It should not be confused with the classification (1 to 5 stars) of official organisations.*

FUMEL

47500 – Michelin map **336** H3 – pop. 5 186 – alt. 70
▶ Paris 594 – Agen 55 – Bergerac 64 – Cahors 48

⚠ Village Vacances Domaine de Guillalmes

(rental of chalets only)

📞 05 53 71 01 99. www.domainedeguillalmes.com

Address : La Gaillarde (3km east along the D 911, follow the signs for Cahors, at Condat exit follow right turn for 1km; beside the Lot river)

Opening times : from beginning March to end Nov.

3 ha flat, grassy

Rental rates : ♿ (1 chalet) – 1 🏠 – 18 🏡 – 2 gîtes. Per night from 60 to 80€ – Per week from 390 to 710€ – Reservation fee 10€

🚐 8 📷 14€

Surroundings : 🚲 ♨
Leisure activities : 🍷 🍴 🏄 🚴 🏊 🛶 🚿
Facilities : 🚿 🅿 🍴 🍴 🛶

GPS Longitude : 1.00955
Latitude : 44.48343

⚠ Les Catalpas

📞 05 53 71 11 99. www.les-catalpas.com

Address : La Tour, chemin de la plaine de Condat (situated 2km east along the D 911, follow the signs for Cahors; at the Condat exit, follow the road to the right for 1.2km; beside the Lot river)

Opening times : from beginning April to mid Nov.

2 ha (80 pitches) flat, grassy, hard surface areas

Tariff : 21.50€ 🚶🚶 🚗 📷 (½) (10A) – Extra per person 5.50€

Rental rates : (from mid March to mid Nov.) – 4 🏠 – 3 🏡 – 1 gîte. Per night from 35 to 65€ – Per week from 200 to 590€

🚐 8 📷 17.50€

Cycle tourists are welcome.

Surroundings : 🚲 ♨
Leisure activities : 🏄 🛶
Facilities : 🚿 🍴 🛶

GPS Longitude : 0.99737
Latitude : 44.48916

We have selected the best campsites in France with our usual care, listing those with the best facilities in the most pleasant surroundings.

GABARRET

40310 – Michelin map **335** L11 – pop. 1 270 – alt. 153
▶ Paris 715 – Agen 66 – Auch 76 – Bordeaux 140

⚠ Parc Municipal Touristique la Chêneraie

📞 05 58 44 92 62. la-cheneraie@orange.fr

Address : take the eastern exit along the D 35, follow the signs for Castelnau-d'Auzan and take the road to the right

Opening times : from beginning March to end Oct.

0.7 ha (36 pitches) relatively flat, flat, grassy, sandy

Tariff : (2014 Price) 🚶 2.73€ 🚗 1.24€ 📷 2.52€ – (½) (10A) 2€

Rental rates : (2014 Price) Permanent – 4 🏠 – 10 gîtes. Per night from 49 to 57€ – Per week from 164 to 297€

Surroundings : 🚲 ♨
Leisure activities : 🏄 🚴
Facilities : ♿ 🚿 🍴 🍴 🛶
Nearby : 🏊 🛶

GPS Longitude : 0.01622
Latitude : 43.98361

GRADIGNAN

33170 – Michelin map **335** H6 – pop. 23 386 – alt. 26
▶ Paris 592 – Bordeaux 9 – Lyon 550 – Nantes 336

⛰ Beausoleil

℘ 05 56 89 17 66. www.camping-gradignan.com

Address : 371 cours du Général de Gaulle (on the bypass (rocade), take exit 16 for Gradignan)

Opening times : Permanent

0.5 ha (31 pitches) relatively flat, flat, grassy, fine gravel

Tariff : 20€ ⚭⚭ ⬅ 国 ⚡ (10A) – Extra per person 3.50€
Rental rates : Permanent ⚮ – 4 ⏚. Per week from 260 to 410€
There's a shuttle bus for the tram to Bordeaux.

Surroundings : ⏃ 🄀🄀
Facilities : ⚅ ⚮ ⍔ ⊞ ⚒ ⚮ ⚘ launderette

G P S Longitude : -0.6278
Latitude : 44.75573

GROLÉJAC

24250 – Michelin map **329** I7 – pop. 654 – alt. 67
▶ Paris 537 – Gourdon 14 – Périgueux 80 – Sarlat-la-Canéda 13

⛰⛰ Les Granges ⚬⚬

℘ 05 53 28 11 15. www.lesgranges-fr.com – limited spaces for one-night stay

Address : in the village

Opening times : from end April to mid Sept.

6 ha (188 pitches) terraced, flat and relatively flat, grassy

Tariff : 30.80€ ⚭⚭ ⬅ 国 ⚡ (6A) – Extra per person 8€ – Reservation fee 25€

Rental rates : (from end April to mid Sept.) – 55 ⏚ – 16 ⏚ – 8 tent lodges. Per night from 37 to 115€ – Per week from 257 to 802€ – Reservation fee 25€

Surroundings : ⚮ ⏃ 🄀🄀
Leisure activities : ⚐✗ 🖼 ⚘⚘ ⚒ ⚘⚘
⚒
Facilities : ⚅ ⚮ ⚑ ⚒ ⚒ launderette ⚮
Nearby : ⚒

G P S Longitude : 1.29117
Latitude : 44.81579

⛰ Le Lac de Groléjac

℘ 05 53 59 48 70. www.camping-dulac-dordogne.com

Address : Le Roc Percé (situated 2km south along the D 704, D 50, follow the signs for Domme and turn left, following signs for Nabirat)

Opening times : from beginning May to mid Sept.

2 ha (92 pitches)

Tariff : 20.20€ ⚭⚭ ⬅ 国 ⚡ (10A) – Extra per person 5.50€ – Reservation fee 15€

Rental rates : (from beginning May to mid Sept.) – 19 ⏚ – 9 canvas bungalows. Per night from 35 to 55€ – Per week from 215 to 740€ – Reservation fee 15€

⏚ borne – ⚒ ⚡ 12€

Surroundings : ⚮ ⚒ 🄀🄀 ⚠
Leisure activities : ⚮ ⚒ pedalos ⚮
Facilities : ⚅ ⚮ (July-Aug.) ⚒ ⚒ ⚒ ⚒
Nearby : ⚒

G P S Longitude : 1.29441
Latitude : 44.802

HAGETMAU

40700 – Michelin map **335** H13 – pop. 4 539 – alt. 96
▶ Paris 737 – Aire-sur-l'Adour 34 – Dax 45 – Mont-de-Marsan 29

⛰ Municipal de la Cité Verte

℘ 05 58 79 79 79. www.laciteverte.com

Address : chemin des Loussets (to the south along the av. du Dr-Édouard-Castera, near some arenas and the swimming pool; beside a river)

Opening times : from beginning June to end Sept.

0.4 ha (24 pitches) flat, grassy

Tariff : (2014 Price) 22.50€ ⚭⚭ ⬅ 国 ⚡ (16A)

Close to municipal sports buildings and leisure facillities.

Surroundings : ⚮ ⏃ 🄀🄀
Leisure activities : ✗ 🖼 ⚘⚘ ⚮
Facilities : ⚮ ⚑ ⍔ – 24 individual sanitary facilities (⚒ ⚒ ⚒ wc) ⚮ ⚒
Nearby : ⚒ 🖼 ⚒ sports trail

G P S Longitude : -0.59215
Latitude : 43.65233

HAUTEFORT

24390 – Michelin map **329** H4 – pop. 1 086 – alt. 160
▶ Paris 466 – Bordeaux 190 – Périgueux 60 – Brive-la-Gaillarde 57

⛰⛰ Village Vacances Les Sources (rental of chalets only)

℘ 05 53 51 96 56. www.dordogne-gite.fr

Address : La Génèbre (2.6km south along the D 704 and the D 62E4)

Opening times : from beginning April to mid Nov.

30 ha/5 for camping undulating

Rental rates : ⚑ – 15 ⏚ – 15 gîtes. Per night from 150 to 200€ – Per week from 240 to 890€

Surroundings : ⚮ ≺ Château de Hautefort
Leisure activities : ⚐ 🖼 ⚘⚘ ⚒ paintballing
Facilities : ⚅ ⚮ ⚒ ⚒ launderette

G P S Longitude : 1.12641
Latitude : 45.25085

HENDAYE

64700 – Michelin map **342** B4 – pop. 14 412 – alt. 30
▶ Paris 799 – Biarritz 31 – Pau 143 – St-Jean-de-Luz 12

⛰⛰ Eskualduna ⚬⚬

℘ 05 59 20 04 64. www.camping-eskualduna.fr

Address : route de la Corniche (situated 2km east, rte da la Corniche; beside a stream)

Opening times : from beginning May to end Sept.

10 ha (330 pitches) undulating

Tariff : (2014 Price) ⚭ 10€ ⬅ 6€ 国 9€ – ⚡ (10A) 6€ – Reservation fee 20€

Rental rates : (2014 Price) (from mid April to mid Oct.) ⚅ (2 mobile homes) – 70 ⏚ – 11 ⏚. Per night from 65 to 125€ – Per week from 240 to 1,610€ – Reservation fee 20€

⏚ borne 5€ – 20 国 12€

A free shuttle service to the beach, choose the pitches away from the road.

Surroundings : 🄀🄀
Leisure activities : ⚐✗ 🖼 ⚘ ⚒ ⚒ ⚒
multi-sports ground
Facilities : ⚅ ⚮ ⚒ ⚒ ⚒ launderette ⚒
⚮ refrigerators

G P S Longitude : -1.73925
Latitude : 43.37555

This guide is updated regularly, so buy your new copy every year!

⁂ Club Airotel Ametza

𝄢 05 59 20 07 05. www.camping-ametza.com

Address : boulevard de l'Empereur (located 1km east)

Opening times : from mid April to end Sept.

4.5 ha (230 pitches) terraced, relatively flat, flat, grassy

Tariff : (2014 Price) 40.50 € ✦✦ ⇔ 🔲 🔌 (6A)

Extra per person 7.60 € – Reservation fee 15 €

Rental rates : (from mid April to end Sept.) ♿ (1 mobile home) ⚿ – 30 🚐 – 3 🏠 – 3 tent lodges. Per night from 30 to 50 € – Per week from 200 to 1,225 € – Reservation fee 15 €

🚻 borne

Pitches for tents and caravans are available, as well as owner-occupier and rental mobile homes.

Surroundings : 🏞 ⌗ ♤♤		G P S	Longitude : -1.75578
Leisure activities : ♟ ✕ 🎦 🕴 ⛹ ⚿ ⚑			Latitude : 43.37285
Facilities : ♿ ⚿ ⚐ launderette 🗑 ⚒			

⁂ Dorrondeguy

𝄢 05 59 20 26 16. www.camping-dorrondeguy.com

Address : rue de la Glacière

Opening times : from beginning April to mid Oct.

4 ha (127 pitches) terrace, relatively flat, flat, grassy

Tariff : 31 € ✦✦ ⇔ 🔲 🔌 (8A) – Extra per person 6.50 € – Reservation fee 15 €

Rental rates : (from beginning April to end Oct.) ♿ (1 mobile home) ⚿ Ⓟ – 31 🚐 – 13 🏠 – 4 canvas bungalows. Per week from 250 to 1,090 € – Reservation fee 20 €

A pretty little chalet village.

Surroundings : 🏞 ⌗ ♤♤		G P S	Longitude : -1.74727
Leisure activities : ♟ ✕ 🎦 ⛹ ⚑ Basque pelota walled court			Latitude : 43.36867
Facilities : ♿ ⚿ ⚐ ♟ launderette ⚒			

HOURTIN

33990 – Michelin map **335** E3 – pop. 3 001 – alt. 18

▶ Paris 638 – Andernos-les-Bains 55 – Bordeaux 65 – Lesparre-Médoc 17

⁂ La Rotonde - Le Village Western ♣♣

𝄢 05 56 09 10 60. www.village-western.com

Address : chemin de Bécassine (head 1.5km west along the av. du Lac and take road to the left, 500m from the lake (direct access)

Opening times : from mid April to end Sept.

17 ha/11 for camping (300 pitches)

Tariff : (2014 Price) 37 € ✦✦ ⇔ 🔲 🔌 (10A) – Extra per person 8 €

Rental rates : (2014 Price) (from mid April to end Sept.) – 91 🚐 – 4 🏠 – 12 tipis – 5 canvas bungalows – 5 tent lodges. Per night from 30 to 193 € – Per week from 210 to 1,351 €

🚻 borne 2 € – ⛽ 8 €

A distinctive Wild West décor, next to a riding centre.

Surroundings : 🏞 ♤		G P S	Longitude : -1.07468
Leisure activities : ♟ ✕ 🎦 🕴 nighttime ⛹ ⚑ 🚴 ⚑ 🐎			Latitude : 45.17935
Facilities : ♿ ⚿ ⚐ ⚒ ♟ launderette 🗑 ⚒			
Nearby : ✂ 🎣			

⛰ Les Ourmes ♣♣

ESE communication

𝄢 05 56 09 12 76. www.lesourmes.com

Address : 90 avenue du Lac (located 1.5km west)

7 ha (300 pitches)

Rentals : ⚿ – 37 🚐.

🚻 borne

Surroundings : 🏞 ♤♤		G P S	Longitude : -1.07584
Leisure activities : ♟ ✕ 🎦 🕴 nighttime ⛹ ⚑ ⚑			Latitude : 45.18204
Facilities : ♿ ⚿ ⚐ ♟ launderette 🗑 ⚒			
Nearby : ✂ 🎣 🐎			

⚠ Aires Naturelles l'Acacia et le Lac

𝄢 05 56 73 80 80. www.campinglacacia.com

Address : route de Carcans (7km southwest along the D 3 and take the road to the right)

Opening times : from mid June to end Sept.

5 ha/2 for camping (50 pitches) adjacent pine trees

Tariff : 22 € ✦✦ ⇔ 🔲 🔌 (6A) – Extra per person 6 €

Surroundings : 🏞 ♤♤		G P S	Longitude : -1.06361
Leisure activities : ⚑ 🚴			Latitude : 45.13561
Facilities : ⚿ ♟ launderette			

HOURTIN-PLAGE

33990 – Michelin map **335** D3

▶ Paris 556 – Andernos-les-Bains 66 – Bordeaux 76 – Lesparre-Médoc 26

⁂ Club Airotel La Côte d'Argent ♣♣

ESE

𝄢 05 56 09 10 25. www.cca33.com

Address : 500m from the beach

Opening times : from mid May to mid Sept.

20 ha (870 pitches)

Tariff : 60 € ✦✦ ⇔ 🔲 🔌 (10A) – Extra per person 11 € – Reservation fee 35 €

Rental rates : (from mid May to mid Sept.) ⚿ – 255 🚐. Per night from 53 to 264 € – Per week from 212 to 1,848 € – Reservation fee 35 €

🚻 borne – 70 🔲 60 €

Surroundings : 🏞 ♤♤		G P S	Longitude : -1.16446
Leisure activities : ♟ ✕ 🎦 🕴 ⛹ 🎯 ⚑ 🚴 ✂ ⚑ ⚑ 🏃 multi-sports ground			Latitude : 45.22259
Facilities : ♿ ⚿ 📷 ⚐ ♟ launderette 🗑 ⚒ refrigerated food storage facilities			

Using the traditional Michelin classification method, the guide provides you with an easy, speedy reference for assessing the category of each site: 1 to 5 tents (see page 10).

LA HUME

33470 – Michelin map **335** E7
▶ Paris 645 – Bordeaux 59 – Mérignac 62 – Pessac 56

⛰ Verdalle

🖉 05 56 66 12 62. www.campingdeverdalle.com

Address : 2 allée de l'Infante (continue north along the av. de la Plage and take the road to the right; beside the Bassin d'Arcachon, direct access to the beach)

Opening times : from mid April to end Sept.

1.5 ha (108 pitches)

Tariff : (2014 Price) 27 € ★★ ⇌ 🗉 – Extra per person 6 € – Reservation fee 12 €

Rental rates : (2014 Price) ⬠ – 6 canvas bungalows. Per night from 30 to 110 € – Per week from 210 to 750 € – Reservation fee 12 €

Surroundings : ⬡ ◁ ▭ ♤♤	**G** Longitude : -1.11099
Facilities : ⬡ ☞ ⚐ ▨	**P** Latitude : 44.64397
Nearby : ⛴	**S**

Some information or pricing may have changed since the guide went to press. We recommend you check the price list online in advance or at the entrance to the campsite and enquire about possible restrictions.

ITXASSOU

64250 – Michelin map **342** D3 – pop. 2 031 – alt. 39
▶ Paris 787 – Bayonne 24 – Biarritz 25 – Cambo-les-Bains 5

⛰ Hiriberria

🖉 05 59 29 98 09. www.hiriberria.com

Address : located 1km northwest along the D 918, follow the signs for Cambo-les-Bains and take the road to the right

Opening times : Permanent

4 ha (228 pitches)

Tariff : 26 € ★★ ⇌ 🗉 ⚡ (10A) – Extra per person 7 €

Rental rates : (from beginning March to end Nov.) – 14 ⬛ – 19 ⌂. Per night from 55 to 100 € – Per week from 255 to 675 €

⬛ borne 3.50 € – 180 🗉 26 €

A small, pretty chalet village. Choose the pitches furthest away from the road in preference.

Surroundings : ◁ ▭ ♤♤	**G** Longitude : -1.40137
Leisure activities : ▱ ⚜ 🖾 (open air in season)	**P** Latitude : 43.33887
Facilities : ⬡ ☞ ▦ ♨ ⚐ ✲ ⚑ launderette	**S**

The prices listed were supplied by the campsite owners in 2014 (if prices were not available, those from the previous year are given). The fees should be regarded as basic charges and may fluctuate with inflation.

LABENNE-OCÉAN

40530 – Michelin map **335** C13
▶ Paris 763 – Bordeaux 185 – Mont-de-Marsan 98 – Pau 129

⛰⛰ Yelloh! Village le Sylvamar ♟♦

Yelloh! Village le Sylvamar

🖉 05 59 45 75 16. www.sylvamar.fr

Address : avenue de l'Océan (continue along the D 126, follow the signs for the beach, near Le Boudigau)

Opening times : from end March to beginning Oct.

25 ha (750 pitches)

Tariff : 57 € ★★ ⇌ 🗉 ⚡ (10A) – Extra per person 9 €

Rental rates : (from end March to beginning Oct.) ⬡ (2 chalets) ⬠ – 250 ⬛ – 60 ⌂ – 1 cabin in the trees – 1 gîte. Per night from 39 to 299 € – Per week from 273 to 2,093 €

A large water park with a covered paddling pool and play area; a range of luxury rental options.

Surroundings : ⬡ ▭ ♤♤	
Leisure activities : �ⓡ ✕ ⌂ ⊡ (open-air theatre) ⚜ ♬ ♨ hammam, jacuzzi ⚓ ⚙ ✕ ▱ ⚓ multi-sports ground, spa centre	**G** Longitude : -1.45687 **P** Latitude : 43.59532 **S**
Facilities : ⬡ ☞ ⚐ ♨ ⚐ ✲ ⚑ launderette ▨ ⚐ refrigerated food storage facilities	
Nearby : ⚞ ⛁ wildlife park	

⛰ Côte d'Argent ♟♦

🖉 05 59 45 42 02. www.camping-cotedargent.com

Address : 60 avenue de l'Océan (along the D 126, follow the signs for the beach)

Opening times : from end March to end Oct.

4 ha (215 pitches)

Tariff : 42.80 € ★★ ⇌ 🗉 ⚡ (6A) – Extra per person 6.50 € – Reservation fee 25 €

Rental rates : (from end March to end Oct.) – 23 ⬛ – 35 ⌂ – 3 apartments – 12 canvas bungalows. Per week from 217 to 1,045 € – Reservation fee 25 €

⬛ borne 3.80 €

Surroundings : ▭ ♤♤	
Leisure activities : ⓡ ✕ ⊡ daytime ⚜ ⚓ ⚙ ♨ ▱ multi-sports ground	**G** Longitude : -1.45687 **P** Latitude : 43.59532 **S**
Facilities : ⬡ ☞ ⬛ ♨ ⚐ ✲ ⚑ launderette ⚐	
Nearby : ▱ ✕⚙	

Michelin classification:

⛰⛰⛰⛰⛰	*Extremely comfortable, equipped to a very high standard*
⛰⛰⛰⛰	*Very comfortable, equipped to a high standard*
⛰⛰⛰	*Comfortable and well equipped*
⛰⛰	*Reasonably comfortable*
⛰	*Satisfactory*

⛰ Municipal Les Pins Bleus

🕿 05 59 45 41 13. www.lespinsbleus.com

Address : avenue de l'Océan (along the D 126 follow the signs for the beach; beside the Boudigau river)

Opening times : from beginning April to end Oct.

6.5 ha (120 pitches)

Tariff : 10€ ✷✷ ⮘ 🅴 ⚡ (16A) – Extra per person 7€ – Reservation fee 18.50€

Rental rates : (from beginning April to end Oct.) ♿ (1 chalet) – 22 🛖 – 10 🏠 – 10 canvas bungalows. Per night from 28 to 92€ – Per week from 152 to 645€ – Reservation fee 18.50€

🚐 borne 2€ – 14 🅴 9€ – ⚡13€

Surroundings : 🌳🌳
Leisure activities : ✗ 🏛 🏊 🚣 🚴 ⛵
Facilities : ⚡ 🍴 launderette, refrigerated food storage facilities

GPS Longitude : -1.45687
Latitude : 43.60229

LACANAU

33680 – Michelin map **335** E5 – pop. 4 412 – alt. 17
▶ Paris 625 – Bordeaux 47 – Mérignac 45 – Pessac 51

⛰ FranceLoc Talaris Vacances ♣

🕿 05 56 03 04 15. www.talaris-vacances.fr

Address : at Le Moutchic (5km west along the D 6, follow the signs for Lacanau-Océan)

Opening times : from mid April to mid Sept.

10 ha (476 pitches) flat, grassy, small lake

Tariff : (2014 Price) 45€ ✷✷ ⮘ 🅴 ⚡ (10A) – Extra per person 7€ Reservation fee 27€

Rental rates : (2014 Price) (from mid April to mid Sept.) – 270 🛖 – 15 canvas bungalows – 9 tent lodges. Per night from 40 to 185€ – Per week from 161 to 1,295€ – Reservation fee 27€

🚐 borne

In a pleasant wooded setting.

Surroundings : 🌳🌿
Leisure activities : 🍴 ✗ 🏛 🏊 🚣 🚴 ⛵ 🏊 multi-sports ground
Facilities : ♿ ⚡ 🍴 launderette 🏪

GPS Longitude : -1.11236
Latitude : 45.008

⛰ Le Tedey ♣

Le Tedey

🕿 05 56 03 00 15. www.le-tedey.com (July–Aug.)

Address : at Le Moutchic, route de Longarisse (3km south and take road to the left)

Opening times : from end April to mid Sept.

14 ha (700 pitches) adjacent wooded dunes

Tariff : (2014 Price) 32.90€ ✷✷ ⮘ 🅴 Extra per person 6.40€ – Reservation fee 20€

Rental rates : (2014 Price) (from end April to mid Sept.) – 38 🛖. Per week from 340 to 795€ –Reservation fee 20€

In a pleasant location beside the Lac de Lacanau, shaded by pine trees, but with poor sanitary facilities.

Surroundings : 🌊 🌳🌳
Leisure activities : 🍴 🏛 🏊 🚣 🚴 ⛵
Facilities : ♿ ⚡ 🍴 launderette 🏪

GPS Longitude : -1.13652
Latitude : 44.9875

LACANAU-OCÉAN

33680 – Michelin map **335** D4 – pop. 3 142
▶ Paris 636 – Andernos-les-Bains 38 – Arcachon 87 – Bordeaux 63

⛰ Yelloh! Village Les Grands Pins ♣

Yelloh! Village Les Grands Pins

🕿 05 56 03 20 77. www.lesgrandspins.com

Address : Plage Nord (north of the resort, 500m from the beach (direct access)

Opening times : from end April to end Sept.

11 ha (570 pitches) terraced, undulating, sandy

Tariff : 57€ ✷✷ ⮘ 🅴 ⚡ (10A) –

Extra per person 9€

Rental rates : (from end April to end Sept.) – 233 🛖 – 11 tent lodges. Per night from 35 to 279€ – Per week from 245 to 1,953€

🚐 borne

One part of the site is vehicle-free.

Surroundings : 🌊 🌳🌳
Leisure activities : 🍴 ✗ 🏛 🏊 🚣 hammam jacuzzi 🚣 🚴 ⛵ 🏊 fitness trail multi-sports ground spa centre
Facilities : ♿ ⚡ 🅿 🍴 launderette 🏪 refrigerated food storage facilities

GPS Longitude : -1.19517
Latitude : 45.01088

⛰ Club Airotel de l'Océan ♣

🕿 05 56 03 24 45. www.airotel-ocean.com

Address : 24 rue du Repos, Plage Nord (North Beach)

Opening times : from mid April to end Oct.

9 ha (550 pitches) terraced, undulating, sandy

Tariff : (2014 Price) 54€ ✷✷ ⮘ 🅴 ⚡ (15A) – Extra per person 10€ Reservation fee 28€

Rental rates : (2014 Price) (from mid April to end Oct.) – 250 🛖. Per night from 50 to 140€ – Per week from 350 to 1,715€ – Reservation fee 28€

A pleasant water park, partly covered.

Surroundings : 🌳🌳
Leisure activities : 🍴 ✗ 🏛 🏊 🚣 hammam jacuzzi 🚣 🚴 ⛵ disco, surfing spa centre
Facilities : ♿ ⚡ 🍴 launderette 🏪 refrigerated food storage facilities

GPS Longitude : -1.1928
Latitude : 45.00868

*For more information on visiting particular towns or regions, consult the relevant regional **MICHELIN** Green Guide. We also recommend you use the appropriate Michelin regional map to locate your selected campsite, to calculate distances and to work out the best route.*

LAMONZIE-MONTASTRUC

24520 – Michelin map **329** E6 – pop. 632 – alt. 50
▶ Paris 587 – Bordeaux 131 – Périgueux 46 – Agen 103

🔺 L'Escapade 👥

📞 0553572379. www.campinglescapade.com

Address : Les Roussilloux (follow the signs for St-Alvère)

Opening times : from beginning April to beginning Sept.

4.5 ha (85 pitches)

Tariff : (2014 Price) 33 € 👫 🚐 🔲 📳 (10A) – Extra per person 7 €
Reservation fee 26 €

Rental rates : (from beginning April to beginning Sept.) ♿ –
70 🚐 – 10 🏠. Per night from 42 to 140 € – Per week
from 294 to 980 € – Reservation fee 26 €

🚏 borne

Surroundings : 🌳 🏞 🎣
Leisure activities : 🍴 🍽 🏊 ♣ 🎣
hammam, jacuzzi 🚣 🚴 🎮 🎿 donkey
rides, multi-sports ground
Facilities : ♿ 🔌 🍳 🍴 launderette 🚿

G P S Longitude : 0.60793
Latitude : 44.88636

*A chambre d'hôte is a guesthouse or B & B-style
accommodation.*

LANOUAILLE

24270 – Michelin map **329** H3 – pop. 989 – alt. 209
▶ Paris 446 – Brantôme 47 – Limoges 55 – Périgueux 46

🔺 Village Vacances Le Moulin de la Jarousse

(rental of chalets, yurts, cabins in the trees and gîtes only)

📞 0553523791, www.location-en-dordogne.com

Address : at Payzac, La Jarousse (continue 9km northeast along the
D 704 to l'Hépital, then take right turn along the D 80)

Opening times : Permanent

8 ha terraced, lake, forest

Rental rates : (2014 Price) ♿ (1 gîte) – 8 🏠 – 8 yurts – 9 cabins
in the trees – 3 gîtes. Per night from 70 to 260 € – Per week
from 350 to 860 €

In an unspoilt, wooded setting overlooking the lake.

Surroundings : 🌳 ≤ 🏞
Leisure activities : 🚣 🚴 🎮 (open air in
season) 🎿 🎣 pedalos 🚤
Facilities : 🔌 🔲 🍳 🍴 📳

G P S Longitude : 1.18411
Latitude : 45.43694

LARRAU

64560 – Michelin map **342** G4 – pop. 204 – alt. 636
▶ Paris 840 – Bordeaux 254 – Pamplona 110 – Donostia-San
Sebastián 142

🔺 Village Vacances Les Chalets d'Iraty

(rental of chalets only)

📞 0559285129. www.chalets-iraty.com – alt. 1 327

Address : at the Col de Bagargui pass (14km west along the D 19,
follow the signs for St-Jean-Pied-de-Port)

Opening times : Permanent

2 000 ha/4 for camping undulating

Rental rates : (2014 Price) 🔲 – 40 🏠. Per night from 40 to 70 € –
Per week from 305 to 490 €

*The site is laid out in the Forêt d'Iraty (forest), between the Col
de Bagargui and the Col Hegui Xouri (mountain passes).*

Surroundings : 🌲 🏞
Leisure activities : 🚴 ✂️
Facilities : 🔌 🔲 🍴 📳
Nearby : 🏊 🍴 🍽 ⛷ 🎣 🐎 cross-country
skiing

G P S Longitude : -1.03532
Latitude : 43.03638

LARUNS

64440 – Michelin map **342** J5 – pop. 1 326 – alt. 523
▶ Paris 811 – Argelès-Gazost 49 – Lourdes 51 – Oloron-Ste-Marie 34

🔺 Les Gaves

📞 0559053237, www.campingdesgaves.com – limited spaces for
one-night stay

Address : Pon district (located 1.5km southeast of Larun, follow the
signs for Le Col d'Aubisque and take the road to the left; beside the
Gave d'Ossau (river)

Opening times : Permanent

2.4 ha (101 pitches) flat, grassy

Tariff : (2014 Price) 26.60 € 👫 🚐 🔲 📳 (10A) –
Extra per person 4.80 € – Reservation fee 20 €

Rental rates : (2014 Price) Permanent 🔲 – 14 🚐 – 5 🏠 –
5 apartments – 1 gîte. Per night from 37 to 101 € – Per week
from 259 to 707 € – Reservation fee 20 €

🚏 borne – 8 🔲 14.80 € – 🚐 11 €

*A pleasant camping area, with varied rental options, but the
rather jaded sanitary facilities are not of a high standard; many
owner-occupier mobile homes.*

Surroundings : ❄️ 🏔 ≤ 🏞 🎣
Leisure activities : 🍴 🏊 🚣
Facilities : 🔌 🔲 🎿 🍴 launderette

G P S Longitude : -0.41772
Latitude : 42.98306

*We value your opinion and welcome your feedback.
Do email us at campingfrance@tp.michelin.com*

LÈGE-CAP-FERRET

33950 – Michelin map **335** E6 – pop. 7 527 – alt. 9
▶ Paris 629 – Arcachon 65 – Belin-Beliet 56 – Bordeaux 50

🔺 La Prairie

📞 0556600975. www.campinglaprairie.com

Address : 93 avenue du Médoc (located 1km northeast along the D 3,
follow the signs for Le Porge)

Opening times : from beginning March to end Oct.

2.5 ha (118 pitches)

Tariff : (2014 Price) 21.30 € 👫 🚐 🔲 📳 (10A) – Extra per person 4 €

Rental rates : (2014 Price) (from beginning April to mid Oct.) –
16 🚐 – 4 tent lodges. Per night from 41 to 108 € – Per week
from 232 to 655 €

🚏 borne – 20 🔲 17.60 € – 🚐 9 €

Surroundings : 🏞 🎣
Leisure activities : 🏊 🚣 🎿
Facilities : ♿ 🔌 🍴 📳

G P S Longitude : -1.13375
Latitude : 44.80271

LÉON

40550 – Michelin map **335** D11 – pop. 1 830 – alt. 9
▶ Paris 724 – Castets 14 – Dax 30 – Mimizan 42

⛰ FranceLoc Punta Lago ♣♟

☏ 05 58 49 24 40. www.camping-puntalago.com

Address : 1165 avenue du Lac (1.5km northwest along the D 142, opposite the municipal stadium, 200m from the lake)

Opening times : from beginning April to end Sept.

5.5 ha (300 pitches)

Tariff : (2014 Price) 48€ ♣♣ ⇔ 国 ⑭ (10A) – Extra per person 7€

Rental rates : (2014 Price) (from end April to end Sept.) – 80 ⛺. Per night from 39 to 208€ – Per week from 273 to 1,456€

Surroundings : ⟨icons⟩
Leisure activities : ⟨icons⟩
multi-sports ground
Facilities : ⟨icons⟩ launderette ⟨icon⟩
Nearby : ⟨icons⟩

GPS Longitude : -1.31342
Latitude : 43.88382

LESCUN

64490 – Michelin map **342** I5 – pop. 178 – alt. 900
▶ Paris 846 – Lourdes 89 – Oloron-Ste-Marie 37 – Pau 70

⛰ Le Lauzart

☏ 05 59 34 51 77. www.camping-lescun.com

Opening times : from beginning April to end Sept.

1 ha (55 pitches) flat and relatively flat

Tariff : (2014 Price) ♣ 3.50€ ⇔ 1.50€ 国 4.50€ – ⑭ (10A) 4.50€

A magnificent mountain site, although with ageing sanitary facilities. Half board available.

Surroundings : ⟨icons⟩
Leisure activities : ⟨icon⟩
Facilities : ⟨icons⟩

GPS Longitude : -0.64217
Latitude : 42.92761

LIMEUIL

24510 – Michelin map **329** G6 – pop. 328 – alt. 65
▶ Paris 528 – Bergerac 43 – Brive-la-Gaillarde 78 – Périgueux 48

⛰ La Ferme des Poutiroux

☏ 05 53 63 31 62. www.poutiroux.com

Address : take the northwestern exit along the D 31, follow the signs for Trémolat then continue 1km along the road for Paunat to the right

Opening times : from beginning April to end Sept.

2.5 ha (45 pitches)

Tariff : ♣ 5.80€ ⇔ 国 6.40€ – ⑭ (6A) 4.20€ – Reservation fee 13€

Rental rates : (from beginning April to end Sept.) ⟨icon⟩ – 20 ⛺. Per night from 24 to 81€ – Per week from 170 to 620€ – Reservation fee 13€

⟨borne icon⟩ borne 3€ – 8 国 15€

Surroundings : ⟨icons⟩
Leisure activities : ⟨icons⟩
Facilities : ⟨icons⟩ launderette

GPS Longitude : 0.87946
Latitude : 44.89332

The guide covers all 22 regions of France – see the map and list of regions on pages 4–5.

LINXE

40260 – Michelin map **335** D11 – pop. 1 236 – alt. 33
▶ Paris 712 – Castets 10 – Dax 31 – Mimizan 37

⛰ FranceLoc Domaine Lila

☏ 05 58 43 96 25. www.franceloc.fr – limited spaces for one-night stay

Address : 190 route de Mixe (located 1.5km northwest along the D 42, follow the signs for St-Girons and take D 397, turning to the right)

Opening times : from mid June to mid Sept.

2 ha (159 pitches)

Tariff : (2014 Price) 30€ ♣♣ ⇔ 国 ⑭ (16A) – Extra per person 7€ Reservation fee 27€

Rental rates : (2014 Price) (from mid June to mid Sept.) – 200 ⛺. Per night from 42 to 82€ – Per week from 168 to 1,232€ – Reservation fee 27€

A good number of mobile homes and pitches for tents and caravans arranged around an eco swimming pool (no chemicals).

Surroundings : ⟨icon⟩
Leisure activities : ⟨icons⟩
Facilities : ⟨icons⟩ launderette

GPS Longitude : -1.25758
Latitude : 43.93185

The information in the guide may have changed since going to press.

LIT-ET-MIXE

40170 – Michelin map **335** D10 – pop. 1 497 – alt. 13
▶ Paris 710 – Castets 21 – Dax 42 – Mimizan 22

⛰ Tohapi Les Vignes ♣♟

(rental of mobile homes, chalets and canvas bungalows only)

☏ 05 58 42 85 60. www.village-center.fr

Address : 2.7km southwest along the D 652 and take the D 88, to the right, follow the signs for Le Cap de l'Homy

Opening times : from beginning April to end Sept.

15 ha (495 pitches)

Rental rates : ⟨icon⟩ (2 mobile homes) – 280 ⛺ – 40 ⟨chalet icon⟩ – 19 canvas bungalows. Per night from 24 to 234€ – Per week from 168 to 1,638€ – Reservation fee 10€

Leisure activities : ⟨icons⟩ (big top staging activities and shows) ⟨icons⟩ cinema, multi-sports ground
Facilities : ⟨icons⟩ launderette ⟨icons⟩

GPS Longitude : -1.28275
Latitude : 44.02401

⛰ Municipal du Cap de l'Homy

☏ 05 58 42 83 47. www.camping-cap.com

Address : at Cap-de-l'Homy, 600 avenue de l'Océan (8km west along the D 652 and take D 88 to the right; 300m from the beach (direct access)

Opening times : from beginning May to end Sept.

10 ha (474 pitches)

Tariff : (2014 Price) 31.30€ ♣♣ ⇔ 国 ⑭ (6A) –

Extra per person 7.10€ – Reservation fee 30€

Rental rates : (2014 Price) (from beginning May to mid Sept.) ⟨icon⟩ – 15 canvas bungalows. Per week from 230 to 720€ – Reservation fee 30€

⟨borne icon⟩ borne 6.75€

In the shade of a pleasant pine wood.

Surroundings :
Leisure activities : 🏛 🚴
Facilities : 🚿 ⊶ 📮 ♨ ¶ launderette
refrigerated food storage facilities
Nearby : 🏖 ¶ ✕ 🛶 surfing

GPS	Longitude : -1.33435 Latitude : 44.03712

MARCILLAC-ST-QUENTIN

24200 – Michelin map **329** I6 – pop. 791 – alt. 235
▶ Paris 522 – Brive-la-Gaillarde 48 – Les Eyzies-de-Tayac 18
Montignac 21

⛰ **Les Tailladis**

✆ 05 53 59 10 95. www.tailladis.com

Address : Les Tailladis (situated 2km to the north, near the D 48;
beside the Beune river and a lake)

Opening times : from mid March to end Oct.

25 ha/8 for camping (90 pitches)

Tariff : 25.75 € ✹ ✹ ⇌ 🗉 🔌 (10A) – Extra per person 6.85 € –
Reservation fee 12.50 €

Rental rates : (from mid March to end Oct.) – 3 🛖 – 4 🏠 –
2 canvas bungalows – 2 tent lodges. Per night from 25 to 65 € –
Per week from 395 to 725 € – Reservation fee 12.50 €

Surroundings :
Leisure activities : ¶ ✕ 🛶 🎣
Facilities : 🚿 ⊶ 🏛 ♨ ¶ launderette 🏖 🍴

GPS	Longitude : 1.18789 Latitude : 44.97465

MAULÉON-LICHARRE

64130 – Michelin map **342** G5 – pop. 3 205 – alt. 140
▶ Paris 802 – Oloron-Ste-Marie 31 – Orthez 39 – Pau 60

⛰ **Uhaitza - Le Saison**

✆ 05 59 28 18 79. www.camping-uhaitza.com

Address : located 1.5km south along the D 918, follow the signs for
Tardets-Sorholus; beside the Saison river

Opening times : from beginning April to mid Oct.

1 ha (50 pitches) terraced, flat, grassy

Tariff : (2014 Price) 26.10 € ✹ ✹ ⇌ 🗉 🔌 (10A) – Extra per person 6 €
Reservation fee 10 €

Rental rates : (2014 Price) (from beginning March to mid Nov.)
🏕 (from mid July to end Aug.) – 2 🛖 – 5 🏠. Per week
from 286 to 617 € – Reservation fee 10 €

🚐 borne 5.25 € – 🚽 11 €

*Choose the pitches near the stream and further away from
the road.*

Surroundings : 🌲 🚏 ♨♨
Leisure activities : ¶ 🏛 🚴 🏊 🛶
Facilities : 🚿 ⊶ 📮 ♨ 🚿 ¶ launderette

GPS	Longitude : -0.8972 Latitude : 43.20789

⛺ **Aire Naturelle La Ferme Landran**

✆ 05 59 28 19 55. www.gites64.com/la-ferme-landran

Address : at Ordiarp, Larréguy district (4.5km southwest along the
D 918, follow the signs for St-Jean-Pied-de-Port then continue 1.5km
along the road for Lambarre to the right)

Opening times : from beginning April to end Sept.

1 ha (25 pitches) sloping, flat, grassy

Tariff : 14.60 € ✹ ✹ ⇌ 🗉 🔌 (6A) – Extra per person 3.10 €

Rental rates : Permanent – 2 🏠 – 1 gîte. Per night from €60 –
Per week from 280 to 380 €

🚐 borne 3.50 €

A farm campsite.

Surroundings : 🌲 ≤ ♨♨
Leisure activities : 🏛 🛶
Facilities : 🚿 ⊶ 📮 📶

GPS	Longitude : -0.93933 Latitude : 43.20185

MESSANGES

40660 – Michelin map **335** C12 – pop. 986 – alt. 8
▶ Paris 734 – Bayonne 45 – Castets 24 – Dax 33

⛰⛰ **Club Airotel Le Vieux Port** 🅰👥

✆ 08 25 70 40 40. www.levieuxport.com

Address : route de la Plage Sud (2.5km southwest along the D 652,
follow the signs for Vieux-Boucau-les-Bains then continue 800m
along the road to the right; 500m from the beach -direct access)

Opening times : from beginning April to end Sept.

40 ha/30 for camping (1546 pitches) undulating, flat, grassy, sandy

Tariff : (2014 Price) 69 € ✹ ✹ ⇌ 🗉 🔌 (8A) – Extra per person 9.90 €
Reservation fee 40 €

Rental rates : (2014 Price) (from beginning April to end Sept.) 🚿
(1 mobile home) 🏕 – 380 🛖 – 75 🏠. Per night from 50 to
258 € – Per week from 315 to 2,205 € – Reservation fee 40 €

*A spacious landscaped water park with plenty of shops and
services at the entrance.*

Surroundings : ♨♨
Leisure activities : ¶ ✕ 🏛 📺 (cinema/
theatre) 🎯 🛝 hammam, jacuzzi 🏊 🚴
🎰 🎠 🏊 🛶 multi-sports ground,
spa centre
Facilities : 🚿 ⊶ 🗉 ♨ 🚿 ¶ launderette
🛒 🍴 refrigerated food storage facilities

GPS	Longitude : -1.39995 Latitude : 43.79773

⛰⛰ **Village Vacances Club Airotel Lou Pignada** 🅰👥

(rental of caravans, mobile homes and chalets only)

✆ 08 25 70 40 40. www.loupignada.com

Address : route d'Azur (situated 2km south along the D 652 then
continue 500m down road to the left)

Opening times : from beginning April to end Sept.

8 ha (430 pitches)

Rental rates : (2014 Price) 🚿 (1 mobile home) 🏕 – 120 🛖 –
25 🏠. Per night from 46 to 220 € – Per week from 195 to 1,540 €
Reservation fee 40 €

Surroundings : 🚏 ♨♨
Leisure activities : ¶ ✕ 📺 🎯 🛝 🛝 🏊 🚴
🎰 🏊 🛶 multi-sports ground
Facilities : 🚿 ⊶ ♨ ¶ launderette 🏖 🍴
refrigerated food storage facilities
Nearby : 🛒

GPS	Longitude : -1.38245 Latitude : 43.79747

*There are several different types of sani-station
('borne' in French) – sanitation points providing
fresh water and disposal points for grey water.
See page 12 for further details.*

🏔 La Côte

📞 05 58 48 94 94. www.campinglacote.com

Address : chemin de la Côte (2.3km southwest along the D 652, follow the signs for Vieux-Boucau-les-Bains and take the road to the right)

Opening times : from beginning April to end Sept.

3.5 ha (143 pitches)

Tariff : 31.50 € ♦♦ ⇔ 国 ⚡ (10A) – Extra per person 6.40 € – Reservation fee 19 €

Rental rates : Permanent ⚒ – 11 ▣ – 3 gîtes. Per week from 250 to 840 € – Reservation fee 20 €

🚰 borne

Surroundings : ⛰ ♞♞
Leisure activities : ▦ jacuzzi ⛵⚓
Facilities : ♿ ⚡ ⛺♨ launderette, refrigerated food storage facilities
Nearby : 🛒

GPS	Longitude : -1.39171
	Latitude : 43.80035

⛺ Les Acacias

📞 05 58 48 01 78. www.lesacacias.com

Address : 101 chemin du Houdin, Delest district (situated 2km south along the D 652, follow the signs for Vieux-Boucau-les-Bains then continue 1km along the turning to the left)

Opening times : from end March to end Oct.

1.7 ha (128 pitches)

Tariff : 24.50 € ♦♦ ⇔ 国 ⚡ (10A) – Extra per person 4.90 € – Reservation fee 15 €

Rental rates : (from end March to end Oct.) – 13 ▣. Per night from 55 to 105 € – Per week from 240 to 730 €

🚰 borne 9 € – 3 国 24.50 €

Surroundings : ⛰ ♀
Leisure activities : ▦ ⛵
Facilities : ♿ ⚡ ⛺♨ launderette
Nearby : 🛒

GPS	Longitude : -1.37567
	Latitude : 43.79757

MÉZOS

40170 – Michelin map **335** E10 – pop. 866 – alt. 23
▶ Paris 700 – Bordeaux 118 – Castets 24 – Mimizan 16

🏔 Club Airotel Le Village Tropical Sen Yan ♦♦

📞 05 58 42 60 05. www.sen-yan.com

Address : avenue de la Gare (located 1km east, follow the signs for Le Cout)

Opening times : from beginning June to mid Sept.

8 ha (310 pitches)

Tariff : 45.50 € ♦♦ ⇔ 国 ⚡ (10A) – Extra per person 9 € – Reservation fee 26 €

Rental rates : (from beginning May to mid Sept.) ⚒ – 150 ▣ – 41 ▣. Per night from 60 to 180 € – Per week from 420 to 1,260 € Reservation fee 26 €

A pretty site with swimming pools, palm trees, plantations and a small ecological lake.

Surroundings : ⛰ ♞♞
Leisure activities : � ▦ ♨♨♨ ⛵⚓ ♣♣ ♒♒ ⛵ (lake) ⚾ multi-sports ground
Facilities : ♿ ⚡ ⛺♨ launderette

GPS	Longitude : -1.15657
	Latitude : 44.07164

MIALET

24450 – Michelin map **329** G2 – pop. 665 – alt. 320
▶ Paris 436 – Limoges 49 – Nontron 23 – Périgueux 51

🏔 Village Vacances L'Étang de Vivale

(rental of chalets only)

📞 05 53 52 66 05. www.vivaledordogne.com

Address : 32 avenue de Nontron (700m west along the D 79; beside the lake)

Opening times : from beginning April to beginning Nov.

30 ha

Rental rates : (2014 Price) – 20 ▣. Per night from 80 to 100 € – Per week from 420 to 800 €

Surroundings : ⛰ ≤ ▣ ♀
Leisure activities : ♥ ▦ ⛵⚓ ☸ ♒♒ ⛵ boats to hire ⚒
Facilities : ♿ ⚡ Ⓟ ♨ ▣

GPS	Longitude : 0.89788
	Latitude : 45.54793

MIMIZAN

40200 – Michelin map **335** D9 – pop. 7 000 – alt. 13
▶ Paris 692 – Arcachon 67 – Bayonne 109 – Bordeaux 109

⛺ Municipal du Lac

📞 05 58 09 01 21, www.mimizan-camping.com

Address : avenue de Woolsack (situated 2km north along the D 87, follow the signs for Gastes; beside the Lac d'Aureilhan)

Opening times : from beginning May to beginning Sept.

8 ha (466 pitches)

Tariff : (2014 Price) 21.49 € ♦♦ ⇔ 国 ⚡ (6A) –

Extra per person 8.10 € – Reservation fee 21 €

Rental rates : (2014 Price) (from beginning May to beginning Sept.) – 19 canvas bungalows. Per night from 27 to 46 € – Per week from 190 to 532 € – Reservation fee 21 €

🚰 borne 2 € – 21 国 19.24 €

Surroundings : ♀
Leisure activities : ✗ ♒♒
Facilities : ♿ ⚡ ▣ ♨ ⛺ ♨
Nearby : ≈ ⚓ ◊ pedalos

GPS	Longitude : -1.2299
	Latitude : 44.21968

MIMIZAN-PLAGE

40200 – Michelin map **335** D9
▶ Paris 706 – Bordeaux 128 – Mont-de-Marsan 84

🏔 Club Airotel Marina-Landes ♦♦

📞 05 58 09 12 66. www.marinalandes.com

Address : 8 rue Marina (500m from La Plage du Sud (beach))

Opening times : from beginning May to end Sept.

9 ha (536 pitches)

Tariff : (2014 Price) 57 € ♦♦ ⇔ 国 ⚡ (10A) – Extra per person 10 € Reservation fee 35 €

Rental rates : (2014 Price) (from beginning May to end Sept.) – 100 ▣ – 6 ▣ – 24 apartments – 17 tent lodges. Per night from 35 to 194 € – Per week from 196 to 1,360 € – Reservation fee 35 €

🚰 borne

Surroundings : ▣ ♞♞
Leisure activities : ♥ ✗ ▦ ♣♣ ♒♒ ⛵⚓ ♣♣ ☸ ♨ ▣ ⚾ ⚾ multi-sports ground, entertainment room
Facilities : ♿ ⚡ ▥ ⛺ ♨ launderette ♨♨ ⛺
Nearby : 🐎

GPS	Longitude : -1.2909
	Latitude : 44.2043

ᴍᴍ Municipal de la Plage ♣▲

℘ 05 58 09 00 32. www.mimizan-camping.com

Address : boulevard de l'Atlantique (northern suburb)

Opening times : from mid April to mid Sept.

16 ha (608 pitches)

Tariff : (2014 Price) 24.25€ ☆☆ ⇔ 🔲 ⚡ (10A) –
Extra per person 10.15€ – Reservation fee 21€

Rental rates : (2014 Price) (from mid April to mid Sept.) ℗ –
36 🚐 – 15 🏠 – 2 tent lodges. Per week from 175 to 785€ –
Reservation fee 21€

🚰 borne 2€ – 18 🔲 11.20€

The site welcomes groups of surfers.

Surroundings : 🗔
Leisure activities : ✗ ⑨ ⚡ 🚤 climbing
wall, multi-sports ground
Facilities : ♿ ⚬ 🛁 🍴 launderette ⚌ 🚿
refrigerated food storage facilities

G P S Longitude : -1.28384
Latitude : 44.21719

MOLIETS-PLAGE

40660 – Michelin map **335** C11
▶ Paris 716 – Bordeaux 156 – Mont-de-Marsan 89 – Bayonne 67

ᴍᴍ Le Saint-Martin ♣▲

℘ 05 58 48 52 30. www.camping-saint-martin.fr

Address : avenue de l'Océan (on the D 117, direct access to the
beach)

Opening times : from beginning April to beginning Nov.

18 ha (660 pitches)

Tariff : (2014 Price) 45.20€ ☆☆ ⇔ 🔲 ⚡ (10A) –
Extra per person 8.90€ – Reservation fee 35€

Rental rates : (2014 Price) (from beginning April to
beginning Nov.) – 40 🚐 – 137 🏠 – 6 canvas bungalows.
Per week from 205 to 1,540€ – Reservation fee 35€

🚰 borne – 45 🔲 51.90€

Surroundings : 🗔 ♀
Leisure activities : ▼ ✗ ⌂ ⑨ ⚡ ⟐ 🚤
🏊 🛝 multi-sports ground
Facilities : ♿ ⚬ 🛁 🍴 launderette 🚿
refrigerated food storage facilities
Nearby : 🚲 ⛳ ✗

G P S Longitude : -1.38731
Latitude : 43.85259

MONPAZIER

24540 – Michelin map **329** G7 – pop. 522 – alt. 180
▶ Paris 575 – Bergerac 47 – Fumel 26 – Périgueux 75

ᴍᴍ Le Moulin de David ♣▲

℘ 05 53 22 65 25. www.moulindedavid.com

Address : 3km southwest along the D 2, follow the signs for Villeréal
and take road to the left; beside a stream

Opening times : from mid April to end Sept.

16 ha/4 for camping (160 pitches)

Tariff : 30€ ☆☆ ⇔ 🔲 ⚡ (10A) – Extra per person 6€ – Reservation
fee 18€

*The Michelin classification (ᴍᴍᴍ ... ᴧ) is totally
independent of the official star classification system
awarded by the local prefecture or other official
organisation.*

Rental rates : (from mid April to end Sept.) – 56 🚐 – 3 canvas
bungalows – 7 tent lodges. Per week from 169 to 920€ –
Reservation fee 18€

🚰 borne

Surroundings : 🐚 🗔 ♀♀
Leisure activities : ▼ ✗ ⌂ ⑨ ⚡ 🚤 🏊 🛝
(stream) ⟐
Facilities : ♿ ⚬ 🛁 🍴 launderette ⚌
🚿

G P S Longitude : 0.87873
Latitude : 44.65979

MONTIGNAC

24290 – Michelin map **329** H5 – pop. 2 851 – alt. 77
▶ Paris 513 – Brive-la-Gaillarde 39 – Périgueux 54 – Sarlat-la-
Canéda 25

ᴍᴍ Le Moulin du Bleufond

℘ 05 53 51 83 95. www.bleufond.com

Address : avenue Aristide Briand (500m south along the D 65 follow
the signs for Sergeac; near the Vézère river)

Opening times : from beginning April to mid Oct.

1.3 ha (84 pitches) flat, grassy

Tariff : (2014 Price) ☆ 7.40€ ⇔ 🔲 8.95€ – ⚡ (10A) 5.15€

Rental rates : (2014 Price) (from end March to mid Oct.) – 21 🚐.
Per week from 260 to 790€

The attractive pitches are based around an old mill.

Surroundings : 🐚 🗔 ♀♀
Leisure activities : ✗ ⌂ ⧈ jacuzzi ⚡ 🚤
Facilities : ♿ ⚬ ▥ 🛁 🍴 launderette
🚿
Nearby : ✗ 🎣

G P S Longitude : 1.15864
Latitude : 45.05989

*Routes nationales are main roads and their identifying
numbers begin with N or RN. Routes départementales are
generally quieter roads and begin with D or DN.*

MONTPON-MÉNESTÉROL

24700 – Michelin map **329** B5 – pop. 5 535 – alt. 93
▶ Paris 532 – Bergerac 40 – Bordeaux 75 – Libourne 43

ᴧ La Cigaline

℘ 05 53 80 22 16. www.lacigaline.fr

Address : 1 rue de la Paix (take the northern exit along the D 708,
follow the signs for Ribérac and take the turning to the left before
the bridge)

Opening times : Permanent

2 ha (120 pitches) flat, grassy

Tariff : 16.40€ ☆☆ ⇔ 🔲 ⚡ (10A) – Extra per person 4.60€ –
Reservation fee 12€

Rental rates : Permanent – 10 🚐 – 2 tent lodges. Per night
from 45 to 60€ – Per week from 260 to 550€ – Reservation
fee 12€

🚰 10 🔲 12€ – 🚿 8€

Situated beside the Isle river.

Surroundings : 🗔 ♀♀
Leisure activities : ⌂ 🚤
Facilities : ♿ ⚬ 🛁 🍴 🔳
Nearby : 🏊

G P S Longitude : 0.15839
Latitude : 45.01217

NAVARRENX

64190 – Michelin map **342** H3 – pop. 1 104 – alt. 125
▶ Paris 787 – Oloron-Ste-Marie 23 – Orthez 22 – Pau 43

⛰ Beau Rivage

🔗 05 59 66 10 00. www.beaucamping.com

Address : allée des Marronniers (to the west of the town between the Gave d'Oloron (river) and the village ramparts)

Opening times : from end March to mid Oct.

2.5 ha (70 pitches)

Tariff : 28€ ✶✶ ⬅ 🅴 (10A) – Extra per person 6.40€
Rental rates : (from end March to mid Oct.) ♿ (1 chalet) – 10 🏠.
Per week from 310 to 765€
🚐 borne – 18 🅴 17.50€
By the Gave d'Oloron river and the old village fortifications.

Surroundings : 🐟 ⛱ ♤♤
Leisure activities : 🛶 ⛵ ⛴
Facilities : ♿ ⛐ 🆒 🛁☂🚰 ⊺ launderette
Nearby : ✂ 🎣

Longitude : -0.76121
Latitude : 43.32003

Some campsites benefit from proximity to a municipal leisure centre.

NONTRON

24300 – Michelin map **329** E2 – pop. 3 421 – alt. 260
▶ Paris 464 – Bordeaux 175 – Périgueux 49 – Angoulême 47

⛰ Camping De Nontron

🔗 05 53 56 02 04. www.campingdenontron.com

Address : at St-Martial-de-Valette (located 1km south on the D 675, follow the signs for Périgueux)

Opening times : from beginning Jan to mid Dec.

2 ha (70 pitches) flat, grassy, beside river

Tariff : (2014 Price) 16.80€ ✶✶ ⬅ 🅴 (10A) – Extra per person 4€
Rental rates : (2014 Price) (from beginning Jan to mid Dec.)
✂ – 4 🚐 – 1 🛖 – 6 studios. Per night from 50€ – Per week from 219 to 572€
🚐 borne
Situated beside a large indoor water park.

Surroundings : ⛱ ♤♤
Leisure activities : 🛶 ⛴
Facilities : ♿ ⛐ 🆒 🛁☂🆒 🚰
Nearby : ≋ hammam, jacuzzi 🎣 🏊

Longitude : 0.65807
Latitude : 45.51951

ONDRES

40440 – Michelin map **335** C13 – pop. 4 479 – alt. 37
▶ Paris 761 – Bayonne 8 – Biarritz 15 – Dax 48

⛰ Du Lac

🔗 05 59 45 28 45. www.camping-du-lac.fr

Address : 518 rue de Janin (2.2km north along the N 10 then take the D 26, follow the signs for Ondres-Plage then head towards Le Turc, road to the right; near a lake)

Opening times : from mid March to end Oct.

3 ha (115 pitches)

Tariff : (2014 Price) 43€ ✶✶ ⬅ 🅴 (10A) – Extra per person 7.50€
Reservation fee 18€

Rental rates : (2014 Price) (from mid March to end Oct.) ✂ (from mid March to end June) – 27 🚐 – 3 🏠 – 7 canvas bungalows.
Per night from 31 to 226€ – Per week from 217 to 1,582€ – Reservation fee 20€

Surroundings : 🐟 ⛱ ♤♤
Leisure activities : 🍹 ✕ 🛶 ≋ hammam 🏄 🚴 ⛴
Facilities : ♿ ⛐ 🆒 🛁⊺ launderette 🚰
Nearby : 🎣

Longitude : -1.45249
Latitude : 43.56499

PARCOUL

24410 – Michelin map **329** B4 – pop. 363 – alt. 70
▶ Paris 503 – Bergerac 69 – Blaye 72 – Bordeaux 75

⛰ Le Paradou

🔗 05 53 91 42 78. www.leparadou24.fr

Address : at the Vaure leisure centre (situated 2km southwest along the D 674, follow the signs for La Roche-Chalais)

Opening times : Permanent

20 ha/4 for camping (100 pitches)

Tariff : (2014 Price) 25.10€ ✶✶ ⬅ 🅴 (10A) –
Extra per person 5.80€ – Reservation fee 15€
Rental rates : (2014 Price) Permanent ♿ (1 chalet) – 56 🚐 – 4 🏠. Per week from 200 to 760€ – Reservation fee 15€

Surroundings : ⛱ ♤♤
Leisure activities : 🛶 🏄 ✂ 🎣 ⛴ ≋ (lake) 🏊
Facilities : ♿ ⛐ 🛁🚰 launderette refrigerators
Nearby : 🍹 ✕ 🚣 pedalos

Longitude : 0.02578
Latitude : 45.19038

PARENTIS-EN-BORN

40160 – Michelin map **335** E8 – pop. 5 187 – alt. 32
▶ Paris 658 – Arcachon 43 – Bordeaux 76 – Mimizan 25

⛰ Le Pipiou ⛺

🔗 05 58 78 57 25. www.camping-pipiou.fr

Address : 382 route des Campings (2.5km west along the D 43 and take the turning to the right, 100m from the lake)

Opening times : from mid April to mid Oct.

6 ha (324 pitches) Tariff : (2014 Price) 24€ ✶✶ ⬅ 🅴 (10A)
Extra per person 5.50€ – Reservation fee 15€
Rental rates : (2014 Price) (from mid April to mid Oct.) – 25 🚐 – 3 canvas bungalows. Per week from 210 to 700€ – Reservation fee 15€

Surroundings : 🐟 ⛱
Leisure activities : 🍹 ✕ 🏹 🎣 🏄 🚴 ⛴ 🏊 multi-sports ground
Facilities : ♿ ⛐ 🆒 🛁☂🚰 ⊺ launderette 🏊🚣
Nearby : 🎣 ≋ (beach) 🎣 ♨

Longitude : -1.10135
Latitude : 44.3457

⛰ L'Arbre d'Or

🔗 05 58 78 41 56. www.arbre-dor.com

Address : 75 route du lac (located 1.5km west along the D 43)

Opening times : from beginning April to end Oct.

4 ha (200 pitches) flat, grassy, sandy

Tariff : (2014 Price) 29.20€ ✶✶ ⬅ 🅴 (10A) –
Extra per person 6.65€

Rental rates : (2014 Price) (from beginning April to end Oct.) – 17 – 1 🏠 – 2 canvas bungalows. Per night from 60 to 100€ – Per week from 205 to 1,080€

Surroundings : ♀
Leisure activities : 🍴 ✕ 🏖 🎿 ⚓ 🎯 ⛴ multi-sports ground
Facilities : ♿ ⚡ 🔌 launderette ♨ refrigerators

Longitude : -1.09232
Latitude : 44.34615

PAUILLAC

33250 – Michelin map **335** G3 – pop. 5 135 – alt. 20
▶ Paris 625 – Arcachon 113 – Blaye 16 – Bordeaux 54

⚠ Municipal Les Gabarreys

🕿 05 56 59 10 03. www.pauillac-medoc.com

Address : route de la Rivière (located 1km to the south, near the Gironde river)

Opening times : from beginning April to mid Oct.

1.6 ha (59 pitches)

Tariff : 23.50€ ✝✝ ⚓ 🔲 🔌 (10A) – Extra per person 5€ – Reservation fee 12€

Rental rates : (2014 Price) (from beginning April to mid Oct.) ♿ (1 mobile home) – 7 . Per night from 44 to 102€ – Per week from 254 to 610€

🚐 borne 4.70€ – 🚐 14€

There's an outdoor jacuzzi in an elevated position, with a panoramic view of the Gironde river.

Surroundings : 🌳 ⛰ ♀
Leisure activities : 🍴 🏖 jacuzzi ⚓ 🏔 m
Facilities : ♿ ⚡ launderette

Longitude : -0.74226
Latitude : 45.18517

PETIT-PALAIS-ET-CORNEMPS

33570 – Michelin map **335** K5 – pop. 676 – alt. 35
▶ Paris 532 – Bergerac 51 – Castillon-la-Bataille 18 – Libourne 20

⚠ Flower Le Pressoir

🕿 05 57 69 73 25. www.campinglepressoir.com

Address : 29 Queyrai (1.7km northwest along the D 21, follow the signs for St-Médard-de-Guizières and take road to the left)

Opening times : Permanent

2 ha (100 pitches)

Tariff : 18€ ✝✝ ⚓ 🔲 🔌 (10A) – Extra per person 4€ – Reservation fee 15€

Rental rates : Permanent – 30 – 10 canvas bungalows. Per night from 33 to 142€ – Per week from 231 to 994€ – Reservation fee 15€

🚐 15 🔲 16€

Surroundings : 🌳 ⛰ ⛱ ♀
Leisure activities : 🍴 ✕ 🏖 ⚓ 🚲 ⛴
Facilities : ♿ ⚡ 🔌 launderette

Longitude : -0.06301
Latitude : 44.99693

PEYRIGNAC

24210 – Michelin map **329** I5 – pop. 514 – alt. 200
▶ Paris 508 – Brive-la-Gaillarde 33 – Juillac 33 – Périgueux 44

⚠ La Garenne

🕿 05 53 50 57 73. www.lagarennedordogne.com

Address : Le Combal (800m north of the village, near the stadium)

Opening times : Permanent

4 ha/1.5 (70 pitches)

Tariff : 21.25€ ✝✝ ⚓ 🔲 🔌 (10A) – Extra per person 5€

Rental rates : Permanent – 19 – 14 🏠 – 2 canvas bungalows. Per night from 33 to 113€ – Per week from 205 to 789€

Surroundings : 🌳 ♀♀
Leisure activities : 🏖 🏊 hammam, jacuzzi ⚓ ⛴
Facilities : ♿ ⚡ 🎱 ♨ ⚗ 🍴 🔲 ♨
Nearby : ✕ 🎣

PEYRILLAC-ET-MILLAC

24370 – Michelin map **329** J6 – pop. 213 – alt. 88
▶ Paris 521 – Brive-la-Gaillarde 45 – Gourdon 23 – Sarlat-la-Canéda 22

⚠ Au P'tit Bonheur

🕿 05 53 29 77 93. www.camping-auptitbonheur.com

Address : Combe de Lafon (2.5km north along the follow the signs for Le Bouscandier)

Opening times : from beginning April to end Sept.

2.8 ha (113 pitches)

Tariff : (2014 Price) 22.70€ ✝✝ ⚓ 🔲 🔌 (10A) – Extra per person 5.65€ – Reservation fee 16€

Rental rates : (2014 Price) (from beginning April to end Sept.) – 25 – 9 🏠 – 3 canvas bungalows. Per night from 36 to 108€ – Per week from 246 to 752€ – Reservation fee 16€

🚐 borne

Surroundings : 🌳 ⛱ ♀♀
Leisure activities : 🍴 ✕ 🏖 🏊 jacuzzi ⚓ 🚲 ⛴
Facilities : ♿ ⚡ ♨ ⚗ 🍴 🔲 ♨

Longitude : 1.40356
Latitude : 44.93214

PISSOS

40410 – Michelin map **335** G9 – pop. 1 315 – alt. 46
▶ Paris 657 – Arcachon 72 – Biscarrosse 34 – Bordeaux 75

⚠ Municipal de l'Arriu

🕿 05 58 08 90 38. www.pissos.fr – 🏮

Address : 525 chemin de l'Arriu (1.2km east along the D 43, follow the signs for Sore and take the road to the right, after the swimming pool)

Opening times : from beginning July to mid Sept.

3 ha (74 pitches)

Tariff : 12€ ✝✝ ⚓ 🔲 🔌 (12A) – Extra per person 3€

Rental rates : (from beginning July to mid Sept.) – 3 canvas bungalows. Per week from 261€

Surroundings : 🌳 ♀♀
Facilities : ♿ ⚡ 🍴 ♨ ⚗
Nearby : 🔲 🏖 🚲 ✕ ⛴ 🐴

Longitude : -0.77047
Latitude : 44.3027

In order for the guide to remain wholly objective, the selection of campsites is made on an entirely independent basis.

PLAZAC

24580 – Michelin map **329** H5 – pop. 725 – alt. 110
▶ Paris 527 – Bergerac 65 – Brive-la-Gaillarde 53 – Périgueux 40

🏞 Le Lac ♠♦

𝒫 05 53 50 75 86. www.campinglelac-dordogne.com

Address : at the lake (800m southeast along the D 45, follow the signs for Thonac)

Opening times : from mid May to end Sept.

7 ha/2.5 for camping (130 pitches)

Tariff : (2014 Price) ✤ 5.70€ ⇦ 🄴 5.70€ – 🄗 (10A) 3.70€ – Reservation fee 12€

Rental rates : (2014 Price) (from mid May to end Sept.) 🕭 (1 mobile home) – 40 🛏 – 4 🏠. Per night from 35 to 100€ – Per week from 235 to 720€ – Reservation fee 12€

🚐 2 🄴 20€

Beside the lake, in the shade of walnut and Holm oak trees.

Surroundings : 🏞 ⌂ ♨♨ ⛰
Leisure activities : 🍽 ✕ 🎦 ⛹ ⛷ ✖ ⛏ ⛷ multi-sports ground
Facilities : 🔥 ⊶ 🛁 🚿 🚰 launderette 🛒
G P S Longitude : 1.14794
Latitude : 45.03125

To make the best possible use of this guide, please read pages 2–15 carefully.

PONT-DU-CASSE

47480 – Michelin map **336** G4 – pop. 4 305 – alt. 67
▶ Paris 658 – Bordeaux 147 – Toulouse 122 – Montauban 96

⚠ Village Vacances de Loisirs Darel

(rental of chalets only)

𝒫 05 53 67 96 41, accueil@ville-pontducasse.fr

Address : Darel (7km northeast along the D 656, follow the signs for Cahors and take a right turn towards St-Ferréol)

Opening times : Permanent

34 ha/2 for camping undulating

Rental rates : (2014 Price) 🅿 – 15 🏠. Per night from 70€ – Per week from 202 to 386€ – Reservation fee 13€

In a pleasant location surrounded by trees, near a large riding centre.

Surroundings : 🏞 ♨♨
Leisure activities : 🎦 ⛷ ⛹
Facilities : 🎦 🔲
G P S Longitude : 0.68536
Latitude : 44.21698

LE PORGE

33680 – Michelin map **335** E5 – pop. 2 428 – alt. 8
▶ Paris 624 – Andernos-les-Bains 18 – Bordeaux 47 – Lacanau-Océan 21

🏞 Municipal la Grigne ♠♦

𝒫 05 56 26 54 88. www.camping-leporge.fr

Address : 35 avenue de l'Océan (9.5km west along the D 107, 1km from Le Porge-Océan)

Opening times : from beginning April to end Sept.

30 ha (700 pitches)

Tariff : 32.10€ ✤✤ ⇦ 🄴 🄗 (10A) – Extra per person 6.80€ – Reservation fee 21€

Rental rates : (from beginning April to end Sept.) ⚡ – 24 🛏 – 10 canvas bungalows. Per week from 350 to 995€ – Reservation fee 21€

🚐 borne 3€

Surroundings : ♨♨
Leisure activities : 🍽 ✕ 🎦 ⛹ ⛷ ⛷ ⛷ ✖ ⛏
Facilities : 🔥 ⊶ 🛁 🚿 🚰 launderette 🛒
Nearby : forest trail
G P S Longitude : -1.20314
Latitude : 44.89363

PYLA-SUR-MER

33115 – Michelin map **335** D7
▶ Paris 648 – Arcachon 8 – Biscarrosse 34 – Bordeaux 66

🏞 Yelloh! Village Panorama du Pyla ♠♦

𝒫 05 56 22 10 44. www.camping-panorama.com

Address : route de Biscarrosse (7km south along the D 218)

Opening times : from mid April to end Sept.

15 ha/10 for camping (450 pitches)

Tariff : 47€ ✤✤ ⇦ 🄴 🄗 (10A) – Extra per person 8€

Rental rates : (from mid April to end Sept.) – 80 🛏 – 5 🏠 – 15 tent lodges. Per night from 34 to 175€ – Per week from 238 to 1,225€

🚐 borne

Access to the beach via a pedestrian path and steep steps.

Surroundings : 🏞 ≤ ⌂ ♨♨
Leisure activities : 🍽 ✕ 🎦 ⛹ ⛷ ⛷ ⛷ ✖ ⛏ ⛷ ⛷ hang-gliding skate park
Facilities : 🔥 ⊶ 🚿 🚰 launderette 🛒 refrigerated food storage facilities
G P S Longitude : -1.22502
Latitude : 44.57738

🏞 FranceLoc Domaine Le Petit Nice ♠♦

𝒫 05 56 22 74 03. www.petitnice.com

Address : route de Biscarrosse

Opening times : from beginning April to end Sept.

5 ha (209 pitches) very uneven, terraced, flat, sandy

Tariff : (2014 Price) 39€ ✤✤ ⇦ 🄴 🄗 (10A) – Extra per person 7€

Reservation fee 30€

Rental rates : (2014 Price) (from beginning April to end Sept.) – 4 caravans – 89 🛏 – 10 tent lodges. Per night from 46 to 170€ – Per week from 182 to 1,372€ – Reservation fee 30€

🚐 borne

Situated at the foot of the Dune du Pyla.

Surroundings : 🏞 ≤ Banc d'Arguin National Park ♨♨
Leisure activities : 🍽 ✕ 🎦 ⛹ ⛷ ⛷ ⛷ ⛷ multi-sports ground
Facilities : 🔥 ⊶ 🚿 🚰 launderette 🛒 refrigerated food storage facilities
Nearby : paragliding
G P S Longitude : -1.22043
Latitude : 44.57274

🏞 Tohapi La Forêt ♠♦

𝒫 05 56 22 73 28. www.village-center.fr

Address : 3 km at the south on the D 218, route Biscarrosse (at the foot of the Dune du Pyla)

Opening times : from beginning April to end Sept.

8 ha (460 pitches) undulating, flat and relatively flat, sandy

Tariff : (2014 Price) 34€ ✤✤ ⇦ 🄴 🄗 (10A) – Extra per person 9€ – Reservation fee 10€

Rental rates : (2014 Price) (from beginning April to end Sept.) ♿ (2 mobile homes) – 95 🚐 – 12 🏠. Per night from 31 to 192€ – Per week from 217 to 1,344€ – Reservation fee 20€
🚐 borne
Situated at the foot of the Dune du Pyla.

Surroundings : 🌊	**G P S**
Leisure activities : 🍷 🍴 🛖 👤 🏃 🚣 🚴 ✂ 🏋 multi-sports ground	Longitude : -1.20857
Facilities : ♿ ⛽ 🚿 🍴 launderette 🧺 🚗	Latitude : 44.58542

RAUZAN

33420 – Michelin map **335** K6 – pop. 1 148 – alt. 69
▶ Paris 596 – Bergerac 57 – Bordeaux 39 – Langon 35

▲ Le Vieux Château

Le Vieux Château

☎ 05 57 84 15 38. www.vieuxchateau.fr
Address : take the northern exit follow the signs for St-Jean-de-Blaignac and take road to the left (1.2km)

Opening times : from beginning April to mid Oct.

2.5 ha (74 pitches)

Tariff : 20.60€ 🚻 🚐 🔌 (6A) – Extra per person 5.50€ – Reservation fee 8€

Rental rates : (2014 Price) (from beginning April to mid Oct.) 🦌 – 10 🚐 – 4 🏠 – 2 canvas bungalows – 1 Swiss Army truck. Per week from 216 to 826€ – Reservation fee 8€
🚐 borne
At the foot of a ruined 12th-century fortress, with a pedestrian path to the village.

Surroundings : 🌊	**G P S**
Leisure activities : 🍷 🍴 🛖 🎣	Longitude : -0.12715
Facilities : ♿ ⛽ 🍴 🧺	Latitude : 44.78213

RIVIÈRE-SAAS-ET-GOURBY

40180 – Michelin map **335** E12 – pop. 1 168 – alt. 50
▶ Paris 742 – Bordeaux 156 – Mont-de-Marsan 68 – Bayonne 44

▲ Lou Bascou

☎ 05 58 97 57 29. www.campingloubascou.fr – limited spaces for one-night stay

Address : 250 route de Houssat (to the northeast of the town)

Opening times : Permanent

1 ha (41 pitches) flat, grassy

Tariff : 28.50€ 🚻 🚐 🔌 (10A) – Extra per person 11€
Rental rates : Permanent – 8 🏠. Per night from 39 to 99€ – Per week from 273 to 693€
🚐 borne 13€ – 15 🔌 13€

Surroundings : 🌊	**G P S**
Leisure activities : 📺 entertainment room	Longitude : -1.14971
Facilities : ♿ ⛽ 🍴 launderette	Latitude : 43.68203
Nearby : 🧺 ✂	

Do not confuse:
▲ to ▲▲▲ : MICHELIN classification with
★ to ★★★★★ : official classification

LA ROCHE-CHALAIS

24490 – Michelin map **329** B5 – pop. 2 857 – alt. 60
▶ Paris 510 – Bergerac 62 – Blaye 67 – Bordeaux 68

▲ Municipal de Gerbes

☎ 05 53 91 40 65. www.larochechalais.com
Address : Les Gerbes (located 1km west; beside the river)

Opening times : from mid April to end Sept.

3 ha (100 pitches) small adjacent wood

Tariff : (2014 Price) 11. 68€ 🚻 🚐 🔌 (10A) – Extra per person 2.50€

Rental rates : (2014 Price) (from mid April to end Sept.) – 4 🚐 – 3 🏠 – 1 gîte. Per night from 55€ – Per week from 90 to 321€ Reservation fee 15€
🚐 borne 9€ – 10 🔌 11€ – 🔌 9€

Surroundings : 🌊 🌊	**G P S**
Leisure activities : 🛖 🚣 🎣	Longitude : -0.00207
Facilities : ♿ ⛽ 🍴	Latitude : 45.14888

LA ROQUE-GAGEAC

24250 – Michelin map **329** I7 – pop. 416 – alt. 85
▶ Paris 535 – Brive-la-Gaillarde 71 – Cahors 53 – Fumel 52

▲▲ Le Beau Rivage 👥

☎ 05 53 28 32 05. www.beaurivagedordogne.com
Address : Le Gaillardou (4km east on the D 46; beside the Dordogne river)

Opening times : from end April to mid Sept.

8 ha (199 pitches)

Tariff : (2014 Price) 27.80€ 🚻 🚐 🔌 (6A)

Extra per person 5.60€ – Reservation fee 20€
Rental rates : (2014 Price) (from end April to mid Sept.) – 44 🚐. Per week from 173 to 923€ – Reservation fee 20€

Surroundings : 🌊 ⛰	**G P S**
Leisure activities : 🍷 🍴 🛖 👤 nighttime 🏃 🚣 ✂ 🎣 🐟	Longitude : 1.21422
Facilities : ♿ ⛽ 🚿 🧺 🍴 launderette 🧺 🚗	Latitude : 44.81587
Nearby : 🚴	

ROUFFIGNAC

24580 – Michelin map **329** G5 – pop. 1 552 – alt. 300
▶ Paris 531 – Bergerac 58 – Brive-la-Gaillarde 57 – Périgueux 32

▲▲ L'Offrerie

☎ 05 53 35 33 26. www.camping-ferme-offrerie.com
Address : Le Grand Boisset (situated 2km south along the D 32, follow the signs for Les Grottes de Rouffignac and take a right turn)

Opening times : from beginning April to beginning Oct.

3.5 ha (48 pitches)

Tariff : (2014 Price) 23.20€ 🚻 🚐 🔌 (10A) – Extra per person 5.60€

Rental rates : (2014 Price) (from beginning April to beginning Oct.) – 19 🚐 – 10 canvas bungalows. Per night from 25 to 55€ – Per week from 155 to 735€
🚐 borne 3€ – 1 🔌 11.50€ – 🔌 11.50€

Surroundings : 🌊 🏕 🌊	**G P S**
Leisure activities : 🍴 🛖 🚣 🏋	Longitude : 0.97109
Facilities : ⛽ 🍴 🧺 🚗	Latitude : 45.02775

La Nouvelle Croze

05 53 05 38 90. www.lanouvellecroze.com

Address : 2.5km southeast along the D 31, follow the signs for Fleurac and take the road to the right

Opening times : from beginning April to end Oct.

1.3 ha (40 pitches) flat, grassy

Tariff : 22.70€ ♣♣ ⟶ 🗉 (16A) – Extra per person 5.70€
Rental rates : (from beginning April to end Oct.) – 16 🚐. Per night from 38 to 70€ – Per week from 221 to 795€

Surroundings : 🐾 ♨
Leisure activities : ♈✗ 🏛 🚣 🛶
Facilities : ♿ o⟶ 🆑 ♨ ♈
Longitude : 0.99783
Latitude : 45.02412

Bleu Soleil

05 53 05 48 30. www.camping-bleusoleil.com

Address : Domaine Touvent (located 1.5km north along the D 31, follow the signs for Thenon and take turning to the right)

Opening times : from mid April to end Sept.

41 ha/7 for camping (110 pitches)

Tariff : (2014 Price) ♣ 5.50€ ⟶ 🗉 7€ – (½) (10A) 3.80€ – Reservation fee 15€
Rental rates : (2014 Price) (from end March to end Sept.) – 21 🏠 – 2 canvas bungalows. Per night from 25 to 60€ – Per week from 308 to 735€ – Reservation fee 15€

Surroundings : 🐾 ⟨ ♨
Leisure activities : ♈✗ 🏛 🚣 🛶 multi-sports ground
Facilities : ♿ o⟶ 🆑 ♨ 🛢 🚿 refrigerated food storage facilities
Longitude : 0.98586
Latitude : 45.05507

SABRES

40630 – Michelin map 335 G10 – pop. 1 200 – alt. 78
Paris 676 – Arcachon 92 – Bayonne 111 – Bordeaux 94

Le Domaine de Peyricat

05 58 07 51 88. www.vtf-vacances.com

Address : take the southern exit along the D 327, follow the signs for Luglon

Opening times : from mid June to mid Sept.

20 ha/2 for camping (69 pitches)

Tariff : (2014 Price) 23€ ♣♣ ⟶ 🗉 – Extra per person 2.80€
Rental rates : (2014 Price) (from mid April to end Sept.) 🚲 – 4 🚐 – 8 🏠. Per week from 309 to 709€

🚐 borne 5€

Lots of activities are available at the adjacent holiday village.

Surroundings : 🗂
Facilities : ♿ o⟶ 🚿 ♈
At Village Vacances : launderette ♈✗ 🏛 🏃 🛶 ✗ 🏊
Longitude : -0.74235
Latitude : 44.144

Do not confuse:
△ to ▲▲▲ : *MICHELIN classification with*
★ to ★★★★★ : *official classification*

ST-AMAND-DE-COLY

24290 – Michelin map 329 I5 – pop. 382 – alt. 180
Paris 515 – Bordeaux 188 – Périgueux 58 – Cahors 104

Yelloh! Village Lascaux Vacances 🚶

05 53 50 81 57. www.campinglascauxvacances.com

Address : Les Malénies (located 1km south along the D 64, follow the signs for St-Geniès)

Opening times : from end May to mid Sept.

12 ha (150 pitches)

Tariff : 36€ ♣♣ ⟶ 🗉 (½) (10A) – Extra per person 7€
Rental rates : (from end May to mid Sept.) – 80 🚐 – 10 🏠 – 2 canvas bungalows – 2 tent lodges. Per night from 39 to 156€ – Per week from 273 to 1,092€

🚐 borne

Surroundings : 🐾 🗂 ♨
Leisure activities : ♈✗ 🏃 🚴 🛶 🎣 🏛 🛶 🏊 multi-sports ground
Facilities : ♿ o⟶ 🆑 ♨ 🚿 ♈ launderette 🚿
Longitude : 1.24191
Latitude : 45.05461

ST-ANTOINE-D'AUBEROCHE

24330 – Michelin map 329 G5 – pop. 145 – alt. 152
Paris 491 – Brive-la-Gaillarde 96 – Limoges 105 – Périgueux 24

La Pélonie

05 53 07 55 78. www.lapelonie.com

Address : La Pélonie (1.8km southwest towards Milhac-Gare - from Fossemagne, continue 6 km along the RN 89 and take the road to the right)

Opening times : from mid April to end Sept.

5 ha (60 pitches)

Tariff : ♣ 5.80€ ⟶ 🗉 6.90€ – (½) (10A) 3.80€ – Reservation fee 10€
Rental rates : (from mid April to end Sept.) – 24 🚐. Per night from 50 to 65€ – Per week from 565 to 750€ – Reservation fee 10€

🚐 10 🗉 18€

Surroundings : 🐾 🗂 ♨
Leisure activities : ♈✗ 🏛 🚣 🛶 🏊
Facilities : ♿ o⟶ 🎩 🆑 ♈ launderette 🚿
Longitude : 0.92845
Latitude : 45.13135

ST-ANTOINE-DE-BREUILH

24230 – Michelin map 329 B6 – pop. 2 073 – alt. 18
Paris 555 – Bergerac 30 – Duras 28 – Libourne 34

La Rivière Fleurie

05 53 24 82 80. www.la-riviere-fleurie.com

Address : at St-Aulaye-de-Breuilh, 180 rue Théophile-Cart (3km southwest, 100m from the Dordogne river)

Opening times : from mid April to mid Sept.

2.5 ha (60 pitches) flat, grassy

Tariff : (2014 Price) 23€ ♣♣ ⟶ 🗉 (½) (4A) – Extra per person 6€ – Reservation fee 18€
Rental rates : (2014 Price) Permanent – 21 🚐 – 2 studios – 2 apartments. Per night from 48 to 52€ – Per week from 240 to 640€ – Reservation fee 20€

Surroundings : 🐾 🗂 ♨
Leisure activities : ♈✗ 🏛 🚣 🛶
Facilities : ♿ o⟶ 🆑 ♨ ♈ launderette 🚿
Nearby : ✗
Longitude : 0.12235
Latitude : 44.82879

ST-AULAYE

24410 – Michelin map **329** B4 – pop. 1 360 – alt. 61
▶ Paris 504 – Bergerac 56 – Blaye 79 – Bordeaux 81

⛰ Municipal de la Plage

☏ 05 53 90 62 20. www.saint-aulaye.com

Address : Les Ponts (take the northern exit along the D 38, follow the signs for Aubeterre; beside the Dronne river)

Opening times : from beginning June to mid Sept.

1 ha (70 pitches) flat, grassy

Tariff : 12€ ♦♦ ⇔ 🔲 🔌 (10A) – Extra per person 2€

Rental rates : (from beginning June to mid Sept.) – 11 🚐 – 14 🏠. Per night from 18 to 58€ – Per week from 125 to 405€

Reservation fee 17€

🚐 borne

Surroundings : 🛒 ♤♤
Leisure activities : 🛶 🏊 🚴 ✂ 🎣 🛶 🛥 🐟
Facilities : ♿ ⚮ 🚮 🛢 🍴 launderette
Nearby : ✗ 🚃 🏖 (beach)

GPS	Longitude : 0.13274
	Latitude : 45.20786

ST-AVIT-DE-VIALARD

24260 – Michelin map **329** G6 – pop. 145 – alt. 210
▶ Paris 520 – Bergerac 39 – Le Bugue 7 – Les Eyzies-de-Tayac 17

⛰ Les Castels St-Avit Loisirs ♦♣

St-Avit Loisirs

☏ 05 53 02 64 00. www.saint-avit-loisirs.com – limited spaces for one-night stay

Address : Malefon (1.8km to the northwest)

Opening times : from end March to mid Sept.

55 ha/15 for camping (400 pitches) natural setting among trees and bushes

Tariff : 72€ ♦♦ ⇔ 🔲 🔌 (6A) – Extra per person 12€ – Reservation fee 19€

Rental rates : (from end March to mid Sept.) – 40 🚐 – 35 🏠 – 30 🛏 – 15 apartments – 2 tent lodges – 1 gîte. Per night from 51 to 190€ – Per week from 357 to 1,330€ –Reservation fee 25€

🚐 16 🔲 57.60€ – 🚐 14€

A spacious, undulating and wooded site with a large, attractive swimming pool complex. High-quality chalets.

Surroundings : 🛒 🛒 ♤♤
Leisure activities : ♈ ✗ 🛖 ⑆ ⋔ 🛶 jacuzzi 🏊 🚴 ✂ 🎣 🛶 🛥 quad biking, multi-sports ground, entertainment room
Facilities : ♿ ⚮ 🛁 🚮 ⚱ 🍴 launderette 🛢 🚿

GPS	Longitude : 0.84971
	Latitude : 44.95174

ST-CRÉPIN-ET-CARLUCET

24590 – Michelin map **329** I6 – pop. 493 – alt. 262
▶ Paris 514 – Brive-la-Gaillarde 40 – Les Eyzies-de-Tayac 29 – Montignac 21

⛰ Les Peneyrals ♦♣

Les Peneyrals

☏ 05 53 28 85 71, www.peneyrals.com

Address : at St Crépin (located 1km south along the D 56, follow the signs for Proissans)

Opening times : from mid May to mid Sept.

12 ha/8 for camping (250 pitches)

Tariff : (2014 Price) ♦ 9.90€ ⇔ 🔲 14.40€ – 🔌 (10A) 4.50€ – Reservation fee 20€

Rental rates : (2014 Price) (from mid May to mid Sept.) ♿ (1 chalet) – 40 🚐 – 32 🏠. Per week from 300 to 1,300€ – Reservation fee 30€

🚐 borne

In a hilly setting, with pitches among trees or beside a lake.

Surroundings : 🛥 🛒 ♤♤
Leisure activities : ♈ ✗ 🛖 ⑆ ⋔ 🛶 🚴 ✂ 🎣 🛥 🏊 🛶 🛥
Facilities : ♿ ⚮ 🆑 🛢 🍴 launderette 🚿 🚃

GPS	Longitude : 1.27267
	Latitude : 44.95785

⛰ Village Vacances Les Gîtes de Combas

(rental of gîtes only)

☏ 05 53 28 64 00. www.perigordgites.com

Address : Les Combas (situated 2km south along the D 56, follow the signs for Proissans)

Opening times : Permanent

4 ha

Rental rates : ♿ (1 gîte) 🅿 – 22 🏠 – 22 gîtes. Per night from 100 to 200€ – Per week from 330 to 1,200€

Some gîtes have been established in the old farm buildings made of local stone.

Surroundings : 🛥 🎣
Leisure activities : ♈ 🛖 🏊 ✂ 🛶 🛥
Facilities : ⚮ 🆑 🍴 🛢 🚿

GPS	Longitude : 1.27718
	Latitude : 44.94871

The pitches of many campsites are marked out with low hedges of attractive bushes and shrubs.

ST-CYBRANET

24250 – Michelin map **329** I7 – pop. 376 – alt. 78
▶ Paris 542 – Cahors 51 – Les Eyzies-de-Tayac 29 – Gourdon 21

⛰ Bel Ombrage

☏ 05 53 28 34 14. www.belombrage.com

Address : on the D 50 (800m to the northwest; beside the Céou river)

Opening times : from beginning June to beginning Sept.

6 ha (180 pitches) flat, grassy

Tariff : ♦ 5.90€ ⇔ 🔲 7.50€ – 🔌 (10A) 4.10€

Surroundings : 🛥 🛒 ♤♤ 🏔
Leisure activities : 🛖 🏊 🛶
Facilities : ♿ ⚮ 🍴 launderette
Nearby : ✗

GPS	Longitude : 1.16244
	Latitude : 44.79082

The prices listed were supplied by the campsite owners in 2014 (if prices were not available, those from the previous year are given). The fees should be regarded as basic charges and may fluctuate with inflation.

ST-ÉMILION

33330 – Michelin map **335** K5 – pop. 2 005 – alt. 30
▶ Paris 584 – Bergerac 58 – Bordeaux 40 – Langon 49

🏕 **Yelloh! Saint-Émilion** 👥

Yelloh! Saint-Émilion

📞 05 57 24 75 80. www.camping-saint-emilion.com

Address : Les Combes (3km north along the D 122, follow the signs for Lussac and take turning to the right – caravans and camper vans are not permitted to pass through St-Émilion)

Opening times : from end April to end Sept.

4.5 ha (160 pitches) flat, grassy

Tariff : 39€ ✶✶ ⊂⊃ 🗐 🗘 (10A) – Extra per person 7€
Rental rates : (from end April to end Sept.) – 48 📳. Per night from 39 to 195€ – Per week from 273 to 1,365€
🚐 borne – 25 🗐
There's a free shuttle bus to St-Émilion.

Surroundings : 🌿 🖙 ♨♨
Leisure activities : ✗ 🖥 🚶 ⛵ 🚴 ✂ ⛏ 🛶 🏊 🐟 pedalos 🦎
Facilities : 🚿 🕳 🖥 🍴 launderette 🛁 🚿

GPS
Longitude : -0.14241
Latitude : 44.91675

ST-ÉTIENNE-DE-BAIGORRY

64430 – Michelin map **342** D3 – pop. 1 618 – alt. 163
▶ Paris 820 – Bordeaux 241 – Pau 160 – Pamplona 69

⛺ **Municipal l'Irouleguy**

📞 05 59 37 43 96. mairie.baigorri@orange.fr

Address : Borciriette district (take the northeastern exit along the D 15, follow the signs for St-Jean-Pied-de-Port and take road to the left in front of the swimming pool and behind the Irouléguy wine co-operative; beside the Nive river)

Opening times : from beginning March to end Nov.

1.5 ha (67 pitches) flat, grassy

Tariff : 12.70€ ✶✶ ⊂⊃ 🗐 🗘 (6A) – Extra per person 3.10€
In a green setting, with part stretching along the river.

Surroundings : ♨♨
Leisure activities : ⛵
Facilities : 🚿 🗑 🍴 🖥
Nearby : 🛒 🍴 ✗ ✂ 🛶

ST-GENIÈS

24590 – Michelin map **329** I6 – pop. 941 – alt. 232
▶ Paris 515 – Brive-la-Gaillarde 41 – Les Eyzies-de-Tayac 29 Montignac 13

🏕 **Club Airotel La Bouquerie** 👥

📞 05 53 28 98 22. www.labouquerie.com – limited spaces for one-night stay

Address : located 1.5km northwest along the D 704, follow the signs for Montignac and take the road to the right

Opening times : from mid April to beginning Sept.

8 ha/4 for camping (183 pitches)

Tariff : (2014 Price) ✶ 9.50€ ⊂⊃ 🗐 14€ – 🗘 (10A) 4.20€ – Reservation fee 20€

Rental rates : (2014 Price) (from mid April to beginning Sept.)
🚲 (1 mobile homes) – 90 📳 – 50 🏠. Per week from 320 to 2,190€ – Reservation fee 30€
Lovely pitches in the shade of oak trees.

Surroundings : 🌿 🖙 🦎
Leisure activities : 🍴 ✗ 🖥 🚶 🏊 ⛵ ✂ 🛶 🏊 paintballing, multi-sports ground
Facilities : 🚿 🕳 🏧 🖥 🍴 launderette 🛁 🚿
Nearby : 🐎

GPS
Longitude : 1.24594
Latitude : 44.99892

ST-GIRONS-PLAGE

40560 – Michelin map **335** C11
▶ Paris 728 – Bordeaux 142 – Mont-de-Marsan 79 – Bayonne 73

🏕 **Eurosol** 👥

📞 05 58 47 90 14. www.camping-eurosol.com

Address : route de la Plage (350m from the beach)

Opening times : from mid May to mid Sept.

33 ha/18 for camping (510 pitches)

Tariff : (2014 Price) 39€ ✶✶ ⊂⊃ 🗐 🗘 (10A) – Extra per person 6€ Reservation fee 25€
Rental rates : (2014 Price) (from mid May to mid Sept.) 🦎 ℗ – 145 📳 – 15 ⊂⊃ – 2 tent lodges. Per night from 47 to 170€ – Per week from 329 to 1,190€ – Reservation fee 25€
🚐 borne – 20 🗐 20€

Surroundings : 🌿 ♨♨
Leisure activities : 🍴 ✗ 🖥 🚶 🚴 ✂ multi-sports ground
Facilities : 🚿 🕳 🖥 🛁 🗑 🍴 launderette 🚿🚿
Nearby : 🐎

GPS
Longitude : -1.35162
Latitude : 43.95158

🏕 **Campéole les Tourterelles** 👥

Didier CAVAILHES / CAMPEOLE

📞 05 58 47 93 12. www.camping-tourterelles.com

Address : route de la plage (5.2km west along the D 42, 300m from the ocean (direct access)

Opening times : from end April to end Sept.

18 ha (822 pitches)

Tariff : (2014 Price) 36€ ✶✶ ⊂⊃ 🗐 🗘 (10A) – Extra per person 10.30€ – Reservation fee 25€

Rental rates : (2014 Price) (from beginning April to end Sept.) 🚲 (2 mobile homes) – 136 📳 – 20 🏠 – 115 canvas bungalows. Per night from 22 to 158€ – Per week from 154 to 1,106€ – Reservation fee 25€
🚐 borne 18.20€ – 🚐 31.50€
The site welcomes groups of surfers.

Surroundings : ♨♨
Leisure activities : 🖥 🚶 ⛵ 🚴 🛶 multi-sports ground
Facilities : 🚿 🕳 🛁 🗑 🍴 launderette 🚿 refrigerated food storage facilities

GPS
Longitude : -1.35691
Latitude : 43.95439

ST-JEAN-DE-LUZ

64500 – Michelin map **342** C2 – pop. 13 742 – alt. 3
▶ Paris 785 – Bayonne 24 – Biarritz 18 – Pau 129

Club Airotel Itsas Mendi

℘ 05 59 26 56 50. www.itsas-mendi.com

Address : Acotz district, chemin Duhartia (5km to the northeast, 500m from the beach)

Opening times : from end March to beginning Nov.

8.5 ha (475 pitches)

Tariff : (2014 Price) 44€ ♟♟ ⊕ 🗐 🔌 (10A) – Extra per person 7.90€ Reservation fee 20€

Rental rates : (2014 Price) (from end March to beginning Nov.) – 140 🚐. Per night from 30 to 125€ – Reservation fee 20€
🚰 100 🗐 20.50€

In a green setting laid out on terraces, with half the pitches for mobile homes.

Surroundings : ♤♤
Leisure activities : ♟ ✗ 🖾 🖳 ❄ 🏓 🛶 jacuzzi ⚽ 🏓 🖳 🏊 surfing school, multi-sports ground
Facilities : ♿ ☕ 🗑 🍴 launderette 🖳 ♨ refrigerated food storage facilities
G P S Longitude : -1.61726
Latitude : 43.41347

Atlantica ♟♟

℘ 05 59 47 72 44. www.campingatlantica.com

Address : Acotz district, chemin Miquélénia (5km to the northeast, 500m from the beach)

Opening times : from beginning April to end Sept.

3.5 ha (200 pitches)

Tariff : (2014 Price) 39.70€ ♟♟ ⊕ 🗐 🔌 (6A)

Extra per person 8.20€ – Reservation fee 25€

Rental rates : (2014 Price) (from beginning April to end Sept.) – 100 🚐 – 12 tent lodges. Per night from 35 to 75€ – Per week from 360 to 1,150€ – Reservation fee 25€

In a green setting, laid out on terraces, with many rental options of varying types and standards.

Surroundings : ⊏ ♤♤
Leisure activities : ♟ ✗ 🖾 🏓 ❄ jacuzzi ⚽ 🏊 multi-sports ground
Facilities : ♿ ☕ ♨ 🍴 🖳 ♨ refrigerated food storage facilities
G P S Longitude : -1.61688
Latitude : 43.41525

La Ferme Erromardie

℘ 05 59 26 34 26. www.camping-erromardie.com

Address : 40 chemin Erromardie (1.8km to the northeast, near the beach)

Opening times : from mid March to end Sept.

2 ha (176 pitches) flat, grassy

Tariff : (2014 Price) 33€ ♟♟ ⊕ 🗐 🔌 (16A) – Extra per person 6€ Reservation fee 19€

Rental rates : (from mid March to end Sept.) – 42 🚐. Per night from 39 to 170€ – Per week from 234 to 896€ – Reservation fee 19€

The site is divided into three separate sections, almost the length of the beach.

Surroundings : ♤ ⊏ ♤♤
Leisure activities : ♟ ✗ 🖾 ⚽
Facilities : ♿ ☕ ♨ 🍴 launderette 🖳 ♨
G P S Longitude : -1.64202
Latitude : 43.40564

Inter-Plages

℘ 05 59 26 56 94. www.campinginterplages.com

Address : Acotz district, 305 route des Plages (5km to the northeast, 150m from the beach (direct access)

Opening times : from beginning April to end Sept.

2.5 ha (91 pitches)

Tariff : (2014 Price) 38€ ♟♟ ⊕ 🗐 🔌 (10A) – Extra per person 8€ Reservation fee 20€

Rental rates : (2014 Price) (from beginning April to end Sept.) ⚽ – 17 🚐 – 5 🏠. Per night from 45 to 65€ – Per week from 280 to 750€ – Reservation fee 20€
🚰 borne 4€

In an attractive location looking out over the sea.

Surroundings : ♤ ⊲ ⊏ ♤♤
Leisure activities : 🖾 ⚽ 🚲 🏊
Facilities : ♿ ☕ 🗑 🖳 ♨ ⚘ 🍴 launderette
Nearby : 🖳 ♟ ✗ 🚴 🏊 surfing
G P S Longitude : -1.62667
Latitude : 43.41527

Merko-Lacarra

℘ 05 59 26 56 76. www.merkolacarra.com

Address : Acotz district, 820 route des Plages (5km to the northeast, 150m from Acotz beach)

Opening times : from end March to beginning Oct.

2 ha (123 pitches)

Tariff : 34.50€ ♟♟ ⊕ 🗐 🔌 (16A) – Extra per person 8€ –

Reservation fee 16€

Rental rates : (2014 Price) (from end March to beginning Oct.) ⚽ – 27 🚐. Per night from 49 to 85€ – Per week from 287 to 784€ Reservation fee 20€
🚰 borne 6€

A warm welcome, good-quality sanitary facilities and very close to the beach at Mayarco.

Leisure activities : ✗ ⚽
Facilities : ♿ ☕ 🖳 ♨ 🍴 launderette ♨
Nearby : 🖳 ♟ 🏊 surfing
G P S Longitude : -1.62366
Latitude : 43.41855

Les Tamaris-Plage ♟♟

℘ 05 59 26 55 90. www.tamaris-plage.com

Address : Acotz district, 720 route de Plages (5km to the northeast, 80m from the beach)

Opening times : from beginning April to beginning Nov.

1.5 ha (79 pitches)

Tariff : (2014 Price) 20€ ♟♟ ⊕ 🗐 🔌 (8A) – Extra per person 8€ – Reservation fee 30€

Rental rates : (2014 Price) (from beginning April to beginning Nov.) – 29 🚐 – 5 studios – 10 canvas bungalows. Per night from 45 to 69€ – Per week from 392 to 996€

Reservation fee 30€
🚰 borne 20€

Nice lawns, a few trees and so close to the sea and the beach at Mayarco!

Surroundings : ⊏ ♤
Leisure activities : 🖾 🏓 ❄ hammam, jacuzzi ⚽
Facilities : ♿ ☕ 🖳 ♨ ⚘ 🍴 launderette
Nearby : 🖳 ♟ ✗ 🚴 🏊 surfing
G P S Longitude : -1.62387
Latitude : 43.41804

⚠ Le Bord de mer

✆ 0559262461, www.camping-le-bord-de-mer.fr

Address : 71 chemin d'Erromardie (1.8km northeast)

Opening times : from mid April to beginning Nov.

2 ha (78 pitches) terraced, relatively flat, flat, grassy

Tariff : (2014 Price) 33 € ♟♟ 🚐 🔳 🔌 (10A) – Extra per person 8 € Reservation fee 85 €

A small coastal footpath leads to the cliffs and the beach.

Surroundings : ≼ the ocean and La Rhune mountain 🗘	**G** **P** **S**	Longitude : -1.64155
Leisure activities : ✗		Latitude : 43.40678
Facilities : ⚊ 🏕 🖎 🚿 ⛲ launderette		
Nearby : 🏖 ⛱ 🚵		

ST-JEAN-PIED-DE-PORT

64220 – Michelin map **342** E4 – pop. 1 477 – alt. 159

▶ Paris 817 – Bayonne 54 – Biarritz 55 – Dax 105

🔺 Narbaïtz Vacances

✆ 0559371013. www.camping-narbaitz.com

Address : at Ascarat (2.5km northwest along the D 918, follow the signs for Bayonne and take the turning to the left; 50m from the Nive river and beside a stream)

Opening times : from beginning April to mid Sept.

2.5 ha (101 pitches)

Tariff : (2014 Price) 38.50 € ♟♟ 🚐 🔳 🔌 (10A) – Extra per person 6.50 € – Reservation fee 19 €

Rental rates : (2014 Price) Permanent 🦟 – 12 🚐 – 3 gîtes. Per night from 60 to 70 € – Per week from 300 to 750 € – Reservation fee 19 €

🚐 borne

There's an unrestricted view over the Irouléguy vineyards. Choose pitches furthest away from the road.

Surroundings : ≼ 🎋	**G** **P** **S**	Longitude : -1.25911
Leisure activities : 🏛 🎿 🏊		Latitude : 43.17835
Facilities : ⛺ ⚊ ▥ 🚿 ⛲ launderette 🚵		
Nearby : 🎣		

🔺 Europ'Camping

✆ 0559371278. www.europ-camping.com

Address : at Ascarat (situated 2km northwest along the D 918, follow the signs for Bayonne and take road to the left)

Opening times : from beginning April to end Sept.

2 ha (110 pitches)

Tariff : (2014 Price) 38 € ♟♟ 🚐 🔳 🔌 (10A) – Extra per person 6 € Reservation fee 22 €

Rental rates : (2014 Price) (from beginning April to end Sept.) – 45 🚐. Per night from 60 to 80 € – Per week from 270 to 750 € Reservation fee 22 €

There's an attractive view over the Irouléguy vineyards from well-kept pitches.

Surroundings : 🌊 ≼ 🌳	**G** **P** **S**	Longitude : -1.25398
Leisure activities : 🎣 ✗ 🏛 🎿 🏊		Latitude : 43.17279
Facilities : ⛺ ⚊ 🚿 🔧 ⛲ launderette 🚵		
Nearby : 🎣		

ST-JULIEN-DE-LAMPON

24370 – Michelin map **329** J6 – pop. 613 – alt. 120

▶ Paris 528 – Brive-la-Gaillarde 51 – Gourdon 17 – Sarlat-la-Canéda 17

⚠ Le Mondou

✆ 0553297037. www.camping-dordogne.info

Address : Le Colombier (located 1km east along the D 50, follow the signs for Mareuil and take the road to the right)

Opening times : from beginning April to mid Oct.

1.2 ha (60 pitches)

Tariff : ♟ 5.75 € 🚐 🔳 7.25 € – 🔌 (6A) 4 €

Rental rates : (from beginning April to mid Oct.) 🦟 – 4 🚐 – 1 🏠 – 8 canvas bungalows. Per week from 250 to 825 €

Surroundings : 🌊 🗘 🌳	**G** **P** **S**	Longitude : 1.36691
Leisure activities : 🏛 🎿 🏊		Latitude : 44.86295
Facilities : ⛺ ⚊ 🏕 🚿 ⛲ 🔳 🚵		
Nearby : launderette		

*The classification (1 to 5 tents, **black** or **red**) that we award to selected sites in this guide is our own system. It should not be confused with the classification (1 to 5 stars) of official organisations.*

ST-JULIEN-EN-BORN

40170 – Michelin map **335** D10 – pop. 1 450 – alt. 22

▶ Paris 706 – Castets 23 – Dax 43 – Mimizan 18

🔺 Municipal la Lette Fleurie

✆ 0558427409. www.camping-municipal-plage.com

Address : La Lette, route de l'Océan (4km northwest along the D 41, follow the signs for Contis-Plage)

Opening times : Permanent

8.5 ha (457 pitches)

Tariff : (2014 Price) ♟ 6 € 🚐 🔳 6.80 € – 🔌 (10A) 5.80 € – Reservation fee 15 €

Surroundings : 🌊 🌳	**G** **P** **S**	Longitude : -1.26173
Leisure activities : 🎣 ✗ 🏛 🎿 🦟 🏊		Latitude : 44.08139
Facilities : ⛺ ⚊ 🚿 ⛲ launderette 🏖 🚵 refrigerated food storage facilities		

ST-JUSTIN

40240 – Michelin map **335** J11 – pop. 922 – alt. 90

▶ Paris 694 – Barbotan-les-Thermes 19 – Captieux 41 – Labrit 31

🔺 Le Pin

✆ 0558448891, www.campinglepin.com

Address : route de Roquefort (2.3km north on the D 626; beside a little lake)

Opening times : from beginning April to end Oct.

3 ha (80 pitches)

Tariff : 23 € ♟♟ 🚐 🔳 🔌 (10A) – Extra per person 5 €

Rental rates : (from beginning May to end Oct.) – 6 🚐 – 10 🏠. Per night from 60 to 110 € – Per week from 260 to 800 €

Surroundings : 🌳	**G** **P** **S**	Longitude : -0.23468
Leisure activities : 🎣 ✗ 🎿 🏊 🎣 🐎		Latitude : 44.00188
Facilities : ⛺ ⚊ 🚿 ⛲ launderette 🚵		

ST-LAURENT-MEDOC

33112 – Michelin map **335** G4 – pop. 4 054 – alt. 6
▶ Paris 603 – Bordeaux 45 – Mérignac 41 – Pessac 48

⚲ Le Paradis

℘ 05 56 59 42 15. www.leparadis-medoc.com

Address : Fourthon (2.5km north along the D 1215, follow the signs for Lesparre)

Opening times :

3 ha (70 pitches) flat, grassy

Tariff : (2014 Price) 30€ ✸✸ ⇦ 🗐 ⚡ (10A) – Extra per person 9€ Reservation fee 15€

Rental rates : (2014 Price) (from mid April to mid Oct.) – 29 🚐 – 4 🏠 – 3 canvas bungalows. Per week from 320 to 860€– Reservation fee 15€

Surroundings : 🖵 🎜🎜	**G**	Longitude : -0.83995
Leisure activities : 🍴 🛶 🗖 🎣 🖍	**P**	Latitude : 45.17495
Facilities : ᕦ ⚲ 🍴 🗐 🛒	**S**	

ST-LÉON-SUR-VÉZÈRE

24290 – Michelin map **329** H5 – pop. 428 – alt. 70
▶ Paris 523 – Brive-la-Gaillarde 48 – Les Eyzies-de-Tayac 16 – Montignac 10

⚲ Le Paradis 🌲🌲

℘ 05 53 50 72 64. www.le-paradis.fr

Address : La Rebeyrolle (4km southwest along the D 706, follow the signs for Les Eyzies-de-Tayac; beside the Vézère)

Opening times : from beginning April to end Oct.

7 ha (200 pitches) flat, grassy

Tariff : (2014 Price) 35.70€ ✸✸ ⇦ 🗐 ⚡ (10A) – Extra per person 8.70€ – Reservation fee 20€

Rental rates : (2014 Price) (from beginning April to end Oct.) – 41 🚐 – 5 tent lodges. Per night from 53 to 189€ – Per week from 371 to 1,323€ – Reservation fee 20€

Upmarket facilities based around an old renovated farmhouse.

Surroundings : 🐟 🖵 🎜🎜		
Leisure activities : 🍴 🍽 🗖 🎯 🖍 🛶 🚲 ✂ 🗖 🎜 🚶 multi-sports ground	**G**	Longitude : 1.0712
Facilities : ᕦ ⚲ 🛆 🍴 launderette 🗐 🛒	**P S**	Latitude : 45.00161

ST-MARTIAL-DE-NABIRAT

24250 – Michelin map **329** I7 – pop. 666 – alt. 175
▶ Paris 546 – Cahors 42 – Fumel 45 – Gourdon 11

⚲ Le Convivial

℘ 05 53 28 43 15. www.campingleconvivial.com

Address : Lagrèze (2.2km northwest along the D 46, follow the signs for Domme and take road to the left)

Opening times : from mid June to end Aug.

2.7 ha (50 pitches)

Tariff : (2014 Price) 19€ ✸✸ ⇦ 🗐 ⚡ (6A) – Extra per person 4.90€ Reservation fee 10€

To visit a town or region, use the MICHELIN Green Guides.

Rental rates : (2014 Price) (from mid April to end Oct.) – 19 🚐 – 1 gîte. Per week from 150 to 620€ – Reservation fee 10€

In the shade of 500-year-old chestnut trees!

Surroundings : 🖵 🎜🎜	**G**	Longitude : 1.23951
Leisure activities : 🎣	**P**	Latitude : 44.75444
Facilities : ᕦ ⚲ 🍴 🗐	**S**	

ST-MARTIN-DE-SEIGNANX

40390 – Michelin map **335** C13 – pop. 4 724 – alt. 57
▶ Paris 766 – Bayonne 11 – Capbreton 15 – Dax 42

⚲ Sites et Paysages Lou P'tit Poun 🌲🌲

℘ 05 59 56 55 79. www.louptitpoun.com

Address : 110 avenue du Quartier Neuf (4.7km southwest along the N 117, follow the signs for Bayonne and take road to the left)

Opening times : from mid June to mid Sept.

6.5 ha (168 pitches)

Tariff : (2014 Price) 44.80€ ✸✸ ⇦ 🗐 ⚡ (10A) – Extra per person 8.40€ – Reservation fee 30€

Rental rates : (2014 Price) (from mid June to mid Sept.) ✂ – 10 🚐 – 16 🏠. Per week from 455 to 896€ – Reservation fee 30€ 🚐 borne 7€ – 🔋 16€

Surroundings : 🖵 🎜🎜		
Leisure activities : 🗖 🎯 🛶 🎣	**G**	Longitude : -1.41195
Facilities : ᕦ ⚲ 🛆 🎜 🍴 🗐 🛒	**P S**	Latitude : 43.52437

Some information or pricing may have changed since the guide went to press. We recommend you check the price list online in advance or at the entrance to the campsite and enquire about possible restrictions.

ST-PAUL-LES-DAX

40990 – Michelin map **335** E12 – pop. 12 343 – alt. 21
▶ Paris 731 – Bordeaux 152 – Mont-de-Marsan 53 – Pau 89

⚲ Les Pins du Soleil 🌲🌲

℘ 05 58 91 37 91. www.pinsoleil.com

Address : route des Minières (5.8km northwest along the N 124, follow the signs for Bayonne and take the turning to the left along the D 459)

Opening times : from beginning April to end Sept.

6 ha (145 pitches)

Tariff : (2014 Price) 25€ ✸✸ ⇦ 🗐 ⚡ (10A) – Extra per person 6€ Reservation fee 10€

Rental rates : (2014 Price) (from beginning April to end Oct.) ᕦ (1 chalet) – 45 🚐 – 10 🏠 – 4 canvas bungalows. Per night from 40 to 103€ – Per week from 278 to 719€ – Reservation fee 17€ 🚐 borne

Surroundings : 🖵 🎜🎜		
Leisure activities : 🍴 🍽 🗖 🎯 jacuzzi 🛶 🎣 🎜	**G**	Longitude : -1.09373
Facilities : ᕦ ⚲ 🅲🅲 🍴 🛆 🎜 🗐 🍴 launderette 🛒	**P S**	Latitude : 43.72029

🏔 L'Étang d'Ardy

℘ 05 58 97 57 74. www.camping-ardy.com

Address : allée d'Ardy (5.5km northwest along the N 124, follow the signs for Bayonne then take road to the left before the access road, continuing for 1.7km; beside a lake)

Opening times : from beginning April to mid Oct.

5 ha/3 for camping (102 pitches)

Tariff : 27.25€ ✹✹ ⇔ 🔲 🚽 (10A) – Extra per person 6.50€

Rental rates : (from beginning April to mid Oct.) – 24 🚐 – 7 🏠 – 1 canvas bungalow. Per night from 58 to 103€ – Per week from 280 to 649€

All the pitches for tents and caravans are equipped with individual sanitary facilities ranging from simple and basic to rather old.

Surroundings : 🚣 ⌂ 〰
Leisure activities : 🛶 🎣
Facilities : ᕕ ⟿ – 53 individual sanitary facilities (🔲 ⊕ 🚽 wc) 🌣 ⟿ ! launderette

GPS Longitude : -1.12256
Latitude : 43.72643

⛺ Abesses

℘ 05 58 91 65 34. www.thermes-dax.com

Address : allée du Château (7.5km northwest following signs for Bayonne, D 16 to the right and take the Chemin d'Abesse)

Opening times : from mid March to beginning Nov.

4 ha (198 pitches) small lake

Tariff : (2014 Price) ✹ 3.75€ ⇔ 🔲 5.25€ – 🚽 (6A) 3.25€

Rental rates : (2014 Price) (from mid March to beginning Nov.) – 16 🚐. Per night from 60 to 69€ – Per week from 289 to 330€

A minimum stay of 20 nights.

Surroundings : 🚣 ⌂ 〰
Leisure activities : 🛖 🎣
Facilities : ᕕ ⟿ 🚰🗓📶 🌣 ⟿ ! launderette

GPS Longitude : -1.09715
Latitude : 43.74216

ST-PÉE-SUR-NIVELLE

64310 – Michelin map **342** C2 – pop. 5 550 – alt. 30
▶ Paris 785 – Bayonne 22 – Biarritz 17 – Cambo-les-Bains 17

🏔 L'Ibarron

L'Ibarron

℘ 05 59 54 10 43. www.camping-ibarron.com

Address : Ibarron district (2km, take the western exit, on the D 918, follow the signs for St-Jean-de-Luz, near the Nivelle river)

Opening times : from end April to end Sept.

2.9 ha (142 pitches) flat, grassy

Tariff : (2014 Price) 26.40€ ✹✹ ⇔ 🔲 🚽 (6A) – Extra per person 5.25€ – Reservation fee 10€

Rental rates : (2014 Price) (from beginning May to end Sept.) 🚫 – 23 🚐. Per night from 49 to 95€ – Per week from 240 to 660€ Reservation fee 10€

🚐 borne 5€ – 25 🔲 16.95€

Choose the pitches furthest away from the road.

Surroundings : ⌂ 〰
Leisure activities : 🛖 ⛵ 🎣
Facilities : ᕕ ⟿ ! launderette
Nearby : 🍽 🍹 🗙 🌣 🚲

GPS Longitude : -1.5749
Latitude : 43.3576

🏔 Goyetchea 👥

Christine Mazet

℘ 05 59 54 19 59. www.camping-goyetchea.com

Address : Ibarron district (1.8km north along the D 855, follow the signs for Ahetze and take a right turn)

Opening times : from beginning June to mid Sept.

3 ha (147 pitches) flat and relatively flat, grassy

Tariff : 28.50€ ✹✹ ⇔ 🔲 🚽 (6A)

Extra per person 6€ – Reservation fee 13€

Rental rates : (from end April to mid Sept.) 🚫 – 2 caravans – 33 🚐. Per night from 57 to 63€ – Per week from 265 to 820€ Reservation fee 13€

A view of the pretty Basque houses and La Rhune (mountain).

Surroundings : 🚣 ≪ 〰
Leisure activities : 🗙 🛖 🏋 ⛵ 🛶
Facilities : ᕕ ⟿ 🚿 ! launderette 🌣 refrigerators

GPS Longitude : -1.56683
Latitude : 43.36275

ST-RÉMY

24700 – Michelin map **329** C6 – pop. 432 – alt. 80
▶ Paris 542 – Bergerac 33 – Libourne 46 – Montpon-Ménestérol 10

🏔 Les Cottages en Périgord (rental of chalets only)

℘ 05 53 80 59 46. www.cottagesenperigord.com

Address : Les Pommiers (continue north following signs for Montpon-Ménestérol along the D 708)

Opening times : from mid Jan to mid Dec.

7 ha/1 for camping flat, small lake, adjacent wood

Rental rates : ᕕ (1 chalet) – 3 caravans – 8 🏠. Per night from 70 to 100€ – Per week from 250 to 680€ – Reservation fee 10€

Surroundings : 🚣 〰
Leisure activities : 🛖 ≋ jacuzzi 🛶 🎣
Facilities : ⟿ 🚰🗓📶 ! 📶

GPS Longitude : 0.16333
Latitude : 44.96024

ST-SAUD-LACOUSSIÈRE

24470 – Michelin map **329** F2 – pop. 864 – alt. 370
▶ Paris 443 – Brive-la-Gaillarde 105 – Châlus 23 – Limoges 57

🏔 Kawan Village Château Le Verdoyer 👥

℘ 05 53 56 94 64. www.verdoyer.fr

Address : 2.5km northwest along the D 79, follow the signs for Nontron and take D 96, follow the signs for Abjat-sur-Bandiat; near lakes

Opening times : from end April to end Sept.

15 ha/5 for camping (170 pitches) lakes

Tariff : 55€ ✹✹ ⇔ 🔲 🚽 (10A) – Extra per person 7€ – Reservation fee 20€

Rental rates : (from end April to end Sept.) – 25 🚐 – 20 🏠 – 5 🛏. Per night from 80 to 105€ – Per week from 240 to 735€ Reservation fee 20€

🚐 borne

There are some pitches for tents and caravans with private sanitary facilities and 5 furnished rooms in the château.

Surroundings : 🚣 ⌂ 〰
Leisure activities : 🍹 🗙 🛖 🏋 ⛵ 🚲 🎿 🛶 🎣 ✈
Facilities : ᕕ ⟿ 🔲 🚿 – 14 individual sanitary facilities (🔲 ⊕ 🚽 wc) 🌣 ⟿ ! launderette 🗄 🌣 refrigerated food storage facilities
Nearby : 🏖 (beach)

GPS Longitude : 0.79595
Latitude : 45.55133

ST-VINCENT-DE-COSSE

24220 – Michelin map **329** H6 – pop. 374 – alt. 80
▶ Paris 540 – Bergerac 61 – Brive-la-Gaillarde 65 – Fumel 58

⛰ Le Tiradou

📞 0553303073. www.camping-le-tiradou.com

Address : Larrit (500m southwest of the village; beside a stream)

Opening times : from end April to end Sept.

2 ha (60 pitches) flat, grassy

Tariff : ⚹ 5€ 🚗 🗉 7.50€ – 🔌 (6A) 4€ – Reservation fee 10€
Rental rates : (from end April to end Sept.) – 17 🚐 – 5 🏠 – 2 tent lodges. Per night from 45 to 60€ – Per week from 210 to 690€ – Reservation fee 15€
🚰 4 🗉 11€

Surroundings : 🏕 ♤♤
Leisure activities : ✕ 🏊 jacuzzi 🛶 ⛵
Facilities : ♿ 🚿 🔥 launderette ⚓

GPS Longitude : 1.11268
Latitude : 44.83747

STE-EULALIE-EN-BORN

40200 – Michelin map **335** D9 – pop. 1 116 – alt. 26
▶ Paris 673 – Arcachon 58 – Biscarrosse 98 – Mimizan 11

⛰ Les Bruyères

📞 0558097336. www.camping-les-bruyeres.com

Address : 719 route de Laffont (2.5km north along the D 652)

Opening times : from beginning May to end Sept.

3 ha (177 pitches)

Tariff : (2014 Price) 30.10€ ⚹⚹ 🚗 🗉 🔌 (8A)

Extra per person 8.20€ – Reservation fee 16€

Rental rates : (from beginning May to end Sept.) – 19 🚐 – 1 🏠. Per night from 36 to 87€ – Per week from 245 to 770€ Reservation fee 16€
🚰 borne
Local home-made produce to taste and buy.

Surroundings : 🏊 🏕 ♤♤
Leisure activities : 🍹 ✕ 🏊 ✕ ⛵
Facilities : ♿ 🚿 🔥 ⛵ launderette ⚓ ⚓

GPS Longitude : -1.17949
Latitude : 44.29387

STE-FOY-LA-GRANDE

33220 – Michelin map **335** M5 – pop. 2 544 – alt. 10
▶ Paris 555 – Bordeaux 71 – Langon 59 – Marmande 53

⛰ La Bastide

📞 0557461384. www.camping-bastide.com

Address : at Pineuilh, allée du Camping (take northeastern exit along the D 130; beside the Dordogne river)

Opening times : from beginning April to end Oct.

1.2 ha (38 pitches) flat, grassy

Tariff : (2014 Price) 24€ ⚹⚹ 🚗 🗉 🔌 (10A) – Extra per person 5.80€ Reservation fee 10€
Rental rates : (2014 Price) (from beginning April to end Oct.) – 10 🚐. Per night from 100 to 150€ – Per week from 230 to 695€ Reservation fee 15€
🚰 2 🗉 24€

Surroundings : 🏊 ♤♤
Leisure activities : 🏊 🛶 ⛵
Facilities : ♿ 🚿 🔥 launderette
Nearby : 🏊

GPS Longitude : 0.22462
Latitude : 44.84403

SALIES-DE-BÉARN

64270 – Michelin map **342** G4 – pop. 4 886 – alt. 50 – ♨
▶ Paris 762 – Bayonne 60 – Dax 36 – Orthez 17

⛰ Mosqueros

📞 0559381294. camping2mosqueros@icloud.com

Address : avenue Al Cartero (take the western exit along the D 17, follow the signs for Bayonne, at the outdoor activity centre)

Opening times : from mid March to mid Nov.

0.7 ha (62 pitches)

Tariff : (2014 Price) 16€ ⚹⚹ 🚗 🗉 🔌 (10A) – Extra per person 2.50€
Rentals : 3 🚐.

A pleasant site next to the municipal sports centre. Rather poor and antiquated facillities.

Surroundings : 🏊 ♤♤
Leisure activities : 🏟 multi-sports ground
Facilities : ♿ 🚿 🔥 ⛵ ⚓ launderette
Nearby : ✕ ⛵

GPS Longitude : -0.93814
Latitude : 43.47643

SALIGNAC-EYVIGUES

24590 – Michelin map **329** I6 – pop. 1 141 – alt. 297
▶ Paris 509 – Brive-la-Gaillarde 34 – Cahors 84 – Périgueux 70

⛰ Flower Le Temps de Vivre

📞 0553289321, www.temps-de-vivre.com

Address : located 1.5km south along the D 61 and take the road to the right

Opening times : from mid April to end Sept.

4.5 ha (50 pitches) adjacent wood

Tariff : 28€ ⚹⚹ 🚗 🗉 🔌 (10A) – Extra per person 5.50€ –

Reservation fee 10€
Rental rates : (from mid April to end Sept.) – 18 🚐 – 4 canvas bungalows. Per night from 32 to 104€– Per week from 160 to 728€ Reservation fee 20€
🚰 5 🗉 15.50€ – 🚐 🔌 11€

Surroundings : 🏊 🏕 ♤♤
Leisure activities : 🍹 🏊 🛶 ⛵
Facilities : ♿ 🚿 🔥 launderette ⚓

GPS Longitude : 1.32817
Latitude : 44.96355

SALLES

33770 – Michelin map **335** F7 – pop. 6 044 – alt. 23
▶ Paris 632 – Arcachon 36 – Belin-Béliet 11 – Biscarrosse 122

⛰ Le Park du Val de l'Eyre ♟

📞 0556884703. www.valdeleyre.com

Address : 8 route du Minoy (take the southwestern exit along the D 108e, follow the signs for Lugos; beside the Eyre river and a lake – from the A 63, take exit 21)

Opening times : Permanent

13 ha/4 for camping (150 pitches)

Tariff : ⚹ 9€ 🚗 🗉 20€ 🔌 (6A) – Reservation fee 20€
Rental rates : Permanent – 48 🚐 – 4 🏠 – 4 🚈. Per night from 43 to 132€ – Per week from 253 to 790€ – Reservation fee 20€
🚰 borne 6€

Surroundings : 🏊 ♤♤
Leisure activities : 🍹 ✕ 🏊 🏃 🛶 ⛵ 🏊 🚲
Facilities : ♿ 🚿 ⬛ 🔥 ⛵ launderette ⚓
Nearby : 🛒

GPS Longitude : -0.87399
Latitude : 44.54606

SALLES

47150 – Michelin map **336** H2 – pop. 314 – alt. 120
▶ Paris 588 – Agen 59 – Fumel 12 – Monflanquin 11

⚠ Des Bastides

📞 0553408309. www.campingdesbastides.com

Address : Terre Rouge (located 1km to the northeast, follow the signs for Fumel, at junction of D 150 and D 162)

Opening times : from beginning April to end Sept.

6 ha (96 pitches)

Tariff : 33.90€ ♦♦ ⟚ 🗉 🚿 (6A) – Extra per person 5.20€ – Reservation fee 18€

Rental rates : (from beginning April to end Sept.) – 8 🛖 – 5 🏠 – 1 yurt – 2 canvas bungalows – 4 tent lodges. Per night from 42 to 154€ – Per week from 294 to 1,078€ – Reservation fee 18€

Surroundings : 🖵 🎯
Leisure activities : 🍷 ✗ jacuzzi 🚣 🚴 🛶 ⛵ multi-sports ground
Facilities : 🚿 🖊 🖭 🚽 – 2 individual sanitary facilities (🚿 🚻 wc) 🚰 launderette 🚯
Longitude : 0.88161
Latitude : 44.55263

To visit a town or region, use the MICHELIN Green Guides.

SANGUINET

40460 – Michelin map **335** E8 – pop. 3 133 – alt. 24
▶ Paris 643 – Arcachon 27 – Belin-Béliet 26 – Biscarrosse 120

⚠ Lou Broustaricq 👥

📞 0558827482. www.lou-broustaricq.com – limited spaces for one-night stay 🚭

Address : 2315 route Langeot (2.8km northwest following signs for Bordeaux, 300m from the Étang de Cazaux (lake)

Opening times : from beginning April to end Oct.

18.8 ha (570 pitches)

Tariff : (2014 Price) 45€ ♦♦ ⟚ 🗉 🚿 (10A) – Extra per person 8€

Rental rates : (2014 Price) (from beginning April to end Oct.) 🚭 – 156 🛖. Per night from 39 to 165€ – Per week from 273 to 1,211€

Surroundings : 🏖 🖵 🎯
Leisure activities : 🍷 ✗ 🎬 🖥 👣 jacuzzi 🚣 🚴 🛶 🎣 🖥 ⛵ entertainment room
Facilities : 🚿 🖊 🖭 🚽 🚰 launderette 🚯 🚯
Nearby : 🚣 💧
Longitude : -1.0789
Latitude : 44.50006

SARE

64310 – Michelin map **342** C3 – pop. 2 434 – alt. 70
▶ Paris 794 – Biarritz 26 – Cambo-les-Bains 19 – Pau 138

⚠ La Petite Rhune

📞 0559542397. www.lapetiterhune.com – limited spaces for one-night stay

Address : Lehenbiscaye district (situated 2km south along the road connecting D 406 and D 306)

Opening times : from mid June to mid Sept.

1.5 ha (39 pitches) terraced, relatively flat, flat, grassy

Tariff : (2014 Price) 25.80€ ♦♦ ⟚ 🗉 🚿 (10A)

Extra per person 5.50€ – Reservation fee 10€

Rental rates : (2014 Price) Permanent 🚭 – 15 🏠 – 3 gîtes. Per week from 230 to 670€ – Reservation fee 10€

A small village painted in the Basque colours!

Surroundings : 🏖 ⩽ 🎯
Leisure activities : 🎬 🚣 (small swimming pool) multi-sports ground
Facilities : 🚿 🖊 🖭 🚽 🚰 launderette
Nearby : 🍷 ✗
Longitude : -1.58771
Latitude : 43.30198

This guide is not intended as a list of all the camping sites in France; its aim is to provide a selection of the best sites in each category.

SARLAT-LA-CANÉDA

24200 – Michelin map **329** I6 – pop. 9 541 – alt. 145
▶ Paris 526 – Bergerac 74 – Brive-la-Gaillarde 52 – Cahors 60

⚠ La Palombière 👥

📞 0553592434. www.lapalombiere.fr – limited spaces for one-night stay

Address : at Sainte Nathalène, Galmier (9km northeast on the D 43 and take the turning to the left)

Opening times : from end April to mid Sept.

8.5 ha/4 for camping (177 pitches)

Tariff : ♦ 9.20€ ⟚ 🗉 13.30€ – 🚿 (10A) 3.20€ – Reservation fee 25€

Rental rates : (from end April to mid Sept.) – 51 🛖 – 10 🏠. Per night from 49 to 165€ – Per week from 340 to 1,150€ – Reservation fee 25€

Surroundings : 🏖 🖵 🎯
Leisure activities : 🍷 ✗ 🖥 👣 🔥 hammam 🚣 🚴 🛶 🎣 🖥 ⛵
Facilities : 🚿 🖊 🚽 🎣 🚰 launderette 🚯 🚯
Longitude : 1.29157
Latitude : 44.90639

⚠ Les Castels Le Moulin du Roch 👥

📞 0553592027. www.moulin-du-roch.com 🚭

Address : at St-André d'Allas, on the D 47 (10km to the northwest, follow the signs for Les Eyzies; beside a stream)

Opening times : from mid May to mid Sept.

8 ha (200 pitches) small lake

Tariff : 38€ ♦♦ ⟚ 🗉 🚿 (10A) – Extra per person 10€ – Reservation fee 14€

Rental rates : (from mid May to mid Sept.) 🚭 – 55 🛖. Per night from 40 to 152€ – Reservation fee 14€

Based around an old Périgord windmill.

Surroundings : 🖵 🎯
Leisure activities : 🍷 ✗ 🎬 🖥 👣 🚣 🛶 ⛵ 🎣 multi-sports ground
Facilities : 🚿 🖊 🖭 🚽 🎣 🚰 launderette 🚯 🚯
Longitude : 1.11481
Latitude : 44.90843

⚠ La Châtaigneraie 👥

📞 0553590361, www.camping-lachataigneraie24.com

Address : at Prats de Carlux, La Garrigue Basse (10km east along the D 47 and take turning to the right)

Opening times : from mid May to mid Sept.

9 ha (140 pitches)

Tariff : (2014 Price) 35.50€ ♦♦ ⟚ 🗉 🚿 (10A) – Extra per person 8.90€ – Reservation fee 20€

Rental rates : (2014 Price) (from mid May to mid Sept.) ✂ (from beginning July to end Aug.) – 62 🚐 – 11 🏠 – 3 gîtes. Per week from 230 to 1,030€ – Reservation fee 20€

A pretty water and play park surrounded by low walls made of local stone.

Surroundings : 🏊 🛶 ♨♨
Leisure activities : 🍴 🎱 🏓 🎣 ✂ ⛳ 🎿 ⛷ sports trail
Facilities : 🚿 ⛽ 🍴 🔥 🚰 💧 🍴 launderette 🗑

Longitude : 1.29871
Latitude : 44.90056

🏕 Les Grottes de Roffy 🚹🚺

📞 0553591561, www.roffy.fr

Address : at Ste-Nathalène, Roffy (8km east, along the D 47)

Opening times : from mid April to mid Sept.

5 ha (165 pitches)

Tariff : (2014 Price) 32.40€ 🚹🚺 🚐 🔌 💡 (6A) –

Extra per person 8.50€

Rental rates : (2014 Price) – 28 🚐. Per night from 49 to 132€ – Per week from 343 to 924€

Surroundings : 🏊 🛶 🛖 ♨♨
Leisure activities : 🍴 🍽 🎱 🏓 🎣 ✂ ⛳ 🎿
Facilities : ♿ 🚿 🔥 🍴 🔥 🚰 💧 🍴 launderette 🗑

Longitude : 1.28211
Latitude : 44.90417

🏕 Domaine de Loisirs le Montant 🚹🚺

📞 0553591850. www.camping-sarlat.com

Address : Négrelat (situated 2km southwest along the D 57, follow the signs for Bergerac then continue 2.3km along the road to the right)

Opening times : from mid March to end Sept.

70 ha/8 for camping (135 pitches)

Tariff : (2014 Price) 🚹 8.90€ 🚐 🔌 12.80€ – 💡 (10A) 4.80€ – Reservation fee 19€

Rental rates :(2014 Price) (from mid March to end Sept.) – 26 🚐 – 26 🏠 – 2 gîtes. Per night from 50 to 270€ – Per week from 350 to 1,890€ – Reservation fee 18€

A range of luxury rental options in a naturally wooded and hilly setting.

Surroundings : 🏊 🛶 🛖 ♨♨
Leisure activities : 🍴 🍽 🎱 nighttime 🏓 jacuzzi 🎣 ⛳ 🎿 🎿 multi-sports ground
Facilities : ♿ 🚿 🔥 🍴 🚰 💧 🍴 launderette 🗑

Longitude : 1.18903
Latitude : 44.86573

🏕 Domaine Des Chênes Verts 🚹🚺

📞 0553592107. www.chenes-verts.com – limited spaces for one-night stay

Address : route de Sarlat et Souillac (8.5km southeast)

Opening times : from beginning May to end Sept.

8 ha (143 pitches)

Tariff : 27€ 🚹🚺 🚐 🔌 💡 (6A) – Extra per person 7€ – Reservation fee 20€

Rental rates : (from beginning May to end Sept.) – 72 🚐 – 31 🏠. Per week from 310 to 930€ – Reservation fee 20€

Surroundings : 🏊 🛶 ♨♨
Leisure activities : 🍴 🍽 🎱 🏓 🎣 ⛳ 🎿 🎿
Facilities : ♿ 🚿 🔥 🍴 launderette 🗑🗑

Longitude : 1.2972
Latitude : 44.86321

🏕 La Ferme de Villeneuve 🚹🚺

📞 0553303090. www.fermedevilleneuve.com

Address : at St-André-d'Allas, Villeneuve (8km northwest along the D 47, follow the signs for Les Eyzies-de-Tayac and take turning to the left)

Opening times : from beginning April to end Oct.

20 ha/2.5 for camping (100 pitches) natural setting among trees and bushes, lake

Tariff : (2014 Price) 🚹 6.70€ 🚐 🔌 7.30€ – 💡 (10A) 4.10€

Reservation fee 10€

Rental rates : (2014 Price) (from beginning April to end Oct.) – 2 caravans – 10 🚐 – 4 tipis – 3 canvas bungalows – 2 tent lodges. Per night from 37 to 55€ – Per week from 290 to 739€
Reservation fee 10€

🚮 borne 3€ – 3 🔌 12€

Farm campsite.

Surroundings : 🏊 🛶 ♨♨
Leisure activities : 🍴 🍽 🏓 🎣 ⛳ 🎿
Facilities : ♿ 🚿 🔥 🍴 launderette 🗑
Nearby : cinema/activity centre

Longitude : 1.14051
Latitude : 44.90438

🏕 Les Terrasses du Périgord

📞 0553590225. www.terrasses-du-perigord.com

Address : at Proissans, Pech d'Orance (2.8km to the northeast)

Opening times : from mid April to end Sept.

5 ha (85 pitches)

Tariff : (2014 Price) 24.60€ 🚹🚺 🚐 🔌 💡 (10A)

Extra per person 5.90€ – Reservation fee 8€

Rental rates : (2014 Price) (from mid April to end Sept.) – 10 🚐 – 9 🏠. Per night from 30 to 55€ – Per week from 200 to 615€
Reservation fee 10€

🚮 borne – 10 🔌 24.60€

Surroundings : 🏊 🛶 ♨♨
Leisure activities : 🍽 🎱 jacuzzi 🎣 🏓 🎿 🎿 mountain biking
Facilities : ♿ 🚿 🔥 🍴 🚰 💧 🍴 launderette 🗑🗑

Longitude : 1.23658
Latitude : 44.90617

🏕 Indigo Sarlat - Les Périères

Camping Indigo ©R.Etienne

📞 0553590584. www.camping-indigo.com

Address : rue Jean Gabin (located 1km to the northeast, by the exit from town)

Opening times : from beginning April to end Sept.

11 ha/4 for camping (100 pitches) terraced, flat, grassy

Tariff : (2014 Price) 34.90€ 🚹🚺 🚐 🔌 💡 (6A) Extra per person 7.30€ – Reservation fee 22€

Rental rates : (2014 Price) (from beginning April to beginning Nov.) – 4 caravans – 8 🚐 – 22 tent lodges – 15 gîtes. Per night from 45 to 122€ – Per week from 221 to 854€ – Reservation fee 22€

🚮 borne 7€ – 40 🔌 30.70€

Surroundings : ♨♨
Leisure activities : 🍴 🎱 🛁 🎣 ✂ 🎿 🎿 sports trail
Facilities : ♿ 🚿 🔥 🚰 💧 🍴 launderette

Longitude : 1.22767
Latitude : 44.89357

⚑ Les Charmes

☎ 05 53 31 02 89. www.campinglescharmesdordogne.com

Address : at St-André-d'Allas, Malartigue Haut (10km west along the D 25, follow the signs for Le Bugue and take road to the right)

Opening times : from beginning May to beginning Oct.

5.5 ha/1.8 (100 pitches)

Tariff : (2014 Price) 24.10€ ✖✖ ⇔ 🖹 ⚡ (6A) –

Extra per person 6.10€

Rental rates : (2014 Price) (from beginning May to beginning Oct.) – 6 🚐 – 5 🏠 – 4 canvas bungalows – 3 tent lodges. Per week from 159 to 789€

Surroundings : 🐟 ⌑ ♨ Leisure activities : ♟ ⚓ 🏊 ⚒ multi-sports ground Facilities : ♿ ⚏ 🛖 🖹 ⚒	**GPS** Longitude : 1.11365 Latitude : 44.89412

⚑ Les Acacias

☎ 05 53 31 08 50. www.acacias.fr

Address : Bourg de la Canéda, rue Louis de Champagne (6km southeast along the D 704 and take a right turn at the Leclerc hypermarket)

Opening times : from beginning April to end Sept.

4 ha (122 pitches)

Tariff : 23.30€ ✖✖ ⇔ 🖹 ⚡ (10A) – Extra per person 5.60€ – Reservation fee 10€

Rental rates : (from beginning April to end Sept.) ✄ – 20 🚐. Per night from 45 to 65€ – Per week from 240 to 730€ – Reservation fee 10€

🚰 borne 5€

There's a bus shuttle service to Sarlat.

Surroundings : ⟨ ⌑ ♨ Leisure activities : ♟ ⚓ 🚲 ⚒ multi-sports ground Facilities : ♿ ⚏ 🛖 🖹 ⚒⟿ ♟ launderette ⚒	**GPS** Longitude : 1.23699 Latitude : 44.85711

SAUBION

40230 – Michelin map **335** C12 – pop. 1 323 – alt. 17

▶ Paris 747 – Bordeaux 169 – Mont-de-Marsan 79 – Pau 106

⚑ Club Airotel La Pomme de Pin

☎ 05 58 77 00 71, www.camping-lapommedepin.com

Address : 825 route de Seignosse (2km southeast along the D 652 and D 337)

Opening times : from beginning April to beginning Oct.

5 ha (252 pitches)

Tariff : (2014 Price) 34.25€ ✖✖ ⇔ 🖹 – Extra per person 6.65€ Reservation fee 20€

Rental rates : (2014 Price) (from beginning April to beginning Oct.) – 48 🚐 – 24 canvas bungalows. Per week from 190 to 1,356€ – Reservation fee 20€

🚰 borne

There's an indoor water park; free shuttle buses to the beaches in July and August.

Surroundings : ⌑ ♨ Leisure activities : ♟ ✖ 🏊 ⚙ jacuzzi ⚓ 🏊 (open air in season) Facilities : ♿ ⚏ 🖃 🖹 ⟿ ♟ launderette ⚒ ⚒ refrigerated food storage facilities	**GPS** Longitude : -1.35563 Latitude : 43.67608

SAUVETERRE-LA-LÉMANCE

47500 – Michelin map **336** I2 – pop. 587 – alt. 100

▶ Paris 572 – Agen 68 – Fumel 14 – Monflanquin 27

⚑ Flower Le Moulin du Périé

☎ 05 53 40 67 26. www.camping-moulin-perie.com

Address : Moulin du Périé (3km east following signs for Loubejac; beside a stream)

Opening times : from mid May to mid Sept.

4 ha (125 pitches) flat, grassy

Tariff : (2014 Price) 31.25€ ✖✖ ⇔ 🖹 ⚡ (10A) – Extra per person 7.30€ – Reservation fee 20€

Rental rates : (2014 Price) (from mid May to end Sept.) ✄ – 12 🚐 – 4 🏠 – 16 canvas bungalows. Per night from 33 to 120€ – Per week from 231 to 840€ – Reservation fee 35€

🚰 borne

Surroundings : 🐟 ⌑ ♨ Leisure activities : ♟ ✖ 🏊 ⚓ 🚲 ⚒ ⚏ Facilities : ♿ ⚏ 🖃 🖹 launderette ⚒	**GPS** Longitude : 1.04743 Latitude : 44.5898

A chambre d'hôte is a guesthouse or B & B-style accommodation.

SEIGNOSSE OCÉAN

40510 – Michelin map **335** C12

▶ Paris 763 – Bordeaux 184 – Mont-de-Marsan 89 – Pau 115

⚑ Océliances ♨♟

☎ 05 58 43 30 30. www.oceliances.com

Address : avenue des Tucs (along the D 79e, 500m from the beach at Les Bourdaines)

13 ha (439 pitches)

Rentals : ✄ – 75 🚐 – 20 🏠 – 9 canvas bungalows.

🚰 borne

Surroundings : ♨ Leisure activities : ♟ ✖ 🏊 ⚙ 🏃 🎿 ⚓ 🚲♨ 🏊 surfing multi-sports ground, entertainment room Facilities : ♿ ⚏ 🖹 ⚒ ⟿ ♟ launderette ⚒ ⚒ refrigerated food storage facilities	**GPS** Longitude : -1.43039 Latitude : 43.69358

SIORAC-EN-PÉRIGORD

24170 – Michelin map **329** G7 – pop. 1 015 – alt. 77

▶ Paris 548 – Bergerac 45 – Cahors 68 – Périgueux 60

⚑ Le Port

☎ 05 53 31 63 81, www.campingduport.net

Address : to the northeast of the town, access via the D 25, follow the signs for Buisson-Cussac and take the road in front of Carrefour supermarket; beside the Dordogne and the Nauze rivers

Opening times : from beginning April to end Oct.

2.5 ha (83 pitches) flat, grassy

Tariff : ✖ 4.38€ ⇔ 🖹 3.60€ – ⚡ (10A) 3.10€

Rental rates : (from beginning April to end Oct.) – 10 🚐 – 1 tipi. Per night from 25 to 36€ – Per week from 150 to 465€

Surroundings : ⌑ ♨ Leisure activities : 🏊 ⚓ ⚒ 🏊 Facilities : ♿ ⚏ (mid Jul–mid Aug) 🖃 Nearby : 🍴 ♟ ✖ ✂	**GPS** Longitude : 0.98755 Latitude : 44.82472

SORDE-L'ABBAYE

40300 – Michelin map **335** E13 – pop. 646 – alt. 17
▶ Paris 758 – Bayonne 47 – Dax 27 – Oloron-Ste-Marie 63

⚠ Municipal la Galupe

𝒫 05 58 73 18 13. mairie.sordelabbaye@wanadoo.fr

Address : 242 chemin du Camping (1.3km west along the D 29, follow the signs for Peyrehorade, D 123 to the left and take the road before the bridge; near the Gave d'Oloron (river)

Opening times : from beginning July to end Aug.

0.6 ha (28 pitches)

Tariff : (2014 Price) 11.50€ ★★ ⬅ 🖭 (9A) –

Extra per person 2.50€

| Surroundings : 🏞 ⌂ 🌳 Facilities : ♿ 📷 | **G P S** | Longitude : -1.0561 Latitude : 43.52983 |

Some information or pricing may have changed since the guide went to press. We recommend you check the price list online in advance or at the entrance to the campsite and enquire about possible restrictions.

SOULAC-SUR-MER

33780 – Michelin map **335** E1 – pop. 2 711 – alt. 7
▶ Paris 515 – Bordeaux 99 – Lesparre-Médoc 31 – Royan 12

⚠ Les Lacs ♟

𝒫 05 56 09 76 63. www.camping-les-lacs.com

Address : 126 route des Lacs (continue 3km east along the D 101)

Opening times : from beginning April to beginning Nov.

5 ha (228 pitches)

Tariff : (2014 Price) 36.50€ ★★ ⬅ 🖭 (10A) – Extra per person 6€
Rental rates : (2014 Price) (from beginning April to beginning Nov.) ♿ (1 mobile home) – 70 🚐 – 12 🏠. Per night from 42 to 162€ – Per week from 294 to 1,134€
🚐 2 15€ – 🔌 14€
Organised coach excursions are available.

| Surroundings : 🏞 ⌂ 🌳🌳 Leisure activities : 🍽 ✕ 🎮 🎯 🏃 ⛷ 🎣 🔲 🏊 ⛰ multi-sports ground Facilities : ♿ 🔌 🚿 🚽 🍴 launderette 🔲 🏄 Nearby : 🐎 | **G P S** | Longitude : -1.11932 Latitude : 45.48328 |

⚠ Yelloh! Village Soulac sur Mer ♟

𝒫 05 56 09 77 63. www.camping-club-soulac.com

Address : at L'Amélie-sur-Mer, allée Michel de Montaigne (2.8km east along the D 101 E2 and D 101)

Opening times : from end April to beginning Sept.

4 ha (170 pitches)

Tariff : 46€ ★★ ⬅ 🖭 (10A) – Extra per person 7€
Rental rates : (from end April to beginning Sept.) – 79 🚐 – 10 🏠. Per night from 39 to 254€ – Per week from 273 to 1,778€
🚐 borne

| Surroundings : 🏞 🌳🌳 Leisure activities : 🍽 ✕ 🎮 🏃 ⛴ jacuzzi ⛷ 🏊 ✂ 🔲 🏊 Facilities : ♿ 🔌 🚿 🍴 launderette 🔲 🏄 | **G P S** | Longitude : -1.11886 Latitude : 45.48563 |

⚠ L'Océan

𝒫 05 56 09 76 10. http://perso.wanadoo.fr/camping.ocean

Address : 62 allée de la Négade (take the eastern exit along the D 101e 2 and take the D 101, 300m from the beach)

Opening times : from beginning June to mid Sept.

6 ha (300 pitches)

Tariff : ★ 6€ ⬅ 🖭 15€ – 🔌 (10A) 4.50€ – Reservation fee 20€

In a natural wooded setting.

| Surroundings : 🏞 🌳🌳 Leisure activities : 🍽 🎮 🚲 ✂ Facilities : ♿ 🔌 📷 🍴 launderette 🔲 🏄 | **G P S** | Longitude : -1.14533 Latitude : 45.48043 |

SOUSTONS

40140 – Michelin map **335** D12 – pop. 7 240 – alt. 9
▶ Paris 732 – Biarritz 53 – Castets 23 – Dax 29

⚠ Village Vacances Sunêlia Le Framissima Nature

(rental of mobile homes, chalets and tent lodges only)

𝒫 05 58 77 70 00. www.camping-nature-soustons.fr

Address : Nicot-les-Pins, 63 avenue Port d'Albret (follow the signs for Les Lacs)

Opening times : from mid April to end Sept.

14 ha (250 pitches)

Rental rates : ♿ (1 mobile home) 🚫 🅿 – 200 🚐 – 12 🏠 – 37 tent lodges. Per night from 30 to 228€ – Per week from 210 to 1,596€

Organised excursions are available; an eco swimming pool and plenty of activities for children and teenagers.

| Surroundings : 🏞 🌳🌳 Leisure activities : 🍽 ✕ 🎮 🎯(open-air theatre) 🎣 ⛴ hammam, jacuzzi 🚲 🏊 🏊 multi-sports ground, spa centre, entertainment room Facilities : 🔌 🍴 launderette 🔲 🏄 | **G P S** | Longitude : -1.35999 Latitude : 43.75593 |

⚠ L'Airial

𝒫 05 58 41 12 48. www.campinglairial.fr

Address : 67 avenue de Port d'Albret (situated 2km west along the D 652, follow the signs for Vieux-Boucau-les-Bains, 200m from the Étang de Soustons)

Opening times : from beginning April to beginning Oct.

13 ha (440 pitches)

Tariff : 35€ ★★ ⬅ 🖭 (10A) – Extra per person 7.50€

Reservation fee 20€

Rental rates : (from beginning April to beginning Oct.) ♿ (2 mobile homes) 🚫 – 58 🚐 – 28 🏠. Per night from 85 to 165€ – Per week from 195 to 1,035€
🚐 10 🖭 26€ – 🔌 18€

| Surroundings : 🌳 Leisure activities : 🍽 ✕ 🎮 🎯daytime 🏃 🚲 ✂ ⛰ 🔲 🏊 multi-sports ground Facilities : ♿ 🔌 🚿 🍴 launderette 🔲 🏄 refrigerated food storage facilities | **G P S** | Longitude : -1.35195 Latitude : 43.75433 |

The guide covers all 22 regions of France – see the map and list of regions on pages 4–5.

⛺ Village Vacances Le Dunéa

📞 05 58 48 00 59. www.club-dunea.com

Address : at Souston-Plage, port d'Albret sud, 1 square de l'Herté (200m from the lake)

Opening times : from 11 April to mid Oct.

0.5 ha

Rental rates : (from beginning April to mid Oct.) ⊷ – 20 gîtes. Per night from 65€ – Per week from 260 to 1,090€

Surroundings : 🚲 ⚲
Leisure activities : 🏛 ⟋
Facilities : ⟜ 🅿 ⁎ 🔲
Nearby : ✂ 🐎

Longitude : -1.40065
Latitude : 43.7731

⛰ Village Vacances le Clos du Moulin

(rental of chalets only)

📞 05 53 51 68 95. www.leclosdumoulin.com

Address : Le Moulin de Bouch (6km west de Terrasson-Lavilledieu along the N 89, follow the signs for St-Lazare and take the D 62 following signs for Coly; beside the river)

Opening times : from beginning March to end Nov.

1 ha flat, grassy

Rental rates : (2014 Price) 🅿 – 14 🏠. Per week from 300 to 920€

Surroundings : ⚲
Leisure activities : ⁌ 🚲 ⟋
Facilities : ⟜ ⟜ 🔲 ⁎

Longitude : 1.26337
Latitude : 45.10288

LE TEICH

33470 – Michelin map **335** E7 – pop. 6 485 – alt. 5
▶ Paris 633 – Arcachon 20 – Belin-Béliet 34 – Bordeaux 50

⛰ Ker Helen 👥

📞 05 56 66 03 79. www.kerhelen.com

Address : 119 avenue de la Côte d'Argent (situated 2km west along the D 650, follow the signs for Gujan-Mestras)

Opening times : from mid April to mid Oct.

4 ha (170 pitches) flat, grassy

Tariff : ⅄ 5.50€ ⊷ 🔲 14.30€ – 🔌 (10A) 3.70€ – Reservation fee 18€
Rental rates : (from mid April to mid Oct.) ♿ (1 chalet) – 12 canvas bungalows – 4 tent lodges. Per night from 30 to 120€ – Per week from 180 to 580€ – Reservation fee 18€
🚐 borne 10€

Surroundings : ⟋ ⚲⚲
Leisure activities : ⁌ ✕ 🌙 nighttime 🏃 ⟋⟋
🚲 ⟋
Facilities : ♿ ⟜ ⟜ 🏕 ⁎ launderette ⟋

Longitude : -1.04284
Latitude : 44.63975

LA TESTE-DE-BUCH

33260 – Michelin map **335** E7 – pop. 24 597 – alt. 5
▶ Paris 642 – Andernos-les-Bains 35 – Arcachon 5 – Belin-Béliet 44

⛰ Village Vacances FranceLoc La Pinèda 👥

(rental of mobile homes only)

📞 05 56 22 23 24. www.campinglapinede.net ou franceloc.fr

Address : route de Cazaux (11km south along the D 112; beside the Les Landes canal - 2.5km from Cazaux)

Opening times : from mid April to mid Sept.

5 ha

Rental rates : (2014 Price) ♿ (1 mobile home) – 230 🏠. Per night from 37 to 183€ – Per week from 148 to 1,281€ – Reservation fee 27€

Surroundings : 🚲 ⟋ ⚲⚲
Leisure activities : ⁌ ✕ 🏛 🏖 🏃 ⟋⟋ 🚲
⟋ ⟋ ⟋
Facilities : ♿ ⟜ ⟜ 🏕 ⁎ launderette ⟋
Nearby : ⚓ water skiing

Longitude : -1.15055
Latitude : 44.55516

TERRASSON-LAVILLEDIEU

24120 – Michelin map **329** I5 – pop. 6 222 – alt. 90
▶ Paris 497 – Brive-la-Gaillarde 22 – Juillac 28 – Périgueux 53

⛰ La Salvinie

📞 05 53 50 06 11. www.camping-salvinie.fr

Address : Bouillac Sud (take the southern exit along the D 63, follow the signs for Chavagnac then continue 3.4km, following signs for Condat; on the right after the bridge)

Opening times : from beginning April to end Sept.

2.5 ha (70 pitches) flat, grassy

Tariff : (2014 Price) 21.40€ ⅄⅄ ⊷ 🔲 🔌 (8A) –
Extra per person 5.60€
Rental rates : (2014 Price) (from beginning April to end Sept.) – 9 🏠. Per night from 60 to 120€ – Per week from 250 to 800€
🚐 30 🔲 17.40€ – ⟳ 🔌14.50€

Surroundings : ≼ ⟋ ⚲⚲
Leisure activities : 🏛 🏖 ⟋
Facilities : ♿ ⟜ ⁎ launderette

Longitude : 1.26216
Latitude : 45.12069

Some campsites benefit from proximity to a municipal leisure centre.

THENON

24210 – Michelin map **329** H5 – pop. 1 283 – alt. 194
▶ Paris 515 – Brive-la-Gaillarde 41 – Excideuil 36 – Les Eyzies-de-Tayac 33

⛰ Le Verdoyant

📞 05 53 05 20 78. www.campingleverdoyant.fr

Address : route de Montignac-Lascaux (4km southeast along the D 67, near two lakes)

Opening times : from beginning April to end Sept.

9 ha/3 for camping (67 pitches)

Tariff : (2014 Price) 20.40€ ⅄⅄ ⊷ 🔲 🔌 (10A) –
Extra per person 5.10€
Rental rates : (from beginning April to end Sept.) – 12 🏠 – 2 🏠 –
1 canvas bungalow. Per night from 64 to 120€ – Per week from 87 to 470€
🚐 borne – 10 🔲 12.50€

Surroundings : ≼ ⚲⚲
Leisure activities : ⁌ ✕ ⟋ ⟋
Facilities : ♿ ⟜ 🏕 ⟋ ⁎ launderette ⟋

Longitude : 1.09102
Latitude : 45.11901

To make the best possible use of this guide, please read pages 2–15 carefully.

THIVIERS

24800 – Michelin map **329** G3 – pop. 3 121 – alt. 273
▶ Paris 449 – Brive-la-Gaillarde 81 – Limoges 62 – Nontron 33

🏔 Le Repaire

🕿 05 53 52 69 75. www.camping-le-repaire.fr

Address : situated 2km southeast along the D 707, follow the signs for Lanouaille and take the road to the right

Opening times : from beginning April to end Oct.

10 ha/4.5 for camping (100 pitches) adjacent wood

Tariff : 22.50€ ✶✶ ⇔ 🔲 🄷 (10A) – Extra per person 5.50€
Rental rates : Permanent Ⓟ – 9 🏠. Per night from 55 to 65€ – Per week from 200 to 500€

Attractive pitches set around a small lake.

Surroundings : ⊏🗆 ♀		
Leisure activities : ☂ 🛋 ⊟s jacuzzi 🏊 🛶 fitness trail	**G P S**	Longitude : 0.9321 Latitude : 45.41305
Facilities : ⚙ ⊶ (season) 🏕 🔲		
Nearby : 🍴 ⚓ (beach)		

TOCANE-ST-APRE

24350 – Michelin map **329** D4 – pop. 1 679 – alt. 95
▶ Paris 498 – Brantôme 24 – Mussidan 33 – Périgueux 25

🏕 Municipal le Pré Sec

🕿 05 53 90 40 60. www.campingdupresec.com

Address : north of the town along the D 103, follow the signs for Montagrier, near the stadium; beside the Dronne river

Opening times : from beginning May to end Sept.

1.8 ha (80 pitches)

Tariff : (2014 Price) 10.81€ ✶✶ ⇔ 🔲 🄷 (10A) – Extra per person 1.95€
Rental rates : (2014 Price) Permanent – 14 🏠. Per night from 27 to 40€ – Per week from 245 to 380€
🚐 borne 2€ – 1 🔲 – 🕭 🄷10.81€

Surroundings : 🏕 ⊏🗆 ♀♀		
Leisure activities : 🛋 🏄 🍴 ⚓ (beach) 🏊 🛹 skate park	**G P S**	Longitude : 0.49685 Latitude : 45.25649
Facilities : ⚙ ⊶ 🍴 🔲		

TRENTELS

47140 – Michelin map **336** H3 – pop. 821 – alt. 50
▶ Paris 607 – Agen 42 – Bergerac 72 – Cahors 60

🏕 Village Vacances Municipal de Lustrac

(rental of chalets only)

🕿 05 53 70 72 22. www.campingdelustrac.jimdo.com – traditional camp. spaces also available

Address : at Lustrac (2.5km northeast along the D 911, follow the signs for Fumel and take the road to the right, towards Lustrac; beside the Lot river)

Opening times : Permanent

0.5 ha flat, grassy

Rental rates : (2014 Price) ⚙ – 7 🏠. Per week from 200 to 440€

Surroundings : 🏕 ⊏🗆 ♀♀		
Leisure activities : 🛋	**G P S**	Longitude : 0.88316 Latitude : 44.4335
Facilities : ⊶ 🏕 🍴 launderette		
Nearby : 🍴		

TURSAC

24620 – Michelin map **329** H6 – pop. 319 – alt. 75
▶ Paris 536 – Bordeaux 172 – Périgueux 48 – Brive-la-Gaillarde 57

🏔 Le Vézère Périgord

🕿 05 53 06 96 31. www.levezereperigord.com

Address : 800m northeast along the D 706, follow the signs for Montignac and take the road to the right

Opening times : from mid April to end Oct.

3.5 ha (103 pitches)

Tariff : ✶ 6.20€ ⇔ 🔲 10€ – 🄷 (10A) 3.60€
Rental rates : (from mid April to end Oct.) – 25 🚍 – 2 tent lodges. Per night from 30 to 55€ – Per week from 210 to 750€
🚐 borne

Surroundings : 🏕 ⊏🗆 ♀♀		
Leisure activities : ☂ 🍴 🛋 jacuzzi 🏄 🚲 🍴 🔲 🛶	**G P S**	Longitude : 1.04637 Latitude : 44.97599
Facilities : ⚙ ⊶ 🏕 🍴 launderette 🛒		

Key to rentals symbols:

12 🚍	Number of mobile homes
20 🏠	Number of chalets
6 🛏	Number of rooms to rent
Per night 30–50€	Minimum/maximum rate per night
Per week 300–1,000€	Minimum/maximum rate per week

URDOS

64490 – Michelin map **342** I5 – pop. 69 – alt. 780
▶ Paris 850 – Jaca 38 – Oloron-Ste-Marie 41 – Pau 75

🏕 Municipal Le Gave d'Aspe

🕿 06 08 77 35 97. www.campingaspe.com

Address : rue du Moulin de la Tourette (1.5km northwest along the N 134, take the road in front of the old station)

Opening times : from beginning May to mid Sept.

1.5 ha (80 pitches) open site, relatively flat, flat, grassy

Tariff : ✶ 3.95€ ⇔ 🔲 4.95€ – 🄷 (10A) 3€
Rental rates : Permanent – 2 🏠 – 2 🛏. Per night from 55€ – Per week from 299 to 399€
🚐 borne 2€

Pitches with good shade beside the Aspe mountain stream.

Surroundings : 🏕 ≤ ♀♀		
Leisure activities : 🛋 🏄 🛶	**G P S**	Longitude : -0.55642 Latitude : 42.87719
Facilities : ⚙ ⊶ 🏕 🍴 🔲		

*For more information on visiting particular towns or regions, consult the relevant regional **MICHELIN Green Guide**. We also recommend you use the appropriate Michelin regional map to locate your selected campsite, to calculate distances and to work out the best route.*

URRUGNE

64122 – Michelin map **342** B4 – pop. 8 427 – alt. 34
▶ Paris 791 – Bayonne 29 – Biarritz 23 – Hendaye 8

⚠️ Sunêlia Col d'Ibardin 👥

Col d'Ibardin

𝒫 0559543121, www.col-ibardin.com

Address : route d'Olhette (4km south along the D 4, follow the signs for Ascain and Le Col d'Ibardin; beside a stream)

Opening times : from mid March to mid Nov.

8 ha (203 pitches)

Tariff : (2014 Price) 35€ ✶ ✶ 🚐 🔲 🔌 (10A) – Extra per person 6.50€

Rental rates : (2014 Price) (from mid March to mid Nov.) ♿ (1 mobile home) 🚫 – 56 🚃 – 6 tent lodges. Per night from 48 to 130€ – Per week from 340 to 510€ – Reservation fee 30€

🚃 borne

In the middle of an oak forest; pitches beside a stream. Choose those furthest away from the road.

Surroundings : 🏞 〰〰
Leisure activities : 🍴 ✗ 🏠 🏃 🛷 🎿 🏊 multi-sports ground
Facilities : ♿ 🔌 🍴 ⛺ 🚿 🛗 🛎 launderette 🧺 🚽

G P S Longitude : -1.68461
Latitude : 43.33405

⚠️ Larrouleta

𝒫 0559473784. www.larrouleta.com

Address : Socoa district, 210 route de Socoa (3km to the south)

Opening times : Permanent

5 ha (327 pitches) flat, grassy

Tariff : 25.50€ ✶ ✶ 🚐 🔲 🔌 (10A) – Extra per person 6€

🚃 borne – 27 🔲 20€

A very pleasant site surrounding a small lake (swimming). Choose the pitches away from the road.

Surroundings : 〰〰
Leisure activities : 🍴 ✗ 🏠 🛷 🎿 🏊 (open air in season) 🏖 (beach) 🛶 pedalos
Facilities : ♿ 🔌 🛗 ⛺ 🚿 🛎 launderette 🧺 🚽

G P S Longitude : -1.6859
Latitude : 43.37036

URT

64240 – Michelin map **342** E2 – pop. 2 183 – alt. 41
▶ Paris 757 – Bayonne 17 – Biarritz 24 – Cambo-les-Bains 28

⚠️ Etche Zahar

𝒫 0559562736. www.etche-zahar.fr

Address : 175 allée de Mesplès (located 1km west along the D 257, towards Urcuit and take the turning to the left)

Opening times : from beginning March to mid Nov.

1.5 ha (47 pitches)

Tariff : ✶ 3.90€ 🚐 2.50€ 🔲 9.70€ – 🔌 (10A) 3.40€ – Reservation fee 13€

Rental rates : (from beginning March to mid Nov.) ♿ (2 chalets) – 9 🚃 – 9 🏠 – 5 canvas bungalows – 4 tent lodges. Per night from 27 to 98€ – Per week from 189 to 686€ – Reservation fee 13€

🚃 2 🔲 20€

In a green setting with a variety of rental options.

Surroundings : 🚣 🏞 〰〰
Leisure activities : 🏠 🏃 🚲 🛷
Facilities : ♿ 🔌 🛎 launderette

G P S Longitude : -1.2973
Latitude : 43.4919

VENDAYS-MONTALIVET

33930 – Michelin map **335** E2 – pop. 2 288 – alt. 9
▶ Paris 535 – Bordeaux 82 – Lesparre-Médoc 14 – Soulac-sur-Mer 21

⚠️ La Chesnays

𝒫 0556417274. www.camping-montalivet.com

Address : 8 route de Soulac, at Mayan

Opening times : from beginning May to mid Sept.

1.5 ha (59 pitches) flat, grassy

Tariff : 27.90€ ✶ ✶ 🚐 🔲 🔌 (10A) – Extra per person 5.90€ – Reservation fee 15€

Rental rates : (from beginning May to end Sept.) 🚫 – 5 🚃 – 3 🏠 – 2 canvas bungalows – 2 tent lodges. Per night from 38 to 123€ – Per week from 235 to 780€ – Reservation fee 15€

Surroundings : 🏞 〰〰
Leisure activities : 🏠 🏃 🚲 🛷
Facilities : ♿ 🔌 ⛺ 🛎 🖼

G P S Longitude : -1.08262
Latitude : 45.37602

⚠️ Le Mérin

𝒫 0556417864. www.campinglemerin.com

Address : 7 route du Mérin (3.7km northwest along the D 102, follow the signs for Montalivet and take road to the left)

Opening times : from beginning April to end Oct.

3.5 ha (165 pitches)

Tariff : ✶ 3.90€ 🚐 🔲 9.30€ 🔌 (10A)

Rental rates : (from beginning April to end Oct.) 🚫 – 12 🚃 – 3 🏠. Per night from 30 to 67€ – Per week from 210 to 470€

Surroundings : 🚣 🏞 〰〰
Leisure activities : 🏃
Facilities : 🔌 ⛺ 🛎 🖼

G P S Longitude : -1.09932
Latitude : 45.36703

VENSAC

33590 – Michelin map **335** E2 – pop. 854 – alt. 5
▶ Paris 528 – Bordeaux 82 – Lesparre-Médoc 14 – Soulac-sur-Mer 18

⚠️ Les Acacias

𝒫 0556095881, www.les-acacias-du-medoc.fr

Address : 44 route de St-Vivien (located 1.5km northeast along the N 215, follow the signs for Verdon-sur-Mer and take the road to the right)

Opening times : from end March to end Oct.

3.5 ha (175 pitches)

Tariff : (2014 Price) 30€ ✶ ✶ 🚐 🔲 🔌 (6A) – Extra per person 5.20€

Rental rates : (2014 Price) (from end March to end Oct.) – 80 🚃. Per night from 49 to 130€ – Per week from 343 to 910€

Surroundings : 🏞 〰〰
Leisure activities : ✗ 🏠 🌙 nighttime 🏃 ⛷ 🎿
Facilities : ♿ 🔌 🖼 ⛺ 🚿 🛎 launderette 🚽

G P S Longitude : -1.03252
Latitude : 45.40887

LE-VERDON-SUR-MER

33123 – Michelin map **335** E2 – pop. 1 334 – alt. 3
▶ Paris 514 – Bordeaux 100 – La Rochelle 80

⩗⩗⩗ **Sunêlia La Pointe du Médoc** ⚲⚹

✆ 05 56 73 39 99. www.camping-lapointedumedoc.com

Address : 18 rue Ausone (follow signs for the Pointe de Grave along the D 1215 and turn right)

Opening times : from mid April to mid Sept.

6.5 ha (260 pitches) **Tariff :** 28€ ★★ ⌕ 🖹 🔌 (10A) – Extra per person 6€ – Reservation fee 10€

Rental rates : (from mid April to mid Sept.) ♿ (1 mobile home) – 114 ⍟ – 31 🏠. Per night from 46 to 157€ – Per week from 322 to 1,100€ – Reservation fee 30€

Surroundings : ⚲
Leisure activities : ♟ ✕ ⛱ ⍟ ⩫ ⚡ ⧔ 🚲 ♨ ⬛ ⅄ multi-sports ground, entertainment room
Facilities : ♿ ⟿ 🖹 ⬚ ⤢ ⟟ ♉ launderette ⚌ ⚶

| **G P S** | Longitude : -1.07965 |
| | Latitude : 45.54557 |

These symbols are used for a campsite that is exceptional in its category:

⩗⩗⩗...⩙ *Particularly pleasant setting, quality and range of services available*

🐾🐾 *Tranquil, isolated site – quiet site, particularly at night*

≪≼ *Exceptional view – interesting or panoramic view*

VÉZAC

24220 – Michelin map **329** I6 – pop. 617 – alt. 90
▶ Paris 535 – Bergerac 65 – Brive-la-Gaillarde 60 – Fumel 53

⩗⩗ **Les Deux Vallées**

✆ 05 53 29 53 55. www.campingles2vallees.com

Address : La Gare (to the west, behind the old station; beside a little lake)

Opening times : from end Feb to beginning Nov.

2.5 ha (100 pitches) flat, grassy

Tariff : (2014 Price) ★ 7.60€ ⌕ 🖹 9.90€ – 🔌 (10A) 4.10€ – Reservation fee 15€

Rental rates : (2014 Price) (from end March to end Oct.) – 18 ⍟ – 2 gîtes. Per night from 31 to 61€ – Per week from 199 to 915€ – Reservation fee 15€

Uninterrupted view of the Château de Beynac from some pitches.

Surroundings : 🐾 ≼ ⌕ ⚲
Leisure activities : ♟ ✕ ⛱ ⚡ 🚲 ♨ ⅄ ⬛ ⚲
Facilities : ♿ ⟿ ▥ ⚌ ♉ launderette ⚶ refrigerators

| **G P S** | Longitude : 1.15844 |
| | Latitude : 44.83542 |

VIELLE-SAINT-GIRONS

40560 – Michelin map **335** D11 – pop. 1 160 – alt. 27
▶ Paris 719 – Castets 16 – Dax 37 – Mimizan 32

⩗⩗⩗ **Sunêlia Le Col Vert** ⚲⚹

D. NARBEBURU

✆ 08 90 71 00 01, www.colvert.com

Address : 1548 route de l'Étang (5.5km south along the D 652; beside the Étang de Léon)

Opening times : from beginning April to end Sept.

24 ha (800 pitches)

Tariff : 47.20€ ★★ ⌕ 🖹 🔌 (10A) Extra per person 7.50€ – Reservation fee 30€

Rental rates : (from beginning April to end Sept.) ♿ (1 mobile home) ⌂ – 310 ⍟ – 34 ⌂ – 27 canvas bungalows – 18 tent lodges. Per night from 24 to 119€ – Per week from 168 to 833€ – Reservation fee 33.50€

🏕 borne – 🚰 🔌 12€

A free shuttle service to St-Girons-Plage beach.

Surroundings : ⚲⚲ ⛰
Leisure activities : ♟ ✕ ⛱ ⍟ ⩫ 🎣 ⚑ hammam, jacuzzi ⚡ 🚲 ✂ ⬛ ⅄ ♨ multi-sports ground
Facilities : ♿ ⟿ 🖹 ⬚ – 6 individual sanitary facilities (▥ ⚌ 🚽 wc) ⤢ ⟟ ♉ launderette 🛒 ⚶ refrigerated food storage facilities
Nearby : ⩫ ⧫ 🐎 boats to hire

⩘ **L'Océane**

✆ 05 58 42 94 37. www.camping-oceane.fr – limited spaces for one-night stay

Address : route des Lacs (located 1km to the north)

Opening times : from beginning May to end Sept.

3 ha (99 pitches)

Tariff : (2014 Price) 28€ ★★ ⌕ 🖹 🔌 (10A) – Extra per person 8€
Rental rates : Permanent – 58 ⍟. Per night from 38 to 120€ – Per week from 200 to 820€ – Reservation fee 25€

Pleasant pine grove.

Surroundings : ⚲⚲⚲
Leisure activities : ♟ ✕ ⛱ ⚡ 🚲 ⅄
Facilities : ⟿ (July-Aug.) ♉ launderette ⚶

| **G P S** | Longitude : -1.30611 |
| | Latitude : 43.92278 |

Michelin classification:

⩗⩗⩗ *Extremely comfortable, equipped to a very high standard*

⩗⩗ *Very comfortable, equipped to a high standard*

⩗⩗ *Comfortable and well equipped*

⩘ *Reasonably comfortable*

⩙ *Satisfactory*

VIEUX-BOUCAU-LES-BAINS

40480 – Michelin map **335** C12 – pop. 1 577 – alt. 5
▶ Paris 740 – Bayonne 41 – Biarritz 48 – Castets 28

⚠ Municipal les Sablères

✆ 05 58 48 12 29. www.camping-les-sableres.com

Address : boulevard du Marensin (to the northwest, 250m from the beach (direct access)

Opening times : from end March to mid Oct.

11 ha (517 pitches)

Tariff : (2014 Price) 23.90€ ✶✶ ⇔ 🔲 ⚡ (10A) – Extra per person 4.60€ – Reservation fee 20€

Rental rates : (2014 Price) (from end March to mid Oct.) – 7 🚐 – 11 🏠 – 2 tent lodges. Per night from 38 to 81€ – Per week from 190 to 889€ – Reservation fee 20€

Surroundings : 🌿
Leisure activities : 🏄 multi-sports ground
Facilities : ♿ ⚬ 🚿 🛁 🚮 🍴 launderette refrigerated food storage facilities
Nearby : 🛶 🍴 ✗ ✗

GPS Longitude : -1.40596
Latitude : 43.79326

VILLERÉAL

47210 – Michelin map **336** G2 – pop. 1 286 – alt. 103
▶ Paris 566 – Agen 61 – Bergerac 35 – Cahors 76

⚠ Yelloh! Village Le Château de Fonrives ♣♣

✆ 05 53 36 63 38. www.campingchateaufonrives.com

Address : route d'Issigeac, Rives (2.2km northwest along the D 207 and take the turning to the left, by the château)

Opening times : from mid April to mid Sept.

20 ha/10 for camping (370 pitches)

Tariff : (2014 Price) 27€ ✶✶ ⇔ 🔲 ⚡ (10A) – Extra per person 8€

Rental rates : Permanent – 180 🚐. Per night from 45 to 229€ – Per week from 315 to 1,603€

🚐 6 🔲 18€

Surroundings : 🌿 🎋 🌳🌳
Leisure activities : 🍴 ✗ 🎬 🎯 🏊 🎣 🛶 jacuzzi 🏄 🚲 ✗ 🔲 🛝 🏔 🚶 sports trail
Facilities : ♿ ⚬ 🚿 🛁 🍴 launderette 🛶 🚿

GPS Longitude : 0.7314
Latitude : 44.65739

⚠ Sites et Paysages Fontaine du Roc

✆ 05 53 36 08 16. www.fontaineduroc.com

Address : Dévillac (7.5km southeast along the D 255 and take the turning to the left)

Opening times : from beginning April to beginning Oct.

2 ha (60 pitches) flat, grassy

Tariff : (2014 Price) ✶ 6€ ⇔ 🔲 8€ – ⚡ (10A) 4.50€ – Reservation fee 25€

Rental rates :(2014 Price) (from beginning April to beginning Oct.) – 4 🚐 – 3 🏠. Per night from 50 to 110€ – Per week from 350 to 770€

🚐 borne – ⚡11€

Surroundings : 🌿 🌳🌳
Leisure activities : 🔲 🏊 jacuzzi 🏄 🛝
Facilities : ♿ ⚬ 🛁 🍴 launderette

GPS Longitude : 0.8187
Latitude : 44.61414

VITRAC

24200 – Michelin map **329** I7 – pop. 870 – alt. 150
▶ Paris 541 – Brive-la-Gaillarde 64 – Cahors 54 – Gourdon 23

⚠ Domaine Soleil Plage ♣♣

✆ 05 53 28 33 33. www.soleilplage.fr

Address : Caudon (beside the Dordogne river)

Opening times : from mid April to end Sept.

8 ha/5 for camping (199 pitches) flat, grassy

Tariff : 39.90€ ✶✶ ⇔ 🔲 ⚡ (16A) – Extra per person 8.20€ – Reservation fee 39.90€

Rental rates : (from mid April to end Sept.) 🅿 – 53 🚐 – 27 🏠. Per night from 47 to 209€ – Per week from 306 to 1,350€ – Reservation fee 39.90€

🚐 borne 3€ – 10 🔲 23€

Small but luxurious chalet village, rather pretty.

Surroundings : 🌿 ≤ 🎋 🌳🌳
Leisure activities : 🍴 ✗ 🎬 🎯 🎣 🏄 ✗ 🏊 🔲 🛝 🏔 (beach) 🛶 🚲 🌿 multi-sports ground
Facilities : ♿ ⚬ 🔲🎬 🚿 🛁 🍴 launderette 🛶 🚿

GPS Longitude : 1.25374
Latitude : 44.82387

⚠ La Bouysse de Caudon

✆ 05 53 28 33 05. www.labouysse.com

Address : at Caudon (2.5km east, near the Dordogne river)

Opening times : from mid April to end Sept.

6 ha/3 for camping (160 pitches) flat, grassy, walnut trees

Tariff : (2014 Price) ✶ 4.90€ ⇔ 🔲 6.30€ – ⚡ (10A) 3.20€

Rental rates : (2014 Price) (from mid April to end Sept.) 🌿 (from mid April to end June) 🅿 – 4 🚐 – 9 🏠 – 5 apartments – 2 gîtes. Per night from 120 to 150€ – Per week from 280 to 810€

🚐 borne 3€

Surroundings : 🌿 🎋 🌳🌳
Leisure activities : 🍴 🏄 ✗ 🏊 🏔 (beach) 🚲 🌿
Facilities : ♿ ⚬ 🚿🎬 🛁 🍴 launderette 🛶 🚿 refrigerators

GPS Longitude : 1.25063
Latitude : 44.82357

AUVERGNE

G. Labriet / Photononstop

Shhh! Don't wake the volcanoes. They are the giant sleeping beauties of the Auvergne, a stunning region at the heart of France. Dormant for several millennia, they form a natural barrier that keeps them secure from any encroachment by man. If you listen very carefully, you may just make out a distant rumble from Vulcania, the interactive and educational European Park of Volcanism, where you can learn all you could possibly want to know about volcanoes. The region's domes and peaks, sculpted by volcanic fire, are the source of countless mountain springs that cascade down the steep slopes into brooks, rivers and crystal-clear lakes. Renowned for the therapeutic qualities of its waters, the Auvergne has long played host to well-heeled visitors at its elegant spa resorts, but many find it simply impossible to follow doctor's orders when faced with the tempting aroma of an Auvergne country stew, a savoury *Pounti* cake or a full-bodied Cantal cheese!

Legend:
- Locality with campsite
- Locality with campsite and rental option
- Vannes — Locality with campsite and campervan area
- Moyaux — Locality with at least one pleasant campsite
- Motorway service area for campervans

Saulieu
les Settons
Prémery
Crux-la-Ville
Arnay-le-Duc
Montigny-en-Morvan
N 81
la Charité-sur-Loire
St-Péreuse
Château-Chinon
Épinac
NIÈVRE
D 978
St-Léger-de-Fougeret
Nevers
D 978
Aubois
Autun
N 80
San
St-Honoré-les-Bains
Couches
Luzy
CHAL
Lunery
SAÔNE-ET-
Issy-l'Évêque
Gueugnon
St-Amand-Montrond
Bessais-le-Fromental
Bourbon-Lancy
Palinges
Salornay-s-Guye
Isle-et-Bardais
ALLIER
Moulins
Dompierre-s-Besbre
Digoin
le Bourg-d'Hem
St-Bonnet-Tronçais
Pierrefitte-s-Loire
Charolles
Paray-le-Monial
Dompierre-les-Ormes
Châteaumeillant
Matour
Boussac-Bourg
Treignat
Sazeret
Chambilly
Chauffailles
Châtelus-Malvaleix
MONTLUÇON
N 145
N 79
Lapalisse
la Pacaudière
Belmont-de-la-Loire
Pouilly-s/s-Charlieu
Poule-les-Écharmeaux
Néris-les-Bains
Guéret
Lapeyrouse
Vichy
Cublize
CREUSE
St-Éloy-les-Mines
Abrest
D 2209
Gannat
Bellerive-sur-Allier
Roanne
RHÔ
D 941
St-Gervais-d'A.
Cordelle
Aubusson
MANZAT
Puy-Guillaume
St-Rémy-s-Durolle
St-Paul-de-Vézelin
LA LOIRE
Royère-de-Vassivière
Châtelguyon
HAUT-FOREZ NORD
Balbigny
Volvic
Riom
Orléat
Pontgibaud
PUY-
DE-
DÔME
CLERMONT-FERRAND
HAUT-FOREZ SUD
Feurs
Nebouzat
Royat
Cournon-d'A.
Courpière
Jeansagnière
Poncins
St-Symphorien-s-Coise
CHAVANON
Murat-le-Quaire
Orcet
Billom
Ambert
St-Galmier
St-Sauves-d'A.
Aydat
la Bourboule
le Mont-Dore
St-Nectaire
Issoire
Chambois
Tauves
Chambon-s-Lac
Montaigut-le-Blanc
Murol
St-Germain-l'Herm
ST-ÉTIENNE
Singles
Bagnols
Nonette
St-Genès-Malifaux
Ligiiac
Lanobre
Lempdes-sur-Allagnon
Treignac
Champs-s-Tarentaine
LA FAYETTE
Champagnac-le-Vieux
la Chaise-Dieu
St-Didier-en-Velay
Neuvic
Saignes
Brioude
N 102
Ste-Sigolène
Mauriac
Paulhaguet
Vorey
Auriac
St-Martin-Valmeroux
N 122
Langeac
St-Paulien
Yssingeaux
N 88
Argentat
St-Martin-Cantalès
Neussargues-Moissac
HAUTE-
LOIRE
Lalouvesc
Arnac
CANTAL
St-Jacques-des-Blats
le Chambon-s-Lignon
St-Agrève
Camps
St-Gérons
Ruynes-en-Margeride
Saugues
Monistrol-d'Allier
Mars
Bretenoux
Vic-s-Cère
Neuvéglise
Issarlès
le Cheylard
Pers
Blavignac
St-Sauveur-de-
Lacam-d'Ourcet
Aurillac
Arpajon-s-Cère
St-Just
Alleyras
Thérondels
Chaudes-Aigues
les Olliè-s-Eyrieux
LA LOZÈRE
LA LOZÈRE
ARDÈCHE
Maurs
Pons
St-Alban-s-Limagnole
St-Paul-le-Froid
Naussac
Bagnac-s-Célé
Laguiole
Nasbinals
Chastanier
Figeac
Grand-Vabre
St-Amans-des-Cots
LOZÈRE
Rocles
N 102
Béduer
Flagnac
Entraygues-s-T.
Marvejols
Aubenas
Capdenac-Gare
Conques
Sénergues
Espalion
Mende
Largentière
MONTÉLI
Boisse-Penchot
St-Germain-du-Tel
St-Bauzile
Villefort
Rignac
AVEYRON
la Canourgue
Villefranche-de-Rouergue
St-Geniez-d'Olt
Ste-Enimie
Ispagnac
Bédouès
St-Salvadou
Rodez
L'AVEYRON
Canilhac
St-Georges-de-Lévéjac
Florac
N 106
La Fouillade
Pont-de-Salars
Sévérac-l'Église
Canet-de-Salars
les Vignes

ABREST

03200 – Michelin map **326** H6 – pop. 2 696 – alt. 290
▶ Paris 361 – Clermont-Ferrand 70 – Moulins 63 – Montluçon 94

⛰ La Croix St-Martin ⚏

☎ 04 70 32 67 74. www.camping-vichy.com

Address : 99 avenue des Graviers (to the north, near the Allier)

Opening times : from beginning April to beginning Oct.

3 ha (89 pitches) flat, grassy

Tariff : ☗ 5.20€ ⇔ 国 6.20€ – ⚡ (10A) 3.70€ – Reservation fee 5€
Rental rates : (2014 Price) (from beginning April to beginning Oct.) – 17 ⛺. Per week from 395 to 620€ – Reservation fee 5€
⛽ borne 5€

Shaded pitches beside a walking and cycling path that hugs the Allier river.

Surroundings : ⛰ ⌑ 🌳🌳
Leisure activities : 🏛 🕺 🚣 ⛵ fitness trail, bikepark 🐾
Facilities : ♿ ⛗ 💳 ⛲ 🍴 launderette 🧺
Nearby : 🏊

G P S	Longitude : 3.44012 Latitude : 46.10819

ALLEYRAS

43580 – Michelin map **331** E4 – pop. 173 – alt. 779
▶ Paris 549 – Brioude 71 – Langogne 43 – Le Puy-en-Velay 32

⛺ Municipal Au Fil de l'Eau

☎ 04 71 57 56 86. www.camping-municipal.alleyras.fr – alt. 660

Address : Le Pont-d'Alleyras (2.5km to the northwest, direct access to the Allier)

0.9 ha (60 pitches) flat and relatively flat

Rentals : 6 huts (without sanitary facilities).

Surroundings : ⛰ ≼
Leisure activities : 🚣
Facilities : ♿ ⛗ launderette
Nearby : 🏊 🏊

G P S	Longitude : 3.67005 Latitude : 44.91786

AMBERT

63600 – Michelin map **326** J9 – pop. 6 962 – alt. 535
▶ Paris 438 – Brioude 63 – Clermont-Ferrand 77 – Montbrison 47

⛰ Municipal Les Trois Chênes

☎ 04 73 82 34 68. www.camping-ambert.com

Address : route du Puy (located 1.5km south along the D 906, follow the signs for La Chaise-Dieu; near the Dore river)

Opening times : from end April to end Sept.

3 ha (120 pitches) flat, grassy

Tariff : 20.65€ ☗☗ ⇔ 国 ⚡ (10A) – Extra per person 4.75€
Rental rates : Permanent – 18 ⛺. Per night from 80 to 173€
Per week from 275 to 715€
⛽ borne 2€

In a pleasant leafy setting but choose those pitches furthest away from the road.

Surroundings : ≼ ⌑ 🌳🌳
Leisure activities : 🏛 🚣
Facilities : ♿ ⛗ ⛲ ⚘ 🍴 launderette
Nearby : 🏊 🍷 🍴 🧺 🏓 🏐 🌊 🏊 fitness trail

G P S	Longitude : 3.7291 Latitude : 45.53953

ARNAC

15150 – Michelin map **330** B4 – pop. 148 – alt. 620
▶ Paris 541 – Argentat 38 – Aurillac 35 – Mauriac 36

⛰ Village Vacances La Gineste

(rental of mobile homes and chalets only)

☎ 04 71 62 91 90. www.village-vacances-cantal.com

Address : La Gineste (3km northwest along the D 61, follow the signs for Pleaux then continue 1.2km along the road to the right)

Opening times : Permanent

3 ha terraced

Rental rates : (2014 Price) Ⓟ – 50 ⛺ – 40 ⛺. Per week from 395 to 600€ – Reservation fee 13€
⛽ borne 2€ – 2 国

A pleasant location on a peninsula in the Lac d'Enchanet.

Surroundings : ⛰ ≼ 🌳
Leisure activities : 🍷 🍴 🏛 🛥 🚣 ⛵ 🏊 (beach) 🚤 🐴
Facilities : ⛗ 🚿 🍴 🏛 🧺 ⛲
Nearby : watersports centre

G P S	Longitude : 2.2121 Latitude : 45.08285

We have selected the best campsites in France with our usual care, listing those with the best facilities in the most pleasant surroundings.

ARPAJON-SUR-CÈRE

15130 – Michelin map **330** C5 – pop. 6 009 – alt. 613
▶ Paris 559 – Argentat 56 – Aurillac 5 – Maurs 44

⛺ La Cère

☎ 04 71 64 55 07. www.camping.caba.fr

Address : south of the town, access via the D 920. opposite the Esso service station; beside the river

2 ha (78 pitches) flat, grassy

Rentals : 10 ⛺.

A wooded setting and a well-kept site.

Surroundings : ⌑ 🌳
Leisure activities : 🏛 🚣 🚲 🏊
Facilities : ♿ ⛗ 🍴 🖥
Nearby : 🛒 🏓

G P S	Longitude : 2.46246 Latitude : 44.89858

AURILLAC

15000 – Michelin map **330** C5 – pop. 28 207 – alt. 610
▶ Paris 557 – Brive-la-Gaillarde 98 – Clermont-Ferrand 158 Montauban 174

⛺ Municipal l'Ombrade

☎ 04 71 48 28 87. www.camping.caba.fr

Address : head 1km north along the D 17 and take r. du Gué-Bouliaga to the right; on both sides of the Jordanne

7.5 ha (200 pitches) flat, grassy

Surroundings : 🌳🌳
Leisure activities : 🏛 🚲
Facilities : ♿ ⛗ ⛲ ⚘ 🍴 🖥
Nearby : 🛒

G P S	Longitude : 2.4559 Latitude : 44.93562

AYDAT

63970 – Michelin map **326** E9 – pop. 2 122 – alt. 850
▶ Paris 438 – La Bourboule 33 – Clermont-Ferrand 21 – Issoire 38

⛰ Lac d'Aydat

✆ 0473793809. www.camping-lac-aydat.com
Address : beside the lake, Foret du lot (head 2km northeast along the D 90 and take the road to the right; near the lake)

Opening times : from mid April to mid Sept.

7 ha (150 pitches) terraced, flat, grassy, stony

Tariff : 28€ ★★ ⇌ 🔲 (15A) – Extra per person 6€ – Reservation fee 20€

Rental rates : Permanent ♿ (1 chalet) – 54 🛏 – 17 🏠. Per night from 50 to 110€ – Per week from 350 to 770€ – Reservation fee 20€

🚐 borne
Situated beside a lake, on an undulating and very wooded site.

Surroundings : 🏞 ♤♤
Leisure activities : 🖼 ♨ m
Facilities : ♿ ⚓ 🗑 ⛲ launderette
Nearby : 🛶 🎿 🚠 🚴 🛥 (beach) 🏊 🚣
forest trail

Longitude : 2.98907
Latitude : 45.66903

BAGNOLS

63810 – Michelin map **326** C9 – pop. 496 – alt. 862
▶ Paris 483 – Bort-les-Orgues 19 – La Bourboule 23 – Bourg-Lastic 38

⛰ Municipal la Thialle

✆ 0473222800. www.bagnols63.fr
Address : route de St-Donat (take southeastern exit along the D 25; beside the Thialle river)

Opening times : Permanent

2.8 ha (70 pitches)

Tariff : 19€ ★★ ⇌ 🔲 (3A) – Extra per person 4.20€
Rental rates : Permanent ♿ (1 mobile home) – 8 🏠. Per night from 40 to 59€ – Per week from 241 to 355€

🚐 borne

Surroundings : 🏞 ▭ ♤
Leisure activities : 🖼 ♨ m 🎬 (open air in season)
Facilities : ♿ ⚓ (season) 🗑 ⛲ 🍴
launderette
Nearby : 🛶 🍸 ✕

Longitude : 2.63466
Latitude : 45.49758

BELLERIVE-SUR-ALLIER

03700 – Michelin map **326** H6 – pop. 8 530 – alt. 340
▶ Paris 357 – Clermont-Ferrand 53 – Moulins 58 – Saint-Étienne 147

⛰ Club Airotel Beau Rivage et les Isles 👥

✆ 0470322685. www.camping-beaurivage.com
Address : rue Claude Decloître

Opening times : from beginning April to mid Oct.

7 ha (143 pitches) flat, grassy, fine gravel

Tariff : 20€ ★★ ⇌ 🔲 (10A) – Extra per person 6€ – Reservation fee 5€

Rental rates : (from beginning April to mid Oct.) ♿ (1 mobile home) – 31 🛏 – 4 🏠 – 2 apartments. Per night from 38 to 75€ – Per week from 266 to 469€ – Reservation fee 15€

🚐 borne 10€

The site is in two sections, with shaded pitches beside the Allier river, facing the Vichy parkland on the opposite bank.

Surroundings : 🏞 ▭ ♤♤
Leisure activities : 🍸 ✕ 🖼 🎣 🏇 ♨ 🚴 🎿
(open air in season) 🏊 🚣 pedalos, archery
🦋 entertainment room
Facilities : ♿ ⚓ 🔲 🏚 🗑 ⛲ 🍴 launderette
Nearby : 🛶

Longitude : 3.43192
Latitude : 46.11482

BILLOM

63160 – Michelin map **326** H8 – pop. 4 637 – alt. 340
▶ Paris 437 – Clermont-Ferrand 28 – Cunlhat 30 – Issoire 31

⛰ Municipal le Colombier

✆ 0473689150. www.billom.fr
Address : rue Carnot (To the northeast of the town, follow the signs for Lezoux)

Opening times : from mid June to mid Sept.

1 ha (38 pitches)

Tariff : (2014 Price) ★ 2.50€ ⇌ 🔲 – 🔲 (6A) 3.20€
Rentals : 12 🏠.
The well-marked out pitches are shaded and the chalet village has a pretty view.

Surroundings : 🏞 ▭ ♤♤
Leisure activities : 🖼 ♨
Facilities : ♿ ⚓ 🗑 🍴 launderette
Nearby : ✕ 🎬 🛶

Longitude : 3.3459
Latitude : 45.72839

LA BOURBOULE

63150 – Michelin map **326** D9 – pop. 1 961 – alt. 880 – ♨
▶ Paris 469 – Aubusson 82 – Clermont-Ferrand 50 – Mauriac 71

⛰ Les Clarines

✆ 0473810230. www.camping-les-clarines.com
Address : 1424 avenue du Mar. Leclerc

Opening times : from mid Dec. to end Oct.

3.75 ha (187 pitches) terraced, relatively flat, flat, grassy, fine gravel

Tariff : (2014 Price) 21.55€ ★★ ⇌ 🔲 🔲 (10A) –
Extra per person 4.85€
Rental rates : (2014 Price) (from mid Dec. to end Oct.) – 31 🛏.
Per week from 252 to 686€
🚐 borne 5€ – 10 🔲 10€
A free shuttle to the spa and a bus to the ski resorts.

Surroundings : ❄ ♤♤
Leisure activities : 🖼 ♨ 🚵 mountain bike trail
Facilities : ⚓ 🏚 🗑 🍴 launderette

Longitude : 2.76222
Latitude : 45.59463

⛰ Les Vernières

✆ 0473811020. www.camping-la-bourboule.fr
Address : avenue du Mar. de Lattre-de-Tassigny (take the eastern exit along the D 130, follow the signs for Le Mont-Dore; near the Dordogne)

Opening times : from beginning May to mid Oct.

1.5 ha (174 pitches) terrace, flat, grassy

Tariff : 15.75€ ★★ ⇌ 🔲 🔲 (10A) – Extra per person 4.50€

Rental rates : (from beginning May to mid Oct.) – 6 🏠 – 1 yurt – 6 tent lodges. Per night from 40 to 90€ – Per week from 190 to 590€

🚐 borne – 40 ▤ 15€ – 🛒10€

Very varied rental options and plenty of green space. Choose the pitches furthest away from the road if possible.

Surroundings : ▭ 🌳🌳 Leisure activities : 🍴 🏠 🏃 ⛷️ Facilities : 🚿 🔌 🛒▥ 🍴 launderette Nearby : 🍴 🏊 🎣	**GPS** Longitude : 2.75285 Latitude : 45.58943

BRIOUDE

43100 – Michelin map **331** C2 – pop. 6 688 – alt. 427
▶ Paris 487 – Clermont-Ferrand 71 – Le Puy-en-Velay 59 – Aurillac 105

⚠️ Aquadis Loisirs La Bageasse

📞 0471500770. www.aquadis-loisirs.com

Opening times : from beginning March to beginning Nov.

2.5 ha (49 pitches) terraced, flat, grassy

Tariff : 16.90€ 🚹🚹 🚐 ▤ 🔌 (10A) – Extra per person 4.60€ – Reservation fee 9.90€

Rental rates : (from beginning March to beginning Nov.) 🚿 (1 chalet) – 4 🚐 – 15 🏠. Per night from 60 to 78€ – Per week from 178 to 596€ – Reservation fee 19.90€

A pleasant site near the river.

Surroundings : ▭ 🌳🌳 Leisure activities : 🍴 🍴 Facilities : 🚿 🔌▥ ⛵ 🍴 launderette Nearby : 🏊	**GPS** Longitude : 3.40479 Latitude : 45.28123

LA CHAISE-DIEU

43160 – Michelin map **331** E2 – pop. 730 – alt. 1 080
▶ Paris 503 – Ambert 29 – Brioude 35 – Issoire 59

⚠️ Municipal les Prades

📞 0471000788. otcasadei@wanadoo.fr

Address : situated 2km northeast along the D 906, follow the signs for Ambert, near the small lake at La Tour (direct access)

Opening times : from beginning June to end Sept.

3 ha (100 pitches) relatively flat, grassy

Tariff : (2014 Price) 🚹 3.50€ 🚐 2€ – 🔌 (10A) 4€

Surroundings : 🌳🌳 Leisure activities : ⛵ Facilities : 🚿 ⛵ 🔌 Nearby : 🍴 🏊 🐎	**GPS** Longitude : 3.70496 Latitude : 45.33321

Key to rentals symbols :

12 🚐	*Number of mobile homes*
20 🏠	*Number of chalets*
6🛏️	*Number of rooms to rent*
Per night *30–50€*	*Minimum/maximum rate per night*
Per week *300–1,000€*	*Minimum/maximum rate per week*

CHAMBON-SUR-LAC

63790 – Michelin map **326** E9 – pop. 352 – alt. 885 – Winter sports : 1 150/1 760 m
▶ Paris 456 – Clermont-Ferrand 37 – Condat 39 – Issoire 32

〰️ Yelloh! Village Le Pré Bas

📞 0473886304. www.campingauvergne.com

Address : near the lake (direct access)

Opening times : from mid April to mid Sept.

3.8 ha (180 pitches)

Tariff : 36€ 🚹🚹 🚐 ▤ 🔌 (6A) – Extra per person 7€

Rental rates : (from mid April to mid Sept.) 🚿 (1 mobile home) – 109 🚐 – 2 gîtes. Per night from 39 to 164€ – Per week from 273 to 1,148€

🚐 borne 36€ – 28 ▤ 36€

Good activities for young children, some indoors.

Surroundings : 🌿 ▭ 🌿 Leisure activities : 🍴 🍴 🏠 🎣 🏃 ⛵ hammam, jacuzzi 🏊 🏊 ⛵ spa centre, entertainment room Facilities : 🚿 🔌 ⛵ 🍴 launderette 🚿 Nearby : 🏊 ⛵ (beach) 🎣 🦆 pedalos	**GPS** Longitude : 2.91427 Latitude : 45.57516

⚠️ Les Bombes

📞 0473886403. www.camping-les-bombes.com

Address : Chemin de Pétary (east of Chambon-sur-Lac, head towards Murol and take a right turn; beside the Couze de Chambon river)

Opening times : from beginning May to mid Sept.

5 ha (150 pitches) flat, grassy

Tariff : (2014 Price) 🚹 5.20€ 🚐 ▤ 14.80€ – 🔌 (16A) 4.60€ – Reservation fee 12€

Rental rates : (2014 Price) (from beginning May to mid Sept.) – 2 caravans – 15 🚐 – 3 tent lodges. Per night from 42 to 67€ Per week from 195 to 725€ – Reservation fee 12€

🚐 borne 7€

A variety of rental options with lots of green space, ideal for relaxation.

Surroundings : 🌿 🌿 Leisure activities : 🍴 🍴 🏠 🏊 🚲 ⛵ 🎣 Facilities : 🚿 🔌 ⛵ 🍴 launderette 🚿	**GPS** Longitude : 2.90188 Latitude : 45.56994

⚠️ Serrette

📞 0473886767. www.campingdeserrette.com – alt. 1 000

Address : 2.5km west along the D 996, follow the signs for Le Mont-Dore and take the D 636 (to the left), follow the signs for Chambon-des-Neiges

Opening times : from beginning May to mid Sept.

2 ha (75 pitches) terraced, flat and relatively flat, stony, grassy

Tariff : (2014 Price) 24.55€ 🚹🚹 🚐 ▤ 🔌 (10A) – Extra per person 5.15€ – Reservation fee 12€

Rental rates : (2014 Price) (from beginning May to mid Sept.) 🚿 (1 chalet) – 8 🚐 – 3 🏠. Per night from 30 to 60€ – Per week from 400 to 740€ – Reservation fee 12€

There's a magnificent view over the lake and the surrounding area.

Surroundings : 🌿 ≤ Lac Chambon and the Château de Murol 🌿 Leisure activities : 🍴 🍴 🏠 ⛵ 🏊 (open air in season) Facilities : 🚿 🔌 🍴 launderette 🚿	**GPS** Longitude : 2.89105 Latitude : 45.57099

LE CHAMBON-SUR-LIGNON

43400 – Michelin map **331** H3 – pop. 2 690 – alt. 967
▶ Paris 573 – Annonay 48 – Lamastre 32 – Le Puy-en-Velay 45

⛰ Les Hirondelles

☎ 0471597384. www.campinglehirondelles.fr – alt. 1 000
Address : route de la Suchère (located 1km south along the D 151 and turn left onto D 7)
Opening times : from mid June to beginning Sept.
1 ha (45 pitches) flat, grassy
Tariff : (2014 Price) 18.95€ ✶✶ ⛺ 🔲 (6A) – Extra per person 4.50€
Rental rates : (2014 Price) (from mid April to beginning Nov.) ⚡ – 3 🏠. Per night from 35 to 70€ – Per week from 240 to 485€
🚰 borne 10€
In a pleasant setting overlooking the village.

Surroundings :
Leisure activities :
Facilities :
At the river : sports trail
GPS Longitude : 4.2986 Latitude : 45.05436

⛰ Le Lignon

☎ 0471597286. contact@campingdulignon.com – alt. 1 000
Address : route du Stade (take the southwestern exit along the D 15, follow the signs for Mazet-sur-Voy and take a right turn before the bridge, near the river)
Opening times : from mid April to end Sept.
2 ha (130 pitches) flat, grassy
Tariff : (2014 Price) 20€ ✶✶ ⛺ 🔲 (10A) – Extra per person 6.20€
Rental rates : Permanent – 5 🏠. Per night from 55 to 70€ Per week from 390 to 490€

Surroundings :
Leisure activities :
Facilities :
At the river : sports trail
GPS Longitude : 4.29686 Latitude : 45.05944

CHAMPAGNAC-LE-VIEUX

43440 – Michelin map **331** D1 – pop. 234 – alt. 880
▶ Paris 486 – Brioude 16 – La Chaise-Dieu 25 – Clermont-Ferrand 76

⛰ Le Chanterelle

☎ 0471763400. www.champagnac.com
Address : Le Prat Barrat (1.4km north along the D 5, follow the signs for Auzon, and take the road to the right)
Opening times : from mid April to mid Oct.
4 ha (90 pitches) terraced, flat, grassy
Tariff : ✶ 4€ ⛺ 2.70€ 🔲 6.20€ – (10A) 3.70€
Rental rates : (from mid April to mid Oct.) – 4 🏠 – 20 🏠 – 14 canvas bungalows. Per night from 40 to 114€ – Per week from 280 to 798€ – Reservation fee 16€
A lush, green site near a lake.

Surroundings :
Leisure activities :
Facilities : launderette
Nearby : (beach) fitness trail
GPS Longitude : 3.50575 Latitude : 45.3657

CHAMPS-SUR-TARENTAINE

15270 – Michelin map **330** D2 – pop. 1 035 – alt. 450
▶ Paris 500 – Aurillac 90 – Clermont-Ferrand 82 – Condat 24

⛰ Les Chalets de l'Eau Verte (rental of chalets only)

☎ 0471787878. www.auvergne-chalets.fr
Address : Le Jagounet
Opening times : Permanent
8 ha relatively flat
Rental rates : P – 10 🏠. Per week from 273 to 798€ – Reservation fee 10€
There is a 2-night minimum stay in low season.

Surroundings :
Leisure activities :
Facilities :
Nearby :
GPS Longitude : 2.63853 Latitude : 45.40595

Using the traditional Michelin classification method, the guide provides you with an easy, speedy reference for assessing the category of each site: 1 to 5 tents (see page 10).

CHÂTELGUYON

63140 – Michelin map **326** F7 – pop. 6 223 – alt. 430
▶ Paris 411 – Aubusson 93 – Clermont-Ferrand 21 – Gannat 31

⛰ Le Ranch des Volcans

☎ 0473860247. www.ranchdesvolcans.com
Address : route de la Piscine (take southeastern exit along the D 985, follow the signs for Riom)
Opening times : from mid March to beginning Nov.
4 ha (285 pitches)
Tariff : 24.50€ ✶✶ ⛺ 🔲 (10A) – Extra per person 4.50€
Rental rates : (from mid March to beginning Nov.) – 2 caravans – 35 🏠 – 3 🏠 – 1 studio – 4 tipis. Per night from 60 to 105€ Per week from 250 to 660€ – Reservation fee 10€
🚰 borne – 22 🔲 14.50€
Partially under the shade of birch trees, decorated with an American ranch theme. There's a shuttle bus to the spa centre.

Surroundings :
Leisure activities :
Facilities : launderette
GPS Longitude : 3.07732 Latitude : 45.91491

⛰ La Croze

☎ 0473860827. www.campingcroze.com
Address : at St-Hippolyte, route de Mozac (located 1km southeast along the D 227, follow the signs for Riom)
3.7 ha (98 pitches) terraced, relatively flat, flat, grassy
Rentals : (1 chalet) – 17 🏠 – 9 🏠.
There is a shuttle bus to the spa centre.

Surroundings :
Leisure activities :
Facilities : launderette
GPS Longitude : 3.06083 Latitude : 45.90589

CHAUDES-AIGUES

15110 – Michelin map **330** G5 – pop. 940 – alt. 750 –
▶ Paris 538 – Aurillac 94 – Entraygues-sur-Truyère 62 – Espalion 54

⛺ Le Château du Couffour

☏ 0471235708. www.camping-chaudes-aigues.fr – alt. 900

Address : at the stadium (situated 2km south along the D 921, follow the signs for Laguiole then take the road to the right)

Opening times : from mid April to mid Oct.

2.5 ha (90 pitches) flat, grassy

Located high up, in the heart of the countryside.

Surroundings :
Leisure activities :
Facilities :
Nearby : climbing, casino

GPS Longitude : 3.00071
Latitude : 44.8449

COURNON-D'AUVERGNE

63800 – Michelin map **326** G8 – pop. 19 494 – alt. 380
▶ Paris 422 – Clermont-Ferrand 12 – Issoire 31 – Le Mont-Dore 54

🏔 Municipal le Pré des Laveuses

☏ 0473848130. www.cournon-auvergne.fr/camping

Address : rue des Laveuses (head 1.5km east via road to Billom and take the beach road to the left)

Opening times : Permanent

5 ha (145 pitches)

Tariff : (2014 Price) 24.70€ ★★ ⛺ 🔌 (10A) –
Extra per person 5.70€

Rental rates : (2014 Price) Permanent ♿ (2 chalets) – 15 🚐 –
18 🏠 – 12 canvas bungalows. Per night from 53 to 137€ –
Per week from 187 to 598€

🚐 borne 2.30€ – 10 🔲 4.60€

Near a small artificial lake and the Allier river.

Surroundings :
Leisure activities : launderette
Facilities :
Nearby :

GPS Longitude : 3.22271
Latitude : 45.74029

COURPIÈRE

63120 – Michelin map **326** I8 – pop. 4 514 – alt. 320
▶ Paris 399 – Ambert 40 – Clermont-Ferrand 50 – Issoire 53

⛺ Municipal les Taillades

☏ 0473530121, www.ville-courpiere.fr

Address : Les Taillades (take the southern exit along the D 906, follow the signs for Ambert, take the D 7 to the left, follow the signs for Aubusson-d'Auvergne and take the road to the right; by the swimming pool and near a stream)

0.5 ha (40 pitches) flat, grassy

Rentals : 4 🚐.

The pitches are well marked out; free entry to the swimming pool.

Surroundings :
Leisure activities :
Facilities :
Nearby :

GPS Longitude : 3.5487
Latitude : 45.75354

DOMPIERRE-SUR-BESBRE

03290 – Michelin map **326** J3 – pop. 3 184 – alt. 234
▶ Paris 324 – Bourbon-Lancy 19 – Decize 46 – Digoin 27

⛺ Municipal Les Bords de Bresbre

☏ 0470345557. camping@mairie-dsb.fr

Address : La Madeleine (take the southeastern exit along the N 79, follow the signs for Digoin; near the Besbre river and not far from a lake)

Opening times : from mid May to mid Sept.

2 ha (70 pitches) flat, grassy

Tariff : (2014 Price) ★ 2.65€ ⛺ 🔲 2.15€ – 🔌 (10A) 2.45€

🚐 borne 2€

By a large municipal stadium and 7km from the Le Pal animal and amusement park.

Surroundings :
Leisure activities :
Facilities :

GPS Longitude : 3.68289
Latitude : 46.51373

GANNAT

03800 – Michelin map **326** G6 – pop. 5 853 – alt. 345
▶ Paris 383 – Clermont-Ferrand 49 – Montluçon 78 – Moulins 58

🏔 Municipal Le Mont Libre

☏ 0470901216. www.camping-gannat.fr

Address : 10 route de la Batisse (located 1km south along the N 9 and take turning to the right)

Opening times : Permanent

1.5 ha (70 pitches) terraced, flat, grassy

Tariff : (2014 Price) 11.60€ ★★ ⛺ 🔲 🔌 (10A) –
Extra per person 2.70€

Rental rates : (2014 Price) Permanent – 13 🏠. Per week from 245 to 523€

🚐 borne 4.20€ – 6 🔲 14.90€ – 🔌 14.90€

Surroundings :
Leisure activities : (small swimming pool)
Facilities : launderette
Nearby :

GPS Longitude : 3.19403
Latitude : 46.0916

ISLE-ET-BARDAIS

03360 – Michelin map **326** D2 – pop. 275 – alt. 285
▶ Paris 280 – Bourges 60 – Cérilly 9 – Montluçon 52

🏔 Les Écossais

☏ 0470666257. www.campingtroncais.com

Address : 1km south, follow signs for Chamignoux

Opening times : from beginning April to mid Oct.

2 ha (70 pitches) relatively flat, flat, grassy

Tariff : (2014 Price) ★ 3€ ⛺ 1.40€ 🔲 2.50€ – 🔌 (10A) 3.40€ –
Reservation fee 15€

Rental rates : (2014 Price) (from beginning April to mid Oct.) –
2 🚐 – 7 gîtes. Per night from 50 to 66€ – Per week from 187 to 472€ – Reservation fee 15€

Beside the Lac de Pirot and at the edge of the Tronçais forest.

Surroundings :
Leisure activities : laundrette
Facilities :
Nearby : (beach)

GPS Longitude : 2.78814
Latitude : 46.68278

ISSOIRE

63500 – Michelin map **326** G9 – pop. 13 949 – alt. 400
▶ Paris 446 – Aurillac 121 – Clermont-Ferrand 36 – Le Puy-en-Velay 94

▲▲▲ Château La Grange Fort

𝒫 0473710243. www.lagrangefort.eu

Address : 4km southeast along the D 996, follow the signs for la Chaise-Dieu then take a right turn, 3km along the D 34, follow the signs for Auzat-sur-Allier, from the A 75, take exit 13 towards Parentignat

Opening times : from beginning April to end Oct.

23 ha/4 pitches (120 pitches) relatively flat, flat, grassy, gravelled

Tariff : ♦ 6.25€ ⇔ 3€ 🔲 14.45€ – 🔌 (6A) 3.50€ – Reservation fee 15€

Rental rates : Permanent – 18 ⌂⌂ – 9 ⌂ – 5 ⊨ – 2 apartments – 10 canvas bungalows – 2 tent lodges – 1 gîte. Per night from 61 to 129€ – Per week from 275 to 985€ – Reservation fee 15€

🚗 borne – 12 🔲 17€

The site is based around a picturesque medieval château, with some pitches overlooking the Allier river.

Surroundings : 🌳 ≤ 🗀 ♀
Leisure activities : ♈ ✗ 🖾 🛥 jacuzzi 🚣
🚲 ✂ 🔲 🛝
Facilities : & �o→ 🅿 🎴 🖽 🍴 launderette 🚿

Longitude : 3.28501
Latitude : 45.50859

▲▲▲ Municipal du Mas

𝒫 0473890359. www.camping-issoire.com

Address : rue du Dr Bienfait (2.5km east along the D 9, follow the signs for Orbeil and take a right turn, 50m from a lake and 300m from the Allier river; from A 75 take exit 12)

Opening times : from beginning April to beginning Nov.

3 ha (148 pitches) flat, grassy

Tariff : (2014 Price) 19.50€ ♦♦ ⇔ 🔲 🔌 (13A) – Extra per person 5€
Rental rates : (2014 Price) Permanent & (1 chalet) – 4 ⌂⌂ – 6 ⌂ – 3 canvas bungalows. Per night from 31 to 78€ – Per week from 217 to 546€

🚗 borne 3.55€ – 6 🔲 19.50€

Near the Allier river and a fishing lake.

Surroundings : 🌳 ♀
Leisure activities : 🖾 🚣 🛝 🏹
Facilities : & o→ 🎴 🛝 🚿 🍴 launderette
Nearby : ✗ 🚲 ✂ 🎣 bowling

Longitude : 3.27397
Latitude : 45.55108

LANGEAC

43300 – Michelin map **331** C3 – pop. 4 004 – alt. 505
▶ Paris 513 – Clermont-Ferrand 97 – Le Puy-en-Velay 44 – Aurillac 134

▲▲▲ Les Gorges de l'Allier

𝒫 0471770501. www.campinglangeac.com

Address : Domaine Le Pradeau

Opening times : from beginning April to end Oct.

14 ha (214 pitches) flat, grassy

Tariff : 15.60€ ♦♦ ⇔ 🔲 🔌 (20A) – Extra per person 5.70€ – Reservation fee 15€

Rental rates : (from beginning April to end Oct.) & (2 chalets) – 10 ⌂⌂ – 21 ⌂ – 1 gîte. Per night from 51 to 120€ – Per week from 306 to 780€ – Reservation fee 15€

🚗 borne 2.55€

Surroundings : 🌳 ≤ ♀
Leisure activities : ♈ ✗ 🖾 🛥 🛝 🏹 🚣
multi-sports ground, entertainment room
Facilities : & o→ 🛝 🚿 🍴 launderette
Nearby : 🛥 🚲 ✂ 🏹

Longitude : 3.50069
Latitude : 45.10389

LANOBRE

15270 – Michelin map **330** D2 – pop. 1 400 – alt. 650
▶ Paris 493 – Bort-les-Orgues 7 – La Bourboule 33 – Condat 30

▲▲▲ Le Lac de la Siauve

𝒫 0471403185. www.camping-lac-siauve.fr – alt. 660

Address : rue du Camping (3km southwest along the D 922, follow the signs for Bort-les-Orgues and take turning to the right, 200m from the lake (direct access)

Opening times : from beginning April to mid Oct.

8 ha (220 pitches) terraced, flat, grassy

Tariff : 22€ ♦♦ ⇔ 🔲 🔌 (10A) – Extra per person 5.50€ – Reservation fee 12€

Rental rates : (from beginning April to beginning Oct.) – 14 ⌂⌂ – 19 ⌂ – cabins. Per week from 230 to 620€ – Reservation fee 12€

🚗 borne 4€

Surroundings : 🌳 ≤ 🗀 ♀
Leisure activities : ♈ 🖾 🕐daytime 🚣
🚲🔲
Facilities : & o→ 🛝 🚿 🍴 launderette
Nearby : 🏖 (beach) watersports centre

Longitude : 2.50407
Latitude : 45.4306

We have selected the best campsites in France with our usual care, listing those with the best facilities in the most pleasant surroundings.

LAPALISSE

03120 – Michelin map **326** I5 – pop. 3 162 – alt. 280
▶ Paris 346 – Digoin 45 – Mâcon 122 – Moulins 50

▲ Municipal La Route Bleue

𝒫 0470992631. www.lapalisse-tourisme.com

Address : rue des Vignes (take the southeastern exit along the N7)

Opening times : from beginning April to end Sept.

0.8 ha (66 pitches) flat, grassy

Tariff : (2014 Price) ♦ 2.40€ ⇔ 1.80€ 🔲 1.85€ – 🔌 (25A) 2.40€
Rental rates : (2014 Price) (from beginning April to end Sept.) ✂ – 2 ⌂⌂ – 6 ⌂. Per night from 30 to 60€ – Per week from 150 to 370€

Beside the Besbre river with a small footpath linking the campsite with the town centre.

Surroundings : 🗀 ♀♀
Leisure activities : 🏹
Facilities : & o→ 🛝 🍴 🖾
Nearby : ✂ fitness trail

Longitude : 3.6395
Latitude : 46.2433

LAPEYROUSE

63700 – Michelin map **326** E5 – pop. 561 – alt. 510
▶ Paris 350 – Clermont-Ferrand 74 – Commentry 15
Montmarault 14

⚠ **Municipal les Marins**

✆ 0473936000. www.63lapeyrouse.free.fr

Address : Etang de la Loge (lake) (situated 2km southeast along the D 998, follow the signs for Echassières and turn right onto D 100, follow the signs for Durmignat)

Opening times : from beginning June to beginning Sept.

2 ha (68 pitches) flat, grassy

Tariff : (2014 Price) 15€ ✶✶ ⇘ 🅴 [½] (4A) – Extra per person 3€

Rental rates : (2014 Price) Permanent – 6 🏠. Per night from 340 to 560€ – Per week from 340 to 560€

Hedges and shrubs mark out the pitches; near a small lake.

Surroundings : 🐟 🗔
Leisure activities : 🎪 🏇 🐟
Facilities : ⅙ ⚬━ 🏕 ⑆ 🖩
Nearby : ⛩ 🍴 🏖 (beach)

Longitude : 2.8837
Latitude : 46.22125

LEMPDES-SUR-ALLAGNON

43410 – Michelin map **331** B1
▶ Paris 472 – Clermont-Ferrand 56 – Le Puy-en-Velay 73 – Aurillac 102

⚠ **Pont d'Allagnon**

✆ 0471765369. www.campingenauvergne.com

Address : rue René Filiol

Opening times : from end March to mid Oct.

2 ha (60 pitches) flat, grassy

Tariff : 19.60€ ✶✶ ⇘ 🅴 [½] (10A) – Extra per person 4.50€

Rental rates : Permanent ⅙ (1 chalet) – 2 🛏 – 6 🏠. Per night from 39 to 78€ – Per week from 215 to 515€

🚐 borne 2€ – 5 🅴 15€

There's direct access to the village via a small foot bridge over the Allagnon river.

Surroundings : 🐟 🗔 ♨
Leisure activities : ⛩ 🍴 🎪 🏇 🎿 🧗 🐟 multi-sports ground
Facilities : ⅙ ⚬━ 🏕 ⑆ 🖩 launderette
Nearby : 🏊

Longitude : 3.26624
Latitude : 45.38697

MAURIAC

15200 – Michelin map **330** B3 – pop. 3 854 – alt. 722
▶ Paris 490 – Aurillac 53 – Le Mont-Dore 77 – Riom-és-Montagnes 37

🏔 **Val St-Jean**

✆ 0471673113. www.tourismevalsaintjean.fr

Address : at the leisure centre (2.2km west along the D 681, follow the signs for Pleaux and turn right onto D 682, direct access to a small lake)

Opening times : from beginning May to mid Sept.

3.5 ha (100 pitches) terraced, flat, grassy

Tariff : 24.70€ ✶✶ ⇘ 🅴 [½] (10A) – Extra per person 5.50€

Rental rates : (2014 Price) Permanent ⅙ (1 chalet) – 20 🏠 – 5 tipis. Per night from 45 to 70€ – Per week from 220 to 625€

🚐 borne 2€ – 🚐 [½] 12€

Beside a lake and close to the historic city.

Surroundings : 🐟 ⇜ 🗔 ♨
Leisure activities : 🎪 ③daytime 🏇
Facilities : ⅙ ⚬━ 🖂 ⑆ ⑆ ☂ 🖩 launderette
Nearby : 🏪 🍴 🎪 🚲 🧗 🎿 🏊 (beach) 🏇
🐴 pedalos

Longitude : 2.31657
Latitude : 45.21835

MAURS

15600 – Michelin map **330** B6 – pop. 2 213 – alt. 290
▶ Paris 568 – Aurillac 43 – Entraygues-sur-Truyère 50 – Figeac 22

🏔 **Municipal le Vert**

✆ 0471490415. www.campinglevert-maurs.fr

Address : avenue du stade (800m southeast along the D 663, follow the signs for Décazeville; beside the Rance)

1.2 ha (44 pitches) flat, grassy

Rentals : 4 🏠.

Surroundings : 🗔 ♨♨
Leisure activities : 🎪 🏇 🎿
Facilities : ⅙ ⚬━ 🏕 ⑆ ☂ 🖩 🖩
Nearby : 🏪 🏇

Longitude : 2.2064
Latitude : 44.70507

MONISTROL-D'ALLIER

43580 – Michelin map **331** D4 – pop. 219 – alt. 590
▶ Paris 535 – Brioude 58 – Langogne 56 – Le Puy-en-Velay 28

⚠ **Municipal le Vivier**

✆ 0471572414. www.monistroldallier.com

Address : to the south, near the Allier (direct access)

Opening times : from beginning April to mid Sept.

1 ha (48 pitches)

Tariff : (2014 Price) 14.40€ ✶✶ ⇘ 🅴 [½] (8A)

Extra per person 3.40€

Surroundings : ⇜ ♨
Leisure activities : 🎪
Facilities : ⅙ ⚬━ 🖂
Nearby : 🍴 🏇 🎿 🧗 🐟 rafting and canyoning

Longitude : 3.65348
Latitude : 44.96923

MONTAIGUT-LE-BLANC

63320 – Michelin map **326** F9 – pop. 717 – alt. 500
▶ Paris 443 – Clermont-Ferrand 33 – Issoire 17 – Pontgibaud 46

⚠ **Le Pré**

✆ 0473967507. www.campinglepre.com

Address : in the village

Opening times : from mid April to end Sept.

1.5 ha (100 pitches) flat, grassy

Tariff : (2014 Price) 22€ ✶✶ ⇘ 🅴 [½] (10A) – Extra per person 4.50€ Reservation fee 8€

Rental rates : (2014 Price) (from mid Jan to mid Dec.) ⅙ (1 chalet) – 7 🏠. Per night from 45 to 50€ – Per week from 250 to 600€ Reservation fee 8€

🚐 borne 2€

Beside the Couze de Chambon river with a view of the hilltop village.

Surroundings : 🐟 ⇜ 🗔 ♨♨
Leisure activities : 🎪 🐟
Facilities : ⅙ ⚬━ 🖂 🦺 launderette refrigerators
Nearby : 🏇 🎿 🧗 🎿

Longitude : 3.09162
Latitude : 45.58482

LE MONT-DORE

63240 – Michelin map **326** D9 – pop. 1 391 – alt. 1 050 – ⚜ – Winter sports : 1 050/1 850 m
▶ Paris 462 – Aubusson 87 – Clermont-Ferrand 43 – Issoire 49

🏔 Municipal l'Esquiladou

✆ 0473652374. www.mairie-mont-dore.fr

Address : at Queureuilh, route des Cascades (head along the D 996, following signs for Murat-le-Quaire and take turning to the right)

Opening times : from mid April to beginning Nov.

1.8 ha (100 pitches) terraced, flat, fine gravel

Tariff : ✶ 4€ ⇦ 🚐 📧 4.10€ – (10A) 4€

Rental rates : (from end Dec. to beginning Nov.) – 17 🏠. Per night from 52 to 90€ – Per week from 280 to 555€

🚐 borne

In a mountainous setting, green and wooded, near the town centre.

Surroundings : 🌄 ≤ 🏞	**GPS**
Leisure activities : 🏛 jacuzzi 🚣 🖼 (small swimming pool) (open in season)	Longitude : 2.80162
Facilities : ♿ ⛽ 🏭 🧺 launderette	Latitude : 45.58706

To visit a town or region, use the MICHELIN Green Guides.

MURAT-LE-QUAIRE

63150 – Michelin map **326** D9 – pop. 476 – alt. 1 050
▶ Paris 478 – Clermont-Ferrand 45 – Aurillac 120 – Cournon d'Auvergne 60

🏔 Le Panoramique

✆ 0473811879. www.campingpanoramique.fr/ – limited spaces for one-night stay

Address : 1.4km east along the D 219, follow the signs for Le Mont-Dore and take road to the left

Opening times : from mid April to mid Oct.

3 ha (85 pitches) very uneven, terraced, flat, grassy

Tariff : (2014 Price) 17.90€ ✶✶ ⇦ 📧 (10A) – Extra per person 6.30€

Rental rates : (2014 Price) (from mid April to mid Oct.) – 9 🏠 – 13 🏠. Per night from 49 to 114€ – Per week from 287 to 759€

🚐 borne 4.80€

Situated in an attractive, elevated location.

Surroundings : 🌄 ≤ Les Monts Dore and Dordogne valley	**GPS**
Leisure activities : 🍽 ✗ 🏛 🚣 🖼 wildlife park	Longitude : 2.74779
Facilities : ♿ ⛽ 🏭 🍴 launderette	Latitude : 45.596

🏔 Municipal les Couderts

✆ 0473655481, www.camping-couderts.e-monsite.com/

Address : Les Couderts (take the northern exit; beside a stream)

Opening times : from mid April to mid Nov.

1.7 ha (62 pitches) terraced, relatively flat, flat, grassy

Tariff : (2014 Price) 12.35€ ✶✶ ⇦ 📧 (10A) – Extra per person 2.95€

Rental rates : (2014 Price) Permanent – 1 🏠 – 6 🏠. Per night from 52 to 85€ – Per week from 255 to 530€

🚐 borne 9€

A pleasant and well-organised site for campervans at 500m, open all year.

Surroundings : 🌄 ≤ 🏞 ♨	**GPS**
Leisure activities : 🚣 Finnish kota	Longitude : 2.73511
Facilities : ♿ 🚿 🏭 🍴 launderette	Latitude : 45.59937
Nearby : 🍽 ✗	

MUROL

63790 – Michelin map **326** E9 – pop. 546 – alt. 830
▶ Paris 456 – Besse-en-Chandesse 10 – Clermont-Ferrand 37 Condat 37

🏞 Sunêlia La Ribeyre 👫

Sunêlia La Ribeyre

✆ 0473886429. www.laribeyre.com

Address : Jassat (1.2km to the south, follow the signs for Jassat; beside a stream)

Opening times : from beginning May to mid Sept.

13 ha (460 pitches)

Tariff : 42.70€ ✶✶ ⇦ 📧 (10A) – Extra per person 8.15€ – Reservation fee 30€

Rental rates : (from beginning May to mid Sept.) ♿ (1 mobile home) – 101 🏠. Per night from 36 to 209€ Reservation fee 30€

A lovely water park and small lake for bathing and canoeing.

Surroundings : 🌄 ≤ ♨♨	**GPS**
Leisure activities : 🍽 ✗ 🏛 🎦 🏕 jacuzzi 🚣 🍴 🖼 🏊 (lake) ⛵ 🚲	Longitude : 2.93719
Facilities : ♿ ⛽ 🚿 🍴 launderette 🧺	Latitude : 45.56232
Nearby : 🎣	

🏔 Le Repos du Baladin

✆ 0473886193. www.camping-auvergne-france.com

Address : Groire (located 1.5km east along the D 146, follow the signs for St-Diéry)

Opening times : from mid April to mid Sept.

1.6 ha (88 pitches) terraced, relatively flat, flat, grassy, rocks

Tariff : 24.85€ ✶✶ ⇦ 📧 (6A) – Extra per person 5.35€ – Reservation fee 14€

Rental rates : (from mid April to mid Sept.) – 22 🏠 – 2 🏠. Per night from 49 to 65€ – Per week from 214 to 730€ – Reservation fee 14€

🚐 borne

In a green setting, with a view of the Château de Murol from some pitches.

Surroundings : ≤ 🏞 ♨♨	**GPS**
Leisure activities : 🍽 ✗ 🏛 🚣 🖼	Longitude : 2.95728
Facilities : ♿ ⛽ 🏭 🧺 launderette 🚲	Latitude : 45.57379

This guide is not intended as a list of all the camping sites in France; its aim is to provide a selection of the best sites in each category.

⚠ Les Fougères - Domaine du Marais

𝒫 0473886708. www.camping-auvergne-sancy.com

Address : 0.6km west along the D 996, follow signs for Chambon-Lac

Opening times : from beginning May to mid Sept.

4 ha (135 pitches) very uneven, terraced, flat, grassy

Tariff : (2014 Price) 24.30€ ✚✚ ⇜ 🅴 ⑭ (10A) –
Extra per person 5.20€ – Reservation fee 10€

Rental rates : (2014 Price) (from beginning April to end Oct.) –
39 ⌕ – 29 ⌂ – 2 canvas bungalows. Per night from 36 to 97€
Per week from 226 to 989€ – Reservation fee 10€

The site is in two sections on either side of the road.

Surroundings : ⌕ 🌳🌳 Leisure activities : 🏛 ⛲ jacuzzi ⛷ 🏊 Facilities : ♿ ⛽ ⚒ 🍴 launderette Nearby : 🏊 ✗ 🎣 ⛵ (beach)	**G P S** Longitude : 2.93056 Latitude : 45.57583

NÉBOUZAT

63210 – Michelin map **326** E8 – pop. 774 – alt. 860
▶ Paris 434 – La Bourboule 34 – Clermont-Ferrand 20
Pontgibaud 19

⚠ Les Dômes

𝒫 0473871406. www.les-domes.com – alt. 815

Address : Les Quatre Routes de Nébouzat (along the D 216, follow the signs for Rochefort-Montagne)

Opening times : from end April to beginning Oct.

1 ha (62 pitches) flat, grassy

Tariff : 25.10€ ✚✚ ⇜ 🅴 ⑭ (10A) – Extra per person 10.80€

Reservation fee 10€

Rental rates : (2014 Price) (from end April to beginning Oct.) ♿
(1 chalet) – 10 ⌕ – 5 ⌂. Per night from 55 to 87€ – Per week
from 387 to 716€ – Reservation fee 18€
⌕ borne 6€ – 🔌 ⑭11€

The campsite is in green and well-kept surroundings.

Surroundings : ⩽ 🌳🌳 Leisure activities : 🏛 🖥 (open air in season) Facilities : ⛽ 🚿 ♨ 🍴 launderette Nearby : 🍴 ✗	**G P S** Longitude : 2.89028 Latitude : 45.72538

To make the best possible use of this guide, please read pages 2–15 carefully.

NÉRIS-LES-BAINS

03310 – Michelin map **326** C5 – pop. 2 705 – alt. 364 – ♨
▶ Paris 336 – Clermont-Ferrand 86 – Montluçon 9 – Moulins 73

⚠ Municipal du Lac

𝒫 0470032470. www.ville-neris-les-bains.fr

Address : to the south along the D 155, follow the signs for Villebret

Opening times : from end March to mid Nov.

3.5 ha (129 pitches) terraced, flat and relatively flat, grassy, fine gravel

Tariff : (2014 Price) 15€ ✚✚ ⇜ 🅴 ⑭ (10A) – Extra per person 4.20€

Rental rates : (2014 Price) Permanent ♿ (1 chalet) – 21 ⌕ –
8 ⌂ – 7 apartments. Per night from 32 to 44€ – Per week
from 196 to 500€
⌕ borne – 6 🅴 7€

In two sections: the upper part contains the reception and is near an old station, the lower part is beside a lake. A tariff including spa entry is available.

Surroundings : 🏊 ⌕ 🌳🌳 Leisure activities : 🍴 ✗ 🏛 👫 ⛷ 🏊 Facilities : ♿ ⛽ ♨ 🍴 launderette . Nearby : 🚲 ✗ 🎣 ⛵ 🖥 fitness trail	**G P S** Longitude : 2.65174 Latitude : 46.28702

NEUSSARGUES-MOISSAC

15170 – Michelin map **330** F4 – pop. 959 – alt. 834
▶ Paris 509 – Aurillac 58 – Brioude 49 – Issoire 64

⚠ Municipal de la Prade

𝒫 0471205021, www.neussargues-moissac.fr

Address : route de Murat (take the western exit along the D 304, follow the signs for Murat; beside the Alagnon)

Opening times : from beginning June to end Aug.

2 ha (22 pitches) terraced, flat, grassy, small wood

Tariff : 11.40€ ✚✚ ⇜ 🅴 ⑭ (10A) – Extra per person 2€

Rental rates : Permanent Ⓟ – 8 ⌕ – 6 ⌂. Per night
from 123 to 159€ – Per week from 229 to 494€

On the banks of the river.

Surroundings : 🏊 ⩽ ⌕ 🌳🌳 Leisure activities : 🏛 👫 🏊 Facilities : ♿ 🚿 ♨ ⚒ 🍴 ⚒	**G P S** Longitude : 2.96695 Latitude : 45.12923

These symbols are used for a campsite that is exceptional in its category:

⚠⚠⚠....⚠	*Particularly pleasant setting, quality and range of services available*
🏊🏊	*Tranquil, isolated site – quiet site, particularly at night*
⩽ ⩽	*Exceptional view – interesting or panoramic view*

NEUVÉGLISE

15260 – Michelin map **330** F5 – pop. 1 130 – alt. 938
▶ Paris 528 – Aurillac 78 – Entraygues-sur-Truyère 70 – Espalion 66

⚠ Flower Le Belvédère

𝒫 0471235050. www.campinglebelvedere.com – pitches accessed via steep slope, help moving caravans onto and off pitches available on request – alt. 670

Address : Lanau (6.5km south along the D 48, D 921, follow the signs for Chaudes-Aigues and take the Chemin de Gros to the right)

Opening times : from mid April to end Sept.

5 ha (116 pitches) terraced, flat, grassy

Tariff : 30€ ✚✚ ⇜ 🅴 ⑭ (15A) – Extra per person 6€ – Reservation
fee 17€

Rental rates : (from mid April to end Sept.) – 46 ⌕ – 7 ⌂ –
4 canvas bungalows – 4 tent lodges. Per night from 38 to 127€
Per week from 190 to 889€ – Reservation fee 17€

In an attractive elevated location.

Surroundings : ⩽ Gorges de la Truyère ⌕ ♀ Leisure activities : 🍴 ✗ 🏛 👒 👫 ⛲ 🖥 Facilities : ♿ 🚿 ♨ ⚒ 🍴 launderette 🏊	**G P S** Longitude : 3.00045 Latitude : 44.89534

NONETTE

63340 – Michelin map **326** G10 – pop. 322 – alt. 480
▶ Paris 467 – Clermont-Ferrand 51 – Cournon-d'Auvergne 47 Riom 66

⛰ Les Loges

℘ 04 73 71 65 82. www.lesloges.com

Address : 2km south along the D 722, follow the signs for Le Breuil-sur-Couze then 1km along the road near the bridge

Opening times : from beginning April to mid Sept.

4 ha (126 pitches) flat, grassy

Tariff : (2014 Price) 22.10€ ✹✹ ⇐ 回 [5] (6A) – Extra per person 4.90€ – Reservation fee 6€

Rental rates : (2014 Price) (from beginning April to mid Sept.) – 25 ⏢. Per night from 25 to 85€ – Per week from 170 to 580€– Reservation fee 6€
There's plenty of green space for relaxation and some pitches by the Allier river.

Surroundings : ⊗ ⊏ 00	
Leisure activities : ▾ ✕ ⊜ ⚤ ⊿ △ ⤿	**G** Longitude : 3.27158
Facilities : ⴠ � ⌂ ⊛ launderette ⊰	**P** Latitude : 45.47367 **S**

ORCET

63670 – Michelin map **326** G8 – pop. 2 729 – alt. 400
▶ Paris 424 – Billom 16 – Clermont-Ferrand 14 – Issoire 25

⛰ Clos Auroy

℘ 04 73 84 26 97. www.camping-le-clos-auroy.com

Address : 15 rue de la Narse (200m south of the town, near the Auzon river)

Opening times : Permanent

3 ha (82 pitches) terrace, flat, grassy, fine gravel

Tariff : ✹ 6.50€⇐ 回 14.80€ – [5] (10A) 5.10€ – Reservation fee 20€
Rental rates : (from beginning April to mid Oct.) ⚡ (from beginning April to end June) – 9 ⏢ – 2 tent lodges. Per night from 60 to 75€ – Per week from 250 to 750€ – Reservation fee 20€
⏢ borne 3€
The pitches are attractively marked out with shrubs.

Surroundings : ⊏ 00	
Leisure activities : ✕ ⌂ jacuzzi ⚤ ⊿ ⤿	**G** Longitude : 3.16912
Facilities : ⴠ ⍚ ⌷ ⊛ launderette ⤿	**P** Latitude : 45.70029 **S**
Nearby : ✄	

ORLÉAT

63190 – Michelin map **326** H7 – pop. 2 010 – alt. 380
▶ Paris 440 – Clermont-Ferrand 34 – Roanne 76 – Vichy 38

⛰ Le Pont-Astier

℘ 04 73 53 64 40. www.camping-lepont-astier.fr

Address : at the leisure centre (5km east along the D 85, D 224 and take road to the left; beside the Dore river)

Opening times : from beginning March to end Nov.

2 ha (90 pitches) flat, grassy

Tariff : 16.50€ ✹✹ ⇐ 回 [5] (16A) – Extra per person 5€
Rental rates : (from beginning March to end Nov.) – 8 ⏢. Per night from 60€ – Per week from 260 to 390€ – Reservation fee 8€
⏢ borne 2€

Some pitches that are well marked out look down on the Dore river.

Surroundings : ⊗ ⊏ 00	
Facilities : ⴠ ⍚ ⊛ launderette	**G** Longitude : 3.47664
Nearby : ▾ ✕ ⚤ ⊿ ⤿	**P** Latitude : 45.86813 **S**

PAULHAGUET

43230 – Michelin map **331** D2 – pop. 959 – alt. 562
▶ Paris 495 – Brioude 18 – La Chaise-Dieu 24 – Langeac 15

⛰ La Fridière

℘ 04 71 76 65 54. www.campingfr.nl

Address : 6 route d'Esfacy (located to the southeast along the D 4; beside the Senouire river)

3 ha (45 pitches) flat, grassy

Surroundings : ⊗ ⊏	
Leisure activities : ▾ ⌂ ⚤ ⤿	**G** Longitude : 3.52
Facilities : ⴠ ⍚ ⌷ ⊛ ⊿	**P** Latitude : 45.199 **S**

Some campsites benefit from proximity to a municipal leisure centre.

PERS

15290 – Michelin map **330** B5 – pop. 303 – alt. 570
▶ Paris 547 – Argentat 45 – Aurillac 25 – Maurs 24

⛰ Le Viaduc

℘ 04 71 64 70 08. www.camping-cantal.com

Address : Le Ribeyrès (5km northeast along the D 32 and take the D 61; beside the lake at St-Etienne-Cantalès)

Opening times : from mid April to mid Oct.

1 ha (54 pitches) terraced, flat, grassy

Tariff : (2014 Price) 20.40€ ✹✹ ⇐ 回 [5] (10A) – Extra per person 5€ Reservation fee 14€
Rental rates : (2014 Price) (from mid April to mid Oct.) – 8 ⏢ – 1 ⌂. Per night from 50 to 70€ – Per week from 295 to 540€ Reservation fee 14€
⏢ borne 6€
A pleasant location.

Surroundings : ⊗ ⟨ ⊏ 2	
Leisure activities : ▾ ⌂ ⚤ ⊿ ⤿ ⤿	**G** Longitude : 2.2556
Facilities : ⴠ ⍚ ⊛ launderette ⊰	**P** Latitude : 44.90602 **S**
Nearby : watersports centre	

PIERREFITTE-SUR-LOIRE

03470 – Michelin map **326** J3 – pop. 518 – alt. 228
▶ Paris 324 – Bourbon-Lancy 20 – Lapalisse 50 – Moulins 42

⛰ Municipal le Vernay

℘ 04 70 47 02 49. www.pierrefitte03.fr

Address : Le Vernay (Take the northwestern exit along the N 79, follow the signs for Dompierre, left onto D 295, follow the signs for Saligny-sur-Roudon then continue 900m along the road to the right after the bridge, 200m from the canal)

Opening times : from mid April to mid Oct.

2 ha (52 pitches) flat, grassy, fine gravel

Tariff : (2014 Price) ✹ 2.50€⇐ 回 3.50€ – [5] (6A) 2€

Rental rates : (2014 Price) (from mid April to mid Oct.) &
(3 mobile homes) – 12 🚐. Per night from 50 to 60€ – Per week
from 200 to 300€ – Reservation fee 15€

🚰 borne

Near a small lake, canal and cycle route.

Surroundings : 🏞 Leisure activities : 🚲pedalos Facilities : & 🛁 (July-Aug.) 🛒 🏚 ⚐ 🔥 Nearby : 🍴✗ 🚤 💥 🏊 (beach) 🎣 fitness trail	**GPS** Longitude : 3.80342 Latitude : 46.50857

PONTGIBAUD

63230 – Michelin map **326** E8 – pop. 745 – alt. 735
▶ Paris 432 – Aubusson 68 – Clermont-Ferrand 23 – Le Mont-
Dore 37

⛺ Municipal de la Palle

✆ 04 73 88 96 99. www.campongibaud.free.fr

Address : Route de la Miouze (500m southwest along the D 986,
follow the signs for Rochefort-Montagne; beside the Sioule river)

Opening times : from mid April to mid Oct.

4.5 ha (86 pitches) flat, grassy

Tariff : ✝ 4.20€ 🚗 ▣ 3.70€ – ⚡ (16A) 3.50€
Rental rates : Permanent & (1 chalet) – 6 🏚. Per night
from 40 to 70€ – Per week from 250 to 470€

🚰 borne 2.50€

Choose the pitches furthest away from the road in preference.

Surroundings : 🏞 ♀♀ Leisure activities : 🏤 🚤 🎣 Facilities : & 🛁 ⚐ 🔥 launderette Nearby : 🍴✗	**GPS** Longitude : 2.84516 Latitude : 45.82982

PUY-GUILLAUME

63290 – Michelin map **326** H7 – pop. 2 631 – alt. 285
▶ Paris 374 – Clermont-Ferrand 53 – Lezoux 27 – Riom 35

⛺ Municipal de la Dore

✆ 04 73 94 78 51, www.puy-guillaume.com

Address : 86 rue Joseph-Claussat (take the western exit along the
D 63, follow the signs for Randan and take a right turn before the
bridge, near the river)

Opening times : from mid June to end Aug.

3 ha (100 pitches) flat, grassy

Tariff : (2014 Price) ✝ 3.90€ 🚗 ▣ 4.65€ – ⚡ (60A) 3.90€

Choose the pitches furthest away from the road in preference.

Surroundings : ♀ Leisure activities : 🏤 🚤 🎣 🎣 Facilities : & 🛁 ⚐ 🔥	**GPS** Longitude : 3.46623 Latitude : 45.96223

*There are several different types of sani-station
('borne' in French) – sanitation points providing
fresh water and disposal points for grey water.
See page 12 for further details.*

ROYAT

63130 – Michelin map **326** F8 – pop. 4 431 – alt. 450 – ⚓
▶ Paris 423 – Aubusson 89 – La Bourboule 47 – Clermont-Ferrand 5

🏔 Indigo Royat 🏕

Campingindigo ©R.Etienne

✆ 04 73 35 97 05. www.camping-indigo.
com

Address : route de Gravenoire (situated
2km southeast along the D 941c, follow
the signs for Le Mont-Dore and take
a right turn D 5, follow the signs for
Charade)

Opening times : from end March to
beginning Nov.

7 ha (200 pitches) terraced, relatively
flat, flat, grassy, fine gravel

Tariff : (2014 Price) 31.30€ ✝✝ 🚗 ▣ ⚡ (10A) –
Extra per person 6.40€ – Reservation fee 22€
Rental rates : (2014 Price) (from end March to beginning Nov.) –
8 caravans – 23 🏚 – 6 🏚 – 13 tent lodges. Per night
from 48 to 134€ – Per week from 236 to 938€ – Reservation
fee 22€

🚰 borne 7€ – 40 ▣ 26€

*In a pleasantly leafy setting with shade and a variety of rental
options; the pitches at the top of the site are very peaceful.*

Surroundings : 🌿 🏞 ♀ Leisure activities : 🍴✗ 🏤 🎮 🚴 🚤 🚲 💥 🎣 Facilities : & 🛁 ⚐ 🏚 🔥 launderette	**GPS** Longitude : 3.05452 Latitude : 45.75868

*For more information on visiting particular towns or
regions, consult the relevant regional MICHELIN Green
Guide. We also recommend you use the appropriate
Michelin regional map to locate your selected campsite,
to calculate distances and to work out the best route.*

RUYNES-EN-MARGERIDE

15320 – Michelin map **330** H4 – pop. 640 – alt. 920
▶ Paris 527 – Clermont-Ferrand 111 – Aurillac 86 – Le Puy-en-
Velay 88

⛺ Révéa Le Petit Bois

✆ 04 71 23 42 26. http://www.revea-camping.fr/fr/camping-le-petit-
bois.html

Address : at Lesparot

Opening times : from end April to mid Sept.

4 ha (90 pitches) relatively flat, flat, grassy

Tariff : 20.80€ ✝✝ 🚗 ▣ ⚡ (10A) – Extra per person 4.20€ –
Reservation fee 10€
Rental rates : (from end April to mid Sept.) – 7 🚐. Per night
from 55 to 60€ – Per week from 190 to 540€ – Reservation
fee 25€

🚰 10 ▣ 17.10€

Located in a pleasant pine forest

Surroundings : 🌿 ⩽ ♀♀ Facilities : & 🛁 ⚐ 🔥 launderette Nearby : 🚤 forest trail	**GPS** Longitude : 3.21898 Latitude : 44.99899

SAIGNES

15240 – Michelin map **330** C2 – pop. 892 – alt. 480
▶ Paris 483 – Aurillac 78 – Clermont-Ferrand 91 – Mauriac 26

⚑ Municipal Bellevue

✆ 0471406840. www.saignes-mairie.fr

Address : take the northwestern exit, by the stadium

Opening times : from beginning July to end Aug.

1 ha (42 pitches) flat, grassy

Tariff : (2014 Price) ✻ 2.25€ ⇌ 1.20€ 🔲 1.40€ – ⚡ (16A) 2.45€
Rental rates : (2014 Price) (from beginning July to end Aug.) –
3 🛏. Per night from 50€ – Per week from 250 to 310€

Surroundings : ⪬ 🗔 ♀
Leisure activities : 🎪 🚴
Facilities : & ⚲ 🚿 🖼
Nearby : 🍴 🛶

GPS Longitude : 2.47416
Latitude : 45.33678

ST-BONNET-TRONÇAIS

03360 – Michelin map **326** D3 – pop. 751 – alt. 224
▶ Paris 301 – Bourges 57 – Cérilly 12 – Montluçon 44

🏔 Centre de Tourisme de Champ Fossé

✆ 0470061130. www.campingstroncais.com

Address : place du Champ de Foire (700m southwest)

Opening times : from beginning April to mid Oct.

3 ha (110 pitches)

Tariff : (2014 Price) ✻ 4.60€ ⇌ 1,40€ 🔲 4.60€ – ⚡ (10A) 3.60€ –
Reservation fee 15€

Rental rates : (2014 Price) (from beginning April to mid Oct.) –
12 🛏 – 10 gîtes. Per night from 49 to 123€ – Per week
from 203 to 535€ – Reservation fee 15€

*In an attractive location beside the Lac de St-Bonnet and a
small leisure centre.*

Surroundings : 🌲 ⪬ ♀♀
Leisure activities : 🍷 🎪 🛶
Facilities : ⚲ 🚿 🍴 launderette
Nearby : 🚴 🎾 🏊 🏖 (beach) 🎿 🎣
pedalos

GPS Longitude : 2.68841
Latitude : 46.65687

ST-DIDIER-EN-VELAY

43140 – Michelin map **331** H2 – pop. 3 313 – alt. 830
▶ Paris 538 – Annonay 49 – Monistrol-sur-Loire 11 – Le Puy-en-
Velay 58

⚑ La Fressange

✆ 0471662528. www.saint-didier.com/camping

Address : 800m southeast along the D 45, follow the signs for St-
Romain-Lachalm and take the turning to the left; beside a stream

Opening times : from mid April to mid Oct.

1.5 ha (72 pitches) relatively flat, grassy

Tariff : (2014 Price) 17.95€ ✻✻ ⇌ 🔲 ⚡ (16A) –
Extra per person 4.85€

Rental rates :(2014 Price) (from mid April to mid Oct.) –
11 🏠 – 3 tent lodges. Per night from 78 to 100€ – Per week
from 210 to 480€

A sunny site, on the side of a hill.

Surroundings : ♀
Leisure activities : 🚴
Facilities : & ⚲ 🚿 🍴 🖼
Nearby : 🎾 🛶 🚴 sports trail

GPS Longitude : 4.28302
Latitude : 45.30119

ST-ÉLOY-LES-MINES

63700 – Michelin map **326** E6 – pop. 3 703 – alt. 490
▶ Paris 358 – Clermont-Ferrand 64 – Guéret 86 – Montluçon 31

⚑ Municipal la Poule d'Eau

✆ 0473854547. selm.maire@wanadoo.fr

Address : rue de la Poule d'Eau, near lakes

Opening times : from beginning June to mid Sept.

1.8 ha (50 pitches)

Tariff : (2014 Price) 8.25€ ✻✻ ⇌ 🔲 ⚡ (8A) – Extra per person 2.55€
🚐 borne – 2 🔲 6.70€

Situated in a green setting beside two lakes.

Surroundings : ⪬ 🗔 ♀♀ ⛰
Leisure activities : 🚴 🎣
Facilities : & ⚲ 🍴 🖼
Nearby : 🍷 🍴 🏊 🏖 (beach) fitness trail,
pedalos

GPS Longitude : 2.83057
Latitude : 46.15064

*This guide is not intended as a list of all the camping
sites in France; its aim is to provide a selection of the
best sites in each category.*

ST-GERMAIN-L'HERM

63630 – Michelin map **326** I10 – pop. 508 – alt. 1 050
▶ Paris 476 – Ambert 27 – Brioude 33 – Clermont-Ferrand 66

🏔 St-Éloy

✆ 0473720513. www.camping-le-saint-eloy.com

Address : route de la Chaise-Dieu (take the southeastern exit, on the
D 999)

Opening times : from beginning May to end Sept.

3 ha (63 pitches) terraced, flat, grassy

Tariff : 20.10€ ✻✻ ⇌ 🔲 ⚡ (10A) – Extra per person 4.50€
Rental rates : Permanent & (1 chalet) – 13 🏠. Per week
from 230 to 725€

Good quality chalet rentals and a pretty view over the village.

Surroundings : 🌲 ⪬
Leisure activities : 🍷 🍴 🎪 jacuzzi 🚴 🚲
🏊
Facilities : & ⚲ 🍴 launderette
Nearby : 🎿 🎾 🏖

GPS Longitude : 3.54781
Latitude : 45.45653

ST-GÉRONS

15150 – Michelin map **330** B5 – pop. 209 – alt. 526
▶ Paris 538 – Argentat 35 – Aurillac 24 – Maurs 33

🏔 Les Rives du Lac

✆ 0625346289. www.lesrivesdulac.fr

Address : 8.5km southeast along the follow the signs for Espinet;
300m from the lake at St-Étienne-Cantalès

Opening times : from mid April to mid Nov.

3 ha (100 pitches) relatively flat, flat, grassy

Tariff : 20€ ✻✻ ⇌ 🔲 ⚡ (10A) – Extra per person 5€ – Reservation
fee 10€

Rental rates : (from mid April to mid Dec.) – 11 🛏. Per night
from 60 to 75€ – Per week from 220 to 550€ – Reservation fee 16€
🚐 borne – 🚗 ⚡10€

In a pleasant setting.

Surroundings : 🏞 🛶 ♨♨ **Leisure activities :** 🍴 🚴 🎣 🛷 Facilities : 🔥 🚰 ♨ 🍴 launderette 🏪 **Nearby :** ✕ 🍴 🏊 (beach) 🎣	**G P S** Longitude : 2.23057 Latitude : 44.93523

ST-GERVAIS-D'AUVERGNE

63390 – Michelin map **326** D6 – pop. 1 304 – alt. 725
▶ Paris 377 – Aubusson 72 – Clermont-Ferrand 55 – Gannat 41

⚠ Municipal de l'Étang Philippe

🖉 0473857484. www.ville-stgervais-auvergne.fr

Address : Mazières (take the northern exit along the D 987, follow the signs for St-Éloy-les-Mines; near a small lake)

Opening times : from beginning April to end Sept.

3 ha (130 pitches)

Tariff : (2014 Price) 10.90€ ★ ★ 🚗 🔲 🔌 (10A)

Extra per person 1.50€ – Reservation fee 20€

Rental rates : (2014 Price) Permanent 🔥 (1 chalet) – 11 🏠.
Per night from 25€ – Per week from 290 to 450€

🚐 borne 2€

Good quality chalet rentals, with a pretty view of the lake.

Surroundings : 🏞 ⛰ 🛶 ♨ ⛰ **Leisure activities :** 🎱 Facilities : 🔥 🚰 ♨ 🍴 🏪 **Nearby :** 🚴 🍴 🎣 (beach) 🎣 fitness trail, skatepark	**G P S** Longitude : 2.81804 Latitude : 46.03688

ST-JACQUES-DES-BLATS

15800 – Michelin map **330** E4 – pop. 325 – alt. 990
▶ Paris 536 – Aurillac 32 – Brioude 76 – Issoire 91

⚠ des Blats

🖉 0471470600. www.camping-des-blats.fr

Address : east of the village, follow the signs for Nierevèze, beside the Cère river

Opening times : from beginning May to end Sept.

1.5 ha (50 pitches) flat, grassy

Tariff : ★ 4.60€ 🚗 1.60€ 🔲 2€ – 🔌 (10A) 4€ – Reservation fee 4€
Rental rates : Permanent 🔥 (1 chalet) – 4 🏠 – 1 tent lodge.
Per week from 180 to 550€ – Reservation fee 8€

🚐 borne – 1 🔲 13.80€

Surroundings : ⛰ 🛶 ♨♨ **Leisure activities :** ✕ 🎱 🚴 🚲 🎣 Facilities : 🔥 🚰 ⬛ ♨ 🍴 launderette **Nearby :** 🍴 🎣	**G P S** Longitude : 2.71345 Latitude : 45.05182

Key to rentals symbols:

12 🚐	*Number of mobile homes*
20 🏠	*Number of chalets*
6 🛏	*Number of rooms to rent*
Per night *30–50€*	*Minimum/maximum rate per night*
Per week *300–1,000€*	*Minimum/maximum rate per week*

ST-JUST

15320 – Michelin map **330** H5 – pop. 206 – alt. 950
▶ Paris 531 – Chaudes-Aigues 29 – Ruynes-en-Margeride 22 – St-Chély-d'Apcher 16

⚠ Municipal

🖉 0471737048. www.saintjust.com

Address : in the village (southeast; beside a stream – follow A 75: take exit 31 or 32)

Opening times : from beginning May to end Sept.

2 ha (60 pitches) flat and relatively flat

Tariff : 9.80€ ★ ★ 🚗 🔲 🔌 (10A) – Extra per person 2.10€

Rental rates : Permanent 🔥 (1 mobile home) – 6 🚐 – 5 🏠 –
7 gîtes. Per night from 61 to 138€ – Per week from 203 to 459€
🚐 borne 2€ – 6 🔲 9.80€ – 🔋9.50€

In the heart of the mountains, the site is crossed by a stream.

Surroundings : 🏞 ♨ **Leisure activities :** 🎱 Facilities : 🔥 🚰 ♨ 🍴 launderette **Nearby :** 🏪 🍴 ✕ 🎣 🍴 🎣	**G P S** Longitude : 3.20938 Latitude : 44.88993

ST-MARTIN-CANTALES

15140 – Michelin map **330** B4 – pop. 177 – alt. 630
▶ Paris 546 – Clermont-Ferrand 135 – Le Puy-en-Velay 180 Aurillac 34

⚠ Pont du Rouffet

🖉 0471694276. www.campingpontdurouffet.com

Address : Pont du Rouffet

Opening times : from mid May to mid Sept.

1 ha (30 pitches) terraced, flat, grassy

Tariff : (2014 Price) 18.20€ ★ ★ 🚗 🔲 🔌 (6A) –
Extra per person 3.25€

Rental rates : (2014 Price) (from mid May to mid Sept.) 🏕 –
4 🚐. Per week from 245 to 415€

Surroundings : 🏞 ⛰ ♨♨ **Leisure activities :** 🎱 🏊 🎣 Facilities : 🔥 🚰 ♨ 🍴 🏪	**G P S** Longitude : 2.2585 Latitude : 45.072

ST-MARTIN-VALMEROUX

15140 – Michelin map **330** C4 – pop. 856 – alt. 646
▶ Paris 510 – Aurillac 33 – Mauriac 21 – Murat 53

⚠⚠ Municipal Le Moulin du Teinturier

🖉 0471694312. mairie.saint-martin-valmeroux@wanadoo.fr

Address : 9 rue de Montjoly (take the western exit, on the D 37, follow the signs for Ste-Eulalie-Nozières; beside the Maronne)

Opening times : from mid June to mid Sept.

3 ha (100 pitches) flat, grassy

Tariff : (2014 Price) 17.30€ ★ ★ 🚗 🔲 🔌 (16A) –
Extra per person 3.50€

Rental rates : (2014 Price) Permanent – 10 🏠. Per night
from 35 to 75€ – Per week from 175 to 505€

🚐 borne – 10 🔲

Surroundings : ⛰ 🛶 **Leisure activities :** 🎱 🚴 🎣 Facilities : 🔥 🚰 ♨ ♨ ♨ 🍴 🏪 **Nearby :** 🍴 🎣	**G P S** Longitude : 2.42336 Latitude : 45.11619

ST-NECTAIRE

63710 – Michelin map **326** E9 – pop. 732 – alt. 700 – ⚓
▶ Paris 453 – Clermont-Ferrand 43 – Issoire 27 – Le Mont-Dore 24

⛰ Vallée Verte

☎ 04 73 88 52 68. www.valleeverte.com

Address : 1.5km southeast along the D 996 and take a right turn

Opening times : from mid April to mid Sept.

2.5 ha (91 pitches) terraced, flat, grassy

Tariff : 25.50€ ✶✶ 🚐 🔲 🔌 (8A) – Extra per person 7€ – Reservation fee 9.50€

Rental rates : (from mid April to mid Sept.) – 9 🚌 – 5 🏚. Per night from 51 to 68€ – Per week from 280 to 810€ – Reservation fee 9.50€

🚰 borne 5€ – 🛒🔌14€

Situated near a stream with a view of the sourrounding area.

Surroundings : 🏊 �️ ♨♨ 🔲	
Leisure activities : 🍽✕ 🛶 🎣	**G** Longitude : 3.0008
Facilities : ♿ ⚡ 🚿 🍴 launderette 🧺	**P** **S** Latitude : 45.575
Nearby : 🎣	

⛰ Le Viginet

☎ 04 73 88 53 80. www.camping-viginet.com

Address : take southeastern exit along the D 996 then continue 600m along the road to the left (opposite the Ford garage)

Opening times : from mid April to end Sept.

2 ha (90 pitches) terraced, relatively flat, flat, grassy, stony

Tariff : 23.40€ ✶✶ 🚐 🔲 🔌 (10A) – Extra per person 4.80€ – Reservation fee 7€

Rental rates : (2014 Price) (from mid April to end Sept.) ♿ (1 chalet) – 12 🏚 – 14 cabins. Per night from 25 to 80€ – Per week from 130 to 875€ – Reservation fee 7€

Some chalets look out over the valley; pitches among trees and bushes.

Surroundings : 🏊 ⛰ ♨♨	
Leisure activities : 🛶 🎣 (small swimming pool)	**G** Longitude : 3.00269
Facilities : ♿ ⚡ 🚿 🍴 🗄 🧺 refrigerators	**P** **S** Latitude : 45.57945
Nearby : 🎯 fitness trail	

⛰ La Clé des Champs

☎ 04 73 88 52 33. www.campingcledeschamps.com

Address : take southeastern exit along the D 996 and take D 642, follow the signs for Les Granges; beside a stream and 200m from the Couze de Chambon

Opening times : from beginning April to end Sept.

1 ha (64 pitches) terraced, flat, grassy

Tariff : (2014 Price) 24€ ✶✶ 🚐 🔲 🔌 (6A) – Extra per person 6.20€ Reservation fee 9.50€

Rental rates : (2014 Price) Permanent – 20 🚌 – 9 🏚. Per night from 38 to 100€ – Per week from 190 to 750€ – Reservation fee 9.50€

🚰 borne 4€ – 6 🔲 11.80€

Good quality chalets to rent.

Surroundings : 🚍 ♨♨	
Leisure activities : 🍽✕ 🛶 🎣 🏊	**G** Longitude : 2.99934
Facilities : ♿ ⚡ 🚿 🍴 launderette 🧺	**P** **S** Latitude : 45.57602

ST-PAULIEN

43350 – Michelin map **331** E3 – pop. 2 398 – alt. 795
▶ Paris 529 – La Chaise-Dieu 28 – Craponne-sur-Arzon 25 – Le Puy-en-Velay 14

⛰ La Rochelambert

☎ 04 71 00 54 02. www.camping-rochelambert.com

Address : route de Lanthenas (head 2.7km southwest along the D 13, follow the signs for Allègre and turn left onto D 25, follow the signs for Loudes; near the Borne (direct access)

Opening times : from beginning April to end Sept.

3 ha (100 pitches) flat, grassy

Tariff : 23.80€ ✶✶ 🚐 🔲 🔌 (16A) – Extra per person 5€ – Reservation fee 13€

Rental rates : (from beginning April to end Sept.) – 2 caravans – 12 🏚 – 2 tent lodges. Per night from 60 to 72€ – Per week from 212 to 693€ – Reservation fee 13€

🚰 borne 3€ – 🛒12€

Surroundings : 🚍	
Leisure activities : 🍽✕ 🛶 🎣 🏊	**G** Longitude : 3.81192
Facilities : ♿ ⚡ 🚿 🍴 launderette	**P** **S** Latitude : 45.13547

ST-RÉMY-SUR-DUROLLE

63550 – Michelin map **326** I7 – pop. 1 847 – alt. 620
▶ Paris 395 – Chabreloche 13 – Clermont-Ferrand 55 – Thiers 7

⛰ Révéa Les Chanterelles

☎ 04 73 94 31 71, www.camping-lac.fr

Address : 3km northeast along the D 201 and take the road to the right - take A 72: exit 3

Opening times : from beginning April to beginning Oct.

5 ha (150 pitches) terraced, very uneven, relatively flat, flat, grassy

Tariff : 20.10€ ✶✶ 🚐 🔲 🔌 (10A) – Extra per person 4€

Rental rates : Permanent – 8 🏚 – 2 tent lodges. Per night from 30 to 85€ – Per week from 185 to 598€ – Reservation fee 10€

🚰 borne – 6 🔲 20.10€

In a pleasant location on high ground, near a lake.

Surroundings : 🏊 ⛰ 🌳	
Leisure activities : 🎣 🛶	
Facilities : ♿ ⚡ 🔲 🍴 🗄	**G** Longitude : 3.59918
At the lake : 🏖 🍽✕ 🎯 🍴 🎣 🏊 ⛵ (beach)	**P** **S** Latitude : 45.90308
🏊 🎣 squash	

ST-SAUVES-D'AUVERGNE

63950 – Michelin map **326** D9 – pop. 1 133 – alt. 791
▶ Paris 458 – Clermont-Ferrand 49 – Limoges 181 – Tulle 104

⛰ Sites et Paysages Pont de la Dordogne

☎ 04 73 81 01 92. www.auvergnecampingnature.com

Address : 0.8km south towards Tauve

Opening times : from mid June to end Aug.

3 ha (56 pitches) flat, grassy, fine gravel

Tariff : 23.50€ ✶✶ 🚐 🔲 🔌 (16A) – Extra per person 6€

Reservation fee 10€

Rental rates : (from mid June to end Aug.) ♿ (1 chalet) – 5 caravans – 7 🏚 – 2 yurts – 6 cabins. Per night from 80 to 115€ Per week from 320 to 690€ – Reservation fee 10€

🚰 borne – 20 🔲 – 🛒 🔌15€

Situated beside a lake and near the Dordogne river.

Surroundings : 🐟 ⌂ ♋
Leisure activities : 🍸 ✕ 🏠 hammam, jacuzzi 🛶🚴🏊 🎣 farm or petting farm, freshwater paddling pool, archery
Facilities : 🚿 🏛 ♨ 📶

G P S	Longitude : 2.69002
	Latitude : 45.60281

STE-SIGOLÈNE

43600 – Michelin map **331** H2 – pop. 5 900 – alt. 808
▶ Paris 551 – Annonay 50 – Monistrol-sur-Loire 8 – Montfaucon-en-Velay 14

Kawan Village de Vaubarlet 👥

📞 0471666495. www.vaubarlet.com – alt. 600

Address : head 6km southwest along the D 43, follow the signs for Grazac

Opening times : from beginning May to end Sept.

15 ha/3 pitches (131 pitches) flat, grassy

Tariff : 31€ ✶✶ 🚐 🔲 🔌 (15A) – Extra per person 4€ – Reservation fee 15€

Rental rates : (from beginning May to end Sept.) 🚿 (2 chalets) – 1 caravan – 18 🚐 – 5 🏡 – 5 canvas bungalows – 2 tent lodges. Per night from 40 to 97€ – Per week from 55 to 644€ Reservation fee 30€

🚐 borne – 🔋 🔌16€

In a green valley crossed by the Dunière river.

Surroundings : 🐟 ≤ ♀
Leisure activities : 🍸 ✕ 🏠 ☼daytime ⚽
🛶🚴🏊 🚿 ⛟ 🅴 ♨ – 2 private sanitary facilities (🚽 🚿 wc) 🍴 launderette ⚓

G P S	Longitude : 4.21254
	Latitude : 45.21634

SAUGUES

43170 – Michelin map **331** D4 – pop. 1 873 – alt. 960
▶ Paris 529 – Brioude 51 – Mende 72 – Le Puy-en-Velay 43

🏔 Municipal Sporting de la Seuge

📞 0471778062. www.saugues.fr/tourisme/hebergements/camping

Address : avenue du Gévaudan (take the western exit along the D 589, follow the signs for Le Malzieu-Ville and take a right turn; beside the Seuge river and near two lakes and a pine forest)

Opening times : from beginning April to end Oct.

3 ha (92 pitches) flat, grassy

Tariff : (2014 Price) 11€ ✶✶ 🚐 🔲 🔌 (16A) – Extra per person 3.30€ Reservation fee 15€

Rental rates : (2014 Price) (from beginning April to end Oct.) – 14 🏡 – 5 🛏 – 1 gîte. Per week from 220 to 459€

🚐 borne – 3 🅴 6.10€

A natural pool (clean and filtered but no chemicals).

Surroundings : ≤ ♀
Leisure activities : 🏠 🛶 🎾 🏊 (fresh water) 🎣 multi-sports ground entertainment room
Facilities : 🚿 ♨ 🍴 launderette
Nearby : 🍴 🚵 🏊 🐎 sports trail, pedalos

G P S	Longitude : 3.54073
	Latitude : 44.95818

SAZERET

03390 – Michelin map **326** E4 – pop. 157 – alt. 370
▶ Paris 348 – Gannat 44 – Montluçon 34 – Montmarault 4

🏔 La Petite Valette

📞 0470076457. www.valette.nl – access difficult in some places (track)

Address : 5.5km to the northeast, access via rte Les Deux-Chaises parallel to the N 79 and Chemin des Prugnes on the left - from the A 71, take exit 11.

Opening times : from beginning June to mid Sept.

4 ha (58 pitches) flat, grassy

Tariff : 26.20€ ✶✶ 🚐 🔲 🔌 (6A) – Extra per person 5.50€ – Reservation fee 16€

Rental rates : (from beginning June to mid Sept.) – 8 🚐 – 5 🏡. Per night from 50 to 100€ – Per week from 250 to 450€ Reservation fee 16€

Facilities and activities based around a former traditional Bourbon farm.

Surroundings : 🐟 ⌂ ♋
Leisure activities : ✕ 🏠 🚴 🏊 🎣
Facilities : 🚿 ⛟ 🅿 🏛 🍴 launderette

G P S	Longitude : 2.99231
	Latitude : 46.3596

SINGLES

63690 – Michelin map **326** C9 – pop. 170 – alt. 737
▶ Paris 484 – Bort-les-Orgues 27 – La Bourboule 23 – Bourg-Lastic 20

Le Moulin de Serre 👥

📞 0473211606. www.moulindeserre.com

Address : 1.7km south of the Guinguette, along the D 73, follow the signs for Bort-les-Orgues; beside the Burande river

Opening times : from mid April to mid Sept.

7 ha/2.6 pitches (99 pitches) flat, grassy

Tariff : 24.90€ ✶✶ 🚐 🔲 🔌 (10A) – Extra per person 4.90€ – Reservation fee 16€

Rental rates : (from mid April to mid Sept.) 🚿 (1 mobile home) – 23 🚐 – 12 canvas bungalows. Per night from 26 to 62€ – Per week from 175 to 721€ – Reservation fee 16€

🚐 borne 4€ – 10 🅴 5€

In a green setting in a valley, near a small river.

Surroundings : 🐟 ≤ ⌂ ♋
Leisure activities : 🍸 ✕ 🏠 ☼ ⚽ jacuzzi
🛶🚴🎾🏊 🎣
Facilities : 🚿 ⛟ 🏛 ♨ 🍴 launderette ⚓

G P S	Longitude : 2.54235
	Latitude : 45.54357

Michelin classification:

🏔🏔🏔🏔 *Extremely comfortable, equipped to a very high standard*

🏔🏔🏔 *Very comfortable, equipped to a high standard*

🏔🏔🏔 *Comfortable and well equipped*

🏔🏔 *Reasonably comfortable*

🏔 *Satisfactory*

TAUVES

63690 – Michelin map **326** C9 – pop. 768 – alt. 820
▶ Paris 474 – Bort-les-Orgues 27 – La Bourboule 13 – Bourg-Lastic 29

⛰ Les Aurandeix

✆ 0473211406. www.camping-les-aurandeix.fr

Address : at the stadium (east of the town)

Opening times : from mid April to end Sept.

2 ha (50 pitches) terraced, relatively flat, flat, grassy

Tariff : (2014 Price) 23€ ♟♟ ⇔ 圁 ⚡ (10A) – Extra per person 4.95€
Reservation fee 10€

Rental rates : (2014 Price) (from mid April to end Sept.) – 13 ⛟. Per night from 42 to 125€ – Per week from 195 to 695€ – Reservation fee 19€

⛟ borne 5€ – ⚡ 10€

The pitches and rental accommodations are on terraces overlooking the swimming pool.

Surroundings : ⌂ 🌳 Leisure activities : 🎦 🏄 🏊 multi-sports ground Facilities : 🔥 ⚬ ⛟ 🏕 🚿 launderette Nearby : 🏊 fitness trail	**GPS** Longitude : 2.62473 Latitude : 45.56101

TREIGNAT

03380 – Michelin map **326** B4 – pop. 443 – alt. 450
▶ Paris 342 – Boussac 11 – Culan 27 – Gouzon 25

⛺ Municipal de l'Étang d'Herculat

✆ 0470070389. http://treignat-allier.weebly.com/

Address : 2.3km to the northeast, access via the road to the left, after the church

Opening times : from beginning April to end Sept.

1.6 ha (35 pitches) open site, relatively flat to hilly, flat, grassy

Tariff : (2014 Price) ♟ 1.65€ ⇔ 圁 6€ – ⚡ (30A) 2€

In a pleasant location beside a large lake.

Surroundings : 🌿 ⌂ 🌳 Leisure activities : 🎦 🏄 🐎 Facilities : 🔥 🚿 🏕	**GPS** Longitude : 2.3673 Latitude : 46.35611

We value your opinion and welcome your feedback. Do email us at campingfrance@tp.michelin.com

VIC-SUR-CÈRE

15800 – Michelin map **330** D5 – pop. 1 988 – alt. 678
▶ Paris 549 – Aurillac 19 – Murat 29

⛰ La Pommeraie

✆ 0471475418. www.camping-la-pommeraie.com – alt. 750

Address : Daïsses (2.5km southeast along the D 54. D 154 and take the road to the right)

Opening times : from beginning May to end Aug.

2.8 ha (100 pitches) terraced, flat, grassy

Tariff : (2014 Price) 15€ ♟♟ ⇔ 圁 ⚡ (10A) – Extra per person 5.70€
Reservation fee 19€

Rental rates : (2014 Price) (from beginning May to end Aug.) – 40 ⛟. Per night from 50 to 147€ – Per week from 350 to 1,029€ – Reservation fee 19€

⛟ 2 圁 15€

In an attractive elevated location.

Surroundings : 🌿 ◁ mountain peaks, Vallée de la Cère and small town of Vic-sur-Cère ⌂ 🌳 Leisure activities : ♟ ✗ 🎦 🕓 nighttime 🏃 🎿 🏂 🏊 walking trails Facilities : 🔥 ⚬ 🏕 🏂 🏕 🚿 🏕 launderette 🏊 🏄	**GPS** Longitude : 2.63307 Latitude : 44.9711

⛺ Vic'Nature

✆ 0471475418. www.camping-la-pommeraie.com

Address : route de Salvanhac (beside the Cère river)

Opening times : from mid May to end Sept.

3 ha (200 pitches) flat, grassy

Tariff : (2014 Price) 15€ ♟♟ ⇔ 圁 ⚡ (10A) – Extra per person 4.10€
Reservation fee 8€

Rental rates : (2014 Price) (from mid June to mid Sept.) – 5 ⛟. Per night from 44 to 73€ – Per week from 224 to 434€ – Reservation fee 8€

⛟ 10 圁

Surroundings : ◁ 🌳🌳 Leisure activities : 🎦 🏄 Facilities : 🔥 🚿 🏕 launderette Nearby : 🏊 🏂 🎿 🏄	**GPS** Longitude : 2.62492 Latitude : 44.97986

VOLVIC

63530 – Michelin map **326** F7 – pop. 4 409 – alt. 510
▶ Paris 419 – Clermont-Ferrand 14 – Moulins 99 – Saint-Étienne 160

⛺ Municipal Volvic Pierre et Sources

✆ 0473335016. www.camping-volvic.com

Address : at the exit from the village, towards Châtel-Guyon

Opening times : from beginning May to end Sept.

2 ha (68 pitches) relatively flat, flat, grassy

Tariff : 19€ ♟♟ ⇔ 圁 ⚡ (16A) – Extra per person 4.50€

Rental rates : Permanent 🔥 (1 chalet) – 10 ⛢. Per night from 65 to 95€ – Per week from 250 to 560€

⛟ borne 2€ – 5 圁

The site has well marked-out pitches with a view of the Château de Tournoël.

Surroundings : ⌂ Leisure activities : 🎦 Facilities : 🔥 ⚬ 🏂 🏕 🚿 🏕 launderette Nearby : 🏄 🏂	**GPS** Longitude : 3.04685 Latitude : 45.87234

Key to rentals symbols:

12 ⛟	*Number of mobile homes*
20 ⛢	*Number of chalets*
6 🛏	*Number of rooms to rent*
Per night *30–50€*	*Minimum/maximum rate per night*
Per week *300–1,000€*	*Minimum/maximum rate per week*

VOREY

43800 – Michelin map **331** F2 – pop. 1 428 – alt. 540
▶ Paris 544 – Ambert 53 – Craponne-sur-Arzon 18 – Le Puy en
Velay 23

▲ Pra de Mars

Stéphanie Eizenbuch

✆ 04 71 03 40 86. http://www.
leprademars.com
Address : le Chambon de Vorey
Opening times : from beginning April
to end Sept.
3.6 ha (100 pitches) flat, grassy
Tariff : 19.80€ ♟♟ ⇌ 回 (⚡) (5A) –
Extra per person 3.90€
Rental rates : (from beginning April
to end Sept.) – 7 ⛺ – 1 apartment. Per night from 38 to 72€ –
Per week from 250 to 550€
⛽ borne 3€

Surroundings : ♨ ⩽ ⌂ ♀
Leisure activities : ♟ ✕ ⛱ ⛵ ⚲ ✂ ⚓ ⊿
⇌
Facilities : ⚐ ⚬ ⇱ ⚲ ⚲ ⚲ launderette ⚲

GPS Longitude : 3.9429
Latitude : 45.20352

▲ Les Moulettes

✆ 04 71 03 70 48. www.camping-les-moulettes.fr
Address : chemin de Félines (to the west of the town centre; beside
the Arzon river)
Opening times : from beginning May to mid Sept.
1,3 ha (45 pitches) flat, grassy
Tarif : (2014 Price) ♟ 6€⇌ 回 8€ – (⚡) (10A) 3.50€
Rental rates : (2014 Price) (from beginning May to end Sept.) –
6 ⛺ – 6 ⛺. Per week from 250 to 580€
⛽ borne 3€ – 5 回 2€

Surroundings : ♨ ⌂ ♀♀
Leisure activities : ♟ ✕ ⛱ ⛵ ⊿ ⚲
Facilities : ⚐ ⚬ ⇱ ⚲ ⚲ ⚲ ⚲
Nearby : ✂ ⚲

GPS Longitude : 3.90363
Latitude : 45.18637

*Using the traditional Michelin classification method,
the guide provides you with an easy, speedy reference
for assessing the category of each site: 1 to 5 tents
(see page 10).*

BRITTANY

T. Deschamps / Photononstop

B rittany, or Breizh, as it is known to those lucky enough to live there, is a region of harsh granite coastlines, mysterious dolmens and menhirs, enchanted forests and pretty ports, dotted with colourful fishing boats. Its charm lies in its sea breeze, seafood and sea-faring history; in its varied landscapes, extensive coastline and delightful islands; in its gastronomy, music and traditional festivals. Its inhabitants were born – or so they claim – with a drop of salt water in their blood. Proud of the language handed down from their Celtic ancestors, today's Bretons nurture their identity with lively celebrations of folklore and customs. Naturally, such devotion to culture demands plenty of delicious and wholesome nourishment: sweet and savoury pancakes, thick slices of butter cake and mugs of cold cider. However, Brittany's gastronomic reputation doesn't end there and gourmets can feast on the oysters, lobster and crab for which it is famous. A visit to Brittany is a jigsaw of wonderful experiences.

Legend:

- ● Locality with campsite
- ■ Locality with campsite and rental option
- <u>Vannes</u> Locality with campsite and campervan area
- <u>Moyaux</u> Locality with at least one pleasant campsite
- 🚐 Motorway service area for campervans

MANCHE

Perros-Guirec
Plougrescant
Pleubian
Primel-Trégastel
Trégastel
Trébeurden
Trélévern
Paimpol
Plougasnou
Pleumeur-Bodou
Louannec
Pontrieux
Plouézec
Roscoff
St-Pol-de-Léon
Lannion
D 786
Brignogan-Plages
Plougoulm
St-Jean-du-Doigt
St-Michel-en-Grève
Plouguerneau
Carantec
Plestin-les-Grèves
Bégard
Lantic
Landéda
Plounévez-Lochrist
Lampaul-Ploudalmézeau
Plouigneau
D 167
Guingamp
Île d'Ouessant
Milizac
N 12
Morlaix
N 12
Châteaudren
St-Renan
BREST
Elorn
Locmaria-Plouzané
Sizun
Callac
le Conquet
Plougastel-Daoulas
FINISTÈRE
CÔTES-
le Fret
Camaret-s-Mer
Crozon
N 165
Morgat
Dinéault
Châteaulin
Telgruc-s-Mer
D 887
Aulne
N 164
Pentrez-Plage
Plomodiern
Trébout
Ploéven
Kervel
Poullan-s-M.
Douarnenez
Locronan
Odet
Île de Sein
Plouhinec
St-Yvi
Scaër
Priziac
Pontivy
Primelin
D 765
Quimper
Plozévet
Fouesnant
Le Faouët
D 768
Tréguennec
la Forêt-Fouesnant
Mousterlin
Arzano
Blavet
Plomeur
Bénodet
Concarneau
Quimperlé
Penmarch
Beg-Meil
Moëlan-s-Mer
Pont-Scorff
N 24
Treffiagat
Névez
Camors
Lesconil
Loctudy
le Pouldu
Guidel
N 165
LORIENT
Ste-Anne-d'Auray
Plobannalec-Lesconil
Raguenès-Plage
Larmor-Plage
Plouhinec
Ploemel
Port-Manech
Plougoumelen
Île de Groix
Belz
Erdeven
Crach
Plouharnel
Baden
Carnac
Carnac-Plage
la Trinité
Arzon
Quiberon
St-Philibert
Locmariaquer
le Palais
Bangor
Belle-Île-en-Mer

OCÉAN   ATLANTIQUE

AMBON

56190 – Michelin map **308** P9 – pop. 1 676 – alt. 30
▶ Paris 465 – Muzillac 7 – Redon 42 – La Roche-Bernard 22

D'Arvor

𝒫 02 97 41 16 69. www.campingdarvor.com – limited spaces for one-night stay

Address : 18 Brouel (located 1.5km west along the D 20, follow the signs for Sarzeau and take the turning to the left, follow the signs for Brouel)

4 ha (140 pitches)

Rentals : ♿ (1 chalet) – 60 🏠 – 1 ⛺.

Surroundings : ♨
Leisure activities : ♟ ✗ 🎬 ⚅ ⚞ ⚟ 🚴
🎿 ⚓ ⚁ ⚒
Facilities : ♿ ⚷ ⚑ launderette

| G P S | Longitude : -2.57221 |
| | Latitude : 47.55654 |

ARRADON

56610 – Michelin map **308** O9 – pop. 5 301 – alt. 40
▶ Paris 467 – Auray 18 – Lorient 62 – Quiberon 49

Sites et Paysages Penboch ♣♟

𝒫 02 97 44 71 29. www.camping-penboch.fr

Address : 9 chemin de Penboch (situated 2km southeast following signs for Roguedas, 200m from the beach)

Opening times : from mid April to end Sept.

4 ha (175 pitches)

Tariff : (2014 Price) 39.80€ ♟♟ ⚞ 🔲 ⚡ (10A) – Extra per person 6.50€

Rental rates : (2014 Price) (from mid April to end Sept.) – 45 🏠. Per night from 42 to 170€ – Per week from 280 to 1,190€ – Reservation fee 20€

🚿 borne 5€ – 🔌 ⚡14€

In a leafy location with pleasant shade.

Surroundings : ⚘ ⛭ ♨♨
Leisure activities : ♟ 🎬 ⚞ jacuzzi ⚓ ♪
⚁ ⚒ ⚑ multi-sports ground
Facilities : ♿ ⚷ ▦ ⛭ – 4 individual sanitary facilities (🚿 ⚘ wc) ⚓ ⚑ launderette ⚘ refrigerators
Nearby : ⚞ ⚒

| G P S | Longitude : -2.80085 |
| | Latitude : 47.62217 |

L'Allée

𝒫 02 97 44 01 98. www.camping-allee.com

Address : located 1.5km west, follow the signs for Le Moustoir and take the turning to the left

Opening times : from beginning April to end Sept.

3 ha (148 pitches)

Tariff : (2014 Price) ♟ 5.15€ ⚞ 🔲 9.65€ – ⚡ (10A) 4.60€ – Reservation fee 20€

Rental rates : (2014 Price) Permanent – 28 🏠 – 2 tent lodges – 2 gîtes. Per night from 90 to 110€ – Per week from 205 to 950€ Reservation fee 20€

🚿 borne

Surroundings : ⚘ ⛭ ♨
Leisure activities : 🎬 ⚓ ⚁
Facilities : ♿ ⚷ (July–Aug.) ⚘ ⚑ launderette
Nearby : ✗ ⚒

| G P S | Longitude : -2.84025 |
| | Latitude : 47.62109 |

ARZANO

29300 – Michelin map **308** K7 – pop. 1 403 – alt. 91
▶ Paris 508 – Carhaix-Plouguer 54 – Châteaulin 82 – Concarneau 40

Les Castels Ty Nadan ♣♟

𝒫 02 98 71 75 47. www.tynadan-vacances.fr

Address : Locunolé, route d'Arzano (3km west; beside the Ellé river)

Opening times : from beginning May to beginning Sept.

20.5 ha/5 for camping (325 pitches)

Tariff : 45€ ♟♟ ⚞ 🔲 ⚡ (10A) – Extra per person 9.10€ – Reservation fee 25€

Rental rates : (from beginning May to beginning Sept.) – 80 🏠 – 6 ⛺ – 1 apartment – 4 tent lodges – 1 gîte. Per night from 56 to 119€ – Per week from 336 to 833€ – Reservation fee 30€

🚿 borne 10€

A partially indoor water park with lots of sports activities and lesiure facillities, river swimming and canoeing.

Surroundings : ⚘ ⛭ ♨♨ ⚑
Leisure activities : ♟ ✗ 🎬 ⚞ ⚞ jacuzzi
⚓ 🚴 ✗ ⚁ ⚒ ⚒ (beach) ⚓ ⚞ farm
or petting farm, climbing wall, forest trail ⚞ entertainment room
Facilities : ♿ ⚷ 🔲 ⚘ ⚓ ⚑ launderette
⚁ ⚘

| G P S | Longitude : -3.47461 |
| | Latitude : 47.90476 |

Key to rentals symbols:

12 🏠	Number of mobile homes
20 ⛺	Number of chalets
6 🛏	Number of rooms to rent
Per night 30–50€	Minimum/maximum rate per night
Per week 300–1,000€	Minimum/maximum rate per week

ARZON

56640 – Michelin map **308** N9 – pop. 2 132 – alt. 9
▶ Paris 487 – Auray 52 – Lorient 94 – Quiberon 81

Municipal le Tindio

𝒫 02 97 53 75 59. www.camping-arzon.fr

Address : 2 rue du Bilouris, at Kermers (800m to the northeast)

Opening times : from beginning April to beginning Nov.

5 ha (220 pitches)

Tariff : (2014 Price) ♟ 4.30€ ⚞ 8€ 🔲 8.50€ – ⚡ (10A) 3.40€

Rental rates : (2014 Price) (from beginning April to beginning Nov.) ♿ (3 chalets) – 18 ⛺. Per week from 273 to 698€

🚿 borne 2€ – 19 🔲 10€ – 🔌 ⚡12.90€

Situated beside the sea.

Surroundings : ♨
Leisure activities : 🎬 ⚓ ⚒ multi-sports ground
Facilities : ♿ ⚷ ⚘ ⚓ ⚑ launderette

| G P S | Longitude : -2.8828 |
| | Latitude : 47.55562 |

BADEN

56870 – Michelin map **308** N9 – pop. 4 077 – alt. 28
▶ Paris 473 – Auray 9 – Lorient 52 – Quiberon 40

⋀⋀⋀ Mané Guernehué ♣♣

© Camping Mané Guernehué

📞 02 97 57 02 06. www.camping-baden.com

Address : 52 rue Mané Er Groëz (located 1km southwest, follow the signs for Mériadec and take a right turn)

Opening times : from beginning April to end Oct.

18 ha/8 for camping (377 pitches) undulating, terraced, flat and relatively flat, grassy, pond, natural setting among trees and bushes

Tariff : (2014 Price) 46.20€ ♥♥ ⇌ 🅴 (10A) – Extra per person 8.20€ – Reservation fee 20€

Rental rates : (2014 Price) (from beginning April to end Oct.) ♿ (1 mobile home) – 4 caravans – 161 🛏 – 19 🏠 – 2 tent lodges – 7 gîtes. Per night from 72 to 209€ – Per week from 250 to 1,463€ – Reservation fee 20€

🚐 borne 6.50€ – 💧 ⚡15€

An attractive indoor spa area and riding centre with ponies and horses.

Surroundings : 🐾 🚇 ♀
Leisure activities : ♟ ✗ 🎬 🏃 🔥 ☯
hammam, jacuzzi 🏊 🚵 🎣 🎳 🛝 🏹 🐴
zip wiring, multi-sports ground, spa centre, water park, entertainment room
Facilities : ♿ 🚿 ⟦cc⟧ 🏧 🚙 🔥 🚽 ⚾
launderette 🧹
Nearby : ✗

Longitude : -2.92531
Latitude : 47.61418

BÉGARD

22140 – Michelin map **309** C3 – pop. 4 652 – alt. 142
▶ Paris 499 – Rennes 147 – St-Brieuc 51 – Quimper 132

⋀⋀ Donant

📞 02 96 45 46 46. www.camping-donant-bretagne.com

Address : at Gwénézhan

Opening times : Permanent

3 ha (91 pitches)

Tariff : (2014 Price) ♥ 4€ ⇌ 2.40€ 🅴 4.10€ – ⚡ (36A) 3.60€

Rental rates : (2014 Price) Permanent ♿ (1 chalet) – 15 🏠 – 12 🛏 – 4 canvas bungalows – 1 gîte. Per night from 78 to 100€ – Per week from 149 to 609€

🚐 borne 6€ – 💧 11€

Surroundings : 🚇
Leisure activities : 🎬 🎋 🏊
entertainment room
Facilities : ♿ 🚿 ⟦cc⟧ launderette
Nearby : ♟ 🔥 🎳 🛝 ⚾ leisure park

Longitude : -3.2837
Latitude : 48.61807

Using the traditional Michelin classification method, the guide provides you with an easy, speedy reference for assessing the category of each site (see page 10).

BEG-MEIL

29170 – Michelin map **308** H7
▶ Paris 562 – Rennes 211 – Quimper 23 – Brest 95

⋀⋀ La Piscine ♣♣

📞 02 98 56 56 06. www.campingdelapiscine.com

Address : 51 Hent Kerleya (4km to the northwest)

3.8 ha (199 pitches) flat, grassy, small lake

Rentals : 🚫 – 30 🛏 – 4 🏠.

In a pleasant location near the sea, and with an attractriive pool complex.

Surroundings : 🐾 🚇 ♀
Leisure activities : 🎬 🏃 ☯ hammam, jacuzzi 🏊 🚵 🎳 🛝 🏹 mountain biking
Facilities : ♿ 🚿 🚙 🔥 🚽 launderette 🏊 🍴

Longitude : -4.01579
Latitude : 47.86671

⋀⋀ Le Kervastard

📞 02 98 94 91 52. www.campinglekervastard.com

Address : 56 chemin de Kervastard (150m from the town)

Opening times : from beginning April to end Sept.

2 ha (122 pitches) flat, grassy

Tariff : 32.80€ ♥♥ ⇌ 🅴 ⚡ (10A) – Extra per person 6.10€ – Reservation fee 15€

Rental rates : (from beginning April to end Oct.) – 19 🛏. Per night from 50 to 105€ – Per week from 236 to 730€ – Reservation fee 15€

🚐 borne 5€ – 5 🅴 25€ – 💧 13€

In a pleasant setting with light shade and close to shops.

Surroundings : 🚇 ♀
Leisure activities : 🎬 🏊 🚴 🛝
Facilities : ♿ 🚿 ⟦cc⟧ 🚙 🚽 launderette
Nearby : 🏊 ♟ ✗ 🍴

Longitude : -3.98825
Latitude : 47.86015

*The classification (1 to 5 tents, **black** or red) that we award to selected sites in this guide is our own system. It should not be confused with the classification (1 to 5 stars) of official organisations.*

BELLE-ÎLE

56360 – Michelin map **308** – pop. 2 457 – alt. 7

Bangor 56360 – Michelin map **308** L11 – pop. 926 – alt. 45
▶ Paris 513 – Rennes 162 – Vannes 53

⋀ Municipal de Bangor

📞 02 97 31 89 75. http://www.bangor.fr/hebergements_camping.html

Address : 18 rue Pierre Cadre (to the west of the town)

Opening times : from beginning April to end Sept.

0.8 ha (75 pitches)

Tariff : (2014 Price) ♥ 3.25€ ⇌ 1.60€ 🅴 2.95€ – ⚡ (10A) 2.65€

Rental rates : (2014 Price) (from beginning April to end Sept.) – 6 🛏 – 16 🛏. Per week from 286 to 575€

Surroundings : 🐾 🎋
Leisure activities : 🏊
Facilities : ♿ 🚿 🚽
Nearby : ✗ 🐴

Longitude : -3.19103
Latitude : 47.31453

Le Palais 56360 – Michelin map **308** M10 – pop. 2 545 – alt. 7
▶ Paris 508 – Rennes 157 – Vannes 48

🏔 Bordenéo

📞 02 97 31 88 96. www.bordeneo.com

Address : 1.7km northwest following signs for Port Fouquet, 500m from the sea

Opening times : from mid April to end Sept.

5.5 ha (202 pitches) flat, grassy

Tariff : ✦ 7.35€ � 2.70€ 🔲 11.35€ – 🔌 (5A) 3.65€ – Reservation fee 15€

Rental rates : (from mid April to end Sept.) – 50 🏠 – 10 🏚 – 4 studios – 10 canvas bungalows. Per night from 65 to 225€ – Per week from 310 to 920€ – Reservation fee 16€

Ornamental flowers and shrubs decorate the site.

Surroundings : 🏞 ⌑ 🎣
Leisure activities : 🍽 🎦 ⊙nighttime 🛶 🚴 🏐 🎮 🏊 ⛷
Facilities : ♿ ☕ ⛺ 🚿 🍴 launderette 🔲
Nearby : 🛒 🐎 scuba diving

🏔 L'Océan

📞 02 97 31 83 86. www.camping-ocean-belle-ile.com

Address : at Rosboscer (to the southwest of the town, 500m from the port)

Opening times : Permanent

2.8 ha (125 pitches)

Tariff : (2014 Price) 24.70€ ✦✦ 🚗 🔲 🔌 (3A) – Extra per person 5.50€ Reservation fee 5€

Rental rates : (2014 Price) Permanent ♿ (1 mobile home) – 2 caravans – 16 🏠 – 28 🏚. Per night from 41 to 108€ – Per week from 289 to 768€ – Reservation fee 12€

Surroundings : 🏞 ⌑ 🎣
Leisure activities : 🍽 ✕ 🛶 🏊
Facilities : ♿ ☕ ⛺ 🚿 🍴 launderette 🔲
Nearby : 🛒 🐎 scuba diving

BELZ

56550 – Michelin map **308** L8 – pop. 3 476 – alt. 12
▶ Paris 494 – Rennes 143 – Vannes 34 – Lorient 25

🏔 Le Moulin des Oies

📞 02 97 55 53 26. www.lemoulindesoies.com

Address : 21 rue de la Côte

Opening times : from beginning April to end Sept.

1.9 ha (90 pitches) flat, grassy

Tariff : (2014 Price) 20.80€ ✦✦ 🚗 🔲 🔌 (6A) – Extra per person 5€ Reservation fee 12€

Rental rates : (2014 Price) (from beginning April to end Sept.) – 21 🏠. Per week from 212 to 653€ – Reservation fee 12€

🚐 borne – 🚐 10€

Beside the Ria d'Étel river.

Surroundings : 🏞 ⌑ 🎣
Leisure activities : 🎦 🛶 🏊 (seawater pool) multi-sports ground
Facilities : ♿ ☕ 🍴 launderette

To visit a town or region, use the MICHELIN Green Guides.

BÉNODET

29950 – Michelin map **308** G7 – pop. 3 271
▶ Paris 563 – Concarneau 19 – Fouesnant 8 – Pont-l'Abbé 13

🏔 Sunêlia L'Escale St-Gilles ♣

📞 02 98 57 05 37. www.stgilles.fr – limited spaces for one-night stay
🚫 (from end April to end June)

Address : corniche de la mer (located at La Pointe St-Gilles (headland))

Opening times : from end April to end Sept.

11 ha/7 for camping (467 pitches) flat, grassy

Tariff : 44€ ✦✦ 🚗 🔲 🔌 (10A) – Extra per person 10€ – Reservation fee 35€

Rental rates : (from end April to end Aug.) ♿ (1 mobile home) 🚫 – 160 🏠 – 2 tent lodges. Per night from 39 to 191€ – Per week from 218 to 1,337€ – Reservation fee 35€

An attractive location opposite the ocean, near the beach, with a modern and extensive water park. Option for full and half-board stays.

Surroundings : 🏞 ⌑ 🎣
Leisure activities : 🍽 ✕ 🎦 ⊙ 🏸 🎠 ⛵ hammam jacuzzi 🛶 🚴 🏐 🎮 🏊 ⛷ spa centre water park entertainment room
Facilities : ♿ ☕ 🏢 ⛺ 🚿 🍴 launderette 🔲 🚐
Nearby : 🎣

🏔 Le Letty ♣

📞 02 98 57 04 69. www.campingduletty-benodet.com

Address : impasse de Creisanguer

Opening times : from end June to beginning Sept.

10 ha (542 pitches) flat, grassy

Tariff : 46€ ✦✦ 🚗 🔲 🔌 (10A) – Extra per person 10€ – Reservation fee 12€

🚐 borne

An attractive location close to the beach with a spectacular view of the Mousterlin dunes. Plenty of places for tents and caravans. An extensive and exotic water park.

Surroundings : 🏞 🎣 ⛵
Leisure activities : 🍽 🎦 ⊙ 🏸 🎠 ⛵ hammam, jacuzzi 🏐 🎮 🏊 🎾 beauty treatments 🎣 entertainment room
Facilities : ♿ ☕ ⛺ 🚿 🍴 launderette 🔲 🚐
Nearby : 🎿 🛶 🎣, squash

🏔 Le Poulquer

📞 02 98 57 04 19. www.campingdupoulquer.com

Address : 23 rue du Poulquer (150m from the sea)

Opening times : from beginning May to end Sept.

3 ha (215 pitches)

Tariff : ✦ 7.20€ 🚗 3.20€ 🔲 7.50€ – 🔌 (10A) 5.30€ – Reservation fee 20€

Rental rates : (from beginning May to end Sept.) 🚫 – 33 🏠. Per week from 300 to 850€ – Reservation fee 20€

In a green and shady setting, with spacious pitches for tents and caravans.

Surroundings : ⌑ 🎣
Leisure activities : 🍽 ✕ 🎦 🛶 🏊 🏐 ⛷ entertainment room
Facilities : ♿ ☕ 🍴 launderette
Nearby : 🎾 🎿 🛶 🎣

	GPS
	Longitude : -3.16711
	Latitude : 47.35532

	GPS
	Longitude : -3.13996
	Latitude : 47.53473

	GPS
	Longitude : -3.17603
	Latitude : 47.68045

	GPS
	Longitude : -4.09669
	Latitude : 47.86325

	GPS
	Longitude : -4.08995
	Latitude : 47.86537

	GPS
	Longitude : -4.09844
	Latitude : 47.86794

BINIC

22520 – Michelin map **309** F3 – pop. 3 602 – alt. 35
▶ Paris 463 – Guingamp 37 – Lannion 69 – Paimpol 31

⚠ Le Panoramic

✆ 02 96 73 60 43. www.lepanoramic.net

Address : rue Gasselin

Opening times : Permanent

4 ha (150 pitches) terrace, relatively flat, flat, grassy

Tariff : 29€ ♥♥ ⟺ 📧 ⚡ (10A) – Extra per person 6€ – Reservation fee 10€

Rental rates : (from end March to end Sept.) – 1 caravan – 44 🚐 – 8 🏠 – 2 canvas bungalows. Per night from 30 to 125€ – Per week from 200 to 875€ – Reservation fee 10€

Surroundings : ▭ ♀♀
Leisure activities : ♥ ✕ 🏊 ⛵ 🎣 🔲 (open air in season), multi-sports ground
Facilities : ♿ ⊶ 💳 ▦ ♨ ♨ launderette

GPS Longitude : -2.82304
Latitude : 48.59098

⚠ Municipal des Fauvettes

Municipal des Fauvettes

✆ 02 96 73 60 83. www.ville-binic.fr

Address : rue des Fauvettes

Opening times : from end March to end Sept.

1 ha (83 pitches) terraced, flat and relatively flat, grassy

Tariff : (2014 Price) 22.90€ ♥♥ ⟺ 📧 ⚡ (6A) – Extra per person 5.20€

Rental rates : (2014 Price) (from end March to end Sept.) 🚲 – 4 🚐 – 3 studios. Per night from 99€ – Per week from 260 to 416€ – Reservation fee 65€

🚽 borne – 🔌 9.40€

The rental accommodation is reserved for the Gendarmerie during July and August (beach patrol).

Surroundings : 🍃 ≤ of the Baie de St-Brieuc ♀
Leisure activities : ⛵
Facilities : ♿ ⊶ ♨ ▦

GPS Longitude : -2.82122
Latitude : 48.60635

BRIGNOGAN-PLAGES

29890 – Michelin map **308** F3 – pop. 848 – alt. 17
▶ Paris 585 – Brest 41 – Carhaix-Plouguer 83 – Landerneau 27

⚠ La Côte des Légendes

✆ 02 98 83 41 65. www.campingcotedeslegendes.com

Address : rue Douar ar Pont (situated 2km to the northwest)

Opening times : from end March to mid Nov.

3.5 ha (147 pitches)

Tariff : (2014 Price) 18.95€ ♥♥ ⟺ 📧 ⚡ (5A) – Extra per person 4.80€

Rental rates : (2014 Price) (from end March to mid Nov.) – 11 🚐 – 3 🏠 – 4 canvas bungalows. Per night from 43 to 97€ – Per week from 238 to 680€

🚽 borne 3€ – 4 📧 7.30€ – 🔌 7.30€

Beside La Plage Des Crapauds (beach), an eco-friendly site.

Surroundings : 🍃 ▭ ♀ ⛰
Leisure activities : 🛶 ⛵
Facilities : ♿ ⊶ (July–Aug.) ♨ ▦
Nearby : 🎣

GPS Longitude : -4.32928
Latitude : 48.67284

CALLAC

22160 – Michelin map **309** B4 – pop. 2 359 – alt. 172
▶ Paris 510 – Carhaix-Plouguer 22 – Guingamp 28 – Morlaix 41

⚠ Municipal Verte Vallée

✆ 02 96 45 58 50. commune@mairie-callac.fr

Address : place Jean Auffret (take the western exit along the D 28, follow the signs for Morlaix and turn left onto av. Ernest-Renan; 50m from a small lake)

1 ha (60 pitches)

Surroundings : 🍃 ▭ ♀♀
Leisure activities : ✕ 🏓 🎣
Facilities : ♿ ⊶

GPS Longitude : -3.43765
Latitude : 48.40174

CAMARET-SUR-MER

29570 – Michelin map **308** D5 – pop. 2 576 – alt. 4
▶ Paris 597 – Brest 4 – Châteaulin 45 – Crozon 11

⚠ Le Grand Large

✆ 02 98 27 91 41. www.campinglegrandlarge.com

Address : at Lambézen (3km northeast along the D 355 and take turning to the right; 400m from the beach)

2.8 ha (123 pitches)

Rentals : 27 🚐 – 3 🏠.

The site looks out over the entrance to Brest's natural harbour, with a spectacular view from half of the pitches.

Surroundings : 🍃 ≤ the sea ▭
Leisure activities : ♥ 🏠 ⛵ 🎣 🔲
Facilities : ♿ ⊶ 💳 ♨ ♨ launderette 🏊 🚿

GPS Longitude : -4.56472
Latitude : 48.28083

We have selected the best campsites in France with our usual care, listing those with the best facilities in the most pleasant surroundings.

CAMORS

56330 – Michelin map **308** M7 – pop. 2 788 – alt. 113
▶ Paris 472 – Auray 24 – Lorient 39 – Pontivy 31

⚠ Le Village Insolite

✆ 02 97 39 18 36. www.camping-levillageinsolite.com

Address : rue des Mésanges (located 1km west along the D 189, follow the signs for Lambel-Camors)

Opening times : from mid April to end Sept.

1 ha (30 pitches)

Tariff : (2014 Price) 19.40€ ♥♥ ⟺ 📧 ⚡ (16A) – Extra per person 3.40€ – Reservation fee 6€

Rental rates : (2014 Price) Permanent – 1 caravan – 3 🏠 – 1 yurt – 1 tipi. Per night from 52 to 100€ – Per week from 310 to 645€ – Reservation fee 6€

🚽 borne 6.20€ – 🔌 13.90€

Near lakes and a national forest.

Surroundings : 🍃 ♀
Leisure activities : 🔲
Facilities : ♿ ⊶ 💳 ♨ ♨ ▦
Nearby : ⛵ 🎣

GPS Longitude : -3.01304
Latitude : 47.84613

CANCALE

35260 – Michelin map **309** K2 – pop. 5 374 – alt. 50
▶ Paris 398 – Avranches 61 – Dinan 35 – Fougères 73

⛰⛰ Le Bois Pastel

✆ 02 99 89 66 10. www.campingboispastel.fr

Address : 13 rue de la Corgnais (7km northwest along the D 201 coast road and take the turning to the left)

Opening times : from beginning April to end Sept.

5.2 ha (247 pitches) flat, grassy

Tariff : (2014 Price) ♦ 4.90€ ⇔ 2€ 回 11€ – ⚡ (6A) 4€ – Reservation fee 15€

Rental rates : (2014 Price) (from beginning April to end Sept.) – 20 🚐. Per week from 300 to 710€ – Reservation fee 15€

🚐 borne 4.50€ – 5 回 26.80€

Pitches for tents and caravans among the greenery, often well shaded.

Surroundings : 🏊 ♤♤
Leisure activities : ♟ ⚓ 🖼 (open air in season) multi-sports ground
Facilities : ♿ ⚏ 🚿 launderette 🛒 🚗

G P S	Longitude : -1.86861
	Latitude : 48.68875

CARANTEC

29660 – Michelin map **308** H2 – pop. 3 249 – alt. 37
▶ Paris 552 – Brest 71 – Lannion 53 – Morlaix 14

⛰⛰ Yelloh! Village Les Mouettes 🅰👤

✆ 02 98 67 02 46. www.les-mouettes.com – limited spaces for one-night stay

Address : 50 route de la Grande Grève (located 1.5km southwest following the signs for St-Pol-de-Léon and take right turn.)

Opening times : from mid April to beginning Sept.

4 ha (474 pitches) flat, grassy

Tariff : 50€ ♦♦ ⇔ 回 ⚡ (16A) – Extra per person 9€

Rental rates : (from mid April to beginning Sept.) ♿ Ⓟ – 242 🚐 – 34 🏠. Per week from 273 to 1 687€

🚐 borne

A magnificent water park by the sea, with giant waterslides; upmarket rental options.

Surroundings : 🏊 ♤ ♀
Leisure activities : ♟ ⚓ 🖼 ⛵ 🏃 ⛵ jacuzzi ⚓ 🚲 ⚔ ♣ 🖼 🛝 library, spa centre, entertainment room
Facilities : ♿ ⚏ 🚿 🚰 launderette 🛒 🚗

G P S	Longitude : -3.92802
	Latitude : 48.65922

CARNAC

56340 – Michelin map **308** M9 – pop. 4 362 – alt. 16
▶ Paris 490 – Auray 13 – Lorient 49 – Quiberon 19

⛰⛰ Les Castels La Grande Métairie 🅰👤

La Grande Métairie

✆ 02 97 52 24 01. www.lagrandemetairie.com – limited spaces for one-night stay

Address : route de Kerlescan (2.5km to the northeast)

Opening times : from beginning April to mid Sept.

15 ha/11 for camping (575 pitches)

Tariff : 50€ ♦♦ ⇔ 回 ⚡ (10A) – Extra per person 8.20€

Rental rates : (2014 Price) (from beginning April to mid Sept.) ♿ (1 mobile home) – 8 caravans – 219 🚐 – 2 cabins in the trees. Per night from 78 to 164€ – Per week from 196 to 798€

🚐 borne 7€

The site is beside the Étang de Kerloquet (lake) with a range of good-quality rental options.

Surroundings : 🏞 ♤ ♀
Leisure activities : ♟ ⚔ 🖼 ⛺ (open-air theatre) 🏃 jacuzzi ⚓ 🚲 ⚔ ♣ 🛝 🛝 zip wiring, skate park
Facilities : ♿ ⚏ 🛢 🛒 🚗 🚰 🚰 launderette 🛒 🚗

G P S	Longitude : -3.05975
	Latitude : 47.59647

⛰⛰ Le Moustoir 🅰👤

✆ 02 97 52 16 18. www.lemoustoir.com

Address : 71 route du Moustoir (situated 3km to the northeast)

Opening times : from mid April to end Sept.

5 ha (165 pitches)

Tariff : ♦ 7€ ⇔ 回 45€ ⚡ (10A)

Rental rates : (from mid April to end Sept.) – 84 🚐 – 20 🏠 – 4 🛏. Per night from 32 to 135€ – Per week from 225 to 950€

Reservation fee 8€

🚐 borne – 🔋 ⚡ 16€

Surroundings : 🏞 ♤ ♀
Leisure activities : ♟ ⚔ 🖼 ⛺ 🏃 ⚓ 🚲 ⚔ ♣ 🛝 🛝
Facilities : ♿ ⚏ ☷ 🚿 🚰 🚰 launderette 🛒 🚗

G P S	Longitude : -3.06689
	Latitude : 47.60829

⛰⛰ Moulin de Kermaux 🅰👤

✆ 02 97 52 15 90. www.camping-moulinkermaux.com

Address : route de Kerlescan (2.5km to the northeast)

3 ha (150 pitches)

Rentals : ♿ ⚕ – 55 🚐 – 5 🏠 – 3 canvas bungalows – 3 gîtes.

Surroundings : 🏊 ♤ ♀
Leisure activities : ♟ ⚔ 🖼 ⛺ 🏃 ⛵ jacuzzi ⚓ ♣ 🖼 (open air in season) 🛝 multi-sports ground
Facilities : ♿ ⚏ 🚿 launderette 🚗
Nearby : 🏇

G P S	Longitude : -3.06523
	Latitude : 47.59512

Michelin classification:

⛰⛰⛰⛰ *Extremely comfortable, equipped to a very high standard*
⛰⛰⛰ *Very comfortable, equipped to a high standard*
⛰⛰ *Comfortable and well equipped*
⛰ *Reasonably comfortable*
⛰ *Satisfactory*

⚏ Flower Le Lac

✆ 02 97 55 78 78. www.lelac-carnac.com

Address : Passage du Lac (6.3km to the northeast; beside the lake)

Opening times : from end April to end Sept.

2.5 ha (140 pitches)

Tariff : ✚ 6€⇔ 🅿 19€ – (ᵮ) (6A) 4€ – Reservation fee 8€

Rental rates : (from end April to end Sept.) – 3 caravans – 25 🚐 – 2 ⊨ – 1 tipi – 4 tent lodges. Per night from 30 to 99€ – Per week from 205 to 695€ – Reservation fee 8€

⛽ borne – ♿ (ᵮ)16€

Surroundings : ⌇ ⟨ ⊡ ♀♀
Leisure activities : 🎮 🏓 ⚓ 🚴 ⛵ multi-sports ground
Facilities : ♿ ⚡ ⚏ ⛱ ⛲ ⴳ launderette ⚏
Nearby : 🐎

GPS Longitude : -3.02912
Latitude : 47.61117

⚏ Kérabus

✆ 02 97 52 24 90. www.camping-kerabus.com

Address : 13 allée des Alouettes (situated 2km to the northeast)

Opening times : from beginning April to mid Oct.

1.4 ha (86 pitches) flat, grassy

Tariff : 23.50€ ✚✚ ⇔ 🅿 (ᵮ) (6A) – Extra per person 5.30€ – Reservation fee 10€

Rental rates : (2014 Price) (from beginning April to mid Oct.) – 14 🚐 – 1 tent lodge. Per night from 35 to 97€ – Per week from 180 to 650€

⛽ borne 4€ – ♿ 11.90€

Surroundings : ⌇ ⊡ ♀♀
Leisure activities : ⚓ ⛵ multi-sports ground
Facilities : ♿ ⚏ ⴳ launderette

GPS Longitude : -3.07648
Latitude : 47.59641

⚏ VivaCamp les Bruyères

✆ 02 97 52 30 57. www.camping-lesbruyeres.com

Address : at Kérogile (3km to the north)

Opening times : from beginning April to end Sept.

2 ha (115 pitches) flat, grassy

Tariff : (2014 Price) ✚ 5.40€⇔ 🅿 9.50€ – (ᵮ) (10A) 4.80€ – Reservation fee 10€

Rental rates : (2014 Price) (from beginning April to end Sept.) – 35 🚐 – 3 canvas bungalows – 2 tent lodges. Per night from 27 to 126 € – Per week from 189 to 882€ – Reservation fee 20€

⛽ borne

Surroundings : ⌇ ♀♀
Leisure activities : 🎮 ⚓ 🎾 ⛵ (open air in season), zip wiring
Facilities : ♿ ⚏ ⴳ 🖥
Nearby : bowling

GPS Longitude : -3.08884
Latitude : 47.60437

⚏ L'Étang

✆ 02 97 52 14 06. www.camping-etang.fr

Address : at Kerlann (head 2km north along the D 119 towards Auray then take left turning, 50m from a lake)

Opening times : from beginning April to mid Oct.

2.5 ha (165 pitches) flat, grassy

Tariff : (2014 Price) 21.40€ ✚✚ ⇔ 🅿 (ᵮ) (6A) – Extra per person 5.60€

Rental rates : (2014 Price) Permanent ⚿ – 10 🚐. Per week from 220 to 670€

⛽ borne 21.40€

Surroundings : ⌇ ⊡ ♀
Leisure activities : ⛹ ⚓ 🎾 ⛵ ⛵ multi-sports ground
Facilities : ♿ (summer) ⊡ ⚏ ⴳ launderette
Nearby : ⚓

GPS Longitude : -3.08137
Latitude : 47.60107

⚏ Vacances Directes Le Domaine de Kermario

(rental of mobile homes and gîtes only)

✆ 08 25 13 34 00. www.campingkermario.com

Address : 1 chemin de Kerluir (situated 2km to the northeast)

Opening times : from beginning April to end Sept.

4 ha

Rental rates : (2014 Price) ℗ – 79 🚐 – 9 gîtes. Per night from 31 to 109€ – Per week from 217 to 763€ – Reservation fee 10€

Furnished gîtes are available in old farm buildings that have been beautifully restored.

Surroundings : ⌇ ♀♀
Leisure activities : ✗ 🎮 ⊙ 🏊 ⚓ 🚴 ⛵ ⛵ multi-sports ground, entertainment room
Facilities : ♿ ⚡ ⴳ launderette ⚏

GPS Longitude : -3.06636
Latitude : 47.59521

CARNAC-PLAGE

56340 – Michelin map **308** M9

▶ Paris 494 – Rennes 143 – Vannes 34

⚏ Les Menhirs ♨♀

Les Menhirs

✆ 02 97 52 94 67. www.lesmenhirs.com
limited spaces for one-night stay

Address : allée Saint-Michel

Opening times : from mid April to end Sept.

6 ha (360 pitches) flat, grassy

Tariff : ✚ 8.70€⇔ 🅿 31.90€ – (ᵮ) (10A) 4.90€ – Reservation fee 20€

Rental rates : (from mid April to end Sept.) ♿ (1 mobile home) ⚿ – 62 🚐 – 1 🏠. Per night from 90 to 160€ – Per week from 312 to 1,136€ – Reservation fee 20€

⛽ borne – 8 🅿 31.90€

Situated 400m from the beach and the town centre.

Surroundings : ⌇ ⊡ ♀
Leisure activities : ⛹ 🎮 ⊙ 🏊 ⚓ 🏓 ⟨⟩ jacuzzi ⚓ ⛵ ⛵ multi-sports ground, spa centre, entertainment room
Facilities : ♿ ♿ ⚏ ⚏ ⴳ launderette ⚏ ⚏
Nearby : 🚴

GPS Longitude : -3.06979
Latitude : 47.57683

This guide is not intended as a list of all the camping sites in France; its aim is to provide a selection of the best sites in each category.

⛰ Les Druides

📞 02 97 52 08 18. www.camping-les-druides.com

Address : 55 chemin de Beaumer (To the east, in part of town called Beaumer, 500m from the beach)

Opening times : from mid April to beginning Sept.

2.5 ha (110 pitches)

Tariff : 🚶 6.80€ ➔ 3.50€ 🔲 20.40€ – ⚡ (10A) 6.30€ – Reservation fee 20€

Rental rates : (from mid April to beginning Sept.) ⌇ – 17 🚐 – 3 apartments. Per week from 225 to 805€ – Reservation fee 20€

🚐 borne

Surroundings : ♤♤
Leisure activities : 🏓 🏄 🛶 multi-sports ground
Facilities : ♿ ☎ 🏕 🚿 🍴 launderette
Nearby : 🛒

GPS
Longitude : -3.05689
Latitude : 47.58012

⛰ Le Men-Du

📞 02 97 52 04 23. www.camping-mendu.com

Address : 22bis chemin de Beaumer (in suburb called Le Men-Du, 300m from the beach)

Opening times : from beginning April to beginning Oct.

1.5 ha (100 pitches)

Tariff : 28€ 🚶🚶 ➔ 🔲 ⚡ (10A) – Extra per person 5€ – Reservation fee 15€

Rental rates : (from beginning April to beginning Oct.) ♿ (1 mobile home) – 21 🚐. Per week from 250 to 670€ – Reservation fee 15€

Surroundings : ☐ ♤
Leisure activities : ✗
Facilities : ♿ ☎ 🏕 🚿 launderette
Nearby : 🍴 🎣 🐾

GPS
Longitude : -3.05522
Latitude : 47.57941

⛰ L'Océan

📞 06 31 65 00 75. www.camping-delocean.com – limited spaces for one-night stay

Address : Quartier le Men-Du, impasse des Gabelous (head along the D 186 towards La Trinité sur Mer and take the Chemin de Beaumer; 250m from the beach)

Opening times : from beginning April to mid Oct.

0.5 ha (50 pitches)

Tariff : 18.50€ 🚶🚶 ➔ 🔲 ⚡ (10A) – Extra per person 5€ – Reservation fee 15€

Rental rates : (from beginning April to mid Oct.) – 17 🚐. Per night from 50 to 60€ – Per week from 240 to 640€ – Reservation fee 15€

🚐 borne 2€ – 🔌 ⚡ 14.90€

Surroundings : ♤
Leisure activities : 🏄
Facilities : ♿ ☎ 🏧 🚿 🍴 🖥
Nearby : 🛒 🎣 🐾

GPS
Longitude : -3.05327
Latitude : 47.57849

Some information or pricing may have changed since the guide went to press. We recommend you check the price list online in advance or at the entrance to the campsite and enquire about possible restrictions.

LA CHAPELLE-AUX-FILTZMEENS

35190 – Michelin map **309** L4 – pop. 726 – alt. 40
▶ Paris 388 – Rennes 39 – Saint-Malo 42 – Fougères 83

⛰ Le Domaine du Logis

📞 02 99 45 25 45. www.domainedulogis.com

Address : Le Logis (located 1.5km west on the D 13, follow the signs for St-Dominieuc)

20 ha/6 for camping (188 pitches) flat, grassy
Rentals : ♿ ⌇ – 19 🚐.

In a lovely rural setting, based around a former traditional Breton farm complex.

Surroundings : 🌳 ☐ ♤
Leisure activities : 🍴 ✗ 🏓 🏕 🎣 🚣 🚴 🎯 🛶 mountain biking
Facilities : ♿ ☎ 🚿 launderette 🧺
Nearby : 🎣

GPS
Longitude : -1.83566
Latitude : 48.38306

A chambre d'hôte is a guesthouse or B & B-style accommodation.

CHÂTEAUGIRON

35410 – Michelin map **309** M6 – pop. 6 450 – alt. 45
▶ Paris 336 – Angers 114 – Châteaubriant 45 – Fougères 56

⛰ Les Grands Bosquets

📞 02 99 37 89 02. www.tourisme-payschateaugiron.fr

Address : route d'Ossé (take the eastern exit along the D 34)

Opening times : from beginning April to end Sept.

0.6 ha (33 pitches) flat, grassy

Tariff : (2014 Price) 🚶 2.20€ ➔ 3€ – ⚡ (6A) 2.50€

Beside a lake (suitable for bathing) in a rural setting.

Surroundings : ♤♤
Leisure activities : 🏖 (beach) 🎣
Facilities : 🏕
Nearby : 🏄 🎣

GPS
Longitude : -1.49734
Latitude : 48.04983

CHÂTEAULIN

29150 – Michelin map **308** G5 – pop. 5 337 – alt. 10
▶ Paris 548 – Brest 49 – Douarnenez 27 – Châteauneuf-du-Faou 24

⛰ Le Rodaven

📞 02 98 86 32 93. www.campingderodaven.fr

Address : south of the town, beside the Aulne river (right bank)

Opening times : from beginning April to end Sept.

2.3 ha (94 pitches) flat, grassy

Tariff : 16.50€ 🚶🚶 ➔ 🔲 ⚡ (10A) – Extra per person 3.90€

Rental rates : (2014 Price) (from beginning April to end Sept.) ⌇ – 2 caravans – 3 🚐. Per night from 42 to 62€ – Per week from 190 to 435€

🚐 borne

Beside the Aulne river, attractive pitches for tents and caravans, with shops and restaurants nearby.

Surroundings : ♤
Leisure activities : 🍴 🏄 🎣
Facilities : ♿ ☎ (mid July to mid Aug.) 🏧 🚿 launderette 🧺
Nearby : 🛒 ✗ 🚴 🎣 🏓 🛶 canoeing

GPS
Longitude : -4.08995
Latitude : 48.19012

CHÂTELAUDREN

22170 – Michelin map **309** E3 – pop. 1 047 – alt. 105
▶ Paris 469 – Guingamp 17 – Lannion 49 – St-Brieuc 18

⚠ Municipal de l'Étang

✆ 02 96 74 10 38. www.chatelaudren.fr – ♣

Address : rue de la Gare (in the town; beside a large, beautiful lake)

Opening times : from beginning May to end Sept.

0.2 ha (17 pitches)

Tariff : (2014 Price) ♦ 3€ ⇌ 1€ 🔲 4.20€ – 🔌 (10A) 3€

Surroundings : 🗔 👤	**GPS** Longitude : -2.9709
Leisure activities : 🎣	Latitude : 48.53883
Facilities : 🚻	
Nearby : 🏄	

CHÂTILLON-EN-VENDELAIS

35210 – Michelin map **309** O5 – pop. 1 698 – alt. 133
▶ Paris 311 – Fougères 17 – Rennes 49 – Vitré 13

⚠ Le Lac

✆ 06 03 33 64 35. www.chatillon-en-vendelais.fr

Address : route de Parce, l'Épine (500m north along the D 108; beside the Étang de Châtillon)

0.6 ha (61 pitches)

Rentals : 1 🏠.

In a pleasant natural setting by the lake (Étang de Chatillon).

Surroundings : 🌄 ⬅ 🗔 👤👤 ♨	**GPS** Longitude : -1.18026
Leisure activities : 🎣	Latitude : 48.22909
Facilities : 🏛	
Nearby : ♈ ✕ ✕	

CHERRUEIX

35120 – Michelin map **309** L3 – pop. 1 141 – alt. 3
▶ Paris 377 – Cancale 20 – Dinard 32 – Dol-de-Bretagne 9

⚠ L'Aumône

✆ 02 99 48 84 82. www.camping-de-laumone.com

Address : 0.5km south along the D 797

Opening times : from beginning April to beginning Nov.

1.6 ha (70 pitches) flat, grassy

Tariff : ♦ 4€ ⇌ 🔲 9€ – 🔌 (10A) 3.50€

Rental rates : (from beginning April to end Oct.) – 7 🚐 – 1 tipi – 1 tent lodge – 2 gîtes. Per night from 35 to 120€ – Per week from 105 to 590€

Located behind a beautiful stone building in a leafy setting, with slightly old sanitary facilities.

Surroundings : 👤	**GPS** Longitude : -1.71248
Leisure activities : ♈ ✕ 🏄 🚲 ⛴	Latitude : 48.60172
Facilities : ⚡ 🍴 launderette	

*For more information on visiting particular towns or regions, consult the relevant regional **MICHELIN Green Guide**. We also recommend you use the appropriate Michelin regional map to locate your selected campsite, to calculate distances and to work out the best route.*

CONCARNEAU

29900 – Michelin map **308** H7 – pop. 19 352 – alt. 4
▶ Paris 546 – Brest 96 – Lorient 49 – Quimper 22

🏔 Les Sables Blancs ♣♣

✆ 02 98 97 16 44. www.camping-lessablesblancs.com

Address : rue des Fleurs (100m from the beach)

Opening times : from beginning April to end Oct.

3 ha (149 pitches) terraced, relatively flat, flat, grassy

Tariff : (2014 Price) 30€ ♦♦ ⇌ 🔲 🔌 (10A) – Extra per person 7€

Rental rates : (2014 Price) (from beginning April to end Oct.) – 34 🚐. Per night from 45 to 115€ – Per week from 220 to 784€
🚻 borne

Situated close to the town centre and beaches, with a lovely view of the sea from some pitches.

Surroundings : 🌄 ⬅ Concarneau bay 🗔 👤👤	**GPS** Longitude : -3.92836
Leisure activities : ♈ ✕ 🏛 🏄 jacuzzi 🏄 ⛴	Latitude : 47.88203
Facilities : ⚡ ⚓ 🏕 🍴 launderette 🐕	
Nearby : 💧	

⚠ Les Prés Verts

✆ 02 98 97 09 74. www.presverts.com

Address : Kernous-Plage (3km northwest along the coast road and take a left turn; 250m from the beach (direct access)

3 ha (142 pitches) relatively flat to hilly, flat, grassy

Rentals : 🚐 – 12 🚐.

In a tranquil and pleasant setting, with just a little shade and a view over the Baie de Concarneau (bay) from some pitches.

Surroundings : 🌄	**GPS** Longitude : -3.93333
Leisure activities : 🏛 🏄 🎿 ⛴	Latitude : 47.88333
Facilities : ⚡ ⚓ 🍴 launderette	

LE CONQUET

29217 – Michelin map **308** C4 – pop. 2 635 – alt. 30
▶ Paris 619 – Brest 24 – Brignogan-Plages 59 – St-Pol-de-Léon 85

🏔 Les Blancs Sablons

✆ 02 98 36 07 91. www.les-blancs-sablons.com

Address : Le Théven (5km northeast along the D 67 and take D 28, follow the signs for the beach at Les Blancs Sablons, 400m from the beach – passenger walkway to town)

Opening times : from beginning April to end Sept.

12 ha (360 pitches)

Tariff : (2014 Price) 20€ ♦♦ ⇌ 🔲 🔌 (16A) – Extra per person 4.50€ Reservation fee 9€

Rental rates : (2014 Price) (from beginning April to mid Oct.) – 10 🚐 – 3 🏠. Per night from 57 to 77€ – Per week from 270 to 660€ – Reservation fee 9€

In a natural setting, bordering on the wild.

Surroundings : 🌄	**GPS** Longitude : -4.76071
Leisure activities : ♈ 🏄 ⛴	Latitude : 48.36687
Facilities : ⚡ ⚓ 🍴 launderette	

CRACH

56950 – Michelin map **308** M9 – pop. 3 276 – alt. 35
▶ Paris 482 – Auray 6 – Lorient 46 – Quiberon 29

⏶ Le Fort Espagnol

☎ 02 97 55 14 88. www.fort-espagnol.com

Address : route du Fort Espagnol (800m east, follow the signs for
La Rivière d'Auray)

5 ha (190 pitches)
Rentals : 3 caravans – 83 ⌁ – 4 ⌂ – 4 tent lodges.

Surroundings : ▨ ⌂ ♀♀	G	Longitude : -2.98988
Leisure activities : ⏻ ✕ ▦ ↯ ⌁ ⏦	P	Latitude : 47.61539
Facilities : ⏦ ⌾ ⏦ launderette ⏦	S	
Nearby : ⏦ ✕ ♦		

CROZON

29160 – Michelin map **308** E5 – pop. 7 697 – alt. 85
▶ Paris 587 – Brest 60 – Châteaulin 35 – Douarnenez 40

⏶ Les Pins

☎ 06 60 54 40 09. www.camping-crozon-lespins.com

Address : route de Dinan (situated 2km southwest along the D 308
follow the signs for La Pointe de Dinan (headland)

Opening times : from beginning April to end Sept.

4 ha (155 pitches) open site, flat and relatively flat, grassy, sandy

Tariff : (2014 Price) ⏦ 5€ ⇔ 🅴 9.50€ – (∅) (10A) 3.80€

Rental rates : (2014 Price) (from beginning April to
beginning Nov.) ⏦ (1 mobile home) – 12 ⌁ – 13 ⌂. Per night
from 65€ – Per week from 330 to 680€

*A very peaceful site under the pine trees; ideal for rest and
relaxation.*

Surroundings : ▨ ♀♀	G	Longitude : -4.51462
Leisure activities : ↯ ▨ (small swimming pool)	P	Latitude : 48.24153
Facilities : ⏦ ⌾ ⏦ ⏦ ⏦ 🅱	S	
Nearby : forest trail		

⏶ Plage de Goulien

☎ 06 08 43 49 32. www.presquile-crozon.com

Address : 5km west along the D 308, follow signs for La Pointe de
Dinan and take a right turn, 200m from the beach

Opening times : from mid June to mid Sept.

3.5 ha (135 pitches) terraced, relatively flat, flat, grassy

Tariff : ⏦ 5.35€ ⇔ 🅴 9.75€ – (∅) (10A) 4€ – Reservation fee 5€
Rental rates : (from mid April to mid Sept.) – 24 ⌁ – 4 ⌂.
Per week from 330 to 690€ – Reservation fee 10€
⏦ 5 🅴 20€
Located near a sandy beach.

Surroundings : ▨ ⌂ ♀♀	G	Longitude : -4.54437
Leisure activities : ⏻ ▦ ↯ ⏦	P	Latitude : 48.23908
Facilities : ⏦ ⌾ ⏦ ⏦ launderette ⏦ ⏦	S	

DINÉAULT

29150 – Michelin map **308** G5 – pop. 1 739 – alt. 160
▶ Paris 560 – Rennes 208 – Quimper 36 – Brest 54

⏶ Ty Provost

☎ 02 98 86 29 23. www.typrovost.com

Address : 4km southeast along the C 1, follow the signs for
Châteaulin and take road to the left

Opening times : from beginning June to mid Sept.

1.2 ha (44 pitches) terraced, flat and relatively flat, grassy

Tariff : 16.80€ ⏦⏦ ⇔ 🅴 (∅) (10A) – Extra per person 3.90€
Rental rates : Permanent ⏦ (2 chalets) – 5 ⌁ – 7 ⌂ – 2 gîtes.
Per night from 59 to 79€ – Per week from 297 to 497€
⏦ borne – 4 🅴 16.80€
*In a lovely setting, based at a traditional farm complex with a
panoramic view of the winding Aulne river.*

Surroundings : ▨ ⊰ Aulne valley ♀	G	Longitude : -4.12421
Leisure activities : ⏻ ▦ ↯	P	Latitude : 48.20706
Facilities : ⏦ ⌾ ⏦ ⏦ launderette	S	

DOL-DE-BRETAGNE

35120 – Michelin map **309** L3 – pop. 5 163 – alt. 20
▶ Paris 378 – Alençon 154 – Dinan 26 – Fougères 54

⏶ Les Castels Domaine des Ormes

☎ 02 99 73 53 00. www.lesormes.com – limited spaces for one-night
stay

Address : Épiniac (7.5km south along the D 795, follow the signs for
Combourg then take the road to the left)

Opening times : from beginning April to mid Sept.

200 ha/40 for camping (630 pitches) forest

Tariff : 54.10€ ⏦⏦ ⇔ 🅴 (∅) (10A) – Extra per person 8.30€ –
Reservation fee 20€
Rental rates : Permanent – 1 caravan – 81 ⌁ – 28 ⌂ – 45 ⏦ –
11 studios – 25 apartments – 30 cabins in the trees – 4 gîtes.
Per night from 52 to 256€ – Per week from 360 to 1,795€ –
Reservation fee 20€
⏦ borne
*In the grounds of a 16th-century château, with wide open
spaces and plenty of activities, including a partially covered
water park.*

Surroundings : ▨ ⊰ ♀♀	G	Longitude : -1.72722
Leisure activities : ⏻ ✕ ▦ ⏦ ⏦ ⏦ ↯ ⏦ ✕ ⏦ ▨ ⏦ ↯ ⏦ ⏦ disco, climbing wall, forest trail, paintballing, zip wiring, golf course, driving range, multi-sports ground, entertainment room	P	Latitude : 48.49139
Facilities : ⏦ ⌾ ⏦ launderette ⏦ ⏦	S	

⏶ Le Vieux Chêne

☎ 02 99 48 09 55. www.camping-vieuxchene.fr

Address : route de Pontorson (5km east, along the N 176, follow
the signs for Pontorson, east of Baguer-Pican on the D 57 – Advised
route via the diversion, take exit Dol-de-Bretagne-Est and take D 80,
D 576)

Opening times : from beginning May to mid Sept.

4 ha/2 for camping (213 pitches)

Tariff : 30€ ⏦⏦ ⇔ 🅴 (∅) (10A) – Extra per person 7€
Rental rates : (from mid April to mid Sept.) – 16 ⌁ – 18 ⌂.
Per night from 40 to 114€ – Per week from 200 to 798€
⏦ borne 5€ – 2 🅴 30€

*The classification (1 to 5 tents, **black** or **red**) that we
award to selected sites in this guide is our own system.
It should not be confused with the classification
(1 to 5 stars) of official organisations.*

In a pleasant location beside two natural lakes, a perfect spot for fishing and relaxing.

Surroundings : 🐾 ⌑ 🌳🌳
Leisure activities : ♈ ✕ 🏠 🚣 ✂ ♪ ⛵ 🏹
Facilities : ⚅ ⊶ 🎪 ♨ 🛁 ♻ ♈ launderette 🛋 ⚲

GPS Longitude : -1.68361
Latitude : 48.54945

ERDEVEN

56410 – Michelin map **308** M9 – pop. 3 402 – alt. 18
▶ Paris 492 – Auray 15 – Carnac 10 – Lorient 28

🏕 La Croëz-Villieu

📞 02 97 55 90 43. www.la-croez-villieu.com – limited spaces for one-night stay

Address : Kernogan, route de Kerhillio (located 1km southwest along the beach road at Kerhillio)

Opening times : from beginning May to end Sept.

3 ha (158 pitches) flat, grassy

Tariff : (2014 Price) 30.60€ ♈♈ ⇔ 🔲 ⚡ (10A) –
Extra per person 6.80€

Rental rates : (2014 Price) (from beginning April to mid Oct.) –
30 🛖 – 2 tent lodges. Per night 80€ – Per week from 135 to 805€

The water park is partly under cover.

Surroundings : 🐾 ⌑ 🌳
Leisure activities : ♈ 🏠 hammam, jacuzzi 🚣 ⛵ 🏹 🔲
Facilities : ⊶ ♨ launderette
Nearby : 🛒

GPS Longitude : -3.15838
Latitude : 47.63199

🏕 L' Idéal

📞 02 97 55 67 66. www.camping-l-ideal.com – limited spaces for one-night stay

Address : Lisveur, route de la Plage

Opening times : from beginning April to end Sept.

0.6 ha (30 pitches) flat, grassy

Tariff : 32€ ♈♈ ⇔ 🔲 ⚡ (10A) – Extra per person 6€

Rental rates : (2014 Price) (from beginning April to end Sept.) –
22 🛖 – 3 🏠 – 4 apartments. Per night from 60 to 105€ –
Per week from 220 to 710€ – Reservation fee 25€
🛖 2 🔲 18€ – ⚲13€

Surroundings : 🐾 🌳
Leisure activities : ♈ 🏠 🔲
Facilities : ⚅ ⊶ ♨ launderette

GPS Longitude : -3.16317
Latitude : 47.62115

ERQUY

22430 – Michelin map **309** H3 – pop. 3 802 – alt. 12
▶ Paris 451 – Dinan 46 – Dinard 39 – Lamballe 21

🏕 Le Vieux Moulin ♣♣

📞 02 96 72 34 23. www.camping-vieux-moulin.com

Address : 14 rue des Moulins (situated 2km east)

Opening times : from mid April to beginning Sept.

2.5 ha (173 pitches) flat, grassy

Tariff : ♈ 7€ ⇔ 5€ 🔲 14€ – ⚡ (10A) 6€

Rental rates : (from mid April to beginning Sept.) – 70 🛖.
Per night from 47 to 150€ – Per week from 329 to 1 050€
🛖 borne 5€

In a well-kept, green setting.

Surroundings : ⌑ 🌳🌳
Leisure activities : ♈ ✕ 🏠 🚣 🏹 🚴 🔲 🛶 ⛵ multi-sports ground
Facilities : ⚅ ⊶ 📧 🛁 ♻ ♈ launderette 🛋 ⚲
Nearby : ✂ 🔲 ♪

GPS Longitude : -2.44249
Latitude : 48.63828

🏕 Yelloh! Village Les Pins ♣♣

📞 02 96 72 31 12. www.yellohvillage.fr/camping/les_pins.com

Address : Le Guen, 88 rue des Moulins (located 1km to the north, on the corner of r. des Moulins and r. Léon Hamonet)

Opening times : from mid April to mid Sept.

10 ha (488 pitches)

Tariff : (2014 Price) 20€ ♈♈ ⇔ 🔲 ⚡ (10A) – Extra per person 5€

Rental rates : Permanent ⚅ – 160 🛖 – 5 🏠 – 11 canvas bungalows. Per night from 39 to 129€ – Per week from 273 to 903€

Surroundings : 🐾 ⌑ 🌳🌳
Leisure activities : ♈ ✕ 🏠 🎣 🏹 🚴 🐎 hammam jacuzzi 🚣 ✂ 🔲 🛶 ⛵ spa centre
Facilities : ⚅ ⊶ 🛁 ♈ launderette 🛋 ⚲
Nearby : ♪

GPS Longitude : -2.45573
Latitude : 48.63802

🏕 Sites et Paysages Bellevue ♣♣

📞 02 96 72 33 04. http://campingbellevue.fr

Address : route de la Libération (5.5km southwest)

Opening times : from mid April to mid Sept.

3.5 ha (160 pitches) flat, grassy

Tariff : 29€ ♈♈ ⇔ 🔲 ⚡ (10A) – Extra per person 5.70€

Rental rates : (from mid April to mid Sept.) ⚅ (1 chalet) 🏹 (from beginning July to end Aug.) – 18 🛖 – 5 🏠 – 4 canvas bungalows. Per night from 40 to 117€ – Per week from 280 to 820€
🛖 borne – 100 🔲 24€ – ⚲14€

The entrance is surrounded by flowers, the pitches are surrounded by trees and shrubs.

Surroundings : ⌑ 🌳🌳
Leisure activities : ♈ 🏠 🏹 🚴 ♪ 🔲 (open air in season) multi-sports ground
Facilities : ⚅ ⊶ 🛁 ♈ launderette ⚲
Nearby : 🛋

GPS Longitude : -2.48486
Latitude : 48.59377

🏕 St-Pabu

📞 02 96 72 24 65. www.saintpabu.com

Address : St-Pabu (at the beach at Saint-Pabu, 4km southwest)

Opening times : from beginning April to mid Oct.

5.5 ha (409 pitches)

Tariff : (2014 Price) 26.30€ ♈♈ ⇔ 🔲 ⚡ (10A) –
Extra per person 5.60€ – Reservation fee 20€

Rental rates : (2014 Price) (from beginning April to mid Oct.) –
39 🛖. Per week from 285 to 740€ – Reservation fee 20€
🛖 borne 6€

Opposite the Baie d'Erquy (bay).

Surroundings : 🐾 ⬅ ⌑ ⛰
Leisure activities : ♈ 🏠 🚣
Facilities : ⚅ ⊶ 🛁 ♈ launderette 🛋
Nearby : 🤿 scuba diving

GPS Longitude : -2.49459
Latitude : 48.60878

Les Roches

📞 02 96 72 32 90. www.camping-les-roches.com

Address : rue Pierre Vergos (3km southwest)

Opening times : from mid March to beginning Nov.

3 ha (160 pitches)

Tariff : (2014 Price) 👤 4€ 🚗 3€ 🔲 6.50€ – 🔌 (10A) 3.90€ – Reservation fee 8€

Rental rates : (2014 Price) (from mid March to beginning Nov.) – 18 🛖 – 1 tent lodge. Per night from 40 to 80€ – Per week from 220 to 660€ – Reservation fee 8€

🚐 borne

On the slopes of Caroual Village.

Surroundings : 🌳 ♀
Leisure activities : 🏠 🎣 🏹 ⛰
Facilities : 🚿 ⛽ 🏢 🔥 🍴 launderette ♨

GPS	Longitude : -2.4769
	Latitude : 48.6094

Des Hautes Grées

📞 02 96 72 34 78. www.camping-hautes-grees.com

Address : 123 rue St Michel, Les Hopitaux (3.5km to the northeast, 400m from the St-Michel beach)

Opening times : from mid April to end Sept.

3 ha (177 pitches) flat, grassy

Tariff : (2014 Price) 26.40€ 👥 🚗 🔲 🔌 (10A) – Extra per person 5.60€ – Reservation fee 15€

Rental rates : (2014 Price) (from mid April to end Sept.) – 35 🛖. Per night from 45 to 70€ – Per week from 290 to 720€ – Reservation fee 15€

🚐 borne 14.50€ – 10 🔲 14.50€ – 💧 🔌 14.50€

Surroundings : 🌳 🐚
Leisure activities : 🏠 🎿 ♨ 🎣 🏹 ⛷
Facilities : 🚿 ⛽ 🔥 🍴 launderette

GPS	Longitude : -2.42491
	Latitude : 48.64254

ÉTABLES-SUR-MER

22680 – Michelin map **309** E3 – pop. 3 091 – alt. 65
▶ Paris 467 – Guingamp 31 – Lannion 56 – St-Brieuc 19

L'Abri-Côtier

📞 02 96 70 61 57. www.camping-abricotier.fr

Address : 12 rue De Robien (located 1km north following signs for St-Quay-Portrieux and take the turning to the left)

Opening times : from beginning May to mid Sept.

2 ha (140 pitches)

Tariff : 👤 5.80€ 🚗 🔲 8€ – 🔌 (10A) 4€

Rental rates : (from beginning May to mid Sept.) – 14 🛖 – 5 canvas bungalows. Per night from 50 to 80€ – Per week from 240 to 700€

🚐 borne 2€

Surroundings : 🌳
Leisure activities : 🍸 jacuzzi ♨
Facilities : 🚿 ⛽ 🏢 🔥 🍴 launderette ♨ 🔥
Nearby : ✂ ⛰ 🦆 🏇

GPS	Longitude : -2.83529
	Latitude : 48.6354

This guide is updated regularly, so buy your new copy every year!

LE FAOUËT

56320 – Michelin map **308** J6 – pop. 2 893 – alt. 68
▶ Paris 516 – Carhaix-Plouguer 35 – Lorient 40 – Pontivy 47

Municipal Beg er Roch

📞 02 97 23 15 11. http://campingbegerroch.jimdo.com

Address : route de Lorient (situated 2km southeast along the D 769, follow the signs for Lorient)

3 ha (65 pitches) flat, grassy

Rentals : 8 🛖.

In a pleasant setting beside the Ellé river.

Surroundings : ♀
Leisure activities : 🏠 🎣 🏹 ⛷
Facilities : 🚿 ⛽ 🏢 ♨ launderette

GPS	Longitude : -3.46973
	Latitude : 48.01794

FEINS

35440 – Michelin map **309** M5 – pop. 798 – alt. 104
▶ Paris 369 – Avranches 55 – Fougères 44 – Rennes 30

Domaine de Boulet

📞 02 99 69 63 23. www.pays-aubigne.fr/camping

Address : at Domaine de Boulet (situated 2km northeast along the D 91, follow the signs for Marcillé-Raoul and take road to the left)

Opening times : from mid April to end Sept.

1.5 ha (62 pitches) flat, grassy

Tariff : (2014 Price) 11€ 👥 🚗 🔲 🔌 (10A) – Extra per person 4.50€

Rental rates : (2014 Price) (from mid April to end Sept.) – 6 🛖. Per week from 38 to 50€

In a pleasant location beside the Étang de Boulet (lake), with some unusual-style accommodation.

Surroundings : 🌳 ⛵ ♀ ≈
Leisure activities : 🏠 🎣 🚲 ⛷
Facilities : 🚿 ⛽ (July-Aug.) ♨ 🍴 launderette, refrigerated food storage facilities
Nearby : ✂ 🦆 🏇 watersports centre

GPS	Longitude : -1.63863
	Latitude : 48.33845

LA FORÊT-FOUESNANT

29940 – Michelin map **308** H7 – pop. 3 299 – alt. 19
▶ Paris 553 – Rennes 202 – Quimper 18 – Brest 94

Club Airotel Kérantérec 👥

📞 02 98 56 98 11. www.camping-keranterec.com

Address : at Kerleven (2.8km southeast)

Opening times : from mid April to end Sept.

6.5 ha (265 pitches) very uneven, terraced, relatively flat, flat, grassy

Tariff : 34€ 👥 🚗 🔲 🔌 (16A) – Extra per person 8.50€ – Reservation fee 30€

Rental rates : (from mid April to mid Sept.) – 52 🛖. Per night from 70 to 250€ – Per week from 270 to 950€ – Reservation fee 30€

🚐 borne 4€

With special access to the beach, this site is set amid lovely surroundings and enjoys peace and tranquility.

Surroundings : 🌳 ⛵ ♀ ≈
Leisure activities : 🍸 🍴 🏠 🎣 🎿 🎣 🚲 ✂ 📺 ♨ entertainment room
Facilities : 🚿 ⛽ ♨ 🍴 launderette

GPS	Longitude : -3.95538
	Latitude : 47.89903

▲▲▲ Kerleven ♣♣

✆ 02 98 56 98 83. www.campingdekerleven.com – limited spaces for one-night stay

Address : at Kerleven, 4 route de Port La Forêt, (situated 2km southeast, 200m from the beach)

Opening times : from mid April to end Sept.

4 ha (235 pitches)

Tariff : (2014 Price) 33.20€ ♣♣ ⇔ 回 ⚡ (10A) – Extra per person 7.50€ – Reservation fee 10€

Rental rates : (2014 Price) (from mid April to end Sept.) ✂ (from mid April to end June) – 37 ⏚. Per night from 60 to 85€ – Per week from 240 to 799€ – Reservation fee 10€

borne 2€ – ⚡16€

In a pleasant location based around a former Breton 'longère' farmhouse.

Surroundings : ⌷ ♀♀
Leisure activities : ♈ ✕ 🖼 ☺ 🏃 ⚓ 🖼 🏊 ⛵
Facilities : ♿ ⚷ ⛺ ♈ launderette 🚿 ⚓
Nearby : ♨

GPS Longitude : -3.96788   Latitude : 47.89807

▲▲▲ Les Saules ♣♣

✆ 02 98 56 98 57. www.camping-les-saules.com

Address : at Kerléven, 54 route de la Plage (2.5km southeast; beside the beach at Kerléven (direct access))

Opening times : from beginning May to end Sept.

4 ha (235 pitches)

Tariff : 32€ ♣♣ ⇔ 回 ⚡ (6A) – Extra per person 6.80€ – Reservation fee 18€

Rental rates : (from beginning April to end Sept.) ♿ (1 mobile home) – 37 ⏚. Per night from 90 to 195€ – Per week from 199 to 949€ – Reservation fee 18€

Divided into two sections, with a few special pitches in the lower section near the sea.

Surroundings : ⌷ ♀ ⚠
Leisure activities : ♈ ✕ 🖼 🏃 ⚓ 🏊 ⛵
Facilities : ⚷ ⛺ ♈ launderette 🚿
Nearby : ♨

GPS Longitude : -3.9611   Latitude : 47.899

▲▲ Manoir de Penn ar Ster

✆ 02 98 56 97 75. www.camping-pennarster.com

Address : 2 chemin de Penn-Ar-Ster (take the northeastern exit, follow the signs for Quimper and take the turning to the left)

Opening times : from mid March to mid Nov.

3 ha (97 pitches)

Tariff : 24.50€ ♣♣ ⇔ 回 ⚡ (10A) – Extra per person 7€ – Reservation fee 10€

Rental rates : (from mid March to mid Nov.) ♿ (2 chalets) – 8 ⏚ – 2 🏠 – 1 tent lodge. Per night from 45 to 70€ – Per week from 230 to 690€ – Reservation fee 15€

borne 5€ – 5 回 17€ – ⚡17€

The site adjoins a pretty stone manor house with an adjacent garden.

Surroundings : ⌷ ♀♀
Leisure activities : 🖼 ⚓ ♈
Facilities : ♿ ⚷ 🏛 ⛺ 🚿 ♈ launderette
Nearby : ♈ ✕

GPS Longitude : -3.97977   Latitude : 47.91215

▲▲ FranceLoc Domaine du St-Laurent

✆ 02 98 56 97 65. www.franceloc.fr

Address : at Kerleven (3km southeast, 500m from the large beach at Kerleven)

Opening times : from beginning April to end Sept.

5.4 ha (260 pitches)

Tariff : (2014 Price) 16€ ♣♣ ⇔ 回 ⚡ (10A) – Extra per person 4.70€ Reservation fee 27€

Rental rates : (2014 Price) (from beginning April to end Sept.) ♿ (1 mobile home) – 194 ⏚. Per night from 33 to 119€ – Per week from 133 to 1,218€ – Reservation fee 27€

Some pitches have a view of the sea and the Îles de Glénan (islands). There is an impressive water park with water slides.

Surroundings : ✎ ⌷ ♀♀ ⚠
Leisure activities : ♈ ✕ ☺ 🏃 ⚓ ✂ 🎯 🖼 🏊 ⚓ multi-sports ground
Facilities : ♿ ⚷ ⛺ ♈ launderette ⚓
Nearby : ≈ ♨

GPS Longitude : -3.9547   Latitude : 47.89623

29170 – Michelin map **308** G7 – pop. 9 356 – alt. 30
▶ Paris 555 – Carhaix-Plouguer 69 – Concarneau 11 – Quimper 16

▲▲▲ Sunêlia L'Atlantique ♣♣

✆ 02 98 56 14 44. www.latlantique.fr – limited spaces for one-night stay ✂

Address : 4.5km to the south, towards La Chapelle de Kerbader, 400m from the beach (direct access)

Opening times : from end April to beginning Sept.

10 ha (432 pitches) flat, grassy

Tariff : 46€ ♣♣ ⇔ 回 ⚡ (6A) – Extra per person 8€ – Reservation fee 35€

Rental rates : (from end April to beginning Sept.) ♿ (1 mobile home) ✂ – 200 ⏚ – 4 yurts – 10 tent lodges. Per night from 30 to 196€ – Per week from 210 to 1,372€ – Reservation fee 35€

borne – ⚡16€

Equipped with a pretty swimming area and spa, this site has beach access via a lovely path across the Fouesnant marshland.

Surroundings : ✎ ⌷ ♀♀
Leisure activities : ♈ ✕ 🖼 ☺ 🏃 💆 ⚓ hammam, jacuzzi ⚓ 🚴 ✂ 🎯 🖼 🏊 ⛵ spa centre, entertainment room
Facilities : ♿ ⚷ 回 ⛺ 🚿 ⚓ ♈ launderette 🚿 ⚓

GPS Longitude : -4.01854   Latitude : 47.85487

35300 – Michelin map **309** O4 – pop. 19 820 – alt. 115
▶ Paris 326 – Caen 148 – Le Mans 132 – Nantes 158

▲ Municipal de Paron

✆ 02 99 99 40 81. campingmunicipal35@orange.fr

Address : route de la Chapelle-Janson (located 1.5km east along the D 17, access recommended via the eastern bypass (rocade)

2.5 ha (90 pitches) relatively flat, flat, grassy

borne

In a lovely setting among trees, a stone's throw from the medieval city of Fougères.

Surroundings : ✎ ⌷ ♀♀
Leisure activities : ⚓
Facilities : ⚷ launderette
Nearby : ✂ 🖼 🐎

GPS Longitude : -1.18193   Latitude : 48.35371

LE FRET

29160 – Michelin map **308** D5
▶ Paris 591 – Rennes 239 – Quimper 56 – Brest 10

� Gwel Kaër

☎ 02 98 27 61 06. www.camping-gwel-kaer.com

Address : 40 rue de Pen-An-Ero (take the southeastern exit along the D 55, follow the signs for Crozon; beside the sea)

Opening times : from beginning April to end Sept.

2.2 ha (98 pitches) terraced, flat and relatively flat, grassy

Tariff : (2014 Price) ⚬ 4.60€ ⚬ 2.50€ ⚬ 4.40€ – ⚡ (10A) 3.45€

Rental rates : (2014 Price) (from beginning April to end Sept.) – 7 ⚬. Per night from 42 to 65€ – Per week from 290 to 530€

A peaceful site near the water, with a pretty view of Le Fret port and Brest harbour.

Surroundings : ⚬ ⚬ ⚬
Leisure activities : ⚬
Facilities : ⚬ ⚬ (from mid June to mid Sept) ⚬ ⚬ ⚬

GPS Longitude : -4.50237
Latitude : 48.28132

LE GUERNO

56190 – Michelin map **308** Q9 – pop. 818 – alt. 60
▶ Paris 460 – Muzillac 8 – Redon 30 – La Roche-Bernard 17

⚬ Municipal de Borg-Néhué

☎ 02 97 42 94 76. www.leguerno.fr

Address : rue du Borg Nehué (500m northwest following signs for Noyal-Muzillac)

Opening times : from beginning April to end Oct.

1.4 ha (50 pitches) flat, grassy

Tariff : (2014 Price) 12.30€ ⚬⚬ ⚬ ⚬ ⚡ (6A) – Extra per person 3.10€

Rental rates : (2014 Price) Permanent – 9 ⚬. Per night from 104€ – Per week from 174 to 455€

⚬ borne – 10 ⚬ 12.30€

Surroundings : ⚬ ⚬ ⚬
Leisure activities : ⚬
Facilities : ⚬ ⚬ ⚬ ⚬ ⚬
Nearby : ⚬

GPS Longitude : -2.41557
Latitude : 47.58251

GUIDEL

56520 – Michelin map **308** K8 – pop. 10 174 – alt. 38
▶ Paris 511 – Nantes 178 – Quimper 60 – Rennes 162

⚬⚬⚬ Les Jardins de Kergal

☎ 02 97 05 98 18. www.camping-lorient.com

Address : route des Plages (3km southwest along the D 306, follow the signs for Guidel-Plages and take road to the left)

Opening times : from beginning April to mid Nov.

5 ha (153 pitches) flat, grassy

Tariff : (2014 Price) 31€ ⚬⚬ ⚬ ⚬ ⚡ (16A) – Extra per person 7€ – Reservation fee 20€

Rental rates : (2014 Price) (from beginning April to mid Nov.) ⚬ (1 chalet) – 30 ⚬ – 32 ⚬. Per night from 50 to 100€ – Per week from 210 to 860€ – Reservation fee 20€

A pleasant wooded site.

Surroundings : ⚬ ⚬⚬
Leisure activities : ⚬ ⚬ ⚬ ⚬ ⚬ ⚬ ⚬ ⚬ ⚬ multi-sports ground
Facilities : ⚬ ⚬ ⚬ ⚬ launderette refrigerators
Nearby : ⚬ ⚬ sports trail

GPS Longitude : -3.50734
Latitude : 47.77464

ÎLE-AUX-MOINES

56780 – Michelin map **308** N9 – pop. 601 – alt. 16
▶ Paris 483 – Rennes 132 – Vannes 15 – Lorient 59

⚬ Municipal du Vieux Moulin

☎ 02 97 26 30 68. www.mairie-ileauxmoines.fr ⚬

Address : Le Vieux Moulin (take southeastern exit from town, follow the signs for La Pointe de Brouel (headland)

Opening times : from mid April to mid Sept.

1 ha (44 pitches)

Tariff : (2014 Price) ⚬ 7€ ⚬ ⚡ (0A)

Rental rates : (2014 Price) Permanent ⚬ – 4 canvas bungalows. Per night from 46 to 77€ – Per week from 217 to 434€ – Reservation fee 5€

A site with no electricity supply, reserved for tents.

Surroundings : ⚬
Leisure activities : ⚬
Facilities : ⚬
Nearby : ⚬

GPS Longitude : -2.84514
Latitude : 47.59292

JOSSELIN

56120 – Michelin map **308** P7 – pop. 2 533 – alt. 58
▶ Paris 428 – Dinan 86 – Lorient 76 – Pontivy 35

⚬ Domaine de Kerelly

☎ 02 97 22 22 20. www.camping-josselin.com

Address : Le Bas de la Lande (situated 2km west along the D 778 and take the D 724, follow the signs for Guégon to the left, 50m from the Oust river, take the western exit Guégon along the dual carriageway)

Opening times : from mid April to beginning Oct.

2 ha (60 pitches) terraced, relatively flat, flat, grassy, adjacent pine trees

Tariff : (2014 Price) 20.50€ ⚬⚬ ⚬ ⚬ ⚡ (10A) – Extra per person 4€

Rental rates : (2014 Price) (from beginning April to beginning Oct.) – 8 ⚬ – 3 canvas bungalows. Per night from 50 to 90€ – Per week from 250 to 680€ ⚬ borne

Cyclists are welcome.

Surroundings : ⚬ ⚬
Leisure activities : ⚬ ⚬ ⚬ ⚬
Facilities : ⚬ ⚬ ⚬ ⚬ ⚬ ⚬ launderette
Nearby : ⚬ ⚬

GPS Longitude : -2.57352
Latitude : 47.95239

JUGON-LES-LACS

22270 – Michelin map **309** I4 – pop. 1 683 – alt. 29
▶ Paris 417 – Lamballe 22 – Plancoët 16 – St-Brieuc 59

⚬⚬⚬ Au Bocage du Lac

☎ 02 96 31 60 16. www.camping-location-bretagne.com

Address : rue du Bocage (located 1km southeast along the D 52, follow the signs for Mégrit)

4 ha (180 pitches)

Rentals : 7 ⚬ – 40 ⚬ – 1 cabin in the trees – 1 'floating' chalet.

Situated beside the large Étang de Jugon (lake), with a lovely indoor water park and play area.

Surroundings : ⚬ ⚬
Leisure activities : ⚬ ⚬ ⚬ ⚬ ⚬ ⚬ ⚬ ⚬ wildlife park
Facilities : ⚬ ⚬ ⚬ ⚬ launderette
Nearby : ⚬ ⚬ ⚬ ⚬

GPS Longitude : -2.31663
Latitude : 48.40165

KERVEL

29550 – Michelin map **308** F6
▶ Paris 586 – Rennes 234 – Quimper 24 – Brest 67

▲▲▲ FranceLoc Domaine de Kervel ▲▲

📞 02 98 92 51 54. www.kervel.fr

Address : at Kervel

Opening times : from mid April to mid Sept.

7 ha (316 pitches) flat, grassy

Tariff : (2014 Price) 33€ ♣♣ 🚐 🅴 🔌 (10A) – Extra per person 7€ – Reservation fee 27€

Rental rates : (2014 Price) (from mid April to mid Sept.) ♿ (1 mobile home) – 147 🛖 – 3 🏠. Per night from 37 to 151€ – Per week from 147 to 1,057€ – Reservation fee 27€

Numerous mobile homes beside a large, partially indoor water park.

Surroundings : 🌿🌿
Leisure activities : 🍴✕ 🎦 🛶🚣🏊🚴 ✂🏇🔳🏊⛳ multi-sports ground
Facilities : ♿ ⊶ 🚿♨ 🚾 🍴 launderette 🏖️

GPS	Longitude : -4.26737
	Latitude : 48.11617

We have selected the best campsites in France with our usual care, listing those with the best facilities in the most pleasant surroundings.

KERVOYAL

56750 – Michelin map **308** P9
▶ Paris 471 – Rennes 124 – Vannes 30 – Lorient 87

▲ Oasis

📞 02 97 41 10 52. www.campingloasis.com – 🏧

Address : rue Port Lestre (100m from the beach)

Opening times : from beginning May to end Sept.

3 ha (150 pitches) flat, grassy

Tariff : 23.10€ ♣♣ 🚐 🅴 🔌 (6A) – Extra per person 3.65€

🛖 borne

Surroundings : 🌊🌿🌿
Leisure activities : 🛶🚣
Facilities : ⊶ 🍴 launderette

GPS	Longitude : -2.55013
	Latitude : 47.51897

LAMPAUL-PLOUDALMEZEAU

29830 – Michelin map **308** D3 – pop. 753 – alt. 24
▶ Paris 613 – Brest 27 – Brignogan-Plages 36 – Ploudalmézeau 4

▲ Municipal des Dunes

📞 02 98 48 14 29. lampaul-ploudalmezeau.mairie@wanadoo.fr

Address : Le Vourc'h (700m north of the town, beside the sports field and 100m from the beach (direct access)

Opening times : from mid June to mid Sept.

1.5 ha (150 pitches) open site, flat, grassy, sandy, dunes

Tariff : (2014 Price) ♣ 4.70€ 🚐 – 🔌 (16A) 2.60€

🛖 borne 2.50€

A natural site among the dunes.

Surroundings : 🌊
Leisure activities : 🎦
Facilities : ♿ ⊶ (July–Aug.) 🚿 launderette

GPS	Longitude : -4.65639
	Latitude : 48.56785

LANDÉDA

29870 – Michelin map **308** D3 – pop. 3 620 – alt. 52
▶ Paris 604 – Brest 28 – Brignogan-Plages 25 – Ploudalmézeau 17

▲▲ Les Abers ▲▲

📞 02 98 04 93 35. www.camping-des-abers.com

Address : 51 Toull Tréaz (2.5km to the northwest; by the dunes at Ste-Marguerite)

Opening times : from beginning May to end Sept.

4.5 ha (180 pitches) dunes

Tariff : 21€ ♣♣ 🚐 🅴 🔌 (10A) – Extra per person 4.30€

Rental rates : (from beginning May to end Sept.) ♿ (1 mobile home) – 22 🛖 – 1 studio – 1 apartment. Per week from 280 to 630€

🛖 borne

In a pleasant location close to the beach, the site is well situated among the sand dunes; small islands can be reached at low tide.

Surroundings : 🌊◁⛰️
Leisure activities : 🎦 🛶🚣🏊🚴
Facilities : ♿ ⊶ 🚿 🍴 launderette 🏖️
Nearby : 🍴✕

GPS	Longitude : -4.60306
	Latitude : 48.59306

Some information or pricing may have changed since the guide went to press. We recommend you check the price list online in advance or at the entrance to the campsite and enquire about possible restrictions.

LANLOUP

22580 – Michelin map **309** E2 – pop. 272 – alt. 58
▶ Paris 484 – Guingamp 29 – Lannion 44 – St-Brieuc 36

▲▲▲ Le Neptune

📞 02 96 22 33 35. www.leneptune.com

Address : Ker Guistin (on the D786, south of Plouezec)

Opening times : from beginning April to mid Oct.

2 ha (84 pitches) relatively flat, flat, grassy

Tariff : (2014 Price) ♣ 6€ 🚐 🅴 13€ – 🔌 (10A) 4€ – Reservation fee 10€

Rental rates : (2014 Price) (from beginning April to mid Oct.) – 16 🛖 – 4 🏠 – 1 tent lodge. Per night from 25 to 113€ – Per week from 235 to 837€ – Reservation fee 10€

🛖 borne 8€

In a pleasant setting with trees and shrubs.

Surroundings : 🌳🌿
Leisure activities : 🍴 🎦 🚣🏊 🚴🏓🔳 (open air in season) multi-sports ground
Facilities : ♿ ⊶ 🅲 🚿 🍴 launderette 🏖️
Nearby : ✂

GPS	Longitude : -2.96704
	Latitude : 48.71372

Key to rentals symbols:

12 🛖	*Number of mobile homes*
20 🏠	*Number of chalets*
6 🛏️	*Number of rooms to rent*
Per night 30–50€	*Minimum/maximum rate per night*
Per week 300–1,000€	*Minimum/maximum rate per week*

LANNION

22300 – Michelin map **309** B2 – pop. 19 847 – alt. 12
▶ Paris 516 – Brest 96 – Morlaix 42 – St-Brieuc 65

⋀⋀⋀ Les Plages de Beg-Léguer

☎ 02 96 47 25 00. www.campingdesplages.com

Address : route de la Côte (6km west following signs for Trébeurden and take the turning to the left, 500m from the beach)

Opening times : from beginning May to end Sept.

5 ha (240 pitches)

Tariff : (2014 Price) ♣ 7.70€ ⇔ 🅴 8.80€ – 🔌 (6A) 3.90€

Rental rates : (2014 Price) (from beginning May to end Sept.) 🅿 – 27 🚐 – 7 🏠 – 6 canvas bungalows. Per night from 35 to 109€ – Per week from 210 to 763€

🚰 borne

Surroundings : 🌊 ⌷ ♤♤
Leisure activities : 🍽 ✗ 🛶 ♨ 🚵 ✂ 🗖 🏊 🏄 multi-sports ground
Facilities : & ⚊ ♨ launderette ⚲

G P S Longitude : -3.545
Latitude : 48.73834

⋀ Municipal des 2 Rives

☎ 02 96 46 31 40. www.ville-lannion.fr

Address : rue du Moulin du Duc (situated 2km southeast along the D 767, follow the signs for Guingamp and take the turning to the right after the Leclerc commercial centre)

2.3 ha (116 pitches) flat, grassy

Rentals : & (1 chalet) – 14 🏠 – 4 canvas bungalows.

A site with attractive trees and shrubs on both banks of the Léguer river.

Surroundings : 🌊 ♤
Leisure activities : 🍸 🛶 🎣
Facilities : & ⚊ ♨ 🏊 ♨ launderette
Nearby : 🥾 walking trails

G P S Longitude : -3.44584
Latitude : 48.72293

LANTIC

22410 – Michelin map **309** E3 – pop. 1 483 – alt. 50
▶ Paris 466 – Brest 139 – Lorient 133 – Rennes 116

⋀ Les Étangs

☎ 02 96 71 95 47. www.campinglesetangs.com

Address : rue des Terres Neuvas, Le Pont de la Motte (situated 2km east along the D 4, follow the signs for Binic, near two lakes)

1.5 ha (110 pitches) terrace, relatively flat, flat, grassy

Rentals : 10 🚐 – 1 🏠 – 2 canvas bungalows.

Surroundings : 🌊 ♤♤
Leisure activities : 🛶 🛶 🏊
Facilities : & ⚊ ♨ ♨ 🖻
Nearby : 🛶

G P S Longitude : -2.86254
Latitude : 48.6068

These symbols are used for a campsite that is exceptional in its category:

⋀⋀⋀ ... ⋀   *Particularly pleasant setting, quality and range of services available*

🌊 🌊   *Tranquil, isolated site – quiet site, particularly at night*

≪ ≪   *Exceptional view – interesting or panoramic view*

LARMOR-PLAGE

56260 – Michelin map **308** K8 – pop. 8 423 – alt. 4
▶ Paris 510 – Lorient 7 – Quimper 74 – Vannes 66

⋀ La Fontaine

☎ 02 97 33 71 28. www.campingdelafontaine.fr

Address : Kerdeff, rue de Quéhello (to the west of the resort, 300m from the D 152 recommended route)

Opening times : Permanent

4 ha (130 pitches) relatively flat, flat, grassy

Tariff : (2014 Price) 22.50€ ♣♣ ⇔ 🅴 🔌 (16A) – Extra per person 5.10€

Rental rates : Permanent – 19 🚐. Per night from 50 to 60€ – Per week from 270 to 560€

🚰 borne – 3 🅴 12€

Surroundings : 🌊 ⌷ ♤♤
Leisure activities : 🛶 🏌
Facilities : & ⚊ 🖬 🏊 ♨ launderette

G P S Longitude : -3.39212
Latitude : 47.70912

LESCONIL

29740 – Michelin map **308** F8
▶ Paris 581 – Douarnenez 41 – Guilvinec 6 – Loctudy 7

⋀⋀⋀ La Grande Plage

☎ 02 98 87 88 27. www.campinggrandeplage.com

Address : 71 rue Paul Langevin (located 1km west, follow the signs for Guilvinec, 300m from the beach (direct access)

Opening times : from beginning April to end Sept.

2.5 ha (120 pitches)

Tariff : 26.75€ ♣♣ ⇔ 🅴 🔌 (10A) – Extra per person 5.50€

Rental rates : (from beginning April to end Sept.) – 15 🚐 – 5 canvas bungalows. Per night from 43 to 132€ – Per week from 265 to 860€

🚰 borne 2€

A very pleasant site that has been renovated recently, with a pretty swimming pool and access to the beach at 200m.

Surroundings : ⌷ ♤♤
Leisure activities : 🍸 ✗ 🛶 🛶 🚵 🏊 ♨
Facilities : & ⚊ ♨ ♨ launderette ⚲

G P S Longitude : -4.22897
Latitude : 47.79804

⋀ Les Dunes

☎ 02 98 87 81 78. http://www.camping-desdunes.com

Address : 67 rue Paul-Langevin (located 1km west, follow the signs for Guilvinec; 150m from the beach (direct access)

2.8 ha (120 pitches) flat, grassy

Rentals : 4 🚐.

A pleasant site, set back a bit from the sea.

Surroundings : ⌷ ♤
Leisure activities : 🛶 🛶
Facilities : & ⚊ ♨ ♨ launderette

G P S Longitude : -4.22856
Latitude : 47.79716

⋀ Keralouet

☎ 02 98 82 23 05. www.campingkeralouet.com

Address : 11 rue Eric Tabarly (located 1km east on the Loctudy road)

Opening times : from beginning April to mid Sept.

1 ha (64 pitches) flat, grassy

Tariff : (2014 Price) 21.25€ ♣♣ ⇔ 🅴 🔌 (10A) – Extra per person 4.50€

Rental rates : (2014 Price) (from beginning April to mid Sept.) ♿ (1 chalet) – 19 ⬚ – 4 canvas bungalows – 2 tent lodges. Per night from 39 to 75€ – Per week from 205 to 659€

A well-kept and pleasant site, an interesting and restorative stop for touring cyclists.

Surroundings : ♤♤
Leisure activities : 🏊🚴♒
Facilities : ♿☞🍴📺
Nearby : ◊

GPS Longitude : -4.20595
Latitude : 47.80424

LOCMARIA-PLOUZANÉ

29280 – Michelin map **308** D4 – pop. 4 837 – alt. 65
▶ Paris 610 – Brest 15 – Brignogan-Plages 50 – Ploudalmézeau 23

⚠ Municipal de Portez

☎ 02 98 48 49 85. tourisme@locmaria-plouzane.fr

Address : Portez (3.5km southwest along the D 789 and follow the signs for the beach at Trégana; 200m from the beach)

Opening times : from beginning May to mid Sept.

2 ha (110 pitches) open site, terraced, flat, grassy

Tariff : (2014 Price) 15.14€ ✶✶ ⬅ 回 [2] (8A) – Extra per person 3.50€

Rental rates : (2014 Price) (from beginning May to mid Sept.) – 5 ⬚. Per night from 35 to 70€ – Per week from 220 to 470€ ⬚ borne 4.60€

An attractive location with pleasant pitches and a lovely view of the Anse de Bertheaume (cove).

Surroundings : ♤ ⬚♤
Leisure activities : 🏠 🏊
Facilities : ♿☞ (15 June-15 Sept) ⬚ launderette
Nearby : ♈ ✗

GPS Longitude : -4.66344
Latitude : 48.3582

LOCMARIAQUER

56740 – Michelin map **308** N9 – pop. 1 692 – alt. 5
▶ Paris 488 – Auray 13 – Quiberon 31 – La Trinité-sur-Mer 10

⚠ Lann-Brick

☎ 02 97 57 32 79. www.camping-lannbrick.com

Address : Lann Brick - route de Kérinis (2.5km northwest following signs for Kérinis, 200m from the beach)

Opening times : from beginning March to end Oct.

1.2 ha (98 pitches) flat, grassy

Tariff : 22€ ✶✶ ⬅ 回 [2] (10A) – Extra per person 5€ – Reservation fee 15€

Rental rates : (from mid March to end Oct.) – 20 ⬚ – 2 canvas bungalows. Per night from 65 to 145€ – Per week from 180 to 745€ Reservation fee 15€
⬚ borne 3€ – 🔋 [2]16€

Surroundings : ⬚♤
Leisure activities : ♈🏠🏊🚴♒
Facilities : ♿☞⬚🍴launderette
Nearby : ✗🎣◊

GPS Longitude : -2.97436
Latitude : 47.57838

*The classification (1 to 5 tents, **black** or red) that we award to selected sites in this guide is our own system. It should not be confused with the classification (1 to 5 stars) of official organisations.*

LOCRONAN

29180 – Michelin map **308** F6 – pop. 798 – alt. 105
▶ Paris 580 – Rennes 229 – Quimper 17

⛰ Le Locronan

☎ 02 98 91 87 76. www.camping-locronan.fr

Address : rue de la Troménie

Opening times : from mid April to end Sept.

2.6 ha (100 pitches)

Tariff : (2014 Price) 24€ ✶✶ ⬅ 回 [2] (10A) – Extra per person 5.50€ – Reservation fee 5€

Rental rates : (2014 Price) (from mid April to end Sept.) – 21 ⬚ – 2 canvas bungalows. Per night from 39 to 120€ – Per week from 195 to 825€ – Reservation fee 15€ ⬚ borne

Right in the heart of the countryside.

Surroundings : ♤ ⬚♤♤
Leisure activities : 🏊🎣
Facilities : ♿☞⬚🍴launderette

GPS Longitude : -4.19918
Latitude : 48.09582

LOCTUDY

29750 – Michelin map **308** F8 – pop. 4 207 – alt. 8
▶ Paris 578 – Bénodet 18 – Concarneau 35 – Pont-l'Abbé 6

⛰ Les Hortensias

☎ 02 98 87 46 64. www.camping-loctudy.com

Address : 38 rue des Tulipes (3km southwest following signs for Larvor, 500m from the beach at Lodonnec)

Opening times : from beginning April to end Sept.

1.5 ha (100 pitches) flat, grassy

Tariff : 25.40€ ✶✶ ⬅ 回 [2] (10A) – Extra per person 4.90€ – Reservation fee 10€

Rental rates : (from beginning April to end Sept.) – 1 caravan – 21 ⬚. Per night from 35 to 110€ – Per week from 150 to 760€ – Reservation fee 10€
⬚ borne 5€ – 5 回 25.40€

A good site for tents and caravans, set back a little from the seashore activities.

Surroundings : ♤♤♤
Leisure activities : ♈🏊🚴♒
Facilities : ♿☞⬚🍴launderette 🎣⬚
Nearby : ✗

GPS Longitude : -4.1823
Latitude : 47.81259

LOUANNEC

22700 – Michelin map **309** B2 – pop. 2 946 – alt. 53
▶ Paris 527 – Rennes 175 – St-Brieuc 77 – Lannion 10

⛰ Municipal Ernest Renan

☎ 02 96 23 11 78. www.camping-louannec.fr

Address : located 1km west; beside the sea

Opening times : from beginning April to end Sept.

4 ha (265 pitches) flat, grassy

Tariff : (2014 Price) 18.30€ ✶✶ ⬅ 回 [2] (16A) – Extra per person 3.80€

Rental rates : (2014 Price) Permanent – 14 ⬚ – 2 canvas bungalows. Per night from 42 to 84€ – Per week from 189 to 680€
⬚ borne 10€

Surroundings : ⬚⚠
Leisure activities : ♈🏠🌞daytime 🏊♒◊
Facilities : ♿☞⬚🍴launderette ⬚🎣
Nearby : 🐎

GPS Longitude : -3.42723
Latitude : 48.79666

MARCILLÉ-ROBERT

35240 – Michelin map **309** N7 – pop. 929 – alt. 65
▶ Paris 333 – Bain-de-Bretagne 33 – Châteaubriant 30 – La Guerche-de-Bretagne 11

⚠ Municipal de l'Étang

📞 06 02 08 60 22. camping.marcillerobert@yahoo.fr
Address : rue des Bas Gasts (take the southern exit along the D 32, follow the signs for Arbrissel)
Opening times : Permanent
0.5 ha (22 pitches) pond
Tariff : 12€ ★★ ⇌ 🗉 ⚡ (10A) – Extra per person 3€
Rental rates : Permanent – 1 🚐 – 1 🏠. Per night from 24 to 36€ – Per week from 168 to 230€
A pleasant setting looking out over a lake, at the edge of which is a nature reserve.

Surroundings : 🌾 ⪦ 🏞 🔟
Facilities : 🔥 🚽
Nearby : 🏊 🎾 🛶
Longitude : -1.36471
Latitude : 47.94768

MARTIGNÉ-FERCHAUD

35640 – Michelin map **309** 08 – pop. 2 650 – alt. 90
▶ Paris 340 – Bain-de-Bretagne 31 – Châteaubriant 15 – La Guerche-de-Bretagne 16

⚠ Municipal du Bois Feuillet

📞 06 24 86 65 57. www.ville-martigne-ferchaud.fr
Address : Étang de la Forge (to the northwest of the town)
Opening times : from beginning June to end Sept.
1.7 ha (50 pitches)
Tariff : (2014 Price) ★ 3€ ⇌ 🗉 2€ – ⚡ (6A) 2€
🚐 borne
Comfortable pitches in a pleasant setting with shade, at the edge of a lake.

Surroundings : 🌾 ⪦ 🏞 🔟
Leisure activities : 🔟
Facilities : 🔥 ⚡ (July–Aug.) ⛱ ⚘ 🔟
Nearby : 🏊 🎾 🛥 (beach) 🛶 🚣 pedalos
Longitude : -1.31599
Latitude : 47.83385

MATIGNON

22550 – Michelin map **309** I3 – pop. 1 647 – alt. 70
▶ Paris 425 – Dinan 30 – Dinard 23 – Lamballe 23

🏔 Le Vallon aux Merlettes

📞 02 96 80 37 99. www.campingdematignon.com
Address : 43 rue du Dr-Jobert (to the southwest along the D 13, follow the signs for Lamballe, by the stadium)
Opening times : from beginning April to end Sept.
3 ha (100 pitches)
Tariff : 19.50€ ★★ ⇌ 🗉 ⚡ (10A) – Extra per person 4.20€
Rental rates : (from beginning April to end Sept.) 🚿 – 3 🚐 – 3 tent lodges. Per night from 35 to 85€ – Per week from 220 to 640€
🚐 borne 3.40€ – 3 🗉 11€ – 🔌 ⚡14.50€

Surroundings : 🌾 🔟
Leisure activities : 🔟 🎾 🔞 🔟 (open air in season)
Facilities : 🔥 ⚡ ⛱ 🔟 launderette
Nearby : 🛒
Longitude : -2.29607
Latitude : 48.59168

MERDRIGNAC

22230 – Michelin map **309** H5 – pop. 2 916 – alt. 140
▶ Paris 411 – Dinan 47 – Josselin 33 – Lamballe 40

⚠ Val de Landrouet

📞 02 96 28 47 98. www.valdelandrouet.com
Address : 14 rue du Gouède (0.8km to the north, near the swimming pool and two lakes; at the leisure and activity park)
Opening times : from beginning May to end Sept.
15 ha/2 for camping (45 pitches)
Tariff : ★ 4€ ⇌ 3€ 🗉 5€ – ⚡ (5A) 3€ – Reservation fee 15€
Rental rates : (from beginning Jan. to mid Dec.) 🔥 (9 chalets) – 5 🚐 – 9 🏠. Per night from 38 to 95€ – Per week from 160 to 750€ – Reservation fee 15€
🚐 borne 2€ – 5 🗉 – 🔌 ⚡12€

Surroundings : 🌾 🔟
Leisure activities : 🍴 🔟
Facilities : 🔥 ⚡ ⛱ 🔟 🔟
Nearby : 🏊 🎾 🔟 🔟 🛶
Longitude : -2.41525
Latitude : 48.19843

This guide is not intended as a list of all the camping sites in France; its aim is to provide a selection of the best sites in each category.

MILIZAC

29290 – Michelin map **308** D4 – pop. 3 009 – alt. 89
▶ Paris 598 – Rennes 247 – Quimper 83

🏔 La Récré des 3 Curés

📞 02 98 07 92 17. www.larecredes3cures.fr
Address : situated at the Parc d'Attractions (leisure park)
Opening times : Permanent
3 ha (100 pitches) flat, grassy
Tariff : 25€ ★★ ⇌ 🗉 ⚡ (10A) – Extra per person 4€
Rental rates : Permanent – 38 🚐 – 6 🏠. Per night from 72 to 187€ – Per week from 211 to 824€
🚐 borne – 40 🗉 21€ – 🔌 ⚡19€
A family campsite that enjoys a pleasant location beside a lake and is next to a large amusement park.

Surroundings : ⪦ lake 🏞 🔟
Leisure activities : 🍴 🔟 🏊 🔟 🛶
Facilities : 🔥 ⚡ ⛱ 🔟 launderette
Nearby : 🍴 🔟 🔟 🐎 🔟 amusement park
Longitude : -4.5294
Latitude : 48.47377

MOËLAN-SUR-MER

29350 – Michelin map **308** J8 – pop. 6 956 – alt. 58
▶ Paris 523 – Carhaix-Plouguer 66 – Concarneau 27 – Lorient 27

⚠ L'Île Percée

📞 02 98 71 16 25. www.camping-ile-percee.fr
Address : plage de Trenez (5.8km west along the D 116, follow the signs for Kerfany-les-Pins, then continue 1.7km along the turning to the left)
Opening times : from end March to end Sept.
1 ha (65 pitches) flat, grassy
Tariff : (2014 Price) 21€ ★★ ⇌ 🗉 ⚡ (6A) – Extra per person 4.50€
Reservation fee 8€

Rental rates : (2014 Price) (from end March to end Sept.) – 4 🚐.
Per week from 255 to 529€ – Reservation fee 8€

A pleasant site with a natural feel, at the edge of the coastal path GR34, with pitches looking out over the ocean.

Surroundings : 🏞 ⤠♀⛰
Leisure activities : ❢ 🎣
Facilities : 🚿 ☎ 🏕🗑 🖼
Nearby : ✕ 🐎 walking trails

Longitude : -3.70241
Latitude : 47.78872

MONTERBLANC

56250 – Michelin map **308** O8 – pop. 3 139 – alt. 89
▶ Paris 453 – Nantes 122 – Rennes 102 – Vannes 14

🔺 Le Haras

📞 02 97 44 66 06. www.campingvannes.com
Address : at Kersimon (from Vannes, head north along the D 767 then take the D 778 E, behind Vannes-Meucon-Bretagne-Sud flying club)
Opening times : from mid March to mid Nov.
14 ha/2.5 for camping (140 pitches)
Tariff : 36€ ✵✵ 🚐 🔲 🔌 (16A) –
Extra per person 5€ – Reservation fee 30€
Rental rates : (from beginning April to end Oct.) 🚻 (1 chalet) – 60 🚐 – 7 🏠. Per night from 50 to 180€ – Per week from 350 to 1,260€ – Reservation fee 30€
🚐 borne 16€ – 9 🔲 16€ – 🔌16€

Surroundings : 🏞 ♀♀
Leisure activities : ❢✕ 🕙daytime ⤇ hammam jacuzzi 🏊🚴✕ ♪ 🔲 🎣 🏊 wildlife park multi-sports ground spa centre
Facilities : 🚿 ☎ ▥ 🏕 🗑 🔧 🔌 launderette
Nearby : 🐎

Longitude : -2.72795
Latitude : 47.73035

MORGAT

29160 – Michelin map **308** E5 – pop. 7 535
▶ Paris 590 – Rennes 238 – Quimper 55 – Brest 15

🔺 Les Bruyères

📞 02 98 26 14 87. www.camping-bruyeres-crozon.com
Address : Le Bouis (located 1.5km along the D 255, follow the signs for Le Cap de la Chèvre and take road to the right)
4 ha (130 pitches)
Rentals : 17 🚐.

In a natural setting with access to Morgat via a pedestrian path; the site includes a water park.

Surroundings : 🏞 ♀
Leisure activities : 🏊 🔲 🎣 🏊
Facilities : ☎ 🏕 🔧 launderette
Nearby : 🛒❢✕

Longitude : -4.53183
Latitude : 48.22293

The Michelin classification (🔺🔺🔺... 🔺) is totally independent of the official star classification system awarded by the local prefecture or other official organisation.

MOUSTERLIN

29170 – Michelin map **308** G7
▶ Paris 563 – Rennes 212 – Quimper 22 – Brest 94

🔺 FranceLoc Le Grand Large 🚹🚹

📞 02 98 56 04 06. www.franceloc.fr – limited spaces for one-night stay
Address : 48 route du Grand Large (near the beach)
Opening times : from mid April to beginning Sept.
5.8 ha (287 pitches) flat, grassy
Tariff : (2014 Price) 30€ ✵✵ 🚐 🔲 🔌 (6A) – Extra per person 7€ – Reservation fee 27€
Rental rates : (2014 Price) (from mid April to beginning Sept.) 🚻 (1 mobile home) – 220 🚐. Per night from 33 to 70€ – Per week from 133 to 1,127€ – Reservation fee 27€

Numerous rental options based around a restaurant and a good water park that is partially covered.

Surroundings : 🏞 ♀
Leisure activities : ❢✕ 🖼 🕙🏊 ⤇ 🏊 🚴✕ 🔲 🏊 🏊 multi-sports ground
Facilities : 🚿 ☎ 🏕 🔧 🔌 launderette 🏊🚲

Longitude : -4.0367
Latitude : 47.84809

🔺 Kost-Ar-Moor

📞 02 98 56 04 16. www.camping-fouesnant.com
Address : 17 route du Grand Large (500m from the beach)
Opening times : from mid April to mid Sept.
3.5 ha (177 pitches) flat, grassy
Tariff : 27.50€ ✵✵ 🚐 🔲 🔌 (10A) – Extra per person 5.70€ – Reservation fee 15€
Rental rates : (from mid April to mid Sept.) – 28 🚐 – 5 apartments. Per night from 45 to 65€ – Per week from 200 to 750€ – Reservation fee 15€

A charming, tranquil setting beneath the shade of pine trees, ideal for tents and caravans.

Surroundings : 🏞 ♀♀
Leisure activities : ❢✕ 🖼 🏊 🚴🏊
Facilities : 🚿 ☎ 🏕 🔧 launderette
Nearby : 🌊

Longitude : -4.03421
Latitude : 47.85106

We value your opinion and welcome your feedback. Do email us at campingfrance@tp.michelin.com

NAIZIN

56500 – Michelin map **308** O7 – pop. 1 695 – alt. 106
▶ Paris 454 – Ploërmel 40 – Pontivy 16 – Rennes 106

🔺 Municipal de Coetdan

📞 02 97 27 43 27. www.naizin.fr
Address : rue des Peupliers (600m east along the D 17 and take D 203 towards Réguiny)
Opening times : from beginning June to end Sept.
0.7 ha (28 pitches)
Tariff : (2014 Price) ✵ 3€ 🚐 2€ 🔲 2€ – 🔌 (10A) 3€

A pleasant setting near a small lake.

Surroundings : ▱ ♀♀
Leisure activities : 🎣
Facilities : 🚿 ☎ 🏊🔲
Nearby : 🏊 🔥 fitness trail

Longitude : -2.82616
Latitude : 47.99336

NÉVEZ

29920 – Michelin map **308** I8 – pop. 2 718 – alt. 40
▶ Paris 541 – Concarneau 14 – Pont-Aven 8 – Quimper 40

⌂ Les Chaumières

𝒫 02 98 06 73 06. www.camping-des-chaumieres.com

Address : 24 Hameau de Kerascoet (head 3km south along the D 77 towards Port Manec'h then take the turning to the right)

Opening times : from mid May to mid Sept.

3 ha (110 pitches) flat, grassy

Tariff : 22.80€ ♦♦ ⇌ ▣ ⚡ (10A) – Extra per person 5.20€
Rental rates : (from beginning April to end Sept.) – 6 ⛺. Per night from 35 to 60€ – Per week from 210 to 600€ – Reservation fee 10€
🚐 borne 13.50€

A lush, green and peaceful site, with access to the beach via a beautiful shaded footpath.

Surroundings : 🌊 ⛺ ♀
Leisure activities : ⛵
Facilities : ♿ ⊙⚪ (July–Aug.) ⍾ launderette
Nearby : ♈ ✗

GPS	Longitude : -3.77433
	Latitude : 47.79598

NOYAL-MUZILLAC

56190 – Michelin map **308** Q9 – pop. 2 410 – alt. 52
▶ Paris 468 – Rennes 108 – Vannes 31 – Lorient 88

⌂⌂⌂ Moulin de Cadillac

𝒫 02 97 67 03 47. www.camping-moulin-cadillac.com

Address : 4.5km northwest following signs for Berric

Opening times : from mid April to mid Sept.

7 ha (192 pitches) adjacent wood

Tariff : (2014 Price) ♦ 6.20€ ⇌ ▣ 14.50€ – ⚡ (10A) 3.80€ – Reservation fee 10€
Rental rates : (2014 Price) (from mid April to mid Sept.) – 60 ⛺ – 9 ⛺ – 4 canvas bungalows. Per night from 85 to 160€ – Per week from 240 to 790€ – Reservation fee 10€
🚐 borne

In a pleasant setting, with an indoor water park; beside a stream.

Surroundings : 🌊 ⛺ ♀
Leisure activities : ♈ ⛱ ☺ ⇌ ✗ ⍾ ⛱ ⛱
⛱ ⛏ wildlife park, multi-sports ground, entertainment room
Facilities : ♿ ⊙⚪ ⍾ launderette

GPS	Longitude : -2.50199
	Latitude : 47.61412

PAIMPOL

22500 – Michelin map **309** D2 – pop. 7 828 – alt. 15
▶ Paris 494 – Guingamp 29 – Lannion 33 – St-Brieuc 46

⌂ Municipal de Cruckin-Kérity

𝒫 02 96 20 78 47. www.camping-paimpol.com

Address : Kérity (head 2km southeast along the D 786, follow the signs for St-Quay-Portrieux, next to the stadium, 100m from the beach at Cruckin)

Opening times : from beginning April to beginning Oct.

2 ha (130 pitches) flat, grassy

Tariff : (2014 Price) 20.60€ ♦♦ ⇌ ▣ ⚡ (13A) – Extra per person 4.40€ – Reservation fee 20€

Rental rates : (2014 Price) (from beginning April to beginning Oct.) – 5 canvas bungalows. Per night from 43 to 60€ – Per week from 220 to 360€ – Reservation fee 25€
🚐 borne 6.50€ – 10 ▣ 10€

Surroundings : ⛺ ♀
Leisure activities : ⛱ ⛵
Facilities : ♿ ⍾ ⍾ launderette
Nearby : ✗ ⍾ fitness trail

GPS	Longitude : -3.02224
	Latitude : 48.76972

PAIMPONT

35380 – Michelin map **309** I6 – pop. 1 641 – alt. 159
▶ Paris 390 – Dinan 60 – Ploërmel 26 – Redon 47

⌂ Municipal Paimpont Brocéliande

𝒫 02 99 07 89 16. www.camping-paimpont-broceliande.com

Address : 2 rue du Chevalier Lancelot du Lac (take the northern exit along the D 773, near the lake)

1.5 ha (90 pitches) flat, grassy
Rentals : ♿ (1 chalet) – 6 ⛺.

A setting with only a little shade at the edge of the Forêt de Brocéliande (forest).

Leisure activities : ⛱ ⛵
Facilities : ♿ ⊙⚪ ⍾ launderette
Nearby : ⛱ ✗

GPS	Longitude : -2.17248
	Latitude : 48.02404

PÉNESTIN

56760 – Michelin map **308** Q10 – pop. 1 867 – alt. 20
▶ Paris 458 – La Baule 29 – Nantes 84 – La Roche-Bernard 18

⌂⌂⌂ Le Cénic ♣♣

𝒫 02 99 90 45 65. www.lecenic.com

Address : route de La Roche-Bernard (located 1.5km east along the D 34; beside a lake)

5.5 ha (310 pitches)
Rentals : 60 ⛺ – 8 ⛺.

There's a partially covered water park.

Surroundings : ⛺ ♀♀
Leisure activities : ♈ ⛱ ☺ ⍾ ⛵ hammam
⛵ 🎣 ⛱ ⛱ ⛏ entertainment room
Facilities : ♿ ⊙⚪ ⍾ launderette

GPS	Longitude : -2.45547
	Latitude : 47.47889

⌂⌂ Les Îles ♣♣

𝒫 02 99 90 30 24. www.camping-des-iles.fr

Address : at La Pointe du Bile, 119 route des Trois Îles (4.5km south along the D 201 to the right)

Opening times : from beginning April to end Sept.

3.5 ha (184 pitches)

Tariff : 43€ ♦♦ ⇌ ▣ ⚡ (10A) – Extra per person 6€
Rental rates : (from beginning April to end Sept.) ♿ (1 chalet) – 65 ⛺ – 8 ⛺ – 2 tent lodges. Per night from 45 to 91€ – Per week from 245 to 1,330€
🚐 borne 4€

Situated close to the beach.

Surroundings : ⛺ ♀♀ ⛰
Leisure activities : ♈ ✗ ⛱ ☺ nighttime ⍾
⛵ ⛱ ✗ ⛏ multi-sports ground
Facilities : ♿ ⊙⚪ ▣ ⍾ ⍾ launderette ⛱ ⛱
Nearby : ⛱

GPS	Longitude : -2.48426
	Latitude : 47.44561

⛰ Yelloh! Village Le Domaine d'Inly ♨

🖉 02 99 90 35 09. www.camping-inly.com – limited spaces for one-night stay

Address : route de Couarne (situated 2km southeast along the D 201 and take turning to the left)

Opening times : from mid April to mid Sept.

30 ha/12 for camping (500 pitches)

Tariff : (2014 Price) 42€ ✶✶ 🚗 🔲 🔌 (10A) – Extra per person 7€

Rental rates : (from mid April to mid Sept.) – 152 🛏. Per night from 28 to 178€ – Per week from 196 to 1,211€

Surroundings : ⌇ ⌂ ♊
Leisure activities : ♈ ✕ 🎣 ♿ ⚓ ⛷ ⚲ ✧ 🎾 🎿 ♒ ♨ pedalos ⚕
Facilities : 🚻 ⚐ 🚿 💧 ♈ launderette 🌊 ⚕

Longitude : -2.46694
Latitude : 47.47138

⛰ Les Parcs

🖉 02 99 90 30 59. www.camping-lesparcs.com

Address : route de la Roche-Bernard (500m east along the D 34)

3 ha (100 pitches) relatively flat, flat, grassy

Rentals : 20 🛏.

Surroundings : ⌂ ♊
Leisure activities : ♈ 🎿 (open air in season)
Facilities : ♿ 🚻 ♈ launderette
Nearby : 🛒

PENMARCH

29760 – Michelin map **308** E8 – pop. 5 749 – alt. 7
▣ Paris 585 – Audierne 40 – Douarnenez 45 – Pont-l'Abbé 12

⛰ Yelloh! Village La Plage ♨

🖉 02 98 58 61 90. www.villagelaplage.com

Address : route des Fusillés de Poulguen (situated 100m from the beach (direct access)

Opening times : from mid April to mid Sept.

14 ha (410 pitches)

Tariff : 47€ ✶✶ 🚗 🔲 🔌 (10A) – Extra per person 8€

Rental rates : (from mid April to mid Sept.) – 240 🛏 – 2 cabins in the trees – 8 tent lodges. Per night from 39 to 239€ – Per week from 273 to 1,673€

🚰 borne

In a beachside setting with lots of activities;'huts in the trees' with ocean views.

Surroundings : ♊
Leisure activities : ♈ ✕ 🎣 ♿ ⚓ 🎿 ⚲
🚣 ✧ 🎾 ♒ 🎿 🏊 pedal go-carts,
multi-sports ground
Facilities : ♿ 🚻 ♈ launderette 🌊 ⚕
Nearby : ⚕

Longitude : -4.31194
Latitude : 47.8035

Michelin classification:

⛰⛰⛰⛰ *Extremely comfortable, equipped to a very high standard*

⛰⛰⛰ *Very comfortable, equipped to a high standard*

⛰⛰⛰ *Comfortable and well equipped*

⛰⛰ *Reasonably comfortable*

⛺ *Satisfactory*

⛺ Municipal de Toul ar Ster

🖉 02 98 58 86 88. www.penmarch.fr/Office-de-Tourisme

Address : 110 rue Edmond Michelet (1.4km southeast following signs for Guilvinec along the coast and take turning to the right, 100m from the beach (direct access)

Opening times : from mid June to mid Sept.

3 ha (202 pitches)

Tariff : (2014 Price) ✶ 3.45€ 🚗 2.40€ 🔲 3.30€ – 🔌 (10A) 3€
🚰 borne 13€

In a pleasant setting close to a sailing centre.

Surroundings : ⌇
Leisure activities : 🎣 ⚓
Facilities : ♿ 🚻 (July-Aug) 🚿 ♈ launderette
Nearby : ♨

Longitude : -4.33726
Latitude : 47.81246

PENTREZ-PLAGE

29550 – Michelin map **308** F5
▣ Paris 566 – Brest 55 – Châteaulin 18 – Crozon 18

⛰ Homair Vacances Le Ker'Ys ♨

🖉 0820 201 207. www.homair.com/camping/le-domaine-de-ker-ys – limited spaces for one-night stay

Address : chemin des Dunes (opposite the beach)

Opening times : from mid April to end Sept.

3.5 ha (190 pitches)

Tariff : 29.70€ ✶✶ 🚗 🔲 🔌 (8A) – Extra per person 5.50€ – Reservation fee 49€

Rental rates : (from mid April to end Sept.) – 160 🛏. Per night from 17 to 130€ – Per week from 119 to 910€ – Reservation fee 49€

A good water park, lots of boating activities and the beach is nearby.

Surroundings : ⌂ ♨
Leisure activities : 🎣 ♿ daytime ⚓ 🛶 ⛵
jacuzzi 🚣 ✧ 🎿 🏊
Facilities : ♿ 🚻 ℹ 🚿 ♈ launderette
Nearby : ♈ ✕

Longitude : -4.30137
Latitude : 48.19249

---

*To visit a town or region, use the **MICHELIN Green Guides.***

PERROS-GUIREC

22700 – Michelin map **309** B2 – pop. 7 375 – alt. 60
▣ Paris 527 – Lannion 12 – St-Brieuc 76 – Tréguier 19

⛰ Yelloh! Village Le Ranolien ♨

🖉 02 96 91 65 65. www.leranolien.fr

Address : at Ploumanac'h, boulevard du Sémaphore (located 1km southeast along the D 788, 200m from the sea)

15 ha (525 pitches) very uneven, flat and relatively flat, grassy, rocks
Rentals : 5 caravans – 330 🛏.
🚰 borne

There's a very pleasant spa centre (open all year round).

Surroundings : ≤ ⌂ ♨
Leisure activities : ♈ ✕ 🎣 ♿ ⚓ 🛶
⛵ hammam, jacuzzi 🚣 🏊 🎿 🏊
disco multi-sports ground, spa centre,
entertainment room
Facilities : ♿ 🚻 🏛 🚿 ♈ launderette 🛒 ⚕

Longitude : -3.4747
Latitude : 48.82677

⚴ Claire Fontaine

📞 02 96 23 03 55. www.camping-claire-fontaine.com

Address : rue de Toul al Lann (2.6km southwest along the r. des Frères- Mantrier, follow the signs for Pleumeur-Bodou and take turning to the right)

3 ha (180 pitches)

Rentals : 2 🏠 – 6 🛏 – 1 gîte.

A pleasant setting for this site based around an old renovated farmhouse of great character.

Surroundings : ⬡ 🟢🟢
Leisure activities : 🖼
Facilities : ⚲ 🚿 🍴 launderette

GPS Longitude : -3.46538
Latitude : 48.80598

PLANCOËT

22130 – Michelin map **309** I3 – pop. 3 079 – alt. 41
▶ Paris 417 – Dinan 17 – Dinard 20 – St-Brieuc 46

⚴ Municipal Les Vergers

📞 02 96 84 03 42. mairie-plancoet@wanadoo.fr

Address : rue du Verger (Continue towards southeastern exit, follow the signs for Dinan, behind the fire station; beside the Arguenon river and a small lake)

1.2 ha (100 pitches) flat, grassy

Surroundings : ⬡ the village of Plancoët 🚐 🟢
Leisure activities : 🦢
Facilities : ⚲ 🚿 launderette
Nearby : 🏄

GPS Longitude : -2.23366
Latitude : 48.52041

PLÉNEUF-VAL-ANDRÉ

22370 – Michelin map **309** G3 – pop. 3 942 – alt. 52
▶ Paris 446 – Dinan 43 – Erquy 9 – Lamballe 16

⚴ Campéole Les Monts Colleux 🔥👥

📞 02 96 72 95 10. www.camping-montscolleux.com

Address : 26 rue Jean Lebrun

Opening times : from beginning April to end Sept.

5 ha/200 for camping

Tariff : (2014 Price) 25.80€ 🔥🔥 🚗 🔲 🔌 (6A) – Extra per person 7.20€
Reservation fee 15€

Rental rates : (from beginning April to end Sept.) ⚲ (1 mobile home) – 43 🛖 – 23 🏠. Per night from 38 to 62€ – Per week from 266 to 840€ – Reservation fee 25€

🚮 borne

Surroundings : ⬡ ⬡
Leisure activities : 🔥 🏄
Facilities : 🚿 🍴 launderette 🧺
Nearby : 🎿

GPS Longitude : -2.5508
Latitude : 48.5898

These symbols are used for a campsite that is exceptional in its category:

🅰🅰🅰 ... ⚴ *Particularly pleasant setting, quality and range of services available*

🦢🦢 *Tranquil, isolated site – quiet site, particularly at night*

⬡⬡ *Exceptional view – interesting or panoramic view*

PLESTIN-LES-GRÈVES

22310 – Michelin map **309** A3 – pop. 3 644 – alt. 45
▶ Paris 528 – Brest 79 – Guingamp 46 – Lannion 18

🏔 Municipal St-Efflam

📞 02 96 35 62 15. www.camping-municipal-bretagne.com

Address : at St-Efflam, place de Lan-Carré (3.5km to the northeast, follow the signs for St-Michel-en-Grève; 200m from the sea)

Opening times : from beginning April to beginning Oct.

4 ha (190 pitches) terraced, relatively flat, flat, grassy

Tariff : (2014 Price) 18€ 🔥🔥 🚗 🔲 🔌 (10A) – Extra per person 3.70€
Rental rates : (2014 Price) (from beginning April to beginning Oct.)
⚲ (1 mobile home) – 10 🛖 – 9 🏠. Per night from 40 to 70€ – Per week from 205 to 560€
🚮 borne 3€ – 10 🔲 16€

Surroundings : ⬡ 🟢
Leisure activities : 🔥 🖼 🏄 🎿
Facilities : ⚲ 🚿 (July-Aug) 🍴 launderette
Nearby : ✕ 🎣

GPS Longitude : -3.60108
Latitude : 48.66834

⚴ Aire Naturelle Ker-Rolland

📞 02 96 35 08 37. www.camping-ker-rolland.com

Address : Ker Rolland (2.2km southwest along the D 786, follow the signs for Morlaix and take the turning to the left, following signs for Plouégat-Guérand)

Opening times : from mid June to mid Sept.

1.6 ha (22 pitches) flat, grassy

Tariff : 12€ 🔥🔥 🚗 🔲 🔌 (13A) – Extra per person 2.80€
Rental rates : Permanent – 3 🛖. Per night from 35 to 52€ – Per week from 200 to 375€
🚮 borne

This is a farm campsite (with a market garden).

Surroundings : ⬡
Leisure activities : 🖼
Facilities : ⚲ 🚿 🍴 🎪 🍴 🔲

GPS Longitude : -3.64337
Latitude : 48.64338

The prices listed were supplied by the campsite owners in 2014 (if prices were not available, those from the previous year are given). The fees should be regarded as basic charges and may fluctuate with inflation.

PLEUBIAN

22610 – Michelin map **309** D1 – pop. 2 577 – alt. 48
▶ Paris 506 – Lannion 31 – Paimpol 13 – St-Brieuc 58

🏔 Port la Chaîne

📞 02 96 22 92 38. www.portlachaine.com

Address : situated 2km north along the D 20, follow the signs for Larmor-Pleubian and take turning to the left

4.9 ha (200 pitches) terraced, relatively flat, flat, grassy

Rentals : 42 🛖 – 3 canvas bungalows.

There's plenty of shade from centuries-old maritime pines; situated beside the sea.

Surroundings : ⬡ 🟢🟢 ⛰
Leisure activities : 🔥 🖼 🏄 🎿 🏊
Facilities : ⚲ 🚿 🍴 🧺 🍴 launderette

GPS Longitude : -3.13284
Latitude : 48.85545

PLEUMEUR-BODOU

22560 – Michelin map **309** A2 – pop. 4 039 – alt. 94
▶ Paris 523 – Lannion 8 – Perros-Guirec 10 – St-Brieuc 72

⛰ Le Port

✆ 02 96 23 87 79. www.camping-du-port-22.com

Address : 3 chemin des Douaniers (6km to the north, to the south of Trégastel-Plage)

Opening times : from end March to mid Oct.

2 ha (80 pitches) open site, flat and relatively flat, grassy, rocks

Tariff : 21.90€ ✶✶ 🚐 🅴 🅐 (15A) – Extra per person 2€

Rental rates : (from end March to mid Oct.) – 27 🛖 – 6 🏠 – 2 canvas bungalows – 2 tent lodges. Per night from 40 to 70€ – Per week from 150 to 770€ – Reservation fee 15€

🚐 20 🅴 18€ – 🔋 15€

Situated beside the sea, with some pitches virtually 'on top of the water'.

Surroundings : 🏖 ⬅🏔
Leisure activities : 🍹 ✗ 🚣 🚴 🛝
Facilities : 🚿 🔌 🛁 🚰 🍽 launderette

GPS Longitude : -3.54278
Latitude : 48.81029

PLÉVEN

22130 – Michelin map **309** I4 – pop. 587 – alt. 80
▶ Paris 431 – Dinan 24 – Dinard 28 – St-Brieuc 38

⛰ Municipal

✆ 02 96 84 46 71. www.pleven.fr

Address : in the village (in the grounds of the town hall)

Opening times : from beginning April to mid Nov.

1 ha (40 pitches)

Tariff : ✶ 1.70€ 🚐 1€ 🅴 2€ – 🅐 (10A) 1.70€

Surroundings : 🌳🌳
Facilities : 🚿 🔌 🚰 🍽
Nearby : 🛒 ✗

GPS Longitude : -2.31911
Latitude : 48.48914

PLOBANNALEC-LESCONIL

29740 – Michelin map **308** F8 – pop. 3 326 – alt. 16
▶ Paris 578 – Audierne 38 – Douarnenez 38 – Pont-l'Abbé 6

⛰ Yelloh! Village L'Océan Breton 🎣

✆ 02 98 82 23 89. www.camping-bretagne-oceanbreton.fr – limited spaces for one-night stay

Address : route de Plobannalec, Le Manoir de Kerlut (1.6km south along the D 102, follow the signs for Lesconil and take the road to the left)

Opening times : from mid April to beginning Sept.

12 ha/8 for camping (240 pitches) flat, grassy

Tariff : 51€ ✶✶ 🚐 🅴 🅐 (10A) – Extra per person 8€

Rental rates : (from mid April to beginning Sept.) – 176 🛖 – 8 🏠 – 3 yurts – 6 tent lodges. Per night from 35 to 239€ – Per week from 245 to 1,673€

🚐 borne

A very pleasant site, laid out around a delightful water park; access to the beach via a free shuttle service.

Surroundings : 🏖 🌳🌳
Leisure activities : 🍹 ✗ 🏛 🎣 🏃 🎣 🛶
🚣 🚴 ✗ 🎯 🏊 ⛳ forest trail
Facilities : 🚿 🔌 🛁 🚰 🍽 launderette 🚮 🛁

GPS Longitude : -4.22574
Latitude : 47.81167

PLOEMEL

56400 – Michelin map **308** M9 – pop. 2 508 – alt. 46
▶ Paris 485 – Auray 8 – Lorient 34 – Quiberon 23

⛰ Municipal St-Laurent 🎣

✆ 02 97 56 85 90. www.camping-saint-laurent.fr

Address : Kergonvo (2.5km to the northwest, follow the signs for Belz, near D 22 junction, take D 186)

Opening times : from mid April to end Oct.

3 ha (90 pitches)

Tariff : 22.20€ ✶✶ 🚐 🅴 🅐 (10A) – Extra per person 5.35€ – Reservation fee 10€

Rental rates : (from mid April to end Oct.) – 21 🛖 – 2 canvas bungalows – 6 tent lodges. Per night from 48 to 117€ – Per week from 331 to 820€ – Reservation fee 10€

🚐 borne – 🔋 12€

Surroundings : 🌳🌳
Leisure activities : ✗ 🏃 🚣 🎯
Facilities : 🔌 🛁 🍽 🖥 🚮

GPS Longitude : -3.10013
Latitude : 47.66369

⛰ Kergo

✆ 02 97 56 80 66. www.campingkergo.com

Address : situated 2km southeast along the D 186, follow the signs for La Trinité-sur-Mer and take the turning to the left

Opening times : from beginning May to end Oct.

2.5 ha (135 pitches)

Tariff : (2014 Price) 18.95€ ✶✶ 🚐 🅴 🅐 (10A) – Extra per person 4.20€

Rental rates : (2014 Price) (from beginning April to mid Nov.) – 10 🛖. Per night from 38 to 80€ – Per week from 230 to 560€ Reservation fee 10€

🚐 borne 5€

Surroundings : 🏖 🌿
Leisure activities : 🏛 ⛲ jacuzzi 🚣 🚴
Facilities : 🚿 🔌 🛁 🍽 🖥

GPS Longitude : -3.05362
Latitude : 47.64403

There are several different types of sani-station ('borne' in French) – sanitation points providing fresh water and disposal points for grey water. See page 12 for further details.

PLOÉVEN

29550 – Michelin map **308** F6 – pop. 505 – alt. 60
▶ Paris 585 – Brest 64 – Châteaulin 15 – Crozon 25

⛰ La Mer

✆ 02 98 81 29 19. www.campingdelamer29.fr

Address : Ty Anquer Plage (3km southwest, 300m from the beach)

1 ha (54 pitches) flat, grassy

Rentals : 1 🛖 – 6 canvas bungalows.

A charming, small campsite where peace and tranquillity are guaranteed, 100m from an unspoilt beach.

Surroundings : 🏖 🌿
Facilities : 🔌 🍽 🚮

GPS Longitude : -4.26796
Latitude : 48.14806

PLOMEUR

29120 – Michelin map **308** F7 – pop. 3 634 – alt. 33
▶ Paris 579 – Douarnenez 39 – Pont-l'Abbé 6 – Quimper 26

⚠ Aire Naturelle Kéraluic

📞 02 98 82 10 22. www.keraluic.fr ✆ (from beginning July to end Aug.)

Address : Keraluic (4.3km northeast along the D 57, follow the signs for Plonéour-Lanvern)

Opening times : from mid April to mid Oct.

1 ha (25 pitches) flat, grassy

Tariff : 20.90€ ♣♣ 🚗 🔋 (6A) – Extra per person 5.50€
Rental rates : Permanent ✆ – 2 🛏 – 3 studios – 1 apartment – 2 canvas bungalows. Per week from 395 to 450€

Old farmhouse buildings that have been attractively renovated; wide pitches for tents and caravans.

Surroundings : ⛰ ♨
Leisure activities : 🎱 ⛵
Facilities : 🚿 🍴 🛁 ⛽
G P S Longitude : -4.26624
Latitude : 47.86148

⚠ Lanven

📞 02 98 82 00 75. www.campinglanven.com

Address : La Chapelle de Beuzec (3.5km northwest along the D 57, follow the signs for Plonéour-Lanvern then take the road to the left)

Opening times : from beginning April to end Sept.

3.7 ha (132 pitches) flat, grassy

Tariff : (2014 Price) 20€ ♣♣ 🚗 🔋 (10A) – Extra per person 4.20€
Rental rates : (2014 Price) (from beginning April to mid Nov.) – 6 🚐. Per night from 35 to 76€ – Per week from 385 to 532€

A pleasant setting in the heart of the countryside; around half the site is occupied by children's summer camps in July and August.

Surroundings : ⛰ ♨
Leisure activities : ♨ ✗ ⛵
Facilities : 🍴 launderette
G P S Longitude : -4.30663
Latitude : 47.8505

PLOMODIERN

29550 – Michelin map **308** F5 – pop. 2 182 – alt. 60
▶ Paris 559 – Brest 60 – Châteaulin 12 – Crozon 25

⛰ La Mer d'Iroise

📞 02 98 81 52 72. www.camping-iroise.fr

Address : plage de Pors-Ar-Vag (5km southwest, 100m from the beach)

Opening times : from mid April to beginning Oct.

2.5 ha (132 pitches) terraced, flat and relatively flat, grassy

Tariff : ♣ 6.10€ 🚗 🔋 12.10€ – 🔋 (6A) 3.80€ – Reservation fee 16€
Rental rates : Permanent – 2 caravans – 12 🚐 – 16 🏠. Per night from 38 to 96€ – Per week from 262 to 860€ – Reservation fee 16€
🚐 borne

A good camp site equipped to a high standard, with a fine view of the sea from some pitches.

Surroundings : ⛰ ≤ Baie de Douarnenez ♨
Leisure activities : ♨ 🎱 ⛵
Facilities : 🚿 🛁 🍴 launderette 🚗
Nearby : ✗ watersports centre
G P S Longitude : -4.29397
Latitude : 48.17006

PLOUÉZEC

22470 – Michelin map **309** E2 – pop. 3 368 – alt. 100
▶ Paris 489 – Guingamp 28 – Lannion 39 – Paimpol 6

⛰ Domaine du Launay

📞 02 96 20 63 15. www.domaine-du-launay.com

Address : 11 route de Toul Veign (3.1km southwest along the D 77, follow the signs for Yvias and take turning to the right)

Opening times : from beginning April to end Oct.

4 ha (90 pitches) terraced, flat, grassy

Tariff : (2014 Price) ♣ 3.50€ 🚗 🔋 5.50€ – 🔋 (16A) 16€ – Reservation fee 10€
Rental rates : (2014 Price) (from beginning April to end Sept.) ✆ – 10 🚐 – 2 canvas bungalows. Per night from 85€ – Per week from 240 to 490€ – Reservation fee 10€
🚐 borne 3.50€ – 8 🔋 12€ – 🚐 🔋 15€

The site has decorative trees and shrubs .

Surroundings : ⛰ ≤ 🏡 ♨
Leisure activities : ♨ 🎱 ⛵ 🚲 ⛳ 🎯
entertainment room
Facilities : 🚿 🍴 launderette
Nearby : ✗ 🐴
G P S Longitude : -3.00286
Latitude : 48.73523

⛰ Le Cap Horn Cap des Îles

📞 02 96 20 64 28. www.lecaphorn.com

Address : rue de Port Lazo (2.3km northeast along the D 77, direct access to the beach)

4 ha (149 pitches) terraced, relatively flat, stony, grassy

Rentals : 40 🚐 – 1 cabin in the trees.

The site overlooks the Anse de Paimpol (bay) and the Île de Bréhat (island).

Surroundings : ⛰ ≤ 🏡
Leisure activities : ♨ 🎱 ⛵ 🚲 🎯 ✈
Facilities : 🚿 🍴 🛁 launderette 🚗
Nearby : ✗ 🎯 🐴
G P S Longitude : -2.96311
Latitude : 48.76

PLOUGASNOU

29630 – Michelin map **308** I2 – pop. 3 268 – alt. 55
▶ Paris 545 – Brest 76 – Guingamp 62 – Lannion 34

⛰ Flower Domaine de Mesqueau

📞 02 98 67 37 45. www.domaine-de-mesqueau.com

Address : 870 route de Mesqueau (3.5km south along the D 46, follow the signs for Morlaix then continue 800m along the turning to the left, 100m from a small lake (direct access)

Opening times : from end March to end Sept.

7.5 ha (100 pitches) flat, grassy

Tariff : 25€ ♣♣ 🚗 🔋 (10A) – Extra per person 6€ – Reservation fee 10€
Rental rates : (from end March to end Sept.) Ⓟ – 40 🚐 – 4 canvas bungalows – 4 tent lodges. Per night from 31 to 123€ – Per week from 196 to 861€ – Reservation fee 10€

Tranquil and spacious pitches in the heart of the countryside.

Surroundings : ⛰ ♨
Leisure activities : 🎱 ⛵ 🚲 ✗ 🎯 ✈
multi-sports ground
Facilities : 🚿 🍴 🛁 🍴
Nearby : ✗ 🚗 ⛵
G P S Longitude : -3.78101
Latitude : 48.66462

PLOUGASTEL-DAOULAS

29470 – Michelin map **308** E4 – pop. 13 304 – alt. 113
▶ Paris 596 – Brest 12 – Morlaix 60 – Quimper 64

🏕 St-Jean 👥

𝒫 02 98 40 32 90. www.campingsaintjean.com

Address : Saint-Jean (4.6km northeast along the D 29 and N 165, take the exit for the Leclerc commercial centre)

Opening times : from mid April to mid Sept.

203 ha (125 pitches)

Tariff : (2014 Price) 24.50€ 👫 🚐 🔲 🐕 (10A) – Extra per person 5.30€

Rental rates : (2014 Price) (from mid April to mid Sept.) – 44 🛖. Per night from 70 to 100€ – Per week from 224 to 694€ – Reservation fee 20€

A pleasant site and location beside the estuary of the Elorn river, ideal for birdwatching.

Surroundings : 🌲 🗄 ♀ ⛲
Leisure activities : 🎯 ✗ 🎣 🌙nighttime 🏃
🚣 🚲 🏊 🛶 multi-sports ground
Facilities : 👤 ⚡ 🎛 🍴 launderette 🧺

Longitude : -4.35334
Latitude : 48.40122

PLOUGOULM

29250 – Michelin map **308** G3 – pop. 1 805 – alt. 60
▶ Paris 560 – Brest 58 – Brignogan-Plages 27 – Morlaix 24

⛺ Municipal du Bois de la Palud

𝒫 02 98 29 81 82. www.plougoulm.fr

Address : Creach ar Feunteun (900m west of the D 10-D 69 junction (Criossant de Plougoulm), following signs for Plouescat and take the road to the right)

0.7 ha (34 pitches) terraced, relatively flat, grassy

A lovely wooded setting, with some beautiful expanses of field nearby.

Surroundings : 🌲 ≤ 🗄 ♀♀
Facilities : 👤 ⚡ 🧺
Nearby : 🚣

Longitude : -4.05323
Latitude : 48.67236

PLOUGOUMELEN

56400 – Michelin map **308** N9 – pop. 2 378 – alt. 27
▶ Paris 471 – Auray 10 – Lorient 51 – Quiberon 39

⛺ La Via Natura Fontaine du Hallate

𝒫 06 16 30 08 33. www.camping-en-morbihan.fr

Address : 8 chemin de Poul Fetan (3.2km southeast towards Ploeren and follow the signs for Baden to the right; at Hallate)

Opening times : from beginning April to end Oct.

3 ha (94 pitches)

Tariff : 19.90€ 👫 🚐 🔲 🐕 (6A) – Extra per person 3.20€

Rental rates : (from beginning April to end Oct.) 🛖 – 8 🛖 – 1 yurt. Per night from 60 to 90€ – Per week from 195 to 590€ Reservation fee 30€

Surroundings : 🌲 ≤ 🗄 ♀
Leisure activities : 🚣
Facilities : 👤 ⚡ 🎛 🍴 launderette

Longitude : -2.8989
Latitude : 47.6432

PLOUGRESCANT

22820 – Michelin map **309** C1 – pop. 1 347 – alt. 53
▶ Paris 516 – Lannion 26 – Perros-Guirec 23 – St-Brieuc 68

⛺ Le Gouffre

𝒫 02 96 92 02 95. www.camping-gouffre.com – limited spaces for one-night stay

Address : Hent Crec'h Kermorvant (2.7km north following signs for La Pointe du Château (headland))

Opening times : from beginning April to end Sept.

3 ha (130 pitches)

Tariff : 12€ 👫 🚐 🔲 🐕 (6A) – Extra per person 4€

Rental rates : (from beginning April to end Sept.) – 13 🛖. Per night from 48 to 140€ – Per week from 150 to 550€
🚐 borne – 🚰12€

Surroundings : 🌲 🗄
Facilities : 👤 ⚡ (July–Aug) 🍴 🖼

Longitude : -3.22749
Latitude : 48.86081

⛺ Le Varlen

𝒫 02 96 92 52 15. www.levarlen.com

Address : 4 Pors Hir (2km to the northeast, follow the signs for Pors Hir, 200m from the sea)

Opening times : from beginning April to beginning Nov.

1 ha (60 pitches) flat, grassy

Tariff : 🧍 4.50€ 🚐 2.20€ 🔲 4.80€ – 🐕 (10A) 4.10€ – Reservation fee 8€

Rental rates : Permanent – 13 🛖 – 2 studios – 1 canvas bungalow. Per night from 38 to 142€ – Per week from 206 to 320€ Reservation fee 8€
🚐 borne 13€

Surroundings : 🌲 🗄
Leisure activities : 🎯 🎣 🚣
Facilities : 👤 ⚡ ♿ 🍴 launderette 🧺
Nearby : ✗

Longitude : -3.21873
Latitude : 48.86078

Do not confuse:
⛺ to 🏕 : *MICHELIN classification with*
★ to ★★★★★ : *official classification*

PLOUGUERNEAU

29880 – Michelin map **308** D3 – pop. 6 411 – alt. 60
▶ Paris 604 – Brest 27 – Landerneau 33 – Morlaix 68

🏕 La Grève Blanche

𝒫 02 98 04 70 35. www.campinggreveblanche.com

Address : St-Michel (4km north along the D 32, follow the signs for St Michel and take a left turn; beside beach)

Opening times : from beginning April to mid Oct.

2.5 ha (100 pitches)

Tariff : (2014 Price) 🧍 3.60€ 🚐 1.70€ 🔲 5.10€ – 🐕 (10A) 2.95€

Rental rates : (2014 Price) Permanent 🛖 – 2 caravans – 2 🛖 – 2 🏠 – 2 tipis. Per night 42€ – Per week from 210 to 530€
🚐 borne 4€ – 🚰9€

In a natural setting among rocks overlooking the beach.

Surroundings : ≤ the bay ⛰
Leisure activities : 🎯 🚣
Facilities : 👤 ⚡ 🍴

Longitude : -4.523
Latitude : 48.6305

⚠ Du Vougot

⚲ 02 98 25 61 51. www.campingduvougot.com

Address : route de Prat Ledan (7.4km northeast along the D 13 and the D 10, follow the signs for Guisseny, then take the D 52; along the bank of the Vougot, 250m from the sea)

Opening times : from beginning April to mid Oct.

2.5 ha (55 pitches)

Tariff : 21€ ✶✶ ⇌ 🔲 🔌 (10A) – Extra per person 3.90€ – Reservation fee 15€

Rental rates : (from beginning April to mid Oct.) – 15 . Per night from 58 to 80€ – Per week from 230 to 600€

🚐 borne 4€ – 🚐 8€

A haven of peace in a well-preserved natural setting.

Surroundings : 🐟 ⬚ Leisure activities : ♟ 🏄 Facilities : ⚬ 🔲 🍴 launderette Nearby : watersports centre	**GPS** Longitude : -4.45 Latitude : 48.63132

🏔 PLOUHARNEL

56340 – Michelin map **308** M9 – pop. 2 000 – alt. 21
▶ Paris 490 – Auray 13 – Lorient 33 – Quiberon 15

🏔 Kersily

⚲ 02 97 52 39 65. www.camping-kersily.com

Address : Ste-Barbe (2.5km northwest along the D 781, follow the signs for Lorient)

Opening times : from beginning April to end Oct.

2.5 ha (120 pitches)

Tariff : (2014 Price) ✶ 5.80€ ⇌ 🔲 9.60€ – 🔌 (10A) 4€ – Reservation fee 10€

Rental rates : (2014 Price) (from beginning April to end Oct.) – 27 . Per night from 52 to 72€ – Per week from 200 to 700€ Reservation fee 10€

🚐 borne 2€ – 🚐 10€

Surroundings : 🐟 ♡♡ Leisure activities : ♟ ✗ 🎱 🌙 nighttime 🏄 ✗ 🛝 entertainment room Facilities : 🚿 ⚬ 🧺 🍴 launderette	**GPS** Longitude : -3.1316 Latitude : 47.61107

⚠ Les Goélands

⚲ 02 97 52 31 92. www.camping-lesgoelands.com

Address : Kergonan (located 1.5km east along the D 781, follow the signs for Carnac then continue 500m along the turning to the left)

Opening times : from beginning April to end Sept.

1.6 ha (80 pitches) flat, grassy

Tariff : (2014 Price) 17€ ✶✶ ⇌ 🔲 🔌 (10A) – Extra per person 5€ – Reservation fee 15€

Rental rates : (2014 Price) (from beginning April to end Sept.) – 2 – 2 🏠. Per night from 40 to 60€ – Per week from 268 to 598€ – Reservation fee 15€

Surroundings : 🐟 ♡ Leisure activities : 🏄 🛝 Facilities : ⚬ 🧺 🍴 🔲 Nearby : ✗	**GPS** Longitude : -3.09657 Latitude : 47.59461

To make the best possible use of this guide, please read pages 2–15 carefully.

29780 – Michelin map **308** E6 – pop. 4 217 – alt. 101
▶ Paris 594 – Audierne 5 – Douarnenez 18 – Pont-l'Abbé 27

🏔 Kersiny-Plage

Kersiny-Plage

⚲ 02 98 70 82 44. www.kersinyplage.com

Address : 1 rue Nominoé (take the western exit along the D 784, follow the signs for Audierne then continue 1km south following signs for Kersiny, 100m from the beach (direct access)

Opening times : from mid May to mid Sept.

2 ha (70 pitches) terraced, relatively flat, grassy

Tariff : 19.40€ ✶✶ ⇌ 🔲 🔌 (8A) – Extra per person 5.90€ – Reservation fee 10€

Rental rates : (from mid May to mid Sept.) 🚿 – 4 – 3 🏠. Per night from 45 to 75€ – Per week from 260 to 530€ – Reservation fee 10€

🚐 borne

An attractive site beside the sea with no shade, but all the pitches have a beautiful view of the ocean.

Surroundings : 🐟 ≤ ocean ⬚ Facilities : ⚬ 🍴 🔲 Nearby : ✗	**GPS** Longitude : -4.50819 Latitude : 48.00719

56680 – Michelin map **308** L8 – pop. 4 922 – alt. 10
▶ Paris 503 – Auray 22 – Lorient 18 – Quiberon 30

🏔 Moténo 👥

⚲ 02 97 36 76 63. www.camping-le-moteno.com

Address : rue du Passage d'Étel (4.5km southeast along the D 781 and take a right turn, follow the signs for Le Magouër)

4 ha (256 pitches) flat, grassy

Rentals : 90 – 22 🏠.

Surroundings : ⬚ ♡ Leisure activities : ♟ ✗ 🎱 🌙 🎣 ♨ jacuzzi 🏄 🚲 🛝 🛝 multi-sports ground, entertainment room Facilities : 🚿 ⚬ 🧺 🍴 launderette 🛝	**GPS** Longitude : -3.22127 Latitude : 47.66492

29610 – Michelin map **308** I3 – pop. 4 685 – alt. 156
▶ Paris 526 – Brest 72 – Carhaix-Plouguer 43 – Guingamp 44

🏔 Aire Naturelle la Ferme de Croas Men

⚲ 02 98 79 11 50. http://ferme-de-croasmen.com

Address : Croas Men (2.5km northwest along the D 712 and the D 64, follow the signs for Lanmeur then continue 4.7km following signs for Lanleya to the left, then follow the signs for Garlan)

Opening times : from beginning April to end Oct.

1 ha (25 pitches) flat, grassy, fruit trees

Tariff : (2014 Price) ✶ 3.50€ ⇌ 🔲 7€ – 🔌 (6A) 3.50€

Rental rates : (2014 Price) Permanent – 2 caravans – 4 – 3 🏠 – 2 tent lodges. Per night from 60 to 80€ – Per week from 350 to 550€

🚐 borne 18€ – 🚐 8€

A working educational farm, with a museum of agricultural tools. A leafy setting for tents and caravans.

Surroundings : 🐾 ♀
Leisure activities : 🏕 🎣
Facilities : ♿ ⛟ 🍴 launderette
Nearby : ⛳ 🐎

GPS Longitude : -3.73792
Latitude : 48.60465

PLOUNÉVEZ-LOCHRIST

29430 – Michelin map **308** F3 – pop. 2 398 – alt. 70
▶ Paris 576 – Brest 41 – Landerneau 24 – Landivisiau 22

△ Municipal Odé-Vras

📞 02 98 61 65 17. www.plounevez-lochrist.fr

Address : Ode Vras (4.5km to the north, along the D 10, 300m from the Baie de Kernic (direct access)

Opening times : from beginning June to mid Sept.

3 ha (135 pitches)

Tariff : (2014 Price) 🚶 2.80€ 🚐 1€ 🔲 1.40€ – 🔌 (10A) 2.45€

Rental rates : (2014 Price) (from beginning June to mid Sept.) – 1 🛖. Per night from 50€ – Per week from 265 to 340€

A site charmingly situated beside unspoilt sand dunes.

Surroundings : 🏞 ♀
Leisure activities : 🏕 🎣
Facilities : ⛟ 🛒 ⛱ launderette

GPS Longitude : -4.23942
Latitude : 48.64564

The information in the guide may have changed since going to press.

PLOZÉVET

29710 – Michelin map **308** E7 – pop. 2 988 – alt. 70
▶ Paris 588 – Audierne 11 – Douarnenez 19 – Pont-l'Abbé 22

⛰ La Corniche

📞 02 98 91 33 94. www.campinglacorniche.com

Address : chemin de la Corniche (take the southern exit along the coast road)

Opening times : from beginning April to end Oct.

2 ha (120 pitches) flat, grassy

Tariff : 23.90€ 🚶🚶 🚐 🔲 🔌 (10A) – Extra per person 4.90€ – Reservation fee 12€

Rental rates : (from beginning April to end Oct.) – 16 🛖 – 9 🏠 – 5 tent lodges. Per night from 41 to 61€ – Per week from 308 to 721€ – Reservation fee 12€

🚐 borne 4€

A haven of peace in the middle of the Baie d'Audierne (bay), 500m from the centre of the village.

Surroundings : 🐾
Leisure activities : 🍴 🏕 🎣 🏊
Facilities : ♿ ⛟ 🔲 ⛱ 🏊 💈 🍴 launderette

GPS Longitude : -4.4287
Latitude : 47.98237

The Michelin classification (△△△ ... △) is totally independent of the official star classification system awarded by the local prefecture or other official organisation.

PLURIEN

22240 – Michelin map **309** H3 – pop. 1 396 – alt. 48
▶ Paris 436 – Dinard 34 – Lamballe 25 – Plancoët 23

△ Municipal la Saline

📞 02 96 72 17 40. http://campinglessalines.fr

Address : rue du Lac, Sables d'or-Les Pins (1.2km northwest along the D 34, follow the signs for Sables-d'Or-les-Pins; 500m from the sea)

Opening times : from beginning April to end Oct.

3 ha (150 pitches) terraced, flat, grassy

Tariff : 15.40€ 🚶🚶 🚐 🔲 🔌 (6A) – Extra per person 3.40€

Rental rates : (from beginning April to end Oct.) – 8 🛖 – 2 tent lodges. Per night from 38 to 90€ – Per week from 210 to 537€

🚐 borne 2€

Surroundings : ≤ ♀
Leisure activities : 🎣
Facilities : ♿ 🛒 launderette

GPS Longitude : -2.41396
Latitude : 48.63281

In order for the guide to remain wholly objective, the selection of campsites is made on an entirely independent basis.

PONTRIEUX

22260 – Michelin map **309** D2 – pop. 1 053 – alt. 13
▶ Paris 491 – Guingamp 18 – Lannion 27 – Morlaix 67

△ Traou-Mélédern

📞 02 96 95 69 27. www.camping-pontrieux.com

Address : 400m south of the town; beside the Trieux river

Opening times : Permanent

1 ha (50 pitches)

Tariff : 🚶 4.20€ 🚐 🔲 5.30€ – 🔌 (10A) 3.20€

Rental rates : Permanent – 1 🛖 – 2 gîtes. Per night from 50€ – Per week from 260 to 360€

Surroundings : 🏞 ♀♀
Leisure activities : 🎣
Facilities : ♿ 🛒 (from mid June to mid Sept) 🔲 🍴 🏊
Nearby : marina

GPS Longitude : -3.16355
Latitude : 48.6951

PONT-SCORFF

56620 – Michelin map **308** K8 – pop. 3 167 – alt. 42
▶ Paris 509 – Auray 47 – Lorient 11 – Quiberon 56

△ Ty Nénez

📞 02 97 32 51 16. www.lorient-camping.com

Address : route de Lorient (1.8km southwest along the D 6)

Opening times : Permanent

2.5 ha (93 pitches)

Tariff : 22.40€ 🚶🚶 🚐 🔲 🔌 (16A) – Extra per person 5€

Rental rates : Permanent ♿ (1 mobile home) – 17 🛖. Per night from 53 to 109€ – Per week from 318 to 763€

🚐 borne 3€ – 20 🔲 10.60€ – 🚐 10.60€

Surroundings : 🏞 ♀
Leisure activities : 🍴 🎣 🖼
Facilities : ♿ ⛟ 🏛 🏊 🍴 launderette

GPS Longitude : -3.40664
Latitude : 47.82081

PORDIC

22590 – Michelin map **309** F3 – pop. 5 923 – alt. 97
▶ Paris 459 – Guingamp 33 – Lannion 65 – St-Brieuc 11

⚠ Les Madières

⚲ 02 96 79 02 48. www.campinglesmadieres.com

Address : Le Vau Madec (situated 2km northeast following signs for Binic and take a right turn)

Opening times : from beginning April to end Oct.

1.6 ha (93 pitches)

Tariff : (2014 Price) 24.10€ ✯✯ ⇔ 🅴 (∅) (10A) –
Extra per person 5.80€

Rental rates : (2014 Price) (from beginning April to end Oct.) –
9 🛏. Per night from 70€ – Per week from 320 to 590€ –
Reservation fee 10€

🔌 8 🅴 17.50€ – ⚡(∅)15€

A pleasant leafy setting, attractively shady; some pitches with a view of the sea and the port at St-Quay-Portrieux.

Surroundings : ⛰ ⌂ ♨
Leisure activities : 🍹 ✗ ⛵
Facilities : ♿ ⚮ ▦ ⚐ launderette

GPS Longitude : -2.80475
Latitude : 48.58266

⚠ Le Roc de l'Hervieu

⚲ 02 96 79 30 12. www.campinglerocdelhervieu.fr – limited spaces for one-night stay

Address : 19 rue d'Estienne d'Orves (3km northeast following signs for La Pointe de Pordic (headland) and take the road to the right)

Opening times : from beginning May to end Sept.

2.5 ha (166 pitches) flat, grassy

Tariff : ✯ 4.50€ ⇔ 3.80€ 🅴 4.50€ – (∅) (10A) 3.80€

Rental rates : (from beginning May to end Sept.) – 20 🛏.
Per week from 330 to 450€

🔌 borne 4€

Surroundings : ⛰ ⌂
Leisure activities : 🛶 ⚓
Facilities : ♿ ⚮ ⚐ ▦

GPS Longitude : -2.7811
Latitude : 48.58188

PORT-MANECH

29920 – Michelin map **308** I8
▶ Paris 545 – Carhaix-Plouguer 73 – Concarneau 18 – Pont-Aven 12

⚠ St-Nicolas

⚲ 02 98 06 89 75. www.campinglesaintnicolas.com

Address : at Port-Manech, 8 Kergouliou (north of the town, 200m from the beach)

3 ha (180 pitches) terraced, relatively flat, flat, grassy

Rentals : 18 🛏.

The site is in two sections, with decorative flowers and shrubs.

Surroundings : ⛰ ⌂ ♨
Leisure activities : 🛶 ⚓ 🗺 ⚓ ⛷
Facilities : ♿ ⚮ ⚐ launderette
Nearby : ⚓ 🍹 ✗ 🛶

GPS Longitude : -3.74541
Latitude : 47.80512

LE POULDU

29360 – Michelin map **308** J8
▶ Paris 521 – Concarneau 37 – Lorient 25 – Moëlan-sur-Mer 10

⚠ Les Embruns

⚲ 02 98 39 91 07. www.camping-les-embruns.com

Address : rue du Philosophe-Alain (in the town, 350m from the beach)

Opening times : from beginning April to mid Sept.

5.5 ha (176 pitches) fruit trees

Tariff : 37.50€ ✯✯ ⇔ 🅴 (∅) (16A) – Extra per person 7.50€ –
Reservation fee 20€

Rental rates : (from beginning April to mid Sept.) ♿ (1 mobile home) – 35 🛏. Per night from 110 to 190€ – Per week from 275 to 1,310€ – Reservation fee 20€

🔌 borne 6€ – 14 🅴 9.90€

A charming family campsite, in green and landscaped surroundings, offering a warm welcome and excellent activities.

Surroundings : ⌂ ♨
Leisure activities : 🍹 🛶 ☺ 🛁 ≋ hammam
🏊 🚲 (open air in season) ⚘ wildlife park, spa centre
Facilities : ♿ ⚮ ▦ ☂ ⚓ ⚐ launderette
Nearby : ⚓ ✗ ☕ ✗ 🛶

GPS Longitude : -3.54696
Latitude : 47.76947

⚠ Keranquernat

⚲ 02 98 39 92 32. www.camping.keranquernat.com

Address : Keranquernat (at the roundabout, take northeastern exit)

Opening times : from end April to beginning Sept.

1.5 ha (100 pitches)

Tariff : ✯ 4€ ⇔ 🅴 9€ – (∅) (6A) 4€

Rental rates : (from end April to beginning Sept.) 🏖 – 10 🛏.
Per night from 45 to 110€ – Per week from 210 to 490€

🔌 borne 10€

In a pleasant setting shaded by apple trees and covered in flowers.

Surroundings : ⛰ ⌂ ♨
Leisure activities : 🛶 🛁 ⚓ ⛷
Facilities : ♿ ⚮ (July-Aug) ☂ ⚓ ⚐ launderette
Nearby : ⚓ ✗ ☕ 🛶

GPS Longitude : -3.54332
Latitude : 47.7727

⚠ Locouarn

⚲ 02 98 39 91 79. www.camping-locouarn.com

Address : situated 2km north along the D 49, follow the signs for Quimperlé

Opening times : from beginning June to beginning Sept.

2.5 ha (100 pitches) open site, relatively flat, flat, grassy

Tariff : ✯ 3.60€ ⇔ 🅴 6.90€ – (∅) (10A) 4.20€

Rental rates : (from beginning May to mid Sept.) – 6 🛏 – 8 🏠.
Per night from 50€ – Per week from 160 to 490€ – Reservation fee 5€

A pleasant site surrounded by fields.

Surroundings : ⛰ ♨
Leisure activities : ⛷
Facilities : ♿ ⚮ ☂ ⚓ ⚐ launderette
Nearby : ⚓ 🍹 ✗ 🐎

GPS Longitude : -3.54793
Latitude : 47.7855

⚠ Les Grands Sables

📞 02 98 39 94 43. www.camping-lesgrandssables.com

Address : 22 rue Philosophe Alain (in the town, 200m from the beach)

Opening times : from mid April to mid Sept.

2.4 ha (128 pitches) terraced, flat and relatively flat, sandy, grassy

Tariff : (2014 Price) 21.30€ ♛♛ ⬟ 国 🚿 (10A) – Extra per person 5€
Reservation fee 9€

Rental rates : (2014 Price) (from mid April to mid Sept.) – 18 🚐. Per night from 30 to 87€ – Per week from 215 to 610€– Reservation fee 9€

🚐 borne 4€

In a green and leafy location with shade and a view of the pretty chapel of Notre-Dame-de-la-Paix.

Surroundings : 🦢 ⚓		**G**	Longitude : -3.54716
Leisure activities : 🏊 🚴		**P**	Latitude : 47.7683
Facilities : ⚡ 🚿 🏕 🚰 launderette		**S**	
Nearby : 🏖 ✕ ✂ 🚣			

⚠ Croas An Ter

📞 02 98 39 94 19. www.campingcroasanter.com

Address : Quelvez (located 1.5km north along the D49, follow the signs for Quimperlé)

Opening times : from beginning May to mid Sept.

3.5 ha (90 pitches)

Tariff : 16.20€ ♛♛ ⬟ 国 🚿 (6A) – Extra per person 3.80€

Rental rates : (from beginning June to mid Sept.) – 2 🚐 – 1 tent lodge. Per night from 35 to 55€ – Per week from 290 to 440€

A site with good shade and integrated well in the natural surroundings; a perfect spot for touring cyclists.

Surroundings : 🦢 🚐 🎾		**G**	Longitude : -3.54104
Leisure activities : ✕ 🚴 🚲		**P**	Latitude : 47.78515
Facilities : ⚡ 🚿 🏕 🚰 launderette		**S**	
Nearby : 🏖 🚣			

Routes nationales are main roads and their identifying numbers begin with N or RN. Routes départementales are generally quieter roads and begin with D or DN.

POULLAN-SUR-MER

29100 – Michelin map **308** E6 – pop. 1 499 – alt. 79
▶ Paris 596 – Rennes 244 – Quimper 30 – Brest 80

⚠⚠⚠ La Baie de Douarnenez ♟♟

📞 02 98 74 26 39. www.camping-douarnenez.com

Address : 30 rue Luc Robet (600m east of the town along the D7)

5.7 ha (190 pitches) flat, grassy

Rentals : 74 🚐 – 20 🏠 – 3 canvas bungalows – 6 tent lodges.

The pitches are laid out around a partially covered water park.

Surroundings : 🦢 🚐 🎾		**G**	Longitude : -4.40634
Leisure activities : 🍸 ✕ 🏊 🌙nighttime		**P**	Latitude : 48.08162
🏸 🚴 🚲 ✂ 🎱 🏓 🛝 🎣 multi-sports ground		**S**	
Facilities : ⚡ 🚿 🏕 🚰 🚽 launderette 🏖 🚣			

PRIMEL-TRÉGASTEL

29630 – Michelin map **308** I2
▶ Paris 554 – Rennes 198 – Quimper 105 – Brest 79

⚠ Municipal de la Mer

📞 02 98 72 37 06. www.camping-plougasnou.fr

Address : 15 route de Karreg An Ty (4km north along the D 46)

Opening times : from beginning April to end Oct.

1 ha (63 pitches)

Tariff : (2014 Price) 14.20€ ♛♛ ⬟ 国 🚿 (10A) – Extra per person 3.70€

Rental rates : (2014 Price) (from beginning April to end Oct.) – 2 canvas bungalows. Per night from 40 to 60€ – Per week from 250 to 350€

🚐 borne 2.20€

An exceptional location beside the sea, with an unrestricted sea view. Make sure tents are well secured as the site is exposed to the wind.

Surroundings : 🦢 ⛰Île de Batz and Roscoff ⛰		**G**	Longitude : -3.81527
Leisure activities : 🛶 🚴 🚲 🏄		**P**	Latitude : 48.71477
Facilities : ♿ 🚿 (July-Aug) 🚰 launderette		**S**	
Nearby : 🍸 ✕			

For more information on visiting particular towns or regions, consult the relevant regional MICHELIN Green Guide. We also recommend you use the appropriate Michelin regional map to locate your selected campsite, to calculate distances and to work out the best route.

PRIMELIN

29770 – Michelin map **308** D6 – pop. 742 – alt. 78
▶ Paris 605 – Audierne 7 – Douarnenez 28 – Quimper 44

⚠ Municipal de Kermalero

📞 02 98 74 84 75. www.primelin.fr

Address : route de l'Océan (take the western exit towards the port)

Opening times : from mid March to end Oct.

1 ha (75 pitches)

Tariff : (2014 Price) 15€ ♛♛ ⬟ 国 🚿 (6A) – Extra per person 3.50€
Reservation fee 10€

🚐 borne 2€ – 6 国 3€

A simple but pleasant site beside the sea.

Surroundings : 🦢 ⛰ 🚐		**G**	Longitude : -4.61067
Leisure activities : 🛶 🚴		**P**	Latitude : 48.02544
Facilities : ♿ 🚿 (July-Aug) 🏕 🚽 🚰 launderette		**S**	
Nearby : ✂			

The prices listed were supplied by the campsite owners in 2014 (if prices were not available, those from the previous year are given). The fees should be regarded as basic charges and may fluctuate with inflation.

PRIZIAC

56320 – Michelin map **308** K6 – pop. 1 046 – alt. 163
▶ Paris 498 – Concarneau 55 – Lorient 42 – Pontivy 39

⚠ Municipal Bel Air

☎ 02 97 34 61 26. www.priziac.com

Address : Lac du Bel Air (lake) (500m north along the D 109 and take the turning to the left)

Opening times : from beginning April to end Oct.

1.5 ha (60 pitches) flat, grassy

Tariff : (2014 Price) ★ 2.50€ ⟵ 1.25€ 🔲 1.75€ – (½) (10A) 2€ –
Reservation fee 10€

Rental rates : (2014 Price) (from beginning April to end Oct.) –
4 🚐. Per night from 45 to 50€ – Per week from 180 to 352€
Reservation fee 10€

🚐 borne – 🖫3€

In a green setting with plenty of shade, near a small lake.

Surroundings : 🌿 ⚲ ⚠ Leisure activities : 🏛 Facilities : ♿ launderette Nearby : 🍽 ⛵ 🎯 ⛱ (beach) 🐟 ♨ watersports centre	**GPS** Longitude : -3.41418 Latitude : 48.06155

The pitches of many campsites are marked out with low hedges of attractive bushes and shrubs.

QUIBERON

56170 – Michelin map **308** M10 – pop. 5 027 – alt. 10
▶ Paris 505 – Auray 28 – Concarneau 98 – Lorient 47

🏔 Flower Le Bois d'Amour ♟⚤

☎ 02 97 50 13 52. www.quiberon-camping.com

Address : rue Saint-Clément (located 1.5km southeast, 300m from the sea and sea spa centre)

Opening times : from beginning April to end Sept.

4.6 ha (272 pitches)

Tariff : 16€ ★★ ⟵ 🔲 (½) (10A) – Extra per person 4.20€ – Reservation fee 15€

Rental rates : (from beginning April to end Sept.) – 90 🚐 –
18 🏚 – 18 canvas bungalows – 10 tent lodges. Per night from 32 to 111€ – Per week from 220 to 693€ – Reservation fee 20€

🚐 borne

Surroundings : ⌂ ⚲ Leisure activities : 🍽 ✕ 🏛 🎯 🏃 🏄 🚴 🛶 Facilities : ♿ ⚡ ⛺ 🍴 launderette 🧺 Nearby : 🎯 🐎 ⚞	**GPS** Longitude : -3.10427 Latitude : 47.47632

🏔 Do.Mi.Si.La.Mi. ♟⚤

☎ 02 97 50 22 52. www.domisilami.com

Address : St-Julien-Plage, 31 rue de la Vierge (600m to the north, 100m from the beach)

Opening times : from beginning April to end Oct.

4.4 ha (350 pitches)

Tariff : ★ 5€ ⟵ 🔲 14€ – (½) (10A) 4.20€
Reservation fee 20€

Rental rates : (from beginning April to end Oct.) 🏃 – 80 🚐.
Per night from 32 to 147€ – Per week from 192 to 882€

🚐 borne 8€ – 5 🔲 13.80€

Camping DOMISILAMI

There's a free shuttle service to Quiberon.

Surroundings : ⌂ ⚲ Leisure activities : 🍽 ✕ 🏛 🏃 🏄 🚴 multi-sports ground Facilities : ♿ ⚡ ⛺ 🍴 launderette 🧺🚿	**GPS** Longitude : -3.12045 Latitude : 47.49937

🏔 Les Joncs du Roch

☎ 02 97 50 24 37. www.lesjoncsduroch.com

Address : rue de l'Aérodrome (situated 2km southeast, 500m from the sea)

2.3 ha (163 pitches) flat, grassy

Rentals : 26 🚐 – 2 canvas bungalows.

Surroundings : ⌂ ⚲ Leisure activities : 🏛 🏄 🎱 (open air in season) multi-sports ground, entertainment room Facilities : ♿ ⚡ ⛺ 🍴 launderette Nearby : ⚞ 🐎 ♨ 🏇	**GPS** Longitude : -3.10098 Latitude : 47.47946

⚠ Beauséjour

☎ 02 97 30 44 93. www.campingbeausejour.com

Address : boulevard du Parco (800m to the north, 50m from the beach)

2.4 ha (160 pitches) flat and relatively flat, grassy, sandy
Rentals : 15 🚐.

Leisure activities : 🏛 🏄 multi-sports ground Facilities : ♿ ⚡ ▣ ⛺ 🍴 launderette Nearby : 🍽 🍴 ✕ 🏄	**GPS** Longitude : -3.12027 Latitude : 47.5003

QUIMPER

29000 – Michelin map **308** G7 – pop. 63 387 – alt. 41
▶ Paris 564 – Brest 73 – Lorient 67 – Rennes 215

🏔 Les Castels L'Orangerie de Lanniron ♟⚤

☎ 02 98 90 62 02. www.lanniron.com

Address : allée de Lanniron (3km south along the ring road (périphérique), then take the exit towards Bénodet and a right turn; near the leisure centre at Creac'h Gwen)

Opening times : from beginning April to beginning Nov.

38 ha/6.5 for camping (235 pitches) flat, grassy

Tariff : (2014 Price) ★ 8.50€ ⟵ 5.60€ 🔲 27.60€ – (½) (10A) 27.60€
Reservation fee 25€

Rental rates : (2014 Price) Permanent – 46 🚐 – 12 studios –
3 tent lodges – 5 gîtes. Per night from 80 to 140€ – Per week from 455 to 980€ – Reservation fee 25€

🚐 borne

Situated in the magnificent park and grounds of a 17th-century château; beside the Odet river, with a 9-hole golf course and pretty water park.

Surroundings : ⌂ ⚲⚲ Leisure activities : 🍽 ✕ 🏛 🎯 🏃 jacuzzi 🏄 🚴 🎯 🐎 🐟 🏌 9-hole golf course 🎣 Facilities : ♿ ⚡ ▣ ⛺ 🍴 launderette 🧺 🚿	**GPS** Longitude : -4.10338 Latitude : 47.97923

QUIMPERLÉ

29300 – Michelin map **308** J7 – pop. 11 384 – alt. 30
▶ Paris 517 – Carhaix-Plouguer 57 – Concarneau 32 – Pontivy 76

⚠ Municipal de Kerbertrand

📞 02 98 39 31 30. www.quimperle-tourisme.com

Address : 2 rue de Kermaria (located 1.5km west along the D 783, follow the signs for Concarneau and take the road to the right, after the stadium, opposite the Leclerc commercial centre)

1 ha (40 pitches) flat, grassy

A simple but attractive municipal campsite.

Surroundings : 🌿 ౮౮
Leisure activities : 🎏 ⛵
Facilities : ⊶
Nearby : 🛒 ✗ 🎣 🏊

Longitude : -3.57044
Latitude : 47.872

Using the traditional Michelin classification method, the guide provides you with an easy, speedy reference for assessing the category of each site: 1 to 5 tents (see page 10).

RAGUENÈS-PLAGE

29920 – Michelin map **308** I8
▶ Paris 545 – Carhaix-Plouguer 73 – Concarneau 17 – Pont-Aven 12

🏔 Les Deux Fontaines 👥

📞 02 98 06 81 91. www.les2fontaines.com

Address : Feunten Vihan (1.3km north following signs for Névez and Trémorvezen)

Opening times : from end April to beginning Sept.

9 ha (270 pitches) flat, grassy

Tariff : (2014 Price) 38.90€ ✶ ✶ ⛺ 🔲 (10A) – Extra per person 7€ – Reservation fee 15€

Rental rates : (2014 Price) (from end April to beginning Sept.) – 60 🚐 – 11 🏠. Per night from 49 to 161€ – Per week from 199 to 1,127€ – Reservation fee 15€

🚐 borne 5€ – 🔵 15€

A water park with good facilities for children, partially open air; sub aqua lessons for beginners are available.

Surroundings : 🌿 ⌂ ౮౮
Leisure activities : 🎏 ✗ 🎏 🛖 🚸 🛝 ⛷ ✗
🔲 🏊 farm or petting farm, pool, scuba diving
Facilities : 🚻 ⊶ 🔲 🧺 launderette

Longitude : -3.79129
Latitude : 47.7992

🏔 Club Airotel Le Raguenès-Plage 👥

Le Raguenès-Plage

📞 02 98 06 80 69. www.camping-le-raguenes-plage.com

Address : 19 rue des Îles (400m from the beach, direct access)

Opening times : from mid April to end Sept.

6 ha (287 pitches) flat, grassy

Tariff : (2014 Price) 39.50€ ✶ ✶ ⛺ 🔲 🔲 (10A) – Extra per person 6.20€

Rental rates : (2014 Price) (from mid April to end Sept.) – 60 🚐. Per night from 38 to 128€ – Per week from 295 to 890€

🚐 borne

In a pleasant setting, laid out around an attractive water park.

Surroundings : ౮౮
Leisure activities : 🎏 ✗ 🎏 🛖 🚸 🛝 ⛷
🚴 🏊 ⛷
Facilities : 🚻 ⊶ 🔲 🧺 launderette 🏊 🚐

Longitude : -3.80085
Latitude : 47.79373

🏔 Le Vieux Verger - Ty Noul

📞 02 98 06 86 08. www.campingduvieuxverger.com

Address : 20 Kéroren (take the northern exit, follow the signs for Névez)

1.2 ha (42 pitches) flat, grassy
Rentals : 10 🚐 – 1 apartment.

A pretty water park; attractive pitches for tents and caravans.

Surroundings : ౮
Leisure activities : ⛷ 🚴 🏊 ⛷
Facilities : 🚻 ⊶ 🧺 🔲

Longitude : -3.79777
Latitude : 47.79663

⚠ L'Océan

📞 02 98 06 87 13. www.camping-ocean.fr

Address : 15 impasse des Mouettes, at Kéroren (take the northern exit, follow the signs for Névez and take a right turn, 350m from the beach (direct access)

Opening times : from mid May to mid Sept.

2.2 ha (150 pitches)

Tariff : 28€ ✶ ✶ ⛺ 🔲 🔲 (6A) – Extra per person 6.40€

Rental rates : (from mid May to mid Sept.) 🚐 – 8 🚐. Per week from 330 to 600€

🚐 borne – 🔵 🔲 24€

Quiet, peaceful pitches; a spacious site with flowers and a panoramic view of the ocean.

Surroundings : 🌿 ⌂ ⌂
Leisure activities : 🎏 ⛷ 🔲 (open air in season)
Facilities : 🚻 ⊶ 🏊 🧺 launderette
Nearby : ✗ 🍺

Longitude : -3.79789
Latitude : 47.79471

RENNES

35000 – Michelin map **309** L6 – pop. 206 604 – alt. 40
▶ Paris 349 – Angers 129 – Brest 246 – Caen 185

⚠ Municipal des Gayeulles

📞 02 99 36 91 22. www.camping-rennes.com

Address : rue Professeur Maurice-Audin (take the northeastern exit towards the N 12, follow the signs for Fougères then take the av. des Gayeulles near a small lake)

Opening times : Permanent

3 ha (178 pitches) flat, grassy

Tariff : (2014 Price) 🔲 4€ ⛺ 1.70€ 🔲 7€ – 🔲 (16A) 3.50€

🚐 borne 2€ – 30 🔲 7.80€

Situated in the middle of the immense wooded park at Les Gayeulles, in a natural setting shared with rabbits!

Surroundings : 🌿 ⌂ ౮౮
Leisure activities : ⛷
Facilities : 🚻 ⊶ (July-Aug) 🎏 🏊 🧺 🔲 launderette 🏊
Nearby : 🛒 ✗ 🎣 🏂 🔲 (open air in season) skating rink, wildlife park

Longitude : -1.64772
Latitude : 48.13455

LA ROCHE-BERNARD

56130 – Michelin map **308** R9 – pop. 757 – alt. 38
▶ Paris 444 – Nantes 70 – Ploërmel 55 – Redon 28

⚠ Municipal le Pâtis

📞 02 99 90 60 13. www.camping-larochebernard.com

Address : 3 chemin du Pâtis (to the west of the town towards the marina)

Opening times : from beginning April to mid Oct.

1 ha (58 pitches) flat, grassy

Tariff : (2014 Price) 21.70€ ✶✶ ⇎ 🗉 (6A) – Extra per person 3.60€

Rental rates : (2014 Price) Permanent – 2 🚐. Per night from 38 to 100€ – Per week from 215 to 590€

🚰 borne 2€ – 18 🗉 9.90€

Situated beside the Vilaine river, opposite the port.

Surroundings : ▭ ♀
Leisure activities : 🛶 𝟞
Facilities : ⅙ ⊙ (July-Aug) 🎴 ♨ ⛾ launderette
Nearby : 🛶 ♨

Longitude : -2.30523
Latitude : 47.51923

This guide is not intended as a list of all the camping sites in France; its aim is to provide a selection of the best sites in each category.

ROCHEFORT-EN-TERRE

56220 – Michelin map **308** Q8 – pop. 662 – alt. 40
▶ Paris 431 – Ploërmel 34 – Redon 26 – Rennes 82

⚠ Sites et Paysages Au Gré des Vents

📞 02 97 43 37 52. www.campingaugredesvents.com

Address : 2 chemin de Bogeais (located 1km southwest along the D 774, follow the signs for Péaule and take the road to the right; 500m from a small lake)

Opening times : from beginning April to end Sept.

2.5 ha (60 pitches)

Tariff : (2014 Price) 25.60€ ✶✶ ⇎ 🗉 (10A) – Extra per person 5.65€

Rental rates : (2014 Price) Permanent – 6 🚐 – 2 tent lodges. Per night from 58 to 86€ – Per week from 276 to 603€

🚰 borne 2.50€ – 🚐 11€

Surroundings : ⛰
Leisure activities : 🛶 ✂ 🖼 (open air in season)
Facilities : ⅙ ⊙ ⛾⛾ launderette
Nearby : ✗ ☷ (beach) ⚓

Longitude : -2.34736
Latitude : 47.69587

ROHAN

56580 – Michelin map **308** O6 – pop. 1 637 – alt. 55
▶ Paris 451 – Lorient 72 – Pontivy 17 – Quimperlé 86

⚠ Municipal le Val d'Oust

📞 02 97 51 57 58. www.rohan.fr

Address : rue de St-Gouvry (take the northwestern exit)

Opening times : from beginning May to mid Sept.

1 ha (45 pitches) flat, grassy

Tariff : (2014 Price) ✶ 3.50€ ⇎ 1.50€ 🗉 2€ – (10A) 3.40€

🚰 borne

Situated beside the Nantes–Brest canal and near a small lake.

Surroundings : ♀♀
Leisure activities : 🛶 𝟞
Facilities : ⅙ ⛾ 🖼
Nearby : 🍴 ✗ ✂ ☷ (beach) ⚓ sports trail

Longitude : -2.7548
Latitude : 48.07077

ROZ-SUR-COUESNON

35610 – Michelin map **309** M3 – pop. 1 034 – alt. 65
▶ Paris 365 – Rennes 82 – Caen 134 – St-Lô 99

⚠ Les Couesnons

📞 02 99 80 26 86. www.lescouesnons.com

Address : l'Hopital (situated 2km southeast on the D 797)

Opening times : from beginning April to end Oct.

1 ha (50 pitches) flat, grassy

Tariff : (2014 Price) 22€ ✶✶ ⇎ 🗉 (10A) – Extra per person 5.30€

Rental rates : (2014 Price) (from beginning April to end Oct.) – 1 caravan – 8 🚐. Per night from 110 to 260€ – Per week from 310 to 680€

Choose the pitches furthest away from the road in preference.

Surroundings : ▭ ♀♀
Leisure activities : 🍴 ✗ 🏛
Facilities : ⅙ ⊙ 🎴 ⛾⛾ 🖼

Longitude : -1.60904
Latitude : 48.59597

ST-BRIAC-SUR-MER

35800 – Michelin map **309** J3 – pop. 1 955 – alt. 30
▶ Paris 411 – Dinan 24 – Dol-de-Bretagne 34 – Lamballe 41

⚠ Émeraude

📞 02 51 22 22 36. www.campingleparadis.com

Address : 7 chemin de la Souris

Opening times : Permanent

3.2 ha (196 pitches)

Tariff : (2014 Price) 13€ ✶✶ ⇎ 🗉 (12A) – Extra per person 5€ – Reservation fee 25€

Rental rates : (2014 Price) Permanent ⅙ (1 mobile home) – 83 🚐 – 9 🏠 – 10 canvas bungalows. Per night from 18 to 58€ – Per week from 126 to 900€ – Reservation fee 25€

There's an attractive swimming area and restaurant, surrounded by palm trees.

Surroundings : ⛰ ♀
Leisure activities : 🍴 ✗ 🖼 🛶 𝟞 ♨ ⛲ entertainment room
Facilities : ⅙ ⊙ ⛾ ♨⛾ launderette 🛶

Longitude : -2.13012
Latitude : 48.62735

ST-CAST-LE-GUILDO

22380 – Michelin map **309** I3 – pop. 3 500 – alt. 52
▶ Paris 427 – Avranches 91 – Dinan 32 – St-Brieuc 50

⚠ Les Castels Le Château de la Galinée ♣♣

📞 02 96 41 10 56. www.chateaudegalinee.com

Address : rue de Galinée (7km to the south, access via the D 786, near the crossroads with the road to St-Cast-le-Guildo)

Opening times : from mid May to beginning Sept.

14 ha (272 pitches) flat, grassy

Tariff : ✶ 7.30€ ⇎ 🗉 21€ – (10A) 6.20€ – Reservation fee 20€

Rental rates : (from mid April to beginning Sept.) ⚡ – 2 caravans – 45 🚐 – 5 🏠 – 5 canvas bungalows. Per night from 41 to 165€ – Per week from 287 to 1,155€ – Reservation fee 20€

🚰 borne

Surroundings : 🐾 ▭ ♨♨
Leisure activities : 🍴 🏛 🏊 🏃 🎣 🏄
🎯 🔲 🎱 🎿 🏐 multi-sports ground, entertainment room
Facilities : 🚿 🔌 ⬚▥ 🛁 – 4 individual sanitary facilities (🚿 🚽 wc) 🛒 🚮 🍴 launderette 🚮 🛒

GPS Longitude : -2.25725
Latitude : 48.58403

⛰ **Le Châtelet** 👥

📞 02 96 41 96 33. www.lechatelet.com – limited spaces for one-night stay

Address : rue des Nouettes (located 1km west, 250m from the beach (direct access)

Opening times : from mid April to mid Sept.

9 ha/3.9 for camping (216 pitches) small lake

Tariff : (2014 Price) 🚶 7.20€ 🚗 🔲 22.50€ – ⚡ (8A) 6.20€ –Reservation fee 23€

Rental rates : (2014 Price) (from mid April to mid Sept.) – 52 🚐 – 1 tipi – 6 tent lodges. Per night from 48 to 135€ – Per week from 335 to 1,290€ – Reservation fee 23€

🚰 borne

The site overlooks the Baie de la Frênaye (bay).

Surroundings : 🐾 ≼ ▭ ♀
Leisure activities : 🍴 🏛 🏊 🏃 🎣 🔲 (open air in season) 🎣
Facilities : 🚿 🔌 🛁 🛒 🚮 🍴 launderette 🚮 🛒
Nearby : 🛒 ✕ 🚲

GPS Longitude : -2.26959
Latitude : 48.63773

⛰ **Vert-Bleu Les Mielles**

📞 02 96 41 87 60. www.campings-vert-bleu.com

Address : boulevard de la Vieux-Ville (take the southern exit along the D 19, follow the signs for St-Malo, right next to the stadium and 200m from the beach)

Opening times : from mid March to mid Nov.

3.5 ha (160 pitches) flat, grassy

Tariff : (2014 Price) 29.20€ 🚶🚶 🚗 🔲 ⚡ (10A) – Extra per person 6.10€ – Reservation fee 20€

Rental rates : (2014 Price) (from mid March to mid Nov.) –15 🚐. Per night from 65 to 130€ – Per week from 390 to 910€ – Reservation fee 20€

🚰 borne – 🚐 ⚡22.70€

Surroundings : ▭ ♀
Leisure activities : 🏛 🎣 🔲
Facilities : 🚿 🔌 🛁 🍴 launderette
Nearby : 🍴 🔲 🚤

GPS Longitude : -2.25402
Latitude : 48.62694

ST-COULOMB

35350 – Michelin map **309** K2 – pop. 2 454 – alt. 35
▶ Paris 398 – Cancale 6 – Dinard 18 – Dol-de-Bretagne 21

⛰ Le Tannée

📞 02 99 89 41 20. www.campingdetannee.com – limited spaces for one-night stay

Address : rue de Tannée

0.6 ha (30 pitches) flat and relatively flat

Rentals : 16 🚐.

Good-quality mobile home rentals with lovely terraces.

Surroundings : 🐾 ▭
Leisure activities : hammam 🎣 🔲 (open air in season)
Facilities : 🚿 🔌 🛁 🍴 launderette

GPS Longitude : -1.889
Latitude : 48.68655

⛰ **Duguesclin**

📞 02 99 89 03 24. www.camping-duguesclin.com – limited spaces for one-night stay

Address : rue de Tannée (2.5km northeast along the D 355, follow the signs for Cancale and take turning to the left)

Opening times : from end March to beginning Nov.

0.9 ha (41 pitches)

Tariff : 20.90€ 🚶🚶 🚗 🔲 ⚡ (10A) – Extra per person 4.80€

Rental rates : (from end March to beginning Nov.) – 15 🚐 – 1 apartment – 1 gîte. Per week from 250 to 660€ – Reservation fee 15€

Only a few pitches for tents and caravans; a pretty vegetable garden is shared by campers.

Surroundings : 🐾 ≼ ▭ ♀
Leisure activities : 🔲 🎣 jacuzzi 🎣 🚲
Facilities : 🚿 🔌 ⬚ 🛁 🛒 🚮 🍴 ▥

GPS Longitude : -1.89027
Latitude : 48.68628

ST-GILDAS-DE-RHUYS

56730 – Michelin map **308** N9 – pop. 1 647 – alt. 10
▶ Paris 483 – Arzon 9 – Auray 48 – Sarzeau 7

⛰ **Le Menhir** 👥

📞 02 97 45 22 88. www.camping-bretagnesud.com

Address : route de Clos er Bé (3.5km north - recommended route via the D 780, follow the signs for Port-Navalo)

Opening times : from mid April to mid Sept.

5 ha/3 for camping (176 pitches)

Tariff : 33.80€ 🚶🚶 🚗 🔲 ⚡ (6A) – Extra per person 6.50€ – Reservation fee 18.50€

Rental rates : (from mid April to mid Sept.) ⚡ – 49 🚐. Per night from 50 to 140€ – Per week from 200 to 980€ – Reservation fee 18.50€

Surroundings : ▭ ♨♨
Leisure activities : 🍴 🏛 🏃 🎣 🎯 🔲 🎱 🎿
Facilities : 🚿 🔌 🛁 🛒 🚮 🍴 launderette 🚮 🛒

GPS Longitude : -2.84781
Latitude : 47.52874

⛰ **Goh'Velin**

📞 02 97 45 21 67. www.camping-gohvelin.fr

Address : 89 rue Guernevé (located 1.5km to the north, 300m from the beach)

Opening times : from beginning April to end Sept.

1 ha (93 pitches) flat, grassy

Tariff : 27.50€ 🚶🚶 🚗 🔲 ⚡ (16A) – Extra per person 5.50€ – Reservation fee 10€

Rental rates : (from beginning April to end Sept.) ⚡ – 19 🚐. Per night from 100 to 150€ – Per week from 260 to 760€ – Reservation fee 10€

Surroundings : ▭ ♀
Leisure activities : 🏛 🎣 🔲
Facilities : 🔌 🍴 ▥
Nearby : 🎿 🚤

GPS Longitude : -2.84515
Latitude : 47.51204

ST-JEAN-DU-DOIGT

29630 – Michelin map **308** I2 – pop. 623 – alt. 15
▶ Paris 544 – Brest 77 – Guingamp 61 – Lannion 33

⛺ Municipal du Pont Ar Gler

☎ 02 98 67 32 15. http://campingstj.jimdo.com/ – 🏴

Address : Pont ar Gler (in the town)

Opening times : from end June to end Aug.

1 ha (33 pitches)

Tariff : (2014 Price) 🚶 3.35 € ⛺ 1.75 € 🔲 3.15 € – 🔌 (6A) 2.90 €

A municipal site that is very green and natural, on the edge of a charming traditional village.

Surroundings : 🔲 🏞 ♀
Leisure activities : 🎪 ⛹
Facilities : ᴴ ⊶ 🍴 ⚌ 🏠
Nearby : 🛝 ♈ ✗

G P S	Longitude : -3.77487
	Latitude : 48.69405

ST-JOUAN-DES-GUÉRETS

35430 – Michelin map **309** K3 – pop. 2 699 – alt. 31
▶ Paris 396 – Rennes 63 – St-Helier 10 – St-Brieuc 85

⛰ Le P'tit Bois ♣♣

☎ 02 99 21 14 30. www.ptitbois.com

Address : La Chalandouze (access via the N 137)

Opening times : from mid April to mid Sept.

6 ha (275 pitches) flat, grassy

Tariff : 47 € 🚶🚶 ⛺ 🔲 🔌 (10A) – Extra per person 9 €

Rental rates : (from mid April to mid Sept.) – 168 🛏. Per night from 39 to 225 €

🚐 borne 7 €

A pleasant rural site with an extensive water park.

Surroundings : 🔲 ♀
Leisure activities : ♈ ✗ 🎪 🏓 🏃 hammam jacuzzi ⛹ 🚲 ✂ 🎣 ⛱ ⛳ multi-sports ground, entertainment room
Facilities : ᴴ ⊶ ⚌ 🏠 🚿 🍴 launderette 🛝 ⚗

G P S	Longitude : -1.9869
	Latitude : 48.60966

ST-LUNAIRE

35800 – Michelin map **309** J3 – pop. 2 309 – alt. 20
▶ Paris 410 – Rennes 76 – St-Helier 16 – St-Brieuc 83

⛰ La Touesse

☎ 02 99 46 61 13. www.campinglatouesse.com

Address : 171 rue Ville Géhan (situated 2km east along the D 786, follow the signs for Dinard; 400m from the beach)

Opening times : from beginning April to end Sept.

2.5 ha (141 pitches) flat, grassy

Tariff : (2014 Price) 🚶 5.60 € ⛺ 3.20 € 🔲 8.20 € – 🔌 (10A) 3.80 € – Reservation fee 16 €

Rental rates : (2014 Price) (from beginning April to end Sept.) – 65 🛏 – 3 studios – 11 apartments – 2 gîtes. Per night from 40 to 98 € – Per week from 196 to 686 € – Reservation fee 16 €

🚐 borne 6 €

A pleasant, green site with access to Fourberie beach via a small path (700m).

Surroundings : ♀♀
Leisure activities : ♈ ✗ 🎪 🏊 ⛹
Facilities : ᴴ ⊶ 🍴 ⚌ 🏠 🚿 🍴 launderette 🛝 ⚗
Nearby : 🐎

G P S	Longitude : -2.08425
	Latitude : 48.63086

ST-MALO

35400 – Michelin map **309** J3 – pop. 47 045 – alt. 5
▶ Paris 404 – Alençon 180 – Avranches 68 – Dinan 32

⛰⛰ Domaine de la Ville Huchet ♣♣

☎ 02 99 81 11 83.

Address : route de la Passagère, Quelmer (5km south along the D 301, follow the signs for Dinard and take turning for La Grassinais to the left in front of the Mercedes showroom)

6 ha (198 pitches) flat, grassy

Rentals : ᴴ (1 mobile home) – 85 🛏 – 6 🏠 – 3 studios.

A pleasant site based around a small château, with an attractive pool area.

Surroundings : 🔲 ♀♀
Leisure activities : ♈ ✗ 🎪 🏃 🏊 🚲 🎣 ⛱ ⛳ multi-sports ground
Facilities : ᴴ ⊶ 🍴 ⚌ 🍴 launderette 🛝 ⚗

G P S	Longitude : -1.98704
	Latitude : 48.61545

ST-MARCAN

35120 – Michelin map **309** M3 – pop. 455 – alt. 60
▶ Paris 370 – Dinan 42 – Dol-de-Bretagne 14 – Le Mont-St-Michel 17

⛰ Le Balcon de la Baie

☎ 02 99 80 22 95. www.lebalcondelabaie.com

Address : Le Verger (500m southeast along the D 89, follow the signs for Pleine-Fougères and turn left after the cemetery)

Opening times : from mid April to end Oct.

4 ha (80 pitches) flat, grassy

Tariff : 22.10 € 🚶🚶 ⛺ 🔲 🔌 (6A) – Extra per person 5.40 €

Rental rates : (from beginning April to end Oct.) – 12 🛏. Per night from 38 to 58 € – Per week from 264 to 400 €

In a very pleasant setting with views over the Baie du Mont-Saint-Michel (bay).

Surroundings : 🏞 ≼ Baie du Mont-St-Michel 🔲 ♀♀
Leisure activities : 🎪 ⛹ 🏊
Facilities : ᴴ ⊶ ⚌ 🍴 launderette

G P S	Longitude : -1.62929
	Latitude : 48.58942

ST-MICHEL-EN-GRÈVE

22300 – Michelin map **309** A2 – pop. 480 – alt. 12
▶ Paris 526 – Guingamp 43 – Lannion 11 – Morlaix 31

⛰⛰ Sites et Paysages Les Capucines

☎ 02 96 35 72 28. www.lescapucines.fr

Address : Voie Romaine, at Kervourdon (located 1.5km north following signs for Lannion and take road to the left)

Opening times : from beginning April to end Sept.

4 ha (100 pitches)

Tariff : 28.20 € 🚶🚶 ⛺ 🔲 🔌 (16A) – Extra per person 5.80 € – Reservation fee 15 €

Rental rates : (from beginning April to end Sept.) ᴴ (1 chalet) – 11 🛏 – 5 🏠 – 1 tent lodge. Per night from 55 to 174 € – Per week from 230 to 1,218 € – Reservation fee 15 €

🚐 borne 5 € – 🔌 14 €

Surroundings : 🏞 🔲 ♀
Leisure activities : ♈ 🎪 ⛹ 🚲 🎣 🖼 (open air in season) multi-sports ground
Facilities : ᴴ ⊶ ⚌ 🏠 🚿 🍴 launderette ⚗

G P S	Longitude : -3.55694
	Latitude : 48.69278

ST-PÈRE

35430 – Michelin map **309** K3 – pop. 2 289 – alt. 50
▶ Paris 392 – Cancale 14 – Dinard 15 – Dol-de-Bretagne 16

🏔 Bel Évent

🖉 02 99 58 83 79. www.camping-bel-event.com

Address : Bellevent (located 1.5km southeast along the D 74, follow the signs for Châteauneuf and take the road to the right)

Opening times : from mid April to end Sept.

2.5 ha (120 pitches) flat, grassy

Tariff : (2014 Price) 23.80€ ✹ ✹ ⇌ 🗉 🔌 (10A) – Extra per person 3.70€

Rental rates : (2014 Price) (from mid April to end Sept.) – 17 ⌷⌷ – 1 🏚. Per week from 240 to 740€

The pitches are well marked out and there are plenty of owner-occupier mobile homes.

Surroundings : 🖛 ♀		
Leisure activities : 👔 🛖 ⚒ 🎣 🏊 ⌇ multi-sports ground	**G**	Longitude : -1.91838
Facilities : 🚿 🔚 🛁 🚾 launderette	**P** **S**	Latitude : 48.57347

ST-PHILIBERT

56470 – Michelin map **308** N9 – pop. 1 520 – alt. 15
▶ Paris 486 – Auray 11 – Locmariaquer 7 – Quiberon 27

🏔 Les Palmiers

🖉 02 97 55 01 17. www.campinglespalmiers.com

Address : Kernivilit (situated 2km west, 500m from the river at Crach (sea))

Opening times : from beginning April to mid Oct.

3 ha (115 pitches)

Tariff : 21.30€ ✹ ✹ ⇌ 🗉 🔌 (6A) – Extra per person 3.90€ – Reservation fee 19.50€

Rental rates : (from beginning April to mid Oct.) – 48 ⌷⌷ – 48 🏚 – 2 ▭ – 1 apartment. Per night from 50 to 95€ – Per week from 199 to 700€ – Reservation fee 19.50€

🖼 borne 3€ – 10 🗉 9€ – 🚽 13.50€

The site is based around an old renovated farmhouse.

Surroundings : ♀		
Leisure activities : 👔 ✗ 🛖 ⚒ 🚴 🏊 ⌇ entertainment room	**G**	Longitude : -3.01504
Facilities : 🚿 🔚 🛁 🚾 launderette	**P** **S**	Latitude : 47.58831
Nearby : ✗		

🏔 L'Évasion

🖉 02 97 55 04 90. www.campinglevasion.com

Address : le Congre (located 1km to the north)

Opening times : from beginning April to end Oct.

1.7 ha (98 pitches)

Tariff : (2014 Price) ✹ 5.50€ ⇌ 🗉 9€ – 🔌 (10A) 4.10€ – Reservation fee 20€

Rental rates : (2014 Price) (from beginning April to end Oct.) – 35 ⌷⌷ – 2 canvas bungalows. Per night from 35 to 75€ – Per week from 170 to 690 € – Reservation fee 20€

Surroundings : 🖛 ♀♀		
Leisure activities : 🛖 ⚒ 🏊 ⌇	**G**	Longitude : -2.99778
Facilities : 🚿 🔚 🛁 🚾 launderette	**P** **S**	Latitude : 47.59591
Nearby : 🛒 ✗ ♨		

ST-POL-DE-LÉON

29250 – Michelin map **308** H2 – pop. 7 043 – alt. 60
▶ Paris 557 – Brest 62 – Brignogan-Plages 31 – Morlaix 21

🏔 Ar Kleguer 👥

🖉 02 98 69 18 81. www.camping-ar-kleguer.com

Address : plage Ste-Anne (east of the town)

Opening times : from beginning April to end Sept.

5 ha (182 pitches)

Tariff : (2014 Price) 29.90€ ✹ ✹ ⇌ 🗉 🔌 (10A) – Extra per person 6.50€ – Reservation fee 18€

Rental rates : (2014 Price) (from beginning April to end Sept.) – 45 ⌷⌷ – 5 🏚 – 3 gîtes. Per week from 290 to 840€ – Reservation fee 18€

🖼 borne

A pleasant landscaped site near the sea, among rocks and pines, with an educational farm for children.

Surroundings : 🦌 ⪦ 🖛 ♀ ⛰		
Leisure activities : 👔 🛖 🎣 ⚒ ✂ 🗉 🏊 ⌇ multi-sports ground	**G**	Longitude : -3.9677
Facilities : 🚿 🔚 🎱 🛁 🚾 launderette	**P** **S**	Latitude : 48.6907

🏔 Le Trologot

🖉 02 98 69 06 26. www.camping-trologot.com

Address : Grève du Man (To the east, follow the signs for Îlot St-Anne; near the beach)

Opening times : from beginning May to end Sept.

2 ha (100 pitches) flat, grassy

Tariff : (2014 Price) ✹ 5€ ⇌ 2.15€ 🗉 7.10€ – 🔌 (10A) 3.85€

Rental rates : (2014 Price) (from beginning May to end Sept.) – 15 ⌷⌷. Per week from 270 to 685€

🖼 borne 19.45€

In a simple and pleasant setting by the sea.

Surroundings : 🖛 ♀		
Leisure activities : ⚒ 🏊	**G**	Longitude : -3.9698
Facilities : 🚿 🔚 🛁 🚾 launderette	**P** **S**	Latitude : 48.6935

ST-RENAN

29290 – Michelin map **308** D4 – pop. 7 468 – alt. 50
▶ Paris 605 – Brest 14 – Brignogan-Plages 43 – Ploudalmézeau 14

🏔 Municipal de Lokournan

🖉 02 98 84 37 67. www.saint-renan.fr

Address : route de l'Aber (take northwestern exit along the D 27 and take the road to the right; near the stadium)

Opening times : from mid June to mid Sept.

0.8 ha (70 pitches) flat, grassy, sandy

Tariff : (2014 Price) ✹ 3.40€ ⇌ 🗉 3.40€ – 🔌 (12A) 3.60€

🖼 borne – 20 🗉

In a well-shaded, natural setting near a small lake.

Surroundings : 🦌 🖛 ♀♀		
Leisure activities : 🛖	**G**	Longitude : -4.62929
Facilities : 🚿 🔚 🚽 🎴	**P** **S**	Latitude : 48.43991
Nearby : 🎽		

ST-SAMSON-SUR-RANCE

22100 – Michelin map **309** J4 – pop. 1 514 – alt. 64
▶ Paris 401 – Rennes 57 – St-Brieuc 64 – St-Helier 34

⚐ Municipal Beauséjour

✆ 02 96 39 53 27. www.beausejour-camping.com

Address : La Hisse (3km east, along the D 57 and take the D 12 to the right, 200m from the port - access via steep slope)

3 ha (120 pitches) flat, grassy

Rentals : 🚿 – 6 🚐 – 12 🛏 – 3 gîtes.
The pretty gîtes are in the local stone.

Surroundings : 🐾
Leisure activities : 🏛 ⚓
Facilities : ⚹ ⚖ ☂ launderette
Nearby : 🍷 ⚶ ⚓

GPS Longitude : -2.00889
Latitude : 48.48889

ST-YVI

29140 – Michelin map **308** H7 – pop. 2 755 – alt. 105
▶ Paris 563 – Rennes 212 – Quimper 17 – Vannes 119

⚐ Tohapi Le Bois de Pleuven

✆ 08 25 00 20 30. www.village-center.fr

Address : Kerancolven

Opening times : from mid April to mid Sept.

17 ha/10 for camping (260 pitches) flat, grassy

Tariff : (2014 Price) 17€ ✚✚ ⚓ 🔌 (6A) – Extra per person 6€ – Reservation fee 10€

Rental rates : (2014 Price) (from mid April to mid Sept.) – 73 🚐 – 17 canvas bungalows. Per night from 20 to 75€ – Per week from 140 to 525€ – Reservation fee 10€

A natural, unspoilt setting among trees and bushes.

Surroundings : 🐾 🏕 〰
Leisure activities : 🍷 ✕ 🏛 ⚓ ⚶ 🚴 ⚒ ♨
🖥 ⚓ ⚘
Facilities : ⚹ ⚖ ☂ launderette ⚘

GPS Longitude : -3.97056
Latitude : 47.95028

STE-ANNE-D'AURAY

56400 – Michelin map **308** N8 – pop. 2 347 – alt. 42
▶ Paris 475 – Auray 7 – Hennebont 33 – Locminé 27

⚐ Municipal du Motten

✆ 02 97 57 60 27. contact@sainte-anne-auray.com

Address : allée des Pins (located 1km southwest along the D 17, follow the signs for Auray and take r. du Parc to the right)

1.5 ha (115 pitches) flat, grassy

Surroundings : ♨♨
Leisure activities : 🏛 ⚓ ⚒
Facilities : ⚹ ⚖ 🔲
Nearby : 🔲

GPS Longitude : -2.96251
Latitude : 47.69831

We value your opinion and welcome your feedback.
Do email us at campingfrance@tp.michelin.com

SARZEAU

56370 – Michelin map **308** O9 – pop. 7 659 – alt. 30
▶ Paris 478 – Nantes 111 – Redon 62 – Vannes 23

⚐ FranceLoc Domaine An Trest ⚶⚶

✆ 02 97 41 79 60. www.franceloc.fr

Address : 1 chemin du Treste (2.5km to the south, follow the signs for Le Roaligen)

Opening times : from mid April to mid Sept.

5 ha (225 pitches) terraced, flat, grassy

Tariff : (2014 Price) 33€ ✚✚ ⚓ 🔲 🔌 (16A) – Extra per person 7€ – Reservation fee 27€

Rental rates : (2014 Price) (from mid April to mid Sept.) ⚹ (1 mobile home) – 146 🚐. Per night from 40 to 120€ – Per week from 150 to 1,100€ – Reservation fee 27€

A partially covered water park, with some impressive chutes.

Surroundings : ♨
Leisure activities : 🍷 ✕ 🏛 ⚓ ⚶ ⚒ 🚴 ⚘
🖥 ⚓ ⚒
Facilities : ⚹ ⚖ ☂ 🍴 launderette
Nearby : ⚶ ⚓

GPS Longitude : -2.77208
Latitude : 47.50612

⚐ Lodge Club Presqu'Île de Rhuys ⚶⚶

✆ 02 97 41 29 93. www.lodgeclub.fr

Address : Le Bas Bohat (2.8km west)

15 ha/10 for camping (250 pitches) flat, grassy, adjacent forest

Rentals : 18 🚐 – 6 tent lodges.

Surroundings : 🐾 ♨
Leisure activities : 🍷 ✕ 🏛 ⚶ ⚒ 🚴 🖥
🖥 ⚓ ⚒ multi-sports ground
Facilities : ⚹ ⚖ ☂ ⚓ ⚒ 🍴 launderette ⚘

GPS Longitude : -2.79722
Latitude : 47.5225

⚐ Ferme de Lann Hoedic

✆ 02 97 48 01 73. www.camping-lannhoedic.fr

Address : rue Jean de La Fontaine

Opening times : from beginning April to end Oct.

3.6 ha (128 pitches)

Tariff : (2014 Price) ⚹ 5€ ⚓ 🔲 8.90€ – 🔌 (10A) 3.70€ – Reservation fee 10€

Rental rates : (2014 Price) (from beginning April to end Oct.) 🚿 – 12 🚐. Per week from 200 to 690€ – Reservation fee 10€
🚐 borne 12€ – 🔋 🔌11€

Surroundings : 🐾 ♨
Leisure activities : ⚓ ⚶ 🚴
Facilities : ⚹ ⚖ ⚓ ⚒ 🍴 launderette

GPS Longitude : -2.76249
Latitude : 47.5068

⚐ La Grée Penvins

✆ 02 97 67 33 96. www.campinglagreepenvins.com

Address : 8 route de la Chapelle (9km southeast along the D 198)

2.5 ha (125 pitches)

Rentals : 🚿 – 12 🚐.

Direct access to the beach at La Pointe de Penvins (headland).

Surroundings : 🐾 ♨ ⚓
Facilities : ⚹ ⚖ ⚓ 🍴 🔲
Nearby : 🍷 ✕ ⚒

GPS Longitude : -2.68242
Latitude : 47.49665

SCAËR

29390 – Michelin map **308** I6 – pop. 5 244 – alt. 190
▶ Paris 544 – Carhaix-Plouguer 38 – Concarneau 29 – Quimper 35

⚑ Municipal de Kérisole

𝒫 02 98 57 60 91. www.ville-scaer.fr ✖

Address : rue Louis Pasteur (take the eastern exit following signs for Le Faouët)

Opening times : from mid June to end Aug.

4 ha/2.3 for camping (83 pitches)

Tariff : (2014 Price) ♀ 2.70€ 🚗 1.90€ 🔲 3.20€ – ⚡ (10A) 2.75€

Rental rates : (2014 Price) (from mid June to end Aug.) ✖ – 3 🚐. Per night from 53 to 68€ – Per week from 295 to 352€
🚐 borne

In a tranquil and pleasant setting among trees, near the new town library.

Surroundings : 🌲 ♀
Leisure activities : 🛶
Facilities : ♿ 🚮 launderette
Nearby : ✖ 🏊 fitness trail

G P S Longitude : -3.69756
Latitude : 48.0278

SÉRENT

56460 – Michelin map **308** P8 – pop. 2 985 – alt. 80
▶ Paris 432 – Josselin 17 – Locminé 31 – Ploërmel 19

⚑ Municipal du Pont Salmon

𝒫 02 97 75 91 98. www.serent.fr

Address : 29 rue du Général de Gaulle (in the town, follow the signs for Ploërmel)

1 ha (30 pitches) flat, grassy

Rentals : ♿ (1 chalet) – 4 🚐.

There's free use of the municipal swimming pool.

Surroundings : ♀♀
Leisure activities : 🛶
Facilities : ⚡ 🚮 launderette
Nearby : ✖ 🏊

G P S Longitude : -2.50191
Latitude : 47.82506

SIZUN

29450 – Michelin map **308** G4 – pop. 2 221 – alt. 112
▶ Paris 572 – Brest 37 – Carhaix-Plouguer 44 – Châteaulin 36

⚑ Municipal du Gollen

𝒫 02 98 24 11 43. www.mairie-sizun.fr – ℍℝ

Address : Le Gollen (located 1km south along the D 30, follow the signs for St-Cadou and take the turning to the left; beside the Elorn river)

Opening times : from beginning April to end Sept.

0.6 ha (29 pitches)

Tariff : (2014 Price) ♀ 3€ 🚗 2€ 🔲 2.50€ – ⚡ (10A) 2.50€
🚐 borne 2€

The site is located on a large field near the Elorn river.

Surroundings : 🌲 ♀
Leisure activities : 🎣
Facilities : ⚡ 🚮 🚿
Nearby : ✖ 🏊

G P S Longitude : -4.07659
Latitude : 48.4

SULNIAC

56250 – Michelin map **308** P8 – pop. 3 133 – alt. 125
▶ Paris 457 – Rennes 106 – Vannes 21 – Nantes 112

⚑ Village Vacances La Lande du Moulin

(rental of chalets, gîtes and mobile homes only)

𝒫 02 97 53 29 39. www.la-lande-du-moulin.com

Address : Le Nounène (located 1.5km east along the D 104 and follow the signs for Theix)

12 ha

Rentals : ♿ (3 chalets) – 2 🚐 – 50 🚐 – 17 gîtes.

Full and half-board accommodation options are available.

Surroundings : 🌲 ♀
Leisure activities : ♀ ✖ 🏠 ▦ 🎣 🚴 ⛳ 🏊
🚲 ✖ 🔲 🏊 🎠 🎣
Facilities : 🔌 ▦ ⛲ launderette 🚿

G P S Longitude : -2.56557
Latitude : 47.66686

TADEN

22100 – Michelin map **309** J4 – pop. 2 340 – alt. 46
▶ Paris 404 – Rennes 71 – St-Brieuc 64 – St-Helier 34

⚑ Municipal de la Hallerais

𝒫 02 96 39 15 93. http://www.camping-lahallerais.com

Address : 4 rue de la Robardais (to the southwest of the town)

Opening times : from mid March to mid Nov.

7 ha (225 pitches)

Tariff : (2014 Price) 21.90€ ♀♀ 🚗 🔲 ⚡ (10A) – Extra per person 4€

Rental rates : (2014 Price) (from mid March to mid Nov.) – 9 🚐 – 11 🚐. Per night from 27 to 68€ – Per week from 177 to 476€
🚐 borne – 7 🔲

Surroundings : 🌲 🚐 ♀♀
Leisure activities : ♀ ✖ 🏠 🛶 ✖ 🎣 🏊
multi-sports ground
Facilities : ⚡ 🔌 ▦ 🚿 ⛲ launderette 🚿 🚮
Nearby : 🎯 🐟 💧

G P S Longitude : -2.0232
Latitude : 48.47181

TAUPONT

56800 – Michelin map **308** Q7 – pop. 2 140 – alt. 81
▶ Paris 422 – Josselin 16 – Ploërmel 5 – Rohan 37

⚑ La Vallée du Ninian

𝒫 02 97 93 53 01. www.camping-ninian.fr

Address : Ville Bonne, le Rocher (take the northern exit along the D 8, follow the signs for la Trinité-Phoët, then continue 2.5km along the turning to the left, direct access to the river)

Opening times : from beginning April to end Sept.

2.7 ha (100 pitches) flat, grassy, fruit trees

Tariff : (2014 Price) 20.90€ ♀♀ 🚗 🔲 ⚡ (10A) –
Extra per person 4.70€ – Reservation fee 10€

Rental rates : (2014 Price) (from beginning April to end Sept.) – 10 🚐 – 2 canvas bungalows – 3 tent lodges. Per night from 35 to 70€ – Per week from 160 to 630€ – Reservation fee 10€
🚐 borne 4€ – 🚐 ⚡14€

There are evening events organised, gathering around the bread oven or the apple press.

Surroundings : 🌲 🚐 ♀♀
Leisure activities : ♀ 🏠 🛶 🔲 🎣
Facilities : ⚡ 🔌 🛁 🚿 ⛲ launderette 🚿

G P S Longitude : -2.47
Latitude : 47.96928

TELGRUC-SUR-MER

29560 – Michelin map **308** E5 – pop. 2 088 – alt. 90
▶ Paris 572 – Châteaulin 25 – Douarnenez 29 – Quimper 39

⛰ Armorique

✆ 02 98 27 77 33. www.campingarmorique.com

Address : 112 rue de la Plage (1.2km southwest following signs for Trez-Bellec-Plage)

Opening times : from beginning April to end Sept.

2.5 ha (98 pitches) terraced, relatively flat, flat, grassy

Tariff : (2014 Price) 25.33€ ✶✶ ⇌ 🔲 🔌 (10A) – Extra per person 5.25€ – Reservation fee 16€

Rental rates : (2014 Price) (from beginning April to end Sept.) – 25 🛖 – 4 🏠 – 6 canvas bungalows. Per night from 48 to 86€ – Per week from 252 to 750€ – Reservation fee 16€

🚐 borne – 🔋🔌14€

The site is on different levels, with lovely terraces.

Surroundings : 🏖 ⛵ 🛶 ⌇ ♨		
Leisure activities : ▾ ✗ 🏠 🛶 🛷	G P S	Longitude : -4.37085
Facilities : ♿ ⊶ 🔳 ♨ ♨ launderette 🚿		Latitude : 48.22531

THEIX

56450 – Michelin map **308** P9 – pop. 6 765 – alt. 5
▶ Paris 464 – Ploërmel 51 – Redon 58 – La Roche-Bernard 33

🏕 Rhuys

✆ 02 97 54 14 77. http://campingderhuys.free.fr

Address : rue Dugay Trouin, Le Poteau Rouge (3.5km to the northwest, along the N 165; if coming from Vannes, take Sarzeau exit)

2 ha (66 pitches)

Rental rates : – 6 🛖 – 2 🏠.

Surroundings : ♨		
Leisure activities : 🛶 🛷 (small swimming pool)	G P S	Longitude : -2.69413
Facilities : ♿ ⊶ 🔳 ♨ ♨ 🔳		Latitude : 47.64108
Nearby : 🛒 ▾ ✗ 🔲		

TINTÉNIAC

35190 – Michelin map **309** K5 – pop. 3 304 – alt. 40
▶ Paris 377 – Avranches 70 – Dinan 28 – Dol-de-Bretagne 30

⛰ Domaine Les Peupliers

✆ 02 99 45 49 75. www.domainelespeupliers.fr

Address : at the Domaine de la Besnelais (situated 2km southeast along the old road to Rennes; near lakes, along the N 137, take the exit for Tinténiac Sud)

Opening times : from beginning April to end Sept.

4 ha (93 pitches) flat, grassy

Tariff : 25.50€ ✶✶ ⇌ 🔲 🔌 (8A) – Extra per person 6€

Rental rates : (from mid March to mid Nov.) – 5 🛖 – 2 🏠 – 1 gîte. Per night from 55 to 100€ – Per week from 250 to 630€

🚐 borne – 5 🔲 17€ – 🔋🔌16€

In a lovely setting and location near a natural lake.

Surroundings : ⌇ ♨		
Leisure activities : ▾ 🏠 🛶 🚲 ⚽ 🛷 ♨	G P S	Longitude : -1.82167
Facilities : ♿ ⊶ 🔳 ♨ ♨ launderette 🚿		Latitude : 48.30917

LE TOUR-DU-PARC

56370 – Michelin map **308** P9 – pop. 1 105
▶ Paris 476 – La Baule 62 – Redon 57 – St-Nazaire 81

⛰ Le Cadran Solaire

✆ 02 97 67 30 40. www.campingcadransolaire.fr

Address : rue de Banastère (situated 2km south along the D 324, follow the signs for Sarzeau)

Opening times : from beginning April to end Oct.

2 ha (115 pitches) flat, grassy

Tariff : ✶ 4.60€ ⇌ 🔲 9.50€ – 🔌 (10A) 3.50€

Rental rates : (from beginning April to end Oct.) ⚡ – 15 🛖. Per week from 200 to 600€

🚐 borne

Surroundings : ⌇ ♨		
Leisure activities : 🏠 🛷 🔧	G P S	Longitude : -2.65748
Facilities : ♿ ⊶ 🔳 ♨ launderette		Latitude : 47.5208

TRÉBEURDEN

22560 – Michelin map **309** A2 – pop. 3 714 – alt. 81
▶ Paris 525 – Lannion 10 – Perros-Guirec 14 – St-Brieuc 74

🏕 L'Espérance

✆ 07 86 17 48 08. www.camping-esperance.com

Address : rue de Kéralégan (5km northwest along the D 788, follow the signs for Trégastel; near the sea)

1 ha (70 pitches)

Rentals : 6 🛖.

Surroundings : ⛵ ⌇ ♨		
Leisure activities : ▾ 🏠	G P S	Longitude : -3.55743
Facilities : ♿ ⊶ launderette		Latitude : 48.79096

The guide covers all 22 regions of France – see the map and list of regions on pages 4–5.

TRÉBOUL

29100 – Michelin map **308** E6
▶ Paris 591 – Rennes 239 – Quimper 29 – Brest 75

⛰ Indigo Douarnenez le Bois d'Isis 👥

Campingindigo ©R. Etienne

✆ 02 98 74 05 67. www.camping-indigo.com

Address: 15 chemin de Kerleyou

Opening times : from end April to end Sept.

3.2 ha (124 pitches) terraced, flat, grassy

Tariff : (2014 Price) 26.90€ ✶✶ ⇌ 🔲 🔌 (13A) – Extra per person 4.90€

Rental rates : (2014 Price) (from end April to end Sept.) – 6 caravans – 32 tent lodges. Per night from 45 to 89€ – Per week from 252 to 623€

🚐 borne 7€

The pitches are in a natural wooded setting overlooking the Baie d'Douarnenez (bay).

Surroundings : 🏖 ⛵ Douarnenez bay ♨		
Leisure activities : ▾ 🏠 🛝 🛶 🛷	G P S	Longitude : -4.3589
Facilities : ♿ ⊶ 🔳 ♨ ♨ ♨ launderette		Latitude : 48.10299
Nearby : 🏊 ✗ 🚣 🎣		

🏔 Kerleyou

📞 02 98 74 13 03. www.camping-kerleyou.com

Address : 15 chemin de Kerleyou (located 1km to the west)

3.5 ha (100 pitches)

Rentals : ♿ (1 chalet) – 42 🛏 – 4 🏠.

There are some lovely pitches for tents and caravans not far from the dolmens and menhirs.

Surroundings : 🏞 🗐 ♨♨
Leisure activities : 🍴 🏠 ⛵ 🗐
Facilities : ♿ ⛲ 🚿 launderette ⚑

Longitude : -4.36198
Latitude : 48.09842

🏔 Trézulien

📞 02 98 74 12 30. www.camping-trezulien.com

Address : 14 route de Trézulien (via the r. Frédéric-Le-Guyader)

Opening times : from beginning April to end Sept.

5 ha (199 pitches) very uneven, terraced, relatively flat, flat, grassy

Tariff : 🚶 4.40€ ⛟ 2.80€ 🔲 5.50€ – 🔌 (10A) 3.80€

Rental rates : (from beginning April to mid Oct.) ♿ (1 mobile home) – 12 🛏 – 4 🏠 – 1 tent lodge – 1 gîte. Per night from 35 to 117€ – Per week from 170 to 830€ – Reservation fee 13€

🚰 60 🔲 21.50€

In a pleasant, partially wooded setting, with large pitches under poplar trees.

Surroundings : 🏞 ⪝ ♨
Leisure activities : 🍴 🏠 ⛵ 🗐 ☍ ♨
Facilities : ♿ ⛲ (season) 🚿 launderette
Nearby : 🐎

Longitude : -4.34931
Latitude : 48.09311

TREFFIAGAT

29730 – Michelin map **308** F8 – pop. 2 343 – alt. 20
▶ Paris 582 – Audierne 39 – Douarnenez 41 – Pont-l'Abbé 8

⛺ Les Ormes

📞 02 98 58 21 27. www.campingdesormesleguilvinec.fr

Address : Kerlay (situated 2km to the south, follow the signs for Lesconil and take the turning to the right 400m from the beach (direct access)

Opening times : from beginning April to end Sept.

2 ha (76 pitches) flat, grassy

Tariff : (2014 Price) 🚶 4.20€ ⛟ 2.55€ 🔲 4.20€ – 🔌 (6A) 3.60€ – Reservation fee 6.25€

Rental rates : (2014 Price) (from beginning April to end Sept.) 🏊 – 2 🏠. Per week from 300 to 465€

🚰 borne

A small and attractive site in the countryside, not far the sea.

Surroundings : 🏞 🗐 ♨
Leisure activities : ⛵
Facilities : ⛲ 🏊 launderette
Nearby : ♨

There are several different types of sani-station ('borne' in French) – sanitation points providing fresh water and disposal points for grey water. See page 12 for further details.

TRÉGASTEL

22730 – Michelin map **309** B2 – pop. 2 435 – alt. 58
▶ Paris 526 – Lannion 11 – Perros-Guirec 9 – St-Brieuc 75

🏔 Tourony-Camping

📞 02 96 23 86 61. www.camping-tourony.com

Address : 105 rue de Poul Palud (1.8km east along the D 788, follow the signs for Perros-Guirec; 500m from the beach)

Opening times : from mid April to mid Sept.

2 ha (100 pitches) flat, grassy

Tariff : 24.10€ 🚶🚶 ⛟ 🔲 🔌 (10A) – Extra per person 5.80€ – Reservation fee 14€

Rental rates : (from mid April to mid Sept.) – 17 🛏 – 2 🏠. Per night from 50 to 76€ – Per week from 235 to 635€ – Reservation fee 14€ 🚰 borne – 10 🔲 11.30€

Situated opposite the marina.

Surroundings : ♨
Leisure activities : 🍴 ✕ ⛵
Facilities : ♿ ⛲ 📵 🏊 🚿 🚻 launderette
Nearby : 🛒 ⚔ 🎣

TRÉGUENNEC

29720 – Michelin map **308** F7 – pop. 348 – alt. 31
▶ Paris 582 – Audierne 27 – Douarnenez 27 – Pont-l'Abbé 11

🏔 Kerlaz

📞 02 98 87 76 79. www.kerlaz.com

Address : route de la Mer (in the village, along the D 156)

Opening times : from beginning April to end Sept.

1.25 ha (65 pitches) flat, grassy

Tariff : (2014 Price) 🚶 4.20€ ⛟ 2.35€ 🔲 5.70€ – 🔌 (10A) 3.80€ – Reservation fee 10€

Rental rates : (from beginning April to end Sept.) – 10 🛏 – 5 🏠 – 3 tent lodges. Per night from 53 to 75€ – Per week from 225 to 645€ – Reservation fee 10€ 🚰 borne 8€

In a pleasant setting with little shade.

Surroundings : ♨
Leisure activities : 🍴 ⛵ 🚲 🗐 (open air in season)
Facilities : ♿ (July-Aug) 🚿 launderette
Nearby : 🏊 🐎

TRÉGUNC

29910 – Michelin map **308** H7 – pop. 6 785 – alt. 45
▶ Paris 543 – Concarneau 7 – Pont-Aven 9 – Quimper 29

🏔 La Pommeraie 👥

📞 02 98 50 02 73. www.campingdelapomeraie.com

Address : Kerdalidec (6km south along the D 1, follow the signs for La Pointe de Trévignon (headland) and take the turning to the left following signs for St-Philibert)

Opening times : from beginning April to mid Sept.

7 ha (198 pitches) flat, grassy

Tariff : 41€ 🚶🚶 ⛟ 🔲 🔌 (10A) – Reservation fee 16€

Rental rates : (from beginning April to mid Sept.) – 34 🛏 – 5 tent lodges. Per week from 230 to 1,310€ – Reservation fee 16€

Tranquil family site beside the sea, with a good aquatic and spa area.

Surroundings : 🗐 ♨
Leisure activities : 🍴 ✕ 🏠 🎮 ⛵ 🛁 jacuzzi ⛵ 🚲 🗐 ☍ ♨ 🐎 multi-sports ground entertainment room
Facilities : ♿ ⛲ 📵 🏊 🚿 🚻 launderette ⚑

Longitude : -3.49131
Latitude : 48.82565

Longitude : -4.32848
Latitude : 47.89457

Longitude : -3.83698
Latitude : 47.80786

Longitude : -4.25518
Latitude : 47.79666

TRÉLÉVERN

22660 – Michelin map **309** B2 – pop. 1 390 – alt. 76
▶ Paris 524 – Lannion 13 – Perros-Guirec 9 – St-Brieuc 73

🏔 RNC Port-l'Épine

✆ 02 96 23 71 94. www.rcn.fr

Address : 10 Venelle de Pors Garo (1.5km northwest then take a road to the left; at Port-l'Épine)

3 ha (160 pitches) terraced, relatively flat, flat, grassy
Rentals : 45 🛖.

Surroundings : 🌿 ≤ Baie de Perros-Guirec 🗔 ⚲ ♨	GPS	Longitude : -3.38594
Leisure activities : 🍹 ✗ 🚣 🚲 🛹		Latitude : 48.8128
Facilities : ♿ ⚲ 🏕 🗑 🚰 🚿 launderette 🛋		

LA TRINITÉ-SUR-MER

56470 – Michelin map **308** M9 – pop. 1 622 – alt. 20
▶ Paris 488 – Auray 13 – Carnac 4 – Lorient 52

🏔 La Plage 👫👤

La Plage

✆ 02 97 55 73 28. www.camping-plage.com

Address : plage de Kervillen (located 1km to the south, direct access to the beach)

Opening times : from beginning May to mid Sept.

3 ha (200 pitches)

Tariff : 46.40€ 👫👫 🚗 🔟 📶 (10A) – Extra per person 6.20€ – Reservation fee 15€

Rental rates : (from beginning May to mid Sept.) – 34 🛖 – 6 canvas bungalows. Per night from 35 to 95€ – Per week from 199 to 940€ – Reservation fee 15€

🚐 borne 4€

Surroundings : 🗔 ⚲ ♨ 🛋	GPS	Longitude : -3.02869
Leisure activities : 🛖 🎣 🕴 jacuzzi 🚣 🛹 🛶 ⚓		Latitude : 47.57562
Facilities : ♿ ⚲ 🏕 🗑 🚰 🚿 launderette		
Nearby : 🛋 🍹 ✗ 🚣 ✗ ⛵		

🏔 Kervilor

✆ 02 97 55 76 75. www.camping-kervilor.com

Address : route du Latz (1.6km to the north)

Opening times : from beginning April to mid Sept.

5 ha (230 pitches)

Tariff : (2014 Price) 👤 5.80€ 🚗 4.15€ 🔟 15.30€ – 📶 (10A) 5€ – Reservation fee 18€

Rental rates : (2014 Price) (from beginning April to mid Sept.) – 68 🛖. Per night from 108 to 190€ – Per week from 280 to 984€ – Reservation fee 18€

Surroundings : 🌿 🗔 ⚲ ♨	GPS	Longitude : -3.03588
Leisure activities : 🍹 🛖 ♨ 🎣 jacuzzi 🚣 🛹		Latitude : 47.60168
✗ 🛶 🛶 multi-sports ground		
Facilities : ♿ ⚲ 🏕 🚿 launderette 🛋 🗑 refrigerators		

🏔 La Baie 👫👤

✆ 02 97 55 73 42. www.campingdelabaie.com – limited spaces for one-night stay

Address : plage de Kervillen (located 1.5km to the south, 100m from the beach)

Opening times : from beginning May to mid Sept.

2.2 ha (170 pitches)

Tariff : (2014 Price) 👤 8.60€ 🚗 🔟 28.55€ – 📶 (10A) 5.45€ – Reservation fee 22€

Rental rates : (2014 Price) (from beginning May to mid Sept.) – 42 🛖. Per night from 49 to 138€ – Per week from 266 to 966€ – Reservation fee 22€

Surroundings : 🌿 🗔 ⚲	GPS	Longitude : -3.02789
Leisure activities : 🛖 🎣 🕴 🚣 🚲 🛹		Latitude : 47.57375
Facilities : ♿ ⚲ 🏕 🗑 🚿 🚰 launderette		
Nearby : 🛋 🍹 ✗ 🚣 ✗ ⛵ 🛶		

🏔 APV Plijadur 👫👤

✆ 02 97 55 72 05. www.camping-apv.com

Address : 94 route de Carnac (1.3km northwest on the D 781)

Opening times : from mid April to end Sept.

5 ha (198 pitches)

Tariff : (2014 Price) 23.10€ 👫👫 🚗 🔟 📶 (10A) – Extra per person 7.60€ – Reservation fee 28€

Rental rates : (2014 Price) (from mid April to end Sept.) – 127 🛖 – 2 apartments. Per night from 38 to 77€ – Per week from 231 to 994€ – Reservation fee 28€

🚐 borne 15.50€ – 10 🔟 15.50€

Choose pitches away from the road in preference.

Surroundings : 🗔 ♨ ♨	GPS	Longitude : -3.04394
Leisure activities : 🍹 🛖 🎣 🕴 ♨ 🛶		Latitude : 47.60464
hammam, jacuzzi 🚣 🛹 🛶 🛶 🛶 ⚓		
Facilities : ♿ ⚲ 🏕 🚿 launderette 🛋		

VANNES

56000 – Michelin map **308** O9 – pop. 52 683 – alt. 20
▶ Paris 459 – Quimper 122 – Rennes 110 – St-Brieuc 107

🏔 Flower Le Conleau

✆ 02 97 63 13 88. www.vannes-camping.com

Address : at la Pointe de Conleau (to the south, towards the Parc du Golfe (leisure park), on the Avenue du Maréchal Juin)

Opening times : from beginning April to end Sept.

5 ha (260 pitches)

Tariff : 29€ 👫👫 🚗 🔟 📶 (10A) – Extra per person 6€ – Reservation fee 15€

Rental rates : (from beginning April to end Sept.) – 71 🛖 – 6 canvas bungalows. Per night from 44 to 120€ – Per week from 196 to 840€ – Reservation fee 20€

🚐 borne 5.50€ – 35 🔟 12€

Pleasant location opposite the Golfe du Morbihan (gulf).

Surroundings : ≤ ♨	GPS	Longitude : -2.77994
Leisure activities : 🍹 🛖 🎣 🕴 🚣 🚲		Latitude : 47.63326
Facilities : ♿ ⚲ 🏕 🚿 🚰 launderette, refrigerated food storage facilities		
Nearby : 🛒		

BURGUNDY

H. Lenain / hemis.fr

A visit to Burgundy takes you back in time to an era when the influence of the mighty Burgundian dukes rivalled that of the kings of France. Stately castles and imposing abbeys still bear witness to a past golden age of ostentation and power. It is hard now to reproach the dukes too much for a flamboyance that has today made Dijon a world-renowned city of art, endowed with an exceptional architectural heritage. And who would dispute their claim to be the lords of the best wines in Christendom when wine lovers still flock to the region in search of the finest cellars and vintages? A dedication to time-honoured traditions remains at the heart of the cuisine of the region, from the pungent *Époisses* cheese to the delicious local gingerbread dripping with honey. After indulging yourself in such gourmet delights, what could be better than a delightful barge trip along the canals and rivers of the region to relax in peace amid the gloriously unspoilt countryside?

ANDRYES

89480 – Michelin map **319** D6 – pop. 471 – alt. 162
▶ Paris 204 – Auxerre 39 – Avallon 44 – Clamecy 10

⛰ Sites et Paysages Au Bois Joli

✆ 03 86 81 70 48. www.campingauboisjoli.fr

Address : 2 route de Villeprenoy (800m southwest)

Opening times : from beginning April to beginning Nov.

5 ha (100 pitches) sloping, flat, grassy

Tariff : 29.50€ ✶✶ ⛺ 🔲 (10A) – Extra per person 6€ –
Reservation fee 9.50€

Rental rates : (from beginning April to beginning Nov.) ✂ –
5 🏠 – 1 tent lodge. Per night from 80 to 150€ – Per week
from 350 to 800€ – Reservation fee 9.50€

🚐 borne 8€ – 3 🔲 16€ – 🚐 10€
A wooded campsite.

Surroundings : 🌳 ♀♀		
Leisure activities : 🏠 🚣 🚲 🎣	G	Longitude : 3.47969
Facilities : 🚿 🚰 🏪 ⛱ 🛒 🍴 🚮	P	Latitude : 47.51655
Nearby : 🚵 🍴	S	

To visit a town or region, use the MICHELIN Green Guides.

ARNAY-LE-DUC

21230 – Michelin map **320** G7 – pop. 1 674 – alt. 375
▶ Paris 285 – Autun 28 – Beaune 36 – Chagny 38

⛰ VivaCamp l'Étang de Fouché

✆ 03 80 90 02 23. www.campingfouche.com

Address : rue du 8 mai 1945 (700m east along the D 17c, follow the
signs for Longecourt)

Opening times : from mid April to mid Oct.

8 ha (209 pitches) flat, grassy

Tariff : 27€ ✶✶ ⛺ 🔲 (10A) – Extra per person 7€ – Reservation
fee 7.50€

Rental rates : (from mid April to mid Oct.) – 18 🏠 – 19 🏡 –
6 canvas bungalows. Per night from 40 to 115€ – Per week
from 168 to 805 € – Reservation fee 15€

🚐 borne – 3 🔲
A pleasant location beside a lake.

Surroundings : 🌳 ⛵ ♀ ⛰		
Leisure activities : 🍴 ✗ 🏠 🎦 daytime 🏓		
🚣 🚲 pedalos	G	Longitude : 4.49802
Facilities : 🚿 🚰 🏪 ⛱ 🛒 🍴 launderette	P	Latitude : 47.13414
🚮 🚵	S	
Nearby : 🍴 🏖 (beach) 🎣		

ASQUINS

89450 – Michelin map **319** F7 – pop. 324 – alt. 146
▶ Paris 219 – Dijon 123 – Auxerre 49 – Avallon 17

⛺ Municipal le Patis

✆ 03 86 33 30 80. www.asquins-sous-vezelay-camping-roulottes.com

Address : route de Givry (500 m, after the bridge on the left)

Opening times : from end April to end Sept.

1 ha (33 pitches) flat, grassy

Tariff : (2014 Price) ✶ 2€ ⛺ 2€ 🔲 2€ – (6A) 3€

Rental rates : (2014 Price) Permanent – 2 caravans. Per night
from 75 to 95€ – Per week from 450 to 570€

Surroundings : ♀		
Leisure activities : 🏠 🚣	G	Longitude : 3.75899
Facilities : 🚿 ⛱ 🏪 ⛱ 🚮	P	Latitude : 47.48293
Nearby : 🏊	S	

AUTUN

71400 – Michelin map **320** F8 – pop. 14 496 – alt. 326
▶ Paris 287 – Auxerre 128 – Avallon 78 – Chalon-sur-Saône 51

⛰ Aquadis Loisirs La Porte d'Arroux

✆ 03 85 52 10 82. www.aquadis-loisirs.com

Address : rue du Traité d'Anvers : Les Chaumottes (take the northern
exit along the D 980, follow the signs for Saulieu, Arroux suburb;
beside the Ternin river)

Opening times : from beginning April to end Oct.

2.8 ha (81 pitches) flat, grassy

Tariff : 20.20€ ✶✶ ⛺ 🔲 (10A) – Extra per person 3.70€ –
Reservation fee 9.90€

Rental rates : (from beginning April to end Oct.) – 6 🏠
Per night from 62€ – Per week from 189 to 499 v – Reservation
fee 19.90€

🚐 borne 5.70€ – 2 🔲 14.30€ – 🚐 11€
Pretty, shady pitches beside the Ternin river.

Surroundings : 🏞 ♀♀		
Leisure activities : 🍴 ✗ 🏠 🚣 🚲 🎣 ✈	G	Longitude : 4.29358
Facilities : 🚿 🚰 🏪 🍴 🚮 🚵	P	Latitude : 46.96447
	S	

AUXERRE

89000 – Michelin map **319** E5 – pop. 36 702 – alt. 130
▶ Paris 166 – Bourges 144 – Chalon-sur-Saône 176 – Chaumont 143

⛰ Municipal

✆ 03 86 52 11 15. camping.mairie@auxerre.com

Address : 8 route de Vaux (to the southeast of the town, near the
stadium, 150m from the Yonne river)

Opening times : from mid April to mid Sept.

4.5 ha (164 pitches) flat, grassy

Tariff : (2014 Price) ✶ 4.37€ ⛺ 🔲 3.82€ – (5A) 3.59€

🚐 borne 3.36€

Surroundings : ♀		
Leisure activities : 🏠 🚣 🚲 🎣	G	Longitude : 3.58703
Facilities : 🚿 🚰 ⛱ launderette 🚮	P	Latitude : 47.7865
Nearby : 🍴 🏖 🎦 🏊	S	

Michelin classification:

⛰⛰⛰⛰ *Extremely comfortable, equipped to a very high
standard*

⛰⛰⛰ *Very comfortable, equipped to a high standard*

⛰⛰ *Comfortable and well equipped*

⛰ *Reasonably comfortable*

⛺ *Satisfactory*

AVALLON

89200 – Michelin map **319** G7 – pop. 7 252 – alt. 250
▶ Paris 220 – Dijon 106 – Auxerre 55 – Autun 80

⚠ Municipal Sous Roches

🕾 03 86 34 10 39. www.campingsousroches.com

Address : route de Méluzien

Opening times : from beginning April to end Oct.

2.7 ha (98 pitches) terraced, flat, grassy

Tariff : (2014 Price) 17.20€ ✖✖ ⬅ 🔲 🔌 (10A)

Extra per person 3.60€

Rental rates : (2014 Price) (from beginning March to end Dec.)
♿ (1 chalet) 💱 – 4 🏠. Per night from 65 to 85€ – Per week
from 260 to 540€

🚐 borne 5€ – 15 🔲 17.20€

Surroundings : 🏖
Leisure activities : 🍴 ⛵ 🎣
Facilities : ♿ ⚬ 🚾 launderette 🧺

G P S Longitude : 3.91293
Latitude : 47.47993

BEAUNE

21200 – Michelin map **320** I7 – pop. 22 516 – alt. 220
▶ Paris 308 – Autun 49 – Auxerre 149 – Chalon-sur-Saône 29

⚠⚠ Municipal les Cent Vignes

🕾 03 80 22 03 91, campinglescentvignes@mairie-beaune.fr

Address : 10 rue Auguste Dubois (take the northern exit along the r.
du Faubourg-St-Nicolas and take D 18 to the left)

Opening times : from mid March to end Oct.

2 ha (116 pitches) flat, grassy

Tariff : (2014 Price) 20.90€ ✖✖ ⬅ 🔲 🔌 (10A) –
Extra per person 4.60€

*The pitches are attractively marked out; the entrance is sur-
rounded by flowers.*

Surroundings : 🗭 ♀
Leisure activities : 🍴 ✖ 🍽 ⛵ multi-
sports ground
Facilities : ♿ ⚬ 🏢 🚾 🚾 launderette 🧺

G P S Longitude : 4.8386
Latitude : 47.03285

BOURBON-LANCY

71140 – Michelin map **320** C10 – pop. 5 275 – alt. 240 – ⚓
▶ Paris 308 – Autun 62 – Mâcon 110 – Montceau-les-Mines 55

⚠⚠ Aquadis Loisirs Les Chalets du Breuil

🕾 03 85 89 20 98. www.aquadis-loisirs.com

Address : 11 rue des Eurimants (towards the southwestern exit,
follow the signs for Digoin; by the swimming pool)

Opening times : from end March to end Oct.

2 ha (63 pitches) flat, grassy

Tariff : 18.50€ ✖✖ ⬅ 🔲 🔌 (10A) – Extra per person 4.75€ –
Reservation fee 9.90€

Rental rates : (from end March to end Oct.) ♿ (1 chalet) – 4 🚐 –
22 🏠. Per night from 89€ – Per week from 266 to 599€ –
Reservation fee 19.90€

🚐 5 🔲 15.90€

Camping pitches around 200m from a small lake.

Surroundings : 🗭 ♀
Leisure activities : 🍴 🐎
Facilities : ⚬ 🏢 🧺 🚾 🚾 📷
Nearby : 🛒 ✖ ⛵ ✂ 🎿 ⛵ (beach) 🎣
casino

G P S Longitude : 3.76646
Latitude : 46.62086

CHABLIS

89800 – Michelin map **319** F5 – pop. 2 383 – alt. 135
▶ Paris 181 – Dijon 138 – Orléans 172 – Troyes 76

⚠ Municipal du Serein

🕾 03 86 42 44 39. www.chablis.net

Address : quai Paul Louis Courier (600m west along the D 956, follow
the signs for Tonnerre and take the road to the right after the bridge;
beside the Serein river)

Opening times : from end May to mid Sept.

2 ha (43 pitches) flat, grassy

Tariff : (2014 Price) ✖ 3€ ⬅ 🔲 6€ – 🔌 (6A) 2€

🚐 borne

In a green setting beside the Serein river.

Surroundings : 🗭 ♀
Leisure activities : ⛵ 🍽 🚾 🍴
Facilities : ♿ ⚬ 🚾 🍴
Nearby : 🚲

G P S Longitude : 3.80596
Latitude : 47.81368

CHAGNY

71150 – Michelin map **320** I8 – pop. 5 525 – alt. 215
▶ Paris 327 – Autun 44 – Beaune 15 – Chalon-sur-Saône 20

⚠⚠ Le Pâquier Fané

🕾 03 85 87 21 42. www.camping-chagny.com

Address : rue du Pâquier fané (to the west; beside the Dheune river)

Opening times : from beginning April to end Oct.

1.8 ha (85 pitches) flat, grassy

Tariff : (2014 Price) 16.70€ ✖✖ ⬅ 🔲 🔌 (16A) –
Extra per person 4.20€

Rental rates : (2014 Price) (from beginning April to end Oct.) –
10 🏠. Per night from 50 to 120€ – Per week from 350 to 840€
Reservation fee 15€

🚐 borne – 12 🔲 16€

Pleasant setting beside the Dheune river.

Surroundings : 🗭 ♀
Leisure activities : ⛵
Facilities : ♿ ⚬ 🚾 launderette 🧺
Nearby : 🚲 ✂ 🎿

G P S Longitude : 4.74574
Latitude : 46.91193

CHAMBILLY

71110 – Michelin map **320** E12 – pop. 523 – alt. 249
▶ Paris 363 – Chauffailles 28 – Digoin 27 – Dompierre-sur-Besbre 55

⚠ La Motte aux Merles

🕾 03 85 25 37 67. campingpicard@yahoo.fr

Address : route de la Palisse (5km southwest along the D 990 and
take road to the left)

Opening times : from beginning April to end Oct.

1 ha (25 pitches) flat

Tariff : ✖ 3€ ⬅ 🔲 4€ – 🔌 (6A) 2.40€

🚐 borne 4€ – 5 🔲 4€

Surroundings : 🏖 ⬚
Leisure activities : ⛵ 🎿 (small swimming
pool)
Facilities : ♿ ⚬ 🚾 🍴 📷

G P S Longitude : 3.95755
Latitude : 46.26443

LA CHARITÉ-SUR-LOIRE

58400 – Michelin map **319** B8 – pop. 5 203 – alt. 170
▶ Paris 212 – Bourges 51 – Clamecy 54 – Cosne-sur-Loire 30

⚠ Municipal la Saulaie

✆ 03 86 70 00 83. www.lacharitesurloire-tourisme.com

Address : quai de La Saulaie (southwestern exit)

Opening times : from mid April to end Sept.

1.7 ha (90 pitches) flat, grassy

Tariff : (2014 Price) 17.60€ ✶✶ ⇌ 🔲 [⚡] (16A) –
Extra per person 4.20€

Rental rates : (2014 Price) (from mid April to end Sept.) ♿ (1
'gypsy' caravan) ⊗ – 2 caravans – 1 canvas bungalow – 3 tent
lodges. Per night from 25 to 89€ – Per week from 150 to 540€

Situated on the Île de la Saulaie (island), near the beach.

Surroundings : ♀
Leisure activities : 🏛 🛶
Facilities : ♿ ⚬ 🗱 🛒 🌳
Nearby : ✂ 🖼

GPS Longitude : 3.00927
Latitude : 47.17879

CHAROLLES

71120 – Michelin map **320** F11 – pop. 2 807 – alt. 279
▶ Paris 374 – Autun 80 – Chalon-sur-Saône 67 – Mâcon 55

⚠ Municipal

✆ 03 85 24 04 90. www.ville-charolles.fr

Address : route de Viry (take the northeastern exit, follow the signs
for Mâcon and turn left onto D 33)

Opening times : from beginning April to end Sept.

1 ha (50 pitches) flat, grassy

Tariff : (2014 Price) ✶ 2.50€ ⇌ 2€ 🔲 4.20€ – [⚡] (16A) 2.50€
🚐 borne 3€ – 10 🔲 3€

A pleasant setting beside the Arconce river.

Surroundings : 🗂 ♀
Leisure activities : ⛲ 🎣 🛶 🚲
Facilities : ♿ ⚬ 🗱 🛒 🌳 🍴
Nearby : 🏛 🏊 🛶

GPS Longitude : 4.28209
Latitude : 46.43959

CHÂTEAU-CHINON

58120 – Michelin map **319** G9 – pop. 2 137 – alt. 510
▶ Paris 281 – Autun 39 – Avallon 60 – Clamecy 65

⚠ Municipal du Perthuy d'Oiseau

✆ 03 86 85 08 17. mairiechateauchinonville@wanadoo.fr

Address : rue du Perthuy d'Oiseau (take the southern exit along the
D 27, follow the signs for Luzy and take a right turn)

Opening times : from beginning May to end Sept.

1 ha (50 pitches) relatively flat to hilly, grassy

Tariff : (2014 Price) ✶ 2€ ⇌ 2.50€ 🔲 1.50€ – [⚡] (10A) 2.50€
🚐 borne

At the edge of a forest.

Surroundings : 🌄 ⇞ 🗂 ♀
Leisure activities : 🏛
Facilities : 🗱 🛒

GPS Longitude : 3.92613
Latitude : 47.05518

CHÂTILLON-SUR-SEINE

21400 – Michelin map **320** H2 – pop. 5 613 – alt. 219
▶ Paris 233 – Auxerre 85 – Avallon 75 – Chaumont 60

⚠ Municipal Louis-Rigoly

✆ 03 80 91 03 05. www.mairie-chatillon-sur-seine.fr

Address : esplanade St-Vorles (follow the signs for Langres)

Opening times : Permanent

0.8 ha (46 pitches) flat and relatively flat, grassy, hard surface areas

Tariff : (2014 Price) ✶ 4.20€ ⇌ 1.70€ 🔲 5.10€ – [⚡] (6A) 4.80€

Rental rates : (2014 Price) (from beginning April to end Sept.) –
2 🛏. Per night from 48 to 63€ – Per week from 252 to 365€
🚐 borne 4€

A leafy, shaded site, near the town swimming pool.

Surroundings : 🌿 🗂 ♀
Leisure activities : 🏛
Facilities : ♿ ⚬ 🛒 🌳
Nearby : ⛾ ✗ 🖼 🏊

GPS Longitude : 4.56969
Latitude : 47.87051

CHAUFFAILLES

71170 – Michelin map **320** G12 – pop. 3 939 – alt. 405
▶ Paris 404 – Charolles 32 – Lyon 77 – Mâcon 64

⛰ Municipal les Feuilles

✆ 03 85 26 48 12. www.chauffailles.com

Address : 18 rue de Châtillon (to the southwest along the r. du
Chatillon)

Opening times : from beginning May to end Sept.

4 ha (67 pitches) flat and relatively flat, grassy

Tariff : (2014 Price) 17.90€ ✶✶ ⇌ 🔲 [⚡] (10A) –
Extra per person 3.30€

Rental rates : (from beginning May to end Sept.) – 2 🛏
– 14 canvas bungalows. Per night from 36 to 75€ – Per week
from 141 to 500€ – Reservation fee 35€

In a green setting beside the Botoret river.

Surroundings : 🗂 ♀
Leisure activities : 🏛 🎣 ⛾ 🛶
Facilities : ♿ ⚬ 🗱 🛒 🌳 🍴
Nearby : 🏊

GPS Longitude : 4.33817
Latitude : 46.20004

CLAMECY

58500 – Michelin map **319** E7 – pop. 4 238 – alt. 144
▶ Paris 208 – Auxerre 42 – Avallon 38 – Bourges 105

⚠ Le Pont Picot

✆ 03 86 27 05 97. clamecycamping@orange.fr

Address : rue de Chevroches (to the south; beside the Yonne and the
Nivernais canal, recommended route via Beaugy)

Opening times : from end March to end Sept.

1 ha (90 pitches) flat, grassy

Tariff : (2014 Price) 15€ ✶✶ ⇌ 🔲 [⚡] (6A) – Extra per person 3€
Rental rates : (2014 Price) (from end March to end Sept.) – 7 🛏.
Per night from 35 to 70€ – Per week from 220 to 400€

A pleasant location on a small island.

Surroundings : 🌿 ⇞ ♀
Leisure activities : 🛶
Facilities : ♿ ⚬ 🍴 launderette

GPS Longitude : 3.52784
Latitude : 47.45203

CLUNY

71250 – Michelin map **320** H11 – pop. 4 624 – alt. 248
▶ Paris 384 – Chalon-sur-Saône 49 – Charolles 43 – Mâcon 25

⚠ Municipal St-Vital

Municipal St-Vital

✆ 03 85 59 08 34. www.cluny-camping.blogspot.com

Address : 30 rue des Griottons (take the eastern exit along the D 15, follow the signs for Azé)

Opening times : from end April to beginning Oct.

3 ha (174 pitches) flat, grassy

Tariff : (2014 Price) 18.50€ ✱ ✱ ⇌ 回 (≨) (6A) – Extra per person 4.35€

⊡ borne 5€
The site has a view of the old town of Cluny.

Surroundings : ⩻ ♀		
Leisure activities : ♽	**G**	Longitude : 4.66778
Facilities : ᴫ ⌘ ▥ ⍑ ▧	**P**	Latitude : 46.43088
Nearby : ✗ ⌦ ⚐ ♞	**S**	

CORMATIN

71460 – Michelin map **320** I10 – pop. 544 – alt. 212
▶ Paris 371 – Chalon-sur-Saône 37 – Mâcon 36 – Montceau-les-Mines 41

⚠ Le Hameau des Champs

✆ 03 85 50 76 71, www.le-hameau-des-champs.com

Address : take the northern exit along the D 981, follow the signs for Chalon-sur-Saône

Opening times : from beginning April to end Sept.

5.2 ha (50 pitches) flat, grassy

Tariff : (2014 Price) ✱ 4€ ⇌ 回 6€ – (≨) (10A) 3.50€
Rental rates : (2014 Price) Permanent ᴫ (1) – 10 🛖. Per night from 65 to 88€ – Per week from 360 to 503€
Situated 150m from a lake and the Givry-Cluny Voie Verte (cycle trail).

Surroundings : ⌦		
Leisure activities : ⍑ ⚐ ♽	**G**	Longitude : 4.68391
Facilities : ᴫ ⌘ ⚐ ⍑ ▧	**P**	Latitude : 46.54868
Nearby : ⚐ ✗ ✗ ⚐	**S**	

COUCHES

71490 – Michelin map **320** H8 – pop. 1 493 – alt. 320
▶ Paris 328 – Autun 26 – Beaune 31 – Le Creusot 16

⚠ La Gabrelle

✆ 03 85 45 59 49. www.lagabrelle.com

Address : 1.7km northwest along the D 978, follow the signs for Autun, near a small lake

Opening times : from mid June to mid Sept.

1 ha (50 pitches) terraced, flat, grassy

Tariff : ✱ 3€ ⇌ 3€ 回 3.50€ – (≨) (6A) 3€
⊡ borne 4€

Surroundings : ⌀		
Leisure activities : ⍑ ✗ ⌦ ⚐	**G**	Longitude : 4.5588
Facilities : ᴫ ⌘ ⌀ ⍑	**P**	Latitude : 46.87586
	S	

CRÊCHES-SUR-SAÔNE

71680 – Michelin map **320** I12 – pop. 2 838 – alt. 180
▶ Paris 398 – Bourg-en-Bresse 45 – Mâcon 9 – Villefranche-sur-Saône 30

⚠ Municipal Port d'Arciat

✆ 03 85 37 11 83. http://pagesperso-orange.fr/campingduportdarciat

Address : route du Port d'Arciat (located 1.5km east along the D 31, follow the signs for Pont de Veyle)

Opening times : from mid May to mid Sept.

5 ha (160 pitches) flat, grassy

Tariff : (2014 Price) 16.30€ ✱ ✱ ⇌ 回 (≨) (6A)

Extra per person 4.25€

Beside the Saône river and near a small lake; direct access.

Surroundings : ♀		
Leisure activities : ⚐ ⍑	**G**	Longitude : 4.80581
Facilities : ᴫ ⌘ ⍑ ▧	**P**	Latitude : 46.24037
Nearby : ⍑ ⚐ ⚐ ⍑	**S**	

CRUX-LA-VILLE

58330 – Michelin map **319** E9 – pop. 410 – alt. 319
▶ Paris 248 – Autun 85 – Avallon 138 – La Charité-sur-Loire 45

⚠ Aquadis Loisirs Le Merle

✆ 03 86 58 38 42. www.aquadis-loisirs.com

Address : Le Merle (4.5km southwest along the D 34, follow the signs for St-Saulge and turn right onto D 181, follow the signs for Ste-Marie; beside the lake)

Opening times : from beginning April to end Oct.

2.6 ha (43 pitches) flat, grassy

Tariff : 17.30€ ✱ ✱ ⇌ 回 (≨) (10A) – Extra per person 4.80€ – Reservation fee 9.90€
Rental rates : (from beginning April to end Oct.) – 11 ⬚ – 5 🛖. Per night from 62 to 68€ – Per week from 189 to 599€ – Reservation fee 19.90€

Surroundings : ⍑ ♀♀ ⛰		
Leisure activities : ⍑ ⌦ ⚐ ♽ ⍑	**G**	Longitude : 3.52478
Facilities : ᴫ ⌘ ⌈⌉ ⍑ ▧	**P**	Latitude : 47.1624
Nearby : pedalos	**S**	

DIGOIN

71160 – Michelin map **320** D11 – pop. 8 460 – alt. 232
▶ Paris 337 – Autun 69 – Charolles 26 – Moulins 57

⚠ Flower La Chevrette

✆ 03 85 53 11 49. www.lachevrette.com

Address : rue de la Chevrette (take the western exit towards Moulins, towards the municipal swimming pool; near the Loire river)

Opening times : from beginning April to mid Oct.

1.6 ha (81 pitches) flat

Tariff : (2014 Price) 20.90€ ✱ ✱ ⇌ 回 (≨) (10A) – Extra per person 4.90€
Rental rates : (2014 Price) (from beginning April to mid Oct.) ⚭ – 2 ⬚ – 2 🛖. Per night from 49 to 81€ – Per week from 196 to 567€
⊡ borne 14€

Surroundings : ⌷ ♀		
Leisure activities : ✗ ⌦ ⍑ (small swimming pool)	**G**	Longitude : 3.96768
Facilities : ᴫ ⌘ ▥ ⚐ ⍑ launderette	**P**	Latitude : 46.47983
Nearby : ⚐ ⍑ ⍑	**S**	

DOMPIERRE-LES-ORMES

71520 – Michelin map **320** G11 – pop. 922 – alt. 480
▶ Paris 405 – Chauffailles 28 – Cluny 23 – Mâcon 35

⚞⚞⚞ Le Village des Meuniers

✆ 03 85 50 36 60. www.villagedesmeuniers.com

Address : 344 rue du Stade (take the northwestern exit along the D 41, follow the signs for La Clayette and take the road to the right, near the stadium)

Opening times : from beginning April to end Oct.

3 ha (113 pitches) terraced

Tariff : 29€ ✦✦ ⇔ 🆑 🔌 (16A) – Extra per person 7€ – Reservation fee 6€

Rental rates : Permanent ⚐ (1) – 16 🚐 – 8 🏠 – 3 gîtes. Per night from 45 to 126€ – Per week from 270 to 882€ – Reservation fee 15€

🚐 10 🆑 29€ – 🚮 13.50€
In an elevated location with lovely views.

Surroundings : 🐾 ← 🏞
Leisure activities : ♈ ✗ 🏠 🕯 nighttime
🏊 🚵 🎣 🛶
Facilities : ⚐ 🔑 🗑 🚻 🖼
Nearby : 🚲 🍴
GPS Longitude : 4.47468
Latitude : 46.36393

Using the traditional Michelin classification method, the guide provides you with an easy, speedy reference for assessing the category of each site: 1 to 5 tents (see page 10).

ÉPINAC

71360 – Michelin map **320** H8 – pop. 2 357 – alt. 340
▶ Paris 304 – Arnay-le-Duc 20 – Autun 19 – Chagny 29

⚞⚞ Municipal le Pont Vert

✆ 03 85 82 00 26. www.campingdupontvert.com

Address : rue de la Piscine (take the southern exit along the D 43 and take the road to the right; beside the Drée river)

2.9 ha (71 pitches) flat, grassy
Rentals : 1 🚐.

Surroundings : 🐾 🏞 ♀
Leisure activities : 🏠
Facilities : ⚐ 🔑 🚻 🖼
Nearby : ♈ ✗ 🏊 🎣 🎿
GPS Longitude : 4.50617
Latitude : 46.98577

GIGNY-SUR-SAÔNE

71240 – Michelin map **320** J10 – pop. 522 – alt. 178
▶ Paris 355 – Chalon-sur-Saône 29 – Le Creusot 51 – Louhans 30

⚞⚞⚞ Les Castels Château de l'Épervière 👥

✆ 03 85 94 16 90. www.domaine-eperviere.com – limited spaces for one-night stay

Address : 6 rue du Château (located 1km to the south; at Épervière)

Opening times : from beginning April to end Sept.

7 ha (100 pitches) flat, grassy

Tariff : ✦ 8.90€ ⇔ 🆑 16.50€ – 🔌 (10A) 5.60€ – Reservation fee 10€
Rental rates : (from beginning April to end Sept.) 🦟 – 5 🚐 – 3 gîtes. Per week from 449 to 889€ – Reservation fee 20€

🚐 borne

A pleasant wooded park beside a lake. Burgundy wines can be tasted in the château's vaulted cellar.

Surroundings : 🐾 🏞 ♀♀
Leisure activities : ♈ ✗ 🏠 🏃 🎣 jacuzzi
🏊 🚵 🎣 🎿 🦆 (pool) 🌊 paddling pool
Facilities : ⚐ 🔑 🗑 🚻 🖼 🚿 🖼
Nearby : 🍴
GPS Longitude : 4.94386
Latitude : 46.65446

GUEUGNON

71130 – Michelin map **320** E10 – pop. 7 638 – alt. 243
▶ Paris 335 – Autun 53 – Bourbon-Lancy 27 – Digoin 16

⚞ Municipal de Chazey

✆ 03 85 85 23 11, www.ccpaysgueugnon.fr

Address : zone de Chazey (4km south along the D 994, follow the signs for Digoin and take the road to the right)

1 ha (20 pitches) flat, grassy
Rentals : 3 🏠 – 6 tent lodges – chalets (without sanitary facilities).

Near a small canal and two lakes.

Surroundings : 🐾 🏞
Leisure activities : 🏠 🎣
Facilities : ⚐ 🔑 🚿 🖼
Nearby : 🌊
GPS Longitude : 4.05386
Latitude : 46.57077

L'ISLE-SUR-SEREIN

89440 – Michelin map **319** H6 – pop. 747 – alt. 190
▶ Paris 209 – Auxerre 50 – Avallon 17 – Montbard 36

⚞ Municipal le Parc du Château

✆ 03 86 33 93 50. www.isle-sur-serein.fr

Address : route d'Avallon (800m south along the D 86; by the stadium, 150m from the Serein river)

1 ha (30 pitches) flat, grassy
Rentals : 4 🚐.

Surroundings : ♀
Facilities : 🔑 🏛 🚿 🖼
Nearby : 🎣 🍴 sports trail
GPS Longitude : 4.00542
Latitude : 47.58119

ISSY-L'ÉVÊQUE

71760 – Michelin map **320** D9 – pop. 842 – alt. 310
▶ Paris 325 – Bourbon-Lancy 25 – Gueugnon 17 – Luzy 12

⚞⚞ L'Etang Neuf

✆ 03 85 24 96 05. camping-etangneuf@orange.fr

Address : rue de l'Étang (located 1km west along the D 42, follow the signs for Grury and take the road to the right)

6 ha/3 pitches (71 pitches) flat
Rentals : 2 🚐 – 6 🏠.

A pleasant location beside a lake and a wood.

Surroundings : 🐾 ← 🏞
Leisure activities : ♈ ✗ 🏠 🎣 🎿
Facilities : ⚐ 🔑 🚻 🖼
Nearby : 🎿 🦆 🎣 🐎
GPS Longitude : 3.9602
Latitude : 46.7078

LAIVES

71240 – Michelin map **320** J10 – pop. 997 – alt. 198
▶ Paris 355 – Chalon-sur-Saône 20 – Mâcon 48 – Montceau-les-Mines 49

⛰ Les Lacs de Laives - la Héronnière

✆ 03 85 44 98 85. www.camping-laheronniere.com

Address : route de la Ferté (4.2km north along the D 18, follow the signs for Buxy and take right turn)

Opening times :

1.5 ha (80 pitches) flat, grassy

Tariff : (2014 Price) 26.80€ ✶✶ ⛆ 回 ⑭ (6A) –Extra per person 5.80€
Rental rates : (2014 Price) (from end March to mid Oct.) – 1 caravan - 2 🚐 – 2 🏠. Per night from 59 to 74€ – Per week from 322 to 994€
Situated close to the lakes at Laives.

Surroundings : 🏞 🚙 ♨
Leisure activities : 🚴 ⛷
Facilities : 🚿 🚰 🚽 🔌
Nearby : 🍷 🍴 ⚓

G P S Longitude : 4.83426
Latitude : 46.67448

LIGNY-LE-CHÂTEL

89144 – Michelin map **319** F4 – pop. 1 334 – alt. 130
▶ Paris 178 – Auxerre 22 – Sens 60 – Tonnerre 28

⛰ Municipal Parc de la Noue Marrou

✆ 03 86 47 56 99. www.tourisme-camping-municipal-de-la-noue-marrou.fr

Address : avenue de la Noue Marrou (take the southwestern exit along the D 8, follow the signs for Auxerre and take road to the left; beside the Serein)

Opening times : from beginning May to end Sept.

2 ha (50 pitches) flat, grassy

Tariff : 12.40€ ✶✶ ⛆ 回 ⑭ (16A) – Extra per person 2.50€
🚐 borne 3.50€
On the edge of the Othe forest and the Serein river.

Surroundings : 🏞
Leisure activities : 🍷 🎣
Facilities : 🚿 🚰 🛁 🚽 🏪
Nearby : 🛒 🚴 ⚓ ⚓

G P S Longitude : 3.75274
Latitude : 47.89597

LORMES

58140 – Michelin map **319** F8 – pop. 1 389 – alt. 420
▶ Paris 255 – Dijon 135 – Nevers 73 – Auxerre 76

⛰ L'Étang du Goulot

✆ 03 86 22 82 37. www.campingetangdugoulot.com

Address : 2 rue des campeurs

Opening times : from beginning May to end Sept.

2.5 ha (64 pitches) flat, grassy

Tariff : (2014 Price) 18€ ✶✶ ⛆ 回 ⑭ (16A) – Extra per person 6€
Rental rates : (2014 Price) (from beginning May to end Sept.) – 1 caravan – 1 🚐 – 2 yurts – 1 tipi – 3 tent lodges. Per night from 70 to 95€ – Per week from 230 to 550€
🚐 borne 3€ – 2 回 18€

Surroundings : 🏞 🚙 ♨
Leisure activities : 🍷 🍴 ⚓ ⚓ 🎣
Facilities : 🚿 🚰 🛁 🚽
Nearby : ⚓ 🚴 🍴

G P S Longitude : 3.82297
Latitude : 47.28268

LOUHANS

71500 – Michelin map **320** L10 – pop. 6 451 – alt. 179
▶ Paris 373 – Bourg-en-Bresse 61 – Chalon-sur-Saône 38 – Dijon 85

⛰ Municipal

✆ 03 85 75 19 02. www.louhans-chateaurenaud.fr

Address : 10 chemin de La Chapellerie (located 1km southwest along the D 971, follow the signs for Tournus and take the D 12, following signs for Romenay, turn left after the stadium)

Opening times : from beginning April to end Sept.

1 ha (60 pitches) flat, grassy

Tariff : (2014 Price) 15€ ✶✶ ⛆ 回 ⑭ (6A) – Extra per person 2.50€
Rental rates : (2014 Price) (from beginning April to end Sept.) – 2 🚐. Per night from 70 to 90€ – Per week from 280 to 380€
🚐 45 回 15€
In a green setting beside river.

Surroundings : 🚙 ♨♨
Facilities : 🚿 (July–Aug.) 🚽 🚰
Nearby : 🍴 ⚓ ⚓

G P S Longitude : 5.21714
Latitude : 46.62436

LUZY

58170 – Michelin map **319** G11 – pop. 2 018 – alt. 275
▶ Paris 314 – Autun 34 – Château-Chinon 39 – Moulins 62

⛰ Club Airotel Château de Chigy 👥

✆ 03 86 30 10 80. www.chateaudechigy.com.fr

Address : at Tazilly (4km southwest along the D 973, follow the signs for Bourbon-Lancy then take the road to the left)

Opening times : from end April to end Sept.

70 ha/15 pitches (135 pitches) flat, grassy

Tariff : (2014 Price) ✶ 5€ ⛆ 26€ 回 ⑭ (6A)
Rental rates : (2014 Price) (from end April to mid Oct.) – 6 🚐 – 29 🏠 – 3 apartments – 6 gîtes. Per night from 59 to 178€ – Per week from 140 to 1,246€

A spacious site laid out around a château, with meadows, woods and lakes.

Surroundings : 🏞 ‹
Leisure activities : 🍷 🍴 🏠 📷 🎿 ⚓ ⚓ 🔫 ⛷ ⚓ 🎣 multi-sports ground
Facilities : 🚿 🚰 🛁 🏪 🚰

G P S Longitude : 3.94445
Latitude : 46.75716

MACON

71000 – Michelin map **320** I12 – pop. 34 000 – alt. 175
▶ Paris 398 – Dijon 128 – Lyon 72 – Bourg-en-Bresse 37

⛰ Municipal

✆ 03 85 38 16 22. www.macon.fr/tourisme/camping – 🏃

Address : at Sancé, 1 rue des Grandes Varennes

Opening times : from mid March to end Oct.

5 ha (266 pitches) flat, grassy

Tariff : (2014 Price) 25.10€ ✶✶ ⛆ 回 ⑭ (10A) – Extra per person 5.40€

Surroundings : 🚙 ♨♨
Leisure activities : 🍷 🍴 🏠 ⚓ ⚓ 🎣
Facilities : 🚿 🚰 🛁 🚽 launderette ♨ 🚰
Nearby : ⚓ marina

G P S Longitude : 4.84372
Latitude : 46.3301

MATOUR

71520 – Michelin map **320** G12 – pop. 1 095 – alt. 500
▶ Paris 405 – Chauffailles 22 – Cluny 24 – Mâcon 36

⚠ Flower Le Paluet

✆ 03 85 59 70 92. www.matour.com

Address : 2 rue de la Piscine (located to the west; follow the signs for la Clayette and take a left turn)

Opening times : from mid April to end Sept.

3 ha (73 pitches) flat and relatively flat

Tariff : 21€ ✶✶ ⇌ 🅴 (10A) – Extra per person 5.10€ – Reservation fee 12€

Rental rates : (from mid March to mid Nov.) – 10 🏠 – 6 canvas bungalows – 2 gîtes. Per night from 46 to 103€ – Per week from 322 to 721€ – Reservation fee 25€

🚐 borne

Beside a lake and near a leisure centre.

Surroundings : 🐾 ⛱ ♨
Leisure activities : 🎦 ⏱daytime ⛵ ✂ 🎣
🛶⛷ multi-sports ground
Facilities : ⚿ ⊶ (season) ⚆ 🍴 launderette

G P S Longitude : 4.48232
Latitude : 46.30677

To make the best possible use of this guide, please read pages 2–15 carefully.

MEURSAULT

21190 – Michelin map **320** I8 – pop. 1 542 – alt. 243
▶ Paris 326 – Dijon 56 – Chalon-sur-Saône 28 – Le Creusot 40

⚠ La Grappe d'Or

✆ 03 80 21 22 48. www.camping-meursault.com

Address : 2 route de Volnay

Opening times : from beginning April to mid Oct.

4.5 ha (130 pitches) terraced, flat, grassy

Tariff : 24.50€ ✶✶ ⇌ 🅴 (12A) – Extra per person 4.20€ – Reservation fee 10€

Rental rates : (from mid April to beginning Oct.) ✂ – 19 🚐 – 1 apartment – 1 gîte. Per night from 45 to 89€ – Per week from 315 to 554€ – Reservation fee 15€

🚐 borne 5€ – 10 🅴 20€

The site overlooks the old village of Mersault and the vineyards.

Surroundings : ≼ ♨
Leisure activities : ✗ ⛵ 🚲 ✂ 🛶 ⛷
Facilities : ⚿ ⊶ 🏛 🍴 🛶 🚿

G P S Longitude : 4.76987
Latitude : 46.98655

MIGENNES

89400 – Michelin map **319** E4 – pop. 7 360 – alt. 87
▶ Paris 162 – Dijon 169 – Auxerre 22 – Sens 46

⚠ Les Confluents

✆ 03 86 80 94 55. www.les-confluents.com

Address : allée Léo Lagrange (near the stadium)

Opening times : from beginning April to end Oct.

1.5 ha (61 pitches) flat, grassy

Tariff : ✶ 4.40€ ⇌ 🅴 5.75€ – (10A) 4.30€

Rental rates : (from beginning April to end Oct.) ✂ – 12 🚐. Per night from 44 to 72€ – Per week from 275 to 387€

🚐 borne 3.30€ – 8 🅴 14€ – ⚡(10A)12.95€

On the banks of the Yonne river.

Surroundings : ⛱ ♨
Leisure activities : 🎦 ⛵ 🚲 🛶
Facilities : ⊶ 🏛 🛶 🚿 ⚆ 🍴 🛶 🚿
Nearby : ✗ ✂ 🎣 watersports centre

G P S Longitude : 3.5095
Latitude : 47.95613

MONTBARD

21500 – Michelin map **320** G4 – pop. 5 527 – alt. 221
▶ Paris 240 – Autun 87 – Auxerre 81 – Dijon 81

⚠ Municipal les Treilles

✆ 03 80 92 69 50. www.montbard.com

Address : rue Michel Servet (along the D 980 diversion northwest of the town, near the swimming complex)

Opening times : from mid March to end Oct.

2.5 ha (80 pitches) flat, grassy

Tariff : 19.30€ ✶✶ ⇌ 🅴 (16A) – Extra per person 5.10€ – Reservation fee 4€

Rental rates : (2014 Price) (from mid April to end Oct.) – 2 🚐. Per night from 90 to 95€ – Per week from 255 to 555€ – Reservation fee 6€

🚐 borne 3.10€ – 6 🅴 19.30€ – ⚡11€

Attractive trees and shrubs surround some pitches.

Surroundings : ≼ ⛱ ♨
Leisure activities : 🎦 ⏱daytime ⛵
multi-sports ground
Facilities : ⚿ ⊶ 🏛 🛶 ⚆ 🍴 🛶
Nearby : ♨ hammam 🏸 🛶 🛶 ⛷

G P S Longitude : 4.33129
Latitude : 47.63111

Key to rentals symbols:

12 🚐	*Number of mobile homes*
20 🏠	*Number of chalets*
6 🛏	*Number of rooms to rent*
Per night 30–50€	*Minimum/maximum rate per night*
Per week 300–1,000€	*Minimum/maximum rate per week*

MONTIGNY-EN-MORVAN

58120 – Michelin map **319** G9 – pop. 319 – alt. 350
▶ Paris 269 – Château-Chinon 13 – Corbigny 26 – Nevers 64

⚠ Municipal du Lac

✆ 03 86 84 71 77. www.montigny-en-morvan.fr – 🏕

Address : Continue 2.3km northeast along the D 944, D 303 towards the dam at Pannecière-Chaumard and take the road to the right.

Opening times : from beginning May to end Sept.

2 ha (59 pitches) undulating, flat, grassy

Tariff : (2014 Price) ✶ 2.50€ ⇌ 1.70€ – (25A) 2€

🚐 borne 3.90€

In a pleasant location near a lake.

Surroundings : 🐾 ♨
Leisure activities : ⛵ 🛶
Facilities : ⚿ ⊶ 🛶 🏛
Nearby : 🛶

G P S Longitude : 3.8735
Latitude : 47.15573

NEVERS

58000 – Michelin map **319** B10 – pop. 36 762 – alt. 194
▶ Paris 247 – Dijon 187 – Bourges 68 – Moulins 57

⚠ Nevers

𝒫 06 84 98 67 79. www.campingnevers.com

Address : rue de la Jonction

Opening times : from mid April to mid Oct.

1.6 ha (73 pitches) terraced, flat, grassy

Tariff : (2014 Price) 21.64€ ✝✝ ⇔ ▣ 🔌 (6A) –Extra per person 3.30€
Rental rates : (2014 Price) (from mid April to mid Oct.) – 2 🚐.
Per night from 56€ – Per week from 335 to 480€ – Reservation fee 10.50€

🚐 borne 2.50€

Situated on the banks of the Loire river, with a view of the cathedral, Ducal Palace and the stone bridge.

Surroundings : ≤ 👤 Leisure activities : 🍴🍽🏠 🏊🎿 🎣 Facilities : 👤🔌 🚽🚿🏢 🖙🛁 launderette 🧺 Nearby : 🏊🚲	**G P S** Longitude : 3.16095 Latitude : 46.98222

NOLAY

21340 – Michelin map **320** H8 – pop. 1 510 – alt. 299
▶ Paris 316 – Autun 30 – Beaune 20 – Chalon-sur-Saône 34

⚠ Municipal les Chaumes du Mont

𝒫 03 45 63 40 01, campingleschaumes@sfr.fr

Address : 0.8km southwest along the D 33A, follow the signs for Couches

1.5 ha (70 pitches) terraced, relatively flat, flat, grassy

Situated near a lake.

Surroundings : ≤ 🏕👤⛰ Leisure activities : 🎿🍽 Facilities : 👤🔌 🖼	**G P S** Longitude : 4.62457 Latitude : 46.94682

⚠ La Bruyère

𝒫 03 80 21 87 59. www.bourgogne-sante-services.com

Address : rue de Moulin Larché (1.2km west along the D 973, follow the signs for Autun and take road to the left)

Opening times : Permanent

1.2 ha (22 pitches) flat, grassy

Tariff : (2014 Price) 14.80€ ✝✝ ⇔ ▣ 🔌 (16A) –
Extra per person 2.50€

🚐 borne

Surroundings : 🌳 ≤ Leisure activities : 🏠 Facilities : 👤🔌🏢🍴 launderette	**G P S** Longitude : 4.62202 Latitude : 46.95055

These symbols are used for a campsite that is exceptional in its category:

🔺🔺🔺...🔺 *Particularly pleasant setting, quality and range of services available*

🌿🌿 *Tranquil, isolated site – quiet site, particularly at night*

≤≤ *Exceptional view – interesting or panoramic view*

PALINGES

71430 – Michelin map **320** F10 – pop. 1 512 – alt. 274
▶ Paris 352 – Charolles 16 – Lapalisse 70 – Lyon 136

⚠ Le Lac

𝒫 03 85 88 14 49. www.campingdulac.eu

Address : at Lac du Fourneau (located 1km northeast along the D 128, rte de Génelard)

Opening times : from beginning April to end Oct.

1.5 ha (44 pitches) terraced, flat, grassy

Tariff : (2014 Price) 23€ ✝✝ ⇔ ▣ 🔌 (10A) – Extra per person 4.10€
Rental rates : (2014 Price) (from beginning April to end Oct.) 👤
(1) – 6 🏠. Per night from 46 to 165€ – Per week from 250 to 750€

🚐 borne – 12 ▣ 23€

Near a small lake.

Surroundings : 🌿 Leisure activities : 🏠 🎿 Facilities : 👤🔌 🚽 🖙🍴 🖼 refrigerators Nearby : 🏊 🍽 ☡ (beach) 🎣	**G P S** Longitude : 4.22521 Latitude : 46.56106

The prices listed were supplied by the campsite owners in 2014 (if prices were not available, those from the previous year are given). The fees should be regarded as basic charges and may fluctuate with inflation.

PARAY LE MONIAL

71600 – Michelin map **320** E11 – pop. 9 115 – alt. 245
▶ Paris 377 – Dijon 149 – Mâcon 66 – Moulins 69

🔺 Mambre

𝒫 03 85 88 89 20. www.campingdemambre.com

Address : 19 rue du Gué Léger

6 ha (161 pitches) flat, grassy

Rentals : 20 🚐.

Surroundings : 👤👤 Leisure activities : 🍴 🎿🚲 🏊 Facilities : 👤🔌🏢 🖙launderette 🛒 Nearby : 🍽	**G P S** Longitude : 4.10479 Latitude : 46.45743

PRÉMERY

58700 – Michelin map **319** C8 – pop. 2 031 – alt. 237
▶ Paris 231 – La Charité-sur-Loire 28 – Château-Chinon 57 Clamecy 41

⚠ Municipal

𝒫 09 65 21 65 56. www.mairie-premery.fr rubrique camping

Address : chemin des Prés de la Ville (take the northeastern exit along the D 977, follow the signs for Clamecy and take the road to the right)

1.6 ha (50 pitches) flat and relatively flat

Rentals : 10 🏠.

Situated near the Nièvre river and a lake.

Leisure activities : 🚲🎣 multi-sports ground Facilities : 👤🔌 🛁🍴 🖼 Nearby : 🏊🎿 🍽 ☡	**G P S** Longitude : 3.33683 Latitude : 47.1781

ST-GERMAIN-DU-BOIS

71330 – Michelin map **320** L9 – pop. 1 935 – alt. 210
▸ Paris 367 – Chalon-sur-Saône 33 – Dole 58 – Lons-le-Saunier 29

⚠ Municipal de l'Étang Titard

🕿 03 85 72 06 15. www.st-germaindubois.fr

Address : route de Louhans (take the southern exit along the D 13)

Opening times : from beginning May to mid Sept.

1 ha (40 pitches) flat, grassy

Tariff : (2014 Price) ✹ 2.30€ ⇌ 1.50€ 🔲 1.20€ – ⚡ (60A) 2.50€

Rental rates : (2014 Price) Permanent ♿ (1) ⚑ – 5 🏠. Per night from 84 to 120€ – Per week from 294 to 420€

Situated near a lake.

Surroundings : ♀	**G** Longitude : 5.24617
Leisure activities : 🏛	**P**
Facilities : ♿ 🚻 ♨ 🚿 🗑	**S** Latitude : 46.74635
Nearby : ✕ 🏊 ⤢ 🎣 sports trail	

ST-HONORÉ-LES-BAINS

58360 – Michelin map **319** G10 – pop. 841 – alt. 300 – ♨
▸ Paris 303 – Château-Chinon 28 – Luzy 22 – Moulins 69

🏔 Camping et Gîtes des Bains

🕿 03 86 30 73 44. www.campinglesbains.com

Address : 15 avenue Jean Mermoz (take the western exit, follow the signs for Vandenesse)

Opening times :

4.5 ha (130 pitches) flat, grassy

Tariff : (2014 Price) 20€ ✹✹ ⇌ 🔲 ⚡ (6A) – Extra per person 4.60€ Reservation fee 8€

Rental rates : (from end March to end Oct.) – 4 🚐 – 3 apartments – 20 gîtes – 1 hut. Per week from 195 to 565€ – Reservation fee 8€

🚰 borne

Surroundings : 🗩 ♀	**G** Longitude : 3.82832
Leisure activities : ♋ ✕ ⤢ 🛝 ⤢ ⛰	**P**
Facilities : ♿ 🔑 🚿 🚻 launderette	**S** Latitude : 46.90684
Nearby : ✕ 🎣	

⚠ Municipal Plateau du Gué

🕿 03 86 30 76 00. http://www.st-honore-les-bains.com/index.php?cat=campings

Address : 13 rue Eugène-Collin (in the town, 150m from the post office)

Opening times : from beginning April to end Oct.

1.2 ha (73 pitches) flat and relatively flat, grassy

Tariff : (2014 Price) ✹ 2.86€ ⇌ 2€ 🔲 2.31€ – ⚡ (15A) 3.30€

🚰 borne 2.10€ – 10 🔲 2.31€

Surroundings : ♀	**G** Longitude : 3.83918
Leisure activities : 🏛 ⤢	**P**
Facilities : ♿ 🚻 🛉 🚿 🗑	**S** Latitude : 46.90376

ST-LÉGER-DE-FOUGERET

58120 – Michelin map **319** G9 – pop. 289 – alt. 500
▸ Paris 308 – Dijon 122 – Nevers 65 – Le Creusot 69

⚠ Sites et Paysages Étang de la Fougeraie

🕿 03 86 85 11 85. www.campingfougeraie.com

Address : at Hameau de Champs (2.4km southeast along the D 157, follow the signs for Onlay)

Opening times : from end March to beginning Oct.

7 ha (60 pitches) flat, grassy

Tariff : 26.50€ ✹✹ ⇌ 🔲 ⚡ (10A) – Extra per person 7€ – Reservation fee 9€

Rental rates : Permanent – 5 🏠 – 4 tent lodges. Per night 75€ – Per week from 60 to 100€ – Reservation fee 16€

🚰 borne – 2 🔲 26.50€ – 🔌 ⚡12€

In a rural setting beside a lake.

Surroundings : 🐟 ≼	**G** Longitude : 3.90492
Leisure activities : ♋ ✕ 🚲 🎣 ⤢ ⚓	**P**
Facilities : ♿ 🔑 🛉 🚻 launderette ⤢	**S** Latitude : 47.00616
refrigerators	

*For more information on visiting particular towns or regions, consult the relevant regional **MICHELIN Green Guide**. We also recommend you use the appropriate Michelin regional map to locate your selected campsite, to calculate distances and to work out the best route.*

ST-PÉREUSE

58110 – Michelin map **319** F9 – pop. 280 – alt. 355
▸ Paris 289 – Autun 54 – Château-Chinon 15 – Clamecy 57

🏔 Le Manoir de Bezolle

Le Manoir de Bezolle

🕿 03 86 84 42 55. www.camping-bezolle.com ⚑

Address : to the southeast along the D 11, 300m from the D 978, follow the signs for Château-Chinon

Opening times : from mid March to end Sept.

8 ha/5 pitches (140 pitches) terraced, flat, grassy, small lakes

Tariff : 30.44€ ✹✹ ⇌ 🔲 ⚡ (10A) – Extra per person 5.50€

Rental rates : (from mid April to end Sept.) ⚑ – 2 caravans – 4 🚐 – 12 🏠 – 2 yurts. Per night from 37 to 108€ – Per week from 259 to 887€

🚰 borne 5€

In the grounds of the manor house.

*The classification (1 to 5 tents, **black** or red) that we award to selected sites in this guide is our own system. It should not be confused with the classification (1 to 5 stars) of official organisations.*

Surroundings : 🐟 ≼ ♀♀	**G** Longitude : 3.8158
Leisure activities : ♋ ✕ 🏛 🏛 ⤢ ⛰ ⤢ ⚓	**P**
Facilities : ♿ 🔑 🔲 🛉 🚿 ⤢ 🚻	**S** Latitude : 47.05732
launderette ⤢ ⤢	

ST-POINT

71520 – Michelin map **320** H11 – pop. 341 – alt. 335
▶ Paris 396 – Beaune 90 – Cluny 14 – Mâcon 26

⚠ Lac de St-Point-Lamartine

📞 03 85 50 52 31, www.campingsaintpoint.com

Address : take the southern exit along the D 22, follow the signs for Tramayes; beside a lake

Opening times : from beginning April to end Oct.

3 ha (102 pitches) flat and relatively flat, grassy

Tariff : 18€ ♦♦ ⇌ 🔲 (13A) – Extra per person 4€
Rental rates : (from beginning April to end Oct.) – 2 🚐 – 11 🏠.
Per night from 45 to 60€– Per week from 200 to 400€ –
Reservation fee 80€
🚰 60 🔲 10€ – 🔌 🖋16.50€
Situated beside a lake.

Surroundings : 🌊 ≤ 🖵
Leisure activities : 🛶 🏊 🚲 🎣
Facilities : 🚿 ⚓ 🗻 🍴 🖼
Nearby : 🍷 🍴 🚣 🐟 pedalos

| | GPS | Longitude : 4.61175 |
| | | Latitude : 46.33703 |

ST-SAUVEUR-EN-PUISAYE

89520 – Michelin map **319** C6 – pop. 946 – alt. 259
▶ Paris 174 – Dijon 184 – Moulins 146 – Tours 242

🏔 Parc des Joumiers

📞 03 86 45 66 28. www.camping-motel-joumiers.com

Address : 2.3km northwest along the D 7 and take the road to the right

Opening times : from end March to mid Oct.

21 ha/7 pitches (100 pitches) flat and relatively flat, grassy

Tariff : (2014 Price) 17€ ♦♦ ⇌ 🔲 (10A) – Extra per person 4.80€
Rental rates : Permanent – 13 🚐 – 3 🏠 – 10 🛏. Per night from 55 to 149€ – Per week from 380 to 781€
🚰 borne 5€ – 2 🔲 13€
Situated beside a lake.

Surroundings : 🌊 🖵 🔺
Leisure activities : ✗ 🏊 🛶 🎣
Facilities : 🚿 ⚓ 🗻 🍴 🖼
Nearby : boats to hire

| | GPS | Longitude : 3.19357 |
| | | Latitude : 47.63082 |

SALORNAY-SUR-GUYE

71250 – Michelin map **320** H10 – pop. 826 – alt. 210
▶ Paris 377 – Chalon-sur-Saône 51 – Cluny 12 – Paray-le-Monial 44

⚠ Municipal de la Clochette

📞 03 85 59 90 11, www.salornay-sur-guye.fr

Address : place de la Clochette (in the village, access via the road in front of the post office)

Opening times : from end May to beginning Sept.

1 ha (60 pitches) flat

Tariff : ♦ 3.50€ ⇌ 🔲 3€ – (10A) 3€ – Reservation fee 5€
🚰 borne 5€
Situated beside the Gande river.

Surroundings : 🖵 ♀
Leisure activities : 🎣
Facilities : 🚿 🗻 🍴 🖼
Nearby : 🏊 ✗

| | GPS | Longitude : 4.59907 |
| | | Latitude : 46.51659 |

SANTENAY

21590 – Michelin map **320** I8 – pop. 827 – alt. 225 – ⚓
▶ Paris 330 – Autun 39 – Beaune 18 – Chalon-sur-Saône 25

🏔 Aquadis Les Sources

📞 03 80 20 66 55. www.aquadis-loisirs.com

Address : avenue des Sources (head 1km southwest following signs for Cheilly-les-Maranges, near the spa centre)

Opening times : from beginning April to end Oct.

3.1 ha (150 pitches) flat and relatively flat

Tariff : 21.50€ ♦♦ ⇌ 🔲 (10A) – Extra per person 3.90€ – Reservation fee 9.90€
🚰 borne 5.50€

Surroundings : ≤ ♀
Leisure activities : 🏊 🚣
Facilities : 🚿 ⚓ 🍴 🖼 🚿 🚗
Nearby : ✗ 🛶

| | GPS | Longitude : 4.6857 |
| | | Latitude : 46.90716 |

SAULIEU

21210 – Michelin map **320** F6 – pop. 2 574 – alt. 535
▶ Paris 248 – Autun 40 – Avallon 39 – Beaune 65

🏔 Aquadis Loisirs Saulieu

📞 03 80 64 16 19. www.aquadis-loisirs.com

Address : located 1km northwest along the N 6, follow the signs for Paris; near a lake

Opening times : from beginning March to beginning Nov.

6 ha (100 pitches) flat and relatively flat, grassy

Tariff : 21.50€ ♦♦ ⇌ 🔲 (10A) – Extra per person 3.70€ – Reservation fee 9.90€
Rental rates : (from beginning March to beginning Nov.) – 6 🚐 – 6 🏠. Per night from 62 to 85€ – Per week from 194 to 639€
Reservation fee 19.90€
🚰 14 🔲 14.30€

Leisure activities : 🍷 🛶 🏊 🚲 ✗ 🎣
Facilities : 🚿 ⚓ 🗻 🍴 🖼
| | GPS | Longitude : 4.22373 |
| | | Latitude : 47.28934 |

The Michelin classification (🏔🏔🏔... ⚠) is totally independent of the official star classification system awarded by the local prefecture or other official organisation.

SAVIGNY-LÈS-BEAUNE

21420 – Michelin map **320** I7 – pop. 1 371 – alt. 237
▶ Paris 314 – Dijon 39 – Mâcon 93 – Lons-le-Saunier 109

⚠ Les Premiers Prés

📞 03 80 26 15 06. www.camping-savigny-les-beaune.fr

Address : route de Bouilland (located 1km northwest along the D 2)

1.5 ha (88 pitches) flat and relatively flat

In a green setting beside a stream.

Surroundings : ♀
Leisure activities : 🍷 🏊
Facilities : 🚿 ⚓ 🍴 🚗

| | GPS | Longitude : 4.82192 |
| | | Latitude : 47.06246 |

LES SETTONS

58230 – Michelin map **319** H8
▶ Paris 259 – Autun 41 – Avallon 44 – Château-Chinon 25

⛰ Plage du Midi

🕿 03 86 84 51 97. www.settons-camping.com

Address : on the right bank of Lac des Settons, Les Branlasses (2.5km southeast along the D 193 and take turning to the right)

4 ha (110 pitches) relatively flat

Rentals : ♿ (1) – 2 caravans – 27 🏠 – 1 cabin in the trees.

Situated beside a lake.

Surroundings : ⩽ ♀ ⛰ Leisure activities : ♟ ⛵ 🛝 (open air in season) Facilities : ♿ ⛽ ♨ ⌇ launderette ♒ Nearby : ✗ ✗ ♪ pedalos	**GPS** Longitude : 4.07056 Latitude : 47.18578

🛆 Les Mésanges

🕿 03 86 84 55 77. www.campinglesmesanges.fr

Address : on the left bank of Lac des Settons, L'Huis-Gaumont (4km south along the D193, D 520, follow the signs for Planchez and turn left towards Chevigny, 200m from the lake)

Opening times : from mid May to mid Sept.

5 ha (100 pitches) relatively flat

Tariff : (2014 Price) 21€ ✹✹ ⬅ 🔲 ⚡ (16A) – Extra per person 5.30€
🚐 borne – 🔋11€

In a pleasant location beside a lake.

Surroundings : ♒ ⛵ ♀ ⛰ Leisure activities : ⛵ ↘ Facilities : ♿ ⛽ ♨ ♒ ⌇ ⌇ launderette Nearby : ⛴	**GPS** Longitude : 4.05385 Latitude : 47.18077

🛆 La Plage des Settons

🕿 03 86 84 51 99. www.camping-chalets-settons.com

Address : on the left bank of Lac des Settons (300m south of the dam)

Opening times : from beginning May to mid Sept.

2.6 ha (60 pitches) terraced, flat, grassy

Tariff : (2014 Price) 20€ ✹✹ ⬅ 🔲 ⚡ (10A) – Extra per person 6€
Rental rates : (from beginning April to mid Nov.) ♿ (2 chalets) – 14 🏠. Per night from 50 to 95 € – Per week from 332 to 665€

Pleasant pitches set on terraces, opposite the lake.

Surroundings : ♒ ⩽ ⛰ Leisure activities : 🏠 ⛵ pedalos Facilities : ♿ ⛽ ♒ 🔲 Nearby : ♟ ✗ ♒	**GPS** Longitude : 4.06132 Latitude : 47.18958

Key to rentals symbols:

12	*Number of mobile homes*
20 🏠	*Number of chalets*
6 🛏	*Number of rooms to rent*
Per night *30–50€*	*Minimum/maximum rate per night*
Per week *300–1,000€*	*Minimum/maximum rate per week*

TONNERRE

89700 – Michelin map **319** G4 – pop. 5 246 – alt. 156
▶ Paris 199 – Auxerre 38 – Montbard 45 – Troyes 60

🛆 La Cascade

🕿 03 86 55 15 44. http://www.revea-camping.fr/fr/accueil-camping-la-cascade.html

Address : avenue Aristide-Briand (take the northern exit along the D 905, follow the signs for Troyes and take D 944, towards the town centre; beside the Yonne canal)

Opening times : from mid April to end Sept.

3 ha (107 pitches) flat, grassy

Tariff : 17.10€ ✹✹ ⬅ 🔲 ⚡ (5A) – Extra per person 4€ – Reservation fee 10€

Rental rates : (from mid April to end Sept.) – 10 🏠. Per night from 70 to 85€ – Per week from 210 to 540€ – Reservation fee 25€
🚐 3 🔲 17.10€

Surroundings : ♀ Leisure activities : 🏠 🚲 Facilities : ♿ ⛽ ⌇ ⌇ ⌇ ⌇ 🔲 Nearby : ⛴ ↘	**GPS** Longitude : 3.98415 Latitude : 47.8603

TOURNUS

71700 – Michelin map **320** J10 – pop. 5 884 – alt. 193
▶ Paris 360 – Bourg-en-Bresse 70 – Chalon-sur-Saône 28 – Lons-le-Saunier 58

⛰ Camping de Tournus

🕿 03 85 51 16 58. www.camping-tournus.com

Address : 14 rue des Canes (located 1km north of the town; take the r. St-Laurent opposite the station. situated right next to the swimming pool and 150m from the Saône (direct access)

Opening times : from beginning April to end Sept.

2 ha (90 pitches) flat, grassy

Tariff : 26.80€ ✹✹ ⬅ 🔲 ⚡ (10A) – Extra per person 6.20€
🚐 borne – 26 🔲 26.80€ – 🔋11€

Leisure activities : 🏠 Facilities : ♿ ⛽ ⌇ ♒ ⌇ 🔲 Nearby : ✗ ✗ ⛵ ♒	**GPS** Longitude : 4.90932 Latitude : 46.57375

VANDENESSE-EN-AUXOIS

21320 – Michelin map **320** H6 – pop. 279 – alt. 360
▶ Paris 275 – Arnay-le-Duc 16 – Autun 42 – Châteauneuf 3

⛰ Sunêlia Le Lac de Panthier ♟♟

🕿 03 80 49 21 94. www.lac-de-panthier.com

Address : situated 2.5km northeast along the D 977bis; follow the road to Commarin and take turning to the left; near the lake

Opening times : from mid April to beginning Oct.

5.2 ha (210 pitches) terraced

Tariff : 28€ ✹✹ ⬅ 🔲 ⚡ (6A) – Extra per person 7€ – Reservation fee 15€

Rental rates : (from mid April to beginning Oct.) – 63 🚐. Per night from 43 to 148€ – Per week from 301 to 1,036€ – Reservation fee 30€
🚐 borne 5€

Surroundings : ♒ ⩽ ⛴ ♀ ⛰ Leisure activities : ♟ ✗ 🏠 ⛰ ↗ ⛴ ⛵ 🚲 🛝 ♒ ♒ ↘ Facilities : ♿ ⛽ ♒ ⌇ 🔲 ♒ ♒ Nearby : ⛴ ♪	**GPS** Longitude : 4.62507 Latitude : 47.24935

VARZY

58210 – Michelin map **319** D7 – pop. 1 329 – alt. 249
▶ Paris 224 – La Charité-sur-Loire 37 – Clamecy 17 – Cosne-sur-Loire 43

⚠ Municipal du Moulin Naudin

𝒫 03 86 29 43 12. mairievarzy@wanadoo.fr ✄

Address : route de Corvol (located 1.5km north along the D 977)

Opening times : from mid May to end Sept.

3 ha (50 pitches) flat

Tariff : (2014 Price) 12€ ✝✝ ⇌ 🔲 (½) (5A) – Extra per person 2.90€

Situated near a small lake.

Surroundings : ⌁ ♀ Leisure activities : ⸞ Facilities : ⤶ᵴ ⟲ ♨ ➣ 🖼 Nearby : ✗ ⤓	**G P S** Longitude : 3.38312 Latitude : 47.3722

VENAREY-LES-LAUMES

21150 – Michelin map **320** G4 – pop. 2 981 – alt. 235
▶ Paris 259 – Avallon 54 – Dijon 66 – Montbard 15

⚠ Municipal Alésia

𝒫 03 80 96 07 76. www.venareyleslaumes.fr

Address : rue du Dct Roux (take the western exit along the D 954, follow the signs for Semur-en-Auxois and take a right turn before the bridge; beside the Brenne and near a small lake)

Opening times : from beginning April to mid Oct.

1.5 ha (67 pitches) flat, grassy

Tariff : 15.70€ ✝✝ ⇌ 🔲 (½) (16A) – Extra per person 3.50€ – Reservation fee 5€

Rental rates : Permanent ᵴ (1 chalet) – 5 🏠 – 1 ⛺. Per night from 50 to 70€ – Per week from 300 to 400€ – Reservation fee 5€

🚐 borne 3€ – 10 🔲 11.70€ – ⬤ (½)11.70€

Surroundings : ⌁ ♀ Leisure activities : ⸞ ⛹ ⸞ Facilities : ⤶ᵴ ⟲ ♨ ➣ ➣ ♨ 🖼 Nearby : ✗ ⤓ (beach)	**G P S** Longitude : 4.45151 Latitude : 47.54425

VERMENTON

89270 – Michelin map **319** F6 – pop. 1 183 – alt. 125
▶ Paris 190 – Auxerre 24 – Avallon 28 – Vézelay 28

🏔 Municipal les Coullemières

𝒫 03 86 81 53 02. www.camping-vermenton.com

Address : Les Coullemières (to the southwest of the town, behind the station)

Opening times : from beginning April to end Sept.

1 ha (53 pitches) flat, grassy

Tariff : (2014 Price) 16€ ✝✝ ⇌ 🔲 (½) (6A) – Extra per person 3.50€

Rental rates : (2014 Price) Permanent ᵴ (1) ✄ (from beginning July to end Aug.) – 6 🚐. Per night from 64 to 75€ – Per week from 370 to 485€

🚐 3 🔲 16€

A pleasant setting near a wide stretch of the Cure river.

Surroundings : ♀♀ ⚠ Leisure activities : ⸞ ⛹ ⸞ 🚲 ✗ Facilities : ᵴ ⟲ (season) ♨ ♨ 🖼 Nearby : ⛟ ⤓ (beach) sports trail	**G P S** Longitude : 3.73123 Latitude : 47.65843

VIGNOLES

21200 – Michelin map **320** J7 – pop. 810 – alt. 202
▶ Paris 317 – Dijon 40 – Chalon-sur-Saône 34 – Le Creusot 51

⚠ Les Bouleaux

𝒫 03 80 22 26 88. camping-les-bouleaux@hotmail.fr

Address : 11 rue Jaune (located at Chevignerot ; beside a stream)

Opening times : Permanent

1.6 ha (46 pitches) flat, grassy

Tariff : (2014 Price) ✝ 4.10€ ⇌ 2.20€ 🔲 3.70€ – (½) (6A) 3.90€

Surroundings : ⌁ ♀♀ Leisure activities : ⸞ Facilities : ᵴ ⟲ ➣ ➣ ♨ ♨ 🖼 Nearby : ▨ ⛏	**G P S** Longitude : 4.88298 Latitude : 47.02668

There are several different types of sani-station ('borne' in French) – sanitation points providing fresh water and disposal points for grey water. See page 12 for further details.

VINCELLES

89290 – Michelin map **319** E5 – pop. 841 – alt. 110
▶ Paris 180 – Auxerre 14 – Avallon 38 – Clamecy 39

🏔 Les Ceriselles ♟♟

𝒫 03 86 42 50 47. www.campingceriselles.com

Address : route de Vincelottes (north of the village, along the D 38)

1,5 ha (80 pitches) flat, grassy

Rentals : ᵴ (1 chalet) – 16 🚐 – 2 🏠.

Beside the Nivernais canal and 150m from the Yonne river.

Surroundings : ⸞ ♀ Leisure activities : ♟ ✗ ⸞ ⛹ ⛹ 🚲 ▨ (open air in season) ✗ Facilities : ᵴ ⟲ ♨ ➣ ➣ ➣ launderette ⤓ Nearby : ▨ ✗ ⚓ ⛏	**G P S** Longitude : 3.63536 Latitude : 47.70705

Ph. Body / hemis.fr

Sleeping Beauty is said to slumber still within the thick stone walls of one of the Loire's fairy-tale castles. Does she await that kiss in Chambord, Azay-le-Rideau, Chenonceau, or perhaps one of the many other wonderful châteaux that lie in wait for you? To list all the Centre's architectural wonders set in the most glorious of gardens would take far too long, but visitors can appreciate some of the Loire's treasures during a season of spectacular *son et lumière* (sound and light) shows. The landscape of the region has inspired a host of writers, from Pierre de Ronsard, the 16th-century 'Prince of Poets', to Balzac and Georges Sand. All succumbed to the charm and beauty of this valley of kings, with its untamed river and atmospheric woodlands. In order to savour the region's twin talents for storytelling and culinary arts to the full, enjoy a plate of delicious chicken stew before settling down to listen to your host's tales of werewolves and other local legends!

Legend:

- Locality with campsite
- Locality with campsite and rental option
- Vannes — Locality with campsite and campervan area
- Moyaux — Locality with at least one pleasant campsite
- Motorway service area for campervans

AUBIGNY-SUR-NÈRE

18700 – Michelin map **323** K2 – pop. 5 879 – alt. 180
▶ Paris 180 – Bourges 48 – Cosne-sur-Loire 41 – Gien 30

⚑ Flower Les Étangs

℘ 02 48 58 02 37. www.camping-aubigny.com

Address : route de Oizon (1.4km east along the D 923, near a lake (direct access)

Opening times : from beginning April to end Sept.

3 ha (100 pitches) flat, grassy

Tariff : 24€ ★★ ⬌ 🗐 🗗 (10A) – Extra per person 5€ – Reservation fee 10€

Rental rates : Permanent – 1 caravan – 8 🛖 – 6 🏠 – 2 canvas bungalows. Per night from 30 to 107€ – Per week from 150 to 749€ Reservation fee 15€

The pitches are well shaded, some are situated on the lake shore.

Surroundings : ⌂ ♀♀	**G**	Longitude : 2.46101
Leisure activities : 🖼 🛶 🎣	**P**	Latitude : 47.48574
Facilities : ♿ ⚏ ⚐ 🛁 🍴 launderette ⚒	**S**	
Nearby : 🍴 🖼 🎣		

AZAY-LE-RIDEAU

37190 – Michelin map **317** L5 – pop. 3 418 – alt. 51
▶ Paris 265 – Châtellerault 61 – Chinon 21 – Loches 58

⛺ Municipal le Sabot

℘ 02 47 45 42 72. www.azaylerideau.fr

Address : rue du Stade (take the eastern exit along the D 84, follow the signs for Artannes and take turning to the right)

Opening times : from beginning April to end Oct.

6 ha (256 pitches) flat, grassy

Tariff : (2014 Price) 11.50€ ★★ ⬌ 🗐 🗗 (8A) – Extra per person 3.10€ 🛒 borne 3€ – 196 🗐 11.50€ – 🔌15.39€

Pleasant location close to the château and beside the Indre river.

Surroundings : ⚘ ♀	**G**	Longitude : 0.46963
Leisure activities : 🖼 🛶 🚲 🎣	**P**	Latitude : 47.25863
Facilities : ♿ ⚏ ⚐ 🍴 launderette	**S**	
Nearby : 🍴 🔫 🎣		

BALLAN-MIRÉ

37510 – Michelin map **317** M4 – pop. 8 152 – alt. 88
▶ Paris 251 – Azay-le-Rideau 17 – Langeais 20 – Montbazon 13

⚑ Club Airotel la Mignardière

℘ 02 47 73 31 00. www.mignardiere.com

Address : 22 avenue des Aubépines (2.5km northeast of the town, not far from the small lake at Joué-Ballan)

Opening times : from beginning April to mid Sept.

2.5 ha (177 pitches) flat, grassy, small adjacent wood

Tariff : 29.60€ ★★ ⬌ 🗐 🗗 (10A) – Extra per person 6€

Rental rates : (from beginning April to mid Sept.) – 4 caravans – 19 🛖 – 20 🏠. Per night 77€ – Per week from 273 to 749€ Reservation fee 15€

🛒 borne 4€

Surroundings : ⌂ ♀	**G**	Longitude : 0.63402
Leisure activities : 🏊 🛶 🚲 🔫 🖼 🎣	**P**	Latitude : 47.35524
Facilities : ♿ ⚏ ▥ ⚐ 🛁 🍴 🖼 ⚒	**S**	
Nearby : 🍴 🔫 🎣 🐎		

BARAIZE

36270 – Michelin map **323** F8 – pop. 313 – alt. 240
▶ Paris 318 – Orléans 192 – Châteauroux 47 – Guéret 86

⛺ Municipal Montcocu

℘ 02 54 25 34 28. syndicat.laceguzon@wanadoo.fr – for caravans – from the 'Montcocu' locality, 12% gradient for 1km

Address : Montcocu (4.8km southeast along the D 913, follow the signs for Éguzon and take D 72, take left turn for Pont-de-Piles)

Opening times : from beginning June to end Sept.

1 ha (26 pitches)

Tariff : (2014 Price) 10.80€ ★★ ⬌ 🗐 🗗 (8A) – Extra per person 2.45€

Rental rates : (2014 Price) (from beginning May to end Oct.) – 4 🏠 – 5 canvas bungalows. Per night 11€ – Per week from 140 to 437€

In a pleasant location and setting in the Creuse valley.

Surroundings : ⚘ ⌂ ♀ ⚑	**G**	Longitude : 1.60023
Leisure activities : 🍴 🖼 🛶 🔫 🎣	**P**	Latitude : 46.47159
Facilities : ♿ ⚏ ⚐ 🛁 🍴	**S**	

The pitches of many campsites are marked out with low hedges of attractive bushes and shrubs.

LA BAZOCHE-GOUET

28330 – Michelin map **311** B7 – pop. 1 314 – alt. 185
▶ Paris 146 – Brou 18 – Chartres 61 – Châteaudun 33

⛺ Municipal la Rivière

℘ 02 37 49 36 49. commune-bazoche-gouet-28330@wanadoo.fr

Address : located 1.5km southwest along the D 927, follow the signs for la Chapelle-Guillaume and take road to the left

Opening times : from end April to end Sept.

1.8 ha (30 pitches) flat, grassy

Tariff : (2014 Price) ★ 5.22€ ⬌ – 🗐 (10A) 3.82€

Rental rates : (2014 Price) Permanent – 1 🛖. Per night from 52€ – Per week from 205 to 263€

Beside the Yerre river and close to some lakes.

Leisure activities : 🛶 🚲 🎣	**G**	Longitude : 0.9689
Facilities : ♿ ⚐ 🛁	**P**	Latitude : 48.129
Nearby : 🍴	**S**	

BEAULIEU-SUR-LOIRE

45630 – Michelin map **318** N6 – pop. 1 779 – alt. 156
▶ Paris 170 – Aubigny-sur-Nère 36 – Briare 15 – Gien 27

⛺ Municipal Touristique du Canal

℘ 02 38 35 32 16. www.beaulieu-sur-loire.fr

Address : route de Bonny-sur-Loire (take the eastern exit along the D 926, near the canal)

Opening times : from beginning April to beginning Nov.

0.6 ha (37 pitches) flat, grassy

Tariff : (2014 Price) ★ 2.70€ ⬌ 🗐 1.50€ – 🗗 (10A) 3.30€

Surroundings : ⌂ ♀	**G**	Longitude : 2.8176
Facilities : ♿ 🛁 ⚒	**P**	Latitude : 47.5435
Nearby : 🍴 🎣 ⚓	**S**	

BESSAIS-LE-FROMENTAL

18210 – Michelin map **323** M6 – pop. 313 – alt. 210
▶ Paris 300 – Orléans 172 – Bourges 51 – Moulins 66

⚲ Le Village de Goule

𝒫 02 48 60 82 66. www.levillagedegoule.com

Address : 1 route de Goule (4.7km southeast along the D 110 and D 110E)

Opening times : from end April to end Sept.

120 ha/2 for camping (75 pitches) flat, grassy

Tariff : (2014 Price) 18.50€ ♣★ ⊕ 🗉 🖾 (10A) –
Extra per person 3.70€ – Reservation fee 10€

Rental rates : (2014 Price) Permanent ⅛ (1 chalet) – 15 🏠 –
1 yurt – 5 tipis – 5 canvas bungalows. Per week from 200 to 595€
Reservation fee 10€

🚐 borne 2€

In a leafy, green setting beside a lake, with various rental options.

Surroundings : 🏞 🗁 ♉♉ ⚘
Leisure activities : ✗ 🏖 🎣 ⚐ 🐎 𝄞
pedalos 🚣
Facilities : ⅍ ⊙ 🖾 ✨ launderette

GPS Longitude : 2.79853
Latitude : 46.73515

BONNEVAL

28800 – Michelin map **311** E6 – pop. 4 565 – alt. 128
▶ Paris 117 – Ablis 61 – Chartres 31 – Châteaudun 14

⚲ Le Bois Chièvre

𝒫 02 37 47 54 01. www.campingduboisdechievre.fr

Address : route de Vouvray (located 1.5km south following signs for Conie and take turning to the right; beside the Loir)

Opening times : from beginning April to mid Oct.

4.5 ha/2.5 for camping (104 pitches) relatively flat, flat, grassy, gravelled, adjacent wood

Tariff : 18€ ♣★ ⊕ 🗉 🖾 (10A) – Extra per person 5€

Rental rates : (from beginning April to mid Oct.) – 3 🚍 –
1 studio. Per night from 60 to 82€ – Per week from 320 to 430€

🚐 borne – 20 🗉 18€

The site is set among oak trees beside the Loir river.

Surroundings : 🏞 🗁 ♨
Leisure activities : 🏖 🎣 🎣 🐎
Facilities : ⅍ ⊙ 🎋 ⚘ ✨ 🍴 🚿 🛁
Nearby : 🍴 🖾

GPS Longitude : 1.3864
Latitude : 48.1708

BOURGES

18000 – Michelin map **323** K4 – pop. 66 786 – alt. 153
▶ Paris 244 – Châteauroux 65 – Dijon 254 – Nevers 69

⚱ Municipal Robinson

𝒫 02 48 20 16 85. www.ville.bourges.fr

Address : 26 boulevard de l'Industrie (head towards the southern exit along the N 144. follow the signs for Montluçon and take the turning to the left, near the Lac d'Auron, take exit A 71 and follow the signs for Bourges Centre)

Opening times : from mid March to mid Nov.

2.2 ha (107 pitches)

Tariff : 22€ ♣★ ⊕ 🗉 🖾 (16A) – Extra per person 4.40€

🚐 borne

Not far from the town centre (1.2km), in a green setting, but choose the pitches away from the road.

Surroundings : 🗁 ♉♉
Leisure activities : 🏄
Facilities : ⅍ ⊙ 🖾 🎋 ⚘ 🛁 🚿 🍴 launderette
Nearby : 🍴 🖾 🏊

GPS Longitude : 2.39488
Latitude : 47.07232

BOURGUEIL

37140 – Michelin map **317** J5 – pop. 3 924 – alt. 42
▶ Paris 281 – Angers 81 – Chinon 16 – Saumur 23

⚱ Municipal Parc Capitaine

𝒫 02 47 97 85 62. www.bourgueil.fr

Address : 31 avenue du Général de Gaulle (1.5 km south along the D 749, follow the signs for Chinon)

Opening times : from mid May to mid Sept.

2 ha (87 pitches) flat, grassy

Tariff : (2014 Price) ♣ 2.25€ ⊕ 🗉 6.65€ – 🖾 (12A) 2.50€

🚐 borne 11.15€

In a green setting with plenty of shade near a lake.

Surroundings : 🗁 ♀
Leisure activities : 🎣 🐎
Facilities : ⅍ ⊙ 🍴 🖾
Nearby : 🛒 🍷 🏄 ✗ 🖾 🏊 🏄 🛶 pedalos

GPS Longitude : 0.16684
Latitude : 47.27381

The Michelin classification (⚲⚲⚲... ⚱) is totally independent of the official star classification system awarded by the local prefecture or other official organisation.

BRACIEUX

41250 – Michelin map **318** G6 – pop. 1 256 – alt. 70
▶ Paris 185 – Blois 19 – Montrichard 39 – Orléans 64

⚲ Indigo Les Châteaux

Camping Indigo ©R.Etienne

𝒫 02 54 46 41 84. www.camping-indigo.com

Address : 11 rue Roger-Brun (take the northern exit, follow the signs for Blois; beside the Beuvron)

Opening times : from beginning April to beginning Nov.

8 ha (350 pitches) flat, grassy

Tariff : (2014 Price) 30€ ♣★ ⊕ 🗉 🖾 (10A) – Extra per person 6.30€ –

Reservation fee 22€

Rental rates :(2014 Price) (from beginning April to beginning Nov.) ⅛ (1 chalet) – 6 caravans – 20 🚍 – 10 🏠 – 26 tent lodges. Per night from 40 to 107€ – Per week from 224 to 712€ – Reservation fee 22€

🚐 borne 7€ – 40 🗉 24.70€

In a wooded setting with a variety of tree species.

Surroundings : 🏞 ♉♉
Leisure activities : 🏖 🎣 ✗ 🛶
Facilities : ⅍ ⊙ 🍴 launderette

GPS Longitude : 1.53821
Latitude : 47.55117

BRIARE

45250 – Michelin map **318** N6 – pop. 5 688 – alt. 135
▶ Paris 160 – Orléans 85 – Gien 11 – Montargis 50

⚠ Onlycamp Le Martinet

📞 02 38 31 24 50. www.campinglemartinet.fr

Address : Val Martinet (located 1km north via town centre, between the Loire river and the canal)

Opening times : from beginning April to end Sept.

4.5 ha (160 pitches) flat, grassy

Tariff : (2014 Price) 18.60€ ✦✦ ⬠ 🔲 (10A) – Extra per person 4€
⛲ borne 3€

Surroundings : 🌳 ♨
Leisure activities : 🎣
Facilities : ⚂ ⚆ 🗄 ⚘ ⚟ ⚘ 🖥
Nearby : ⚓ ⚓

GPS Longitude : 2.72441
Latitude : 47.64226

BUZANÇAIS

36500 – Michelin map **323** E5 – pop. 4 501 – alt. 111
▶ Paris 286 – Le Blanc 47 – Châteauroux 25 – Châtellerault 78

⛰ La Tête Noire

📞 02 54 84 17 27. www.camping-latetenoire.com

Address : to the northwest along the r. des Ponts; beside the Indre river, near the stadium

Opening times : from mid April to end Oct.

2.5 ha (100 pitches) flat, grassy

Tariff : (2014 Price) ✦ 3.65€ ⬠ 🔲 3.65€ – (16A) 3.65€
Rental rates : (from mid April to end Oct.) – 4 🚐 – 2 yurts – Finnish kota. Per night from 36 to 52€ – Per week from 195 to 295€
⛲ borne 4€ – (¶)11€

Surroundings : 🌳 ♨
Leisure activities : 🎪 ♨ 🏊
Facilities : ⚂ ⚆ 🍳 ⚟ 🖥
Nearby : ⚓ ⚔ ⚓

GPS Longitude : 1.41805
Latitude : 46.89285

CANDÉ-SUR-BEUVRON

41120 – Michelin map **318** E7 – pop. 1 462 – alt. 70
▶ Paris 199 – Blois 15 – Chaumont-sur-Loire 7 – Montrichard 21

⛰ Kawan Village La Grande Tortue

📞 02 54 44 15 20. www.la-grande-tortue.com

Address : 3 route de Pontlevoy (500m south along the D 751, follow the signs for Chaumont-sur-Loire and take the turning to the left, follow the signs for La Pieuse, not far from the Beuvron river)

Opening times : from beginning April to end Sept.

5 ha (208 pitches) flat and relatively flat, grassy, sandy

Tariff : 44€ ✦✦ ⬠ 🔲 (16A) – Extra per person 10.50€ – Reservation fee 12€
Rental rates : (from beginning April to end Sept.) – 36 🚐 – 7 🏠. Per night from 290 to 872€ – Per week from 556 to 930€ Reservation fee 12€
⛲ borne

Surroundings : 🌳 ♨
Leisure activities : ♟ ✗ 🎪 ♨ 🔲 (open air in season)
Facilities : ⚂ ⚆ 🍳 ⚟ 🖥 ⚓

GPS Longitude : 1.2583
Latitude : 47.48992

CHAILLAC

36310 – Michelin map **323** D8 – pop. 1 136 – alt. 180
▶ Paris 333 – Argenton-sur-Creuse 35 – Le Blanc 34 – Magnac-Laval 34

⚠ Municipal les Vieux Chênes

📞 02 54 25 61 39. www.chaillac36.fr

Address : allée des Vieux Chênes (southwest of the town, 500m from a lake)

2 ha (40 pitches)

Rentals : 3 🏠.

A green, well-kept site with flowers, close to the stadium and beside a lake.

Surroundings : 🌳 ♨
Leisure activities : ♨ 🏊 fitness trail
Facilities : ⚆ 🗄 🍳
Nearby : ✗ ⚔ pedalos

GPS Longitude : 1.29539
Latitude : 46.43224

*We value your opinion and welcome your feedback.
Do email us at campingfrance@tp.michelin.com*

CHARTRES

28000 – Michelin map **311** E5 – pop. 39 122 – alt. 142
▶ Paris 92 – Orléans 84 – Dreux 38 – Rambouillet 45

⚠ Les Bords de l'Eure

📞 02 37 28 79 43. www.auxbordsdeleure.com

Address : 9 rue de Launay

4 ha (110 pitches) flat, grassy

Rentals : 2 caravans – 1 🚐.

In a pleasant wooded setting near the river.

Surroundings : ♨
Leisure activities : 🎪 ♨ 🎣 pedalos
Facilities : ⚂ ⚆ 🗄 🍳 ⚟ 🖥
Nearby : ✗ ⚓ sports trail

GPS Longitude : 1.4951
Latitude : 48.43265

CHÂTEAUMEILLANT

18370 – Michelin map **323** J7 – pop. 2 082 – alt. 247
▶ Paris 313 – Aubusson 79 – Bourges 66 – La Châtre 19

⛰ Municipal l'Étang Merlin

📞 02 48 61 31 38. http://ot.chateaumeillant.free.fr

Address : route de Vicq (located 1km northwest along the D 70, follow the signs for Beddes and take D 80 to the left)

Opening times : from beginning May to end Sept.

1.5 ha (30 pitches) flat, grassy

Tariff : (2014 Price) ✦ 2.90€ ⬠ 🔲 3.40€ – (5A) 2.30€
Rental rates : (2014 Price) Permanent ⚂ ✗ – 2 🚐 – 6 🏠 – 10 🏡 – 1 gîte. Per night from 27 to 49€ – Per week from 157 to 293€

The chalets are in a pleasant site beside the lake.

Surroundings : ♨ ♨
Leisure activities : 🎪 ♨ 🚲 🎣
Facilities : ⚂ ⚆ 🍳 ⚟ 🖥
Nearby : ✗ ⚓

GPS Longitude : 2.19034
Latitude : 46.56818

CHÂTEAUROUX

36000 – Michelin map **323** G6 – pop. 46 386 – alt. 155
▶ Paris 265 – Blois 101 – Bourges 65 – Châtellerault 98

⚠ Aquadis Loisirs Le Rochat Belle-Isle

✆ 02 54 08 96 29. www.aquadis-loisirs.com

Address : 17 avenue du Parc de Loisirs (continue north along the av. de Paris and take turning to the left; beside the Indre river and 100m from a small lake)

Opening times : from beginning April to end Oct.

4 ha (205 pitches) flat, grassy

Tariff : 19.30€ ★★ ⇔ 🔳 🚿 (10A) – Extra per person 4.30€ – Reservation fee 9.90€

Rental rates : (from beginning April to end Oct.) – 6 🚐. Per night from 68€ – Per week from 178 to 525€ – Reservation fee 19.90€

🚰 borne 5€ – 10 🔳 15.90€ – 🚐 11€

There's a free bus service nearby to the town centre.

Surroundings : 🗒 🌳🌳
Leisure activities : 🛶🚣 🏇
Facilities : 🚿 🔛 🖭 🚗 🚿 🏐 launderette
Nearby : 🏕 🍴 🗙 🛶 🚣 🏊 🏄 🎣 bowling, fitness trail

G P S Longitude : 1.69472
Latitude : 46.8236

CHÂTILLON-COLIGNY

45230 – Michelin map **318** O5 – pop. 1 962 – alt. 130
▶ Paris 140 – Auxerre 70 – Gien 26 – Joigny 48

⚠ Municipal de la Lancière

✆ 06 16 09 30 26. lalanciere@wanadoo.fr – limited spaces for one-night stay

Address : route de la Lancière (south of the town, between the Loing river and the Briare canal)

1.9 ha (55 pitches) flat, grassy

Surroundings : 🗒 🌳🌳
Leisure activities : 🚣 🛶 (small swimming pool)
Facilities : 🚿 launderette, refrigerated food storage facilities
Nearby : ⚓

G P S Longitude : 2.84394
Latitude : 47.81816

CHAUMONT-SUR-LOIRE

41150 – Michelin map **318** E7 – pop. 1 037 – alt. 69
▶ Paris 201 – Amboise 21 – Blois 18 – Contres 24

⚠ Municipal Grosse Grève

✆ 02 54 20 95 22. www.chaumont-sur-loire.fr – 🅿

Address : 81 rue de Marue de Lattre-de-Tassigny (take the eastern exit along the D 751, follow the signs for Blois and take the turning to the left, before the bridge; beside the Loire river)

Opening times : from end April to end Sept.

4 ha (150 pitches)

Tariff : ★ 3.10€ ⇔ 1€ 🔳 2.10€ – 🚿 (10A) 2.10€

🚰 borne 2€

Leisure activities : 🚣 🎣
Facilities : 🚿 🔛 🚗 🏐 launderette
Nearby : 🚲

G P S Longitude : 1.1999
Latitude : 47.48579

CHÉMERY

41700 – Michelin map **318** F7 – pop. 940 – alt. 90
▶ Paris 213 – Blois 32 – Montrichard 29 – Romorantin-Lanthenay 29

⚠ Municipal le Gué

✆ 02 54 32 97 40. www.camping-le-gue.com – 🅿

Address : route de Couddes (to the west of the village; beside a stream)

Opening times : from beginning April to end Oct.

1.2 ha (50 pitches) flat, grassy

Tariff : 14.80€ ★★ ⇔ 🔳 🚿 (10A) – Extra per person 2.50€

Rental rates : (from mid March to mid Dec.) 🚫 – 2 🚐. Per week from 365 to 599€

🚰 borne 3.50€ – 🚐 11€

Surroundings : 🏖 ♨
Leisure activities : 🚣
Facilities : 🚿 🚗 🖭 🏐 🖭
Nearby : 🎣

G P S Longitude : 1.47388
Latitude : 47.34562

CHEMILLÉ-SUR-INDROIS

37460 – Michelin map **317** P6 – pop. 221 – alt. 97
▶ Paris 244 – Châtillon-sur-Indre 25 – Loches 16 – Montrichard 27

⚠ Les Coteaux du Lac

✆ 02 47 92 77 83. www.lescoteauxdulac.com

Address : at the leisure centre (to the southwest of the town)

Opening times : from end March to beginning Oct.

1 ha (72 pitches)

Tariff : 27.40€ ★★ ⇔ 🔳 🚿 (16A) – Extra per person 6.10€ – Reservation fee 14€

Rental rates : (from end March to beginning Oct.) – 29 🚐 – 4 tent lodges. Per night from 28 to 92€ – Per week from 195 to 644€ Reservation fee 14€

🚰 borne – 4 🔳 12€ – 🚐 12€

In an attractive location near a lake.

Surroundings : ⚘
Facilities : 🚿 🏐
Nearby : 🍴 🗙 🚣 🚵 🏄 🏊 🎣 🎣 pedalos

G P S Longitude : 1.15889
Latitude : 47.15772

CHEVERNY

41700 – Michelin map **318** F7 – pop. 939 – alt. 110
▶ Paris 194 – Blois 14 – Châteauroux 88 – Orléans 73

⚠ Sites et Paysages Les Saules 🔼

Les Saules

✆ 02 54 79 90 01. www.camping-cheverny.com

Address : route de Contres (3km southeast along the D 102)

Opening times : from beginning April to mid Sept.

8 ha (164 pitches) flat, grassy

Tariff : 35.50€ ★★ ⇔ 🔳 🚿 (10A) – Extra per person 4.50€

Rental rates : (from beginning April to mid Sept.) 🛠 (1 chalet) 🚫 – 11 🚐 – 4 tent lodges. Per night from 40 to 75€ – Per week from 280 to 700€

🚰 borne – 🚐 14€

Surroundings : 🌳🌳
Leisure activities : 🍴 🗙 🎱 🚵 🚣 🚴 🏄 🎣 sports trail
Facilities : 🛠 🚿 🚗 🏐 launderette 🖭 🖭

G P S Longitude : 1.45184
Latitude : 47.47871

CHINON

37500 – Michelin map **317** K6 – pop. 7 986 – alt. 40
▶ Paris 285 – Châtellerault 51 – Poitiers 80 – Saumur 29

⛰ Intercommunal de l'Île Auger

📞 02 47 93 08 35. www.camping-chinon.com – 🏧

Address : quai Danton

Opening times : from beginning April to end Oct.

4.5 ha (277 pitches) flat, grassy

Tariff : (2014 Price) 13.50€ ✚✚ 🚐 🗐 (≱) (12A) – Extra per person 3€
Rental rates : (2014 Price) (from beginning May to end Sept.) –
4 canvas bungalows. Per night from 37 to 47€ – Per week
from 222 to 282€
🚐 50 🗐 10.20€ – 🐷 (≱)9€

*In a pleasant location opposite the château and beside the
Vienne river.*

Surroundings : ≼ town and Château de Chinon ♀ Leisure activities : 🛥 🎣 Facilities : 🚿 ☕ (summer) 👣 🍴 🗄 Nearby : ✕ 🏖 🛶	**GPS** Longitude : 0.23654 Latitude : 47.16379

CLOYES-SUR-LE-LOIR

28220 – Michelin map **311** D8 – pop. 2 692 – alt. 97
▶ Paris 143 – Blois 54 – Chartres 57 – Châteaudun 13

⛰ Parc de Loisirs - Le Val Fleuri

📞 02 37 98 50 53. www.val-fleuri.fr – limited spaces for one-night stay

Address : route de Montigny (take the northern exit along the N 10,
follow the signs for Chartres then turn left onto D 23)

5 ha (196 pitches) flat, grassy
Rentals : 10 🛖

In a pleasant location beside the Loir river.

Surroundings : 🏞 ♀ Leisure activities : 🍴 ✕ 🏛 🛥 🚴 🛶 🛶 🎣 pedalos ⛳ Facilities : 🚿 ☕ 🗄 🍴 launderette 🗄 Nearby : ✕ ♨	**GPS** Longitude : 1.2333 Latitude : 48.0024

COURVILLE-SUR-EURE

28190 – Michelin map **311** D5 – pop. 2 776 – alt. 170
▶ Paris 111 – Bonneval 47 – Chartres 20 – Dreux 37

⛰ Municipal les Bords de l'Eure

📞 02 37 23 76 38. www.courville-sur-eure.fr

Address : rue Thiers (take the southern exit along the D 114)

1.5 ha (56 pitches) flat, grassy
🚐 borne – 12 🗐

In a wooded setting on the banks of the river.

Surroundings : 🏞 ♀ Leisure activities : 🎣 Facilities : 🚿 ☕ 🗄 Nearby : 🛥	**GPS** Longitude : 1.2414 Latitude : 48.4462

*The guide covers all 22 regions of France – see the map
and list of regions on pages 4–5.*

DESCARTES

37160 – Michelin map **317** N7 – pop. 3 817 – alt. 50
▶ Paris 292 – Châteauroux 94 – Châtellerault 24 – Chinon 51

⛰ Municipal la Grosse Motte

📞 02 47 59 85 90. www.ville-descartes.fr

Address : allée Léo Lagrange (take the southern exit along the D 750,
follow the signs for Le Blanc and take boulevard to the right; beside
the Creuse river)

Opening times : from beginning May to end Sept.

1 ha (50 pitches)

Tariff : (2014 Price) 9.20€ ✚✚ 🚐 🗐 (≱) (5A) – Extra per person 2.40€
Rental rates : (2014 Price) Permanent ⛺ – 8 🏠. Per week
from 250 to 390€
🚐 5 🗐 9.20€

*In a shady park next to a leisure centre and the municipal
gardens.*

Surroundings : 🏞 🚐 ♀♀ Leisure activities : 🎣 Facilities : 👣 🍴 Nearby : 🛥 ✕ 🏇 🛶 🛥	**GPS** Longitude : 0.69715 Latitude : 46.96961

ÉGUZON

36270 – Michelin map **323** F8 – pop. 1 362 – alt. 243
▶ Paris 319 – Argenton-sur-Creuse 20 – La Châtre 47 – Guéret 50

⛰ Municipal du Lac Les Nugiras

📞 02 54 47 45 22. www.campingmunicipal-eguzon.com

Address : route de Messant (3km southeast along the D 3, follow the
signs for the Lac de Chambon then continue 500m along the turning
to the right; 450m from the lake)

Opening times : Permanent

4 ha (180 pitches)

Tariff : (2014 Price) 13€ ✚✚ 🚐 🗐 (≱) (10A) – Extra per person 3.42€
Rental rates : (2014 Price) (from beginning March to end Nov.)
⛺ – 7 🏠 – 5 canvas bungalows. Per night from 34 to 131€ –
Per week from 151 to 474€
🚐 borne 5.20€

*A peaceful site laid out on terraces, near a well-equipped
boating centre.*

Surroundings : ≼ ♀ Leisure activities : 🍴 🏛 🛥 multi-sports ground Facilities : 🚿 ☕ 🗄 🍴 🗄 Nearby : 🚴 🛳 (beach) 🛶 🎣 ♨ water skiing	**GPS** Longitude : 1.604 Latitude : 46.433

FONTAINE-SIMON

28240 – Michelin map **311** C4 – pop. 870 – alt. 200
▶ Paris 117 – Chartres 40 – Dreux 40 – Évreux 66

⛰ Du Perche

📞 02 37 81 88 11. www.campingduperche.com

Address : rue de la Ferrière (1.2km north following signs for
Senonches and take turning to the left)

Opening times : Permanent

5 ha (115 pitches) flat, grassy

Tariff : (2014 Price) 30€ ✚✚ 🚐 🗐 (≱) (6A) – Extra per person 4€

Rental rates : (2014 Price) Permanent ⚷ – 2 ⬛ – 2 🏠.
Per week from 340 to 900€
🚐 borne – 7 ▣
Situated beside the Eure river and a lake.

Leisure activities : 🏊‍♂️ 🎣
Facilities : & ⚷ (July–Aug.) 🍴 🏧
Nearby : ✕ 🖼 🛶 ⛵

GPS Longitude : 1.0194
Latitude : 48.5132

GARGILESSE-DAMPIERRE

36190 – Michelin map **323** F7 – pop. 326 – alt. 220
▶ Paris 310 – Châteauroux 45 – Guéret 59 – Poitiers 113

⚠ La Chaumerette

✆ 02 54 47 84 22. www.gargilesse.fr

Address : Le Moulin (1.4km southwest along the D 39, follow the
signs for Argenton-sur-Creuse and take the road to the left leading to
the Barrage de La Roche au Moine (dam)

Opening times : from beginning May to end Sept.

2.6 ha (72 pitches) flat, grassy

Tariff : (2014 Price) 🚶 1.85€ 🚗 ▣ 6.40€ – 🔌 (10A) 4.65€
Rental rates : (2014 Price) (from beginning March to end Nov.) –
8 🏠. Per night from 26 to 42€ – Per week from 175 to 294€
In a picturesque setting, part of the site is on an island in the
Creuse river.

Surroundings : 🏞 ♨♨
Leisure activities : 🍷 ✕ 🎣
Facilities : & ⚷ 🍴

GPS Longitude : 1.58346
Latitude : 46.5077

GIEN

45500 – Michelin map **318** M5 – pop. 15 161 – alt. 162
▶ Paris 149 – Auxerre 85 – Bourges 77 – Cosne-sur-Loire 46

⚠⚠ Kawan Village Les Bois du Bardelet 👥

✆ 02 38 67 47 39. www.bardelet.com

Address : Le Petit Bardelet, route de Bourges (5km southwest along
the D 940 and 2km along the turning to the left – recommended
route for vehicles coming from Gien, take the D 53, follow the signs
for Poilly-lez-Gien and take first turning to the right)

Opening times : from mid April to end Sept.

15 ha/8 for camping (260 pitches)

Tariff : 29€ 🚶🚶 🚗 ▣ 🔌 (10A) – Extra per person 7.40€ – Reservation
fee 9€
Rental rates : (from mid April to end Sept.) Ⓟ – 33 ⬛ – 45 🏠.
Per night from 50 to 156€ – Per week from 350 to 1,092€ –
Reservation fee 9€
🚐 borne – 25 ▣ 27€ – 💧 🔌12€

Surroundings : 🏞 ♨♨
Leisure activities : 🍷 ✕ 🏊‍♀️ 🎏 ⛵ jacuzzi

Facilities : & ⚷ 🔒🛏 🍽 – 4 individual
sanitary facilities (🍽 🚿 wc) 🍴 🍴
launderette 🧺 🚿

GPS Longitude : 2.61619
Latitude : 47.64116

In order for the guide to remain wholly objective,
the selection of campsites is made on an entirely
independent basis.

LA GUERCHE-SUR-L'AUBOIS

18150 – Michelin map **323** N5 – pop. 3 395 – alt. 184
▶ Paris 242 – Bourges 48 – La Charité-sur-Loire 31 – Nevers 22

⚠ Municipal le Robinson

✆ 02 48 74 18 86. www.camping-robinson-la-guerche-sur-aubois.fr

Address : 2 rue de Couvache (1.4km southeast along the D 200,
follow the signs for Apremont then take a right turn, 600m along the
D 218 and take road to the left)

Opening times : Permanent

1.5 ha (33 pitches)

Tariff : 15€ 🚶🚶 🚗 ▣ 🔌 (16A) – Extra per person 2.50€
Rental rates : Permanent – 6 🏠. Per night from 50 to 62€ –
Per week from 320 to 417€
🚐 borne 12€ – 💧 🔌10€
A pleasant location beside a small lake with very old chalets,
some adjacent to each other.

Surroundings : 🏞 🛶 ♨♨
Leisure activities : 🎮 🚲 🎣
Facilities : & ⚷ 🍴 🏧
Nearby : 🍷 🏊‍♂️ ⛵ pedalos

GPS Longitude : 2.95872
Latitude : 46.94029

Do not confuse:
⚠ to ⚠⚠ : *MICHELIN classification with*
★ to ★★★★★ : *official classification*

L'ÎLE-BOUCHARD

37220 – Michelin map **317** L6 – pop. 1 754 – alt. 41
▶ Paris 284 – Châteauroux 118 – Châtellerault 49 – Chinon 16

⚠ Les Bords de Vienne

✆ 02 47 95 23 59. http://www.campingbordsdevienne.com

Address : 4 allée du camping (near the quartier St-Gilles, upstream of
the bridge over the Vienne, near the river)

1 ha (90 pitches) flat, grassy

Rentals : 4 ⬛ – 1 gîte.

Surroundings : ♨♨
Leisure activities : 🏊‍♂️ 🎣
Facilities : & ⚷ 🍴 🏧
Nearby : 🛒 🍽 🛶

GPS Longitude : 0.42833
Latitude : 47.12139

ISDES

45620 – Michelin map **318** K5 – pop. 612 – alt. 152
▶ Paris 174 – Bourges 75 – Gien 35 – Orléans 40

⚠ Municipal les Prés Bas

✆ 06 78 43 46 28. www.isdes.fr

Address : take the northeastern exit along the D 59, near a lake

Opening times : from beginning April to end Oct.

0.5 ha (20 pitches) flat, grassy

Tariff : (2014 Price) 🚶 3€ 🚗 1.50€ ▣ 5€ 🔌 (6A)
🚐 borne 5€

Surroundings : 🛶
Leisure activities : 🎣
Facilities : & 🛏 🍴 🚿
Nearby : 🏊‍♂️

GPS Longitude : 2.2565
Latitude : 47.6744

LORRIS

45260 – Michelin map **318** M4 – pop. 2 941 – alt. 126
▶ Paris 132 – Gien 27 – Montargis 23 – Orléans 55

⚠️ L'Étang des Bois

📞 02 38 92 32 00. www.canal-orleans.fr

Address : 6km west along the D 88, follow the signs for Châteauneuf-sur-Loire, near the lake at Les Bois

Opening times : from beginning April to end Sept.

3 ha (150 pitches) grassy

Tariff : (2014 Price) ⚹ 3.80€ ⇦ 🅿 6.20€ – 🔌 (10A) 4.65€

Rental rates : (2014 Price) (from beginning April to end Sept.) – 4 🛖. Per night from 52 to 67€ – Per week from 320 to 435€

A wooded setting in a pleasant location.

Surroundings : 🔲 🌳🌳
Leisure activities : 🎣 ⛰
Facilities : ⚏ 🚿 🚰 🚻 🔧
Nearby : 🍴 🏊 🏖 (beach) 🐎

GPS Longitude : 2.44454
Latitude : 47.87393

LUÇAY-LE-MÂLE

36360 – Michelin map **323** E4 – pop. 1 496 – alt. 160
▶ Paris 240 – Le Blanc 73 – Blois 60 – Châteauroux 43

⚠️ Municipal la Foulquetière

📞 02 54 40 43 31. www.lucaylemale.fr

Address : La Foulquetière (3.8km southwest along the D 960, follow the signs for Loches, D 13, follow the signs for Ecueillé to the left and take the road to the right)

Opening times : from beginning April to mid Oct.

1.5 ha (30 pitches) flat and relatively flat, grassy

Tariff : (2014 Price) ⚹ 2€ ⇦ 🅿 2.50€ – 🔌 (6A) 1.50€

Rental rates : Permanent 🏕 – 3 🛖 – 2 gîtes. Per night from 90€ – Per week from 270 to 338€

🚐 borne 3€

80m from a small lake that is very popular with anglers.

Surroundings : 🔲 🌳
Leisure activities : 🎣
Facilities : ⚏ 🚿 🚰 🚻 🔧
Nearby : 🍷 🍴 🚣 🏊 ⛰ 🏖 (beach) 🐟 pedalos

GPS Longitude : 1.40417
Latitude : 47.1109

LUNERY

18400 – Michelin map **323** J5 – pop. 1 449 – alt. 150
▶ Paris 256 – Bourges 23 – Châteauroux 51 – Issoudun 28

⚠️ Intercommunal de Lunery

📞 02 48 68 07 38. www.cc-fercher.fr

Address : 6 rue de l'Abreuvoir (in the town, near the church)

Opening times : from mid April to mid Sept.

0.5 ha (37 pitches) flat, grassy

Tariff : (2014 Price) 12€ ⚹⚹ ⇦ 🅿 🔌 (10A) – Extra per person 3€

Near the remains of an old windmill, near the Cher river.

Surroundings : 🌿 🔲 🌳🌳
Leisure activities : 🎣 🎣
Facilities : ⚏ 🚿 🚰 🔧
Nearby : 🍷 🍴 🏊

GPS Longitude : 2.27038
Latitude : 46.93658

MARCILLY-SUR-VIENNE

37800 – Michelin map **317** M6 – pop. 559 – alt. 60
▶ Paris 280 – Azay-le-Rideau 32 – Chinon 30 – Châtellerault 29

⚠️ Intercommunal la Croix de la Motte

📞 02 47 65 20 38. www.cc-saintemauredetouraine.fr

Address : 1.2km north along the D 18, follow the signs for L'Ile-Bouchard and take turning to the right

1.5 ha (61 pitches) flat, grassy

Rentals : 🏕 – 2 🛖 – 1 tent lodge.

Situated in pleasant, shaded surroundings near the Vienne river.

Surroundings : 🐟 🔲 🌳
Leisure activities : 🎣 🐟
Facilities : ⚏ 🚿 🚰 🔧

GPS Longitude : 0.54337
Latitude : 47.05075

MENNETOU-SUR-CHER

41320 – Michelin map **318** I8 – pop. 878 – alt. 100
▶ Paris 209 – Bourges 56 – Romorantin-Lanthenay 18 – Selles-sur-Cher 27

⚠️ Municipal Val Rose

📞 02 54 98 11 02. mairie.mennetou@wanadoo.fr

Address : rue de Val Rose (south of the town, to the right after the bridge over the canal, 100m from the Cher river)

Opening times : from mid May to mid Sept.

0.8 ha (50 pitches) flat, grassy

Tariff : (2014 Price) ⚹ 2€ ⇦ 🅿 3€ – 🔌 (6A) 2.50€
🚐 borne 2€ – 🚐 8€

Surroundings : 🔲 🌳
Leisure activities : 🎣
Facilities : ⚏ 🚿 🚰
Nearby : 🍴 🏊 🐟 🚣

GPS Longitude : 1.86173
Latitude : 47.26937

To make the best possible use of this guide, please read pages 2–15 carefully.

MESLAND

41150 – Michelin map **318** D6 – pop. 547 – alt. 79
▶ Paris 205 – Amboise 19 – Blois 23 – Château-Renault 20

⛰ Yelloh! Village Le Parc du Val de Loire 👥

📞 02 54 70 27 18. www.parcduvaldeloire.com

Address : 155 route de Fleuray (located 1.5km west)

Opening times : from mid April to mid Sept.

15 ha (300 pitches)

Tariff : 18€ ⚹⚹ ⇦ 🅿 🔌 (10A) – Extra per person 6€

Rental rates : (from mid April to mid Sept.) 🏕 – 150 🛖 – 10 🏠 – 4 tent lodges. Per night from 39 to 141€ – Per week from 273 to 987€

In a wooded setting opposite a vineyard.

Surroundings : 🌿 🔲 🌳🌳
Leisure activities : 🍷 🍴 🎣 🏃 🎣 🚲 🏊
⛰ 🏊 🏊 ⛸
Facilities : ⚏ 🚿 🚰 🚻 🔧

GPS Longitude : 1.10477
Latitude : 47.51001

MONTARGIS

45200 – Michelin map **318** N4 – pop. 15 020 – alt. 95
▶ Paris 109 – Auxerre 252 – Nemours 36 – Nevers 126

⚑ Municipal de la Forêt

☏ 02 38 98 00 20. camping@agglo-montargoise.fr

Address : 38 avenue Louis-Maurice Chautemps (take the northern exit along the D 943 and continue 1km along the D 815, follow the signs for Paucourt)

Opening times : from beginning Feb. to end Nov.

5.5 ha (100 pitches) flat, grassy, stony, sandy

Tariff : (2014 Price) ♦ 3.10€ ⇆ 2.40€ 🅴 3.10€ – 🔋 (10A) 7.80€
🚐 borne 3.80€ – 🛁 🔋 8.30€

Surroundings : 🌳
Leisure activities : 🛶 🏄
Facilities : ♿ ⛽ �🏛 🍴 ⚐ 🚿
Nearby : 🍽 ⛵

Longitude : 2.75102
Latitude : 48.00827

MONTBAZON

37250 – Michelin map **317** N5 – pop. 3 904 – alt. 59
▶ Paris 247 – Châtellerault 59 – Chinon 41 – Loches 33

⚑⚑ La Grange Rouge

☏ 02 47 26 06 43. www.camping-montbazon.com

Address : route de Tours, road RD 910 (after the bridge over the Indre; behind the tourist office and near the stadium)

Opening times : from beginning April to mid Oct.

2 ha (108 pitches) flat, grassy

Tariff : 20.50€ ♦♦ ⇆ 🅴 🔋 (10A) – Extra per person 4.20€
Rental rates : (from beginning April to mid Oct.) 🏷 – 15 🛖.
Per night from 55 to 94€ – Per week from 290 to 630€

In a pleasant location beside the Indre river and near the town centre.

Surroundings : 🏞
Leisure activities : ✖ 🛶 ⛵
Facilities : ♿ ⛽ 🍴 🚿 🖼
Nearby : 🍽 🎣 🔥 sports trail

MONTLOUIS-SUR-LOIRE

37270 – Michelin map **317** N4 – pop. 10 448 – alt. 60
▶ Paris 235 – Amboise 14 – Blois 49 – Château-Renault 32

⚑⚑ Aquadis Loisirs Les Peupliers

☏ 02 47 50 81 90. www.aquadis-loisirs.com

Address : located 1.5km west along the D 751, follow the signs for Tours, 100m from the Loire river

Opening times : from beginning April to end Oct.

6 ha (252 pitches) flat, grassy

Tariff : 17.70€ ♦♦ ⇆ 🅴 🔋 (10A) – Extra per person 3.85€ – Reservation fee 9.90€

Rental rates : (from beginning April to end Oct.) – 11 🛖.
Per night from 84 to 94€ – Per week from 249 to 533€ – Reservation fee 19.90€

🚐 borne 5.90€ – 18 🅴 17.70€ – 🛁 11€
A pleasant wooded site.

Surroundings : 🌳 🏞
Leisure activities : 🍴 🛶 🏄
Facilities : ♿ ⛽ 🆒 🚿 🍴 🖼 🚿
Nearby : 🍽 ⛵ ⛵

Longitude : 0.81144
Latitude : 47.39437

MONTOIRE-SUR-LE-LOIR

41800 – Michelin map **318** C5 – pop. 4 081 – alt. 65
▶ Paris 186 – Blois 52 – Château-Renault 21 – La Flèche 81

⚑⚑ Municipal les Reclusages

☏ 02 54 85 02 53. www.mairie-montoire.fr

Address : Les Reclusages (southwestern exit, follow the signs for Tours and follow the signs for Lavardin to the left after the bridge)

Opening times : from end April to end Sept.

2 ha (133 pitches) flat, grassy

Tariff : (2014 Price) ♦ 3.74€ ⇆ 🅴 2.10€ – 🔋 (10A) 3.93€
Rental rates : (2014 Price) (from end April to end Sept.) – 4 🛖.
Per night from 63 to 90€ – Per week from 214 to 343€

Situated beside the Loir river.

Surroundings : 🏞
Leisure activities : 🍴 🛶 ⛵
Facilities : ♿ ⛽ 🍴 🖼
Nearby : 🏄 🔥 ⛵ ⛵

Longitude : 0.86289
Latitude : 47.74788

There are several different types of sani-station ('borne' in French) – sanitation points providing fresh water and disposal points for grey water. See page 12 for further details.

MORÉE

41160 – Michelin map **318** E4 – pop. 1 117 – alt. 96
▶ Paris 154 – Blois 42 – Châteaudun 24 – Orléans 58

⚑ Municipal de la Varenne

☏ 02 54 89 15 15. mairie-de-moree@wanadoo.fr

Address : chemin de la Varenne (to the west of the town; beside a small lake, recommended route via the D 19, follow the signs for St-Hilaire-la-Gravelle and take road to the left)

Opening times : from beginning March to end Nov.

0.8 ha (43 pitches) flat, grassy

Tariff : (2014 Price) ♦ 4€ ⇆ 🅴 3.50€ – 🔋 (8A) 3€
Rental rates : (2014 Price) (from beginning March to end Nov.) – 2 🛖 – 2 🏠. Per night from 32 to 50€ – Per week from 180 to 400€

🚐 borne 3€ – 20 🅴 9€ – 🛁 8€

Surroundings : 🏖
Leisure activities : 🏖 (beach) ⛵
Facilities : ♿ ⛽ 🚿 🍴
Nearby : 🏄

Longitude : 1.23424
Latitude : 47.9031

These symbols are used for a campsite that is exceptional in its category:

⚑⚑⚑…⚑ *Particularly pleasant setting, quality and range of services available*

🏞🏞 *Tranquil, isolated site – quiet site, particularly at night*

≤≤ *Exceptional view – interesting or panoramic view*

MUIDES-SUR-LOIRE

41500 – Michelin map **318** G5 – pop. 1 350 – alt. 82
▶ Paris 169 – Beaugency 17 – Blois 20 – Chambord 9

🏔 Château des Marais 👫

📞 02 54 87 05 42. www.camping-des-marais.com

Address : 27 rue de Chambord (to the southeast along the D 103, follow the signs for Crouy-sur-Cosson - for caravans, access via the D 112 and take D 103 to the right)

Opening times : from beginning May to mid Sept.

8 ha (299 pitches) flat, grassy

Tariff : 51€ ♦♦ ⇔ 🔲 🔋 (10A) – Extra per person 9€ – Reservation fee 15€

Rental rates : (2014 Price) (from beginning May to end Oct.) 🚫 – 8 🛏 – 31 🏠 – 1 cabin in the trees. Per night from 58 to 182€ – Per week from 406 to 1,274€ – Reservation fee 15€

🚐 borne – 22 🔲 50€

In the pleasant wooded grounds of a 17th-century château.

Surroundings : 🌊 🏕 🎭
Leisure activities : ♈ ✗ 🎬 🍸 nighttime ⚟
🛶 hammam 🛝 🎣 ⚜ 🔊 🏊 🎣 ⚜
Facilities : ♿ ⚡ ⚐ 🚻 ⚗ ⚐ ⛲ launderette
🎣🛶

G P S Longitude : 1.52897
Latitude : 47.66585

🏔 Municipal Bellevue

📞 02 54 87 01 56. mairie.muides@wanadoo.fr – ♻

Address : avenue de la Loire (north of the town along the D 112, follow the signs for Mer and take the turning to the left before the bridge; near the Loire)

Opening times : from mid April to mid Sept.

2.5 ha (100 pitches)

Tariff : 14.85€ ♦♦ ⇔ 🔲 🔋 (5A) – Extra per person 4.20€

🚐 borne 9.10€

Facilities : ♿ ⚡ (June–Aug.) ⛲ 📷
Nearby : 🛝 🎣

G P S Longitude : 1.52607
Latitude : 47.67178

Some campsites benefit from proximity to a municipal leisure centre.

NEUNG-SUR-BEUVRON

41210 – Michelin map **318** H6 – pop. 1 223 – alt. 102
▶ Paris 183 – Beaugency 33 – Blois 39 – Lamotte-Beuvron 20

🏔 Municipal de la Varenne

📞 02 54 83 68 52. www.neung-sur-beuvron.fr

Address : 34 rue de Veillas (located 1km to the northeast, access via the turning to the left of the church; near the Beuvron)

Opening times : from beginning April to mid Oct.

4 ha (73 pitches) relatively flat, flat, grassy, sandy

Tariff : (2014 Price) ♦ 2.70€ ⇔ 🔲 3.20€ – 🔋 (10A) 3.20€

Rental rates : (2014 Price) (from beginning April to end Oct.) – 4 🛏. Per night from 57€ – Per week from 237 to 412€

🚐 borne

A pleasant wooded site.

Surroundings : 🌊 🏕 🎭
Leisure activities : 🎬 🎣 🎣
Facilities : ♿ ⚡ ⛲ 📷

G P S Longitude : 1.81507
Latitude : 47.53849

NEUVY-ST-SÉPULCHRE

36230 – Michelin map **323** G7 – pop. 1 690 – alt. 186
▶ Paris 295 – Argenton-sur-Creuse 24 – Châteauroux 29 – La Châtre 16

🏔 Municipal les Frênes

📞 02 54 30 82 51. www.campingdeneuvy.fr.nf – ♻

Address : route de l'Augère (take the western exit along the D 927, follow the signs for Argenton-sur-Creuse then continue 600m along the turning to the left and take the road to the right, 100m from a lake and the Bouzanne river)

Opening times : from mid June to mid Sept.

1 ha (35 pitches) flat, grassy

Tariff : (2014 Price) 11.50€ ♦♦ ⇔ 🔲 🔋 (9A) – Extra per person 2€

Rental rates : (2014 Price) Permanent 🚫 – 2 🏠. Per night from 90€ – Per week from 240 to 270€

Surroundings : 🌊 🏕 🎭
Leisure activities : 🛝 🎣
Facilities : ♿ ⚡ ⚐ ⚗ ⛲ launderette
Nearby : ♈ ✗ 🎣 🎣

G P S Longitude : 1.7828
Latitude : 46.5903

NOUAN-LE-FUZELIER

41600 – Michelin map **318** J6 – pop. 2 439 – alt. 113
▶ Paris 177 – Blois 59 – Cosne-sur-Loire 74 – Gien 56

🏔 La Grande Sologne 👫

📞 02 54 88 70 22. www.campinggrandesologne.com

Address : rue des Peupliers (take the southern exit along the D 2020, then the road to the left opposite the station)

Opening times : from beginning April to mid Oct.

10 ha/4 for camping (180 pitches) flat, grassy

Tariff : (2014 Price) ♦ 6€ ⇔ 🔲 8.50€ – 🔋 (10A) 3.10€

Rental rates : (2014 Price) (from beginning April to mid Oct.) – 9 🛏 – 4 canvas bungalows – 1 'floating' tent. Per night from 26 to 78€ – Per week from 182 to 695€

🚐 borne

In a wooded setting beside a lake.

Surroundings : 🎭
Leisure activities : ✗ 🎬 ⚟ 🛝 🚲 🎣 🎣
Facilities : ♿ ⚡ 🔲 ⚗ ⛲ 📷 ⚜
Nearby : ♈ 🎣 🏊

G P S Longitude : 2.03631
Latitude : 47.53337

OLIVET

45160 – Michelin map **318** I4 – pop. 19 806 – alt. 100
▶ Paris 137 – Orléans 4 – Blois 70 – Chartres 78

🏔 Municipal

📞 02 38 63 53 94. www.camping-olivet.org

Address : rue du Pont Bouchet (situated 2km southeast along the D 14, follow the signs for St-Cyr-en-Val)

Opening times : from beginning April to mid Oct.

1 ha (46 pitches) flat, grassy

Tariff : (2014 Price) 18.40€ ♦♦ ⇔ 🔲 🔋 (16A) – Extra per person 4.50€

🚐 borne 5.50€ – 10 🔲 18.50€

A pleasant location where the Loiret and Dhuy rivers meet.

Surroundings : 🏕 🎭
Leisure activities : 🎣
Facilities : ♿ ⚡ 🔲 ⚗ ⛲ 📷
Nearby : 🎣 🏊

G P S Longitude : 1.92543
Latitude : 47.85601

PIERREFITTE-SUR-SAULDRE

41300 – Michelin map **318** J6 – pop. 848 – alt. 125
▶ Paris 185 – Aubigny-sur-Nère 23 – Blois 73 – Bourges 55

ᴬᴬᴬᴬ Les Alicourts ♣♣

📞 02 54 88 63 34. www.lesalicourts.com

Address : at Domaine des Alicourts (6km northeast along the D 126 and take the D 126b; beside a small lake)

Opening times : from beginning May to beginning Sept.

21 ha/10 for camping (420 pitches)

Tariff : 50€ ♦♦ ⇔ 🔲 ⚡ (6A) – Extra per person 12€
Rental rates : (from beginning May to beginning Sept.) ⚐ (3 chalets) ⚑ – 170 🛏 – 110 ⌂ – 8 cabins in the trees. Per night from 44 to 220€ – Per week from 308 to 1,652€
🚐 borne

A pretty, partially enclosed swimming area, upmarket spa centre and good quality rental options.

Surroundings : ⛵ ⊡ ♀♀
Leisure activities : ♈ ✕ 🖼 🏃 ♨ 🎣 hammam jacuzzi 🛶 🚲 ⚔ m 🏊 ≋ (beach) ⛷ pedalos 🌊 spa centre entertainment room, skate park
Facilities : ♿ ⚷ ♨ 🚿 🚰 ♈ launderette 🗑 🚿

G P S Longitude : 2.191
Latitude : 47.54482

Routes nationales are main roads and their identifying numbers begin with N or RN. Routes départementales are generally quieter roads and begin with D or DN.

PREUILLY-SUR-CLAISE

37290 – Michelin map **317** O7 – pop. 1 075 – alt. 80
▶ Paris 299 – Le Blanc 31 – Châteauroux 64 – Châtellerault 35

ᴬ Municipal

📞 02 47 94 50 04. www.preuillysurclaise.fr

Address : to the southwest of the town; near the swimming pool, the Claise river and a small lake

Opening times : from beginning June to end Sept.

0.7 ha (37 pitches) flat, grassy

Tariff : 8€ ♦♦ ⇔ 🔲 ⚡ (6A) – Extra per person 2.50€
Rental rates : (from beginning May to end Sept.) ⚑ – 2 🛏. Per night from 50€ – Per week from 200 to 250€
🚐 borne 10€

In a green setting In the middle of a leisure centre.

Surroundings : ⊡ ♀
Leisure activities : 🎣
Facilities : ⚷ 🚿 ♈ 📶
Nearby : 🏊 ⚔ m 🏊 sports trail

G P S Longitude : 0.92618
Latitude : 46.85305

Michelin classification:

ᴬᴬᴬᴬ *Extremely comfortable, equipped to a very high standard*
ᴬᴬᴬ *Very comfortable, equipped to a high standard*
ᴬᴬᴬ *Comfortable and well equipped*
ᴬᴬ *Reasonably comfortable*
ᴬ *Satisfactory*

RILLÉ

37340 – Michelin map **317** K4 – pop. 300 – alt. 82
▶ Paris 282 – Orléans 158 – Tours 47 – Nantes 160

ᴬᴬ Huttopia Rillé

© Huttopia R. Etienne

📞 02 47 24 62 97. www.huttopia.com

Address : at the lake Rillé (situated 2km to the east along the D49)

Opening times : from mid April to mid Oct.

5 ha (120 pitches) flat, grassy

Tariff : (2014 Price) 35€ ♦♦ ⇔ 🔲 ⚡ (10A) – Extra per person 8.20€ – Reservation fee 22€
Rental rates : (2014 Price) (from mid April to mid Oct.) – 10 caravans – 22 ⌂ – 19 tent lodges. Per night from 49 to 167€ – Per week from 258 to 1,169€ – Reservation fee 22€
🚐 borne 7€ – 20 🔲 29.20€

Surroundings : ♀♀
Leisure activities : ♈ ✕ 🖼 ☀ daytime 🏃 🚲 ⚔ 🌊 🎣
Facilities : ♿ ⚷ Ⓟ 🔥 launderette 🔲 🚿
Nearby : 🏇

G P S Longitude : 0.33278
Latitude : 47.44584

ROMORANTIN-LANTHENAY

41200 – Michelin map **318** H7 – pop. 17 092 – alt. 93
▶ Paris 202 – Blois 42 – Bourges 74 – Châteauroux 72

ᴬᴬ Tournefeuille

📞 02 54 76 16 60. www.campingtournefeuille-sologne.com

Address : 32 rue des Lices (take the eastern exit, follow the signs for Salbris and then Long-Eaton; beside the Sauldre river)

Opening times :

1.5 ha (103 pitches) flat, grassy

Tariff : 19.30€ ♦♦ ⇔ 🔲 ⚡ (10A) – Extra per person 7.10€ – Reservation fee 5€
Rental rates : Permanent – 6 ⌂. – Reservation fee 5€
🚐 borne 3.10€ – 15 🔲 10.80€ – ⚡10.80€

Surroundings : ⛵ ♀
Leisure activities : ✕ 🖼 🏃 🚲
Facilities : ♿ ⚷ 🔲 🚿 ♈ 📶
Nearby : 🗑 ✕ 🎣 🏊

G P S Longitude : 1.75586
Latitude : 47.35503

ROSNAY

36300 – Michelin map **323** D6 – pop. 615 – alt. 112
▶ Paris 307 – Argenton-sur-Creuse 31 – Le Blanc 16 – Châteauroux 44

ᴬ Municipal

📞 02 54 37 80 17. rosnay-mairie@wanadoo.fr

Address : route de St-Michel-en-Brenne (500m north along the D 44)

Opening times : from mid Feb. to mid Nov.

2 ha (36 pitches) flat, grassy

Tariff : (2014 Price) 10.50€ ♦♦ ⇔ 🔲 (6A) – Extra per person 2€
🚐 borne – 9 🔲 10.50€

A small, pleasant site near a lake.

Surroundings : ⛵ ♀♀
Leisure activities : 🏃 ⚔ 🎣
Facilities : 🚿 📶 ♨ ♈ 📶

G P S Longitude : 1.21172
Latitude : 46.70645

ST-AMAND-MONTROND

18200 – Michelin map **323** L6 – pop. 10 952 – alt. 160
▶ Paris 282 – Bourges 52 – Châteauroux 65 – Montluçon 56

⚠ Municipal de la Roche

𝒫 02 48 96 09 36. www.entreprisefrery.com

Address : chemin de La Roche (take the southwestern exit along the D 2144, follow the signs for Montluçon, take the Chemin de la Roche to the right before the canal; near the Cher river)

Opening times : from beginning April to end Sept.

4 ha (120 pitches)

Tariff : (2014 Price) 17.10€ ♣♣ ⇔ ⊡ ⚡ (6A) – Extra per person 1.90€
Rental rates : (2014 Price) (from beginning April to end Sept.) – 3 canvas bungalows. Per night from 96€ – Per week from 161 to 230€

Attractive pitches in a green setting by a canal and the Cher river, but the sanitary facilities are rather old and basic.

Surroundings : ⌇ ▱ ♉♉
Leisure activities : ⌱ ⚴ ✘
Facilities : ⅗ ⚭ ▥ ᵞ launderette
Nearby : ⤳

G P S Longitude : 2.49108
Latitude : 46.71816

ST-AVERTIN

37550 – Michelin map **317** N4 – pop. 13 946 – alt. 49
▶ Paris 245 – Orléans 121 – Tours 7 – Blois 70

⚠ Tour Val de Loire - St Avertin

𝒫 02 47 27 87 47. http://valdeloire.onlycamp.fr/fr/

Address : 61 rue de Rochepinard (to the north along the left bank of the Cher river)

Opening times : from mid March to mid Nov.

2 ha (90 pitches) flat, grassy

Tariff : (2014 Price) 21€ ♣♣ ⇔ ⊡ ⚡ (10A) – Extra per person 4.20€
Rental rates : (2014 Price) (from mid March to end Nov.) – 12 ⌂ – 2 canvas bungalows. Per night from 29 to 99€ – Per week from 180 to 589€
⌲ 20 ⊡ 21€

Situated near a small lake.

Surroundings : ▱ ♉
Facilities : ⅗ ⚭ ▥ ♉ᵞ launderette
Nearby : ⚴ ✘ ▧ ⤳ ♨

G P S Longitude : 0.72296
Latitude : 47.37064

ST-PÈRE-SUR-LOIRE

45600 – Michelin map **318** L5 – pop. 1 056 – alt. 115
▶ Paris 147 – Aubigny-sur-Nère 38 – Châteauneuf-sur-Loire 40 Gien 25

⚠ Le Jardin de Sully

𝒫 02 38 67 10 84. www.camping-lejardindesully.fr

Address : 1 route de St-Benoit (to the west along the D 60, follow the signs for Châteauneuf-sur-Loire; near the river)

Opening times : Permanent

2.7 ha (80 pitches)

Tariff : (2014 Price) 15€ ♣♣ ⇔ ⊡ ⚡ (10A) – Extra per person 5€
Rental rates : (2014 Price) Permanent – 18 ⌂ – 8 canvas bungalows. Per night from 35 to 100€ – Per week from 175 to 560€

Leisure activities : ⌱ ⚴
Facilities : ⅗ ⚭ ▥ ♉ ᵞ launderette
Nearby : ✘ ⤳

G P S Longitude : 2.36229
Latitude : 47.7718

ST-PLANTAIRE

36190 – Michelin map **323** G8 – pop. 549 – alt. 300
▶ Paris 339 – Orléans 214 – Châteauroux 68 – Limoges 95

⛰ Municipal de Fougères

𝒫 02 54 47 20 01. www.www.saint-plantaire.fr

Address : 19 plage de Fougères

Opening times : from beginning April to end Oct.

4.5 ha (150 pitches) flat, grassy

Tariff : (2014 Price) ♣ 4.30€ ⇔ 1.60€ ⊡ 12€ – ⚡ (10A) 3.80€
Rental rates : (2014 Price) (from beginning March to end Dec.) – 7 ⌂ – 13 ⌂ – 4 canvas bungalows. Per night from 38 to 120€ – Per week from 149 to 608€

In a pleasant location beside the Lac de Chambon

Surroundings : ≤ ♉
Leisure activities : ⌱ ⚴ ✘ ▧ ⥿ ≍ ⤳
Facilities : ⅗ ⚭ ᵞ launderette ⚲
Nearby : ✘ ♊ pedalos

G P S Longitude : 1.61952
Latitude : 46.42756

To visit a town or region, use the MICHELIN Green Guides.

ST-SATUR

18300 – Michelin map **323** N2 – pop. 1 627 – alt. 155
▶ Paris 194 – Aubigny-sur-Nère 42 – Bourges 50 – Cosne-sur-Loire 12

⛰ Flower Les Portes de Sancerre

𝒫 02 48 72 10 88. www.camping-cher-sancerre.com

Address : quai de Loire (located 1km east along the D 2)

Opening times : from beginning April to end Sept.

1 ha (87 pitches) flat, grassy

Tariff : (2014 Price) 22€ ♣♣ ⇔ ⊡ ⚡ (6A) – Extra per person 4.50€
Reservation fee 10€
Rental rates : (2014 Price) (from beginning April to end Sept.) ⅗ (1 mobile home) – 20 ⌂ – 3 tent lodges. Per night from 41 to 75€ – Per week from 287 to 525€ – Reservation fee 15€
⌲ borne

Well-shaded pitches and rental options beside the Loire river and near a small leisure centre.

Surroundings : ⌇ ▱ ♉♉
Leisure activities : ⌱ ✘
Facilities : ⅗ ⚭ ♉ ⤢ ᵞ ▣
Nearby : ♇ ♣ ♊ ▧ ⤳ ♘

G P S Longitude : 2.86671
Latitude : 47.34251

STE-CATHERINE-DE-FIERBOIS

37800 – Michelin map **317** M6 – pop. 657 – alt. 114
▶ Paris 263 – Azay-le-Rideau 25 – Chinon 37 – Ligueil 19

⛰ Les Castels Parc de Fierbois ♣♣

𝒫 02 47 65 43 35. www.fierbois.com

Address : 1.2km to the south

Opening times : from beginning May to beginning Sept.

30 ha/12 for camping (420 pitches)

Tariff : 52€ ♣♣ ⇔ ⊡ ⚡ (10A) – Extra per person 9€
Rental rates : (from beginning May to beginning Sept.) – 130 ⌂ – 30 ⌂ – 8 cabins in the trees – 8 gîtes. – Per night from 45 to 215€ – Per week from 315 to 1,505€
⌲ borne – ⛟ 14€

A pleasant and spacious site with woods, lake and a water park.

Surroundings : 🛏 🏛 ⛰
Leisure activities : 🍽 🗙 🛎 🗐 🧗 🎣 🏇 🚴
🗙 🔥 🛝 🛀 🌊 (beach) 🛶
Facilities : 🚿 ☕ ⛱ 🔧 🚰 🍴 launderette 🚮
🍴 refrigerated food storage facilities
Nearby : adventure park

GPS Longitude : 0.6549
Latitude : 47.1486

Rental rates : (from end March to mid Oct.) – 6 canvas bungalows.
Per night from 43 to 65€ – Per week from 210 to 430€
🚐 borne 4.60€ – 🔌 🚰16€

Surroundings : 🐟 🎣
Leisure activities : 🏊
Facilities : 🚿 ☕ 🔧 ⛱ 🔧 🚰 🍴 🖨
Nearby : 🛒 🗙 🛝 🛶 🏇

GPS Longitude : 0.13937
Latitude : 47.20039

STE-MAURE-DE-TOURAINE

37800 – Michelin map **317** M6 – pop. 4 072 – alt. 85
▶ Paris 273 – Le Blanc 71 – Châtellerault 39 – Chinon 32

⛺ Municipal de Marans

📞 02 47 65 44 93. camping@sainte-maure-de-touraine.fr – 🏨

Address : rue de Toizelet (located 1.5km southeast along the D 760, follow the signs for Loches, and take the turning to the left; 150m from a small lake)

Opening times : from beginning April to end Sept.

1 ha (66 pitches)

Tariff : (2014 Price) 11.50€ 🚹🚹 🚗 🔲 🚽 (20A) – Extra per person 3€

🚐 borne

Leisure activities : 🏃 sports trail
Facilities : 🚿 ☕ 🔧 ⛱ 🍴
Nearby : 🛝 🛶

GPS Longitude : 0.6252
Latitude : 47.10509

SALBRIS

41300 – Michelin map **318** J7 – pop. 5 682 – alt. 104
▶ Paris 187 – Aubigny-sur-Nère 32 – Blois 65 – Lamotte-Beuvron 21

⛺ Le Sologne

📞 02 54 97 06 38. www.campingdesologne.fr

Address : 8 allée de la Sauldre (take northeastern exit along the D 55, follow the signs for Pierrefitte-sur-Sauldre; beside a lake and near the Sauldre river)

Opening times : from beginning April to end Sept.

2 ha (81 pitches) flat, grassy

Tariff : 19.75€ 🚹🚹 🚗 🔲 🚽 (10A) – Extra per person 4.90€
Rental rates : (from beginning April to end Sept.) 🏊 – 5 🚐 – 1 🏠. Per night from 58 to 94€ – Per week from 235 to 512€
🚐 borne

Surroundings : 🛏 🎣
Leisure activities : 🏞 🛶
Facilities : 🚿 ☕ ⛱ 🚰 🍴 🖨
Nearby : 🛒 🗙 🎣 🛝 🛀

GPS Longitude : 2.05522
Latitude : 47.43026

SAVIGNY-EN-VÉRON

37420 – Michelin map **317** J5 – pop. 1 447 – alt. 40
▶ Paris 292 – Chinon 9 – Langeais 27 – Saumur 20

⛰ La Fritillaire

📞 02 47 58 03 79. www.camping-la-fritillaire.fr

Address : rue Basse (to the west of the town centre; 100m from a lake)

Opening times : from end March to mid Oct.

2.5 ha (100 pitches) flat, grassy, adjacent wood

Tariff : 17.60€ 🚹🚹 🚗 🔲 🚽 (10A) – Extra per person 3€

SAVONNIÈRES

37510 – Michelin map **317** M4 – pop. 3 041 – alt. 47
▶ Paris 263 – Orléans 139 – Tours 17 – Blois 88

⛺ Onlycamp Confluence

📞 02 47 50 00 25. www.onlycamp.fr

Address : route du Bray (take the northern exit from the town; beside the Cher river)

Opening times : from mid April to end Sept.

Flat, grassy

Tariff : (2014 Price) 18.60€ 🚹🚹 🚗 🔲 🚽 (10A) – Extra per person 4€
Rental rates : (2014 Price) (from mid April to end Sept.) – 2 canvas bungalows – 4 tent lodges. Per night from 29 to 52€ – Per week from 180 to 329€
🚐 borne 2€ – 10 🔲 10.40€

Situated beside the Cher river and a cycle path.

Surroundings : 🛏 🎣
Leisure activities : 🏊 🏃 🛶 🦆
Facilities : 🚿 ☕ ⛱ 🚰 🍴 🖨
Nearby : 🛒 🍽 🗙

GPS Longitude : 0.55006
Latitude : 47.34887

This guide is not intended as a list of all the camping sites in France; its aim is to provide a selection of the best sites in each category.

SENONCHES

28250 – Michelin map **311** C4 – pop. 3 186 – alt. 223
▶ Paris 115 – Chartres 38 – Dreux 38 – Mortagne-au-Perche 42

⛰ Huttopia Senonches 🧍🧍

© Huttopia R. Etienne

📞 02 37 37 81 40. www.huttopia.com

Address : Etang de Badouleau (lake)

Opening times : from end April to beginning Oct.

10.5 ha (126 pitches)

Tariff : (2014 Price) 33.80€ 🚹🚹 🚗 🔲 🚽 (10A) – Extra per person 6.80€ – Reservation fee 22€
Rental rates : (2014 Price) (from end April to beginning Oct.) 🅿 – 10 🏠 – 26 tent lodges. Per night from 59 to 149€ – Per week from 371 to 939€ – Reservation fee 22€
🚐 borne 7€ – 20 🔲 28€

Beside the lake and on the edge of the national forest at Senonches.

Surroundings : 🎣🎣 ⛰
Leisure activities : 🏞 🗐 daytime 🏃 🏊
🛝 🛶
Facilities : ☕ 🅿 🔧 🛁 launderette 🚮
Nearby : 🛒 🗙 🏃 🏇

GPS Longitude : 1.0435
Latitude : 48.553

SONZAY

37360 – Michelin map **317** L3 – pop. 1 298 – alt. 94
▶ Paris 257 – Château-la-Vallière 39 – Langeais 26 – Tours 25

⛰ L'Arada Parc ♣♣

☎ 02 47 24 72 69. www.laradaparc.com

Address : rue de la Baratière (take the western exit along the D 68, follow the signs for Souvigné and take a right turn)

1.7 ha (94 pitches)
Rentals : 21 🚐 – 3 🏠 – 5 tent lodges.

Surroundings : 🐟 🖼
Leisure activities : ♈ ✕ 🎪 🏕 🏃 ᵍ🖼
hammam, jacuzzi 🏍 ✗ 🚴 🎣 ⛷ 🏊
Facilities : ♿ ⛐ ♨ 🚿 🚾 ᵗ launderette
Nearby : ✂ 🐟

G P S Longitude : 0.45069
Latitude : 47.52615

SUÈVRES

41500 – Michelin map **318** F5 – pop. 1 481 – alt. 83
▶ Paris 170 – Beaugency 18 – Blois 15 – Chambord 16

⛰ Les Castels Le Château de la Grenouillère ♣♣

☎ 02 54 87 80 37. www.camping-loire.com ✸

Address : 3km northeast on the D 2152

Opening times : from mid April to mid Sept.

11 ha (250 pitches) flat, grassy

Tariff : 33€ ✶✶ 🚐 🖼 🔌 (10A) – Extra per person 8€ – Reservation fee 10€
Rental rates : (from mid April to mid Sept.) ✸ – 140 🚐 – 20 🏠. Per night from 40 to 120€ – Per week from 300 to 870 € Reservation fee 15€

🚐 borne
In wooded parkland, with oak and apple trees.

Surroundings : 🖼 ♨♨
Leisure activities : ♈ ✕ 🖼 ᵍ 🏃 jacuzzi
🏍 ✗ 🚴 ✂ 🎣 ⛷ 🏊
Facilities : ♿ ⛐ ♨ 🚿 🚾 ᵗ launderette
🔥 🏊

G P S Longitude : 1.48512
Latitude : 47.68688

THORÉ-LA-ROCHETTE

41100 – Michelin map **318** C5 – pop. 899 – alt. 75
▶ Paris 176 – Blois 42 – Château-Renault 25 – La Ferté-Bernard 58

⛰ Intercommunal la Bonne Aventure

la Bonne Aventure

☎ 02 54 72 00 59. www.camping-la-bonne-aventure.fr

Address : route de la Cunaille (head 1.7km north along the D 82, follow the signs for Lunay and take turning to the right; near the stadium; beside the Loir)

Opening times : from beginning May to end Sept.

2 ha (60 pitches) flat, grassy

Tariff : (2014 Price) 12.50€ ✶✶ 🚐 🖼
🔌 (6A) – Extra per person 3.50€
Rental rates : (2014 Price) Permanent ✸ – 2 🚐. Per night from 50 to 75€ – Per week from 190 to 330€ – Reservation fee 15€

Surroundings : 🐟 ♀ ⛰
Leisure activities : 🖼 🏍 🚴 🎣 🏊
Facilities : ♿ ⛐ ᵗ 🖼
Nearby : ᐅ

G P S Longitude : 0.95855
Latitude : 47.80504

VALENÇAY

36600 – Michelin map **323** F4 – pop. 2 617 – alt. 140
▶ Paris 233 – Blois 59 – Bourges 73 – Châteauroux 42

⛰ Municipal les Chênes

☎ 02 54 00 03 92. commune@mairie-valencay.fr

Address : located 1km west on the D 960, follow the signs for Luçay-le-Mâle

Opening times : from beginning May to mid Sept.

5 ha (50 pitches) relatively flat, open site

Tariff : (2014 Price) ✶ 4€ 🚐 🖼 4.60€ – 🔌 (10A) 4.70€

🚐 borne 4.20€
In a pleasant green setting beside a lake.

Surroundings : 🖼 ♨♨
Leisure activities : 🏍 ✗ 🏊
Facilities : ♿ ⛐ 🖼

G P S Longitude : 1.55542
Latitude : 47.15808

VATAN

36150 – Michelin map **323** G4 – pop. 2 059 – alt. 140
▶ Paris 235 – Blois 78 – Bourges 50 – Châteauroux 31

⛰ Municipal

☎ 02 54 49 91 37. www.vatan-en-berry.com

Address : rue du Collège (take the western exit along the D 2, follow the signs for Guilly and take the turning to the left)

Opening times : from mid April to mid Sept.

2.4 ha (55 pitches) flat, grassy

Tariff : 12€ ✶✶ 🚐 🖼 🔌 (16A) – Extra per person 4.50€
Rental rates : (from beginning April to end Sept.) – 3 🏠. Per night from 50€ – Per week from 200 to 250€

🚐 borne 5€
Situated beside a delightful lake.

Surroundings : 🖼 ♨♨
Leisure activities : 🏍 ᐅ
Facilities : ♿ ⛐ 🚐 🚾 ᵗ 🖼
Nearby : ✂ 🏊

G P S Longitude : 1.80601
Latitude : 47.07146

This guide is updated regularly, so buy your new copy every year!

VEIGNÉ

37250 – Michelin map **317** N5 – pop. 6 055 – alt. 58
▶ Paris 252 – Orléans 128 – Tours 16 – Joué-lès-Tours 11

⛰ Onlycamp La Plage

☎ 02 47 34 95 39. www.onlycamp.fr

Address : route de Tours (take the northern exit along the D 50)

Opening times : from beginning May to end Sept.

2 ha (110 pitches) flat, grassy

Tariff : (2014 Price) 18.60€ ✶✶ 🚐 🖼 🔌 (10A) – Extra per person 4€
Rental rates : (2014 Price) (from mid May to mid Sept.) – 10 canvas bungalows. Per night from 42 to 62€ – Per week from 264 to 390€

🚐 borne 2€

Surroundings : ♀
Leisure activities : ♈ ✕ 🖼 🏕 🚴 🎣 ⛷ 🏊
Facilities : ♿ (season) ♨ ᵗ launderette

G P S Longitude : 0.73464
Latitude : 47.28929

LA VILLE-AUX-DAMES

37700 – Michelin map **317** N4 – pop. 4 889 – alt. 50
▶ Paris 244 – Orléans 120 – Tours 7 – Blois 53

⚠ Les Acacias

℘ 02 47 44 08 16. www.camplvad.com

Address : rue Berthe Morisot (to the northeast of the town, near the D 751)

Opening times : Permanent

2.6 ha (90 pitches) flat, grassy

Tariff : 20€ ⚹⚹ 🚐 🔲 🔌 (10A) – Extra per person 3.50€

Rental rates : Permanent – 16 🚕. Per night from 70 to 110€ – Per week from 290 to 560€ – Reservation fee 10€

🚻 borne

Surroundings : 🌳🌿
Leisure activities : ✗ 🏊
Facilities : 🚿 ⛽ 🔋 🍴 laundrette
Nearby : 🍷 🎿 🔲 fitness trail

G P S Longitude : 0.7772
Latitude : 47.40224

VILLIERS-LE-MORHIER

28130 – Michelin map **311** F4 – pop. 1 338 – alt. 99
▶ Paris 83 – Orléans 108 – Chartres 24 – Versailles 61

⚠ Les Îlots de St-Val

Les Îlots de St-Val

℘ 02 37 82 71 30. www.campinglesilotsdestval.com – limited spaces for one-night stay

Address : Le Haut Bourray (4.5km northwest along the D 983, follow the signs for Nogent-le-Roi then continue 1km along the D 1013, follow the signs for Neron to the left)

Opening times : from beginning Feb. to mid Dec.

10 ha/6 for camping (153 pitches) flat and relatively flat, grassy, stony

Tariff : 26€ ⚹⚹ 🚐 🔲 🔌 (10A) – Extra per person 6€

Rental rates : Permanent 🏊 – 16 🚕 – 4 🏠. Per week from 260 to 427€

🚻 borne 7€

Surroundings : 🏞
Leisure activities : 🏛 🏊 🎿
Facilities : 🚿 ⛽ 🔋 🍴
Nearby : 🚣 🐴

G P S Longitude : 1.5476
Latitude : 48.6089

VITRY-AUX-LOGES

45530 – Michelin map **318** K4 – pop. 1 826 – alt. 120
▶ Paris 111 – Bellegarde 17 – Châteauneuf-sur-Loire 11 – Malesherbes 48

⚠ Étang de la Vallée

℘ 06 10 53 35 37. www.campingdeletangdelavallee.fr

Address : at the leisure centre (3.3km to the northwest, 100m from the lake)

3.7 ha (180 pitches) flat, grassy

In a pleasant wooded setting near a leisure centre.

Surroundings : 🌅 🌿
Leisure activities : 🏊 m
Facilities : 🚿 ⛽ 🔲 🍴 🔋
Nearby : 🍷 ✗ 🏖 (beach) 🚣 pedalos

G P S Longitude : 2.28162
Latitude : 47.95868

CHAMPAGNE-ARDENNE

G. Labriet / Photononstop

It's easy to spot visitors heading to the Champagne-Ardenne region by the sparkle in their eyes and the look of pure anticipation and delight on their faces as they gaze out at endless vineyards. They are already picturing themselves sipping the famous delicacy that was once known as 'devil's wine' before a monk discovered the secret of its divine bubbles. As those lucky enough to taste the delights of Champagne continue their voyage, they will see the beautiful cathedral of Reims rise up ahead. They will drink in the sight of the delightful half-timbered houses of Troyes and savour the taste of *andouillettes* (chitterling sausages). Visitors can then explore the Ardennes forest by bike or by walking along its hiking trails. This ancient woodland paradise, bordered by the gentle river Meuse, has other delights as well: watch the graceful flight of the crane over a lake as smooth as glass, or succumb to the temptation of a plate of local wild boar.

BANNES

52360 – Michelin map **313** M6 – pop. 401 – alt. 388
▶ Paris 291 – Chaumont 35 – Dijon 86 – Langres 9

⚠ Hautoreille

✆ 03 25 84 83 40. www.campinghautoreille.com

Address : 6 rue du Boutonnier (take the southwestern exit along the D 74, follow the signs for Langres then continue 700m along the road to the left)

Opening times : from beginning Jan. to end Nov.

3.5 ha (100 pitches)

Tariff : ♦ 5.50€ ⇌ 🔲 5.50€ – ⚡ (10A) 4€

Surroundings : 🏊 ♡♡
Leisure activities : ♈ ✕ 🏛 🏠
Facilities : ♿ ⚎ ▥ ♨♈ 📷

GPS Longitude : 5.39519
Latitude : 47.89508

BOURBONNE-LES-BAINS

52400 – Michelin map **313** O6 – pop. 2 255 – alt. 290 – ⚕
▶ Paris 313 – Chaumont 55 – Dijon 124 – Langres 39

⚠ Le Montmorency

✆ 03 25 90 08 64. www.camping-montmorency.com

Address : rue du Stade (take the western exit following signs for Chaumont and take turning to the right; 100m from the stadium)

Opening times : from beginning April to end Oct.

2 ha (74 pitches)

Tariff : ♦ 4.50€ ⇌ 🔲 5.10€ – ⚡ (10A) 3.70€

Rental rates : (from beginning April to end Oct.) – 11 🚐.
Per night from 35 to 41€ – Per week from 245 to 287€

🚐 borne 12.50€ – 10 🔲 15.20€

Surroundings : 🏊 ♡♡
Facilities : ⚎ ▥ ♨♈ launderette
Nearby : ✂ 🔲 (open air in season)

GPS Longitude : 5.74027
Latitude : 47.95742

BOURG-STE-MARIE

52150 – Michelin map **313** N4 – pop. 94 – alt. 329
▶ Paris 330 – Châlons-en-Champagne 153 – Chaumont 50 – Metz 142

⚠ Les Hirondelles

✆ 03 10 20 61 64. www.camping-les-hirondelles.eu

Address : at Romain-sur-Meuse, rue du Moulin de Dona (located 1.5km to the south, along the D 74, follow the signs for Montigny-le-Roi)

Opening times : from mid Feb. to beginning Dec.

4.6 ha (54 pitches)

Tariff : ♦ 4.20€ ⇌ 🔲 5€ – ⚡ (10A) 3.70€

Rental rates : (from beginning Feb. to mid Dec.) – 8 🏠 – 1 gîte.
Per night from 35 to 90 € – Per week from 210 to 322€

🚐 borne 4.50€ – 20 🔲 14€ – 🔋 ⚡14€

Surroundings : 🏊 ♡♡
Leisure activities : 🏛 🚴
Facilities : ♿ ⚎ ♨♈ launderette

GPS Longitude : 5.55533
Latitude : 48.17234

BRAUCOURT

52290 – Michelin map **313** I2
▶ Paris 220 – Bar-sur-Aube 39 – Brienne-le-Château 29 – Châlons-en-Champagne 69

⛰ La Presqu'île de Champaubert ♣♦

✆ 03 25 04 13 20. www.lescampingsduder.com

Address : 3km northwest along the D 153

Opening times : from mid April to end Nov.

3.6 ha (200 pitches)

Tariff : (2014 Price) 25€ ♦♦ ⇌ 🔲 ⚡ (6A) – Extra per person 5€

Rental rates : (2014 Price) (from mid April to end Nov.) – 50 🚐.
Per night from 35 to 70€ – Per week from 210 to 490€

🚐 borne – 20 🔲 18€

In a pleasant location beside the Lac du Der-Chantecoq.

Surroundings : 🏊 ⬱ 🚤 ♡♡ ⚓
Leisure activities : ♈ ✕ 🏛 🎣🏊🏄 ✂ 🔲
Facilities : ♿ ⚎ ♨♈ launderette
Nearby : 🏊 ⚓ pedalos

GPS Longitude : 4.562
Latitude : 48.55413

We have selected the best campsites in France with our usual care, listing those with the best facilities in the most pleasant surroundings.

BUZANCY

08240 – Michelin map **306** L6 – pop. 372 – alt. 176
▶ Paris 228 – Châlons-en-Champagne 86 – Charleville-Mézières 58 – Metz 130

⚠ La Samaritaine

✆ 03 24 30 08 88. www.campinglasamaritaine.com

Address : 3 rue des Étangs (1.4km southwest along the road to the right near the leisure and activity park)

Opening times : from mid April to mid Sept.

2 ha (110 pitches)

Tariff : ♦ 3.50€ ⇌ 2.50€ 🔲 6.50€ – ⚡ (10A) 3.60€

Rental rates : (from mid April to mid Sept.) – 6 🚐 – 9 🏠.
Per night from 48 to 67€ – Per week from 320 to 595€ – Reservation fee 5€

🚐 borne 3€ – 9 🔲 12€

Surroundings : 🏊 🏛 ♡
Leisure activities : 🏛 🚤
Facilities : ♿ ⚎ ♨♈ ▥ 📷
Nearby : 🏊 (lake)

GPS Longitude : 4.9402
Latitude : 49.42365

Michelin classification:

 Extremely comfortable, equipped to a very high standard

Very comfortable, equipped to a high standard

Comfortable and well equipped

Reasonably comfortable

Satisfactory

CHÂLONS-EN-CHAMPAGNE

51000 – Michelin map **306** I9 – pop. 46 236 – alt. 83
▶ Paris 188 – Charleville-Mézières 101 – Metz 157 – Nancy 162

⚊ Aquadis Loisirs Châlons en Champagne

✆ 03 26 68 38 00. www.aquadis-loisirs.com

Address : rue de Plaisance (take the southeastern exit along the N 44, follow the signs for Vitry-le François and take D 60, following signs for Sarry)

Opening times : from beginning March to beginning Nov.

3.5 ha (148 pitches)

Tariff : 22.90€ ★★ ⬛ 🅴 (10A) – Extra per person 5.40€ – Reservation fee 9.90€

Rental rates : (from beginning March to beginning Nov.) – 8 🚐. Per night from 70 € – Per week from 217 to 519€ – Reservation fee 19.90€

🚐 borne 7.20€ – 20 🅴 18.90€ – 🚐 14€

An entrance decorated with flowers and a pleasant setting beside a lake.

Surroundings : ⬭ 🌳🌳	**G**	Longitude : 4.38309
Leisure activities : ✗ 🛖 ⛵ ⚔ 🏹 🚣	**P**	Latitude : 48.98582
Facilities : ♿ ⚲ 🅒 🏛 🚿 ♨ 🍴 launderette	**S**	

---

*To visit a town or region, use the **MICHELIN** Green Guides.*

CHARLEVILLE-MÉZIÈRES

08000 – Michelin map **306** K4 – pop. 49 975 – alt. 145
▶ Paris 233 – Châlons-en-Champagne 130 – Namur 149 – Arlon 120

⚊ Municipal du Mont Olympe

✆ 03 24 33 23 60. camping-charlevillemezieres@wanadoo.fr

Address : 174 rue des Paquis (in the town centre)

Opening times : from beginning April to beginning Oct.

2.7 ha (120 pitches) flat, grassy

Tariff : (2014 Price) ★ 4.50€ ⬛ 🅴 11€ (10A)

🚐 borne

In a bend of the Meuse river, with pedestrian access to the town centre and the Rimbaud museum via a walkway.

Surroundings : 🏊 ⬭ 🌳🌳	**G**	Longitude : 4.72091
Leisure activities : 🛖 ⛵	**P**	Latitude : 49.77914
Facilities : ♿ ⚲ 🅒 🅟 🚿 ♨ 🍴 launderette	**S**	
Nearby : 🍴 ✗ 🚴 🛶 hammam, jacuzzi 🛶 🏄 ⚓ marina		

DIENVILLE

10500 – Michelin map **313** H3 – pop. 828 – alt. 128
▶ Paris 209 – Bar-sur-Aube 20 – Bar-sur-Seine 33 – Brienne-le-Château 8

⚊ Le Tertre

✆ 03 25 92 26 50. www.campingdutertre.fr

Address : 1 route de Radonvilliers (take the western exit on the D 11)

Opening times : from end March to mid Oct.

3.5 ha (155 pitches)

Tariff : ★ 5€ ⬛ 🅴 10.20€ – (10A) 4.20€ – Reservation fee 12€

Rental rates : Permanent – 13 🏠. Per night from 125 to 290€ – Per week from 200 to 550€ – Reservation fee 12€

🚐 2 🅴 25€

Opposite the sailing centre of the leisure and activity park.

Surroundings : ⬭	**G**	Longitude : 4.52737
Leisure activities : 🍴 ✗ ⛵ 🚣	**P**	Latitude : 48.34888
Facilities : ♿ ⚲ 🅒 🚿 ♨ 🍴 🅿	**S**	
Nearby : ✂ 🛶 🎣 water skiing		

ÉCLARON

52290 – Michelin map **313** J2 – pop. 1 991 – alt. 132
▶ Paris 255 – Châlons-en-Champagne 71 – Chaumont 83 – Bar-le-Duc 37

⚊ Yelloh! Village en Champagne-Les Sources du Lac 🧍🧍

✆ 03 25 06 34 24. www.yellohvillage.com – limited spaces for one-night stay

Address : RD 384 (situated 2km to the south, follow the signs for Montier-en-Der; beside the Lac du Der)

Opening times : from mid April to end Sept.

3 ha (120 pitches)

Tariff : 36€ ★★ ⬛ 🅴 (10A) – Extra per person 7€

Rental rates : (from mid April to end Sept.) – 50 🚐. Per night from 30 to 165€ – Per week from 210 to 1,155€

Choose the pitches furthest away from the road in preference.

Surroundings : ⬭ 🌳🌳	**G**	Longitude : 4.84798
Leisure activities : 🍴 🏖 🚶 ⛵ 🚴 🚣 🎣 multi-sports ground	**P**	Latitude : 48.57179
Facilities : ♿ ⚲ 🚿 ♨ 🍴 launderette 🐾	**S**	

ÉPERNAY

51200 – Michelin map **306** F8 – pop. 24 317 – alt. 75
▶ Paris 143 – Amiens 199 – Charleville-Mézières 113 – Meaux 96

⚊ Municipal

✆ 03 26 55 32 14. www.epernay.fr

Address : allée de Cumières (located 1.5km north along the D 301; beside the Marne river)

Opening times : from end April to beginning Oct.

2 ha (109 pitches) flat, grassy

Tariff : ★ 5€ ⬛ 2.50€ 🅴 5€ – (10A) 4€

🚐 borne 2€

Surroundings : ⬭ 🌳🌳	**G**	Longitude : 3.95026
Leisure activities : ⛵ 🚴	**P**	Latitude : 49.05784
Facilities : ♿ ⚲ 🏛 🍴 launderette	**S**	
Nearby : ⚓		

ERVY-LE-CHÂTEL

10130 – Michelin map **313** D5 – pop. 1 224 – alt. 160
▶ Paris 169 – Auxerre 48 – St-Florentin 18 – Sens 62

⚊ Municipal les Mottes

✆ 03 25 70 07 96. www.ervy-le-chatel.reseaudescommunes.fr/communes

Address : chemin des Mottes (1.8km east along the D 374, follow the signs for Auxon, D 92 and take the road to the right after the level crossing)

Opening times : from beginning May to beginning Oct.

0.7 ha (53 for camping) flat, grassy

Tariff : (2014 Price) ★ 3.50€ ⬛ 3€ 🅴 3€ – (6A) 3.50€

The site is beside a small river and a wood.

Surroundings : 🦢
Leisure activities : 🎣
Facilities : ♿ 🛢🗄🚿

G P S Longitude : 3.91827
Latitude : 48.04069

GIFFAUMONT-CHAMPAUBERT

51290 – Michelin map **306** K11 – pop. 261 – alt. 130
▶ Paris 213 – Châlons-en-Champagne 67 – St-Dizier 25 – Bar-le-Duc 52

⏶⏶⏶ Village Vacances Marina-Holyder

(rental of small houses only)

📞 03 26 72 84 04. www.marina-holyder.com

Address : rue de Champaubert, Presqu'île de Rougemer (peninsula in the Lac du Der))

Opening times : Permanent

2 ha flat

Rental rates : **P** – 43 🏠. Per night from 89 to 149€ – Per week from 399 to 949€

Surroundings : 🦢
Leisure activities : 🍸✕🎮🏸 🎱⛳
hammam, jacuzzi 🚣🏊🎱🛶🚤 forest trail
Facilities : 🏚🚿 launderette ⚄
Nearby : 🚲

G P S Longitude : 4.77328
Latitude : 48.54987

LANGRES

52200 – Michelin map **313** L6 – pop. 8 066 – alt. 466
▶ Paris 295 – Châlons-en-Champagne 197 – Chaumont 36 – Dijon 79

⏶⏶⏶ Kawan Village Le Lac de la Liez 👤👥

📞 03 25 90 27 79. www.campingliez.com

Address : at Peigney water park (5km east along the D 284)

Opening times : from beginning April to end Sept.

4.5 ha (190 pitches)

Tariff : 36€ 👤👤 🚗 🔲 🔌 (10A) – Extra per person 8.50€ – Reservation fee 15€

Rental rates : (from end March to end Sept.) – 2 caravans – 2 🚐 – 24 🏠. Per night from 39 to 120€ – Per week from 273 to 840€ Reservation fee 30€

🚽 borne 6€ – 10 🔲 – 🚐🔌10€

Surroundings : 🦢 ⬿ lake, countryside and the town of Langres 🚗 🌳🌳
Leisure activities : 🍸✕🎮🏸 🎱⛳
🔲🎱🚤 ♿ 🔓🖋🏚 🚿– 16 individual sanitary facilities (🚿🚽🚾 wc) 🚿🚿 launderette ⚄🚿
Nearby : 🚲🏖(beach) 🎣 water skiing

G P S Longitude : 5.3807
Latitude : 47.87146

MESNIL-ST-PERE

10140 – Michelin map **313** G4 – pop. 415 – alt. 131
▶ Paris 209 – Châlons-en-Champagne 98 – Troyes 25 – Chaumont 79

⏶⏶⏶ Kawan Le Lac d'Orient 👤👥

📞 03 25 40 61 85. www.camping-lacdorient.com

Address : route du Lac

Opening times : from beginning April to end Sept.

4 ha (199 pitches) flat, grassy

Tariff : 35.40€ 👤👤 🚗 🔲 🔌 (10A) – Extra per person 8.50€ Reservation fee 10€

Rental rates : (from beginning April to end Sept.) 🚿 – 2 caravans – 15 🚐 – 2 🏠. Per night from 51 to 130€ – Per week from 306 to 910€ – Reservation fee 10€

🚽 borne – 9 🔲 16.40€

Surroundings : 🦢🌿
Leisure activities : 🍸🎮🏸🚣🎿🔲🎱🚤 multi-sports ground
Facilities : ♿ 🔓🆑 🎱🚿🚿🏚 launderette ⚄🚿
Nearby : 🎣🐎🏇

G P S Longitude : 4.34624
Latitude : 48.26297

MONTIGNY-LE-ROI

52140 – Michelin map **313** M6 – pop. 2 168 – alt. 404
▶ Paris 296 – Bourbonne-les-Bains 21 – Chaumont 35 – Langres 23

⏶ Municipal du Château

📞 03 25 87 38 93. www.campingduchateau.com

Address : rue Hubert Collot (access via the town centre and take the pedestrian path to the village)

Opening times : from mid April to end Sept.

6 ha/2 for camping (75 pitches)

Tariff : (2014 Price) 👤 5.80€ 🚗 5.80€ 🔲 5.80€ – 🔌 (10A) 4.80€

🚽 borne 2€

In a wooded park overlooking the Vallée de la Meuse.

Surroundings : ⬿ 🌳🌳
Leisure activities : 🚣🎿🚤
Facilities : ♿ 🔓🏚 🎱🚿
Nearby : ✕

G P S Longitude : 5.4965
Latitude : 48.00068

RADONVILLIERS

10500 – Michelin map **313** H3 – pop. 384 – alt. 130
▶ Paris 206 – Bar-sur-Aube 22 – Bar-sur-Seine 35 – Brienne-le-Château 6

⏶ Le Garillon

📞 03 25 92 21 46. www.campinglegarillon.fr

Address : take the southwestern exit along the D 11, follow the signs for Piney and take turning to the right; beside a stream and 250m from the lake, (top of dike via steps)

Opening times : from beginning April to beginning Oct.

1 ha (55 pitches) flat, grassy

Tariff : (2014 Price) 21€ 👤👤 🚗 🔲 🔌 (16A) – Extra per person 4€

Rental rates : (2014 Price) (from beginning April to beginning Oct.) – 10 🚐. Per night from 34 to 83€ – Per week from 204 to 498€

Leisure activities : 🚤
Facilities : ♿ 🔓🚿
Nearby : ✕

G P S Longitude : 4.50206
Latitude : 48.3586

SÉZANNE

51120 – Michelin map **306** E10 – pop. 5 268 – alt. 137
▶ Paris 116 – Châlons-en-Champagne 59 – Meaux 78 – Melun 89

🔺 Municipal

✆ 03 26 80 57 00. campingdesezanne@wanadoo.fr

Address : route de Launat (take the western exit along the D 373, follow the signs for Paris (near N 4) then continue 700m along the road to the left and take turning to the right)

1 ha (79 pitches)

Surroundings : ♀
Leisure activities : 🛶 🏓 ⛸
Facilities : ♿ ⚓ ⁕ 🖥
Nearby : ✗

G P S	Longitude : 3.70212
	Latitude : 48.72154

SIGNY-L'ABBAYE

08460 – Michelin map **306** I4 – pop. 1 365 – alt. 240
▶ Paris 208 – Charleville-Mézières 31 – Hirson 41 – Laon 74

🔺 Municipal l'Abbaye

✆ 03 24 52 87 73. www.signy-abbaye.fr – 🅵

Address : r. de l'Abbaye (situated north, near the stadium, beside the Vaux river)

Opening times : from beginning May to end Sept.

1.2 ha (60 pitches) flat, grassy, fine gravel

Tariff : (2014 Price) ⚬ 2€ ⟺ 1.50€ 🅴 1.70€ – (2) (15A) 3.20€

Surroundings : ♤ ♀
Facilities : ⌷ ✐ 🏚
Nearby : ✗

G P S	Longitude : 4.41967
	Latitude : 49.70134

SOULAINES-DHUYS

10200 – Michelin map **313** I3 – pop. 311 – alt. 153
▶ Paris 228 – Bar-sur-Aube 18 – Brienne-le-Château 17 – Chaumont 48

🔺 La Croix Badeau

✆ 03 25 27 05 43. www.croix-badeau.com

Address : 6 rue de La Croix Badeau (to the northeast of the town, near the church)

Opening times : from beginning April to end Sept.

1 ha (39 pitches)

Tariff : (2014 Price) 19€ ⚬⚬ ⟺ 🅴 (2) (10A) – Extra per person 3.80€
Rental rates : (2014 Price) (from beginning April to end Sept.) – 1 🚐. Per night from 50 to 70€ – Per week from 180 to 470€

🚐 borne 3€ – 39 🅴 19€

Surroundings : ⛩
Leisure activities : ♟ 🏚 ⛸
Facilities : ♿ ⚓ 🏚 ⛺ ⁕ ⁕
Nearby : 🛶 ✗

G P S	Longitude : 4.73846
	Latitude : 48.37672

THONNANCE-LES-MOULINS

52230 – Michelin map **313** L3 – pop. 120 – alt. 282
▶ Paris 254 – Bar-le-Duc 64 – Chaumont 48 – Commercy 55

🔼 Les Castels La Forge de Sainte Marie 🅰

✆ 03 25 94 42 00. www.laforgedesaintemarie.com

Address : route de Joinville (1.7km west along the D 427; beside the Rongeant river)

Opening times : from mid April to beginning Sept.

32 ha/3 for camping (133 pitches) terraced, relatively flat, flat, grassy, pond

Tariff : 32.50€ ⚬⚬ ⟺ 🅴 (2) (6A) – Extra per person 10€
Rental rates : (from mid April to beginning Sept.) – 45 🚐 – 15 gîtes. Per night from 70 to 150€ – Per week from 290 to 999€
Reservation fee 15€

🚐 borne – 10 🅴 30.50€

In a pleasant green setting based around an old restored forge.

Surroundings : ♤ ⛩ ♀
Leisure activities : ♟ ✗ 🏚 ⛸ 🏃 🛶 🚴 ⛳ ⛵
Facilities : ♿ ⚓ 🅴 ⛺ ⛲ ⁕ ⁕ launderette ⛲ ⛲

G P S	Longitude : 5.27097
	Latitude : 48.40629

*For more information on visiting particular towns or regions, consult the relevant regional **MICHELIN Green Guide**. We also recommend you use the appropriate Michelin regional map to locate your selected campsite, to calculate distances and to work out the best route.*

TROYES

10000 – Michelin map **313** E4 – pop. 61 188 – alt. 113
▶ Paris 170 – Dijon 185 – Nancy 186

🔼 Municipal

✆ 03 25 81 02 64. www.troyescamping.net

Address : at Pont Sainte-Marie, 7 rue Roger Salengro (situated 2km to the northeast, follow the signs for Nancy)

Opening times : from beginning April to mid Oct.

3.8 ha (150 pitches) flat, grassy

Tariff : (2014 Price) ⚬ 6.20€ ⟺ 🅴 9.20€ – (2) (10A) 3.20€
🚐 borne 3.50€ – 15 🅴 18.60€

Close to the bus stop for Troyes town centre and factory outlets at Pont Sainte-Marie.

Surroundings : ♀
Leisure activities : 🏚 🛶 🚴 🎣 ⛸
Facilities : ♿ ⚓ 🏚 ⁕ launderette
Nearby : ⛲ ⛵

G P S	Longitude : 4.09682
	Latitude : 48.31112

CORSICA

M. Rock / Cephas / Photononstop

Corsica emerges from the Mediterranean like a glinting jewel. It is indeed the 'Isle of Beauty'. Follow its twisting roads to ancient citadels, perched on the island's rocky flanks in spectacular cliff-top settings, and your efforts will be more than rewarded. Enjoy panoramic views and inhale the fragrance of wild rosemary as you make your way up the rugged hills, clad in *maquis* (Mediterranean shrubs and herbs). The sudden sight of a secluded chapel or timeless village, or indeed an unscheduled encounter with a herd of mountain sheep, are among the many lasting memories that those discovering Corsica on foot, by bike or in their cars take home with them. After exploring the wild interior of the island, plunge into the impossibly clear turquoise waters that surround it and recharge your solar batteries on its warm sandy beaches, dreaming of an *assiette de charcuterie* (pork platter) and traditional cheese. Corsica seduces the eyes and taste buds of every visitor.

Centuri

Pietracorbara

Marine de Farinole

Bastia

D 81

Lumio

Calvi

N 197

Moltifao

Castellare-di-Casinca

N 193

N 198

D 81

HAUTE - CORSE

Calacuccia

Corte

Porto

Piana

Vivario

Aléria

Cargèse

Tiuccia

N 193

Sagone

Casaglione

Calcatoggio

Ghisonaccia

D 81

CORSE

Ajaccio

DU

Solenzara

Zonza

Olmeto

Ste-Lucie-de-Porto-V.

Propriano

N 196

Pinarellu

Belvédère-Campomoro

SUD

Sartène

N 198

Porto-Vecchio

Figari

Bonifacio

●	Locality with campsite
■	Locality with campsite and rental option
Vannes	Locality with campsite and campervan area
Moyaux	Locality with at least one pleasant campsite
🚻	Motorway service area for campervans

AJACCIO

20000 – Michelin map **345** B8 – pop. 64 306
▶ Bastia 147 – Bonifacio 131 – Calvi 166 – Corte 80

⚠ Les Mimosas

✆ 04 95 20 99 85. www.camping-lesmimosas.com – 🏤 ⬜

Address : route d'Alata (5km, take the northern exit along the D 61 and take the turning to the left, follow the signs for Les Milelli)

Opening times : from beginning April to mid Oct.

2.5 ha (70 pitches)

Tariff : ♦ 6€ ⬅ 3€ 🔲 3€ – ⚡ (6A) 3€

Rental rates : Permanent ⬜ – 12 🚐 – 4 🏠 – 1 studio. Per week from 280 to 580€

🚽 borne 8€

Mobile homes and chalets to rent beneath pleasant shade from eucalyptus trees.

Surroundings : 🌲 ♊
Facilities : ♿ ⚲ 🚐 ☗ 🍽 launderette refrigerators

G P S Longitude : 8.73069
Latitude : 41.94066

ALÉRIA

20270 – Michelin map **345** G7 – pop. 1 996 – alt. 20
▶ Bastia 71 – Corte 50 – Vescovato 52

⛰⛰⛰ Marina d'Aléria ♣♟

✆ 04 95 57 01 42, www.marina-aleria.com

Address : plage de Padulone (3km east of Cateraggio along the N 200; beside the Tavignano river)

Opening times : from end April to beginning Oct.

17 ha/7 for camping (335 pitches)

Tariff : (2014 Price) 45.70€ ♦♦ ⬅ 🔲 ⚡ (9A) – Extra per person 7.40€ Reservation fee 25€

Rental rates : (from end April to beginning Oct.) ⬜ (from end April to end June) 🅿 (mobile homes) – 151 🚐 – 31 🏠. Per week from 220 to 1,200€ – Reservation fee 25€

Shady and sunny pitches laid out along the beach.

Surroundings : 🌲 ≼ sea and mountain ♊ ⛰
Leisure activities : 🍴 ✗ 🎮 ⏱daytime 🏃
🚣 🎠 🎯 ✖
Facilities : ♿ ⚲ ☗ 🍽 launderette ☁ 🍢 refrigerated food storage facilities

G P S Longitude : 9.55
Latitude : 42.11139

BASTIA

20200 – Michelin map **345** F3 – pop. 43 545
▶ Ajaccio 148 – Bonifacio 171 – Calvi 92 – Corte 69

⛰⛰⛰ San Damiano

✆ 04 95 33 68 02, www.campingsandamiano.com

Address : Lido de la Marana (9km southeast along the N 193 and turn left onto D 107)

Opening times : from beginning April to end Oct.

12 ha (320 pitches)

Tariff : (2014 Price) 31.60€ ♦♦ ⬅ 🔲 ⚡ (6A) – Extra per person 8.70€

Rental rates : (2014 Price) (from end March to beginning Nov.) ⬜ – 58 🚐 – 56 🏠. Per night from 49 to 185€ – Per week from 347 to 1,295€

🚽 borne

Some luxury chalets, some with with a sea view, and a bar-restaurant right next to the water.

Surroundings : 🌲 ⬜ ♊ ⛁
Leisure activities : 🍴 ✗ 🎮 🚣 ✖ 🐎 🎯 🏊
Facilities : ♿ ⚲ ☗ 🍽 launderette 🍢 🍢
Nearby : 🚣 🐎

G P S Longitude : 9.46718
Latitude : 42.63114

BELVÉDÈRE-CAMPOMORO

20110 – Michelin map **345** B10 – pop. 135 – alt. 5
▶ Ajaccio 88 – Bonifacio 72 – Porto 82 – Sartène 24

⚠ La Vallée

✆ 04 95 74 21 20. www.campomoro-lavallee.com ⬜

Address : at Campomoro (on the D 121, 400m from the beach)

Opening times : from beginning May to end Sept.

3.5 ha (199 pitches) terraced, flat and relatively flat, grassy, stony

Tariff : (2014 Price) ♦ 9€ ⬅ 5€ 🔲 10€ – ⚡ (16A) 6€

Rental rates : (2014 Price) (from beginning May to end Sept.) ⬜ 🅿 – 12 🏠 – 3 apartments. Per week from 750 to 1,200€ Reservation fee 40€

There's a view of the sea and the Genoese tower from some pitches and chalets.

Surroundings : 🌲 ♊
Facilities : ♿ ⚲ 🍽 🍢
Nearby : 🏊

G P S Longitude : 8.81625
Latitude : 41.62815

BONIFACIO

20169 – Michelin map **345** D11 – pop. 2 919 – alt. 55
▶ Ajaccio 132 – Corte 150 – Sartène 50

⛰⛰⛰ Pertamina Village - U-Farniente ♣♟

✆ 04 95 73 05 47. www.camping-pertamina.com

Address : Canelli (5km northeast along the N 198, follow the signs for Porto-Vecchio - Bastia)

Opening times : from beginning April to end Oct.

20 ha/8 for camping (150 pitches)

Tariff : 44€ ♦♦ ⬅ 🔲 ⚡ (6A) – Extra per person 12.50€ – Reservation fee 26€

Rental rates : (from beginning April to end Oct.) ♿ (1 mobile home) – 23 🚐 – 11 canvas bungalows. Per night from 50 to 171€ – Per week from 350 to 1,160€ – Reservation fee 26€

A pleasant, undulating site with plenty of shade and a variety of rental options, some of which are quite luxurious.

Surroundings : 🌲 ⬜ ♊
Leisure activities : 🍴 ✗ 🎮 ⏱ 🏃 🛀jacuzzi 🚣 ✖ 🎯 🏊
Facilities : ♿ ⚲ 🆑 ☗ 🍽 launderette ☁ 🍢 refrigerated food storage facilities

G P S Longitude : 9.17905
Latitude : 41.41825

Michelin classification:

⛰⛰⛰⛰ *Extremely comfortable, equipped to a very high standard*
⛰⛰⛰ *Very comfortable, equipped to a high standard*
⛰⛰⛰ *Comfortable and well equipped*
⛰⛰ *Reasonably comfortable*
⛰ *Satisfactory*

⚶⚶⚶ Rondinara

📞 04 95 70 43 15. www.rondinara.fr ⚓

Address : Suartone (18km northeast along the N 198, follow the signs for Porto-Vecchio and take D 158 to the right, follow the signs for La Pointe de la Rondinara (headland); 400m from the beach)

5 ha (120 pitches) terraced, relatively flat, flat, grassy, stony

Rentals : ⚓ – 36 🚐.

Situated in the heart of the maquis (typical shrubland), with a swimming pool, a restaurant and a panoramic view of the sea and Sardinia.

Surroundings : ⚶ ⚶ ⚶
Leisure activities : ⚶ ✗ ⚶ ⚶ ⚶
Facilities : ⚶ ⚶ ⚶ ⚶ ⚶ ⚶ refrigerated food storage facilities
Nearby : pedalos, bar-restaurant on the beach

GPS Longitude : 9.26289
Latitude : 41.47322

⚶⚶⚶ Les Îles

📞 04 95 73 11 89. www.camping-desiles.com ⚓

Address : route de Piantarella (4.5km east, follow the signs for Piantarella, towards the landing stage at Cavallo)

8 ha (150 pitches) undulating, relatively flat, flat, grassy, stony

Rentals : ⚶ (1 mobile home) ⚓ – 17 🚐 – 20 🏠.

Some pitches have a panoramic view over to Sardinia and nearby islands.

Surroundings : ⚶ ⚶ ⚶ ⚶
Leisure activities : ✗ ⚶ ⚶ ⚶ ⚶ ⚶
Facilities : ⚶ ⚶ ⚶ ⚶ ⚶ ⚶

GPS Longitude : 9.21034
Latitude : 41.37818

⚶⚶⚶ Campo-di-Liccia

📞 04 95 73 03 09. www.campingdiliccia.com ⚓

Address : Parmentil (5.2km northeast along the N 198, follow the signs for Porto-Vecchio)

Opening times : from mid April to end Sept.

5 ha (161 pitches) terrace, flat, stony

Tariff : (2014 Price) ⚶ 7.90€ ⚶ 3.70€ – ⚶ (10A) 4€ – Reservation fee 16€

Rental rates : (2014 Price) (from mid April to end Sept.) ⚓ – 52 🚐 – 16 🏠. Per night from 46 to 155€ – Per week from 288 to 950€ – Reservation fee 16€

🚰 borne 5€

Centuries-old Holm oaks, eucalyptus and olive trees provide generous amounts of shade; a mobile home park of a good standard.

Surroundings : ⚶ ⚶
Leisure activities : ⚶ ✗ ⚶ ⚶ ⚶
Facilities : ⚶ ⚶ (July-Aug.) ⚶ ⚶ ⚶ ⚶ ⚶ refrigerated food storage facilities

GPS Longitude : 9.17893
Latitude : 41.41943

⚶⚶ Pian del Fosse

📞 04 95 73 16 34. www.piandelfosse.com

Address : 3.8 km northeast along the D 58 - or 5km along the N 198 following the signs for Porto-Vecchio and take the D 60 following signs for Santa-Manza

Opening times : from mid April to mid Oct.

5.5 ha (100 pitches) terraced, flat and relatively flat, stony

Tariff : (2014 Price) ⚶ 8.50€ ⚶ 4.50€ ⚶ 7€ – ⚶ (16A) 4.50€ – Reservation fee 15€

Rental rates : (2014 Price) (from mid April to mid Oct.) ⚓ (from mid April to mid Oct.) – 1 🚐 – 5 🏠 – 6 studios – 12 canvas bungalows. Per night from 45 to 143€ – Per week from 250 to 930€ – Reservation fee 15€

🚰 borne

The pitches lie in the shade of mulberry or plane trees, pines and 400-year-old olive trees.

Surroundings : ⚶ ⚶ ⚶
Leisure activities : ✗ ⚶
Facilities : ⚶ ⚶ ⚶ ⚶ ⚶ launderette
Nearby : ⚶

GPS Longitude : 9.20083
Latitude : 41.39972

CALACUCCIA

20224 – Michelin map **345** D5 – pop. 316 – alt. 830
▶ Ajaccio 107 – Bastia 76 – Porto-Vecchio 146 – Corte 27

⚶ Acquaviva

📞 04 95 48 00 08. www.acquaviva-fr.com

Address : 500m southwest along the D 84 and take road to the left, opposite the service station

Opening times : from mid April to mid Oct.

4 ha (50 pitches) flat and relatively flat, stony, grassy

Tariff : ⚶ 7€ ⚶ 4€ ⚶ 6€ – ⚶ (16A) 4€

Rental rates : (from mid April to mid Oct.) – 2 caravans – 14 🛏 – 8 gîtes. Per night from 50 to 60€ – Per week from 350 to 420€

The site looks out over the lake with some shade; hotel and restaurant services are provided by the site owner.

Surroundings : ⚶ ⚶ Lake and mountains ⚶
Leisure activities : ⚶ ⚶
Facilities : ⚶ ⚶ ⚶ ⚶ ⚶
Nearby : ⚶ ✗ ⚶ ⚶

GPS Longitude : 9.01049
Latitude : 42.33341

---

*For more information on visiting particular towns or regions, consult the relevant regional **MICHELIN Green Guide**. We also recommend you use the appropriate Michelin regional map to locate your selected campsite, to calculate distances and to work out the best route.*

CALCATOGGIO

20111 – Michelin map **345** B7 – pop. 522 – alt. 250
▶ Ajaccio 23 – Bastia 156

⚶⚶ La Liscia

📞 04 95 52 20 65. www.la-liscia.com

Address : route de Tiuccia (5km northwest along the D 81; beside the river, in the Golfe de La Liscia (bay), 500m from the beach)

3 ha (100 pitches)

Rentals : ⚓ – 7 🚐 – 1 🏠 – 3 studios.

The site is partly laid out across well-shaded terraces, but choose the pitches furthest away from the road. Basic sanitary facilities.

Surroundings : ⚶
Leisure activities : ⚶ ✗ ⚶ ⚶ ⚶
Facilities : ⚶ ⚶ ⚶ ⚶ launderette ⚶ refrigerators

GPS Longitude : 8.75526
Latitude : 42.04678

CALVI

20260 – Michelin map **345** B4 – pop. 5 377
▶ Bastia 92 – Corte 88 – L'Ile-Rousse 25 – Porto 73

▲▲▲ La Pinède ♣♣

📞 04 95 65 17 80. www.camping-calvi.com

Address : route de la Pinède (300m from the beach)

5 ha (262 pitches)

Rentals : ♿ – 14 caravans – 20 🚐 – 80 🏠.

Choose the pitches away from the road in preference.

Surroundings : ♤♤
Leisure activities : ♈ ✕ 🏚 ⚗ ⚓ ✂ ♨ ⚒
multi-sports ground
Facilities : ♿ ⚡ ⚒♈ launderette ⚗⚒
refrigerated food storage facilities
Nearby : 🛒

G P S Longitude : 8.76795
Latitude : 42.55318

▲▲▲ Les Castors

📞 04 95 65 13 30. www.camping-castors.fr ✗

Address : route de Piétramaggiore (located 1km south along the N 197 towards L'Île Rousse and follow the signs for Pietra-Major to the right)

Opening times : from beginning April to end Oct.

2 ha (105 pitches)

Tariff : (2014 Price) ♈ 7€ ⚐ 2€ 📧 3€ – (½) (15A) 4.50€
Rental rates : (from beginning April to end Oct.) ✗ – 36 🚐 – 28 studios – 11 apartments. Per night from 60 to 212€ – Per week from 371 to 1,295€

🚽 borne

Well shaded, in many cases by eucalyptus trees; many different rental options.

Surroundings : ⚘♤♤
Leisure activities : ♈ ✕ ⚓ ⚒ ⚒
Facilities : ♿ ⚡ ⚒♈ 📧

G P S Longitude : 8.7561
Latitude : 42.55735

▲▲ Bella Vista

📞 04 95 65 11 76. www.camping-bellavista.com – 🍴

Address : route de Pietramaggiore (head 1.5km south along the N 197 towards l'Île Rousse and follow the signs for Pietra-Major to the right)

Opening times : from beginning April to end Sept.

6 ha/4 for camping (152 pitches)

Tariff : (2014 Price) ♈ 8.50€ ⚐ 4.50€ 📧 4.50€ – (½) (10A) 4.50€
Rental rates : (2014 Price) (from beginning April to mid Oct.) ✗ – 21 🏠. Per night from 60 to 150€ – Per week from 220 to 980€ Reservation fee 15€

🚽 20 📧 9€

In the shade of pine and eucalyptus trees and oleanders.

Surroundings : ⚘♤♤
Leisure activities : ✕ ⚓
Facilities : ♿ ⚡ Ⓟ ⚗⚒♈♈ 📧⚒⚒

G P S Longitude : 8.75334
Latitude : 42.55068

There are several different types of sani-station ('borne' in French) – sanitation points providing fresh water and disposal points for grey water. See page 12 for further details.

▲▲ Paradella

📞 04 95 65 00 97. www.camping-paradella.fr ✉ 20214 Calenzana

Address : route de la forêt de Bonifato (9.5km southeast along the N 197, follow the signs for l'Ile-Rousse and take D 81 to the right, follow the signs for the airport and Bonifato)

Opening times : from beginning April to end Sept.

5 ha (150 pitches)

Tariff : 28.50€ ♈♈ ⚐ 📧 (½) (8A) – Extra per person 8.60€

Reservation fee 10€

Rental rates : (from beginning April to end Sept.) ✗ (from beginning July to end Aug.) – 2 🚐 – 18 🏠. Per week from 290 to 790€ – Reservation fee 10€

🚽 borne 5€

Choose the pitches away from the road in preference, sheltered by pines and eucalyptus trees.

Surroundings : ⚏♤♤
Leisure activities : ⚓ ⚒ ⚒
Facilities : ♿ ⚡ ⚗♈ 📧⚒
Nearby : 🏇

G P S Longitude : 8.79166
Latitude : 42.50237

▲ Paduella

📞 04 95 65 06 16. www.campingpaduella.com

Address : route de Bastia (1.8km southeast along the N 197, follow the signs for l'Ile-Rousse; 400m from the beach)

Opening times : from beginning May to beginning Oct.

4.5 ha (160 pitches)

Tariff : ♈ 8.50€ ⚐ 3.60€ 📧 3.60€ – (½) (8A) 3.80€

Rental rates : (from beginning May to beginning Oct.) – 38 canvas bungalows. Per night from 55 to 85€ – Per week from 385 to 595€

🚽 borne

Some pitches are well marked out in the shade of a beautiful pine wood.

Surroundings : ♤♤
Leisure activities : ♈ ⚓
Facilities : ♿ ⚡ ⚏ ⚗ ⚒♈ 📧⚒
Nearby : 🛒

G P S Longitude : 8.76429
Latitude : 42.55219

We have selected the best campsites in France with our usual care, listing those with the best facilities in the most pleasant surroundings.

▲ Dolce Vita

📞 04 95 65 05 99. www.dolce-vita.fr ✗

Address : 4.5km southeast along the N 197, follow the signs for l'Ile-Rousse; at the mouth of the Figarella river, 200m from the sea

Opening times : from mid May to mid Sept.

6 ha (200 pitches)

Tariff : (2014 Price) ♈ 9.90€ ⚐ 3.50€ 📧 7€ – (½) (10A) 4.50€

Choose the pitches near the sea, away from the road and the Calvil'–Île Rousse railway line.

Surroundings : ⚒⚒⚒
Leisure activities : ✕ ⚓ ⚓ ⚒ ⚓
Facilities : ♿ ⚡ ⚏⚐ ⚒ ♈ launderette ⚗⚒
Nearby : ⚓

G P S Longitude : 8.78972
Latitude : 42.55582

CARGÈSE

20130 – Michelin map **345** A7 – pop. 1 117 – alt. 75
▶ Ajaccio 51 – Calvi 106 – Corte 119 – Piana 21

⛰ Torraccia

✆ 04 95 26 42 39. www.camping-torraccia.com

Address : at Bagghiuccia (4.5km north along the D 81, follow the signs for Porto)

Opening times : from end April to end Sept.

3 ha (90 pitches) terraced, flat, grassy, stony

Tariff : (2014 Price) ♟ 9.70€ ⮐ 4.50€ ▣ 4.50€ – (⚡) (10A) 4.50€ – Reservation fee 18.50€

Rental rates : (2014 Price) (from end April to end Sept.) – 25 ⌂. Per night from 60 to 120€ – Per week from 335 to 920€ – Reservation fee 18.50€

Choose the pitches furthest away from the road. Good sanitary facilities and some chalets have a panoramic view.

Surroundings : ⩽ 💧💧	**GPS** Longitude : 8.59797
Leisure activities : 🍸 jacuzzi ⮐ 🏊	Latitude : 42.16258
Facilities : ♿ ⚐ 🍴 🧺	

The prices listed were supplied by the campsite owners in 2014 (if prices were not available, those from the previous year are given). The fees should be regarded as basic charges and may fluctuate with inflation.

CASAGLIONE

20111 – Michelin map **345** B7 – pop. 365 – alt. 150
▶ Ajaccio 33 – Bastia 166

⛰ U Sommalu

✆ 04 95 52 24 21, www.usommalu-camping.fr

Address : route de Casaglione (3km northeast along the D 81, then right onto the D 25, 600m from La plage de Liamone (beach)

Opening times : from beginning April to end Sept.

4 ha (123 pitches) terraced, flat and relatively flat, stony, grassy

Tariff : (2014 Price) ♟ 8.50€ ⮐ 4€ ▣ 4€ – (⚡) (16A) 4.50€

Rental rates : (2014 Price) (from mid April to end Sept.) – 36 🚐 – 12 ⌂. Per week from 385 to 840 € – Reservation fee 5€

🚐 borne

Shady pitches arranged in terraces, some of which have a sea view.

Surroundings : 🌲 💧💧	**GPS** Longitude : 8.73126
Leisure activities : 🍸 🏠 ⮐ 🏊	Latitude : 42.07027
Facilities : ♿ ⚐ 🍴 launderette	

CASTELLARE-DI-CASINCA

20213 – Michelin map **345** F5 – pop. 557 – alt. 140
▶ Paris 943 – Ajaccio 136 – Bastia 31

⛰ Tohapi Domaine d'Anghione 👥

(rental of mobile homes and gîtes only)

✆ 04 95 36 50 22, www.village-center.fr

Address : at Anghione (6km along the D 106)

Opening times : from beginning April to mid Oct.

40 ha/26 for camping flat

Rental rates : (2014 Price) – 95 🚐 – 155 gîtes. Per night from 36 to 164€ – Per week from 252 to 1,148€ – Reservation fee 10€

A holiday village close to the beach with plenty of green spaces.

Surroundings : 🌲 💧💧 ⛰	**GPS** Longitude : 9.52707
Leisure activities : 🍸 ✗ 🏠 🎣 ⛹ ⮐ 🎿 🚵 multi-sports ground	Latitude : 42.47547
Facilities : ♿ ⚐ 🍴 launderette ⚘	
Nearby : 🐎	

CENTURI

20238 – Michelin map **345** F2 – pop. 221 – alt. 228
▶ Ajaccio 202 – Bastia 55

⛰ Isulottu

✆ 04 95 35 62 81, www.isulottu.fr

Address : Marine de Mute (head along the D 35 following the signs for Morsiglia, 200m from the beach)

Opening times : from beginning May to end Sept.

2.3 ha (150 pitches)

Tariff : (2014 Price) 26.30€ ♟♟ ⮐ ▣ (⚡) (20A) – Extra per person 7.60€

🚐 borne 7€

Well-shaded pitches laid out across a series of small terraces, some of which have a view of the sea or the village.

Surroundings : 🌲 ⩽ 💧💧	**GPS** Longitude : 9.3515
Leisure activities : 🍸 ⮐	Latitude : 42.96048
Facilities : ♿ ⚐ 🍴 🧺 ⚘	
Nearby : scuba diving	

CORTE

20250 – Michelin map **345** D6 – pop. 6 744 – alt. 396
▶ Ajaccio 81 – Bastia 68

⛰ Aire Naturelle St-Pancrace

✆ 04 95 46 09 22, www.campingsaintpancrace.fr

Address : Saint-Pancrace district (located 1.5km north along the Cours Paoli and take road to the left after the Sous-Préfecture)

Opening times : from mid April to mid Oct.

12 ha/1 camping (25 pitches)

Tariff : ♟ 6€ ⮐ 3€ ▣ 4€ – (⚡) (45A) 4€

🚐 borne

A farm campsite with produce for sale: ewe's milk and tomme cheese and a range of jams.

Surroundings : 🌲 ⩽ 💧💧	**GPS** Longitude : 9.14696
Leisure activities : 🏠	Latitude : 42.32026
Facilities : ⚐ 🍴 ⛺	

FARINOLE (MARINA DE)

20253 – Michelin map **345** F3 – pop. 224 – alt. 250
▶ Bastia 20 – Rogliano 61 – St-Florent 13

⛰ A Stella

✆ 04 95 37 14 37. www.campingastella.com

Address : along the D 80; beside the sea

3 ha (100 pitches) terraced, relatively flat, flat, grassy, stony

Rentals : 2 apartments.

Some sunny pitches are available with a sea view; close to a pebble beach.

Surroundings : 🏖 ⬅ ♨ ⚠
Leisure activities : 🎦
Facilities : ⚡ 🅿 🚿

GPS Longitude : 9.34259
Latitude : 42.72911

FIGARI

20114 – Michelin map **345** D11 – pop. 1 217 – alt. 80
▶ Ajaccio 122 – Bonifacio 18 – Porto-Vecchio 20 – Sartène 39

⚠ U Moru

📞 04 95 71 23 40. www.u-moru.com

Address : 5km northeast along the D 859

Opening times : from mid June to mid Sept.

6 ha/4 for camping (100 pitches) flat and relatively flat, sandy

Tariff : 🚹 8.20€ ⬅ 3.80€ 🅴 5.80€ – 🔌 (6A) 5€

Rental rates : (from mid June to mid Sept.) ♿ (1 mobile home) – 12 🛖. Per week from 590 to 970€

The pitches are well shaded and the mobile home terraces are well equipped.

Surroundings : ⊏ ♨
Leisure activities : 🎦 ⛵ 🏊
Facilities : ♿ ⚡ 🍴 🅿 🧺, refrigerators

GPS Longitude : 9.16564
Latitude : 41.53096

GHISONACCIA

20240 – Michelin map **345** F7 – pop. 3 669 – alt. 25
▶ Bastia 85 – Aléria 14 – Ghisoni 27 – Venaco 56

🏕 Arinella-Bianca ♟♟

📞 04 95 56 04 78. www.arinellabianca.com

Address : route de la mer (3.5km east along the D 144 then continue 700m along the road to the right)

Opening times : from mid April to end Sept.

10 ha (416 pitches)

Tariff : 54€ 🚹🚹 ⬅ 🅴 🔌 (10A) – Extra per person 16€ – Reservation fee 50€

Rental rates : (from mid April to beginning Oct.) ♿ – 180 🛖 – 56 🛖. Per night from 55 to 90€ – Per week from 305 to 1,590€ Reservation fee 50€

🚐 borne 8€

A pretty seaside area with a pleasant 'zen' water park, several luxurious rental options and a relaxation area close to the beach.

Surroundings : ♨ ⚠
Leisure activities : 🍴 ✗ 🎦 🏕 ⛹ ⛷ ♨ hammam, jacuzzi ⛵ ✗ 🏊 🎾 tourist information , multi-sports ground, spa centre, water park
Facilities : ♿ ⚡ 🚿 🍴 🧺 🧺, refrigerated food storage facilities
Nearby : 🎣 ⚓

GPS Longitude : 9.44331
Latitude : 41.9972

🏕 Homair Vacances Marina d'Erba Rossa ♟♟

📞 04 95 56 25 14. www.marina-erbarossa.com

Address : route de la Mer (4km east along the D 144; beside the beach)

Opening times : from April to Oct.

12 ha/8 for camping (588 pitches) flat, grassy

Tariff : 27€ 🚹🚹 ⬅ 🅴 🔌 (8A) – Extra per person 10.50€ – Reservation fee 49€

Rental rates : (from beginning April to mid Oct.) ✂ – 350 🛖 – 90 🛖 – 25 gîtes. Per night from 28 to 219€ – Per week from 196 to 1,533€ – Reservation fee 49€

In a green and shaded setting, with a relaxation area close to the beach. There's an option for full-board or half-board stays.

Surroundings : ⊏ ♨ ⚠
Leisure activities : 🍴 ✗ 🎦 ⛹ 🏕 ♨ jacuzzi ⛵ ✗ 🏊 wildlife park, spa centre
Facilities : ♿ ⚡ 🅴 🅿 🍴 🍴 launderette 🧺, 🧺 refrigerated food storage facilities
Nearby : 🤿 scuba diving

🏕 Sunêlia Perla Di Mare

Perla Di Mare

(rental of mobile homes, gîtes and apartments only)

📞 04 95 56 53 10. www.perla.di.mare.fr

Address : plage de Vignale

Opening times : Permanent

10 ha (174 pitches) undulating

Rental rates : ♿ (2 mobile homes) ✂ – 100 🛖 – 4 studios – 50 apartments. Per night from 50 to 178€ – Per week from 350 to 1,246€ – Reservation fee 30€

A range of rental options with a relaxation area close to the beach.

Surroundings : 🏖 ♟ ⚠
Leisure activities : 🍴 ✗ 🎦 ⛹ 🏕 hammam, jacuzzi ⛵ 🚲 🏊 archery, spa centre
Facilities : ⚡ 🍴 launderette 🧺

GPS Longitude : 9.4558
Latitude : 42.00647

LUMIO

20260 – Michelin map **345** B4 – pop. 1 250 – alt. 150
▶ Ajaccio 158 – Bastia 83 – Corte 77 – Calvi 10

⚠ Le Panoramic

📞 04 95 60 73 13. www.le-panoramic.com

Address : route de Lavatoggio (situated 2km northeast on the D 71, follow the signs for Belgodère)

6 ha (108 pitches)

Rentals : ✂ – 7 🛖.

Some of the pitches have a panoramic view of the sea.

Surroundings : 🏖 ⬅ ♨
Leisure activities : ✗ 🏊
Facilities : ⚡ 🅿 🧺

GPS Longitude : 8.84805
Latitude : 42.58973

MOLTIFAO

20218 – Michelin map **345** D5 – pop. 724 – alt. 420
▶ Ajaccio 113 – Bastia 58

⚠ E Canicce

📞 04 95 35 16 75. http://www.campingecanicce.com

Address : Vallée de l'Asco (3km south on the D 47; beside the Asco river)

Opening times : from beginning March to end Oct.

1 ha (25 pitches)

Tariff : 23€ ✶✶ ⬅ 🔲 (10A) – Extra per person 6€

Rental rates : (from beginning Jan. to end Nov.) ✗ – 3 🛏 – 3 apartments – 3 gîtes. Per night from 50 to 70€ – Per week from 550 to 690€

In the heart of the maquis (typical shrubland), at the foot of mountains and beside a stream.

Surroundings : ⛰ ⬳ Monte Cinto and Scala di Santa Régina (gorge) ♨♨ Leisure activities : ♒ Facilities : ⚬ ⬆ ⏚ 🔲	**G P S**	Longitude : 9.13444 Latitude : 42.47573

OLMETO

20113 – Michelin map **345** C9 – pop. 1 230 – alt. 320
▶ Ajaccio 64 – Propriano 8 – Sartène 20

⚠ L'Esplanade

📞 04 95 76 05 03, www.camping-esplanade.com

Address : at Olmeto-plage (1.6km along the D 157, 100m from the beach - direct access)

4.5 ha (100 pitches) extremely uneven

Rentals : ✗ Ⓟ (chalets) – 8 caravans – 53 🛏 – 6 tipis – 2 tent lodges.

Choose the pitches furthest away from the road. There's a panoramic view from some chalets, a swimming pool and a restaurant.

Surroundings : ⛰ ♨♨ Leisure activities : ✗ 🍴 ⬆ ⛵ Facilities : ♿ ⚬ 🔲 ⏚ ⬆	**G P S**	Longitude : 8.88868 Latitude : 41.69562

PIANA

20115 – Michelin map **345** A6 – pop. 450 – alt. 420
▶ Ajaccio 72 – Calvi 85 – Évisa 33 – Porto 13

⚠ Plage d'Arone

📞 04 95 20 64 54– 🅵

Address : route Danièle Casanova (11.5km southwest along the D 824; 500m from the beach - direct access)

Opening times : from mid May to end Sept.

3.8 ha (125 pitches) terraced, open site, flat, grassy, stony

Tariff : (2014 Price) ✶ 9€ ⬅ 6€ 🔲 7€ – 🔌 (6A) 3€

Situated 500m from the beach in the maquis (typical shrubland), shaded by olive, eucalyptus, bay and other trees and Mediterranean shrubs.

Surroundings : ⛰ ⬳ ♨♨ Facilities : ♿ ⚬ 🔲 ⬆ ⏚ 🔲 ⬆	**G P S**	Longitude : 8.58092 Latitude : 42.20843

PIETRACORBARA

20233 – Michelin map **345** F2 – pop. 573 – alt. 150
▶ Paris 967 – Ajaccio 170 – Bastia 21 – Biguglia 31

⛰ La Pietra

📞 04 95 35 27 49. www.la-pietra.com

Address : head 4km southeast along the D 232 and take road to the left; 500m from the beach

Opening times : from mid March to beginning Nov.

3 ha (80 pitches)

Tariff : ✶ 9.95€ ⬅ 3.80€ 🔲 5€ – 🔌 (6A) 3.50€

🚐 borne

A well-maintained campsite with shaded, marked-out pitches or on a sunny meadow.

Surroundings : ⛰ ⬳ 🏠 ♨♨ Leisure activities : ✗ 🍴 ⬆ ⛵ ⛱ Facilities : ♿ ⚬ ⬆ ⏚ 🔲 🔲, refrigerated food storage facilities Nearby : 🐎	**G P S**	Longitude : 9.4739 Latitude : 42.83939

To make the best possible use of this guide, please read pages 2–15 carefully.

PINARELLU

20124 – Michelin map **345** F9
▶ Ajaccio 146 – Bonifacio 44 – Porto-Vecchio 16

⚠ California

📞 04 95 71 49 24. www.camping-california.net ✉ 20144 Ste-Lucie-de-Porto-Vecchio ✈ (July–Aug.)

Address : 800m south along the D 468 and 1.5km along the road to the left; beside the beach

Opening times : from beginning June to end Sept.

7 ha/5 for camping (100 pitches)

Tariff : (2014 Price) ✶ 11€ ⬅ 3€ 🔲 11€ – 🔌 4€

Situated near lakes and the sea, in an exclusive location in an unspoilt setting.

Surroundings : ⛰ ♨♨ ⬆ Leisure activities : ✗ ⬆ ⛵ Facilities : ♿ ⚬ Ⓟ 🔲 🔲 🔲 ⏚ 🔲 ⬆	**G P S**	Longitude : 9.38084 Latitude : 41.66591

PORTO

20150 – Michelin map **345** B6 – pop. 544
▶ Ajaccio 84 – Calvi 73 – Corte 93 – Évisa 23

⛰ Les Oliviers ♟♟

📞 04 95 26 14 49. www.camping-oliviers-porto.com ✉ 20150 Ota ✈

Address : Pont de Porto (just off the D81, beside the Porto river, 100m from the town)

Opening times : from end March to beginning Nov.

5.4 ha (216 pitches) very uneven, terraced, flat, stony, rocks

Tariff : ✶ 10.80€ ⬅ 4€ 🔲 7.80€ – 🔌 (5A) 4.50€ – Reservation fee 15€

Rental rates : (from end March to beginning Nov.) ✗ – 6 caravans – 40 🛏. Per night from 58 to 222€ – Per week from 320 to 1,589€ – Reservation fee 16€

🚐 3 🔲

An attractive swimming pool area in a natural setting with trees and shrubs.

Surroundings : 🏖 🌳 🗻
Leisure activities : 🍴 🍽 🎯 🏓 🏊 hammam 🛶 🏊 diving (sub aqua) school, spa centre
Facilities : ♿ ⚡ 🅿 🚿 🧺 launderette 🛒 refrigerated food storage facilities
Nearby : 🍴🐎🎣

GPS Longitude : 8.71005
Latitude : 42.26242

🔺🔺🔺 Sole e Vista

📞 04 95 26 15 71, www.camping-sole-e-vista.com ✉ 20150 Ota

Address : in the village (main access via the supermarket car park – secondary access: head 1km east along the D 124, follow the signs for Ota, 150m from the Porto and the town)

Opening times : from mid March to mid Nov.

4 ha (170 pitches) very uneven, terraced, flat, stony, rocks Tariff : 28€ ★★ 🚐 🔲 🚐 (10A) – Extra per person 9€
Rental rates : Permanent 🏠 – 34 🏠. Per night from 50 to 100€ – Per week from 280 to 1,350€
🚐 borne – 30 🔲 28€ – 🚰 28€

In a natural, wooded setting with pitches on numerous small terraces. There's a panoramic view of the sea and the mountains from the swimming pool and restaurant.

Surroundings : 🏖 🌳 🗻
Leisure activities : 🍴 🛶 🏊
Facilities : 🚿 🍴 launderette, refrigerators
Nearby : 🍴🐎🎣

GPS Longitude : 8.71114
Latitude : 42.26313

🔺🔺 Funtana a l'Ora

📞 04 95 26 11 65. www.funtanaalora.com ✉ 20150 Ota

Address : route d'Évisa (1.4km southeast along the D 84, 200m from the Porto)

Opening times : from beginning April to mid Nov.

2 ha (70 pitches) very uneven, terraced, flat and relatively flat, stony, rocks

Tariff : ★ 9.40€ 🚐 4€ 🔲 7€ – 🚐 (10A) 4€ – Reservation fee 15€
Rental rates : (from beginning April to mid Nov.) – 7 🏠. Per night from 46 to 236€ – Per week from 290 to 1,500€ – Reservation fee 15€
🚐 borne – 10 🔲 5€

Pitches with good amounts of shade on numerous small terraces, in a natural and unspoilt setting.

Surroundings : 🏖 🌳 🗻
Leisure activities : 🎮 🛶 multi-sports ground
Facilities : ♿ 🚿 🍴 launderette 🛒 refrigerated food storage facilities

GPS Longitude : 8.71528
Latitude : 42.25887

These symbols are used for a campsite that is exceptional in its category:

🔺🔺🔺...🔺 *Particularly pleasant setting, quality and range of services available*

🏖 🏖 *Tranquil, isolated site – quiet site, particularly at night*

≪ ≪ *Exceptional view – interesting or panoramic view*

🔺 Casa del Torrente (rental of chalets only)

📞 04 95 22 45 14. www.casadeltorrente.com ✉ 20150 Ota

Address : route Evisa (located 1km southeast along the D 84; beside the Porto river (direct access)

Opening times : from beginning April to mid Nov.

1.5 ha terraced

Rental rates : 🏠 – 12 🏠. Per night from 46 to 236€ – Per week from 290 to 1,500€

Gîtes for large families and free use of the leisure facilities and services at the Funtana a l'Ora campsite 200m on the other side of the road.

Surroundings : 🏖 🌿
Leisure activities : 🛶
Facilities : 🚿 🍴 🍴 🖼
Nearby : 🛶

GPS Longitude : 8.70824
Latitude : 42.26209

Do not confuse:
🔺 *to* 🔺🔺🔺 : *MICHELIN classification with*
★ *to* ★★★★★ : *official classification*

PORTO-VECCHIO

20137 – Michelin map **345** E10 – pop. 11 005 – alt. 40
▶ Ajaccio 141 – Bonifacio 28 – Corte 121 – Sartène 59

🔺🔺🔺 Golfo di Sogno

📞 04 95 70 08 98. www.golfo-di-sogno.fr 🏠

Address : route de Cala-Rossa (6km northeast along the D 468)

Opening times : from beginning May to end Sept.

22 ha (650 pitches)

Tariff : (2014 Price) 30€ ★★ 🚐 🔲 🚐 (6A) – Extra per person 9.90€
Rental rates : (2014 Price) (from beginning May to end Sept.) – 12 🏠 – 61 🏠 – 12 gîtes – 138 bungalows (without sanitary facilities). Per week from 290 to 2,240€

In a very pleasant pine wood beside the sea; a spacious site with a range of rental options of varying degrees of quality.

Surroundings : 🌳 🌿 🏖
Leisure activities : 🍴 🍽 🛶 🏓 🎣 🚣 watersports centre, multi-sports ground
Facilities : 🚿 🖼 🧺 launderette 🍴 🛒
Nearby : ⚓

GPS Longitude : 9.31297
Latitude : 41.62975

🔺🔺 Pitrera

📞 04 95 70 20 10. www.pitrera.com

Address : La Trinite (head 5.8km north along the N 198, follow the signs for Bastia and take road to the right)

Opening times : from end March to beginning Oct.

4 ha (95 pitches)

Tariff : (2014 Price) ★ 7.90€ 🚐 4.10€ 🔲 8€ – 🚐 (6A) 3.50€ – Reservation fee 15€
Rental rates : (2014 Price) (from end March to beginning Oct.) – 1 🏠 – 56 🏠 – 1 yurt. Per night from 57 to 114€ – Per week from 399 to 1,309€ – Reservation fee 10€

Well-shaded pitches, a lovely swimming pool area and a panoramic sea view from some chalets.

Surroundings : 🗻
Leisure activities : 🍴 🛶 🛶 🏊 🏄
Facilities : ♿ 🚿 🍴 🍴 🖼 🛒

GPS Longitude : 9.29535
Latitude : 41.63461

▲▲ U Pirellu

✆ 04 95 70 23 44. www.u-pirellu.com – acces to some pitches via steep slope – 🏕 ⚡

Address : route de Palombaggia (located 9km to the east, at Piccovagia)

Opening times : from mid April to end Sept.

5 ha (150 pitches) very uneven, terraced, flat and relatively flat, grassy, stony

Tariff : (2014 Price) 🚶 9.80€ ⇔ 4€ 🔲 4.50€ – 🔌 (6A) 4€

Rental rates : (2014 Price) (from mid April to end Sept.) ⚡ – 17 🏠. Per night from 60 to 180€ – Per week from 360 to 1,550€ Reservation fee 10€

Some chalets have a panoramic view of the sea and La Pointe de la Chiappa (headland).

Surroundings : ⬚ ⊏⊐ ♤♤
Leisure activities : 🍸 ✕ ⛵ ⊐
Facilities : ♿ ⚷ 🅿 ⛺♀ 🔲 ⊒ ⊒
Nearby : ⛺

▲▲ La Vetta

✆ 04 95 70 09 86. www.campinglavetta.com

Address : La Trinité (5.5km north on N 198, follow the signs for Bastia)

8 ha (100 pitches) terraced, sloping, flat, grassy, stony, rocks

Rentals : ⚡ – 41 ⛟ – 6 🏠.

In an unspoilt and natural setting with some high-quality rental options, but choose the pitches away from the road in preference.

Surroundings : ♤♤
Leisure activities : ✕ ⛵ ⊐
Facilities : ♿ ⚷ ⊒♀ 🔲

▲▲ Arutoli

✆ 04 95 70 12 73, www.arutoli.com

Address : route de l'Ospédale (situated 2km northwest along the D 368)

Opening times : from beginning April to beginning Nov.

4 ha (150 pitches)

Tariff : 24.45€ 🚶🚶 ⇔ 🔲 🔌 (6A) – Extra per person 7€

Rental rates : Permanent – 28 🏠 – 28 gîtes. Per night from 54 to 205€ – Per week from 393 to 1,057€ – Reservation fee 12€

🚐 borne

Well-shaded pitches with a variety of rental options.

Surroundings : ♤♤
Leisure activities : ✕ ⌂ ⊐
Facilities : ♿ ⚷ ⊒♀ 🔲 ⊒ ⊒
Nearby : 🏇

GPS Longitude : 9.3322
Latitude : 41.58962

GPS Longitude : 9.29356
Latitude : 41.63285

GPS Longitude : 9.26556
Latitude : 41.60186

Using the traditional Michelin classification method, the guide provides you with an easy, speedy reference for assessing the category of each site: 1 to 5 tents (see page 10).

▲▲ Bella Vista

✆ 04 95 70 58 01, www.bella-vista.cc ⚡

Address : route de Palombaggia (located 9.3km to the east, at Piccovagia)

Opening times : from end May to mid Sept.

2.5 ha (100 pitches) very uneven, terraced, flat, grassy, stony

Tariff : 🚶 8€ ⇔ 4€ 🔲 4€ – 🔌 (6A) 4€

Rental rates : Permanent ⚡ – 8 🏠. Per week from 450 to 1,500€

Some chalets have a panoramic view of the sea and La Pointe de la Chiappa (headland).

Surroundings : ⬚ ≤ ♤♤
Leisure activities : ✕ ⊐
Facilities : ♿ ⚷ ⊒♀ 🔲

GPS Longitude : 9.3367
Latitude : 41.58672

▲ Les Ilots d'Or

✆ 04 95 70 01 30. www.campingleslilotsdor.com

Address : route Pezza Cardo (head 6km northeast along the D 568 or the N 198, follow the signs for Bastia and take a right turn along the D 468 b before La Trinité)

4 ha (176 pitches) terraced, flat, grassy, flat, rocks

Rentals : ⚡ – 3 ⛟ – 23 🏠.

Some pitches are virtually on top of the water!

Surroundings : ⬚ ⊏⊐ ♤♤ ⬔
Leisure activities : ✕
Facilities : ♿ ⚷ ⊒♀ 🔲
Nearby : ⚓

GPS Longitude : 9.30819
Latitude : 41.6275

▲ Les Jardins du Golfe

✆ 04 95 70 46 92, www.a-stella.org

Address : route de Palombaggia (5.2km to the south)

4 ha (200 pitches) sloping, flat, grassy, sandy

Rentals : 9 🏠.

Surroundings : ♤♤
Leisure activities : 🍸 ⊐ (small swimming pool)
Facilities : ⚷ ⛺♀ 🔲
Nearby : ⊒

GPS Longitude : 9.2905
Latitude : 41.57353

PROPRIANO

20110 – Michelin map **345** C9 – pop. 3 292 – alt. 5
▶ Ajaccio 70 – Bastia 202 – Olbia 126 – Sassari 32

▲▲▲ Village Vacances U Livanti (rental of chalets only)

✆ 04 95 76 08 06. www.ulivanti.com

Address : at Portigliolo - route de Campomoro (8km south along the RN 196 and take D 121; in the Gulf of Le Valinco)

6 ha terraced

Rentals : ⚡ 🅿 – 89 🏠.

A chalet village of various standards, from basic to high quality, with pretty, well-kept terraces and a restaurant right beside the water.

Surroundings : ⬚ ♀ ⬔
Leisure activities : 🍸 ✕ ⛹
Facilities : ⚷⊐ ⛺♀ 🔲
Nearby : ⚓ water skiing

GPS Longitude : 8.86912
Latitude : 41.64491

SAGONE

20118 – Michelin map **345** B7
▶ Ajaccio 38 – Calvi 119 – Corte 106 – Sartène 110

⚠ Le Sagone ♣♣

📞 0495280415. www.camping-sagone.com

Address : route de Vico (2km north along the D 70)

Opening times : from beginning April to end Sept.

30 ha/9 for camping (300 pitches) flat, grassy

Tariff : ♦ 9.20€ ⬅ 2.60€ 📧 8.50€ – (⚡) (10A) 5.50€ – Reservation fee 5€

Rental rates : (from beginning April to end Oct.) ♿ (2 mobile homes) – 160 🖬 – 160 🛖 – 18 canvas bungalows. Per night from 35 to 221€ – Per week from 240 to 1,549€ – Reservation fee 5€

🚐 borne 4€

In the middle of olive, orange, mandarin and lemon trees; some high-quality rental options and themed stays possible.

Surroundings : 🏞 🎶
Leisure activities : ✗ 🎪 🎯 🏋 🎣 🎢 🏊 ✗ 🏓 (open air in season) sports trail, use of golf buggies, multi-sports ground entertainment room
Facilities : ♿ 🚿 🍴 🗑 🍽 launderette 🧺 refrigerated food storage facilities
Nearby : 🍴

G P S Longitude : 8.70553
Latitude : 42.1311

To visit a town or region, use the MICHELIN Green Guides.

STE-LUCIE-DE-PORTO-VECCHIO

20144 – Michelin map **345** F9
▶ Ajaccio 142 – Porto-Vecchio 16

⚠ Homair Vacances Acqua E Sole ♣♣

(rental of mobile homes and chalets only)

📞 0495501575. www.homair.com

Address : Pianu Di Conca (located 1km northeast along the N 198; follow the signs for Solenzara and take road to the left)

Opening times : from April to Oct.

5 ha

Rental rates : ♿ (1 mobile home) – 117 🖬 – 28 🛖 – 7 🏠. Per night from 19 to 212€ – Per week from 133 to 1,484€ – Reservation fee 49€

A selection of mobile homes and good-quality chalets.

Surroundings : 🏞 ♀
Leisure activities : 🍴 ✗ 🎪 🏋 🎯 🎢
Facilities : 🚿 📧 🍽 🍴 launderette 🧺
Nearby : 🏇

G P S Longitude : 9.35129
Latitude : 41.70328

⚠ Santa-Lucia ♣♣

Santa-Lucia

📞 0495714528. www.campingsantalucia.com

Address : road RN 198 (in the village)

Opening times : from beginning April to beginning Oct.

3 ha (160 pitches)

Tariff : (2014 Price) ♦ 9.75€ ⬅ 3.75€ 📧 7€ – (⚡) (6A) 2.90€ – Reservation fee 10€

Rental rates : (2014 Price) (from beginning April to beginning Oct.)
🚲 – 21 🛖 – 22 canvas bungalows. Per week from 195 to 955€ Reservation fee 15€

Well-shaded pitches with good sanitary facilities and a charming small chalet village.

Surroundings : 🏞 🎶
Leisure activities : ✗ 🏋 🎯 🎣 🏊
Facilities : ♿ 🚿 🍴 🍽 📧 🧺
Nearby : 🍴

G P S Longitude : 9.3434
Latitude : 41.6966

⚠ Fautea

📞 0495714151 🚲

Address : at Fautea, towards the sea (5km northeast on the N 198, follow the signs for Solenzara)

5 ha (100 pitches)

Choose the pitches on the small terraces with a panoramic sea view, furthest away from the road.

Surroundings : ⟨ 🏞 🎶 🏖
Leisure activities : ✗ 🎯
Facilities : ♿ 🚿 🍴 📧 🧺
Nearby : ✗

G P S Longitude : 9.40191
Latitude : 41.71557

SOLENZARA

20145 – Michelin map **345** F8 – pop. 1 169
▶ Paris 1017 – Ajaccio 131 – Bastia 105

⚠ Homair Vacances Sole di Sari ♣♣

(rental of mobile homes, chalets and tent lodges only)

📞 0495570770. www.soledisari.com

Address : route de Bavella (1.5km northwest along the D 268)

Opening times : from beginning April to mid Oct.

4 ha terraced

Rental rates : ♿ (1 mobile home) 🚲 – 50 🖬 – 44 🛖 – 16 tent lodges. Per night from 30 to 214 € – Per week from 210 to 1,498€ Reservation fee 49€

An attractive site with some high-end rental options.

Surroundings : 🏞
Leisure activities : ✗ 🕐daytime 🏋 🎯 🏊 🏖 🎣
Facilities : ♿ 🚿 📧 🍴 launderette 🧺

G P S Longitude : 9.38396
Latitude : 41.86493

TIUCCIA

20111 – Michelin map **345** B7
▶ Ajaccio 30 – Cargèse 22 – Vico 22

⚠ Les Couchants

📞 0495522660. http://camping-lescouchants.fr
✉ 20111 Casaglione

Address : route de Casaglione (4.9km north along the D 81 and turn right onto the D 25)

5 ha (120 pitches)

Rentals : 8 🛖.

The pitches are surrounded by lovely olive, eucalyptus and laurel trees.

Surroundings : 🏞 ⟨ 🎶
Leisure activities : 🍴 ✗ 🎯 🎣
Facilities : ♿ 🚿 🍴 🍽 📧 🧺

G P S Longitude : 8.74894
Latitude : 42.08114

VIVARIO

20219 – Michelin map **345** E6 – pop. 532 – alt. 850
▶ Bastia 89 – Aléria 49 – Corte 22 – Bocognano 22

⚠ Aire Naturelle le Soleil

✆ 04 95 47 21 16. camping-lesoleil@orange.fr – alt. 800

Address : Tattone (6km southwest along the N 193, follow the signs for Ajaccio, near the small Tattone railway station)

Opening times : from beginning May to end Sept.

1 ha (25 pitches)

Tariff : 🚶 7€ 🚗 4€ 🗐 4€ – ⚡ (20A) 4€
 16 🗐 21€

Partly shaded by fruit trees looking out over the mountains.

Surroundings : 🐾 ⩤ ⚏	**G** Longitude : 9.15186
Leisure activities : 🍷 ✕ 🏛	**P** Latitude : 42.1532
Facilities : ⊶ 🚿 🍴	**S**
Nearby : 🐾	

ZONZA

20124 – Michelin map **345** E9 – pop. 1 802 – alt. 780
▶ Ajaccio 93 – Porto-Vecchio 40 – Sartène 38 – Solenzara 40

⚠ Municipal

✆ 04 95 78 62 74. campingmunzonza@voila.fr

Address : route de Porto-Vecchio (3km southeast along the D 368)

2 ha (120 pitches) undulating, terraced, flat, stony

 borne

Situated in the shade of pretty pine trees, beside the river.

Surroundings : 🐾 ⚏	**G** Longitude : 9.19563
Leisure activities : 🐾	**P** Latitude : 41.7504
Facilities : ♿	**S**

FRANCHE-COMTÉ

H. Hughes / hemis.fr

Once upon a time in a land called Franche-Comté . . . many of France's tales and legends begin in the secret wilderness of this secluded region on the Swiss border. The high peaks and protected valleys of Jura, cloaked in fragrant conifers, cast a gentle charm over all who explore them. And an irresistible magic spell is woven by its cascading waterfalls, fascinating grottoes and mysterious lakes. The dark blue waters reflect the hills around them while forming a dramatic contrast with the lush green pastures. Nimble-fingered craftsmen transform the local wood into clocks, toys and pipes to the delight of all those who love and appreciate fine craftsmanship. Hungry travellers may want to savour the lovely hazelnut tang of Comté cheese but should beware the region's powerful gastronomic spell. The delicate smoked and salted meats, in which you can almost taste the pine and juniper, along with Franche-Comté's subtle but fruity wines, will have you coming back for more!

BELFORT

90000 – Michelin map **315** F11 – pop. 50 199 – alt. 360
▶ Paris 422 – Lure 33 – Luxeuil-les-Bains 52 – Montbéliard 23

⚠ L'Étang des Forges

✆ 03 84 22 54 92. www.camping-belfort.com

Address : rue du Général Béthouart (located 1.5km north along the D 13, follow the signs for Offemont and take a right turn – from the A 36. take exit 13)

Opening times : from mid April to end Sept.

3.4 ha (90 pitches)

Tariff : (2014 Price) 21.50€ ✱✱ ⬅ 🔲 ⌀ (6A) – Extra per person 4.50€
Rental rates : (2014 Price) (from mid April to end Sept.) ⅙ (1 chalet) – 5 🚐 – 9 🏠 – 1 canvas bungalow. Per night from 60 to 100€ – Per week from 280 to 511€
🚐 borne
A smart and well-maintained with a great variety of trees.

Surroundings : ⪡ ♀
Leisure activities : 🍽 🎦 🛶 🛷
Facilities : ⅙ ⌸ cc 🏧 ᵱ ᵺ ᵗ launderette
Nearby : ⌀

	Longitude : 6.86436
GPS	Latitude : 47.65341

This guide is updated regularly, so buy your new copy every year!

BONLIEU

39130 – Michelin map **321** F7 – pop. 253 – alt. 785
▶ Paris 439 – Champagnole 23 – Lons-le-Saunier 32 – Morez 24

⚠ L'Abbaye

✆ 03 84 25 57 04. www.camping-abbaye.com

Address : 2 route du Lac (located 1.5km east along the N 78, follow the signs for St-Laurent-en-Grandvaux)

Opening times : from beginning May to end Sept.

3 ha (88 pitches)

Tariff : 20.40€ ✱✱ ⬅ 🔲 (10A) – Extra per person 4.80€
Rental rates : (2014 Price) (from beginning May to end Sept.) ⅙ – 4 🚐 – 2 🏠 – 1 studio – 1 gîte. Per night from 48€ – Per week from 295 to 525€
🚐 borne 9€ – 4 🔲 9€
On a pretty site at the base of the cliffs, not far from the Le Hérisson waterfall.

Surroundings : ⪢ ⪡ ⌷
Leisure activities : 🍽 ✗ 🛷
Facilities : ⅙ ⌸ ᵱ ᵗ launderette ⌿
Nearby : 🐎 canoeing

	Longitude : 5.87562
GPS	Latitude : 46.59199

BONNAL

25680 – Michelin map **321** I1 – pop. 21 – alt. 270
▶ Paris 392 – Besançon 47 – Belfort 51 – Épinal 106

⚠⚠ Les Castels Le Val de Bonnal ♙♙

✆ 03 81 86 90 87. www.camping-valdebonnal.com

Address : 1 chemin du Moulin

Opening times : from beginning May to beginning Sept.

140 ha/15 for camping(280 pitches) flat, grassy

Tariff : (2014 Price) 49.75€ ✱✱ ⬅ 🔲 ⌀ (10A) – Extra per person 14€
Reservation fee 20€

Rental rates : (2014 Price) (from beginning May to beginning Sept.) ⅙ – 29 🚐 – 8 tent lodges. Per night 95€ – Per week from 340 to 1.290€
🚐 borne
In a pleasant location beside the Ognon river and near a lake.

Surroundings : ⪢ ⌷ ♀
Leisure activities : 🍽 ✗ 🎦 ☾nighttime 🕺
🛷 🚲 🛶 🛷
Facilities : ⅙ ⌸ ᵱ ᵱ ᵗ launderette ⌿ ⌿
Nearby : ⪜ forest trail

	Longitude : 6.35619
GPS	Latitude : 47.50734

CHALEZEULE

25220 – Michelin map **321** G3 – pop. 1 180 – alt. 252
▶ Paris 410 – Dijon 96 – Lyon 229 – Nancy 209

⚠ Municipal de la Plage

✆ 03 81 88 04 26. www.campingdebesancon.com

Address : 12 route de Belfort (4.5km northeast along the N 83; beside the Doubs river)

Opening times : from beginning April to end Sept.

2.5 ha (152 pitches)

Tariff : ✱ 5.75€ ⬅ 🔲 7.95€ – ⌀ (16A) 3.95€
Rental rates : (2014 Price) Permanent – 10 🚐 – 2 canvas bungalows. Per night from 36 to 95€ – Per week from 252 to 665€
🚐 15 🔲 7.85€
Particular attention has been paid to the floral decoration. A tram stop into the town centre is 500m away.

Surroundings : ♀♀
Leisure activities : ✗ 🛷
Facilities : ⅙ ⌸ ⎏ ᵱ ᵗ launderette
Nearby : ✗ ♫ 🛶 🛷

	Longitude : 6.07103
GPS	Latitude : 47.26445

For more information on visiting particular towns or regions, consult the relevant regional MICHELIN Green Guide. We also recommend you use the appropriate Michelin regional map to locate your selected campsite, to calculate distances and to work out the best route.

CHAMPAGNEY

70290 – Michelin map **314** H6 – pop. 3 728 – alt. 370
▶ Paris 413 – Besançon 115 – Vesoul 48

⚠ Domaine Des Ballastières

✆ 03 84 23 11 22. www.campingdesballastieres.com

Address : 20 rue du Pâquis

Opening times : from beginning April to end Oct.

5 ha (110 pitches)

Tariff : 17.10€ ✱✱ ⬅ 🔲 ⌀ (16A) – Extra per person 3.70€ – Reservation fee 10€
Rental rates : (from beginning April to end Oct.) ⅙ (1 mobile home) – 10 🚐 – 8 canvas bungalows. Per night from 18 to 75€ – Per week from 90 to 610€
🚐 borne 3.50€
Situated beside a small lake.

Leisure activities : 🎦 🕺 🛷 🚲 🛷
Facilities : ⅙ ⌸ cc ᵗ launderette
Nearby : ⪜ ♫ 🐎 pedalos

	Longitude : 6.67414
GPS	Latitude : 47.70615

CHAMPAGNOLE

39300 – Michelin map **321** F6 – pop. 8 088 – alt. 541
▶ Paris 420 – Besançon 66 – Dole 68 – Genève 86

🏕 Municipal de Boyse 🔺👤

📞 03 84 52 00 32. www.camping-boyse.com

Address : 20 rue Georges Vallerey (take the northwestern exit along the D 5, follow the signs for Lons-le-Saunier and take turning to the left)

Opening times : from end May to end Oct.

9 ha/7 for camping(240 pitches)

Tariff : (2014 Price) 22.30 € ✶✶ 🚐 🅴 – Extra per person 6 €
Rental rates : (2014 Price) (from end May to end Oct.) ♿ (2 chalets) – 25 🏠. Per week from 240 to 575 €
🚰 borne 3.80 € – 7 🅴 6 €

A pretty site on a hillside, looking out over the Ain river from an elevation of 30m. Direct access along a road to the river.

Surroundings : 🌿 ⚒
Leisure activities : 🗡 🎮 🚶 ⛷ 🎠 🛶
Facilities : ♿ ⚡ 🐎🏛 launderette 🚿
Nearby : 🎣 🎿 ⛷ sports trail

GPS	Longitude : 5.89741
	Latitude : 46.74643

CHÂTILLON

39130 – Michelin map **321** E7 – pop. 131 – alt. 500
▶ Paris 421 – Champagnole 24 – Clairvaux-les-Lacs 15 – Lons-le-Saunier 19

🏕 Kawan Village Domaine de l'Épinette 🔺👤

📞 03 84 25 71 44. www.domaine-epinette.com

Address : 15 rue de l'Epinette (1.3km south along the D 151)

7 ha (150 pitches)

Rentals : – 71 🚐 – 2 🏠 – 4 canvas bungalows.
🚰 borne

The site is laid out on terraces on the side of a valley and overlooking a river.

Surroundings : 🌿 ⚒
Leisure activities : 🏛 🚶 ⛷ 🛶 ⛵ 🛷 ⛰
Facilities : ♿ ⚡ 🏛 launderette 🚿 🚿

GPS	Longitude : 5.72218
	Latitude : 46.6513

CHAUX DES CROTENAY

39150 – pop. 412 – alt. 735
▶ Paris 440 – Besançon 88 – Lons-le-Saunier 48

🏕 Municipal du Bois Joli

📞 03 84 51 50 82. www.chaletsalesiajura.com

Address : 8 route de la Piscine

Opening times : from beginning July to end Aug.

1 ha (42 pitches) flat, grassy

Tariff : (2014 Price) ✶ 3.50 € 🚐 🅴 5.50 € ⚡ (10A)
Rental rates : (2014 Price) Permanent ♿ (1 chalet) – 8 🏠. Per night from 80 to 100 € – Per week from 370 to 480 €

A pretty view of the surrounding hills.

Surroundings : ⚒ mountains
Leisure activities : 🏛 ⛷
Facilities : ♿ 🚐 launderette
Nearby : 🏊 ✶ 🚴 ⛷ 🎣

GPS	Longitude : 5.96072
	Latitude : 46.66307

CLAIRVAUX-LES-LACS

39130 – Michelin map **321** E7 – pop. 1 454 – alt. 540
▶ Paris 428 – Bourg-en-Bresse 94 – Champagnole 34 – Lons-le-Saunier 22

🏕 Yelloh! Village Le Fayolan 🔺👤

📞 03 84 25 88 52. www.campinglefayolan.fr

Address : rue du Langard (1.2km southeast along the D 118)

17 ha/13 for camping(516 pitches) pine trees
Rentals : – 133 🚐 – 10 tent lodges.
🚰 borne

Situated beside a lake, with numerous services and leisure facilities.

Surroundings : ⚒ 🔲 🛁 ⛱
Leisure activities : ✶ 🗡 🛶 ⛷ 🏊 hammam 🛷 🛷 🏊 entertainment room
Facilities : ♿ ⚡ 🐎🏛 🚿 ✶ launderette 🏊 🚿
Nearby : 🎣 fitness trail

GPS	Longitude : 5.75
	Latitude : 46.56667

🏕 Flower Le Grand Lac 🔺👤

📞 03 84 25 22 14. www.odesia-clairvaux.com

Address : chemin du Langard (800m southeast along the D 118, follow the signs for Châtel-de-Joux and take the road to the right)

Opening times : from mid May to end Sept.

2.5 ha (191 pitches)

Tariff : (2014 Price) 27.80 € ✶✶ 🚐 🅴 – Extra per person 5 €

Situated beside the lake with a beautiful beach and an impressive diving board!

Surroundings : ⚒ 🛁 ⛱
Leisure activities : 🎮 🚶 🛷 ⛷ 🏊 (beach) 🎣 pedalos
Facilities : ♿ ⚡ 🏛 launderette
Nearby : ✶

GPS	Longitude : 5.75507
	Latitude : 46.56823

DOLE

39100 – Michelin map **321** C4 – pop. 24 906 – alt. 220
▶ Paris 363 – Besançon 55 – Chalon-sur-Saône 67 – Dijon 50

🏕 Le Pasquier

📞 03 84 72 02 61. www.camping-le-pasquier.com

Address : 18 chemin Victor et Georges Thévenot (to the southeast along the av. Jean-Jaurès)

Opening times : from mid March to end Oct.

2 ha (120 pitches)

Tariff : (2014 Price) 20.50 € ✶✶ 🚐 🅴 – Extra per person 4.30 € – Reservation fee 15 €
Rental rates : (2014 Price) (from mid March to end Oct.) – 10 🚐 – 4 canvas bungalows. Per night from 35 to 93 € – Per week from 195 to 560 €– Reservation fee 15 €

In a lush, green setting near the Doubs river, with a view of the Dole collegiate church.

Surroundings : 🛁
Leisure activities : ✶ 🗡 🎮 daytime 🛷 ⛷ (small swimming pool)
Facilities : ♿ ⚡ 🐎🏛 🚿 ✶ launderette
Nearby : 🏊 🎣

GPS	Longitude : 5.50357
	Latitude : 47.08982

DOUCIER

39130 – Michelin map **321** E7 – pop. 296 – alt. 526
▶ Paris 427 – Champagnole 21 – Lons-le-Saunier 25

⚑ Domaine de Chalain ♠♠

✆ 03 84 25 78 78. www.chalain.com

Address : 3km to the northeast

Opening times : from end April to mid Sept.

30 ha/18 for camping(712 pitches)

Tariff : (2014 Price) 42€ ★★ ⇔ 🅴 [≢] (10A) – Extra per person 7€ – Reservation fee 20€

Rental rates : (2014 Price) (from end April to mid Sept.) ⚑ – 50 🚐 – 35 🏠. Per night from 43 to 156€ – Per week from 301 to 1,092€ – Reservation fee 20€

🔧 borne 2€ – 6 🅴 40€

In an attractive location on a bay ringed by cliffs, between a forest and the Lac de Chalain.

Surroundings : ≤ ♀ ⛰
Leisure activities : ♈ ✕ 🏠 ☺ ⚶ ᚶ ⚑ hammam, jacuzzi ⚓ ⚛ ⚶ ☰ 🔳 🔳 🟰
Facilities : & ⚲ ⚎ ☐ ♨ ⚄ ♈ launderette 🟰 🟰 refrigerated food storage facilities

G P S Longitude : 5.81395
Latitude : 46.66422

FONCINE-LE-HAUT

39460 – Michelin map **321** G7 – pop. 1 027 – alt. 790
▶ Paris 444 – Champagnole 24 – Clairvaux-les-Lacs 34 – Lons-le-Saunier 62

⚑ Les Chalets du Val de Saine   (rental of chalets only)

✆ 03 84 51 93 11. www.camping-haut-jura.com – alt. 900 – traditional camp. spaces also available

Address : take the southwestern exit along the D437, follow the signs for St-Laurent-en-Grandvaux and take the turning to the left, by the stadium; beside the Saine river

Opening times : Permanent

1.2 ha flat

Rental rates : Ⓟ – 19 🏠. Per night from 60 to 200€ – Per week from 250 to 595€

🔧 borne 3.50€

Surroundings : ⚑
Leisure activities : ⚑
Facilities : ⚎ ♈ launderette
Nearby : 🟰 ♈ ✕ ⚸ 🖼

G P S Longitude : 6.07253
Latitude : 46.65888

To make the best possible use of this guide, please read pages 2–15 carefully.

FRESSE

70270 – Michelin map **314** H6 – pop. 725 – alt. 472
▶ Paris 405 – Belfort 31 – Épinal 71 – Luxeuil-les-Bains 30

⚑ La Broche

✆ 03 84 63 31 40. www.camping-broche.com

Address : Le Volvet (take the western exit, follow the signs for Melesey and then take road to the left)

Opening times : from mid April to mid Oct.

2 ha (50 pitches)

Tariff : ★ 3€ ⇔ 1.50€ 🅴 1.50€ – [≢] (10A) 3€

🔧 borne

Situated in an undulating, wooded site beside a lake.

Surroundings : ⚑ ≤ ♀
Leisure activities : ⚑
Facilities : & ⚲ ⚎ 🟰

G P S Longitude : 6.65269
Latitude : 47.75587

HUANNE-MONTMARTIN

25680 – Michelin map **321** I2 – pop. 83 – alt. 310
▶ Paris 392 – Baume-les-Dames 14 – Besançon 37 – Montbéliard 52

⚑ Le Bois de Reveuge

✆ 03 81 84 38 60. www.campingduboisdereveuge.com

Address : route de Rougemont (1.1km north along the D 113)

Opening times : from end April to beginning Sept.

24 ha/15 for camping(320 pitches)

Tariff : (2014 Price) 35€ ★★ ⇔ 🅴 [≢] (10A) – Extra per person 8.50€ Reservation fee 25€

Rental rates : (2014 Price) (from mid April to beginning Sept.) – 120 🚐 – 32 🏠. Per night from 49 to 209€ – Per week from 294 to 1.463€ – Reservation fee 25€

🔧 borne 20€ – 50 🅴 20€

The site is laid out beside two large lakes on the edge of a wood.

Surroundings : ⚑ ⚎ ♀♀
Leisure activities : ♈ ✕ 🏠 ☺ ⚶ ᚶ ⚑ ⚛ ᚶ 🔳 ⚛ ⚑
Facilities : & ⚲ ⚎ ⚄ ♈ launderette 🟰

G P S Longitude : 6.3447
Latitude : 47.44346

These symbols are used for a campsite that is exceptional in its category:

⚑⚑ ... ⚑ *Particularly pleasant setting, quality and range of services available*

⚑⚑ *Tranquil, isolated site – quiet site, particularly at night*

≤ ≤ *Exceptional view – interesting or panoramic view*

LABERGEMENT-STE-MARIE

25160 – Michelin map **321** H6 – pop. 1 040 – alt. 859
▶ Paris 454 – Champagnole 41 – Pontarlier 17 – St-Laurent-en-Grandvaux 41

⚑ Le Lac

✆ 03 81 69 31 24. www.camping-lac-remoray.com

Address : 10 rue du Lac (take the southwestern exit along the D 437, follow the signs for Mouthe and take turning to the right)

Opening times : from beginning May to end Sept.

1.8 ha (80 pitches)

Tariff : (2014 Price) 22.20€ ★★ ⇔ 🅴 [≢] (6A) – Extra per person 5€ Reservation fee 5€

Rental rates : (2014 Price) (from beginning May to end Sept.) – 4 🚐 – 4 🏠. Per night 83€ – Per week from 210 to 625€ Reservation fee 5€

🔧 borne

300m from the Lac de Remoray.

Surroundings : ≤
Leisure activities : ♈ ✕ 🏠 ⚛
Facilities : & ⚲ ⚄ ♈ launderette 🟰
Nearby : ⚸ 🟰 ⚑

G P S Longitude : 6.27563
Latitude : 46.77134

LACHAPELLE-SOUS-ROUGEMONT

90360 – Michelin map **315** G10 – pop. 549 – alt. 400
▶ Paris 442 – Belfort 16 – Basel 66 – Colmar 55

⚠ Le Lac de la Seigneurie

𝒫 03 84 23 00 13. www.camping-lac-seigneurie.com

Address : 3 rue de la Seigneurie (3.2km north along the D 11, follow the signs for Lauw)

Opening times : from beginning April to end Oct.

4 ha (110 pitches) flat, grassy

Tariff : 20€ ♣♣ ⇔ 圓 ⚡ (6A) –Extra per person 4€
Rental rates : (2014 Price) Permanent ⚡ – 2 🚐 – 4 🏠.
Per night from 88 to 108 € – Per week from 280 to 565€ – Reservation fee 15€

🚰 borne

In a corner of quiet countryside on the edge of a forest and near a lake.

Surroundings : 🌲 🗘 𝟀		
Leisure activities : 🎮 🏄 ⛷	**G**	Longitude : 7.01498
Facilities : 🦽 ⚬ 🍽 launderette	**P**	Latitude : 47.73613
Nearby : ✗ 🎣	**S**	

LEVIER

25270 – Michelin map **321** G5 – pop. 1 949 – alt. 719
▶ Paris 443 – Besançon 45 – Champagnole 37 – Pontarlier 22

⚠ La Forêt

𝒫 03 81 89 53 46. www.camping-dela-foret.com

Address : route de Septfontaines (located 1km northeast along the D 41)

Opening times : from beginning May to mid Sept.

4 ha/2.5 for camping(70 pitches)

Tariff : (2014 Price) 23.70€ ♣♣ ⇔ 圓 ⚡ (10A) –
Extra per person 4.40€ – Reservation fee 10€
Rental rates : (2014 Price) Permanent – 1 caravan – 2 🚐 –
8 🏠. Per night from 30 to 152€ – Per week from 147 to 739€
Reservation fee 10€

🚰 14 圓 15€

Nestling at the edge of a forest in a beautiful setting of fine trees and rocky outcrops.

Surroundings : 🌲 𝟀		
Leisure activities : 🎮 🏄 🚲 ⛷	**G**	Longitude : 6.13308
Facilities : 🦽 ⚬ 🏄 🍽 launderette	**P**	Latitude : 46.95915
Nearby : sports trail	**S**	

LONS-LE-SAUNIER

39000 – Michelin map **321** D6 – pop. 17 907 – alt. 255 – ⚓
▶ Paris 408 – Besançon 84 – Bourg-en-Bresse 73 – Chalon-sur-Saône 61

⚠⚠ La Marjorie

𝒫 03 84 24 26 94. www.camping-marjorie.com

Address : 640 boulevard de l'Europe (to the northeast towards Besançon along the bd de Ceinture)

Opening times : from mid April to beginning Oct.

9 ha/3 for camping(193 pitches) hard surface areas

Tariff : 16.95€ ♣♣ ⇔ 圓 ⚡ (10A) – Extra per person 3.80€ –
Reservation fee 15€

Rental rates : (from beginning April to mid Oct.) 🦽 (1 chalet) –
4 🚐 – 15 🏠. Per night from 50 to 70€ – Per week
from 230 to 680€ – Reservation fee 15€
🚰 borne 4.50€ – 38 圓 16.95€

Attractive trees and shrubs decorate the site; beside a stream.

Surroundings : 🌿 𝟀		
Leisure activities : 🍽 🎮 🌙nighttime 🎿	**G**	Longitude : 5.56855
Facilities : 🦽 ⚬ 🏛 🏄 ⛷ 🍽 launderette	**P**	Latitude : 46.68422
🏊 🏄	**S**	
Nearby : ✗ 🏊 ⛷		

LUXEUIL-LES-BAINS

70300 – Michelin map **314** G6 – pop. 7 370 – alt. 305
▶ Paris 380 – Besançon 88 – Vesoul 35

⚠⚠⚠ Domaine du Chatigny

𝒫 03 84 93 97 97. www.camping.luxeuil.fr

Address : 14 rue Grammont

Opening times : from beginning March to end Oct.

4.5 ha (98 pitches) flat, grassy

Tariff : (2014 Price) ⇔ ⚡ (16A) – Extra per person 4€ – Reservation
fee 8€

Rental rates : (from beginning March to end Oct.) 🦽 (2 chalets) –
20 🚐 – 20 🏠. Per week from 263 to 574€ – Reservation fee 8€
🚰 borne 2€ – 10 圓 20.50€ – 🔌 10€

Located in the town centre, a pleasant, well-maintained green setting.

Surroundings : 🌲 𝟀		
Leisure activities : 🍽 ✗ 🎮 🏄 🚲 🎿 ⛷	**G**	Longitude : 6.37876
multi-sports ground	**P**	Latitude : 47.82259
Facilities : ⚬ 🏛 🏄 🍽 launderette	**S**	
Nearby : 🛒		

The Michelin classification (⚠⚠⚠ … ⚠) is totally independent of the official star classification system awarded by the local prefecture or other official organisation.

MAICHE

25120 – Michelin map **321** K3 – pop. 4 282 – alt. 777
▶ Paris 501 – Baume-les-Dames 69 – Besançon 74 – Montbéliard 43

⚠ Municipal St-Michel

𝒫 03 81 64 12 56. www.mairie-maiche.fr

Address : 23 rue Saint-Michel (head 1.3km south on the D 422 before joining the D 464, follow the signs for Charquemont and take the D 437 heading for Pontarlier - recommended route via the D 437, follow the signs for Pontarlier)

Opening times : from beginning Dec. to mid Nov.

2 ha (70 pitches)

Tariff : (2014 Price) ♣ 3.35€ ⇔ 圓 4.46€ – ⚡ (10A) 4.46€
Rental rates : (2014 Price) (from beginning Dec. to mid Nov.) –
3 🛏 –1 gîte. Per night from 51 to 75€ – Per week from 225 to 340€

Situated near an indoor water park.

Surroundings : 𝟀		
Leisure activities : 🏄	**G**	Longitude : 6.80109
Facilities : 🦽 ⚬ 🏛 🖼	**P**	Latitude : 47.24749
Nearby : 🏊 hammam, jacuzzi 🎿 ⛷	**S**	

MAISOD

39260 – Michelin map **321** E8 – pop. 316 – alt. 520
▶ Paris 436 – Lons-le-Saunier 30 – Oyonnax 34 – St-Claude 29

⚑ Trelachaume

📞 0384420326. www.trelachaume.fr

Address : 50 route du Mont du Cerf (2.2km south along the D 301 and take turning to the right)

Opening times : from mid April to beginning Sept.

3 ha (180 pitches)

Tariff : (2014 Price) 19.70€ ♦♦ ⊷ 🖾 ⛽ (10A) – Extra per person 3€

Rental rates : (2014 Price) (from mid April to mid Sept.) – 5 caravans – 10 🏠 – 6 🏠 – 5 canvas bungalows. Per week from 209 to 662€

Nestling in woods looking down over the Lac de Vouglans.

	G
Surroundings : 🏞 ♀♀	**G** Longitude : 5.68875
Leisure activities : 🏠 ✣ 🚣 cinema	**P** Latitude : 46.46873
Facilities : 🚿 ⊷ 🏠 launderette	**S**

MALBUISSON

25160 – Michelin map **321** H6 – pop. 687 – alt. 900
▶ Paris 456 – Besançon 74 – Champagnole 42 – Pontarlier 16

⚑⚑ Les Fuvettes ♣♣

📞 0381693150. www.camping-fuvettes.com

Address : 24 route de la Plage et des Perrières (located 1km southwest)

Opening times : from beginning April to beginning Oct.

6 ha (306 pitches)

Tariff : 26.90€ ♦♦ ⊷ 🖾 ⛽ (10A) – Extra per person 5.40€ – Reservation fee 10€

Rental rates : (from beginning April to beginning Oct.) 🚿 (1 mobile home) – 40 🏠 – 5 🏠 – 3 canvas bungalows. Per night from 30 to 145€ – Per week from 269 to 929€ – Reservation fee 15€

🚮 borne 3€

Beside the Lac de St-Point, near a mini water activity park.

	G
Surroundings : ← ♀ ⛰	**G** Longitude : 6.29391
Leisure activities : ♈ ✗ 🏠 ✣ 🚣 🏇 🎿	**P** Latitude : 46.79232
🚿 ⛷ mini farm with ponies and alpacas	**S**
Facilities : 🚿 ⊷ 🏠 launderette 🚗 🚙	
Nearby : canoeing, pedalos	

MANDEURE

25350 – Michelin map **321** K2 – pop. 4 959 – alt. 336
▶ Paris 473 – Baume-les-Dames 41 – Maîche 34 – Sochaux 15

⚑ Municipal les Grands Ansanges

📞 0381352379. www.ville-mandeure.com

Address : rue de l'Église (located to the northwest, take exit towards Pont-de-Roide ; beside the Doubs)

1.7 ha (96 pitches) flat, grassy

A very simple site, but perfect for a one-night stay.

	G
Surroundings : ♀	**G** Longitude : 6.80556
Leisure activities : ♈ 🏠 🚣	**P** Latitude : 47.45557
Facilities : launderette	**S**

MARIGNY

39130 – Michelin map **321** E6 – pop. 177 – alt. 519
▶ Paris 426 – Arbois 32 – Champagnole 17 – Doucier 5

⚑⚑⚑ Les Castels La Pergola ♣♣

📞 0384257003. www.lapergola.com

Address : 1 rue des Vernois (800m to the south)

Opening times : from end April to beginning Sept.

10 ha (350 pitches) terraced, flat, grassy, stony

Tariff : 46€ ♦♦ ⊷ 🖾 ⛽ (16A) – Extra per person 7€ – Reservation fee 30€

Rental rates : (from beginning May to beginning Sept.) – 154 🏠. Per night from 53 to 176€ – Per week from 296 to 1.232€ – Reservation fee 30€

🚮 borne

An attractive swimming pool area overlooks the Lac de Chalain ; some high-quality mobile homes.

	G
Surroundings : ← 🖾 ♀ ⛰	**G** Longitude : 5.77984
Leisure activities : ♈ ✗ 🏠 ✣ 🏃 🎿 🚴 🚣	**P** Latitude : 46.67737
🚿 🚣 ♀	**S**
Facilities : 🚿 ⊷ 🖾 🚿 🚗 🚙 launderette	
🚗 🚙	

The prices listed were supplied by the campsite owners in 2014 (if prices were not available, those from the previous year are given). The fees should be regarded as basic charges and may fluctuate with inflation.

MÉLISEY

70270 – Michelin map **314** H6 – pop. 1 699 – alt. 330
▶ Paris 397 – Belfort 33 – Épinal 63 – Luxeuil-les-Bains 22

⚑ La Pierre

📞 0384208438. http://melisey.cchvo.org/index.php?IdPage=1238083072 – limited spaces for one-night stay – 🏠

Address : at Les Granges Baverey (2.7km north on the D 293, follow the signs for Mélay)

Opening times : from beginning May to end Sept.

1.5 ha (58 pitches)

Tariff : 13.60€ ♦♦ ⊷ 🖾 ⛽ (6A) – Extra per person 3.20€

Rental rates : Permanent – 4 🏠 – 2 gîtes. – Per night from 90 to 110€ – Per week from 230 to 380€

🚮 borne 6€ – 8 🖾 13.60€ – 🚐 ⛽10.40€

In a picturesque setting on a wooded site.

	G
Surroundings : 🏞 🖾 ♀	**G** Longitude : 6.58101
Leisure activities : 🏠 🚣	**P** Latitude : 47.77552
Facilities : 🚿 🚽 🖾	**S**

Michelin classification:

⚑⚑⚑⚑ *Extremely comfortable, equipped to a very high standard*

⚑⚑⚑ *Very comfortable, equipped to a high standard*

⚑⚑⚑ *Comfortable and well equipped*

⚑⚑ *Reasonably comfortable*

⚑ *Satisfactory*

MESNOIS

39130 – Michelin map **321** E7 – pop. 202 – alt. 460
▶ Paris 431 – Besançon 90 – Lons 18 – Chalon 77

▲▲▲ Sites et Paysages Beauregard

✆ 03 84 48 32 51. www.juracampingbeauregard.com

Address : 2 Grande-Rue (take the southern exit)

Opening times : from beginning April to end Sept.

6 ha/4.5 for camping(192 pitches)

Tariff : 30.80€ ♦♦ ⇌ 🗉 🗲 (6A) – Extra per person 5.70€ –
Reservation fee 10€

Rental rates : (from beginning April to end Sept.) – 41 🚐 –
5 canvas bungalows. Per night from 45 to 118€ – Per week
from 315 to 826€ – Reservation fee 10€

A partially open-air water park.

Surroundings : ≤ 🏕 ♀		G
Leisure activities : ♈ ✕ 🏛 ≋ hammam, jacuzzi ✦✦ ✕ 🎣 🏹 ⅃ ⅄	Longitude : 5.68878	P
Facilities : ⅄ ⊶ 🖼 ⅂ launderette ⅁	Latitude : 46.60036	S

MONNET-LA-VILLE

39300 – Michelin map **321** E6 – pop. 372 – alt. 550
▶ Paris 421 – Arbois 28 – Champagnole 11 – Doucier 10

▲▲▲ Sous Doriat

✆ 03 84 51 21 43. www.camping-sous-doriat.com

Address : 34 rue Marcel Hugon (take the northern exit along the
D 27e, follow the signs for Ney)

Opening times : from beginning May to end Sept.

3 ha (110 pitches) flat, grassy

Tariff : 20.50€ ♦♦ ⇌ 🗉 🗲 (10A) – Extra per person 4.10€ –
Reservation fee 10€

Rental rates : (from beginning May to end Sept.) – 15 🚐 –
5 🏚 – 4 tent lodges. Per night from 27 to 93€ – Per week
from 189 to 651€ – Reservation fee 10€

🚐 borne 5€

*A simple campsite with a lovely unrestricted view of the Jura
mountains.*

Surroundings : ≤ ♀		G
Leisure activities : 🖼 ✦✦ ⅃ multi-sports area	Longitude : 5.79779	P
Facilities : ⅄ ⊶ ⅂ launderette	Latitude : 46.72143	S
Nearby : ⅏ ♈ ✕		

▲ Du Git

✆ 03 84 51 21 17. www.campingdugit.com

Address : 7 chemin du Git (located 1km southeast along the D 40,
follow the signs for Mont-sur-Monnet and take the road to the right)

Opening times : from beginning June to mid Sept.

6 ha (60 pitches)

Tariff : 16€ ♦♦ ⇌ 🗉 🗲 (5A) – Extra per person 4€

Rental rates : (from beginning June to mid Sept.) – 2 🚐.
Per week from 250 to 450€

🚐 borne 4€

A very simple campsite with poor sanitary facilities.

Surroundings : ⅏ ≤		G
Leisure activities : 🖼 ✦✦	Longitude : 5.79733	P
Facilities : ⅄ ⊶ ⅂ 🖼	Latitude : 46.71234	S

ORNANS

25290 – Michelin map **321** G4 – pop. 4 152 – alt. 355
▶ Paris 428 – Baume-les-Dames 42 – Besançon 26 – Morteau 48

▲▲ Domaine Le Chanet ♣♣

✆ 03 81 62 23 44. www.lechanet.com

Address : 9 chemin du Chanet (located 1.5km southwest along the
D 241, follow the signs for Chassagne-St-Denis and take the road to
the right; 100m from the Loue)

Opening times : from beginning April to beginning Oct.

1.4 ha (95 pitches)

Tariff : 31.20€ ♦♦ ⇌ 🗉 🗲 (6A) – Extra per person 6.30€ –
Reservation fee 7.50€

Rental rates : (from beginning April to beginning Oct.) –
20 🚐 – 2 apartments. Per night from 70 to 125€ – Per week
from 230 to 805€ – Reservation fee 15€

🚐 borne 3.50€ – 5 🗉 16.50€

*In the hills above the town, features an eco (no chemicals)
swimming pool.*

Surroundings : ⅏ ≤ ♀♀		G
Leisure activities : ♈ ✕ 🏛 ✦✦ 🎣 ≋ ✦✦ 🏹	Longitude : 6.12779	P
Facilities : ⅄ ⊶ 🖼 ⅂ launderette	Latitude : 47.10164	S
Nearby : ⅏ ✕		

▲▲▲ Sites et Paysages La Roche d'Ully

✆ 03 81 57 17 79. www.camping-ornans.com

Address : allée de la Tour de Peilz

Opening times : from beginning April to mid Oct.

2 ha (125 pitches) flat, grassy

Tariff : 34€ ♦♦ ⇌ 🗉 🗲 (10A) – Extra per person 6.80€ – Reservation
fee 7.50€

Rental rates : (from beginning April to mid Oct.) – 5 🚐 –
7 🏚 – 10 tent lodges. Per night from 47 to 155€ – Per week
from 220 to 989€ – Reservation fee 15€

🚐 borne 3.50€ – 2 🗉 16€ – ⅃ 🗲16€

Surroundings : 🏕		G
Leisure activities : ♈ ✕ ✦✦ ✦✦ ✦✦	Longitude : 6.15807	P
Facilities : ⅄ ⊶ 🖼 ⅂ 🖼 ⅁	Latitude : 47.10286	S
Nearby : ≋ hammam, jacuzzi 🏹 ⅃ ⅄ ✦		

OUNANS

39380 – Michelin map **321** D5 – pop. 371 – alt. 230
▶ Paris 383 – Arbois 16 – Arc-et-Senans 13 – Dole 23

▲▲▲ La Plage Blanche ♣♣

✆ 03 84 37 69 63. www.la-plage-blanche.com

Address : 3 rue de la Plage (located 1.5km north along the D 71,
follow the signs for Montbarey and take road to the left)

Opening times : from mid May to mid Sept.

7 ha (218 pitches) flat, grassy

Tariff : 29.50€ ♦♦ ⇌ 🗉 🗲 (10A) – Extra per person 5.50€

Rental rates : (from mid May to mid Sept.) – 6 🚐. Per night
from 50 to 105€ – Per week from 350 to 740€

🚐 borne

The site is on the banks of the Loue river.

Surroundings : ⅏ ♀		G
Leisure activities : ♈ ✕ 🖼 🌙nighttime ✦✦ ≋ jacuzzi ✦✦ ⅃ 🏹 ✦ multi-sports ground	Longitude : 5.66333	P
Facilities : ⅄ ⊶ 🖼 ⅂ launderette ⅁ ⅁	Latitude : 47.00276	S
Nearby : ⅏		

⚠ Le Val d'Amour

℘ 03 84 37 61 89. www.levaldamour.com

Address : 1 rue du Val d'Amour (take the eastern exit along the D 472, towards Chamblay)

Opening times : from beginning April to mid Oct.

3.7 ha (97 pitches) flat, grassy, fruit trees

Tariff : (2014 Price) 24€ ★★ ⊂⊐ 回 [₺] (10A) – Extra per person 6€ – Reservation fee 10€

Rental rates : (2014 Price) (from beginning April to end Oct.) – 14 ⊡⊒ – 6 ⌂ – 3 canvas bungalows – 6 tent lodges. Per night from 50 to 100€ – Per week from 190 to 700€ – Reservation fee 10€

⊏⊞ borne 2€ – 3 回 12€ – ⛟ [₺]12€

Pretty floral decoration.

Surroundings : ⅏ ♀♀
Leisure activities : ✗ ⊡ ⊯ ⅋ ᴕ ♒
mountain biking
Facilities : ⅋ ⊶ ⅋ ᵀ launderette
Nearby : ⅏

G P S Longitude : 5.6733
Latitude : 46.99103

PESMES

70140 – Michelin map **314** B9 – pop. 1 111 – alt. 205
▶ Paris 387 – Besançon 52 – Vesoul 64 – Dijon 69

⚠ La Colombière

℘ 03 84 31 20 15. campinglacolombiere70140@orange.fr

Address : take the southern exit along the D 475, follow the signs for Dole; beside the Ognon river

Opening times : from beginning May to end Oct.

1 ha (70 pitches) flat, grassy

Tariff : (2014 Price) 18.50€ ★★ ⊂⊐ 回 [₺] (16A) – Extra per person 3€ Reservation fee 5€

Rental rates : (2014 Price) (from beginning May to end Oct.) – 4 ⊡⊒ – 1 gîte. Per night from 35 to 90€ – Per week from 240 to 450€ – Reservation fee 5€

⊏⊞ borne 3€ – 8 回 6€

Situated beside the river, not far from the centre of the village.

Surroundings : ♀
Leisure activities : ⅋ ᴕ
Facilities : ⅋ ⊶ ⅋⊠ ⊞ ♒
Nearby : ❡ ✗ ᴕ

G P S Longitude : 5.56392
Latitude : 47.27403

POLIGNY

39800 – Michelin map **321** E5 – pop. 4 229 – alt. 373
▶ Paris 397 – Besançon 57 – Dole 45 – Lons-le-Saunier 30

⚠ La Croix du Dan

℘ 03 84 73 77 58. contact@ccgrimont.fr

Address : route de Lons-le-Saunier (located 1km southwest along the N 83 towards Lons-le-Saunier)

Opening times : from mid May to mid Sept.

1.5 ha (87 pitches) flat, grassy

Tariff : (2014 Price) ★ 2.30€ ⊂⊐ 2.40€ 回 3€ – [₺] (10A) 8€

⊏⊞ borne

Situated at the exit from the town, ideal for a stopover.

Surroundings : ⅏ ♀
Leisure activities : ⅋
Facilities : ⅋ ⊶ ⅋ ᵀ

PONTARLIER

25300 – Michelin map **321** I5 – pop. 18 267 – alt. 838
▶ Paris 462 – Basel 180 – Beaune 164 – Belfort 126

⚠ Le Larmont

℘ 03 81 46 23 33. www.camping-pontarlier.fr – alt. 880

Address : 2 chemin du Toulombief (to the southeast towards Lausanne, near the riding centre)

Opening times : from mid Dec. to mid Nov.

4 ha (75 pitches)

Tariff : (2014 Price) 22.30€ ★★ ⊂⊐ 回 [₺] (10A) – Extra per person 4.30€ – Reservation fee 10.20€

Rental rates : (2014 Price) (from mid Dec. to mid Nov.) – 8 ⌂. Per night from 53 to 118€ – Per week from 310 to 674€ – Reservation fee 10.20€

⊏⊞ borne 5.70€ – 20 回 10.70€ – ⛟ [₺]10.70€

Situated on a hillside with well marked-out pitches.

Surroundings : ⅏ ≼ ⊏⊐
Leisure activities : ⊡ ⅋
Facilities : ⅋ ⊶ ⊞ ♒ ⅋ ᴕ ᵀ launderette
Nearby : ⅙ sports trail

G P S Longitude : 6.37349
Latitude : 46.90013

QUINGEY

25440 – Michelin map **321** F4 – pop. 1 300 – alt. 275
▶ Paris 397 – Baume-les-Dames 40 – Besançon 23 – Morteau 78

⚠ Municipal Les Promenades

℘ 03 81 63 74 01. www.campingquingey.fr

Address : at Les Promenades (take the southern exit, follow the signs for Lons-le-Saunier and take road to the right after the bridge)

1.5 ha (75 pitches)

The site is on the bank of the Loue river, near the village centre and a water sports centre.

Surroundings : ⊏⊐ ♀♀
Leisure activities : ⅋ ⅌ ᴕ
Facilities : ⅋ ⊶ ⅋ ᴕ ᵀ launderette
Nearby : ⅏ ✗ ᴕ

G P S Longitude : 5.88928
Latitude : 47.10454

ST-CLAUDE

39200 – Michelin map **321** F8 – pop. 11 355 – alt. 450
▶ Paris 465 – Annecy 88 – Bourg-en-Bresse 90 – Genève 60

⚠ Flower Le Martinet

℘ 03 84 45 00 40. www.camping-saint-claude.fr

Address : 14 route du Martinet (situated 2km southeast following signs for Genève and take the D 290 to the right, where the Flumen and the Tacon rivers meet)

Opening times : from beginning April to end Sept.

2.9 ha (112 pitches)

Tariff : (2014 Price) 19€ ★★ ⊂⊐ 回 [₺] (10A) – Extra per person 4€

Rental rates : (2014 Price) (from beginning April to end Sept. winter school holidays) – 8 ⌂ – 1 tipi – 2 canvas bungalows – 3 cabins. Per night from 37 to 87€ – Per week from 269 to 609€

⊏⊞ borne – 24 回 16€ – ⛟ [₺]14.40€

Nestling in a pleasant mountain setting beside a river.

Surroundings : ≼ ♀♀
Leisure activities : ❡ ✗ ⊡ ⅋
Facilities : ⅋ ⊶ (July–Aug.) ᵀ launderette
⅏
Nearby : ⅌ ⊠ ♒

G P S Longitude : 5.86953
Latitude : 46.37309

ST-HIPPOLYTE

25190 – Michelin map **321** K3 – pop. 917 – alt. 380
▶ Paris 490 – Basel 93 – Belfort 48 – Besançon 89

⚠ Les Grands Champs

✆ 03 81 96 54 53. www.ville.saint-hippolyte.fr

Address : located 1km northeast along the D 121, follow the signs for Montécheroux and take the road to the right, near the Doubs (direct access)

2.2 ha (65 pitches)

An elongated site with pitches laid out across a slope beside the Doubs river.

| Surroundings : 🏞 ⩽ ♨ Leisure activities : 🎣 Facilities : 🔥 ⛽ 🔌 | **G P S** | Longitude : 6.82332 Latitude : 47.32291 |

ST-LAURENT-EN-GRANDVAUX

39150 – Michelin map **321** F7 – pop. 1 779 – alt. 904
▶ Paris 442 – Champagnole 22 – Lons-le-Saunier 45 – Morez 11

⚠ Municipal Champ de Mars

✆ 06 03 61 06 61. www.camping-saint-laurent-jura.fr

Address : 8 rue du Camping (take the eastern exit along the N 5)

Opening times : from mid Dec. to end Sept.

3 ha (133 pitches)

Tariff : 12.70€ ★★ 🚐 🔲 (10A) – Extra per person 3.50€
Rental rates : (from mid Dec. to end Sept.) 🔥 (2 chalets) – 10 🏠. Per week from 308 to 511€
🚐 12 🔲 10.25€ – 🔋 9.65€

Close to the snowshoe hiking trails and cross-country skiing pistes. Higher rates in winter (not given in this guide).

| Surroundings : ❄ ⩽ Leisure activities : 🎣 🚴 Facilities : 🔥 ⛽ 🔌 🏧 ⚒ ☕ launderette | **G P S** | Longitude : 5.96294 Latitude : 46.57616 |

ST-POINT-LAC

25160 – Michelin map **321** H6 – pop. 269 – alt. 860
▶ Paris 453 – Champagnole 39 – Pontarlier 13 – St-Laurent-en-Grandvaux 45

⚠ Municipal

✆ 03 81 69 61 64. www.campingsaintpointlac.com

Address : 8 rue du Port (in the town)

Opening times : from beginning May to end Sept.

1.8 ha (84 pitches)

Tariff : (2014 Price) 18.50€ ★★ 🚐 🔲 (16A) – Extra per person 3.40€

The campervan pitches are close to the campsite.

| Surroundings : ⩽ 🏔 Leisure activities : 🎣 🚴 Facilities : 🔥 ⛽ 🏧 ☕ launderette 🔌 Nearby : 🚤 🏖 watersports centre 🚐 | **G P S** | Longitude : 6.30336 Latitude : 46.81209 |

Some campsites benefit from proximity to a municipal leisure centre.

SALINS-LES-BAINS

39110 – Michelin map **321** F5 – pop. 2 987 – alt. 340 – ⚕
▶ Paris 419 – Besançon 41 – Dole 43 – Lons-le-Saunier 52

⚠ Municipal

✆ 03 84 37 92 70. www.salinscamping.com

Address : place de la Gare (take the northern exit, following signs for Besançon)

Opening times : from beginning April to end Sept.

1 ha (44 pitches)

Tariff : (2014 Price) 18€ ★★ 🚐 🔲 (10A) – Extra per person 4€ – Reservation fee 5€

Rental rates : (2014 Price) (from beginning April to end Sept.) – 1 🏠 – 1 studio. Per week from 200 to 350€ – Reservation fee 5€

In a valley with a superb view of a citadel and surrounding mountains.

| Surroundings : ⩽ 🏕 Leisure activities : 🎪 🚣 🏊 (small swimming pool) Facilities : 🔥 ⛽ 🔌 🚐 ☕ 🏧 | **G P S** | Longitude : 5.87919 Latitude : 46.94625 |

LA TOUR-DU-MEIX

39270 – Michelin map **321** D7 – pop. 226 – alt. 470
▶ Paris 430 – Champagnole 42 – Lons-le-Saunier 24 – St-Claude 36

⛰ Surchauffant

Surchauffant

✆ 03 84 25 41 08. www.camping-surchauffant.fr

Address : at Le Pont de la Pyle (located 1km southeast along the D 470 and take road to the left, 150m from the Lac de Vouglans - direct access)

Opening times : from end April to mid Sept.

2.5 ha (200 pitches)

Tariff : (2014 Price) 25€ ★★ 🚐 🔲 (10A) – Extra per person 6€

Rental rates : (2014 Price) (from end April to mid Sept.) 🔥 – 25 🏠 – 24 🏠. Per night from 31 to 99€ – Per week from 217 to 693€

🚐 borne 2€ – 10 🔲 9€

| Surroundings : 🏞 ⩽ ♨ Leisure activities : 🍴 ⩽ ♨ 🚣 🚴 🏊 Facilities : 🔥 ⛽ (July-Aug.) 🚿 🏧 ☕ launderette 🧊 refrigerated food storage facilities Nearby : 🍷 🏖 (beach) 🎣 | **G P S** | Longitude : 5.6742 Latitude : 46.52298 |

UXELLES

39130 – Michelin map **321** I2 – pop. 49 – alt. 598
▶ Paris 440 – Besançon 93 – Genève 86 – Lausanne 102

⛰ Village Vacances Odesia Les Crozats

(rental of chalets and rooms only)

✆ 03 84 25 51 43. www.odesia-lacs.com

Address : 1 rue Principale

Opening times : from mid Feb. to beginning Jan.

2 ha

Rental rates : (2014 Price) ✹ Ⓟ – 15 ⌂ – 28 ⌷. Per week from 299 to 799€

A small and pretty chalet village in the lake valley with the option for half-board accommodation.

Surroundings : ✺ ⬚
Leisure activities : ♈ ✗ ⌂ ✓ ✟ ⛵ hammam ⚲ ⬚ cinema/activity centre
Facilities : ⌁ ⬚ ⬚ ⬚ ⌇ launderette ⬚

GPS
Longitude : 5.78836
Latitude : 46.60277

VESOUL

70000 – Michelin map **314** E7 – pop. 15 920 – alt. 221
▶ Paris 360 – Belfort 68 – Besançon 47 – Épinal 91

⛰ International du Lac

✆ 03 84 76 22 86. www.camping-vesoul.com
Address : at Vaivre-et-Montoille, avenue des Rives du Lac (2.5km west)
Opening times : Permanent
4 ha (183 pitches) flat, grassy
Tariff : ✿ 4.20€ ⇔ 3.10€ ▣ 4.10€ – 🗲 (10A) 3.10€
Rental rates : Permanent ♿ (1 mobile home) ✹ – 8 .
Per night from 69 to 92€ – Per week from 310 to 549€
⛽ borne 3€ – 40 ▣ 18.90€
Beside a wide lake.

Surroundings : ⬚ ⬚ ⚲
Leisure activities : ⌂ ✓ ⛤ ⛵ ⬚
Facilities : ♿ ⌁ ⬚ ⬚ ⬚ ⬚ ⌇ launderette
Nearby : ♈ ✗ ✻ ⛤ ⛷

GPS
Longitude : 6.13084
Latitude : 47.63121

VILLERSEXEL

70110 – Michelin map **314** G7 – pop. 1 472 – alt. 287
▶ Paris 386 – Belfort 41 – Besançon 59 – Lure 18

⛰ Le Chapeau Chinois

✆ 03 84 63 40 60. www.camping-villersexel.com
Address : 92 rue du Chapeau Chinois (located 1km north along the D 486, follow the signs for Lure and take the road to the right after the bridge)
Opening times : from mid March to end Sept.
2 ha (80 pitches) flat, grassy
Tariff : 19.50€ ✿✿ ⇔ ▣ 🗲 (10A) – Extra per person 3.80€
⛽ borne 4€ – 2 ▣ 19.50€
Beside the Ognon river.

Surroundings : ⬚ ⚲
Leisure activities : ⌂ ⛤ ✻ ⛵ ⬚
Facilities : ♿ ⌁ ⬚ ⬚ ⌇ launderette
Nearby : ✗ ⛺

GPS
Longitude : 6.436
Latitude : 47.55814

Key to rentals symbols:

12	*Number of mobile homes*
20 ⌂	*Number of chalets*
6 ⌷	*Number of rooms to rent*
Per night 30–50€	*Minimum/maximum rate per night*
Per week 300–1,000€	*Minimum/maximum rate per week*

ÎLE-DE-FRANCE

P. Escudero / hemis.fr

Paris, the 'City of Light' on the River Seine, lies at the heart of the Île-de-France. A chic and cosmopolitan capital, it is dominated by the iconic silhouette of the Eiffel Tower. Its former royal palace is now adorned with glass pyramids, a former railway station has been transformed into a magnificent museum and narrow streets lined with bohemian houses branch off from wide, formal, tree-lined boulevards. This is a city of endless contrasts: from busy department stores to elegant cafés, from the *bateaux-mouches* (restaurant boats) that glide along the majestic river at night to the sophisticated glamour of Parisian cabarets. But the region that lies beyond Paris has no intention of remaining in the capital's shadow; it is home to secluded châteaux, the magical world of Disneyland and the relaxed ambience of the summer cafés on the banks of the River Marne. And who could forget the magnificent splendour of Versailles, the most beautiful palace in the world?

Legend:
- ● Locality with campsite
- ■ Locality with campsite and rental option
- <u>Vannes</u> Locality with campsite and campervan area
- <u>Moyaux</u> Locality with at least one pleasant campsite
- Motorway service area for campervans

BAGNEAUX-SUR-LOING

77167 – Michelin map **312** F6 – pop. 1 686 – alt. 45
▶ Paris 84 – Fontainebleau 21 – Melun 39 – Montargis 30

🔺 Municipal de Pierre le Sault

🖉 0164299751, www.camping-bagneaux-sur-loing.fr – limited spaces for one-night stay

Address : chemin des Grèves (to the northeast of the town, near the sports field, between the canal and the Loing river, 200m from a small lake)

Opening times : from beginning April to end Oct.

3 ha (160 pitches)

Tariff : (2014 Price) 13.96€ ✝✝ ⬅ ▣ ⁇ (10A) – Extra per person 3.33€

Located between a canal and the river, but in an industrial quarter.

Surroundings : ⌑ ♀
Leisure activities : 🎣 🏇 ✂
Facilities : ♿ ⌇ ▣ ⑃ ⁇ launderette
Nearby : ⌇

Longitude : 2.70376
Latitude : 48.24069

This guide is not intended as a list of all the camping sites in France; its aim is to provide a selection of the best sites in each category.

BOULANCOURT

77760 – Michelin map **312** D6 – pop. 357 – alt. 79
▶ Paris 79 – Étampes 33 – Fontainebleau 28 – Melun 44

🔺 Île de Boulancourt

🖉 0164241338, www.camping-iledeboulancourt.com – limited spaces for one-night stay

Address : 6 allée des Marronniers (to the south, follow the signs for Augerville-la-Rivière)

Opening times : Permanent

5.5 ha (110 pitches) flat, grassy

Tariff : 14.60€ ✝✝ ⬅ ▣ ⁇ (6A) – Extra per person 4,80€
Rental rates : Permanent ✂ – 4 🚐 – 1 canvas bungalow. Per night from 29 to 146€ – Per week from 165 to 370€
⛽ borne 5€ – 4 ▣ 10.80€

In a pleasant wooded setting near a bend in the Essonne river.

Surroundings : ⌇ ♀♀
Leisure activities : 🎣
Facilities : ⌇ ⁇ ⑃ ⁇ ▣

Longitude : 2.435
Latitude : 48.25583

CHAMPIGNY-SUR-MARNE

94500 – Michelin map **312** E3 – pop. 75 090 – alt. 40
▶ Paris 13 – Créteil 10 – Amiens 150 – Bobigny 13

🔺 Homair Vacances Paris Est

🖉 0143974397, www.campingchampigny.fr – reserved for residents outside the Île de France

Address : boulevard des Alliés

Opening times : Permanent

(383 pitches) flat, grassy

Tariff : 31.90€ ✝✝ ⬅ ▣ ⁇ (10A) – Extra per person 7€ – Reservation fee 49€

Rental rates : Permanent – 200 🚐 – 40 🏠. Per night from 43 to 132€ – Per week from 301 to 924€ – Reservation fee 49€

Beside the Marne river with a view of the Pavillon Baltard (19th-century concert hall).

Leisure activities : ⁇ ✗ jacuzzi 🚲
Facilities : ♿ ⌇ ▣ ⑃ ⁇ ⁇ launderette ⑃
Nearby : ⌇

Longitude : 2.47701
Latitude : 48.82958

CREVECOEUR-EN-BRIE

77610 – Michelin map **312** G3 – pop. 299 – alt. 116
▶ Paris 51 – Melun 36 – Boulogne-Billancourt 59 – Argenteuil 66

🔺 Caravaning des 4 Vents

🖉 0164074111, www.caravaning-4vents.fr – limited spaces for one-night stay

Address : 22 rue de Beauregard (located 1km west following signs for la Houssaye and take turning to the left)

Opening times : from end March to end Oct.

9 ha (199 pitches) flat, grassy

Tariff : 30€ ✝✝ ⬅ ▣ ⁇ (6A) – Extra per person 6€
Rental rates : (from end March to end Oct.) ✂ – 5 🏠. Per night from 83€ – Per week from 560€
⛽ borne – 30 ▣ 30€

In a pleasant leafy setting with large, well marked out pitches.

Surroundings : ⌇ ⌑ ♀
Leisure activities : 🎣 🏇 ⑃
Facilities : ♿ ⌇ ▣ ⑃ ⑃ ⁇ launderette
Nearby : ✂ 🏇

Longitude : 2.89722
Latitude : 48.75065

Key to rentals symbols:
12 🚐 *Number of mobile homes*
20 🏠 *Number of chalets*
6 🛏 *Number of rooms to rent*
Per night *Minimum/maximum rate per night*
30–50€
Per week *Minimum/maximum rate per week*
300–1,000€

ÉTAMPES

91150 – Michelin map **312** B5 – pop. 22 182 – alt. 80
▶ Paris 51 – Chartres 59 – Évry 35 – Fontainebleau 45

🔺 Le Vauvert

🖉 0164942139, caravaning.levauvert@orange.fr – limited spaces for one-night stay

Address : route de Saclas (2.3km south along the D 49)

8 ha (230 pitches) flat, grassy

Only 25 to 30 places for tents and caravans next to 200 pitches for owner-occupiers.

Surroundings : ⌑ ♀
Leisure activities : ⁇ 🎣 🏇 ✂
Facilities : ♿ ⌇ ⑃ ⑃ ⁇
At the leisure/activities centre : ▣ ⑃ 🏇 climbing

Longitude : 2.14532
Latitude : 48.41215

JABLINES

77450 – Michelin map **312** F2 – pop. 629 – alt. 46
▶ Paris 44 – Meaux 14 – Melun 57

▲ L' International

✆ 0160260937, www.camping-jablines.com

Address : at leisure base (situated 2km southwest along the D 45, follow the signs for Annet-sur-Marne, 9km from the Disneyland-Paris park)

Opening times : from beginning April to beginning Nov.

300 ha/4 for camping (154 pitches) flat, grassy

Tariff : 31€ ✠✠ ⇨ ▣ ⚡ (10A) – Extra per person 8€ – Reservation fee 12€

Rental rates : (from beginning April to beginning Nov.) ⚡ – 9 ▢. Per night from 69 to 98€ – Per week from 590 to 690€ Reservation fee 12€

⊞ borne 3€ – 150 ▣ 31€

In an attractive location on a bend in the Marne river, next to a large leisure and activity centre.

Surroundings : ⊗ ⊡ ♀♀
Leisure activities : ◂◂↗
Facilities : ♿ ⊶ ▥ ⟐ ♨ ⟟ launderette ⚱
At the leisure/activities centre : ♀ ✗ ⚱
⚲♒ ⎘ ≊ (fresh water) ♞ cable wakeboarding

Longitude : 2.73437
Latitude : 48.91367

LOUAN VILLEGRUIS FONTAINE

77560 – Michelin map **312** J4 – pop. 512 – alt. 168
▶ Paris 101 – Melun 77 – Provins 21 – Troyes 68

▲ Yelloh! Le Village Nature Cottages

(rental of mobile homes only)

✆ 0164008014, www.yellohvillage-paris-iledefrance.com

Address : at Louan : La Cerclière (D 131)

Opening times : from mid April to mid Nov.

11 ha

Rental rates : (2014 Price) – 220 ▢. Per night from 35 to 199€ – Per week from 245 to 1,393€

In the heart of the forest, surrounded by greenery, 1 hour from Paris and Disneyland-Paris.

Surroundings : ⊗ ♀♀
Leisure activities : ♀ ✗ ⊡ ⎐ ◂◂↗ ⚲♒
⎘ ⚱ ⚓ cinema, zip wiring, forest trail, paintballing, multi-sports ground
Facilities : ♿ ⊶ ▥ ⟟ launderette ⚱ ⚱

Longitude : 3.49077
Latitude : 48.6306

MAISONS-LAFFITTE

78600 – Michelin map **311** I2 – pop. 22 717 – alt. 38
▶ Paris 23 – Versailles 24 – Pontoise 20 – Nanterre 13

▲ Sandaya International

✆ 0139122191, www.sandaya.fr

Address : 1 rue Johnson (on the Île de la Commune)

Opening times : from beginning April to end Oct.

6.5 ha (336 pitches) flat, grassy

Tariff : (2014 Price) 37.50€ ✠✠ ⇨ ▣ ⚡ (10A) – Extra per person 7.50€ – Reservation fee 16€

Rental rates : (2014 Price) (from beginning April to end Oct.)
♿ (1 mobile home) – 62 ▢ – 5 cabins in the trees. Per night from 85 to 150€ – Per week from 595 to 1,050€ – Reservation fee 16€

⊞ borne
On an island in the Seine.

Surroundings : ⊡ ♀
Leisure activities : ♀ ✗ ⊡ ◂◂ ≊
Facilities : ♿ ⊶ ▥ ♨ ⟟ launderette ⚱
Nearby : ✗

Longitude : 2.1458
Latitude : 48.94156

MELUN

77000 – Michelin map **312** E4 – pop. 39 400 – alt. 43
▶ Paris 47 – Chartres 105 – Fontainebleau 18 – Meaux 55

▲ Kawan Village La Belle Étoile

✆ 0164394812, www.campinglabelleetoile.com

Address : 64bis quai Maréchal Joffre (to the southeast along the N 6, follow the signs for Fontainebleau (left bank)

Opening times : from beginning April to mid Oct.

3.5 ha (180 pitches) flat, grassy

Tariff : ✠ 7€ ⇨ ▣ 8€ – ⚡ (6A) 4€ – Reservation fee 8€

Rental rates : (from beginning April to mid Oct.) ⚡ – 11 ▢ – 4 ⌂ – 2 canvas bungalows. Per night from 40 to 100€ – Per week from 200 to 800€ – Reservation fee 8€

⊞ borne 3€
In a very lush setting, right next to the Seine river.

Surroundings : ♀♀
Leisure activities : ⊡ ◂◂ ≊ (pool)
Facilities : ⊶ ▥ ♨ ⟟ launderette
Nearby : ≊ hammam ✗ ⋈ ⊡ ⎐

Longitude : 2.66765
Latitude : 48.50929

PARIS

75000 – pop. 2 234 105 – alt. 30
Au Bois de Boulogne – 75016

▲ Indigo Paris Bois de Boulogne

✆ 0145243000, www.camping-indigo.com – reserved for residents outside the Île de France

Address : 2 allée du Bord de l'Eau (between the bridges at Suresnes and Puteaux; beside the Seine)

Opening times : Permanent

7 ha (510 pitches)

Tariff : (2014 Price) 41.80€ ✠✠ ⇨ ▣ ⚡ (10A) – Extra per person 8€ – Reservation fee 22€

Rental rates : (2014 Price) Permanent ♿ (1 mobile home) – 17 caravans – 58 ▢. Per night from 87 to 154€ – Per week from 548 to 970€ – Reservation fee 22€

⊞ borne 9€ – 40 ▣ 36.20€

Choose the pitches along the Seine river, which are a little more peaceful. There's a bus for Porte Maillot, Paris (RER rail and metro station).

Surroundings : ⊡ ♀♀
Leisure activities : ♀ ✗ ⊡
Facilities : ♿ ⊶ ▥ ♨ ⟟ launderette ⚱ ⚱

Longitude : 2.23464
Latitude : 48.86849

CampingIndigo ©R Etienne

POMMEUSE

77515 – Michelin map **312** H3 – pop. 2 756 – alt. 67
▶ Paris 58 – Château-Thierry 49 – Créteil 54 – Meaux 23

⚠ Iris Parc Le Chêne Gris 👥

📞 01 64 04 21 80, www.irisparc.com ✂

Address : 24 place de la Gare (situated 2km southwest, behind Faremoutiers-Pommeuse station)

Opening times : from end March to beginning Nov.

6 ha (350 pitches)

Tariff : (2014 Price) 44€ ★★ ⛺ 🅴 ⚡ (6A) – Extra per person 5.50€ – Reservation fee 20€

Rental rates : (2014 Price) (from end March to beginning Nov.) – 218 🚐 – 79 canvas bungalows. Per night from 28 to 142€ – Per week from 140 to 994€ – Reservation fee 20€

🚐 borne 2€

There's a well-equipped indoor children's play area.

Surroundings : 🏕 ♨
Leisure activities : ✗ 🏠 🛝 🏃 ⛸ 🏊 🎣
Facilities : 🔧 ⚓ 🚿 🛁 🧺 launderette
🚽 🚰

RAMBOUILLET

78120 – Michelin map **311** G4 – pop. 26 065 – alt. 160
▶ Paris 53 – Chartres 42 – Étampes 44 – Mantes-la-Jolie 50

⚠ Huttopia Rambouillet 👥

© Huttopia R.Étienne

📞 01 30 41 07 34, www.huttopia.com

Address : route du Château d'Eau (head 4km south along the N 10, follow the signs for Chartres)

Opening times : from beginning April to beginning Nov.

8 ha (93 pitches)

Tariff : (2014 Price) 37.70€ ★★ ⛺ 🅴 ⚡ (10A) – Extra per person 8€ – Reservation fee 22€

Rental rates : (2014 Price) (from beginning April to beginning Nov.) 🅿 – 10 caravans – 15 🏠 – 31 tent lodges. Per night from 59 to 152€ – Per week from 372 to 1,064€ Reservation fee 22€

🚐 borne 7€ – 20 🅴 29.90€

Beside a lake, in the heart of the forest.

Surroundings : 🏕 ♨
Leisure activities : ⛱ ✗ 🏠 🏃 ⛸ 🏊 🎣
Facilities : 🔧 ⚓ 🚿 🛁 🧺 launderette
Nearby : 🏊 🚣 wildlife park

TOUQUIN

77131 – Michelin map **312** H3 – pop. 1 095 – alt. 112
▶ Paris 57 – Coulommiers 12 – Melun 36 – Montereau-Fault-Yonne 48

⚠ Les Étangs Fleuris

📞 01 64 04 16 36, www.etangsfleuris.com

Address : route de La Couture (3km east)

Opening times : from beginning April to mid Sept.

5.5 ha (195 pitches)

Tariff : 23€ ★★ ⛺ 🅴 ⚡ (10A) – Extra per person 11.50€

Rental rates : (from beginning April to end Sept.) ✂ – 14 🚐.
Per night from 55 to 90€ – Per week from 395 to 650€

In a green setting, shady, close to the lakes.

Surroundings : 🏊 🏕 ♨
Leisure activities : ⛱ 🏠 🏃 🚴 ⛸ 🏊 🎣 multi-sports ground
Facilities : ⚓ 🚿 🛁 🧺 launderette
Nearby : ✗ 🐎

Longitude : 3.04728
Latitude : 48.73279

The pitches of many campsites are marked out with low hedges of attractive bushes and shrubs.

TOURNAN EN BRIE

77220 – Michelin map **312** F3 – pop. 8 116 – alt. 102
▶ Paris 44 – Melun 29 – Amiens 176 – Créteil 38

⚠ FranceLoc Fredland - Parc de Combreux

📞 01 64 07 96 44, www.campings-franceloc.fr

Address : 1.5 km at the south by the road D 10, route de Liverdy-en-Brie

Opening times : Permanent

26 ha/7 for camping (189 pitches) flat, grassy

Tariff : 40€ ★★ ⛺ 🅴 ⚡ (6A) – Extra per person 7€ – Reservation fee 27€

Rental rates : Permanent – 114 🚐 – 6 🏠 – Reservation fee 27€

Situated 800m from the RER suburban rail station (25 minutes to Paris).

Surroundings : ♨
Leisure activities : ⛱ 🏃 🏊 (small swimming pool) 🎣
Facilities : 🔧 ⚓ 🧺 launderette 🚽

Longitude : 2.76915
Latitude : 48.73517

The Michelin classification (⚠⚠⚠ … ⚠) is totally independent of the official star classification system awarded by the local prefecture or other official organisation.

VENEUX-LES-SABLONS

77250 – Michelin map **312** F5 – pop. 4 788 – alt. 76
▶ Paris 72 – Fontainebleau 9 – Melun 26 – Montereau-Fault-Yonne 14

⚠ Les Courtilles du Lido

📞 01 60 70 46 05, http://www.les-courtilles-du-lido.fr

Address : chemin du Passeur (located 1.5km to the northeast)

Opening times : from end March to end Sept.

5 ha (160 pitches) flat, grassy

Tariff : 19.50€ ★★ ⛺ 🅴 ⚡ (10A) – Extra per person 4€

Rental rates : (from end March to end Sept.) – 15 🚐 – 2 canvas bungalows. Per night from 85 to 140€ – Per week from 250 to 688€

🚐 borne – 🔌 ⚡16€

Surroundings : 🏕 ♨
Leisure activities : ⛱ 🏃 🚴 ⛸ 🎣
Facilities : ⚓ 🛁 🧺 launderette

Longitude : 2.80194
Latitude : 48.38333

VERSAILLES

78000 – Michelin map **311** I3 – pop. 86 477 – alt. 130
▶ Paris 29 – Chartres 80 – Fontainebleau 73 – Rambouillet 35

⚠ Huttopia Versailles

© Huttopia R.Etienne

☎ 01 39 51 23 61, www.huttopia.com

Address : 31 rue Berthelot

Opening times : from end March to beginning Nov.

4.6 ha (180 pitches)

Tariff : (2014 Price) 45.10€ ✿✿ ⇌ 🅴
⚡ (10A) – Extra per person 9.95€
Reservation fee 22€

Rental rates : (2014 Price) (from end March to beginning Nov.) ⚿ (1 chalet) – 9 caravans – 20 🏠 – 26 tent lodges. Per night from 63 to 175€ – Per week from 370 to 1,103€ – Reservation fee 22€

🚐 borne 7€ – 20 🅴 39.30€

A wooded setting close to the town.

Surroundings : 🐾 𖠿		
Leisure activities : ✕ 🏊 ⏛	**G**	Longitude : 2.15912
Facilities : ⚿ o⇌ 🕌 🧺launderette	**P** **S**	Latitude : 48.79441

VILLIERS-SUR-ORGE

91700 – Michelin map **312** C4 – pop. 3 896 – alt. 75
▶ Paris 25 – Chartres 71 – Dreux 89 – Évry 15

⚠ Le Beau Village de Paris

☎ 01 60 16 17 86, www.campingaparis.com – limited spaces for one-night stay

Address : 1 voie des Prés (600m southeast via the le town centre, 800m from St-Geneviève-des-Bois station - from A 6, take exit 6)

Opening times : Permanent

2.5 ha (124 pitches) flat, grassy

Tariff : (2014 Price) 20.60€ ✿✿ ⇌ 🅴 ⚡ (10A) –
Extra per person 5.15€

Rental rates : (2014 Price) Permanent – 20 🚐 – 4 🏠 – 1 studio – 1 apartment – 1 gîte. Per night from 65 to 150€ – Per week from 245 to 590€

🚐 borne 5€ – 20 🅴 15.45€

In a green setting, slightly shady beside the Orge river, with proper pitches for campervans.

Surroundings : 🐾 ⊡ ♀		
Leisure activities : ♀ 🏠 🏊	**G**	Longitude : 2.30421
Facilities : ⚿ o⇌ 🕌 🧺 ⚘launderette	**P** **S**	Latitude : 48.65511
Nearby : ✕ 🖾		

R. Mattes / hemis.fr

Languedoc-Roussillon is a kaleidoscope of landscapes, cultures and sensations. You will be seduced by the feverish rhythm of its festivals, the dizzying beauty of the Tarn gorges and the Pyrenees, the magical spell of its caves and stone statues, the seclusion of its cliff-top 'Citadels of Vertigo' with their panoramic views and the heady perfumes of its sun-drenched *garrigue*, the local scrubland fragrant with wild herbs. Admire the nonchalant flamingoes that thrive on its long stretches of salt flats, enjoy discovering the splendour of Carcassonne's medieval ramparts or explore the quiet waters of the Midi Canal and the harsh majesty of the Cévennes. Taking in so many different sights may exhaust some visitors, but remedies are close at hand: a plate of *aligot*, made from mashed potato, butter, cream, garlic and cheese, and a simmering *cassoulet*, the famously rich combination of duck, sausage, beans and herbs, followed by a slice of Roquefort cheese and a glass of ruby-red wine.

Locality with campsite
Locality with campsite and rental option
Vannes Locality with campsite and campervan area
Moyaux Locality with at least one pleasant campsite
Motorway service area for campervans

AGDE

34300 – Michelin map **339** F9 – pop. 24 031 – alt. 5

▶ Paris 754 – Béziers 24 – Lodève 60 – Millau 118

⚠ Yelloh! Village Mer et Soleil ♣♣

©Mer&Soleil220

📞 04 67 94 21 14. www.camping-mer-soleil.com

Address : chemin de Notre Dame, Saint Martin, route de Rochelongue (3km to the south)

Opening times : from mid April to beginning Oct.

8 ha (477 pitches)

Tariff : 47€ ♦♦ ⇔ 🔲 🔌 (6A) – Extra per person 8€

Rental rates : (from mid April to beginning Oct.) ⚱ (1 mobile home) ⚡ – 231 🚐 – 9 🏠 – 42 tent lodges. Per night from 29 to 245€ – Per week from 203 to 1,715€

An impressive indoor spa area with some luxury mobile homes in a pedestrian zone.

Surroundings : 🌿 🖵 ⚘⚘
Leisure activities : ▾ ✕ 🖭 ⚘ nighttime 🏃
🏊 🛥 jacuzzi 🚴 ⚽ 🎯 🎿 spa centre
Facilities : ♿ ⚓ cc 🚿 ☕ launderette ⚖ ✂
Nearby : 🐎

GPS Longitude : 3.47812
Latitude : 43.28621

⚠ Village Vacances Les Pescalunes

(rental of chalets only)

📞 04 67 01 37 06. www.grandbleu.fr

Address : route de Luxembourg (follow the signs for Le Cap-d'Agde)

Opening times : from beginning April to end Oct.

3 ha

Rental rates : ♿ (2 chalets) 🅿 – 78 🏠. Per night from 70 to 110€ – Per week from 217 to 1,050€

A peaceful chalet village on a hillside, with a view of the surrounding area and the Cévennes mountains.

Surroundings : 🌿 ⛰ ⚘⚘
Leisure activities : 🖭 🏃 🛥 🎿
Facilities : 🏦 ☕ launderette

GPS Longitude : 3.50223
Latitude : 43.30109

⚠ Flower Neptune ♣♣

Flower Neptune

📞 04 67 94 23 94. www.campingleneptune.com

Address : 46 boulevard du Saint-Christ (situated 2km to the south, near the Hérault)

Opening times : from mid April to beginning Oct.

2.1 ha (165 pitches) flat, grassy

Tariff : 38.40€ ♦♦ ⇔ 🔲 🔌 (10A) – Extra per person 8.40€ –

Reservation fee 30€

We have selected the best campsites in France with our usual care, listing those with the best facilities in the most pleasant surroundings.

Rental rates : (from mid April to beginning Oct.) – 20 🚐. Per night from 33 to 150€ – Per week from 231 to 1,050€ – Reservation fee 30€

Flowers and shrubs decorate the site; some high-quality mobile homes.

Surroundings : 🖵 ⚘
Leisure activities : ▾ ✕ 🏃 🛥 🚴 🎿 multi-sports ground
Facilities : ♿ ⚓ ☕ ⚖ ☕ launderette
Nearby : 🎣

GPS Longitude : 3.4581
Latitude : 43.29805

We value your opinion and welcome your feedback. Do email us at campingfrance@tp.michelin.com

⚠ Les Romarins

📞 04 67 94 18 59. www.romarins.com

Address : 6 route du Grau (3km to the south, near the Hérault)

Opening times : from beginning April to end Sept.

2 ha (120 pitches) flat, grassy, sandy

Tariff : (2014 Price) 34€ ♦♦ ⇔ 🔲 🔌 (6A) – Extra per person 8€ – Reservation fee 22€

Rental rates : (2014 Price) (from beginning April to end Sept.) ⚡ – 37 🚐 – 2 studios – 3 tent lodges. Per night from 40 to 134€ – Per week from 270 to 922€ – Reservation fee 22€

🚐 borne 2.50€ – 🚱 11€

Surroundings : 🖵 ⚘⚘
Leisure activities : ▾ ✕ 🖭 🛥 🎿 multi-sports ground
Facilities : ♿ ⚓ cc 🚿 ☕ 📷

GPS Longitude : 3.4468
Latitude : 43.29131

⚠ Le Rochelongue ♣♣

📞 04 67 21 25 51. www.camping-le-rochelongue.fr – limited spaces for one-night stay

Address : route de Rochelongue (4km to the south, 500m from the beach)

2 ha (107 pitches)

Rentals : 27 🚐.

Surroundings : 🖵 ⚘⚘
Leisure activities : ▾ ✕ 🏃 🛥 🎿
Facilities : ♿ ⚓ ☕ ☕ launderette ✂
Nearby : ⚽ 🎯 🐎 watersports centre

GPS Longitude : 3.48139
Latitude : 43.27917

⚠ La Pépinière

📞 04 67 94 10 94. www.campinglapepiniere.com

Address : 3 route du Grau

Opening times : from mid March to mid Oct.

3 ha (100 pitches) flat, grassy

Tariff : (2014 Price) 29.50€ ♦♦ ⇔ 🔲 🔌 (10A) – Extra per person 6.50€ – Reservation fee 25€

Rental rates : (2014 Price) (from mid April to end Sept.) – 29 🚐. Per night from 40 to 88€ – Per week from 280 to 616€

🚐 borne

A family-oriented site very near the Hérault river.

Surroundings : 🌿 🖵
Leisure activities : ▾ ✕ 🏃 🛥 🎿
Facilities : ♿ ⚓ ☕ 📷 ✂
Nearby : 🎣 ⚓

GPS Longitude : 3.45368
Latitude : 43.29488

AIGUES-MORTES

30220 – Michelin map **339** K7 – pop. 8 116 – alt. 3
▶ Paris 745 – Arles 49 – Montpellier 38 – Nîmes 42

Yelloh! Village La Petite Camargue

0466539898. www.yellohvillage-petite.camargue.com

Address : 3.5km west along the D 62, follow the signs for Montpellier

Opening times : from end April to mid Sept.

42 ha/10 for camping (553 pitches)

Tariff : 52€ ✝✝ ⇔ ▣ (16A) – Extra per person 9€

Rental rates : (from end April to mid Sept.) – 300 ⬓. Per night from 39 to 239€ – Per week from 273 to 1,673€

borne

Activities and services suitable for teenagers. There's a free shuttle service to the beaches.

Surroundings : 〇〇
Leisure activities : ▮✗ ⌂ ⚘ 🖈 🏄 🚴 ✂ 〜 🏊 🎣 disco, multi-sports ground
Facilities : ♿ ⊶ 🎱 🔥 ¶ launderette 🏊 ⚲

Longitude : 4.15963
Latitude : 43.56376

ALET-LES-BAINS

11580 – Michelin map **344** E5 – pop. 436 – alt. 186
▶ Paris 786 – Montpellier 187 – Carcassonne 35 – Castelnaudary 49

Val d'Aleth

0468699040. www.valdaleth.com

Address : in the village (D 2118 and take the right turning beside the Aude river)

Opening times : Permanent

0.5 ha (37 pitches)

Tariff : (2014 Price) 22€ ✝✝ ⇔ ▣ (10A) – Extra per person 4.50€
Rentals : Permanent 〜 – 4 🛏.

borne – 8 ▣ 16€

The well-shaded pitches are close to the river and a ruined château.

Surroundings : 〇〇
Leisure activities : 🏄 〜
Facilities : ♿ ⊶ ¶ launderette

Longitude : 2.25564
Latitude : 42.99486

ALLÈGRE-LES-FUMADES

30500 – Michelin map **339** K3 – pop. 695 – alt. 135 – ⚘
▶ Paris 696 – Alès 16 – Barjac 102 – La Grand-Combe 28

FranceLoc Le Domaine des Fumades

0466248078. www.domaine-des-fumades.com

Address : Les Fumade - Les Bains (access via the D 241)

Opening times : from mid April to mid Sept.

15 ha/6 for camping (253 pitches) relatively flat, flat, grassy, stony

Tariff : (2014 Price) 35€ ✝✝ ⇔ ▣ (10A) – Extra per person 7€ – Reservation fee 27€

This guide is not intended as a list of all the camping sites in France; its aim is to provide a selection of the best sites in each category.

Rental rates : (2014 Price) (from mid April to mid Sept.) – 188 ⬓ – 27 🏠 – 5 apartments – 8 tent lodges. Per night from 37 to 130€ – Per week from 147 to 1,344€ – Reservation fee 27€

Beside the Alauzène river and close to the spa centre.

Surroundings : 🏊 ▱ 〇〇
Leisure activities : ▮✗ ⌂ ⚘ 🖈 🏄 ✂ 🏊 🎣 🏊 cinema, multi-sports ground, entertainment room
Facilities : ♿ ⊶ 🔥 ¶ launderette 🏊 ⚲
Nearby : 🐎 🎣

Longitude : 4.22904
Latitude : 44.18484

ANDUZE

30140 – Michelin map **339** I4 – pop. 3 303 – alt. 135
▶ Paris 718 – Alès 15 – Florac 68 – Lodève 84

L'Arche

0466617408. www.camping-arche.fr

Address : 1105 chemin de Recoulin (situated 2km to the northwest; beside the Gardon)

Opening times : from beginning April to end Sept.

5 ha (302 pitches) terraced, relatively flat, flat, grassy, sandy

Tariff : 45€ ✝✝ ⇔ ▣ (10A) – Extra per person 9.50€ – Reservation fee 15€

Rental rates : (2014 Price) (from beginning April to end Sept.) 〜 – 16 ⬓ – 20 🏠. Per night from 58 to 160€ – Per week from 400 to 1,120€ – Reservation fee 15€

borne 2€

A pleasant swimming pool and indoor wellness area.

Surroundings : 🏊 🎣 ▲
Leisure activities : ▮✗ ⌂ ⚘ 🖈 ⇶ hammam 🏄 🏊 🏊 〜 multi-sports ground, spa centre
Facilities : ♿ ⊶ 🎱 🔥 🏊 ⚲ ¶ launderette 🏊 ⚲
Nearby : 🛒

Longitude : 3.97284
Latitude : 44.06873

Cévennes-Provence

0466617310. www.camping-cevennes-provence.fr

Address : at Corbès-Thoiras (by Le Mas du Pont; beside the Gardon de Mialet and near the Gardon de St-Jean (rivers)

Opening times : from end March to end Sept.

30 ha/15 for camping (242 pitches) very uneven, terraced, flat and relatively flat, grassy, stony

Tariff : 32€ ✝✝ ⇔ ▣ (10A) – Extra per person 8.60€ – Reservation fee 15€

Rental rates : (from end March to end Sept.) – 16 🏠. Per week from 350 to 750€

borne

Choose pitches near the river for swimming or higher up for the view over the valley.

Surroundings : 🏊 ≤ ▱ 〇〇 ▲
Leisure activities : ▮✗ ⌂ 🖈 🏄 ✂ ⚘ 🏊 〜
Facilities : ♿ ⊶ 🔥 🏊 ¶ launderette 🏊 ⚲
Nearby : adventure park

Longitude : 3.96643
Latitude : 44.07711

⛰ Les Fauvettes 👫

📞 04 66 61 72 23. www.lesfauvettes.fr

Address : route de St-Jean-du-Gard (1.7km to the northwest)

7 ha/3 for camping (144 pitches) very uneven, terraced, flat and relatively flat, grassy

Rentals : 22 🚐 – 20 🏠.

Choose the pitches away from the road in preference.

Surroundings : 🖵 ⚲	
Leisure activities : 🍹 ✕ 🛖 ☗ 🕺 ⚲ ⚲ entertainment room	**GPS** Longitude : 3.9738
Facilities : 🚿 ⊶ 🗑 🍴 🔲 🛁	Latitude : 44.06027
Nearby : 🚵	

⛰ Le Bel Eté d'Anduze

📞 04 66 61 76 04. www.camping-bel-ete.com

Address : 1870 route de Nîmes (2.5km southeast)

Opening times : from beginning April to end Sept.

2.26 ha (97 pitches) flat, grassy

Tariff : (2014 Price) 35€ 🚻 🚐 🔲 🔌 (16A) – Extra per person 8€ – Reservation fee 20€

Rental rates : (2014 Price) (from beginning April to end Sept.) – 26 🚐. Per night from 55€ – Per week from 270 to 690€ – Reservation fee 20€

Choose the pitches near the Gardon river and away from the road in preference.

Surroundings : ⚲ ⚲	
Leisure activities : ✕ 🛖 🕺 ⚲ ⚲ multi-sports ground	**GPS** Longitude : 3.99468
Facilities : 🚿 ⊶ 🗑 🍴 🔲 🛁 refrigerators	Latitude : 44.03827
Nearby : ⚔ ≋	

ARGELÈS-SUR-MER

66700 – Michelin map **344** J7 – pop. 10 033 – alt. 19

▶ Paris 872 – Céret 28 – Perpignan 22 – Port-Vendres 9

Centre

⛰ Le Front de Mer 👫

📞 04 68 81 08 70. www.camping-front-mer.com

Address : avenue du Grau (250m from the beach)

Opening times : from beginning April to end Sept.

10 ha (588 pitches) flat, grassy

Tariff : 41.90€ 🚻 🚐 🔲 🔌 (6A) – Extra per person 7.40€ – Reservation fee 25€

Rental rates : (from beginning April to end Sept.) – 144 🚐. Per week from 745 to 1,165€ – Reservation fee 25€

A pretty water park and indoor spa area.

Surroundings : 🖵 ⚲ ⚲	
Leisure activities : 🍹 ✕ 🕺 ⚲ hammam, jacuzzi 🕺 ⚲ ⚲ multi-sports ground, spa centre	**GPS** Longitude : 3.04687
Facilities : 🚿 ⊶ 🗑 🍴 launderette 🛁	Latitude : 42.54684

To make the best possible use of this guide, please read pages 2–15 carefully.

⛰ Pujol

📞 04 68 81 00 25. www.campingdepujol.com

Address : avenue de la Rétirada 1939

Opening times : from end April to beginning Oct.

6.2 ha (312 pitches)

Tariff : 38€ 🚻 🚐 🔲 🔌 (6A) – Extra per person 8€ – Reservation fee 15€

Rental rates : (from end April to beginning Oct.) 🚿 – 50 🚐. Per night from 20 to 138€ – Per week from 140 to 966€ – Reservation fee 15€

🚐 10 🔲 14€

Numerous pitches for tents or caravans, many with plenty of shade.

Surroundings : ⚲ ⚲	
Leisure activities : 🍹 ✕ 🎦 nighttime 🕺 🕺 🛖 ⚲	**GPS** Longitude : 3.02768
Facilities : 🚿 ⊶ 🗑 🍴 launderette 🛁	Latitude : 42.55532
Nearby : ⚔ 🐎	

⛰ FranceLoc Paris-Roussillon 👫

📞 04 68 81 19 71. www.parisroussillon.com

Address : avenue de la Retirada

3.5 ha (210 pitches) flat, grassy

Rentals : 100 🚐 – 2 studios – 2 apartments.

In a well-shaded setting; plenty of mobile homes, but also pitches for tents and caravans.

Surroundings : ≋ ⚲ ⚲	
Leisure activities : 🍹 ✕ 🕺 ☗ 🕺 ⚔ ⚲ ⚲ 🛖	**GPS** Longitude : 3.03117
Facilities : 🚿 ⊶ 🗑 🍴 launderette 🛁	Latitude : 42.55782
Nearby : 🐎	

⛰ La Chapelle - Les Ombrages 👫

📞 04 68 81 28 14. www.camping-la-chapelle.com

Address : avenue du Général de Gaulle (400m from the beach)

Opening times : from mid April to mid Sept.

4.1 ha (270 pitches)

Tariff : 46.30€ 🚻 🚐 🔲 🔌 (10A) – Extra per person 12.50€ – Reservation fee 26€

Rental rates : Permanent – 68 🚐. Per night from 60 to 140€ – Per week from 239 to 1,239€ – Reservation fee 26€

🚐 borne 6€ – 8 🔲 34€

Some attractively shaded areas beneath plane trees.

Surroundings : 🖵 ⚲⚲	
Leisure activities : 🛖 ☗ 🕺 🕺 ⚔ 🛖 multi-sports ground	**GPS** Longitude : 3.04214
Facilities : 🚿 ⊶ 🗑 🍴 launderette	Latitude : 42.55074
Nearby : 🚵 ⚓	

⛰ Europe

📞 04 68 81 08 10. www.camping-europe.net

Address : avenue du Général de Gaulle (500m from the beach)

Opening times : from beginning April to end Sept.

1.2 ha (91 pitches) flat, grassy

Tariff : 33€ 🚻 🚐 🔲 🔌 (10A) – Extra per person 7.50€ – Reservation fee 20€

Rental rates : (from beginning April to end Sept.) ᕹ (1 mobile home) – 13 ⛺. Per night from 50 to 110€ – Per week from 220 to 854 € – Reservation fee 20€

🚐 borne

Attractively shaded in places by plane trees, and good sanitary facilities.

Surroundings : ♨
Leisure activities : 🏊 🛶
Facilities : ᕹ ⛽ 🚿 launderette 🚻
Nearby : ⛲

Longitude : 3.04185
Latitude : 42.54987

⛰ Le Stade

📞 0468810440. www.campingdustade.com

Address : 87 avenue du 8 Mai 1945 (known as: rte de la Plage)

Opening times : from beginning April to beginning Oct.

2.4 ha (185 pitches) flat, grassy

Tariff : (2014 Price) 27.50€ ⛺⛺ 🚐 ▣ ⚡ (10A) – Extra per person 6€

Rental rates : (2014 Price) (from beginning April to beginning Oct.) 🚫 – 11 ⛺. Per night from 30 to 96€ – Per week from 210 to 675€ – Reservation fee 10€

Choose pitches away from the road; the sanitary facilities rather old.

Surroundings : ♨
Leisure activities : 🏊
Facilities : ᕹ ⛽ ▣ 🚿 launderette
Nearby : 🛒✕ 🍴 ⛲

Longitude : 3.03544
Latitude : 42.54774

⛰ La Massane

📞 0468810685. www.camping-massane.com

Address : avenue Molière (opposite the "Espace Jean Carrère")

Opening times : from beginning April to end Sept.

2.7 ha (184 pitches) flat, grassy

Tariff : 20€ ⛺⛺ 🚐 ▣ ⚡ (10A) – Extra per person 6.60€ – Reservation fee 12€

Rental rates : (from beginning April to end Sept.) 🚫 – 23 ⛺. Per night from 35 to 88€ – Per week from 250 to 620€ – Reservation fee 12€

Rather old but well-maintained sanitary facilities.

Surroundings : 🏕 ♨
Leisure activities : 🏖 🏊 ⛲
Facilities : ᕹ ⛽ 🚿 launderette
Nearby : ✕

Longitude : 3.03115
Latitude : 42.55137

⛰ Comangès

📞 0468811562. www.campingcomanges.com

Address : avenue Général de Gaulle (300m from the beach)

1.2 ha (90 pitches) flat, grassy

Rentals : 19 ⛺.

Surroundings : ♨
Leisure activities : 🏊
Facilities : ᕹ ⛽ 🚿 ▣
Nearby : 🚲 ✕ ⛲ ♨

Longitude : 3.04423
Latitude : 42.55145

North

⛰ La Sirène et l'Hippocampe ♟

📞 0468810461. www.camping-lasirene.fr

Address : route de Taxo

Opening times : from mid April to end Sept.

21 ha (903 pitches)

Tariff : 55€ ⛺⛺ 🚐 ▣ ⚡ (16A) – Extra per person 11€ – Reservation fee 20€

Rental rates : (from mid April to end Sept.) ᕹ (1 mobile home) – 600 ⛺ – 20 🏠. Per night from 39 to 275€ – Per week from 273 to 1,925€ – Reservation fee 20€

Divided into two sections with two water parks: the 'Hippo-campe' side is more peaceful and family-orientated. Only very few pitches for tents and caravans.

Surroundings : 🏕 ♨
Leisure activities : ♟ ✕ 🏠 🎯 👫 🏊 🚲 🎱 🎣 🏊 🐎 disco, pub, scuba diving, multi-sports ground
Facilities : ᕹ ⛽ 🚿 🏊 🚻 launderette 🚲

Longitude : 3.0326
Latitude : 42.57058

⛰ Le Soleil ♟

📞 0468811448. www.campmed.com

Address : route du Littoral

Opening times : from beginning May to mid Sept.

17 ha (844 pitches)

Tariff : (2014 Price) 48.30€ ⛺⛺ 🚐 ▣ ⚡ (10A) – Extra per person 11.90€ – Reservation fee 25€

Rental rates : (2014 Price) (from beginning May to mid Sept.) – 130 ⛺. Per night from 33 to 190€ – Per week from 231 to 1,330€ – Reservation fee 25€

A lush, green setting with lots of shade, close to the beach.

Surroundings : 🏕 ♨ ⛰
Leisure activities : ♟ ✕ 🏠 🎯 👫 🎣 🚲 🎱 🏊 🐎 disco
Facilities : ᕹ ⛽ 🚻 🏊 🚿 launderette 🚲

Longitude : 3.04618
Latitude : 42.5744

⛰ Les Marsouins ♟

📞 0468811481. http://campsud.com

Address : avenue de la Retirada

Opening times : from beginning April to end Sept.

10 ha (587 pitches) flat, grassy

Tariff : (2014 Price) 42€ ⛺⛺ 🚐 ▣ ⚡ (5A) – Extra per person 8.50€ Reservation fee 20€

Rental rates : (from beginning April to end Sept.) ᕹ (1 mobile home) – 200 ⛺. Per night from 35 to 195€ – Per week from 245 to 1,375€ – Reservation fee 20€

🚐 borne 4€ – 10 ▣ 42€

Attractive pitches for tents and caravans in green and floral surroundings.

Surroundings : 🏕 ♨
Leisure activities : ♟ ✕ 🎯 👫 🏊 🎱 🏊 scuba diving, multi-sports ground
Facilities : ᕹ ⛽ 🚿 🏊 🚻 launderette 🚻 🚲
Nearby : 🐎

Longitude : 3.03471
Latitude : 42.56376

⚠ La Marende ♠♣

☎ 0468811209. www.marende.com

Address : avenue du Littoral (400m from the beach)

3 ha (208 pitches)

Rentals : 67 🚐.

Good shade from pine and eucalyptus trees, but choose pitches away from the road.

Surroundings : 🖵 ♡♡
Leisure activities : ♟ ✕ ☼nighttime ⚡
jacuzzi ⛱ ⛳ ⛵ multi-sports ground
Facilities : ♿ ⚟ ▥ ♨ ♈ launderette ⚒ ⚓
Nearby : ✂ ♞ ♘

**Longitude : 3.0422
Latitude : 42.57395**

⚠ Club Airotel Les Galets ♠♣

☎ 0468810812. http://www.campinglesgalets.fr/ – limited spaces for one-night stay

Address : Route de Taxo a la Mer - north beach

Opening times : from beginning April to end Sept.

5 ha (232 pitches) flat, grassy

Tariff : 44€ ♠♠ ⬤ 🔲 (10A) – Extra per person 9.50€ – Reservation fee 30€

Rental rates : (from beginning April to end Sept.) ♿ (2 mobile homes) – 170 🚐 – 30 🏠. Per night from 34 to 179€ – Per week from 238 to 1,253€ – Reservation fee 30€

🚰 borne 10€ – 4 🔲 10€ – 💧 ⚡10€

Family site with plenty of owner-occupier mobile homes, but few places for tents and caravans.

Surroundings : 🖵 ♡♡
Leisure activities : ♟ ✕ 🚣 ☼nighttime ⚡
⛱ ⚓ multi-sports ground
Facilities : ♿ ⚟ ♨ ♈ launderette ⚓
Nearby : ♞

**Longitude : 3.0144
Latitude : 42.57249**

⚠ Le Roussillonnais ♠♣

☎ 0468811042. www.leroussillonnais.com

Address : boulevard de la mer

10 ha (690 pitches)

Rentals : 105 🚐.

Close to a beach, well shaded, with plenty of pitches for tents and caravans; groups welcome.

Surroundings : ♡♡ ⛰
Leisure activities : ♟ ✕ 🚣 ☼ ⚡ ⛱ ✂
multi-sports ground
Facilities : ♿ ⚟ ▥ ♨ ♈ launderette ⚒ ⚓
Nearby : ♘ ♞

**Longitude : 3.04367
Latitude : 42.56842**

South

⚠ Les Castels Les Criques de Porteils ♠♣

☎ 0468811273. www.lescriques.com

Address : corniche de Collioure, road RD 114

Opening times : from end March to end Oct.

4.5 ha (250 pitches) very uneven, terraced, relatively flat, flat, grassy, stony

Tariff : 54.50€ ♠♠ ⬤ 🔲 (10A) – Extra per person 13€ – Reservation fee 26€

Rental rates : (from end March to end Oct.) – 35 🚐 – 10 canvas bungalows. Per night from 26 to 219€ – Per week from 179 to 1,529€ – Reservation fee 26€

🚰 borne 5€ – 5 🔲 47€

Direct access to the beach via steep steps. A panoramic view of the Baie d'Argelès-sur-Mer (bay) and the Roussillon wine estates.

Surroundings : 🏖 ≤ Baie d'Argelès-sur-Mer
🖵 ♡♡ ⛰
Leisure activities : ♟ ✕ ⛱ ⛳ ⚓ ✂ ⛵ ⚒
scuba diving , multi-sports ground
Facilities : ♿ ⚟ ♨ ♈ launderette ⚒ ⚓
refrigerated food storage facilities

**Longitude : 3.06778
Latitude : 42.53389**

⚠ La Coste Rouge ♠

☎ 0468810894. www.lacosterouge.com – limited spaces for one-night stay

Address : route de Collioure (3km southeast)

Opening times : from beginning April to end Sept.

3.7 ha (145 pitches) terrace, flat and relatively flat, grassy

Tariff : 36€ ♠♠ ⬤ 🔲 (6A) – Extra per person 6.10€ – Reservation fee 20€

Rental rates : (from beginning April to end Sept.) – 45 🚐 – 7 studios. Per night from 36 to 135€ – Per week from 252 to 945€ – Reservation fee 20€

🚰 borne 15€ – 40 🔲 15€

Away from the hustle and bustle of Argelès-sur-Mer, but access to the beaches via a free shuttle service.

Surroundings : 🖵 ♡♡
Leisure activities : ♟ ✕ 🚣 ≤s ⚓ ⚒ ⛵
Facilities : ♿ ⚟ ♨ ♈ launderette ⚒ ⚓
Nearby : ⛳ ♘ ♨ ♞ water skiing

**Longitude : 3.05285
Latitude : 42.53301**

ARLES-SUR-TECH

66150 – Michelin map **344** C8 – pop. 2 757 – alt. 280
▶ Paris 886 – Amélie-les-Bains-Palalda 4 – Perpignan 45 – Prats-de-Mollo-la-Preste 19

⚠ Le Vallespir

☎ 0468399000. http://www.campingvallespir.com/fr/index.html

Address : situated 2km to the northeast, follow the signs for Amélie-les-Bains-Palalda ; beside the Tech river

Opening times : from end March to mid Nov.

2.5 ha (141 pitches)

Tariff : 24€ ♠♠ ⬤ 🔲 (6A) – Extra per person 6.60€

Rental rates : (from end March to mid Nov.) ♿ (2 mobile homes) – 52 🚐. Per night from 36 to 110€ – Per week from 218 to 790€

🚰 borne – 💧 ⚡21.60€

This is an attractive and sheltered site that always has plenty of pitches for tents and caravans.

Surroundings : 🖵 ♡♡
Leisure activities : ♟ ✕ 🚣 ⛱ ⛵ ⚒ ⚓
Facilities : ♿ ⚟ ♨ ♈ launderette

**Longitude : 2.65306
Latitude : 42.46671**

The pitches of many campsites are marked out with low hedges of attractive bushes and shrubs.

BAGNOLS-SUR-CÈZE

30200 – Michelin map **339** M4 – pop. 18 105 – alt. 51
▶ Paris 653 – Alès 54 – Avignon 34 – Nîmes 56

▲▲▲ Les Genêts d'Or

☎ 04 66 89 58 67. www.camping-genets-dor.com 🦌 (from beginning July to mid Aug.)

Address : chemin de Carmignan (take the northern exit along the N 86 then continue 2km along the D 360 to the right; beside the Cèze river)

Opening times : from mid April to mid Sept.

8 ha/3.5 for camping (95 pitches) flat, grassy

Tariff : (2014 Price) 32.50 € ★★ ⬅ 🔲 🔌 (6A) – Extra per person 5.50 € Reservation fee 10 €

Rental rates : (2014 Price) (from mid April to mid Sept.) 🦌 (from beginning July to mid Aug.) – 8 🚐. Per week from 403 to 690 € Reservation fee 10 €

🚐 borne

There are well-shaded pitches beside the river.

Surroundings : 💧💧⛰	**G P S** Longitude : 4.63694 Latitude : 44.17358
Leisure activities : ▼✕ ⬅🚣🛶⛵	
Facilities : ♿ ⛛ 🏛 ⛺🍴 launderette 🚿 🚰 refrigerators	

BALARUC-LES-BAINS

34540 – Michelin map **339** H8 – pop. 6 622 – alt. 3 – ⚕
▶ Paris 781 – Agde 32 – Béziers 52 – Frontignan 8

▲▲▲ Sites et Paysages Le Mas du Padre ▲▴

☎ 04 67 48 53 41. www.mas-du-padre.com

Address : 4 chemin du Mas du Padre (situated 2km northeast along the D 2e and take road to the right)

Opening times : from beginning April to end Oct.

1.8 ha (116 pitches) relatively flat, flat, grassy, fine gravel

Tariff : 38.35 € ★★ ⬅ 🔲 🔌 (10A)
Extra per person 5.60 € – Reservation fee 13 €

Rental rates : (from beginning April to end Oct.) 🦽 (1 chalet) – 16 🚐 – 1 🏠. Per night from 118 to 389 € – Per week from 294 to 973 € – Reservation fee 20.50 €

Pretty shrubs and flowers decorate the site.

Surroundings : 🌳 ⛱💧💧	**G P S** Longitude : 3.6924 Latitude : 43.4522
Leisure activities : 🎣🚣🛶⛵	
Facilities : ♿ ⛛ ⛺🍴 🔲 refrigerators	

Le Mas du Padre

▲▲▲ Les Vignes

☎ 04 67 48 04 93. www.camping-lesvignes.com – limited spaces for one-night stay

Address : 1 chemin des Vignes (1.7km northeast along the D 129, D 2e follow the signs for Sète and take road to the left)

2 ha (169 pitches)

Rentals : ♿ (1 mobile home) – 22 🚐 – 8 🏠.

The pitches are clearly marked out and on a gravel base, usually for people visiting the nearby spa (3 weeks).

Surroundings : ⛱💧💧	**G P S** Longitude : 3.68806 Latitude : 43.45351
Leisure activities : ✕🎣🚣🛶⛵	
Facilities : ♿ ⛛ ⛺🍴 🔲	

LE BARCARÈS

66420 – Michelin map **344** J6 – pop. 4 018 – alt. 3
▶ Paris 839 – Narbonne 56 – Perpignan 23 – Quillan 84

▲▲▲ L'Oasis ▲▴

☎ 04 68 86 12 43. www.camping-oasis.com

Address : route de St-Laurent-de-la-Salanque (1.3km southwest along the D 90)

10 ha (492 pitches)

Rentals : 207 🚐.

A lot of mobile homes, but pitches for tents and caravans are always available.

Surroundings : ⛱ 💧	**G P S** Longitude : 3.02462 Latitude : 42.77619
Leisure activities : ▼✕🛖🎣🚣🛶⛵🏓🎾🏊🏄	
Facilities : ♿ ⛛ ⛺🍴 launderette 🚿 🚰	

▲▲▲ Sunêlia Le California ▲▴

☎ 04 68 86 16 08. www.camping-california.fr

Address : route de St-Laurent (located 1.5km southwest along the D 90 - on D 83, take exit 9: Canet-en-Roussillon)

Opening times : from beginning May to mid Sept.

5 ha (265 pitches)

Tariff : 49.50 € ★★ ⬅ 🔲 🔌 (10A) – Extra per person 6 € – Reservation fee 35 €

Rental rates : (from beginning May to mid Sept.) ♿ (2 mobile homes) – 112 🚐 – 39 🏠 – 7 tent lodges. Per night from 23 to 129 € – Per week from 161 to 903 € – Reservation fee 35 €

🚐 borne 1 € – 81 🔲 14.50 € – 🚐 🔌 14.50 €

A large sports area.

Surroundings : ⛱💧💧	**G P S** Longitude : 3.02346 Latitude : 42.77606
Leisure activities : ▼✕🛖🎣🚣🛶⛵🏓🎾🏊🏄	
Facilities : ♿ ⛛ ⛺🍴 launderette 🚿 🚰	
Nearby : 🛒	

▲▲▲ Yelloh! Village Le Pré Catalan ▲▴

☎ 04 68 86 12 60. www.precatalan.com

Address : route de St-Laurent-de-la-Salanque (located 1.5km southwest along the D 90 then continue 600m along the road to the right)

Opening times : from end April to mid Sept.

4 ha (250 pitches)

Tariff : 47 € ★★ ⬅ 🔲 🔌 (10A) – Extra per person 8 €

Rental rates : (from end April to mid Sept.) – 90 🚐. Per night from 30 to 215 € – Per week from 210 to 1,505 €

🚐 borne 3 €

A pleasant site with activities and services suitable for families with young children.

Surroundings : 🌳⛱💧💧	**G P S** Longitude : 3.02272 Latitude : 42.78086
Leisure activities : ▼✕🛖🎣🚣🛶⛵🏊 multi-sports ground	
Facilities : ♿ ⛛ ⛺🍴 launderette 🚰	
Nearby : 🛒	

To make the best possible use of this guide, please read pages 2–15 carefully.

⛰ L'Europe

✆ 04 68 86 15 36. www.europe-camping.com – limited spaces for one-night stay

Address : route de St-Laurent-de-la-Salanque (situated 2km southwest along the D 90, 200m from the Agly river)

Opening times : Permanent

6 ha (360 pitches) flat, grassy

Tariff : (2014 Price) 52€ ✦✦ ⛺ 🔲 ⚡ (16A) – Extra per person 8€ – Reservation fee 30€

Rental rates : (2014 Price) Permanent – 79 🏠. Per night from 40 to 180€ – Per week from 240 to 1,250€ – Reservation fee 30€

Choose the pitches away from the road. Good-quality rental options in mobile homes as well as some rather old bungalows.

Surroundings : ⌑ ♀
Leisure activities : ♟ ✗ 🎞 ⚅ ⚶ ⚵ ⚶ ⚘
♒ ⚴
Facilities : ♿ ⚬ – 339 individual sanitary facilities (⚲ ⚬ wc) ⚴ ⚴ ⚴ ⚴ ⚴ ⚴ ⚴
GPS Longitude : 3.02064 Latitude : 42.775

⛰ La Croix du Sud ♟♟

✆ 04 68 86 16 61. www.lacroixdusud.fr – limited spaces for one-night stay

Address : route de Saint-Laurent-de-la-Salanque (1.4km southwest along the D 90; from D 83, take exit 10)

3.5 ha (200 pitches) flat, grassy

Rentals : ♿ (2 mobile homes) – 122 🏠 – 22 ⛺.

Numerous rental options, but pitches for tents and caravans are always available.

Surroundings : ⌑ ♀♀
Leisure activities : ♟ ✗ ⚅ ⚶ ⚵ ⚴ ♒ multi-sports ground
Facilities : ♿ ⚬ – ⚴ ⚴ launderette ⚴ refrigerators
GPS Longitude : 3.02757 Latitude : 42.77669

⛰ Flower Le Soleil Bleu ♟♟

(rental of mobile homes and chalets only)

✆ 04 68 86 15 50. www.lesoleilbleu.com

Address : Mas de la Tourre (1.4km southwest along the D 90 follow the signs for St-Laurent-de-la-Salanque; 100m from the Agly river)

Opening times : from beginning April to beginning Oct.

3 ha (175 pitches) flat, grassy

Rental rates : ♿ (1 mobile home) – 158 🏠 – 18 ⛺. Per night from 45 to 199€ – Per week from 225 to 1,393€ – Reservation fee 30€

Choose the sites away from the road in preference.

Surroundings : ⌑ ♀♀
Leisure activities : ♟ ✗ 🎞 ⚅ ⚶ ⚵ ♒ ⚴
multi-sports ground
Facilities : ⚬ – ⚴ ⚴ launderette ⚴ ⚴
GPS Longitude : 3.02842 Latitude : 42.77663

⛰ FranceLoc Las Bousigues ♟♟

✆ 04 68 86 16 19. www.campings-franceloc.fr – limited spaces for one-night stay

Address : avenue des Corbières (900m west)

3 ha (306 pitches)

Rentals : ♿ (2 mobile homes) – 163 🏠 – 4 tipis – 73 bungalows.

A large children's play area and a range of rental options, but the bungalows are old.

Surroundings : ⌑ ♀♀
Leisure activities : ♟ ✗ 🎞 ⚶ ⚵ ⚴ ⚴ ♒ ⚴
multi-sports ground
Facilities : ♿ ⚬ – ⚴ – 31 individual sanitary facilities (⚲ ⚬ wc) ⚴ launderette ⚴

GPS Longitude : 3.0254 Latitude : 42.7869

⛰ Cybele Vacances La Presqu'île ♟♟

✆ 04 68 86 12 80. www.lapresquile.com – limited spaces for one-night stay

Address : rue de la Presquile (to the north, on the D 83 exit 12)

3.5 ha (163 pitches)

Rentals : 83 🏠 – 29 ⛺ – 8 studios.

This site is on a peninsula, surrounded by water, and beside a lake. Some pitches are rather noisy; there is a swimming pool with a snack bar across the road.

Surroundings : ⌑ ♀♀
Leisure activities : ♟ ✗ 🎞 ⚶ jacuzzi ⚴
⚵ ♒ ⚴ ⚴ multi-sports ground
Facilities : ♿ ⚬ – ⚴ ⚴ launderette ⚴ ⚴
Nearby : ⚓
GPS Longitude : 3.02672 Latitude : 42.80528

BARJAC

30430 – Michelin map **339** L3 – pop. 1 546 – alt. 171
▶ Paris 666 – Alès 34 – Aubenas 45 – Pont-St-Esprit 33

⛰ La Combe

✆ 04 66 24 51 21. www.campinglacombe.com

Address : Mas de Reboul (3km west along the D 901, follow the signs for Les Vans and turn right onto the D 384)

Opening times : from beginning May to end Sept.

2.5 ha (100 pitches)

Tariff : 22.50€ ✦✦ ⛺ 🔲 ⚡ (6A) – Extra per person 9€ – Reservation fee 5€

Rental rates : (from beginning May to end Sept.) – 10 🏠 – 4 ⛺ – 1 apartment – 4 canvas bungalows. Per night from 60 to 100€ – Per week from 280 to 650€ – Reservation fee 15€

🅿 borne 4€ – ⚴ 12€

A peaceful, family-orientated site with plenty of shade.

Surroundings : ⚶ ♀♀
Leisure activities : ♟ 🎞 ⚴ ♒
Facilities : ♿ ⚬ – ⚴ ⚴ ⚴
GPS Longitude : 4.34784 Latitude : 44.30917

BÉDOUÈS

48400 – Michelin map **330** J8 – pop. 291 – alt. 565
▶ Paris 624 – Alès 69 – Florac 5 – Mende 39

⛰ Chon du Tarn

✆ 04 66 45 09 14. http://www.camping-chondutarn.com

Address : chemin du Chon du Tarn (take the northeastern exit, follow the signs for Cocurès)

Opening times : from beginning May to beginning Oct.

2 ha (100 pitches)

Tariff : ✦ 4.50€ ⛺ 🔲 4.50€ – ⚡ (6A) 2.30€

borne

In a pleasant setting with lots of green space beside the Tarn river.

Surroundings : 🐾 ⚲ Leisure activities : 🏄 🌊 Facilities : 🚿 🚻 🅿 🏕 ⛲ launderette Nearby : 🍷 ✕ climbing	**GPS** Longitude : 3.60531 Latitude : 44.3446

BELCAIRE

11340 – Michelin map **344** C6 – pop. 440 – alt. 1 002
▶ Paris 810 – Ax-les-Thermes 26 – Axat 32 – Foix 54

⚠ Municipal la Mousquière

📞 04 68 20 39 47. www.camping-pyrenees-cathare.fr

Address : 4 chemin du Lac (take the western exit onto the D 613, follow the signs for Ax-les-Thermes, 150m from a small lake)

Opening times : Permanent

0.6 ha (37 pitches)

Tariff : 17€ ✶✶ 🚗 🔌 (16A) – Extra per person 3€

Rental rates : Permanent – 8 🏠 – 3 canvas bungalows. Per night from 40 to 80€ – Per week from 180 to 420€

An attractively shaded site with a pretty lake nearby.

Surroundings : 🐾 Leisure activities : 🏛 Facilities : 🚿 🚻 🅿 🏕 ⛲ Nearby : 🏄 🎾 🌊 🐎 pedalos	**GPS** Longitude : 1.95022 Latitude : 42.81637

BESSÈGES

30160 – Michelin map **339** J3 – pop. 3 169 – alt. 170
▶ Paris 651 – Alès 32 – La Grand-Combe 20 – Les Vans 18

⚠ Les Drouilhèdes

📞 04 66 25 04 80. www.campingcevennes.com

Address : situated 2km west along the D 17, follow the signs for Génolhac then continue 1km along the D 386 to the right; beside the Cèze river

Opening times : from beginning May to mid Sept.

2 ha (90 pitches)

Tariff : 26.50€ ✶✶ 🚗 🔌 (6A) – Extra per person 5.70€ – Reservation fee 15.50€

Rental rates : (from beginning May to mid Sept.) – 6 🏠. Per week from 365 to 675€ – Reservation fee 15.50€

Surroundings : 🐾 < ⚲ Leisure activities : 🍷 🏄 ⚲ 🐎 Facilities : 🚿 🚻 🅿 🏕 ⛲	**GPS** Longitude : 4.0678 Latitude : 44.29143

BLAVIGNAC

48200 – Michelin map **330** H5 – pop. 236 – alt. 800
▶ Paris 542 – Montpellier 218 – Mende 58 – Clermont-Ferrand 126

⚠ Les Chalets de la Margeride (rental of chalets only)

📞 04 66 42 56 00. www.chalets-margeride.com

Address : Chassagnes (4.5km northwest along the D 989, follow the signs for St-Chély-d'Apcher and take the D 4, following signs for La Garde - from A 75: take exit 32)

Opening times : Permanent

50 ha/2 for camping, terraced

Rental rates : 🚿 (1 chalet) – 21 🏠. Per night from 126 to 139€ – Per week from 298 to 715€ – Reservation fee 9€

In an attractive panoramic location among the Margeride mountains.

Surroundings : 🐾 < Plateau de la Margeride Leisure activities : 🏛 🏄 🚲 🌊 (open air in season) Facilities : 🅿 🏕 ⛲ launderette	**GPS** Longitude : 3.30631 Latitude : 44.87017

BOISSET-ET-GAUJAC

30140 – Michelin map **339** J4 – pop. 2 302 – alt. 140
▶ Paris 722 – Montpellier 103 – Nîmes 53 – Alès 14

⚠ Domaine de Gaujac 🧍

📞 04 66 61 67 57. www.domaine-de-gaujac.com

Address : 2406 chemin de la Madelaine

Opening times : from beginning May to beginning Sept.

10 ha/6.5 for camping (293 pitches) terraced, relatively flat, flat, grassy

Tariff : 39€ ✶✶ 🚗 🔌 (10A) – Extra per person 7.50€ – Reservation fee 20€

Rental rates : (from beginning May to beginning Sept.) – 40 🚐 – 38 🏠. Per night from 42 to 123€ – Per week from 210 to 861€ Reservation fee 20€

borne 10€ – 8 🔲 10€

The lower pitches enjoy lots of shade, those on the terraces get plenty of sun.

Surroundings : ⚲⚲ Leisure activities : 🍷 ✕ 🏛 🎣 🏊 jacuzzi 🏄 🎾 ⛳ 🏊 🌊 Facilities : 🚿 🚻 🅿 🏕 ⛲ launderette 🧺 🔧 Nearby : 🌊 🐎	**GPS** Longitude : 4.02771 Latitude : 44.03471

Some campsites benefit from proximity to a municipal leisure centre.

BOISSON

30500 – Michelin map **339** K3
▶ Paris 682 – Alès 19 – Barjac 17 – La Grand-Combe 28

⚠ Les Castels Le Château de Boisson 🧍

📞 04 66 24 85 61. www.chateaudeboisson.com

Address : Boisson hamlet

Opening times : from mid April to end Sept.

7.5 ha (165 pitches) very uneven, terraced, flat, grassy

Tariff : 43.90€ ✶✶ 🚗 🔌 (10A) – Extra per person 10.50€ – Reservation fee 26€

Rental rates : (from mid April to end Sept.) – 57 🚐 – 11 🏠 – 15 gîtes. Per night from 51 to 201€ – Per week from 217 to 1,267€ Reservation fee 26€

borne 10€

Attractive pitches set near a restored Cévennes château, with a view over the Cévennes from some chalets.

Surroundings : 🐾 🏡 ⚲⚲ Leisure activities : 🍷 ✕ 🏛 🎣 🏊 🏄 🎾 🏊 🌊 Facilities : 🚿 🚻 🅿 🏕 – 7 individual sanitary facilities (🚿 🚻 wc) 🚐 🏕 ⛲ launderette 🧺 🔧 refrigerators	**GPS** Longitude : 4.25673 Latitude : 44.20966

LE BOSC

34490 – Michelin map **339** F6 – pop. 1 046 – alt. 90
▶ Paris 706 – Montpellier 51 – Béziers 58 – Sète 68

▲▲▲ Relais du Salagou (rental of chalets only)

⌀ 04 67 44 76 44. www.relais-du-salagou.com
Address : at Salelles, 8 rue des Terrasses (4.5km southeast along the D 140 - A 75. take exit 56)
12 ha/3 for camping flat
Rentals : ♿ (1 chalet) Ⓟ – 28 🏠.

Surroundings : ♁♁ Leisure activities : ⛨ 🖾 🏊 hammam, jacuzzi ⚡ ✂ 🎣 🔲 🏃 fitness trail, spa centre Facilities : ⊶ 🏛 ⛆ launderette	**GPS** Longitude : 3.41539 Latitude : 43.68268

BRISSAC

34190 – Michelin map **339** H5 – pop. 615 – alt. 145
▶ Paris 732 – Ganges 7 – Montpellier 41 – St-Hippolyte-du-Fort 19

▲▲▲ Le Val d'Hérault

⌀ 04 67 73 72 29. www.camping-levaldherault.com
Address : avenue d'Issensac (4km south along the D 4, follow the signs for Causse-de-la-Selle, 250m from the Hérault river (direct access)
Opening times : from mid March to end Oct.
4 ha (135 pitches) terraced, flat and relatively flat, grassy, stony
Tariff : (2014 Price) 29.90€ ⚤ 🚗 🔳 💡 (10A) – Extra per person 6.80€ – Reservation fee 10€
Rental rates : (2014 Price) (from mid March to end Oct.) – 22 🚐 – 4 🏠 – 10 canvas bungalows. Per night from 40 to 130€ – Per week from 238 to 910€ – Reservation fee 10€
🚐 borne 5€
Well-shaded pitches, some on small, individual terraces.

Surroundings : ♲ ▭ ♁♁ Leisure activities : ⛨ ✗ 🖾 ⊙ nighttime ⚡ 🏃 🛶 Facilities : ♿ ⊶ 🚿 ⛆ ⛆ 🌡 ⛆ 📦 📦 🛒 Nearby : 🏖 (beach) climbing	**GPS** Longitude : 3.70433 Latitude : 43.84677

▲▲▲ Le Domaine d'Anglas 🔒

⌀ 04 67 73 70 18. www.camping-anglas.com
Address : 2km east along the D 108
Opening times : from mid April to end Sept.
115 ha/5 for camping (101 pitches) terraced, flat, grassy, stony
Tariff : (2014 Price) 23.70€ ⚤ 🚗 🔳 💡 (10A) – Extra per person 5€ Reservation fee 17€
Rental rates : (2014 Price) (from mid April to end Sept.) – 4 caravans – 18 🏠 – 5 tent lodges – 1 gîte. Per night from 60 to 195€ – Per week from 255 to 880€ – Reservation fee 17€
🚐 30 🔳 24.50€
Beside the Hérault river and in the heart of the winegrowing region; varied rental options and average sanitary facilities.

Surroundings : ▭ ♁♁ Leisure activities : ✦ ⚡ 🚲 🏖 🛶 zip wiring 🛶 Facilities : ♿ ⊶ 🚿 ⛆ 🌡 ⛆ launderette 📦 🛒	**GPS** Longitude : 3.71615 Latitude : 43.87602

BROUSSES-ET-VILLARET

11390 – Michelin map **344** E2 – pop. 313 – alt. 412
▶ Paris 768 – Carcassonne 21 – Castelnaudary 36 – Foix 88

▲▲▲ Le Martinet-Rouge Birdie

⌀ 04 68 26 51 98. www.camping-martinet.com
Address : 500m south along the D 203 and take the road to the right, 200m from the Dure
Opening times : from beginning May to beginning Sept.
2.5 ha (63 pitches) undulating, flat, grassy, stony, rocks
Tariff : 16€ ⚤ 🚗 🔳 💡 (10A) – Extra per person 7.50€ – Reservation fee 6€
Rental rates : Permanent – 10 🚐 – 1 🏠. Per night from 30 to 105€ – Per week from 210 to 750€ – Reservation fee 6€
A very pleasant site with pitches among the rocks and plenty of shade from small Holm oaks.

Surroundings : ♲ ▭ ♁♁ Leisure activities : ⛨ ✗ 🖾 ⚡ 🏃 🛶 multi-sports ground Facilities : ♿ ⊶ 🚿 🌡 launderette	**GPS** Longitude : 2.0381 Latitude : 43.33088

These symbols are used for a campsite that is exceptional in its category:

▲▲▲…▲ *Particularly pleasant setting, quality and range of services available*

♲♲ *Tranquil, isolated site – quiet site, particularly at night*

⋐⋘ *Exceptional view – interesting or panoramic view*

CANET

34800 – Michelin map **339** F7 – pop. 3 269 – alt. 42
▶ Paris 717 – Béziers 47 – Clermont-l'Hérault 6 – Gignac 10

▲▲▲ Les Rivières

⌀ 04 67 96 75 53. www.camping-lesrivieres.com
Address : La Sablière (1.8km north along the D 131e)
Opening times : from beginning April to end Sept.
9 ha/5 for camping (110 pitches)
Tariff : 31€ ⚤ 🚗 🔳 💡 (10A) – Extra per person 6.50€ – Reservation fee 12€
Rental rates : (from beginning April to mid Oct.) 🛶 – 11 🚐 – 8 🏠 – 3 canvas bungalows – 2 gîtes. Per night from 40 to 79€ – Per week from 210 to 740€ – Reservation fee 12€
🚐 borne 10€ – 7 🔳 10€ – 🛒 8€
A spacious site beside the Hérault river, where swimming is always an option.

Surroundings : ♲ ▭ ♁♁ Leisure activities : ⛨ ✗ 🖾 jacuzzi ⚡ 🚲 🏃 🏖 🛶 climbing wall, multi-sports ground Facilities : ♿ ⊶ 🚿 🌡 📦 🛒 Nearby : 🐎	**GPS** Longitude : 3.49229 Latitude : 43.61792

Routes nationales are main roads and their identifying numbers begin with N or RN. Routes départementales are generally quieter roads and begin with D or DN.

CANET-PLAGE

66140 – Michelin map **344** J6

▶ Paris 849 – Argelès-sur-Mer 20 – Le Boulou 35 – Canet-en-Roussillon 3

⩓⩓⩓ Yelloh! Village Le Brasilia ♠♠

Le Brasilia

📞 04 68 80 23 82. www.brasilia.fr

Address : avenue des Anneaux du Roussillon (beside the Têt river; direct access to the beach)

Opening times : from mid April to beginning Oct.

15 ha (735 pitches)

Tariff : 60.50 € ♥♥ ⇔ 🔲 🔌 (10A) – Extra per person 9 €

Rental rates : (from mid April to beginning Oct.) ⅃ (2 mobile homes) – 241 ⬛ – 47 ⬛ – 2 gîtes. Per night from 38 to 285 €– Per week from 266 to 1,995 €

🚰 borne

Lush green pitches and plenty of shade, small landscaped mobile homes villages and a variety of activities make this a real village club.

Surroundings : ⧖ ⊡ 🎯🎯⚲
Leisure activities : ⧍ ✕ 🎬 📺 🎣 jacuzzi ⛵️🚴🏊⛷ disco, multi-sports ground
Facilities : ⅃ ⊶ ⊞ 🚿 ⚁ 🚰 launderette ⊟
Nearby : 🏇 🐎

| G P S | Longitude : 3.03392 Latitude : 42.69429 |

⩓⩓⩓ Mar Estang ♠♠

📞 04 68 80 35 53. www.marestang.com

Address : route de Saint-Cyprien (1.5km south along the D 18a, near the lake and the beach)

Opening times : Permanent

11 ha (600 pitches) flat, grassy

Tariff : 50 € ♥♥ ⇔ 🔲 🔌 (6A) – Extra per person 13 € – Reservation fee 26 €

Rental rates : Permanent ⅃ (1 mobile homes) 🅿 – 227 ⬛ – 32 canvas bungalows. Per night from 26 to 181 € – Per week from 177 to 1,267 € – Reservation fee 26 €

🚰 borne 4 € – 8 🔲 44 €

Direct access to the beach along an underground passage; the pitches have some shade; activities for young people and teenagers.

Surroundings : ⊡ 🎯🎯
Leisure activities : ⧍ ✕ 🎬 📺 (amphitheatre) 📺 🎣 ⛵️🚴🚴🏊⛷ disco, multi-sports ground
Facilities : ⅃ ⊶ 🚿 🚰 launderette ⊟ ⊟

| G P S | Longitude : 3.03256 Latitude : 42.67262 |

The Michelin classification (⩓⩓⩓ … ⩓) is totally independent of the official star classification system awarded by the local prefecture or other official organisation.

⩓ Les Fontaines

Les Fontaines

📞 04 68 80 22 57. www.camping-les-fontaines.com

Address : 23 avenue de St-Nazaire

Opening times : from beginning May to mid Sept.

5.3 ha (160 pitches)

Tariff : (2014 Price) 36 € ♥♥ ⇔ 🔲 🔌 (10A) – Extra per person 7 € – Reservation fee 15 €

Rental rates : (2014 Price) (from beginning May to mid Sept.) – 105 ⬛. Per night from 32 to 121 € – Per week from 220 to 847 € Reservation fee 15 €

🚰 borne 6 €

A natural site with slight or no shade; choose the pitches near the lake and away from the road in preference.

Surroundings : ⊡
Leisure activities : ⧍ 🎬 🎣 ⛷ wildlife park
Facilities : ⅃ ⊶ (July–Aug.) ⊞ ⚁ 🚰 🚽 launderette

| G P S | Longitude : 2.99892 Latitude : 42.68909 |

Key to rentals symbols:

12 ⬛	*Number of mobile homes*
20 ⬛	*Number of chalets*
6 🛏	*Number of rooms to rent*
Per night 30–50€	*Minimum/maximum rate per night*
Per week 300–1,000€	*Minimum/maximum rate per week*

CANILHAC

48500 – Michelin map **330** G8 – pop. 138 – alt. 700

▶ Paris 593 – La Canourgue 8 – Marvejols 26 – Mende 52

⩓⩓ Municipal la Vallée

📞 04 66 32 91 14. http://www.camping-vallee-du-lot.com

Address : Miège Rivière (12km north along the N 9, follow the signs for Marvejols, turn left onto the D 988, follow the signs for St-Geniez-d'Olt and take the road to the left – from the A 75, take exit 40 towards St-Laurent-d'Olt then continue 5km along the D 988)

Opening times : from mid June to mid Sept.

1 ha (50 pitches) flat, grassy

Tariff : (2014 Price) 12 € ♥♥ ⇔ 🔲 🔌 (16A) – Extra per person 3 €

Rental rates : (2014 Price) (from mid June to mid Sept.) – 3 ⬛. Per night from 36 to 50 € – Per week from 250 to 350 €

🚰 borne – 🔋 11.40 €

In a small but lush green valley by the Lot river.

Surroundings : ⧖ ⊲ ⊡ 🎯🎯
Leisure activities : ⅃ ⛵️🏊⛷ 🏊 🎣
Facilities : ⅃ ⊶ ⚁ 🚰 🔲
Nearby : ✕

| G P S | Longitude : 3.14892 Latitude : 44.4365 |

In order for the guide to remain wholly objective, the selection of campsites is made on an entirely independent basis.

LA CANOURGUE

48500 – Michelin map **330** H8 – pop. 2 112 – alt. 563
▶ Paris 588 – Marvejols 21 – Mende 40 – Millau 53

🏔 Chalets et camping du golf

℘ 04 66 44 23 60. www.lozereleisure.com

Address : route des Gorges du Tarn (3.6km southeast along the D 988, follow the signs for Chanac, after the golf course; beside the Urugne river)

Opening times : from mid April to mid Sept.

8 ha (72 pitches) grassy

Tariff : (2014 Price) 14.50€ ✶ ✶ ⬅ 🔲 ⚡ (6A) – Extra per person 4€
Rental rates : (2014 Price) (from mid April to mid Sept.) – 14 🏠. Per night from 57 to 60€ – Per week from 214 to 626€
🚐 borne – 🔌⚡14.50€

In a green setting, with chalets ranging from basic to more luxurious; very old sanitary facilities for tent and caravan pitches.

Surroundings : 🐟 ☁ ♨♨
Leisure activities : ⚓ ⛴
Facilities : ⚬🔲 🏚 ☝ launderette
Nearby : ☕ ✕ golf

Longitude : 3.24072
Latitude : 44.40842

LE CAP-D'AGDE

34300 – Michelin map **339** G9
▶ Paris 767 – Montpellier 57 – Béziers 29 – Narbonne 59

🏔 La Clape

℘ 04 67 26 41 32. www.camping-laclape.com

Address : 2 rue du Gouverneur (near the beach - direct access)

Opening times : from beginning April to end Sept.

7 ha (450 pitches)

Tariff : (2014 Price) 41.20€ ✶ ✶ ⬅ 🔲 ⚡ (10A) – Extra per person 8€
Reservation fee 27€
Rental rates : (2014 Price) (from beginning April to end Sept.) 🚿 (1 chalet) 🚿 – 89 🏠 – 31 🏠. Per night from 42 to 132€ – Per week from 343 to 924€ – Reservation fee 27€
🚐 borne 2€ – 22 🔲 10€

Services and parking for campervans are available off the site.

Surroundings : ☁ ♨♨
Leisure activities : ☕ ✕ 🏚 ⚓ ⛴ multi-sports ground
Facilities : ⚓ ⚬🔲 🏚 ☝ launderette 🔲🔲 refrigerators

Longitude : 3.5193
Latitude : 43.28534

CARCASSONNE

11000 – Michelin map **344** F3 – pop. 47 854 – alt. 110
▶ Paris 768 – Albi 110 – Béziers 90 – Narbonne 61

🏔 La Cité 👥

℘ 04 68 10 01 00. www.campingcitecarcassonne.com

Address : route de Saint-Hilaire (take the eastern exit along the N 113, follow the signs for Narbonne then continue 1.8km along the D 104, near a branch of the Aude river)

Opening times : from end March to beginning Oct.

7 ha (200 pitches) flat, grassy

Tariff : (2014 Price) 32.40€ ✶ ✶ ⬅ 🔲 ⚡ (10A) – Extra per person 8€

Rental rates : (2014 Price) (from end March to beginning Oct.)
⚓ (2 mobile homes) – 24 🏠 – 17 canvas bungalows. Per night from 60 to 130€ – Per week from 574 to 980€

Very close to the old town of Carcassonne.

Surroundings : ☁ ♨♨
Leisure activities : ☕ ✕ 🏚 ⚓ ⚓ ⛴ multi-sports ground
Facilities : ⚓ ⚬🔲 ☝ launderette 🔲

Longitude : 2.33716
Latitude : 43.19874

CARNON-PLAGE

34280 – Michelin map **339** I7
▶ Paris 758 – Aigues-Mortes 20 – Montpellier 20 – Nîmes 56

🏔 Les Saladelles

℘ 04 67 68 23 71. www.paysdelor.fr

Address : rue de l'Aigoual (head for Carnon-est, D 59, 100m from the beach)

Opening times : from beginning April to end Sept.

7.6 ha (340 pitches)

Tariff : (2014 Price) 22.90€ ✶ ✶ ⬅ 🔲 ⚡ (10A) – Extra per person 4€
Reservation fee 10€
Rental rates : (2014 Price) (from mid April to mid Sept.) 🚿 – 40 🏠. Per week from 260 to 750€ – Reservation fee 10€
🚐 borne 13€ – 18 🔲 13€

Choose the pitches away from the road in preference; parking for campervans nearby but off the site.

Surroundings : ♨♨
Leisure activities : ⚓ multi-sports ground
Facilities : ⚓ ⚬🔲 ⛴ 🏚 ☝ 🔲

Longitude : 3.99464
Latitude : 43.55079

Michelin classification:

🏔🏔🏔🏔 *Extremely comfortable, equipped to a very high standard*
🏔🏔🏔 *Very comfortable, equipped to a high standard*
🏔🏔 *Comfortable and well equipped*
🏔 *Reasonably comfortable*
🏔 *Satisfactory*

CASTEIL

66820 – Michelin map **344** F7 – pop. 120 – alt. 780
▶ Paris 878 – Montpellier 215 – Perpignan 59 – Carcassonne 126

🏔 Domaine St-Martin

℘ 04 68 05 52 09. www.domainesaintmartin.com – help moving caravans onto and off pitches avilable on request

Address : 6 boulevard de la Cascade (take the northern exit along the D 116 and take the road to the right)

4.5 ha (60 pitches) very uneven, terraced, flat, stony, rocks
Rentals : 7 🏠 – 6 tent lodges.

In a natural and unspoilt setting at the foot of the Massif du Canigou (mountains), near a waterfall.

Surroundings : 🐟 ☁ ♨♨♨
Leisure activities : ☕ ✕ 🏚 ⛴
Facilities : ⚓ ⚬🔲 🏚 ☝ launderette
Nearby : ✕

Longitude : 2.39464
Latitude : 42.53296

CASTRIES

34160 – Michelin map **339** I6 – pop. 5 671 – alt. 70
▶ Paris 746 – Lunel 15 – Montpellier 19 – Nîmes 44

⛰ Le Fondespierre

✆ 04 67 91 20 03. www.campingfondespierre.com

Address : 277 chemin Pioch Viala (2.5km northeast along the N 110, follow the signs for Sommières and take turning to the left)

Opening times : from beginning Jan.to mid Dec.

3 ha (103 pitches)

Tariff : (2014 Price) 33€ ✶ ✶ ⇆ 🔲 ⚡ (16A) – Extra per person 6€ – Reservation fee 15€

Rental rates : (2014 Price) Permanent – 30 🚐 – 2 🏠 – 7 canvas bungalows. Per night from 88 to 186€ – Per week from 224 to 760€ – Reservation fee 15€

🚙 borne 4€

Surroundings : 🏞 ⛱ ♨♨	
Leisure activities : 🏌 🚴 ⛲	**G** Longitude : 3.99903
Facilities : ♿ ⚡ 🚿 ♨ launderette	**P** Latitude : 43.69125
Nearby : 🍴	**S**

This guide is updated regularly, so buy your new copy every year!

CELLES

34700 – Michelin map **339** F7 – pop. 22 – alt. 140
▶ Paris 707 – Montpellier 55 – Nîmes 111 – Albi 190

⛰ Municipal les Vailhès

✆ 04 67 44 25 98. www.campinglesvailhes.fr

Address : situated 2km northeast along the D 148E4 follow the signs for Lodève - A75 take exit 54

Opening times : from beginning April to end Sept.

4 ha (246 pitches) terraced, flat, grassy

Tariff : (2014 Price) ✶ 4.20€ ⇆ 🔲 7.20€ – ⚡ (10A) 4.10€

🚙 borne 8€

In an attractive location beside the Lac du Salagou.

Surroundings : 🏞 ⟪ ⛱ ♨♨ ⛰	
Leisure activities : 🏌 ⚓ ⛵ ♨	**G** Longitude : 3.36012
Facilities : ♿ ⚡ ♨ 🔲	**P** Latitude : 43.66865
Nearby : 🎣	**S**

CENDRAS

30480 – Michelin map **339** J4 – pop. 1 930 – alt. 155
▶ Paris 694 – Montpellier 76 – Nîmes 50 – Avignon 76

⛰⛰ La Croix Clémentine

✆ 04 66 86 52 69. www.clementine.fr

Address : route de Mende, La Fare (situated 2km northwest along the D 916 and turn left onto the D 32)

Opening times : from beginning April to mid Sept.

10 ha (250 pitches)

Tariff : 35€ ✶ ✶ ⇆ 🔲 ⚡ (10A) – Extra per person 9€ – Reservation fee 12€

Rental rates : (from beginning April to end Sept.) – 10 🚐 – 30 🏠 – 12 canvas bungalows. Per night from 35 to 150€ – Per week from 200 to 900 € – Reservation fee 12€

🚙 borne 15€ – 4 🔲 15€

In a pleasant wooded setting.

Surroundings : 🏞 ⛱ ♨♨	
Leisure activities : 🍴 ✗ 🔲 🎇 nighttime ⚡	
🚴 ✗ 🎯 ♨ multi-sports ground	**G** Longitude : 4.04333
Facilities : ♿ ⚡ 🔲 🛁 ♨ 🚽 🏌 launderette	**P** Latitude : 44.15167
♨ 🛒 refrigerators	**S**
Nearby : 🎣 🐎	

LE CHAMBON

30450 – Michelin map **339** J3 – pop. 273 – alt. 260
▶ Paris 640 – Alès 31 – Florac 59 – Génolhac 10

⛰ Municipal le Luech

✆ 04 66 61 51 32. mairie-du-chambon@wanadoo.fr – 🅵🆁

Address : Palanquis (600m northwest along the D 29, follow the signs for Chamborigaud)

Opening times : from beginning July to end Aug.

0.5 ha (43 pitches) terraced, relatively flat, grassy, stony

Tariff : (2014 Price) ✶ 2.41€ ⇆ 1.68€ 🔲 3€ – ⚡ (6A) 3.54€

On 2 separate sites on either side of the road beside the Luech river.

Surroundings : ♨♨	
Leisure activities : 🎣	**G** Longitude : 4.00317
Facilities : ♿ 🚿🔲	**P** Latitude : 44.30494
Nearby : 🍴	**S**

For more information on visiting particular towns or regions, consult the relevant regional MICHELIN Green Guide. We also recommend you use the appropriate Michelin regional map to locate your selected campsite, to calculate distances and to work out the best route.

CHASTANIER

48300 – Michelin map **330** K6 – pop. 92 – alt. 1 090
▶ Paris 570 – Châteauneuf-de-Randon 17 – Langogne 10 Marvejols 71

⛰ Pont de Braye

✆ 04 66 69 53 04. www.camping-lozere-naussac.fr

Address : Les Berges du Chapeauroux (located 1km west, near the junction of D 988 and D 34, by the bridge)

Opening times : from beginning May to mid Sept.

1.5 ha (35 pitches)

Tariff : 13.60€ ✶ ✶ ⇆ 🔲 ⚡ (6A) – Extra per person 4€ – Reservation fee 7€

Rental rates : (2014 Price) (from beginning May to mid Sept.) – 3 yurts – 1 apartment – 2 canvas bungalows – 2 tent lodges. Per night from 45 to 65€ – Per week from 189 to 495€ – Reservation fee 7€

🚙 borne 2.50€ – 🚐 8€

Beside the river; a variety of original rental options, with simple facilities.

Surroundings : 🏞 ♨♨	
Leisure activities : 🍴 🔲 🏌 🚴 🎣	**G** Longitude : 3.74755
Facilities : ♿ ⚡ 🔲 ♨ 🚽 ♨ launderette 🛒	**P** Latitude : 44.72656
Nearby : ✗	**S**

CLERMONT-L'HÉRAULT

34800 – Michelin map **339** F7 – pop. 7 627 – alt. 92
▶ Paris 718 – Béziers 46 – Lodève 24 – Montpellier 42

⚠ Municipal Campotel Lac du Salagou

✆ 04 67 96 13 13. www.le-salagou.fr

Address : at Lac du Salagou (lake) (5km northwest along the D 156e 4, 300m from the lake)

Opening times : Permanent

7.5 ha (388 pitches)

Tariff : (2014 Price) 19€ ♣♣ 🚐 🗉 🗱 (10A) – Extra per person 3€ – Reservation fee 15€

Rental rates : (2014 Price) Permanent ♿ (1 mobile home) – 14 🛏 – 14 🏠. Per week from 329 to 680€ – Reservation fee 15€

🚽 borne 2€

A pleasant location close to the lake and the sailing centre.

Surroundings : 🌳 ≤ 🗀 ♧♧
Leisure activities : 🎣 🛶
Facilities : ♿ 🔦 🏧 🚿 🧺 ♒ 🗑 refrigerated food storage facilities
Nearby : 🍷 ✗ 🚣 🚲 🏊 🎣 ♨

G P S Longitude : 3.38957
Latitude : 43.6455

COLLIAS

30210 – Michelin map **339** L5 – pop. 1 002 – alt. 45
▶ Paris 694 – Alès 45 – Avignon 32 – Bagnols-sur-Cèze 35

⚠ Le Barralet

✆ 04 66 22 84 52. www.camping-barralet.com

Address : 6 chemin du Grès (located 1km northeast along the D 3, follow the signs for Uzès and take the road to the right)

2 ha (132 pitches)

Rentals : 18 🛏 – 9 🏠.

There's panoramic view of the village and surrounding area from the swimming pool and the terrace of the bar.

Surroundings : 🌳 ≤ ♧♧
Leisure activities : 🍷 ✗ 🛶 🏊 multi-sports ground
Facilities : ♿ 🔦 ♒ 🗑 🚿

G P S Longitude : 4.48718
Latitude : 43.95769

CONNAUX

30330 – Michelin map **339** M4 – pop. 1 583 – alt. 86
▶ Paris 661 – Avignon 32 – Alès 52 – Nîmes 48

⚠ Le Vieux Verger

✆ 04 66 82 91 62. www.campinglevieuxverger.com

Address : 526 avenue des Platanes (south of the town, 200m from the N 86)

Opening times : Permanent

3 ha (60 pitches)

Tariff : 23.90€ ♣♣ 🚐 🗉 🗱 (10A) – Extra per person 4.80€ – Reservation fee 10€

*The classification (1 to 5 tents, **black** or red) that we award to selected sites in this guide is our own system. It should not be confused with the classification (1 to 5 stars) of official organisations.*

Rental rates : Permanent 🚿 – 9 🛏 – 5 🏠. Per night from 90 to 169€ – Per week from 309 to 760€ – Reservation fee 25€

There are still more places for tents and caravans at the top of the site, plus plenty of shade.

Surroundings : 🗀 ♧
Leisure activities : ✗ 🛶
Facilities : ♿ 🔦 🗺 🧺 🗑
Nearby : 🍽

G P S Longitude : 4.59108
Latitude : 44.08478

CRESPIAN

30260 – Michelin map **339** J5 – pop. 325 – alt. 80
▶ Paris 731 – Alès 32 – Anduze 27 – Nîmes 24

⚠ Kawan Village Le Mas de Reilhe 👥

✆ 04 66 77 82 12. www.camping-mas-de-reilhe.fr

Address : chemin du Mas de Reilhe (take the southern exit along the N 110)

Opening times : from end April to mid Sept.

2 ha (95 pitches)

Tariff : (2014 Price) 31€ ♣♣ 🚐 🗉 🗱 (10A) – Extra per person 7€ – Reservation fee 20€

Rental rates : (2014 Price) (from end April to mid Sept.) – 15 🛏 – 7 🏠 – 4 tent lodges. Per night from 44 to 116€ – Per week from 308 to 812€ – Reservation fee 20€

🚽 borne 31€

Surroundings : 🗀 ♧♧
Leisure activities : 🍷 ✗ 🛶 🚶 🛶 🚲 🏊 multi-sports ground
Facilities : 🔦 🗺 🏧 🛁 🧺 🗑 ♒ launderette 🚿
Nearby : 🍽

G P S Longitude : 4.09676
Latitude : 43.88015

These symbols are used for a campsite that is exceptional in its category:

🏔🏔🏔…🏔 *Particularly pleasant setting, quality and range of services available*

🐾🐾 *Tranquil, isolated site – quiet site, particularly at night*

≤≤ *Exceptional view – interesting or panoramic view*

EGAT

66120 – Michelin map **344** D7 – pop. 453 – alt. 1 650
▶ Paris 856 – Andorra-la-Vella 70 – Ax-les-Thermes 53 – Bourg-Madame 15

⚠ Las Clotes

✆ 04 68 30 26 90. www.pro.pagesjaunes.fr/camping-las-clotes

Address : 400m north of the town; beside a little stream

Opening times : from mid Nov. to mid Oct.

2 ha (80 pitches)

Tariff : 18.50€ ♣♣ 🚐 🗉 🗱 (6A) – Extra per person 4.50€

In an attractive elevated location, on the side of a rocky hill.

Surroundings : 🌳 ≤ Sierra del Cadi and Puigmal (peak) 🗀 ♧♧
Leisure activities : 🎣
Facilities : ♿ 🔦 🚿 🏧 🛁 ♒ 🗑

G P S Longitude : 2.01765
Latitude : 42.499

ERR

66800 – Michelin map **344** D8 – pop. 640 – alt. 1 350 – Winter sports : 1 850/2 520 m

▶ Paris 854 – Andorra-la-Vella 77 – Ax-les-Thermes 52 – Bourg-Madame 10

⚠ Le Puigmal

℘ 0468047183. www.camping-le-puigmal.com

Address : 30 route du Puigmal (along the D 33b; beside a stream)

Opening times : from beginning May to end Sept. , school holidays and weekends in winter

3.2 ha (125 pitches)

Tariff : 14€ ✖✖ ⬅ 🔲 🔌 (10A) – Extra per person 4.60€

Rental rates : (from beginning May to end Sept. , winter school holidays and winter weekends) – 10 🛏. Per night from 59 to 75€ – Per week from 395 to 450€

In pleasant setting, lots of greenery, shaded in places. Good-quality sanitary facilities in the centre.

Surroundings : 🌿 ♢ ♤♤
Leisure activities : 🎯 🛋 ⛷
Facilities : ♿ ⛽ 🏛 🚰 ⓣ launderette
Nearby : ⛵ ⛷

GPS Longitude : 2.03539
Latitude : 42.43751

⚠ Las Closas

℘ 0468047142. www.camping-las-closas.com

Address : 1 place Saint-Génis (along the D 33b)

Opening times : Permanent

2 ha (114 pitches)

Tariff : (2014 Price) 22.50€ ✖✖ ⬅ 🔲 🔌 (10A) – Extra per person 4.50€

Rental rates : Permanent – 15 🛏. Per night from 66 to 73€ – Per week from 405 to 530€

🛏 10 🔲 14€

In the centre of the village close to the church; a pleasant site with good sanitary facilities.

Surroundings : ♢♤
Leisure activities : 🛋 ⛷
Facilities : ♿ ⛽ 🏛 🚰 ⓣ launderette
Nearby : ✖ ⛷ ⛵

GPS Longitude : 2.03138
Latitude : 42.44014

The guide covers all 22 regions of France – see the map and list of regions on pages 4–5.

ESTAVAR

66800 – Michelin map **344** D8 – pop. 429 – alt. 1 200
▶ Paris 852 – Montpellier 247 – Perpignan 97

⚠ L'Enclave ♟♟

℘ 0468047227. www.camping.lenclave.com

Address : 2 rue Vinyals (take the eastern exit along the D 33; beside the Angoust river)

Opening times : from beginning Dec. to beginning Oct.

3.5 ha (175 pitches) terraced, flat and relatively flat, stony, grassy

Tariff : 33.30€ ✖✖ ⬅ 🔲 🔌 (10A) – Extra per person 5.60€ – Reservation fee 10€

Rental rates : Permanent – 30 🛏. Per night from 35 to 100€ – Per week from 190 to 800€ – Reservation fee 10€

🛏 borne 6€

An attractive shady area along a stream with a lovely play-ground at the bottom of the site.

Surroundings : 🌿 ▱ ♢♢
Leisure activities : 🎯 ♣ ⛵ jacuzzi ⛷ ✖ ⛷ 🏊 guided walks , entertainment room
Facilities : ♿ ⛽ 🏛 🚰 ♨ ⓣ launderette
Nearby : ⛵ 🍴 ✖ ⛷ ⛵

GPS Longitude : 1.99813
Latitude : 42.4688

🏠 Yelloh! Village l'Escapade (rental of chalets only)

℘ 0466739739. www.lescapade.com

Address : cami del Segre (800m to the south)

Opening times : Permanent

5 ha flat, grassy

Rental rates : ♿ (5 chalets) – 44 🏠. Per night from 39 to 155€ – Per week from 273 to 1,085€

A village of genuine wooden chalets, very luxurious.

Surroundings : 🌿 ♢
Leisure activities : 🍴 ✖ 🛋 ⛷ multi-sports ground, entertainment room
Facilities : ♿ ⛽ 🏛 ♨ ⓣ launderette ⛵

GPS Longitude : 1.99921
Latitude : 42.46182

FLORAC

48400 – Michelin map **330** J9 – pop. 1 921 – alt. 542
▶ Paris 622 – Alès 65 – Mende 38 – Millau 84

🏠 Municipal le Pont du Tarn ♟♟

Municipal le Pont du Tarn

℘ 0466451826. www.camping-florac.com

Address : route du Pont-de-Montvert (situated 2km north along the N 106, follow the signs for Mende and take D 998 to the right, direct access to the Tarn river)

Opening times : from end March to beginning Nov.

3 ha (181 pitches)

Tariff : (2014 Price) 29.70€ ✖✖ ⬅ 🔲 Extra per person 4.60€ – Reservation fee 12€

Rental rates : (2014 Price) (from end March to beginning Nov.) – 22 🛏 – 6 canvas bungalows. Per week from 190 to 830€ – Reservation fee 12€

🛏 borne 4.50€

Some pitches are beside the Tarn river, but choose those furthest from the road.

Surroundings : ≤ ♢♢
Leisure activities : 🍴 ♣ ⛷ ⛷ 🏊
Facilities : ♿ ⛽ 🏛 ♨ ⛷ ⓣ launderette ⛵
Nearby : ✖

GPS Longitude : 3.59013
Latitude : 44.33625

FONT-ROMEU

66120 – Michelin map **344** D7 – pop. 2 003 – alt. 1 800 – Winter sports : 🎿 ⛷ 🛷
▶ Paris 860 – Montpellier 245 – Perpignan 90 – Canillo 62

⛰ Huttopia Font Romeu 🏕

© Huttopia R. Etienne

📞 04 68 30 09 32. www.huttopia.com – alt. 1 800

Address : route de Mont-Louis (RN 618)

Opening times : from mid June to mid Sept.

7 ha (175 pitches)

Tariff : (2014 Price) 34.10€ 🚶🚶 🚗 🔲 ⚡ (10A) – Extra per person 7.50€ – Reservation fee 22€

Rental rates : (2014 Price) (from mid June to end Sept.) Ⓟ – 34 🛖 – 21 tent lodges. Per night from 65 to 169€ – Per week from 342 to 1,183€ – Reservation fee 22€

🚐 borne 7€ – 20 🔲 28.30€

300m from the cable car station. High quality rental options.

Surroundings : 🏞 ≤ Pyrénées ⚲		GPS
Leisure activities : 🍷 🍽 🎮 🔥 🧗 🛷 🏊		Longitude : 2.04666
Facilities : 🔧 Ⓟ ▥ 🧺 launderette 🧺		Latitude : 42.50628

FORMIGUERES

66210 – Michelin map **344** D7 – pop. 435 – alt. 1 500
▶ Paris 883 – Montpellier 248 – Perpignan 96

⛰ La Devèze

📞 06 37 59 73 89. http://www.campingladeveze.com – alt. 1 600

Address : route de la Devèze

4 ha (117 pitches) terraced, flat, grassy, stony

Rentals : 1 caravan – 13 🔲 – 13 🛖 – 1 tipi – 4 tent lodges.

In a natural setting among pretty mountain pines. Horses and their riders welcome.

Surroundings : 🏞 🔲 ⚲		GPS
Leisure activities : 🍽 🎮 🔥 🛷		Longitude : 2.0922
Facilities : 🔧 🔧 ▥ 🧺 🏊 💧 🍷 launderette 🧺		Latitude : 42.61035

FRONTIGNAN PLAGE

34110 – Michelin map **339** H8 – pop. 23 068 – alt. 2
▶ Paris 775 – Lodève 59 – Montpellier 26 – Sète 10

⛰ Sandaya Les Tamaris 🏕

📞 04 67 43 44 77. www.les-tamaris.fr

Address : 140 avenue d'Ingril (to the northeast along the D 60)

Opening times : from beginning April to mid Oct.

4 ha (250 pitches)

Tariff : (2014 Price) 58€ 🚶🚶 🚗 🔲 ⚡ (6A) – Reservation fee 25€

Rental rates : (2014 Price) (from beginning April to mid Oct.) – 70 🔲 – 30 🛖 – 6 mobile homes (without sanitary facilities). Per night from 31 to 79€ – Per week from 217 to 1,370€ – Reservation fee 25€

🚐 borne 5€

In a pleasant setting close to the beach.

Surroundings : 🏞 🔲 ⚲ 🏖		GPS
Leisure activities : 🍷 🍽 🎮 🔥 🧗 🛷 🏊		Longitude : 3.80572
Facilities : 🔧 🔧 🏊 💧 🍷 launderette 🧊 🧺 refrigerated food storage facilities		Latitude : 43.44993

FUILLA

66820 – Michelin map **344** F7 – pop. 372 – alt. 547
▶ Paris 902 – Font-Romeu-Odeillo-Via 42 – Perpignan 55 – Prades 9

⛰ Le Rotja

📞 04 68 96 52 75. www.camping-lerotja.com

Address : 34 avenue de la Rotja (in the village of Fuilla)

1.6 ha (100 pitches) relatively flat, flat, grassy, stony, fruit trees

Rentals : 10 🔲

The pitches are laid out on terraces, some with shade.

Surroundings : 🏞 ≤ 🔲 ⚲⚲		GPS
Leisure activities : 🍽 🏊 (small swimming pool)		Longitude : 2.35883
Facilities : 🔧 🔧 🏊 🍷 🔲		Latitude : 42.56181
Nearby : 🏊 🍷		

*To visit a town or region, use the **MICHELIN Green Guides**.*

GALLARGUES-LE-MONTUEUX

30660 – Michelin map **339** K6 – pop. 3 257 – alt. 55
▶ Paris 727 – Aigues-Mortes 21 – Montpellier 39 – Nîmes 25

⛰ Les Amandiers 🏕

📞 04 66 35 28 02. www.camping-lesamandiers.fr

Address : 20 rue des stades (southwestern exit, follow the signs for Lunel)

Opening times : from beginning April to end Sept.

3 ha (150 pitches)

Tariff : 27€ 🚶🚶 🚗 🔲 ⚡ (16A) – Extra per person 6€ – Reservation fee 21€

Rental rates : Permanent 🏠 (from beginning April to end Sept.) – 45 🔲. Per night from 24 to 140€ – Per week from 168 to 980€ Reservation fee 21€

A swimming pool area given over to spa and wellness: a large jacuzzi, counterflow swimming, bath with water jets.

Surroundings : 🔲 ⚲⚲		GPS
Leisure activities : 🍷 🍽 🎮 🔥 🧗 🛀 🍸 hammam, jacuzzi 🏊 🏊 spa centre		Longitude : 4.16609
Facilities : 🔧 🔧 🏊 🍷 launderette 🧺		Latitude : 43.71612
Nearby : 🏊		

GIGNAC

34150 – Michelin map **339** G7 – pop. 5 271 – alt. 53
▶ Paris 719 – Béziers 58 – Clermont-l'Hérault 12 – Lodève 25

⛰ Municipal la Meuse

📞 04 67 57 92 97. www.ville-gignac.fr

Address : chemin de la Meuse (1.2km northeast along the D 32, follow the signs for Aniane then take the road to the left, 200m from the Hérault and a water sports centre)

Opening times : from beginning June to mid Sept.

3.4 ha (100 pitches) flat, grassy

Tariff : (2014 Price) 🚶 2.40€ 🚗 🔲 9.70€ – ⚡ (16A) 2.80€ – Reservation fee 7.58€

Rental rates : (2014 Price) (from beginning June to mid Sept.) 🏠 – 9 🔲. Per night from 51 to 70€ – Per week from 400 to 600€ Reservation fee 7.58€

🚐 borne 3€

Pleasant, spacious, marked-out pitches with plenty of shade.

Surroundings : 🏕 ⚘⚘
Leisure activities : ✗ ⚒
Facilities : ♿ ⊶ ⚒ ▣
Nearby : ≋ ⚐ fitness trail

GPS Longitude : 3.55927
Latitude : 43.662

GOUDARGUES

30630 – Michelin map **339** L3 – pop. 1 032 – alt. 77
▶ Paris 667 – Alès 51 – Bagnols-sur-Cèze 17 – Barjac 20

⚘⚘ St-Michelet ♣≈

𝒸 04 66 82 24 99. www.lesaintmichelet.com

Address : route de Frigoulet (located 1km northwest along the
D 371; beside the Cèze river)

Opening times : from end April to mid Sept.

4 ha (160 pitches) terrace, flat and relatively flat, grassy, stony

Tariff : (2014 Price) 30.80€ ✶✶ ⚗ ▣ ⚡ (10A) –
Extra per person 6.80€

Rental rates : (2014 Price) (from end April to mid Sept.) ⚘ –
54 🚐 – 4 canvas bungalows. Per night from 44 to 74€ –
Per week from 300 to 695€

🚐 borne

*The lower part of the site beside the Cèze river is for tents and
caravans and the upper part, where the swimming pool is located, has mobile homes.*

Surroundings : ⚓ 🏕 ⚘⚘
Leisure activities : ❢ ✗ 🎬 ⚑ ⚔ ⚓
≋ ⚐
Facilities : ♿ ⊶ ⚒ ⚒ ▣

GPS Longitude : 4.46271
Latitude : 44.22123

⚘⚘ Les Amarines 2

𝒸 04 66 82 24 92. www.campinglesamarines.com

Address : La Vérune Cornillon (located 1km northeast along the D 23;
beside the Cèze river)

Opening times : from beginning April to end Sept.

3.7 ha (120 pitches) flat, grassy

Tariff : 25€ ✶✶ ⚗ ▣ ⚡ (10A) – Extra per person 6€ – Reservation
fee 15€

Rental rates : (from beginning April to end Sept.) – 22 🚐.
Per night from 50 to 70€ – Per week from 315 to 791€ –
Reservation fee 15€

*Beside the Cèze river, a linear site shaded by poplars and
surrounded by vineyards.*

Surroundings : 🏕 ⚘⚘
Leisure activities : 🎬 ⚔ ⚓ ≋ ⚐
Facilities : ♿ ⊶ ⚒ ⚒ ⚒ ⚒ launderette
refrigerators

GPS Longitude : 4.47924
Latitude : 44.22047

⚘ Sites et Paysages La Grenouille

𝒸 04 66 82 21 36. www.camping-la-grenouille.com

Address : avenue du Lavoir (near the Cèze river - direct access)

Opening times : from beginning April to end Sept.

0.8 ha (50 pitches)

Tariff : (2014 Price) 25.40€ ✶✶ ⚗ ▣ ⚡ (6A) – Extra per person 5.50€
Reservation fee 10€

Rental rates : (2014 Price) (from beginning April to end Sept.) –
7 canvas bungalows. Per night from 40 to 63€ – Per week
from 260 to 440€ – Reservation fee 10€

🚐 borne – 🔌 ⚡ 14.40€

*A small but very pleasant site with a stream running through it,
located in the centre of the village.*

Surroundings : ⚓ 🏕 ⚘⚘
Leisure activities : ⚔ ⚓ (small swimming
pool) ⚐
Facilities : ♿ ⊶ ⚒ ⚒ ▣ refrigerators
Nearby : ⚒

GPS Longitude : 4.46847
Latitude : 44.21468

LA GRANDE-MOTTE

34280 – Michelin map **339** J7 – pop. 8 391 – alt. 1
▶ Paris 747 – Aigues-Mortes 12 – Lunel 16 – Montpellier 28

⚘⚘ Le Garden ♣≈

𝒸 04 67 56 50 09. www.legarden.fr

Address : avenue de la Petite Motte (take the western exit along the
D 59, 300m from the beach)

Opening times : from beginning April to beginning Oct.

3 ha (209 pitches)

Tariff : 44€ ✶✶ ⚗ ▣ ⚡ (10A) – Extra per person 9.80€

Rental rates : (from beginning April to beginning Oct.) ♿
(1 mobile home) – 121 🚐. Per night from 62 to 150 € – Per week
from 315 to 980€ – Reservation fee 20€

Good sanitary facilities and upmarket rental options.

Surroundings : 🏕 ⚘⚘
Leisure activities : ❢ ✗ 🎬 ⚑ ⚔ ⚓
Facilities : ♿ ⊶ ⚘ ⚒ ⚒ ⚒ launderette
⚒ ⚐
Nearby : ⚑ ⚘

GPS Longitude : 4.07235
Latitude : 43.56229

⚘ Les Cigales

𝒸 04 67 56 50 85. www.paysdelor.fr

Address : allée des Pins (take the western exit along the D 59)

Opening times : from mid April to end Sept.

2.5 ha (180 pitches)

Tariff : 23.50€ ✶✶ ⚗ ▣ ⚡ (10A) – Extra per person 6.70€ –
Reservation fee 10€

Rental rates : (from mid April to end Sept.) – 20 🚐. Per week
from 210 to 710€ – Reservation fee 10€

🚐 borne 16€

*There is a large parking area for campervans adjoining the
campsite.*

Surroundings : ⚘⚘
Leisure activities : ⚔
Facilities : ♿ ⊶ ⚒ ⚒ ⚒ launderette
Nearby : ⚘

GPS Longitude : 4.07612
Latitude : 43.56722

Key to rentals symbols:

12 🚐	*Number of mobile homes*
20 🏠	*Number of chalets*
6 🛏	*Number of rooms to rent*
Per night 30–50€	*Minimum/maximum rate per night*
Per week 300–1,000€	*Minimum/maximum rate per week*

LE GRAU-DU-ROI

30240 – Michelin map **339** J7 – pop. 7 995 – alt. 2
▶ Paris 751 – Aigues-Mortes 7 – Arles 55 – Lunel 22

⛰⛰ FranceLoc Le Boucanet ♟♙

☏ 04 66 51 41 48. http://campingboucanet.franceloc.fr/ ✍

Address : route de Carnon (situated 2km northwest of Le Grau-du-Roi (right bank) following signs for la Grande-Motte; beside beach)

Opening times : from beginning April to end Sept.

7.5 ha (462 pitches)

Tariff : (2014 Price) 41 € ✶✶ ⛌ 🔲 🔌 (6A) – Extra per person 9 € – Reservation fee 27 €

Rental rates : (2014 Price) (from beginning April to end Sept.) ✍ – 2 caravans – 313 🛖. Per night from 65 to 204 € – Per week from 259 to 1,687 € – Reservation fee 27 €

🚐 borne 4 € – 5 🔲 41 €

In an exclusive location beside a beautiful beach.

Surroundings : 🌳♀♙
Leisure activities : ♈✕ 🎭 ⛲ 🚴 ⛵ ⛳ ✍ 🔲 🛶 ⛱
Facilities : ♿ ⚡ 🚿♜ launderette 🧺 🍴 refrigerated food storage facilities
Nearby : 🐎

GPS Longitude : 4.10753
Latitude : 43.55428

ISPAGNAC

48320 – Michelin map **330** J8 – pop. 851 – alt. 518
▶ Paris 612 – Florac 11 – Mende 28 – Meyrueis 46

⛰⛰ Municipal du Pré Morjal

☏ 04 66 45 43 57. www.campingdupremorjal.com

Address : chemin du Beldiou (take the western exit along the D 907bis, follow the signs for Millau and take road to the left; near the Tarn)

Opening times : from beginning April to beginning Nov.

2 ha (123 pitches) flat, grassy

Tariff : 22.30 € ✶✶ ⛌ 🔲 🔌 (10A) – Extra per person 4.30 €

Rental rates : (from end March to mid Nov.) – 8 🛖 – 8 canvas bungalows. Per night from 40 to 100 € – Per week from 175 to 595 €

In a pleasant wooded setting at the entrance to the Tarn river gorges.

Surroundings : 🌳≤♀♙
Leisure activities : 🎭 ✍ ⛳ 🛶
Facilities : ♿ ⚡ 🚿♜ launderette
Nearby : ✕ 🐎

GPS Longitude : 3.53038
Latitude : 44.37223

JUNAS

30250 – Michelin map **339** J6 – pop. 1 085 – alt. 75
▶ Paris 730 – Aigues-Mortes 30 – Aimargues 15 – Montpellier 42

⛰⛰ Les Chênes

☏ 04 66 80 99 07. www.camping-les-chenes.com

Address : 95 chemin des Tuileries Basses (1.3km south along the D 140, follow the signs for Sommières and take road to the left)

Opening times : from beginning April to mid Oct.

1.7 ha (90 pitches) terraced, flat and relatively flat, stony

Tariff : 21.50 € ✶✶ ⛌ 🔲 🔌 (10A) – Extra per person 4.70 € – Reservation fee 11 €

Rental rates : (from beginning April to mid Oct.) ✍ – 4 caravans – 10 🛖. Per week from 230 to 590 € – Reservation fee 11 €

Attractively shaded by Holm oaks, with pitches laid out on terraces, some of which are marked out with low stone walls.

Surroundings : 🌳♀♙
Leisure activities : ✍ 🛶
Facilities : ♿ ⚡ 🚿♜

GPS Longitude : 4.123
Latitude : 43.76921

⛺ L'Olivier

☏ 04 66 80 39 52. www.campinglolivier.fr

Address : 112 route de Congenies (take the eastern exit along the D 140 and take the road to the right)

Opening times : from beginning April to end Oct.

1 ha (45 pitches)

Tariff : (2014 Price) 23.90 € ✶✶ ⛌ 🔲 🔌 (10A) – Extra per person 4.80 € – Reservation fee 10 €

Rental rates : (2014 Price) (from beginning April to end Oct.) – 8 🛖 – 6 🛖 – 2 canvas bungalows. Per night from 42 to 62 € – Per week from 185 to 625 € – Reservation fee 10 €

A family-oriented establishment in the shade of Holm oaks near the village.

Surroundings : 🌳♀♙
Leisure activities : ✍ ⛳ 🛶
Facilities : ♿ ⚡ 🚿♜

GPS Longitude : 4.12489
Latitude : 43.77081

LANUÉJOLS

30750 – Michelin map **339** F4 – pop. 334 – alt. 905
▶ Paris 656 – Alès 109 – Mende 68 – Millau 35

⛺ Domaine de Pradines

☏ 04 67 82 73 85. www.domaine-de-pradines.com – alt. 800

Address : route de Millau, D28 (3.5km west along the D 28, follow the signs for Roujarie and take road to the left)

Opening times : from beginning June to mid Sept.

150 ha/30 for camping (75 pitches)

Tariff : ✶ ⛌ 🔲 8.50 € – 🔌 (16A) 3 €

Rental rates : (from beginning April to end Oct.) – 5 🛖 – 5 🛖 – 4 yurts – 4 apartments – 2 tipis – 2 canvas bungalows. Per night from 45 to 78 € – Per week from 250 to 580 €

Right in the heart of the countryside, various rental options, extensive pitches, but only average and rather old sanitary facilities.

Surroundings : 🌳≤♙
Leisure activities : ✕ 🎭 ✍ ⛵ 🛶
Facilities : ♿ ⚡♜ launderette 🧺 🍴

GPS Longitude : 3.34722
Latitude : 44.13306

Michelin classification:

⛰⛰⛰⛰ *Extremely comfortable, equipped to a very high standard*
⛰⛰⛰ *Very comfortable, equipped to a high standard*
⛰⛰ *Comfortable and well equipped*
⛰ *Reasonably comfortable*
⛺ *Satisfactory*

LAROQUE-DES-ALBÈRES

66740 – Michelin map **344** I7 – pop. 2 028 – alt. 100
▶ Paris 881 – Argelès-sur-Mer 11 – Le Boulou 14 – Collioure 18

⋀⋀ Cybele Vacances Les Albères

✆ 04 68 89 23 64. www.camping-des-alberes.com

Address : route du Moulin de Cassagnes (take the northeastern exit along the D 2, follow the signs for Argelès-sur-Mer then continue 0.4km along the road to the right)

Opening times : from beginning April to end Sept.

5 ha (211 pitches) very uneven, terraced, relatively flat, flat, grassy, stony

Tariff : (2014 Price) 18 € ✿✿ ⇔ 🔲 🄵 (6A) – Extra per person 4 € – Reservation fee 25 €

Rental rates : (2014 Price) (from beginning April to end Sept.) – 59 🛏 – 9 🏠 – 3 tent lodges. Per night from 40 to 140 € – Per week from 189 to 849 € – Reservation fee 25 €

The pitches laid out on terraces have plenty of shade.

Surroundings : 🏞 ⌂ ♤♤ Leisure activities : 🍴✗ 🎦 ✶ 🏊 ✗ 🔺 multi-sports ground Facilities : ⚲ ⌿ 🚰 🔲 🗑 ♨	**G P S** Longitude : 2.94418 Latitude : 42.52404

LATTES

34970 – Michelin map **339** I7 – pop. 15 804 – alt. 3
▶ Paris 766 – Montpellier 7 – Nîmes 54 – Béziers 68

⋀⋀ Le Parc

✆ 04 67 65 85 67. www.leparccamping.com

Address : route de Mauguio (situated 2km northeast along the D 172)

Opening times : Permanent

1.6 ha (100 pitches)

Tariff : 29 € ✿✿ ⇔ 🔲 🄵 (10A) – Extra per person 6 € – Reservation fee 15 €

Rental rates : Permanent – 30 🛏 – 2 canvas bungalows. Per night from 55 to 110 € – Per week from 220 to 760 € – Reservation fee 15 €

Close to the tramway (line 3) for Montpellier and Pérols or Lattes.

Surroundings : ⌂ ♤♤ Leisure activities : 🔺 ✶ 🔺 Facilities : ⚲ ⌿ 🚰 launderette Nearby : ✗	**G P S** Longitude : 3.92578 Latitude : 43.57622

LAURENS

34480 – Michelin map **339** E7 – pop. 1 349 – alt. 140
▶ Paris 736 – Bédarieux 14 – Béziers 22 – Clermont-l'Hérault 40

⋀⋀ Sites et Paysages L'Oliveraie ♤♤

✆ 04 67 90 24 36. www.oliveraie.com

Address : 1600 chemin de Bédarieux (situated 2km north and take the road to the right)

Opening times : from beginning March to end Oct.

7 ha (110 pitches) terraced, relatively flat, flat, grassy, stony

Tariff : (2014 Price) 31 € ✿✿ ⇔ 🔲 🄵 (10A) – Extra per person 5 € – Reservation fee 20 €

Rental rates : (2014 Price) (from beginning April to end Oct.) – 12 🛏 – 2 🏠. Per night from 54 to 69 € – Per week from 380 to 710 € – Reservation fee 20 €

This shady site spreads out across terraces, with a swimming pool surrounded by olive trees.

Surroundings : ⌂ ♤♤ Leisure activities : 🍴✗ ⊙nighttime ✶ 🏊 🔺🚲 🏊 ♘ 🔺 Facilities : ⚲ ⌿ 🚰 🗑 🔲 ♨ 🔺	**G P S** Longitude : 3.18571 Latitude : 43.53631

MARSEILLAN-PLAGE

34340 – Michelin map **339** G8
▶ Paris 765 – Montpellier 51 – Nîmes 100 – Carcassonne 114

⋀⋀ Les Méditerranées - Beach Club Nouvelle Floride ♤♤

✆ 04 67 21 94 49. www.lesmediterranees.com

Address : 262 avenue des Campings

Opening times : from end March to end Sept.

7 ha (475 pitches) grassy

Tariff : (2014 Price) 55 € ✿✿ ⇔ 🔲 🄵 (8A) – Extra per person 10 € – Reservation fee 30 €

Rental rates : (from end March to end Sept.) ✄ – 160 🛏 Per night from 45 to 180 € – Per week from 315 to 1,260 €

In a pleasant location near the beach, with free access to the activities at the Les Méditerranées – Beach Garden campsite.

Surroundings : ⌂ ♤♤ 🞈 Leisure activities : 🍴✗ 🎦 ⊙✶ 🔺 jacuzzi 🔺 🏊 multi-sports ground, entertainment room Facilities : ⚲ ⌿ 🚿 ♨ 🔺 🗑 🚰 laundrette 🔺 Nearby : 🔺 disco	**G P S** Longitude : 3.54243 Latitude : 43.30923

⋀⋀ Les Méditerranées - Beach Garden ♤♤

✆ 04 67 21 92 83. www.lesmediterranees.com

Address : avenue des Campings

Opening times : from end March to end Sept.

14 ha (600 pitches)

Tariff : (2014 Price) 53 € ✿✿ ⇔ 🔲 🄵 (8A) – Extra per person 10 € – Reservation fee 30 €

Rental rates : (from end March to end Sept.) ✄ – 104 🛏 Per night from €40 to 180 – Per week from €280 to 1 260

Located close to the beach, with a panoramic restaurant and free access to the activities at the Les Méditerranées - Beach Club Nouvelle Floride campsite.

Surroundings : 🏞 ⌂ ♤♤ 🞈 Leisure activities : 🍴✗ 🎦 ⊙✶ hammam, jacuzzi 🔺 🚲 🏊 🔺 multi-sports ground, spa centre Facilities : ⚲ ⌿ ♨ 🔺 🗑 🚰 laundrette 🔺 Nearby : 🔺	**G P S** Longitude : 3.538 Latitude : 43.3058

⚑ Les Méditerranées - Beach Club Charlemagne

Beach Club Charlemagne

✆ 04 67 21 92 49. www.lesmediterranees.com

Address : avenue des Campings (250m from the beach)

Opening times : from end March to end Sept.

6.7 ha (480 pitches)

Tariff : (2014 Price) 55€ ♣♣ ⇔ 🔲 (8A) – Extra per person 10€ – Reservation fee 30€

Rental rates : (from end March to end Sept.) ⚡ – 171 ⛺. Per night from 40 to 170€ – Per week from 280 to 1,190€

There's free use of the services and leisure facilities at the two other Les Méditerranées - Beach Club campsites, situated opposite and beside the beach.

Surroundings : 🗔 ♀♀
Leisure activities : ♈ ✕ 🎪 🎯 🏹 🏄 🛶 disco
Facilities : 🚿 ⚲ 🧺 🚾 🚽 launderette 🛒 🏊 🛶
Nearby : 🏃 🎣

GPS — Longitude : 3.54337 — Latitude : 43.31052

⚑ Le Galet

✆ 04 67 21 95 61. www.camping-galet.com

Address : avenue des Campings (250m from the beach)

Opening times : from beginning April to end Sept.

3 ha (275 pitches)

Tariff : 43.50€ ♣♣ ♣ ⇔ 🔲 (10A) – Extra per person 7€ – Reservation fee 25€

Rental rates : (from beginning April to end Sept.) – 67 ⛺. Per night from 25 to 140€ – Per week from 175 to 970€ – Reservation fee 25€

An elongated site leading to a pretty water park.

Surroundings : 🗔 ♀
Leisure activities : ✕ 🏹 🏄 🛶
Facilities : 🚿 ⚲ 🧺 launderette
Nearby : 🛒 ♈ 🛶

GPS — Longitude : 3.5421 — Latitude : 43.31108

⚑ La Créole

✆ 04 67 21 92 69. www.campinglacreole.com

Address : 74 avenue des Campings

Opening times : from beginning April to mid Oct.

1.5 ha (110 pitches)

Tariff : 38€ ♣♣ ⇔ 🔲 (10A) – Extra per person 7€ – Reservation fee 17€

Rental rates : (from beginning April to mid Oct.) ⚡ – 18 ⛺. Per week from 200 to 700€ – Reservation fee 17€

⛽ borne – 8 🔲 14€

Situated beside a beautiful beach of fine sand.

Surroundings : 🗔 ♀♀ 🏖
Leisure activities : 🏹 🏄
Facilities : 🚿 ⚲ 🧺 🚽
Nearby : 🏊 ♈ 🛶 🐎

GPS — Longitude : 3.54375 — Latitude : 43.31047

Some campsites benefit from proximity to a municipal leisure centre.

48100 – Michelin map **330** H7 – pop. 5 053 – alt. 650
▶ Paris 573 – Espalion 64 – Florac 50 – Mende 28

⚑ Village VAL V.V.F. et Camping de l'Europe

✆ 04 66 32 03 69. www.vvf-villages.fr

Address : Le Colagnet (1.3km east along the D 999, D 1, follow the signs for Montrodat and take the road to the right; beside the Colagnet – from A 75. take exit 38)

Opening times : Permanent

3 ha (100 pitches) flat, grassy

Tariff : 18.50€ ♣♣ ⇔ 🔲 (6A) – Extra per person 4€ – 30€

Rental rates : (2014 Price) (from mid April to mid Sept.) – 9 ⛺ – 41 apartments. Per night from 45 to 117€ – Per week from 287 to 825€ – Reservation fee 32€

Well-shaded pitches beside the river; basic gîtes available and chalets equipped to a higher standard.

Surroundings : 🞐 🗔 ♀♀
Leisure activities : 🎪 🏄 🏹 ✕ 🛶
multi-sports ground
Facilities : 🚿 ⓟ 🚾 🚽 🚽 launderette
Nearby : 🛒

GPS — Longitude : 3.30432 — Latitude : 44.55075

30140 – Michelin map **339** J4 – pop. 675 – alt. 156
▶ Paris 726 – Montpellier 56 – Nîmes 43 – Avignon 78

⚑ Le Fief d'Anduze 🅰🅰

✆ 04 66 61 81 71. http://www.campinglefiefdanduze.com

Address : at Attuech, 195 chemin du Plan d'Eau (located 1.5km to the north along the D 982, near a lake)

Opening times : from beginning April to end Sept.

5.5 ha (80 pitches) flat, grassy

Tariff : 26.70€ ♣♣ ⇔ 🔲 (10A) – Extra per person 5.30€

Rental rates : Permanent – 21 ⛺. Per night from 52 to 82€ – Per week from 598 to 688€ – Reservation fee 10€

Well-shaded pitches but poor sanitary facilities.

Surroundings : 🞐 🎋
Leisure activities : ♈ ✕ 🎪 🏃 🎯
hammam, jacuzzi 🏄 🛶 multi-sports ground
Facilities : 🚿 ⚲ 🧺 🚽 🎪 🛶
Nearby : 🛶

GPS — Longitude : 4.02576 — Latitude : 44.02946

66210 – Michelin map **344** D7 – pop. 294 – alt. 1 514
▶ Paris 855 – Font-Romeu-Odeillo-Via 20 – Perpignan 92 – Prades 46

⚑ Le Lac

✆ 04 68 30 94 49. www.camping-lac-matemale.com – alt. 1 540 – (limited spaces for one-night stay)

Address : 1.7km southwest along the D 52, follow the signs for Les Angles and take the turning to the left, 150m from the lake

Opening times : Permanent

3.5 ha (110 pitches)

Tariff : ♣ 5.50€ ⇔ 🔲 5€ – (6A) 4.80€

Rental rates : Permanent – 5 🏠. Per week from 250 to 570€

⛽ borne 2.50€

A pleasant mountain location in the shade of a pretty pine forest, direct access to the village along a pedestrian path.

Surroundings : 🐾 ♀♀
Leisure activities : 🏊 ≋ jacuzzi 🚴
Facilities : 🚿 ⛟ 🏧 🔥 ♑ launderette
Nearby : 🍺 🍴 🎿 🎣 ♏ 🚣 ≋ 🐎 sports/
activities centre at 800m

GPS Longitude : 2.10673
Latitude : 42.58164

MAUREILLAS-LAS-ILLAS

66480 – Michelin map **344** H8 – pop. 2 649 – alt. 130
▶ Paris 873 – Gerona 71 – Perpignan 31 – Port-Vendres 31

⛰ Les Bruyères

📞 0468832664. www.camping-lesbruyeres.fr
Address : route de Céret (1.2km west along the D 618)
Opening times : from mid March to mid Nov.
4 ha (106 pitches) very uneven, terraced, flat, grassy, stony
Tariff : 27€ ★★ 🚗 🔲 🔌 (10A) – Extra per person 5.80€ – Reservation fee 8€
Rental rates : (from mid March to mid Nov.) – 22 🚐. Per night from 60 to 130€ – Per week from 340 to 700€ – Reservation fee 8€
🚰 borne 4€ – 2 🔲 7€
In a pleasant wooded setting among cork oaks, but choose the pitches away from the road in preference.

Surroundings : 🏡 ♀♀
Leisure activities : 🏊 🏉 🎣
Facilities : 🚿 ⛟ 🔥 🏧 🛒 ♑
Nearby : 🐎

GPS Longitude : 2.79509
Latitude : 42.49249

MENDE

48000 – Michelin map **330** J7 – pop. 12 285 – alt. 731
▶ Paris 584 – Clermont-Ferrand 174 – Florac 38 – Langogne 46

⛰ Tivoli

📞 0466653110. www.campingtivoli.com
Address : chemin de Tivoli (situated 2km southwest along the N 88, follow the signs for Rodez and take the road to the right, opposite the shopping centre; beside the Lot river)
Opening times : Permanent
1.8 ha (100 pitches) flat, grassy
Tariff : (2014 Price) 24.50€ ★★ 🚗 🔲 🔌 (6A) – Extra per person 7€ Reservation fee 25€
Rental rates : (2014 Price) (from end April to end Sept.) 🏊 – 18 🚐 – 18 🏠. Per night from 60 to 80€ – Per week from 260 to 650€ – Reservation fee 25€
🚰 borne
Below the road to Rodez and opposite a sports complex accessible by footbridge over the Lot river.

Surroundings : ♀♀
Leisure activities : 🏊 🚴 🎣
Facilities : 🚿 ⛟ 🏧 🏧 ♑ 🛒 🛎
Nearby : 🎿

GPS Longitude : 3.45693
Latitude : 44.51268

MEYRUEIS

48150 – Michelin map **330** I9 – pop. 853 – alt. 698
▶ Paris 643 – Florac 36 – Mende 57 – Millau 43

⛰ Kawan Villages le Capelan

📞 0466456050. www.campingcapelan.com
Address : route de Millau (located 1km northwest along the D 996; beside the Jonte)
Opening times : from beginning May to mid Sept.
2.8 ha (100 pitches) flat, grassy
Tariff : 30.50€ ★★ 🚗 🔲 🔌 (10A) – Extra per person 6.10€ – Reservation fee 16€
Rental rates : (from beginning May to mid Sept.) 🏊 – 44 🚐. Per night from 43 to 118€ – Per week from 190 to 820€ – Reservation fee 19€
🚰 borne 4.50€
In a pleasant location in the steep valley of the Jonte river, with a path to the village and swimming pool across the road.

Surroundings : ⛰ 🏡 ♀♀
Leisure activities : 🍺 🏊 🎲 🚴 🎣 ≋ 🏔 climbing
Facilities : 🚿 ⛟ 🔲 🔥 – 3 individual sanitary facilities (🛁 🚽 wc) 🔥 ♑ launderette ⛟

GPS Longitude : 3.4199
Latitude : 44.1859

⛰ Le Champ d'Ayres

📞 0466456051. www.campinglechampdayres.com
Address : route de la Brèze (500m east along the D 57, follow the signs for Campis, near the Brèze)
Opening times : from end April to end Sept.
1.5 ha (91 pitches)
Tariff : 29€ ★★ 🚗 🔲 🔌 (10A) – Extra per person 5.30€ – Reservation fee 15€
Rental rates : (from end April to end Sept.) 🏊 – 19 🚐 – 3 🏠. Per night from 39 to 52 € – Per week from 255 to 720€ Reservation fee 18€
🚰 borne 4.50€
A green and flowery setting.

Surroundings : 🐾 ⛰ 🏡 ♀
Leisure activities : 🍺 🏊 🚴 🎣
Facilities : 🚿 ⛟ 🔥 ♑ launderette
Nearby : 🎿 🐎

GPS Longitude : 3.43536
Latitude : 44.18079

⛰ La Via Natura La Cascade

📞 0466454545. www.camping-la-cascade.com
Address : Salvinsac (3.8km northeast along the D 996, follow the signs for Florac and take the road to the right, near the Jonte river and a waterfall)
Opening times : Permanent
1 ha (54 pitches)
Tariff : 22.80€ ★★ 🚗 🔲 🔌 (16A) – Extra per person 4.30€
Rental rates : Permanent – 13 🚐. Per night from 45 to 70 € – Per week from 275 to 660€
🚰 borne 5€
In the Vallée de la Jonte, the owners have a passion for nature and ecology.

Surroundings : 🐾 ⛰ ♀
Leisure activities : 🏊 🚴 🎣
Facilities : 🚿 ⛟ 🔥 🏧

GPS Longitude : 3.45567
Latitude : 44.19645

⛺ Le Pré de Charlet

📞 04 66 45 63 65. www.camping-cevennes-meyrueis.com

Address : route de Florac (located 1km northeast along the D 996; (beside the Jonte)

2 ha (70 pitches) terraced, relatively flat, flat, grassy

Rentals : 6 🛖 – 3 canvas bungalows.

Situated below the road, with some pitches alongside the river with refurbished sanitary facilities.

Surroundings : 🐾 ♤♤
Leisure activities : 🎮 🏇 🛶
Facilities : 🚿 🔌 🏕 🍽 launderette
Nearby : 🛶

GPS Longitude : 3.43831
Latitude : 44.18587

MONTCLAR

11250 – Michelin map **344** E4 – pop. 186 – alt. 210
▶ Paris 766 – Carcassonne 19 – Castelnaudary 41 – Limoux 15

⛰ Yelloh! Village Domaine d'Arnauteille 🔔👤

📞 04 68 26 84 53. www.camping-arnauteille.com

Address : 2.2km southeast along the D 43

Opening times : from beginning April to mid Sept.

115 ha/12 for camping (198 pitches) very uneven, terraced, relatively flat, flat, grassy

Tariff : 39€ ★★ 🚐 🔲 🔌 (10A) – Extra per person 8€

Rental rates : (from beginning April to mid Sept.) – 80 🛖 – 10 🏠. Per night from 39 to 225€ – Per week from 273 to 1,575€

🚰 borne

On a sloping, spacious and pleasant site set on a hill, with shaded and sunny pitches.

Surroundings : 🐾 ← 🏞 ♤
Leisure activities : 🍴 🎮 🏇 🏊 jacuzzi 🏇
🏊 🎿 🐎 multi-sports ground, spa centre
Facilities : 🚿 🔌 🏕 🍽 launderette 🛁 🛒

GPS Longitude : 2.26107
Latitude : 43.12431

NARBONNE

11100 – Michelin map **344** J3 – pop. 51 227 – alt. 13
▶ Paris 787 – Béziers 28 – Carcassonne 61 – Montpellier 96

⛰ Yelloh! Village Les Mimosas 🔔👤

📞 04 68 49 03 72. www.lesmimosas.com

Address : chaussée de Mandirac (10km to the south, after the suburb La Nautique)

Opening times : from end March to end Oct.

9 ha (266 pitches)

Tariff : 52€ ★★ 🚐 🔲 🔌 (10A) – Extra per person 8€

Rental rates : (from end March to end Oct.) – 85 🛖 – 28 🏠 – 4 studios. Per night from 35 to 210€ – Per week from 245 to 1,470€

Pitches nestling among Languedoc vineyards and a welcoming wine bar for tastings.

Surroundings : 🐾 🏞 ♤
Leisure activities : 🍴 🎮 🏇 🏊 🎣 🚣 🏇
🚴 🎿 🏊 multi-sports ground
Facilities : 🚿 🔌 🏕 🛁 🍽 launderette 🛒
Nearby : 🐎

GPS Longitude : 3.02592
Latitude : 43.13658

⛰ La Nautique

📞 04 68 90 48 19. www.campinglanautique.com

Address : chemin de La Nautique (4km to the south; at Port La Nautique)

Opening times : from beginning March to end Oct.

16 ha (390 pitches)

Tariff : 46.50€ ★★ 🚐 🔲 🔌 (10A) – Extra per person 8.60€

Rental rates : (from beginning March to end Oct.) 🚿 (1 chalet, 4 mobile homes) – 90 🛖 – 1 🏠. Per night from 31 to 142€ – Per week from 228 to 994€

🚰 borne

Beside the Etang de Bages and Etang de Sigean (coastal lagoons).

Surroundings : ← 🏞 ♤
Leisure activities : 🍴 🍽 🎮 🏇 🏊 🚴 🐎 🎿
🎣 🏊 🚣 pedalos
Facilities : 🚿 🔌 – 390 individual sanitary facilities (🚿 🚽 wc) 🛁 🍽 launderette
🛒 🛁
Nearby : ⚓

GPS Longitude : 3.00424
Latitude : 43.14703

NASBINALS

48260 – Michelin map **330** G7 – pop. 498 – alt. 1 180
▶ Paris 573 – Aumont-Aubrac 24 – Chaudes-Aigues 27 – Espalion 34

⛺ Municipal

📞 04 66 32 51 87. mairie.nasbinals@laposte.net – alt. 1 100

Address : route de Saint-Urcize (located 1km northwest along the D 12)

2 ha (75 pitches)

Surroundings : 🐾 ←
Leisure activities : 🎮
Facilities : 🚿 🔌
Nearby : 🐎

GPS Longitude : 3.04016
Latitude : 44.67022

NAUSSAC

48300 – Michelin map **330** L6 – pop. 206 – alt. 920
▶ Paris 575 – Grandrieu 26 – Langogne 3 – Mende 46

⛰ Les Terrasses du Lac

📞 04 66 69 29 62. www.naussac.com

Address : at Lac de Naussac (north of the town along the D 26, follow the signs for Saugues and take the turning to the left; 200m from the lake (direct access)

Opening times : from mid April to end Sept.

6 ha (180 pitches) terraced, relatively flat, flat, grassy

Tariff : 21.50€ ★★ 🚐 🔲 🔌 (10A) – Extra per person 4.90€ – Reservation fee 10€

Rental rates : (from mid April to mid Oct.) – 3 🛖 – 6 🏠 – 17 🛏 – hotel, 9 huts (without sanitary facilities). Per night from 68 to 73€ – Per week from 345 to 675€ – Reservation fee 10€

🚰 borne – 60 🔲 21.50€

All the pitches and rentals benefit from a panoramic view over the large lake.

Surroundings : 🐾 ← Lac de Naussac
Leisure activities : 🍴 🍽 🎮 🏇 🎿 🏊
Facilities : 🚿 🔌 🏕 🍽 launderette 🛒
Nearby : 🏇 🏖 (beach) 🛶 ⚓

GPS Longitude : 3.83505
Latitude : 44.73478

PALAU-DEL-VIDRE

66690 – Michelin map **344** I7 – pop. 2 736 – alt. 26
▶ Paris 867 – Argelès-sur-Mer 8 – Le Boulou 16 – Collioure 15

🏕 Kawan Village Le Haras

𝒫 04 68 22 14 50. www.camping-le-haras.com

Address : 1 ter avenue Juliot Curie, au Domaine Saint-Galdric (take the northeastern exit along the D 11)

Opening times : from beginning April to end Sept.

2.3 ha (131 pitches) flat, grassy

Tariff : 37.50€ ✦✦ ⇔ 🔲 🅷 (10A) – Extra per person 6.70€ – Reservation fee 20€

Rental rates : (from beginning April to end Sept.) – 18 🛏 – 1 canvas bungalow. Per night from 35 to 121€ – Per week from 245 to 847€ – Reservation fee 20€

🚐 borne

Attractively shaded with floral decoration.

Surroundings : 🗨 ♨♨♨
Leisure activities : 🍸✗ 🛖 🚣 ⛵
Facilities : 🚿 ⚲ 🆑 ♨ 🚽 launderette 🔥

GPS Longitude : 2.96474
Latitude : 42.57575

PALAVAS-LES-FLOTS

34250 – Michelin map **339** I7 – pop. 5 996 – alt. 1
▶ Paris 765 – Montpellier 13 – Sète 41 – Lunel 33

🏔 Les Roquilles

𝒫 04 67 68 03 47. www.camping-les-roquilles.fr ✄

Address : 267 bis avenue Saint-Maurice (follow the signs for Carnon-Plage, 100m from the beach)

Opening times : from mid April to mid Sept.

15 ha (792 pitches)

Tariff : (2014 Price) 37.10€ ✦✦ ⇔ 🔲 🅷 (6A) – Extra per person 5.55€ Reservation fee 34€

Rental rates : (2014 Price) (from mid April to mid Sept.) 🚿 (1 mobile home) ✄ –100 🛏 – 40 🏠. Per night from 58 to 99€ – Per week from 295 to 1,315€ – Reservation fee 34€

🚐 borne

Some pitches are beside the lake, which is occasionally frequented by feeding flamingoes.

Surroundings : 🗨 ♀
Leisure activities : 🍸✗ 🛖 🚣⛵ ⚽ ⛷ 🏊 multi-sports ground
Facilities : 🚿 ⚲ ♨ 🔥 🔥

GPS Longitude : 3.96037
Latitude : 43.53851

🏔 Tohapi Palavas 👥

𝒫 04 67 68 01 28. www.palavas-camping.fr – limited spaces for one-night stay ✄

Address : route de Maguelone (right bank)

8 ha (438 pitches)

Rentals : 386 🛏.

A mobile home village with some pitches for tents and caravans beside the sea.

Surroundings : 🌿 ⛰
Leisure activities : 🍸✗ 🛖 🚣 🏄 🚴 ⛷ kite-surfing, multi-sports ground
Facilities : 🚿 ⚲ ♨ 🚽 launderette 🔥 🔥

GPS Longitude : 3.9095
Latitude : 43.51963

LES PLANTIERS

30122 – Michelin map **339** H4 – pop. 252 – alt. 400
▶ Paris 667 – Alès 48 – Florac 46 – Montpellier 85

🏕 Caylou

𝒫 04 66 83 92 85. www.camping-caylou.fr

Address : Le Caylou (located 1km northeast along the D 20, follow the signs for Saumane; beside the Gardon au Borgne)

Opening times : from mid April to mid Oct.

4 ha (75 pitches) terraced, relatively flat, flat, grassy, stony

Tariff : 18€ ✦✦ ⇔ 🔲 🅷 (10A) – Extra per person 5€

Rental rates : (from mid April to mid Oct.) – 4 🛏 – 2 gîtes. Per night from 45 to 60€ – Per week from 280 to 410€

Good-quality gîtes and a nice terrace bar overlooking the valley.

Surroundings : 🌿 ⬿ 🗨 ♨♨
Leisure activities : 🍸✗ 🛖 🚣 ⛷ 🎣 ⛵ entertainment room
Facilities : 🚿 ⚲ 🆑 🔥

GPS Longitude : 3.73101
Latitude : 44.12209

PORT-CAMARGUE

30240 – Michelin map **339** J7
▶ Paris 762 – Montpellier 36 – Nîmes 47 – Avignon 93

🏔 Yelloh! Village Secrets de Camargue

𝒫 04 66 80 08 00. www.yellohvillage-secrets-de-camargue.com (limited spaces for one-night stay)

Address : route de l'Espiguette

Opening times : from beginning April to beginning Nov.

3.5 ha (177 pitches)

Tariff : 52€ ✦✦ ⇔ 🔲 🅷 (6A) – Extra per person 9€

Rental rates : (from beginning April to beginning Nov.) 🅿 – 151 🛏. Per night from 39 to 215€ – Per week from 273 to 1,505€

The campsite is not particularly well suited to families with children. There are some pitches for tents and caravans. A free shuttle service to the beaches.

Surroundings : 🌿 🗨 ♀
Leisure activities : 🍸✗ 🅖daytime 🚴 ⛷
Facilities : 🚿 ⚲ 🅿 🆑 ♨ 🚽 launderette 🔥
Nearby : 🍴 🏊 🐎

GPS Longitude : 4.14105
Latitude : 43.5052

🏔 Yelloh! Village Les Petits Camarguais 👥

(rental of mobile homes only)

𝒫 04 66 51 16 16. www.yellohvillage-petits-camarguais.com

Address : route de l'Espiguette

Opening times : Permanent

3.5 ha

Rental rates : ✄ – 334 🛏. Per night from 39 to 270€ – Per week from 273 to 1,890€

Activities and services suitable for young children. A free shuttle service to the beaches.

Surroundings : 🗨 ♨♨
Leisure activities : 🍸✗ 🅖 🏄 jacuzzi 🚣 🚴 🔲 🏊 ⛷ multi-sports ground, entertainment room
Facilities : 🚿 ⚲ ♨ 🚽 launderette 🔥 🔥
Nearby : 🐎 🏹

GPS Longitude : 4.14456
Latitude : 43.50472

▲▲▲ Vacances Directes La Marine ♣

(rental of mobile homes only)

☏ 0825 13 34 00. www.campinglamarine.com

Address : 2196 route de l'Espiguette

Opening times : from beginning April to end Sept.

5 ha

Rental rates : (2014 Price) ♿ (1 mobile home) – 270 🏠 – 15 tent lodges. Per night from 40 to 168€ – Per week from 280 to 1,176€ Reservation fee 10€

Choose the pitches away from the road in preference. There's a free shuttle service to the beaches

Surroundings : ♤♤
Leisure activities : ♟ ✕ 🏠 🎣 🏃 ⛷ 🚲 🛶 🏊
Facilities : ⊶ cc 🚿 🍴 launderette 🔧 🚗
Nearby : 🛒 🐎, casino

Longitude : 4.1457
Latitude : 43.5074

▲▲▲ Abri de Camargue

Abri de Camargue

☏ 04 66 51 54 83. www.abridecamargue.fr – limited spaces for one-night stay

Address : 320 route de l'Espiguette (near the Casino (gaming) and opposite the fairground)

Opening times : from beginning April to end Sept.

4 ha (277 pitches)

Tariff : 27€ ♣♣ 🚗 🔲 ⚡ (6A) – Extra per person 5€ – Reservation fee 22€

Rental rates : (from beginning April to end Sept.) – 93 🏠. Per night from 61 to 143€ – Per week from 427 to 1,001€ – Reservation fee 22€

🚿 borne 7€
Has a free shuttle service to the beaches.

Surroundings : 🏕 ♤♤
Leisure activities : ♟ ✕ 🎣 🏃 ⛷ 🛶 🏊 cinema, multi-sports ground
Facilities : ⊶ cc 🍴 launderette 🔧 🚗
Nearby : 🛒 🐎 amusement park, casino

Longitude : 4.1488
Latitude : 43.52272

Key to rentals symbols:

12 🏠	*Number of mobile homes*
20 🏡	*Number of chalets*
6 🛏	*Number of rooms to rent*
Per night 30–50€	*Minimum/maximum rate per night*
Per week 300–1,000€	*Minimum/maximum rate per week*

PORTIRAGNES-PLAGE

34420 – Michelin map **339** F9

▶ Paris 768 – Montpellier 72 – Carcassonne 99 – Nîmes 121

▲▲▲ Les Sablons ♣

Les Sablons

☏ 04 67 90 90 55. www.les-sablons.com

Address : Plage Est (take the northern exit)

Opening times : from mid April to end Sept.

15 ha (800 pitches) flat, grassy, sandy, pond

Tariff : 57€ ♣♣ 🚗 🔲 ⚡ (10A) – Extra per person 12€ – Reservation fee 25€

Rental rates : (from mid April to end Sept.) – 210 🏠 – 85 🏡. Per night from 30 to 305€ – Per week from 240 to 2,002€ – Reservation fee 25€

🚿 borne – 🔌 ⚡16€
Close to the beach and a lake.

Surroundings : 🏕 ♤♤ ⛰
Leisure activities : ♟ ✕ 🏠 🎣 🏃 🎿 🛶 🚲 🏊 🏊 disco
Facilities : ♿ ⊶ 🚿 🍴 launderette 🔧 🚗 refrigerated food storage facilities
Nearby : 🎣 💧

Longitude : 3.36469
Latitude : 43.2788

▲▲▲ Les Mimosas ♣

Les Mimosas

☏ 04 67 90 92 92. www.mimosas.com – (limited spaces for one-night stay)

Address : at Port Cassafières

Opening times : from end May to beginning Sept.

7 ha (400 pitches) flat, grassy

Tariff : 46€ ♣♣ 🚗 🔲 ⚡ (6A) – Extra per person 10.50€ – Reservation fee 36€

Rental rates : (from end May to beginning Sept.) ♿ (1 mobile home) – 217 🏠 – 4 🏡 – 12 canvas bungalows. Per night from 35 to 260€ – Per week from 245 to 1,820€ – Reservation fee 36€

🚿 borne 2€
A large water and play park.

Surroundings : 🏕 ♤♤
Leisure activities : ♟ ✕ 🏠 🎣 🏃 🎿 ⛵ 🚲 🛶 🏊 multi-sports ground
Facilities : ♿ ⊶ 🚿 – 17 individual sanitary facilities (🚿 wc) 🍴 launderette 🔧 🚗 refrigerated food storage facilities
Nearby : 🐎 ⚓

Longitude : 3.37305
Latitude : 43.2915

Do not confuse:
▲ *to* ▲▲▲ : *MICHELIN classification with*
★ *to* ★★★★★ : *official classification*

▲▲▲ L'Émeraude

📞 04 67 90 93 76. www.campinglemeraude.com

Address : located 1km north, follow the signs for Portiragnes

Opening times : from end May to beginning Sept.

4.2 ha (280 pitches)

Tariff : (2014 Price) 🚐🔲 45€ – (½) (5A) 5€ – Reservation fee 25€
Rental rates : (2014 Price) (from end May to beginning Sept.) –
166 🚐 – 4 🏠. Per night from 35 to 158€ – Per week
from 245 to 1,106€ – Reservation fee 25€

A pleasant water park.

Surroundings : 〰️
Leisure activities : 🍴✖🏛️ 🛶♨ 🏊
Facilities : 🚿 ⛽ 🍴📶 🏧 refrigerated
food storage facilities
Nearby : 🐎

GPS Longitude : 3.36199
Latitude : 43.28766

*Using the traditional Michelin classification method,
the guide provides you with an easy, speedy reference
for assessing the category of each site: 1 to 5 tents
(see page 10).*

QUILLAN

11500 – Michelin map **344** E5 – pop. 3 352 – alt. 291
▶ Paris 797 – Andorra-la-Vella 113 – Ax-les-Thermes 55
Carcassonne 52

▲▲▲ Village Vacances Domaine de l'Espinet

(rental of studios and maisonnettes only)

📞 04 68 20 88 88. www.lespinet.com

Address : located 1km north along the D 118

Opening times : Permanent

25 ha

Rental rates : (2014 Price) 🚿 🅿 – 24 studios – 158 maisonettes.
Per week from 448 to 2,135€

This is an upmarket, well-appointed holiday village.

Surroundings : 🌲 ⛰️ ♨
Leisure activities : 🍴✖🏛️ 🏃 🎿 ♨
hammam, jacuzzi ♨ ✖ 🏊 🏊 spa centre
Facilities : ⛽ 🍴 launderette

GPS Longitude : 2.19776
Latitude : 42.89268

▲▲ Municipal la Sapinette

📞 04 68 20 13 52. www.villedequillan.fr

Address : 21 avenue René Delpech (0.8km west along the D 79,
follow the signs for Ginoles)

Opening times : from beginning April to end Oct.

1.8 ha (90 pitches) terraced, relatively flat, flat, grassy

Tariff : (2014 Price) 17.60€ ✳✳ 🚐 🔲 (½) (16A) –
Extra per person 4.40€

Rental rates : (2014 Price) (from beginning April to end Oct.) 🚫 –
26 🏠. Per night from 70 to 85€ – Per week from 350 to 729€
🚐 borne 4€ – 6 🔲 11€ – ⛽ (½)12.40€

The pitches are arranged on terraces with a modicum of shade.

Surroundings : 🌲 ⛰️ ♨
Leisure activities : 🏛️ ♨
Facilities : 🚿 ⛽ 🍴

GPS Longitude : 2.18445
Latitude : 42.87495

REMOULINS

30210 – Michelin map **339** M5 – pop. 2 405 – alt. 27
▶ Paris 685 – Alès 50 – Arles 37 – Avignon 23

▲▲▲ La Sousta 👥

📞 04 66 37 12 80. www.lasousta.com

Address : avenue du Pont du Gard (situated 2km to the northwest,
follow the signs for Le Pont du Gard, right bank)

Opening times : from beginning March to end Oct.

14 ha (300 pitches) undulating, relatively flat, flat, grassy, sandy

Tariff : 29.90€ ✳✳ 🚐 🔲 (½) (6A) – Extra per person 9€ – Reservation
fee 15€

Rental rates : (from beginning March to end Oct.) – 60 🚐 –
4 🏠. Per night from 65 to 80€ – Per week from 252 to 874€
Reservation fee 15€
🚐 borne 2€

*In a pleasant wooded setting beside the Gardon river, on the
right bank near the Pont du Gard.*

Surroundings : 🌊 ⛰️
Leisure activities : 🍴✖🏛️ 🏃 ♨ 🚴 ✖ 🏊
🏊 🍴
Facilities : 🚿 ⛽ 📶 🍴 launderette 🏧

GPS Longitude : 4.54
Latitude : 43.94

▲▲▲ FranceLoc Domaine de La Soubeyranne 👥

📞 04 66 37 03 21. www.soubeyranne.com

Address : 1110 route de Beaucaire (2.5km south along the N 86 and
D 986, right bank)

4 ha (200 pitches)

Rentals : 158 🚐 – 4 tent lodges.
🚐 borne

*The numerous mobile homes are well laid out and there's a
very well equipped children's playground.*

Surroundings : 🌊 🚐 ⛰️
Leisure activities : 🍴✖🏛️ 🏃 ♨ ✖ 🎣 🏊 🏊
🏊 multi-sports ground
Facilities : 🚿 ⛽ 🍴 launderette 🏧

GPS Longitude : 4.56236
Latitude : 43.93031

ROCLES

48300 – Michelin map **330** K6 – pop. 209 – alt. 1 085
▶ Paris 581 – Grandrieu 20 – Langogne 8 – Mende 44

▲▲ Rondin des Bois

📞 04 66 69 50 46. www.camping-rondin.com – alt. 1,000

Address : Palhere (3km north following signs for Bessettes and take
road for Vaysset to the right.)

Opening times : from beginning May to end Sept.

2 ha (78 pitches) terraced, relatively flat, flat, stony, rocks

Tariff : 20.50€ ✳✳ 🚐 🔲 (½) (10A) – Extra per person 4.80€ –
Reservation fee 10€

Rental rates : (from beginning April to end Oct.) – 6 🚐 – 8 🏠.
Per night from 50 to 80€ – Per week from 70 to 95€ – Reservation
fee 10€
🚐 borne

*Situated on an unspoilt site; pitches and wooden chalets with
'living' green roofs close to the Lac de Naussac.*

Surroundings : 🌊 ⛰️ 🚐 ♨
Leisure activities : 🍴✖🏛️ 🏃 🏊
forest trail
Facilities : 🚿 ⛽ 🍴 launderette 🏧
Nearby : 🚴 ⛵

GPS Longitude : 3.78105
Latitude : 44.73814

ROQUEFEUIL

11340 – Michelin map **344** C6 – pop. 276 – alt. 900
▶ Paris 813 – Montpellier 226 – Carcassonne 78

⚠ La Mare aux Fées

✆ 04 68 31 11 37. www.pyrenees-camping.com

Address : rue de l'Église (in the village)

Opening times : from mid Jan.to end Oct.

0.5 ha (23 pitches)

Tariff : (2014 Price) 18€ ♣♣ ⟺ ▣ Ⓗ (16A) – Extra per person 5€
Rental rates : (2014 Price) (from mid Jan.to end Oct.) ♿ (1 chalet) – 3 ▣⒣ – 6 ⛺. Per night from 75 to 85€ – Per week from 350 to 550€

🛁 borne 3€ – ⚑17€

A well-maintained site in the shadow of the church bell tower.

Surroundings : 🏞 ▱ ♀		
Leisure activities : ✗ ⛳🏊 (small swimming pool)	**G**	Longitude : 1.9952
Facilities : ♿ ⌫ ▥ ♨ ⚐ ♒ ⛾ ▣ ⤴	**P** **S**	Latitude : 42.8193
Nearby : 🍴		

ROQUEFORT-DES-CORBIÈRES

11540 – Michelin map **344** I5 – pop. 947 – alt. 50
▶ Paris 813 – Montpellier 118 – Carcassonne 78 – Perpignan 45

⚠ Gîtes La Capelle (rental of gîtes only)

✆ 06 19 50 95 26. http://giteslacapelle.chez-alice.fr

Address : 4 rue la Capelle (in the town)

Opening times : Permanent

0.3 ha flat

Rental rates : ℗ – 13 gîtes. Per night from 65 to 155€ – Per week from 270 to 1,290€

A small group of 'semi-detached' gîtes beside a swimming pool.

Surroundings : 🏞 ♀♀		
Leisure activities : 🛋 🏊	**G**	Longitude : 2.95345
Facilities : ⚐ ▥ ⛾ ▣	**P** **S**	Latitude : 42.9897

LA ROQUE-SUR-CÈZE

30200 – Michelin map **339** M3 – pop. 173 – alt. 90
▶ Paris 663 – Alès 53 – Bagnols-sur-Cèze 13 – Bourg-St-Andéol 35

⚠ Les Cascades

✆ 04 66 82 72 97. www.campinglescascades.com

Address : route de Donnat (600m south along the D 166, direct access to the Cèze river)

Opening times : from beginning April to end Sept.

5 ha (118 pitches) terraced, flat and relatively flat, grassy

Tariff : 43€ ♣♣ ⟺ ▣ Ⓗ (10A) – Extra per person 7.50€ – Reservation fee 15€
Rental rates : (from mid April to end Sept.) – 53 ▣⒣. Per night from 24 to 145€ – Per week from 171 to 1,015 €– Reservation fee 15€ 🛁 borne

The pitches arranged on terraces with lots of shade run down to a rocky river with a beach and a bathing place.

Surroundings : 🏞 ▱ ♀♀		
Leisure activities : 🍸✗ ⛵ 🏊 ≋ (beach) 🎣 multi-sports ground	**G**	Longitude : 4.52
Facilities : ♿ ⌫ ▣ ♒ ⚐ ⛾ ▣ ⤴	**P** **S**	Latitude : 44.19

LE ROZIER

48150 – Michelin map **330** H9 – pop. 145 – alt. 400
▶ Paris 632 – Florac 57 – Mende 63 – Millau 23

⚠ Les Prades 👥

✆ 05 65 62 62 09. www. campinglesprades.com
✉ 12720 Peyreleau

Address : on the D 187 (head along the Peyreleau (left bank), 4km west along the D 187; beside the Tarn)

Opening times : from beginning May to mid Sept.

3.5 ha (150 pitches)

Tariff : 35€ ♣♣ ⟺ ▣ Ⓗ (6A) – Extra per person 7€ – Reservation fee 15€
Rental rates : (from beginning May to mid Sept.) 🎿 – 30 ▣⒣ – 3 ⛺. Per night from 36 to 102€ – Per week from 255 to 710 € Reservation fee 15€

🛁 borne

Below the road, some pitches beside the Tarn river with good sanitary facilities and an attractive, small water park.

Surroundings : ♀♀		
Leisure activities : 🍸✗ ⛳ 🎿 ⛵ ≋ 🎣 🌀 🐎 🏊	**G**	Longitude : 3.17332
Facilities : ♿ ⌫ ▥ ♨ ⚐ ⛾ ▣ ⤴	**P** **S**	Latitude : 44.1996

⚠ Le St Pal et son Parc Longue Lègue

✆ 05 65 62 64 46. www.campingsaintpal.com ✉ 12720 Mostuéjouls

Address : La Muse-St Pal, route des Gorges du Tarn (located 1km northwest along the D 907, follow the signs for Millau; beside the Tarn)

Opening times : from mid June to end Aug.

2 ha (105 pitches) flat, grassy

Tariff : 31€ ♣♣ ⟺ ▣ Ⓗ (10A) – Extra per person 6€ – Reservation fee 20€
Rental rates : (from mid June to end Aug.) – 20 ▣⒣ – 5 canvas bungalows. Per night from 54 to 104€ – Per week from 273 to 728€ Reservation fee 20€

Below the road, pitches partly alongside the Tarn river with a good standard of sanitary facilities.

Surroundings : ♀♀ ▲		
Leisure activities : 🍸✗ 🛋 🏊 🎣 🐎	**G**	Longitude : 3.19822
Facilities : ♿ ⌫ ♒ ⛾ launderette ⤴	**P** **S**	Latitude : 44.19639

To make the best possible use of this guide, please read pages 2–15 carefully.

ST-ALBAN-SUR-LIMAGNOLE

48120 – Michelin map **330** I6 – pop. 1 519 – alt. 950
▶ Paris 558 – Montpellier 214 – Mende 39 – Le Puy-en-Velay 76

⚠ Le Galier

✆ 04 66 31 58 80. www.campinglegalier.fr

Address : route de St-Chély-d'Apcher

Opening times : from beginning March to end Sept.

12 ha/3.5 for camping (77 pitches) terraced, flat, grassy, wood

Tariff : 19.40€ ♣♣ ⟺ ▣ Ⓗ (6A) – Extra per person 4.60€ – Reservation fee 15€

Rental rates : (from beginning May to end Sept.) ⚡ – 11 🚐. Per night from 35 to 70€ – Per week from 180 to 595€ – Reservation fee 50€

Some pitches are surrounded by trees and shrubs through which the Limagnole river runs.

Surroundings : 🌿 ♀
Facilities : ₰ ⚬━ 🏢 ⓘ

G P S Longitude : 3.37167
Latitude : 44.7752

ST-ANDRÉ-DE-SANGONIS

34725 – Michelin map **339** G7 – pop. 5 175 – alt. 65
▶ Paris 715 – Béziers 54 – Clermont-l'Hérault 8 – Gignac 5

🔺 Le Septimanien

✆ 0467578423. www.camping-leseptimanien.com

Address : route de Cambous (located 1km southwest along the D 4, follow the signs for Brignac; beside a stream)

Opening times : from end April to mid Sept.

2.6 ha (86 pitches)

Tariff : (2014 Price) 26€ ⚤ 🚗 ⓘ ⓘ (10A) – Extra per person 4.60€ Reservation fee 13€

Rental rates : (2014 Price) (from end April to mid Sept.) – 10 🚐 – 9 🏠. Per week from 290 to 580€ – Reservation fee 13€

This is a peaceful, family-orientated site.

Surroundings : 🌿 ⌂ ♀♀
Leisure activities : ♈ ⛵ ⌘
Facilities : ₰ ⚬━ ⓘ 🖼

G P S Longitude : 3.49508
Latitude : 43.64066

ST-BAUZILE

48000 – Michelin map **330** J8 – pop. 579 – alt. 750
▶ Paris 598 – Chanac 19 – Florac 29 – Marvejols 30

🔺 Municipal les Berges de Bramont

✆ 0466470597. www.saint-bauzile.fr

Address : at Rouffiac (located 1.5km southwest along the D 41. N 106, follow the signs for Mende, near the Bramont and the sports centre)

Opening times : from beginning July to end Sept.

1.5 ha (50 pitches)

Tariff : 12€ ⚤ 🚗 ⓘ ⓘ (50A) – Extra per person 2.50€

Rental rates : (from beginning July to end Aug.) – 4 🏠. Per week from €350

🚐 borne 2.50€

A green setting with wooden chalets equipped to a very good standard.

Surroundings : ≤ ♀
Leisure activities : ⌂ ⛵
Facilities : ₰ ⚬━ 🚿 ⌘ ♨ ⓘ
Nearby : ♈ ✗ 🚲 🍴

G P S Longitude : 3.49428
Latitude : 44.47666

Some information or pricing may have changed since the guide went to press. We recommend you check the price list online in advance or at the entrance to the campsite and enquire about possible restrictions.

ST-CYPRIEN-PLAGE

66750 – Michelin map **344** J7
▶ Paris 870 – Montpellier 173 – Perpignan 21 – Carcassonne 135

🔺🔺🔺 Cala Gogo ⚤

✆ 0468210712. www.camping-le-calagogo.fr

Address : avenue Armand Lanoux - Les Capellans (4km to the south; beside the beach)

Opening times : from end April to end Sept.

11 ha (649 pitches)

Tariff : 48.10€ ⚤ 🚗 ⓘ ⓘ (10A) – Extra per person 11.70€ – Reservation fee 25€

Rental rates : (from end April to end Sept.) ₰ (1 mobile home) – 130 🚐. Per night from 36 to 196€ – Per week from 252 to 1,372€ Reservation fee 25€

🚐 borne

The new rental accommodation is good quality, with a landscaped water park and direct access to the beach.

Surroundings : ⌂ ♀ ⛰
Leisure activities : ♈ ✗ ⌂ ⓘ ⛵ 🍴 ⌘ disco
Facilities : ₰ ⚬━ 🏢 ♨ ⌘ 🚿 ⓘ launderette 🛒🚻

G P S Longitude : 3.03789
Latitude : 42.59998

Michelin classification:

🔺🔺🔺🔺 *Extremely comfortable, equipped to a very high standard*

🔺🔺🔺 *Very comfortable, equipped to a high standard*

🔺🔺🔺 *Comfortable and well equipped*

🔺🔺 *Reasonably comfortable*

🔺 *Satisfactory*

ST-GENIS-DES-FONTAINES

66740 – Michelin map **344** I7 – pop. 2 792 – alt. 63
▶ Paris 878 – Argelès-sur-Mer 10 – Le Boulou 10 – Collioure 17

🔺 La Pinède

✆ 0468897529. www.campinglapinede66.fr

Address : avenue des Albères (south of the town along the D 2)

Opening times : from beginning June to end Aug.

1 ha (71 pitches) flat, grassy

Tariff : (2014 Price) 29.30€ ⚤ 🚗 ⓘ ⓘ (10A) – Extra per person 6.30€ – Reservation fee 19€

Rental rates : (2014 Price) (from beginning June to end Aug.) ⚡ – 10 🚐. Per week from 450 to 550€ – Reservation fee 19€

The site is attractively shaded in places by pine groves; some rental mobile homes are a little old.

Surroundings : ♀♀
Leisure activities : ⌘
Facilities : ₰ ⚬━ 🚿 ♨ 🖼
Nearby : 🍴

G P S Longitude : 2.9245
Latitude : 42.54093

ST-GEORGES-DE-LÉVÉJAC

48500 – Michelin map **330** H9 – pop. 259 – alt. 900
▶ Paris 603 – Florac 53 – Mende 45 – Millau 49

⛰ Cassaduc

℘ 04 66 48 85 80. www.camping-cassaduc.com

Address : route du Point Sublime (1.4km southeast)

Opening times : from beginning July to end Aug.

2.2 ha (75 pitches) terraced, relatively flat, flat, grassy, stony

Tariff : 20€ ✶✶ ⇔ 国 (15A) – Extra per person 6€
Rental rates : (from beginning July to end Aug.) ⤫ – 2 🛏. Per night from 65 to 85€ – Per week from 300 to 490€
🚰 borne 8€ – 6 国 16€

Situated 500m from the Point Sublime (elevated view point); the pitches are on terraces in the shade of a pretty pine wood.

Surroundings : ⤳ ⩽ ♀♀	
Leisure activities : 🎱 ⛄ jacuzzi	**G** Longitude : 3.24282
Facilities : & ⚡ 🍴 🚿 ⚄ ♨ ⛟ 🗑	**P** Latitude : 44.31532
Nearby : ♈ ✗	**S**

ST-GERMAIN-DU-TEIL

48340 – Michelin map **330** H8 – pop. 810 – alt. 760
▶ Paris 601 – Montpellier 166 – Mende 46 – Millau 58

⛰ Les Chalets du Plan d'Eau de Booz

(rental of chalets only)

℘ 04 66 48 48 48. www.lozere-resa.com

Address : near Booz lake (widening in the Lot river) (8km southeast along the D 52, turn onto D 809, after the motorway)

Opening times : from end March to mid Nov.

5 ha flat, grassy, lake
Rental rates : (2014 Price) & (1 chalet) – 43 🛏. Per week from 219 to 649€ – Reservation fee 20€

A wooden chalet village in a green setting, some have a good view over a bend in the Lot river. Half board available.

Surroundings : ♀	
Leisure activities : ♈ ✗ 🎱 ⛹ jacuzzi ⛵ 🛶 💧 pedalos ♒	**G** Longitude : 3.19764
Facilities : ⚡ 🏛 🍴 launderette	**P** Latitude : 44.45787
Nearby : 🚵 forest trail	**S**

ST-HIPPOLYTE-DU-FORT

30170 – Michelin map **339** I5 – pop. 3 803 – alt. 165
▶ Paris 703 – Alès 35 – Anduze 22 – Nîmes 48

⛰ Graniers

℘ 04 66 85 21 44. www.campingdegraniers.com

Address : head 4km northeast following signs for Uzès then take D 133, follow the signs for Monoblet and take the road to the right; beside a stream

Opening times : from beginning March to end Oct.

2 ha (50 pitches) terraced, relatively flat, wood, grassy

Tariff : (2014 Price) 20€ ✶✶ ⇔ 国 ⚡ (6A) – Extra per person 6€
Rental rates : (2014 Price) (from beginning March to end Oct.) ⤫ – 7 🛏 – 3 🛏 – 2 yurts – 3 tent lodges. Per night from 30 to 80€ – Per week from 180 to 690€
🚰 borne

This is a shady site with a range of both old and new rental accommodations.

Surroundings : ⤳ ♀♀	
Leisure activities : ♈ ✗ ⛵ 🚵 🛶	**G** Longitude : 3.88722
Facilities : & ⚡ 🚿 🍴 🗑 ⛟	**P** Latitude : 43.98084
	S

ST-JEAN-DE-CEYRARGUES

30360 – Michelin map **339** K4 – pop. 158 – alt. 180
▶ Paris 700 – Alès 18 – Nîmes 33 – Uzès 21

⛰ Les Vistes

℘ 04 66 83 28 09. www.lesvistes.com

Address : 1 route des Vistes (500m south along the D 7)

Opening times : from beginning April to end Oct. All Saints' Day holiday (1 Nov.)

6 ha/3 for camping (52 pitches) open site, relatively flat, flat, grassy, stony

Tariff : (2014 Price) 27.50€ ✶✶ ⇔ 国 ⚡ (6A) – Extra per person 6.70€
Rental rates : (2014 Price) (from beginning April to end Sept. , All Saints' Day (1 Nov.) and Christmas holidays) & (1 chalet) – 12 🛏 – 5 canvas bungalows. Per week from 247 to 710€

Situated in an attractive, panoramic location.

Surroundings : ⩽ Mt Aigoual ♀♀	
Leisure activities : 🎱 ⛵ 🛶	**G** Longitude : 4.23016
Facilities : & ⚡ 🅿 🚿 ♨ 🍴 🗑 refrigerators	**P** Latitude : 44.04734
	S

ST-JEAN-DU-GARD

30270 – Michelin map **339** I4 – pop. 2 687 – alt. 183
▶ Paris 675 – Alès 28 – Florac 54 – Lodève 91

⛰ Mas de la Cam ▲⚐

℘ 04 66 85 12 02. http://www.camping-cevennes.info/

Address : route de Saint-André-de-Valborgne (3km northwest along the D 907; beside the Gardon de St-Jean)

Opening times : from end April to end Sept.

6 ha (200 pitches)

Tariff : (2014 Price) 39.50€ ✶✶ ⇔ 国 ⚡ (10A) – Extra per person 8.90€ – Reservation fee 17€
Rental rates : (2014 Price) (from end April to end Sept.) ⤫ – 1 studio – 5 gîtes. Per night from 55 to 91€ – Per week from 385 to 635€ – Reservation fee 17€

There's an attractive children's play area.

Surroundings : ⤳ ⩽ ♀♀	
Leisure activities : ♈ ✗ 🎱 ⛹ 🚵 ⛵ 🎯 🛶 ⛷ 🎣 multi-sports ground	**G** Longitude : 3.85319
Facilities : & ⚡ 🚿 🍴 🗑 ⛟ 🛟	**P** Latitude : 44.1123
	S

⛰ Les Sources

℘ 04 66 85 38 03. www.camping-des-sources.fr

Address : route de Mialet (located 1km northeast along the D 983 and D 50)

Opening times : from beginning April to end Sept.

3 ha (92 pitches) terraced, relatively flat, grassy

Tariff : 29€ ✶✶ ⇔ 国 ⚡ (6A) – Extra per person 5.50€ – Reservation fee 15€

Rental rates : (from beginning April to end Sept.) – 3 🏕 – 15 🏠 – 3 canvas bungalows. Per week from 343 to 840€ – Reservation fee 20€

🚐 borne 4€ – 🔌 💧 15.70€

The site enjoys a family atmosphere and has well-shaded pitches.

Surroundings : 🏞 ⟵ 🗒 ♨
Leisure activities : 🍽 ✗ 🏓 🚴 🛷
Facilities : 🚿 🔧 🗒 ♿ 🚻 🍴 launderette 🧺

Longitude : 3.89258
Latitude : 44.11393

⚠ La Forêt

🕿 04 66 85 37 00. www.campingalaforet.com

Address : route de Falguières (situated 2km north along the D 983, follow the signs for St-Étienne-Vallée-Française then continue 2km along the D 333)

Opening times : from mid May to beginning Sept.

3 ha (65 pitches) terraced, flat, grassy, stony

Tariff : (2014 Price) 35.20€ ✠✠ 🚗 🔲 (10A) – Extra per person 7.70€ – Reservation fee 5€

Rental rates : (2014 Price) (from mid May to beginning Sept.) 🏕 – 3 🏠. Per week from 300 to 600€ – Reservation fee 5€

At the edge of a spacious pine grove.

Surroundings : 🏞 ⟵ 🗒 ♨
Leisure activities : 🚴 🛷
Facilities : 🔧 🗒 🍴 🖥 🧺 refrigerators

Longitude : 3.89072
Latitude : 44.12948

ST-PAUL-LE-FROID

48600 – Michelin map **330** J6 – pop. 147 – alt. 1 302 – Winter sports : ⛷
◨ Paris 582 – Montpellier 237 – Mende 54 – Le Puy-en-Velay 61

⚠ Village Vacances les Baraques des Bouviers

(rental chalets and Nordic-style chalets only)

🕿 04 66 48 48 48. www.lesbouviers.com – alt. 1 418

Address : La Baraque des Bouviers (8.5km southeast along the D 58 and D 5, follow the signs for St-Alban-sur-Limagnole)

Opening times : Permanent

20 ha/2 for camping open site, terraced

Rental rates : (2014 Price) 🚿 – 14 🏠. Per week from 191 to 799€

The chalets are well-spaced out across the Plateau de La Margeride, at the foot of cross-country ski pistes and snow-shoe hiking trails.

Surroundings : 🏞 ⟵ ♨
Leisure activities : 🏠
Facilities : 🔧 🗒 🍴 🖥
Nearby : 🍽 ✗ 🚴 climbing

Longitude : 3.50574
Latitude : 44.76617

Michelin classification:

⚠⚠⚠⚠ *Extremely comfortable, equipped to a very high standard*

⚠⚠⚠ *Very comfortable, equipped to a high standard*

⚠⚠⚠ *Comfortable and well equipped*

⚠⚠ *Reasonably comfortable*

⚠ *Satisfactory*

ST-VICTOR-DE-MALCAP

30500 – Michelin map **339** K3 – pop. 683 – alt. 140
◨ Paris 680 – Alès 23 – Barjac 15 – La Grand-Combe 25

⚠⚠⚠ Domaine de Labeiller 👥

🕿 04 66 24 15 27. www.labeiller.fr

Address : 1701 route de Barjac (located 1km southeast, access via the D 51, follow the signs for St-Jean-de-Maruéjols and take road to the left)

Opening times : from mid May to end Aug.

3 ha (132 pitches) terraced, flat, grassy, stony

Tariff : 37€ ✠✠ 🚗 🔲 (6A) – Extra per person 7€ – Reservation fee 15€

Rental rates : (from mid May to end Aug.) – 12 🏕 – 1 🏠. Per night from 40 to 130€ – Per week from 250 to 910€ – Reservation fee 15€

Situated in a pleasant oak wood with an attractive swimming area.

Surroundings : 🏞 🗒 ♨
Leisure activities : 🍽 ✗ 🏓 🚴 🛷 🎿 ⛷ 🏊
Facilities : 🚿 🔧 🏠 🍴 launderette
Nearby : ✂

Longitude : 4.22727
Latitude : 44.24154

The guide covers all 22 regions of France – see the map and list of regions on pages 4–5.

STE-ÉNIMIE

48210 – Michelin map **330** I8 – pop. 525 – alt. 470
◨ Paris 612 – Florac 27 – Mende 28 – Meyrueis 30

⚠⚠⚠ Le Couderc

🕿 04 66 48 50 53. www.campingcouderc.fr

Address : route de Millau (situated 2km southwest along the D 907bis; beside the Tarn river)

Opening times : from beginning April to end Sept.

2.5 ha (130 pitches) terraced, flat, grassy, stony

Tariff : (2014 Price) 28€ ✠✠ 🚗 🔲 (16A) – Extra per person 4€ – Reservation fee 15€

Rental rates : (2014 Price) (from beginning April to end Sept.) – 7 🏕. Per night from 50 to 60€ – Per week from 290 to 690€ Reservation fee 15€

🚐 borne 4€ – 130 🔲 24€

Situated below the road, with very well shaded pitches along the Tarn river.

Surroundings : ♨ ⛰
Leisure activities : 🍽 🏊 🚣 🛶
Facilities : 🚿 🔧 🗒 🍴 launderette

Longitude : 3.39917
Latitude : 44.35194

⚠ Les Fayards

🕿 04 66 48 57 36. www.camping-les-fayards.com

Address : route de Millau (3km southwest along the D 907bis; beside the Tarn river)

2 ha (77 pitches) terraced, flat, grassy, stony

Rentals : 2 caravans – 14 🏕 – 4 🏠.

Situated below the road, with pitches on terraces beside the Tarn river.

Surroundings : 🏞 🗒 ♨
Leisure activities : 🍽 🚴 🏊 🛶 🚣
Facilities : 🚿 🔧 🍴 launderette

Longitude : 3.39504
Latitude : 44.34583

⚠ Le Site

☎ 04 66 48 58 08. www.gorges-du-tarn.fr

Address : Castelbouc (7km southeast along the D 907b, follow the signs for Ispagnac then continue 500m to the right following signs for Castelbouc; beside the Tarn river)

Opening times : from mid April to mid Sept.

1 ha (60 pitches) open site, relatively flat, flat, grassy

Tariff : 18€ ★★ ⇌ 🗐 ⒢ (5A) – Extra per person 4€

Rental rates : (from mid May to mid Sept.) – 10 🛏 – 2 tipis. Per week from 250 to 560€

Bordered by the river and opposite a small waterfall.

Surroundings : 🏊 ☐ ♋♋ ⌂
Leisure activities : 🏊 🎣
Facilities : ♿ ☞ 🏕 ⁱ

GPS Longitude : 3.46571
Latitude : 44.34423

STE-MARIE

66470 – Michelin map **344** J6 – pop. 4 641 – alt. 4
▶ Paris 845 – Argelès-sur-Mer 24 – Le Boulou 37 – Perpignan 14

⚠ Le Palais de la Mer ♣♣

☎ 04 68 73 07 94. www.palaisdelamer.com

Address : avenue de Las Illes (600m north of the resort, 150m from the beach (direct access)

Opening times : from mid May to end Sept.

8 ha/3 for camping (181 pitches)

Tariff : 46€ ★★ ⇌ 🗐 ⒢ (10A) – Extra per person 8.50€ – Reservation fee 35€

In a shaded setting with lots of laurel trees marking out the paths.

Surroundings : ☐ ♋♋
Leisure activities : 🍴 ✗ ☺nighttime 🏃 ♬ hammam, jacuzzi ⛹ 🏓 🦌 wildlife park
Facilities : ♿ ☞ ✉ 🏕 ⌂ ⁱ launderette 🏊 🚿

GPS Longitude : 3.03307
Latitude : 42.74045

⚠ Camp'Atlantique La Pergola

☎ 04 68 73 03 07. www.campinglapergola.com

Address : 21 avenue Frédéric Mistral (500m from the beach)

3.5 ha (181 pitches)

Rentals : 🦌 – 20 🛏 – 9 mobile homes (without sanitary facilities).

Surroundings : ♋♋
Leisure activities : ✗ 🏕 ⛹ 🏊
Facilities : ♿ ☞ 🏕 ⌂ ⁱ launderette 🚿 refrigerators
Nearby : 🏓

GPS Longitude : 3.03315
Latitude : 42.72672

SÉRIGNAN

34410 – Michelin map **339** E9 – pop. 6 631 – alt. 7
▶ Paris 765 – Agde 22 – Béziers 11 – Narbonne 34

⚠ FranceLoc Le Domaine Les Vignes d'Or ♣♣

(rental of mobile homes and chalets only)

☎ 04 67 32 37 18. www.vignesdor.com

Address : chemin de l'Hermitage (3.5km to the south, take the side road located behind the Citroën garage)

Opening times : from mid April to end Sept.

4 ha (227 pitches)

Rental rates : (2014 Price) ♿ (2 mobile homes) – 187 🛏 – 14 ⌂. Per night from 19 to 177€ – Per week from 133 to 1,239€ Reservation fee 27€

Surroundings : 🏊 ♋♋
Leisure activities : 🍴 ✗ ☺ 🏃 ⛹ ☐ 🏊 ♬ multi-sports ground
Facilities : ♿ ☞ 🏕 ⁱ 🖼 🚿
Nearby : 🛒 🏓 🐎 🏕

GPS Longitude : 3.2757
Latitude : 43.2593

⚠ Le Paradis

☎ 04 67 32 24 03. www.camping-leparadis.com 🦌

Address : route de Valras-Plage (located 1.5km to the south)

Opening times : from beginning April to end Sept.

2.2 ha (129 pitches) flat, grassy

Tariff : 34.50€ ★★ ⇌ 🗐 ⒢ (10A) – Extra per person 6.50€ – Reservation fee 18€

Rental rates : (from beginning April to end Sept.) 🦌 – 21 🛏. Per night from 45 to 60€ – Per week from 190 to 650€ – Reservation fee 18€

🚐 borne

A pleasant setting with flowers and large pitches.

Surroundings : ☐ ♋♋
Leisure activities : ✗ 🏕 ⛹ 🏊
Facilities : ♿ ☞ 🎰 🏕 ⌂ ⁱ launderette 🚿
Nearby : 🛒

GPS Longitude : 3.28628
Latitude : 43.26829

⚠ Le Mas des Lavandes (rental of mobile homes only)

☎ 04 67 39 75 88. www.masdeslavandes.fr

Address : chemin de la mer (D 19 follow the signs for Valras-Plage – from the A9 take exit Béziers-est)

Opening times : Permanent

3.8 ha flat

Rental rates : (2014 Price) ♿ (1 mobile home) – 197 🛏. Per week from 190 to 1,080€ – Reservation fee 22€

Luxury mobile homes, but choose those further away from the road in preference.

Surroundings : ☐ ♋♋
Leisure activities : 🍴 ✗ 🏕 🏃 ⛹ 🏓 🏊 ♬
Facilities : ♿ ☞ ⁱ 🖼 🚿
Nearby : 🛒

GPS Longitude : 3.2831
Latitude : 43.25732

SÉRIGNAN-PLAGE

34410 – Michelin map **339** E9
▶ Paris 769 – Montpellier 73 – Carcassonne 100

⚠ Yelloh! Village Le Sérignan Plage ♣♣

Le Sérignan Plage

☎ 04 67 32 35 33. www.leserignanplage.com 🦌

Address : L'Orpellière (on the edge of the beach, direct access)

Opening times : from end April to end Sept.

20 ha (1200 pitches)

Tariff : 58€ ★★ ⇌ 🗐 ⒢ (10A) – Extra per person 10€

Rental rates : (from end April to end Sept.) 🦌 – 399 🛏 – 51 ⌂. Per night from €39 to 314 – Per week from €273 to 2 198

🚐 borne

Natural, sunny pitches, close to the marsh; luxury rental options with plenty of shade close to the beach.

Surroundings : 🏖 ⌷ 🌳🌳 ⛰
Leisure activities : 🍴 ✕ 🏠 ⛱ 🎣 🏊 jacuzzi 🏇 🚴 ✗ 🏊 ⛷ spa centre (naturist in mornings), disco, multi-sports ground
Facilities : ♿ ⚡ 🚿 ♨ launderette 🗑 🚽

Nearby : 🚣 🏇

GPS
Longitude : 3.3213
Latitude : 43.26401

🏔 Yelloh! Village Aloha 🏕

🕿 04 67 39 71 30. www.alohacamping.com

Address : chemin des Dunes

Opening times : from end April to mid Sept.

9.5 ha (444 pitches)

Tariff : 58 € 🏕🏕 ⇔ 🔲 🔌 (10A) – Extra per person 9 €

Rental rates : (from end April to mid Sept.) 🅿 – 184 🛏 – 15 🏠.
Per night from 39 to 375 € – Per week from 273 to 2,625 €

The site lies on both sides of the path leading to the beach, with rental options in a landscaped setting.

Surroundings : 🏖 ⌷ 🌳🌳 ⛰
Leisure activities : 🍴 ✕ 🏠 ⛱ 🎣 🏊 jacuzzi 🏇 🚴 ✗ ⛷ 🏊 multi-sports ground
Facilities : ♿ ⚡ 🚿 ♨ launderette 🗑 🚽

Nearby : 🏊 🏇

GPS
Longitude : 3.33941
Latitude : 43.26745

🏔 Domaine de Beauséjour 🏕

🕿 04 67 39 50 93. www.camping-beausejour.com

Address : beside the beach

10 ha/6 for camping (380 pitches)

Rentals : 84 🛏 – 6 🏠.

There's a very pleasant spa centre, open all year round.

Surroundings : 🏖 ⌷ 🌳🌳 ⛰
Leisure activities : 🍴 ✕ 🕐 nighttime 🎣 🎣 ♨ hammam, jacuzzi 🏇 🚴 ✗ disco, watersports centre, spa centre
Facilities : ♿ ⚡ ♨ launderette 🗑 🚽

GPS
Longitude : 3.33692
Latitude : 43.26711

🏔 Le Clos Virgile 🏕

🕿 04 67 32 20 64. www.leclosvirgile.com

Address : 500m from the beach

5 ha (300 pitches)

Rentals : ✗ – 100 🛏 – 18 🏠.

The pitches are shaded, but the sanitary facilities are somewhat old.

Surroundings : ⌷ 🌳🌳
Leisure activities : 🍴 ✕ 🏠 ⛱ 🎣 jacuzzi 🏇 🏊 ⛷ multi-sports ground
Facilities : ♿ ⚡ ♨ 🔲 🏊 🚽

Nearby : 🏊 🏇

GPS
Longitude : 3.33152
Latitude : 43.27204

There are several different types of sani-station ('borne' in French) – sanitation points providing fresh water and disposal points for grey water. See page 12 for further details.

30250 – Michelin map **339** J6 – pop. 4 496 – alt. 34
▶ Paris 734 – Alès 44 – Montpellier 35 – Nîmes 29

🏔 Les Castels Le Domaine de Massereau

🕿 04 66 53 11 20. www.massereau.com

Address : 1990 route d'Aubais (Les Hauteurs de Sommières (heights)

Opening times : from mid April to end Oct.

90 ha/7.7 for camping (120 pitches) relatively flat, flat, grassy, stony

Tariff : 🏕 12 € ⇔ 5 € 🔲 25 € – 🔌 (16A) 7 € – Reservation fee 25 €

Rental rates : (from mid April to end Oct.) ♿ – 35 🛏 – 24 🏠.
Per night from 50 to 110 € – Per week from 340 to 1,350 € – Reservation fee 25 €

🚰 borne 2 € – 3 🔲 25 € – 💧 🔌 25 €

Luxury rental options, in the middle of a wine-growing area, crossed by a cycle trail (Sommières–Nîmes).

Surroundings : 🏖 ⌷ 🌳🌳
Leisure activities : 🍴 ✕ 🎣 hammam, jacuzzi 🏇 🚴 ✗ 🏊 ⛷ fitness trail, forest trail, zip wiring, multi-sports ground
Facilities : ♿ ⚡ 🚿 🏊 ♨ launderette 🏊 🚽

Nearby : 🎣

GPS
Longitude : 4.09735
Latitude : 43.76574

⛺ Municipal de Garanel

🕿 04 66 80 33 49. camping.garanel@sommieres.fr

Address : chemin Princesse (In the town, near the Vidourle river)

Opening times : from beginning April to end Sept.

7 ha (60 pitches)

Tariff : (2014 Price) 🏕 3.40 € ⇔ 🔲 5 € – 🔌 (8A) 4.50 €

🚰 borne 3.40 €

Very close to sports arena and the town centre.

Surroundings : ⌷ 🌳🌳
Facilities : ♿ ⚡ 🔲 🏊 📷

Nearby : 🏊 🍴 ✕ ✗ 🏊

GPS
Longitude : 4.08703
Latitude : 43.78738

34300 – Michelin map **339** F9
▶ Paris 761 – Montpellier 62 – Béziers 24 – Narbonne 54

🏔 La Tama

🕿 04 67 94 79 46. www.camping-latama.com

Address : 4 rue du Commandant Malet

Opening times : from mid April to mid Sept.

10 ha (700 pitches) undulating, flat and relatively flat, grassy, sandy

Tariff : (2014 Price) 35 € 🏕🏕 ⇔ 🔲 🔌 (10A) – Extra per person 7 € – Reservation fee 20 €

Rental rates : (2014 Price) (from mid April to mid Sept.) ♿ (2 chalets) – 60 🏠 – 30 tent lodges. Per night from 31 to 121 € – Per week from 217 to 847 € – Reservation fee 27 €

A pleasant location beside the sea, sheltered by pine trees.

Surroundings : 🌳🌳 ⛰
Leisure activities : 🏇 🏊 multi-sports ground
Facilities : ♿ ⚡ 🔲 🏊 ♨ launderette, refrigerated food storage facilities

Nearby : 🏊 🍴 ✕ 🚴 🎣

GPS
Longitude : 3.44249
Latitude : 43.28821

TORREILLES-PLAGE

66440 – Michelin map **344** I6

▶ Paris 853 – Montpellier 157 – Perpignan 20 – Carcassonne 119

▲▲▲ Sunêlia Les Tropiques ▲▲

Sunêlia Les Tropiques

℘ 0468280509. www.
campinglestropiques.com

Address : boulevard de la Plage (500m from the beach)

Opening times : from beginning April to beginning Oct.

8 ha (450 pitches)

Tariff : 54€ ✦✦ ⇌ 回 [2] (10A) – Extra per person 10.50€ – Reservation fee 35€

Rental rates : (from beginning April to beginning Oct.) ⴠ (2 mobile homes) – 226 ⌨ – 26 ⌂ – 2 tent lodges. Per night from 42 to 222€ – Per week from 250 to 1,554€ – Reservation fee 35€

⚑ borne – ⴠ 16€

Shady pitches and a pleasant spa centre.

Surroundings : ⊡ 🙼
Leisure activities : 🍽 ✕ ⌂ ⊙ ✣ ⌔ ⊜ hammam, jacuzzi ⛲ ✎ ⌇ disco, multi-sports ground, spa centre
Facilities : ⴠ ⚬ ⊞ ⌄ launderette ⊒ ⌄
Nearby : ⌇ ⛐

Longitude : 3.02972
Latitude : 42.7675

▲▲▲ Mar I Sol ▲▲

℘ 0468280407. www.camping-marisol.com – limited spaces for one-night stay

Address : boulevard de la Plage (150m from the beach - direct access)

Opening times : from mid April to beginning Sept.

7 ha (377 pitches)

Tariff : 64€ ✦✦ ⇌ 回 [2] (10A) – Extra per person 11.60€ – Reservation fee 49.50€

Rental rates : (from mid April to beginning Sept.) – 199 ⌨ – 5 ⌂. Per night from 29 to 398€ – Reservation fee 49.50€

A real village club with lots of activities and a large water park.

Surroundings : ⊡ 🙼
Leisure activities : 🍽 ✕ ⌂ ⊙ ✣ ⌔ ⊜ hammam, jacuzzi ⛲ ⊙ ⌇ disco, multi-sports ground
Facilities : ⴠ ⚬ ⌄ launderette ⌇ ⌄
Nearby : ⌇

Longitude : 3.03327
Latitude : 42.76746

▲▲▲ Le Calypso ▲▲

℘ 0468280947. www.camping-calypso.com – limited spaces for one-night stay

Address : boulevard de la Plage

6 ha (308 pitches)

*The classification (1 to 5 tents, **black** or red) that we award to selected sites in this guide is our own system. It should not be confused with the classification (1 to 5 stars) of official organisations.*

Rentals : ⊗ – 80 ⌨ – 28 ⌂ .

A pretty play and paddling pool area and private sanitary facilities for some pitches.

Surroundings : ⊡ 🙼
Leisure activities : 🍽 ✕ ⌂ ⊙ ✣ ⌔ jacuzzi ⛲ ✎ ⌇ multi-sports ground
Facilities : ⴠ ⚬ ⌄ – 9 individual sanitary facilities (⌄ ⌇ ⌄ wc) ⌄ launderette ⊒ ⌄ refrigerators
Nearby : ⌇ ⛐

Longitude : 3.03043
Latitude : 42.77128

▲▲ Homair Vacances La Palmeraie ▲▲

℘ 0468282064. www.homair.com – limited spaces for one-night stay

Address : boulevard de la Plage

Opening times : from mid April to mid Sept.

4.5 ha (229 pitches)

Tariff : 41€ ✦✦ ⇌ 回 [2] (8A) – Extra per person 8.50€ – Reservation fee 49€

Rental rates : – 220 ⌨. Per night from 17 to 188€ – Per week from 119 to 1,316€ – Reservation fee 49€

There's a good covering of shade for the mobile homes, but very few places for tents and caravans.

Surroundings : ⊡ 🙼
Leisure activities : 🍽 ✕ ⌂ ⊙ nighttime ✣ ⌔ ⊙ ⌇ multi-sports ground
Facilities : ⴠ ⚬ ⊞ ⌄ launderette ⊒ ⌄ refrigerated food storage facilities
Nearby : ⌇ ✕ ⛐

Longitude : 3.02806
Latitude : 42.76361

*For more information on visiting particular towns or regions, consult the relevant regional **MICHELIN** Green Guide. We also recommend you use the appropriate Michelin regional map to locate your selected campsite, to calculate distances and to work out the best route.*

TRÈBES

11800 – Michelin map **344** F3 – pop. 5 416 – alt. 84

▶ Paris 776 – Carcassonne 8 – Conques-sur-Orbiel 9 – Lézignan-Corbières 28

▲ A l'Ombre des Micocouliers ▲

℘ 0468786175. www.campingmicocouliers.com

Address : chemin de la Lande

Opening times : from beginning April to end Sept.

1.5 ha (70 pitches)

Tariff : 24.50€ ✦✦ ⇌ 回 [2] (16A) – Extra per person 5.80€

Rental rates : (from beginning April to end Sept.) – 5 canvas bungalows. Per night from 30 to 50€ – Per week from 140 to 490€

⚑ borne 5€

Situated beside the Aude river in the shade of hackberry trees, but with rather old sanitary facilities.

Surroundings : ⊡ 🙼
Leisure activities : ✕ ⌂ ⛲ ⌇
Facilities : ⴠ ⚬ ⌄ ⌇ ⊞ ⌄
Nearby : ⌇ ✕ ⊡

Longitude : 2.44237
Latitude : 43.20682

UZÈS

30700 – Michelin map **339** L4 – pop. 8 339 – alt. 138
▶ Paris 682 – Alès 34 – Arles 52 – Avignon 38

⚠ Le Moulin Neuf ♣

☎ 04 66 22 17 21. www.le-moulin-neuf.fr

Address : at Saint-Quentin-La-Poterie (4.5km northeast along the D 982, follow the signs for Bagnols-sur-Cèze and take the D 5 to the left)

Opening times : from beginning April to end Sept.

5 ha (140 pitches)

Tariff : 24.50€ ♣♣ ⚌ 回 🗗 (5A) –Extra per person 6.70€ – Reservation fee 10€

Rental rates : Permanent – 35 🏠. Per night from 45 to 100 € – Per week from 252 to 660€ – Reservation fee 10€

🚐 borne

A rectangular site, shaded by poplars, featuring rather old gîtes of 'modest' quality.

Surroundings : 🏞 🏕 ♧♧
Leisure activities : 🍴 ✕ 🏠 🎯 ⚡ 🎣 🍖 ♒ multi-sports ground
Facilities : ♿ ☛ 🚿 🏠 🚾 🏐 🚯 🚱
Nearby : 🏇

G P S | Longitude : 4.45569
Latitude : 44.0321

⚠ Le Mas de Rey

☎ 04 66 22 18 27. www.campingmasderey.com

Address : route d'Anduze (3km southwest along the D 982)

Opening times : from end March to mid Oct.

5 ha/2.5 for camping (66 pitches) flat, grassy

Tariff : (2014 Price) 33€ ♣♣ ⚌ 回 🗗 (10A) – Extra per person 8€ – Reservation fee 10€

Rental rates : (2014 Price) (from end March to mid Oct.) ♿ (1 chalet) – 6 🏠 – 2 tent lodges. Per night from 60 to 110€ – Per week from 375 to 850€ – Reservation fee 10€

Very peaceful pitches and luxurious wooden chalets in pleasant shade.

Surroundings : 🏞 🏕 ♧♧
Leisure activities : 🏠 ⚡ ♒
Facilities : ♿ ☛ 🚿 🏠 🚯

G P S | Longitude : 4.38471
Latitude : 43.99806

VALLABRÈGUES

30300 – Michelin map **339** M5 – pop. 1 318 – alt. 8
▶ Paris 698 – Arles 26 – Avignon 22 – Beaucaire 9

⚠ Lou Vincen

☎ 04 66 59 21 29. www.campinglouvincen.com

Address : to the west of the town, 100m from the Rhône and a small lake

Opening times : from beginning April to end Oct.

1.4 ha (75 pitches) flat, grassy

Tariff : 26.95€ ♣♣ ⚌ 回 🗗 (6A) – Extra per person 7.95€ – Reservation fee 17€

Rental rates : (from mid April to mid Oct.) ♒ – 10 🚐. Per week from 360 to 590€ – Reservation fee 18€

🚐 borne

At the entrance to the town, on the left bank of the Rhône.

Surroundings : 🏞 🏕 ♧♧
Leisure activities : ♒
Facilities : ☛ 🚿 🚾 🏐
Nearby : 🍖

G P S | Longitude : 4.62546
Latitude : 43.85493

VALLERAUGUE

30570 – Michelin map **339** G4 – pop. 1 070 – alt. 346
▶ Paris 684 – Mende 100 – Millau 75 – Nîmes 86

⚠ Le Mourétou

☎ 04 67 82 22 30. www.camping-mouretou.com

Address : route de l'Aigoual and on the right (3km west on the D 986)

Opening times : from mid April to beginning Nov.

1 ha (33 pitches)

Tariff : (2014 Price) 23.90€ ♣♣ ⚌ 回 🗗 (6A) – Extra per person 6€ Reservation fee 15€

Rental rates : (2014 Price) Permanent – 4 🚐 – 2 tent lodges – 2 gîtes. Per night from 26 to 45€ – Per week from 199 to 549€ Reservation fee 15€

Well-shaded pitches beside the Hérault river and a small lake.

Surroundings : 🏕 ♧♧
Leisure activities : ✕ ⚡ ♒ (small swimming pool)
Facilities : 🏐 🚱
Nearby : 🚣 (fresh water)

G P S | Longitude : 3.60785
Latitude : 44.0871

VALRAS-PLAGE

34350 – Michelin map **339** E9 – pop. 4 649 – alt. 1
▶ Paris 767 – Agde 25 – Béziers 16 – Montpellier 76

⚠ Domaine de La Yole ♣

☎ 04 67 37 33 87. www.campinglayole.com

Address : situated 2km southwest, 500m from the beach

Opening times : from end April to mid Sept.

23 ha (1273 pitches)

Tariff : 55€ ♣♣ ⚌ 回 🗗 (6A) – Extra per person 9.75€ – Reservation fee 30€

Rental rates : (from end April to mid Sept.) 🅿 – 278 🚐 – 49 🏠 – 10 canvas bungalows – 10 tent lodges. Per night from 42 to 224€ Reservation fee 30€

🚐 borne

There's a vineyard nearby, plus a farmhouse restaurant.

Surroundings : 🏕 ♧♧
Leisure activities : 🍴 ✕ 🏠 🎲 🎯 ⚡ 🚲 🍖 ♒ 🌲 forest trail , multi-sports ground
Facilities : ♿ ☛ 🚿 🚾 🏐 launderette 🚯 🚱
Nearby : 🏇

G P S | Longitude : 3.27181
Latitude : 43.23639

⚠ La Plage et du Bord de Mer ♣

☎ 04 67 37 34 38. www.camping-plage-mediterranee.com ⚡

Address : route de Vendres (located 1.5km southwest; beside the sea)

Opening times : from end April to end Sept.

13 ha (655 pitches)

Tariff : 48€ ♣♣ ⚌ 回 🗗 (10A) – Extra per person 6€ – Reservation fee 30€

Rental rates : Permanent ⚡ – 59 🚐 – 6 tent lodges. Per night from 40 to 190€ – Per week from 280 to 1,330€ – Reservation fee 30€

A good choice of pitches for tents and caravans, with sanitary facilities that are well maintained but a bit old-fashioned.

Surroundings : 🏕 ♧ ⛱
Leisure activities : 🍴 ✕ 🎲 🎯 ⚡ 🎡 🍖 🎣 ♒ 🏄 multi-sports ground
Facilities : ♿ ☛ 🚿 🚾 🏐 launderette 🚯 🚱
Nearby : 💧 🏇

G P S | Longitude : 3.26889
Latitude : 43.23559

Lou Village

0467373379. www.louvillage.com – limited spaces for one-night stay

Address : chemin des Montilles (2km southwest, 100m from the beach)

Opening times : from end April to mid Sept.

8 ha (470 pitches)

Tariff : (2014 Price) 53€ ★★ ⇔ 🔲 (¼) (10A) – Extra per person 9.50€
Reservation fee 30€

Rental rates : (2014 Price) (from end April to mid Sept.) ⚡ – 100 🔲 – 20 🏠. Per night from 27 to 193€ – Per week from 185 to 1,350€ – Reservation fee 30€

🚐 borne – 🔋 (¼)53€

A water park and direct access to the beach are the site's plus points.

Surroundings : 🔲 ♡♡ ▲
Leisure activities : ▼ ✕ 🔲 ☾nighttime ⚡
⚡ ✕ ☐ 🔲
Facilities : ⚡ ⚘ 🔲 ☐ ☐ 🔲 🔲 ☐ ☐
Nearby : 🐎 jet skis

Longitude : 3.26046
Latitude : 43.23386

Le Méditerranée

0467373429. www.camping-le-mediterranee.com

Address : route de Vendres (located 1.5km southwest, 200m from the beach)

Opening times :

4.5 ha (367 pitches)

Tariff : (2014 Price) 44.50€ ★★ ⇔ 🔲 (¼) (6A) – Extra per person 8€
Reservation fee 25€

Rental rates : (2014 Price) (from end April to beginning Sept.) ⚡ – 65 🔲 – 10 🏠 – 5 mobile homes (without sanitary facilities). Per night from 105 to 125€ – Per week from 310 to 960€ – Reservation fee 25€

The site is well shaded, with numerous pitches for tents and caravans.

Surroundings : ♡♡
Leisure activities : ▼ ✕ 🔲 ⚡ ☐
multi-sports ground
Facilities : ⚡ ⚘ 🔲 launderette ☐ ☐
refrigerators
Nearby : ☐ 🚲 🐎 🔲 🐎

Longitude : 3.26848
Latitude : 43.23592

Les Foulègues

0467373365. www.campinglesfoulegues.com

Address : at Grau-de-Vendres, avenue du Port (5km southwest, 400m from the beach)

Opening times : from mid April to end Sept.

5.3 ha (339 pitches)

Tariff : (2014 Price) 50€ ★★ ⇔ 🔲 (¼) (6A) – Extra per person 8.80€
Reservation fee 30€

Rental rates : (2014 Price) (from beginning May to mid Sept.) – 38 🔲. Per week from 315 to 990€ – Reservation fee 30€

A pleasant site with lots of shade and rather old chalet rental options.

Surroundings : 🔲 ♡♡
Leisure activities : ▼ ✕ 🔲 ☾nighttime ⚡
⚡ ✕ 🔲 ☐
Facilities : ⚡ ⚘ ☐ ☐ 🔲 🔲 ☐ ☐
Nearby : 🐎

Longitude : 3.24222
Latitude : 43.22575

VERNET-LES-BAINS

66820 – Michelin map **344** F7 – pop. 1 432 – alt. 650 – ⚕
▶ Paris 904 – Mont-Louis 36 – Perpignan 57 – Prades 11

L'Eau Vive

0468055414. www.leauvive-camping.com

Address : chemin St Saturnin (take exit towards Sahorre then continue after the bridge 1.3km along the av. St-Saturnin to the right, near the Cady river)

Opening times : from mid April to beginning Oct.

2 ha (90 pitches)

Tariff : (2014 Price) 26.50€ ★★ ⇔ 🔲 (¼) (10A) – Extra per person 5€
Reservation fee 15€

Rental rates : (2014 Price) (from mid April to beginning Oct.) ⚡ (1 chalet) – 8 🔲 – 9 🏠. Per night from 46 to 136€ – Per week from 250 to 740€ – Reservation fee 15€

In a pleasant location.

Surroundings : ⚡ ◁♡
Leisure activities : ▼ ✕ jacuzzi ⚡ ☐
Facilities : ⚡ ⚘ ☐ ☐ 🔲 🔲 🔲

Longitude : 2.38342
Latitude : 42.5527

VERS-PONT-DU-GARD

30210 – Michelin map **339** M5 – pop. 1 696 – alt. 40
▶ Paris 698 – Montpellier 81 – Nîmes 26 – Avignon 27

FranceLoc Gorges du Gardon

0466228181. www.franceloc.fr

Address : 762 chemin Barque-Vieille (to the south, D 981 and D 5; beside the Gardon river)

4 ha (200 pitches)

Rentals : ⚡ (1 mobile home) – 104 🔲 – 4 🏠.

The site has numerous mobile homes and pitches leading down to the banks of the river.

Surroundings : ⚡ 🔲 ♡♡
Leisure activities : ▼ ✕ ⚡ ⚡ ☐ 🔲
🔲 ☐
Facilities : ⚡ ⚘ 🔲 ☐ 🔲 launderette ☐
refrigerators

Longitude : 4.51766
Latitude : 43.95599

VIAS-PLAGE

34450 – Michelin map **339** F9 – pop. 5 386 – alt. 10
▶ Paris 752 – Agde 5 – Béziers 19 – Narbonne 46

Yelloh! Village Club Farret

0467216445. www.camping-farret.com

Address : chemin des Rosses (beside the beach)

Opening times : from beginning April to end Sept.

7 ha (437 pitches)

Tariff : 58€ ★★ ⇔ 🔲 (¼) (10A) – Extra per person 9€

Rental rates : (from beginning April to end Sept.) ⚡ – 326 🔲 – 64 🏠 – 19 studios – 4 apartments. Per night from 30 to 309€– Per week from 210 to 2,163€

🚐 borne

A pretty landscaped mobile home village with different themes: pirates, the Pacific ... and very good sanitary facilities.

Surroundings : ⚡ 🔲 ♡♡ ▲
Leisure activities : ▼ ✕ 🔲 ☐ ⚡ ⚡ ⚡ 🚲
⚡ ☐ ⚡ entertainment room
Facilities : ⚡ ⚘ 🔲 ☐ ☐ 🔲 ⚡ launderette
🔲 ☐
Nearby : ⚡ 🐎

Longitude : 3.419
Latitude : 43.2911

⚑ Sunêlia Domaine de la Dragonnière

Domaine de la Dragonnière

℘ 04 67 01 03 10. www.dragonniere.com (limited spaces for one-night stay)

Address : road RD 612 (5km west, follow the signs for Béziers)

Opening times : from end March to beginning Nov.

30 ha (980 pitches)

Tariff : 69€ ♦♦ ⊯ 🗉 [⚡] (10A) – Extra per person 13€ – Reservation fee 30€

Rental rates : (2014 Price) (from end March to beginning Nov.) – 322 🚐 – 364 ⛺ – 2 tent lodges. Per night from 43 to 309€– Per week from 301 to 2,163€ – Reservation fee 30€

A wide range of accommodation options at different levels of comfort, with an upmarket spa centre and an Olympic-size swimming pool (50m).

Surroundings : 🖵 ♀
Leisure activities : ♀ ✗ 🎦 ⑤ ✦ 🌊 ≈ hammam, jacuzzi ⚴ 🚴 ⚿ 🏊 ⚖ multi-sports ground, spa centre
Facilities : 🚹 ⊶ ▥ – 38 individual sanitary facilities (⌂ ⊜ 🚽 wc) ⚄ ⚡ ⌂ launderette 🛒 🚮 🛒

| | GPS | Longitude : 3.36335 |
| | | Latitude : 43.3126 |

⚑ Le Napoléon ♦♦

℘ 04 67 01 07 80. www.camping-napoleon.fr

Address : 1171 avenue de la Méditerranée (250m from the beach)

Opening times : from beginning April to end Sept.

3 ha (239 pitches)

Tariff : 20€ ♦♦ ⊯ 🗉 [⚡] (10A) – Extra per person 6€ – Reservation fee 28€

Rental rates : (from beginning April to end Sept.) 🚹 (1 mobile home) – 77 🚐 – 39 ⛺ – 2 🛏 – 11 apartments – 5 canvas bungalows. Per night from 34 to 134€ – Per week from 238 to 1,288€ – Reservation fee 28€

🚐 borne 18€ – ⚡22€

Surroundings : 🖵 ♀♀
Leisure activities : ♀ ✗ 🎦 ⑤ ✦ 🌊 ≈ hammam ⚴ 🚴 ⚖ multi-sports ground
Facilities : 🚹 ⊶ ⚄ ⌂ launderette 🛒 🚮 refrigerated food storage facilities
Nearby : disco, sports trail

| | GPS | Longitude : 3.41661 |
| | | Latitude : 43.29179 |

⚑ Méditerranée-Plage

℘ 04 67 90 99 07. www.mediterranee-plage.com

Address : Côte Ouest (6km southwest along the D 137e2)

Opening times : from end March to end Sept.

9.6 ha (490 pitches)

Tariff : (2014 Price) 46€ ♦♦ ⊯ 🗉 [⚡] (6A) – Extra per person 8.50€ Reservation fee 25€

Rental rates : (2014 Price) (from end March to end Sept.) 🚹 (1 mobile home) – 250 🚐. Per week from 220 to 1,375€ – Reservation fee 25€

🚐 borne

A pleasant setting beside the sea with high-quality facilities.

Surroundings : 🐾 🖵 ♀♀ ⚠
Leisure activities : ♀ ✗ 🎦 ⑤ ✦ 🌊 🚴 ⚿ ⌂ 🏊 ⚖ farm or petting farm, multi-sports ground
Facilities : 🚹 ⊶ ⚄ ⌂ launderette 🛒 🚮

| | GPS | Longitude : 3.37106 |
| | | Latitude : 43.28202 |

⚑ Les Flots Bleus ♦♦

℘ 04 67 21 64 80. www.camping-flotsbleus.com

Address : Côte Ouest (to the southwest; beside beach)

Opening times : from end April to end Sept.

5 ha (298 pitches)

Tariff : (2014 Price) 36€ ♦♦ ⊯ 🗉 [⚡] (8A) – Extra per person 7€ – Reservation fee 22€

Rental rates : (2014 Price) Permanent ⚙ – 127 🚐 – 22 ⛺ – 5 apartments. Per night from 28 to 131€ – Per week from 190 to 915€ – Reservation fee 22€

🚐 borne 5€

Jointly run with the France Floride campsite next door.

Surroundings : 🖵 ♀♀
Leisure activities : ♀ ✗ 🎦 ⑤ nighttime ✦ ⚴ 🏊 ⚖ multi-sports ground
Facilities : 🚹 ⊶ ⚄ ⌂ launderette 🛒 🚮

| | GPS | Longitude : 3.4055 |
| | | Latitude : 43.29 |

⚑ Cap Soleil ♦♦

℘ 04 67 21 64 77. www.capsoleil.fr – limited spaces for one-night stay

Address : chemin de la Grande Cosse (Côte Ouest, 600m from the beach)

Opening times : from mid April to end Sept.

4.5 ha (288 pitches) flat, grassy

Tariff : 45€ ♦♦ ⊯ 🗉 [⚡] (10A) – Extra per person 13€ – Reservation fee 25€

Rental rates : (from mid April to end Sept.) 🚹 (1 mobile home) – 100 🚐. Per night from 42 to 157€ – Per week from 179 to 1,450€ – Reservation fee 25€

🚐 borne – 40 🗉 27.50€

The covered swimming pool (uncovered in summer) is reserved for naturists in July and August.

Surroundings : 🖵 ♀♀
Leisure activities : ♀ ✗ 🎦 ⑤ ✦ ⚴ 🚴 ⚿ 🖼 (open air in season) 🏊 ⚖ multi-sports ground
Facilities : 🚹 ⊶ ⚄ – 8 individual sanitary facilities (⌂ ⊜ wc) ⚄ ⚡ ⌂ launderette 🛒 🚮 refrigerators
Nearby : 🐎 🏇

| | GPS | Longitude : 3.39953 |
| | | Latitude : 43.29262 |

These symbols are used for a campsite that is exceptional in its category:

⚑⚑⚑ ... ⚑ *Particularly pleasant setting, quality and range of services available*

🐾 🐾 *Tranquil, isolated site – quiet site, particularly at night*

≪ ≪ *Exceptional view – interesting or panoramic view*

⚠ Californie Plage ⚲

📞 04 67 21 64 69. www.californie-plage.fr

Address : chemin du Trou de Ragout (Côte Ouest, to the southwest along the D 137e and take road to the left; beside the sea)

Opening times : from beginning April to end Sept.

5.8 ha (371 pitches)

Tariff : 45 € ✶✶ 🚐 🔲 (10A) –Extra per person 8.75 € – Reservation fee 25 €

Rental rates : (from beginning April to end Sept.) ✂ – 120 🛏. Per night from 30 to 170 € – Per week from 210 to 1,190 € – Reservation fee 25 €

There's free admission to the water park at the Cap-Soleil campsite (opposite, at 100m).

Surroundings : 🌲 ⛰⛰ ⛰	
Leisure activities : 🍴✗ 🎮 🎣 🏃 🚣 🚴 🏊 multi-sports ground	**G P S** Longitude : 3.39843 Latitude : 43.29051
Facilities : 🚿 🔑 🛁 ⛺ 🍴 launderette 🔌 🚰 refrigerators	
Nearby : ✂ 🏊 🏄	

⚠ L'Air Marin ⚲

📞 04 67 21 64 90. www.camping-air-marin.fr

Address : Côte Est, behind the football pitch

Opening times : from mid April to mid Sept.

5.5 ha (305 pitches)

Tariff : (2014 Price) 42 € ✶✶ 🚐 🔲 (6A) – Extra per person 8 € – Reservation fee 25 €

Rental rates : (2014 Price) (from mid April to mid Sept.) – 70 🛏. Per week from 260 to 1,260 € – Reservation fee 25 €

A linear site in the shade of poplars with an attractive swimming area, very close to the Canal du Midi.

Surroundings : 🌲 ⛰⛰	
Leisure activities : 🍴✗ 🎮 🎣 nighttime 🎪 🚣 ✂ 🏊 boats to hire 🚴 multi-sports ground	**G P S** Longitude : 3.42129 Latitude : 43.30076
Facilities : 🚿 🔑 🚗 ⛺ 🍴 launderette 🔌 🚰	
Nearby : 🎡 amusement park	

⚠ Tohapi Le Petit Mousse ⚲

(rental of mobile homes only)

📞 04 67 90 99 04. www.vacances-directes.com

Address : route de la Grande Cosse

Opening times : from end April to end Sept.

5.2 ha (365 pitches)

Rental rates : – 320 🛏 – 6 🏠 – 28 tent lodges. Per night from 31 to 180 € – Per week from 217 to 1,260 € – Reservation fee 10 €

A site that is virtually 'on top of the water', with some rental accommodation facing the sea.

Surroundings : 🌊 ⛰⛰ ⛰	
Leisure activities : 🍴✗ 🎮 🎣 🏃 🚣 🏊 🏄	**G P S** Longitude : 3.40147 Latitude : 43.28994
Facilities : 🔑 🛁 🍴 launderette 🔌 🚰	

Routes nationales are main roads and their identifying numbers begin with N or RN. Routes départementales are generally quieter roads and begin with D or DN.

⚠ Hélios

📞 04 67 21 63 66. www.camping-helios.com

Address : avenue des Pêcheurs (near the Libron, 250m from the beach)

Opening times : from end April to end Sept.

2.5 ha (215 pitches)

Tariff : (2014 Price) 32 € ✶✶ 🚐 🔲 (6A) – Extra per person 5 € – Reservation fee 10 €

Rental rates : (2014 Price) (from end April to end Sept.) – 30 🛏 – 6 🏠. Per night from 30 to 114 € – Per week from 191 to 793 € Reservation fee 20 €

Beside the Libron river, plenty of shade, with an attractive indoor spa area.

Surroundings : 🌊 ⛰⛰	
Leisure activities : 🍴✗ 🎮 🔥 hammam, jacuzzi 🚣 spa centre	**G P S** Longitude : 3.40764 Latitude : 43.29115
Facilities : 🚿 🔑 🛁 🍴 🔳 🔌 🚰	

LE VIGAN

30120 – Michelin map **339** G5 – pop. 3 959 – alt. 221

▶ Paris 707 – Alès 66 – Lodève 50 – Mende 108

⚠ Le Val de l'Arre

📞 04 67 81 02 77. www.valdelarre.com

Address : Roudoulouse, route du Pont de la Croix (2.5km east along the D 999, follow the rte de Ganges and take road to the right; beside the Arre)

Opening times : from beginning April to end Sept.

4 ha (173 pitches) terraced, relatively flat, flat, grassy

Tariff : 28 € ✶✶ 🚐 🔲 (10A) – Extra per person 7.50 € – Reservation fee 15 €

Rental rates : (from beginning April to end Sept.) ✂ – 35 🛏 – 1 gîte. Per night from 40 to 80 € – Per week from 214 to 815 € Reservation fee 15 €

🚐 borne 3.50 € – 🔋 11 €

Divided into two separate sections on either side of the road; some pitches for tents and caravans with lots of shade, near the river.

Surroundings : ⛰⛰	
Leisure activities : 🎮 🚣 🏊 🎣 🚣	**G P S** Longitude : 3.63751 Latitude : 43.99128
Facilities : 🚿 🔑 ⛺ 🍴 launderette 🔌 🚰	

LES VIGNES

48210 – Michelin map **330** H9 – pop. 103 – alt. 410

▶ Paris 615 – Mende 52 – Meyrueis 33 – Le Rozier 12

⚠ Beldoire

📞 04 66 48 82 79. www.camping-beldoire.com

Address : Les Vignes (south on the D 907)

Opening times : from mid May to mid Sept.

5 ha (142 pitches) terraced, flat, grassy, stony

Tariff : 27 € ✶✶ 🚐 🔲 (6A) – Extra per person 5.50 € – Reservation fee 14 €

Rental rates : (from mid April to end Sept.) – 1 caravan – 9 🛏 – 15 canvas bungalows. Per night from 38 to 50 € – Per week from 289 to 649 € – Reservation fee 14 €

Surroundings : ⛰⛰ ⛰	
Facilities : 🚿 🔑 🍴	**G P S** Longitude : 3.23445 Latitude : 44.28717

⚠ Village Vacances Castel de la Peyre

(rental of small houses only)

𝒫 0466484848. www.lozere-resa.com

Address : located 1km south along the D 16

Opening times : Permanent

1 ha

Rental rates : (2014 Price) – 10 gîtes. Per week from 185 to 726€ Reservation fee 20€

A pretty village of small houses, with a view over the Vallée du Tarn.

Surroundings : ⌂ ≤
Leisure activities : 🎮 🛶
Facilities : ♿ 🏛 ⌂ 🖼

G P S Longitude : 3.2283
Latitude : 44.27292

⚠ La Blaquière

𝒫 0466485493. www.campinggorgesdutarn.fr

Address : 6km northeast along the D 907bis; beside the Tarn river

Opening times : from mid April to mid Sept.

1 ha (79 pitches)

Tariff : (2014 Price) 22€ 🚹🚹 ⛺ ▣ (6A) – Extra per person 5.50€ – Reservation fee 13€

Rental rates : (2014 Price) (from mid April to mid Sept.) 🦢 – 10 🚐 – 3 tent lodges. Per night from 40 to 70€ – Per week from 250 to 650€ – Reservation fee 13€

Below the road, beside the Tarn river, well-shaded pitches.

Surroundings : 🏕 🟡🟡 ⛰
Leisure activities : 🎮 🛶 🎣
Facilities : ♿ 🔑 ⌂ 🖼 🚿 ⛲

G P S Longitude : 3.2685
Latitude : 44.3042

The prices listed were supplied by the campsite owners in 2014 (if prices were not available, those from the previous year are given). The fees should be regarded as basic charges and may fluctuate with inflation.

VILLEFORT

48800 – Michelin map **330** L8 – pop. 618 – alt. 600
▶ Paris 616 – Alès 52 – Aubenas 61 – Florac 63

⚠ La Palhère

𝒫 0466468063. www.campinglapalhere.com – alt. 750

Address : route du Mas de la Barque (4km southwest along the D 66; beside rapids)

Opening times : Permanent

1.8 ha (45 pitches)

Tariff : (2014 Price) 16€ 🚹🚹 ⛺ ▣ (6A) – Extra per person 5€

Rental rates : (2014 Price) (from mid April to mid Nov.) – 3 caravans – 3 🚐 – 4 🏠 – 1 yurt – 2 tipis. Per night from 30 to 50€ – Per week from 180 to 630€

🚐 12 ▣ 17€

Beside a pretty mountain stream with varied rental options.

Surroundings : 🏕 ≤ 🟡🟡
Leisure activities : ✕ 🛶 🎮 🎣
Facilities : 🔑 ♿ ⌂ 🚿 ⛲ 🖼 ⛲

G P S Longitude : 3.91026
Latitude : 44.41862

⚠ Morangiés - Le Lac

𝒫 0466468127. www.camping-lac-cevennes.com – limited spaces for one-night stay

Address : at Morangiés (3.4km north along the D 901, follow the signs for Mende, take D 906, follow the signs for Prévenchère and take turning to the left down the road for Pourcharesses)

Opening times : from beginning May to end Sept.

4 ha (75 pitches)

Tariff : (2014 Price) 16.20€ 🚹🚹 ⛺ ▣ (6A) – Extra per person 4.80€

Rental rates : (2014 Price) Permanent – 32 🚐 – 19 🏠. Per night from 50 to 80€ – Per week from 150 to 770€

🚐 2 ▣ 7€ – ⛽ 9€

An attractive location beside the lake; some of the infrastructure and rental options are a little old. 'Semi-detached' gîtes.

Surroundings : 🏕 ≤ 🛶 🟡🟡
Leisure activities : 🎮 ⛵ 🛶 🎣 🖼
Facilities : ♿ 🔑 ⌂ 🚿 ⛲ 🖼
Nearby : ≈ 🦢 🛥 ⚓

G P S Longitude : 3.92812
Latitude : 44.46183

Key to rentals symbols:

12 🚐 *Number of mobile homes*
20 🏠 *Number of chalets*
6 ⊨ *Number of rooms to rent*
Per night
30–50€ *Minimum/maximum rate per night*
Per week
300–1,000€ *Minimum/maximum rate per week*

VILLEGLY

11600 – Michelin map **344** F3 – pop. 1 020 – alt. 130
▶ Paris 778 – Lézignan-Corbières 36 – Mazamet 46 – Carcassonne 14

⚠ Sites et Paysages Moulin de Ste-Anne

𝒫 0468722080. www.moulindesainteanne.com

Address : 2 chemin de Sainte-Anne (take the eastern exit along the D 435, follow the signs for Villarzel)

Opening times : from beginning April to end Oct.

1.6 ha (60 pitches) terraced, relatively flat, flat, grassy

Tariff : (2014 Price) 28.10€ 🚹🚹 ⛺ ▣ (10A) – Extra per person 5.60€ – Reservation fee 17€

Rental rates : (2014 Price) (from beginning April to end Oct.) ♿ (1 chalet) – 15 🏠 – 2 tent lodges. Per night from 50 to 135€ – Per week from 260 to 750€ – Reservation fee 17€

🚐 borne 6€ – ⛽ 16€

Attractive pitches and good-quality rental options, on shaded terraces.

Surroundings : 🟡🟡
Leisure activities : ♟ ✕ 🎮 🛶 🎣 multi-sports ground
Facilities : ♿ 🔑 🏛 ⌂ 🚿 ⛲ 🖼 ⛲
Nearby : ✕

G P S Longitude : 2.44347
Latitude : 43.28374

*For more information on visiting particular towns or regions, consult the relevant regional **MICHELIN Green Guide**. We also recommend you use the appropriate Michelin regional map to locate your selected campsite, to calculate distances and to work out the best route.*

VILLENEUVE-LÈS-AVIGNON

30400 – Michelin map **339** N5 – pop. 12 463 – alt. 23
▶ Paris 678 – Avignon 8 – Nîmes 46 – Orange 28

⟁ Campéole L'Ile des Papes ♠♠

⌖ 04 90 15 15 90. www.avignon-camping.com

Address : Barrage de Villeneuve (4.5km northeast along the D 980, follow the signs for Roquemaure and take D 780 to the right, between the Rhône and the canal)

Opening times : from end March to beginning Nov.

20 ha (210 pitches)

Tariff : (2014 Price) 32.40€ ♣♣ ⟵ ▣ ⌑ (10A) – Extra per person 5.30€

Rental rates : (2014 Price) (from end March to beginning Nov.) – 119 ⟐ – 64 canvas bungalows. Per night from 26 to 155€ – Per week from 182 to 1,085€

⟐ borne

A spacious site, partially shaded, with a pretty play and paddling pool area.

Surroundings : ⟳ ≺ ▱ ℘℘
Leisure activities : ⛫ ✗ ▱ ☺nighttime ☀
⚓⟳ ⛵ ⅀ ⟍ multi-sports ground
Facilities : ⅖ ⌀▭ Ⓒ⊞ ⌀⛛ launderette
⚐⚑

GPS Longitude : 4.81826
Latitude : 43.99383

⟁ Municipal de la Laune

⌖ 04 90 25 76 06. www.camping-villeneuvelezavignon.com

Address : chemin Saint Honore (to the northeast, access via the D 980, near the stadium and swimming pools)

Opening times : from end March to mid Oct.

2.3 ha (126 pitches)

Tariff : 25€ ♣♣ ⟵ ▣ ⌑ (6A) – Extra per person 6€ – Reservation fee 7.50€

Rental rates : (from end March to mid Oct.) – 4 ⟐ – 4 canvas bungalows. Per night from 40 to 252€ – Per week from 60 to 560€ – Reservation fee 25€

Set among the town's sporting facilities, a well-shaded site with modest sanitary facilities.

Surroundings : ▱ ℘℘
Leisure activities : ▱ ⚓⟳
Facilities : ⅖ ⌀▭ ⌀⛛ ▣
Nearby : ✗ ▱ ⅀

GPS Longitude : 4.79711
Latitude : 43.96331

The guide covers all 22 regions of France – see the map and list of regions on pages 4–5.

LIMOUSIN

N. Thibaut / Photononstop

Life in Limousin is led at its own easy pace: weary Parisians wanting to reconnect with nature come to enjoy the joys of country life, inhale the bracing air of its high plateaus and wander through its woodlands in search of wild mushrooms and chestnuts. The region boasts hills and gorges and lush green meadows. The sight of cattle grazing happily or lambs frolicking in a spring meadow will rejuvenate the spirits of any jaded city dweller. Limousin is home to ancient village churches as well as imposing abbey churches and fortresses. In autumn, the forests are swathed in rich colours, forming a perfect backdrop to the granite and sandstone of the peaceful towns and villages, where ancestral crafts, such as Limoges enamels and porcelain and Aubusson tapestries, still blend the traditional with the best of the new. The food is wholesome – savoury bacon soup, Limousin stew and, as any proud local will tell you, the most tender, succulent beef in the world.

AIXE-SUR-VIENNE

87700 – Michelin map **325** D6 – pop. 5 464 – alt. 204
▶ Paris 400 – Châlus 21 – Confolens 60 – Limoges 14

⚠ Municipal les Grèves

✆ 05 55 70 12 98. www.mairie-aixesurvienne.fr

Address : rue Jean-Claude Papon (beside the Vienne river)

Opening times : from beginning June to end Sept.

3 ha (80 pitches) flat, grassy

Tariff : 15.20€ ✶✶ ⇔ 🔲 [⚡] (10A) – Extra per person 4€

Rental rates : (from beginning April to end Oct.) ⅙ (1 mobile home) – 3 🚐. Per night from 50€ – Per week from 400 to 420€

🚐 borne 3€

Near the town centre, with some pitches beside the Vienne river.

Surroundings : 🏊 ♨♨		
Leisure activities : 🍷 🏠 ⛵ 🎣 ♨		**G** Longitude : 1.1149
Facilities : ⅙ ⛽ 🍴 📷		**P** Latitude : 45.8069
Nearby : 🔳		**S**

*The classification (1 to 5 tents, **black** or red) that we award to selected sites in this guide is our own system. It should not be confused with the classification (1 to 5 stars) of official organisations.*

ARGENTAT

19400 – Michelin map **329** M5 – pop. 3 052 – alt. 183
▶ Paris 503 – Aurillac 54 – Brive-la-Gaillarde 45 – Mauriac 49

⚠⚠⚠ Le Gibanel

✆ 05 55 28 10 11. www.camping-gibanel.com

Address : 4.5km northeast along the D 18, follow the signs for Égletons then take the road to the right

Opening times : from beginning June to end Aug.

60 ha/8.5 for camping (250 pitches)

Tariff : (2014 Price) 30.50€ ✶✶ ⇔ 🔲 [⚡] (10A) – Extra per person 6€ Reservation fee 10€

Rental rates : (2014 Price) (from beginning June to end Aug.) – 10 🚐 – 2 apartments. Per week from 340 to 800€ – Reservation fee 10€

In the grounds of a 16th-century château, beside a lake.

Surroundings : 🏊 ⚓ ♨♨ ⛰		
Leisure activities : 🍷 🏠 🌞daytime ⛵ 🎣 ♨ ⚡ multi-sports ground		**G** Longitude : 1.95852
Facilities : ⅙ ⛽ 🍴 launderette 🔲 🚰		**P** Latitude : 45.1107
		S

⚠⚠ Sunêlia Au Soleil d'Oc 👥

✆ 05 55 28 84 84. www.campingsoleildoc.com

Address : Monceaux-sur-Dordogne (4.5km southwest along the D 12, follow the signs for Beaulieu then take the D 12e, following signs for Vergnolles and take road to the left after the bridge; beside the Dordogne river)

Opening times : from mid April to end Oct.

4 ha (120 pitches)

Tariff : 24.80€ ✶✶ ⇔ 🔲 [⚡] (6A) – Extra per person 6.40€

Rental rates : (from mid April to end Oct.) – 30 🚐 – 8 🏠 – 3 canvas bungalows – 2 tent lodges. Per night from 38 to 112€ – Per week from 150 to 784 €– Reservation fee 18€

🚐 borne – 🔌 [⚡]12€

Some very shady pitches, some of which are beside the Dordogne river.

Surroundings : 🏊 🛶 ♨♨ ⛰		
Leisure activities : 🍷 ✕ 🏠 🎮 🏃 ⛵ 🔐 🎣 🏊		**G** Longitude : 1.91836
Facilities : ⛽ 📷 🔲 🍴 launderette 🚰		**P** Latitude : 45.07618
		S

⚠⚠⚠ Le Vaurette 👥

✆ 05 55 28 09 67. www.vaurette.com

Address : Vaurette (9km southwest along the D 12, follow the signs for Beaulieu; beside the Dordogne river)

Opening times : from beginning May to end Sept.

4 ha (120 pitches)

Tariff : (2014 Price) 31.80€ ✶✶ ⇔ 🔲 [⚡] (6A) – Extra per person 6.40€ Reservation fee 15€

Rental rates : (from mid May to end Sept.) 🚲 – 2 🚐. Per week from 340 to 750€ – Reservation fee 15€

Situated on the Dordogne river, with some pitches by the water.

Surroundings : 🏊 ♨♨ ⛰		
Leisure activities : 🍷 ✕ 🏠 🎮daytime 🏃 ⛵ 🔐 🎣 🚣 entertainment room		**G** Longitude : 1.8825
Facilities : ⅙ ⛽ 🍴 launderette 🚰		**P** Latitude : 45.04568
		S

AUBAZINE

19190 – Michelin map **329** L4 – pop. 852 – alt. 345
▶ Paris 480 – Aurillac 86 – Brive-la-Gaillarde 14 – St-Céré 50

⚠⚠⚠ Campéole Le Coiroux 👥

✆ 05 55 27 21 96. www.camping-coiroux.com

Address : Coiroux tourist zone (5km east along the D 48, follow the signs for Le Chastang, not far from a small lake and a leisure park)

Opening times : from beginning May to end Sept.

165 ha/6 for camping (174 pitches) relatively flat, flat, grassy, wood

Tariff : (2014 Price) 27.50€ ✶✶ ⇔ 🔲 [⚡] (10A) – Extra per person 6.90€ – Reservation fee 25€

Rental rates : (2014 Price) (from mid April to end Sept.) ⅙ (2 mobile homes) – 47 🚐 – 10 🏠 – 27 canvas bungalows. Per night from 21 to 145€ – Per week from 147 to 1,015€ – Reservation fee 25€

🚐 borne 3€

In a spacious, green setting, large pitches and a well-appointed activity centre.

Surroundings : 🏊 🛶 ♨♨		
Leisure activities : 🍷 ✕ 🏠 🎮 🏃 ⛵ 🚣 multi-sports ground		**G** Longitude : 1.70739
Facilities : ⅙ ⛽ 📷 🍴 launderette 🔲 🚰		**P** Latitude : 45.18611
Nearby : 🏊 🎣 (beach) 🎣 forest trail, climbing wall, golf (18 holes)		**S**

Key to rentals symbols:

12 🚐	*Number of mobile homes*
20 🏠	*Number of chalets*
6 🛏	*Number of rooms to rent*
Per night 30–50€	*Minimum/maximum rate per night*
Per week 300–1,000€	*Minimum/maximum rate per week*

AURIAC

19220 – Michelin map **329** N4 – pop. 226 – alt. 608
▶ Paris 517 – Argentat 27 – Égletons 33 – Mauriac 23

⚠ Municipal

✆ 05 55 28 23 02. www.auriac.fr

Address : in the village (take the southeastern exit along the D 65, follow the signs for St-Privat, near a lake and a wooded park)

Opening times : from mid April to end Oct.

1.7 ha (63 pitches) open site

Tariff : (2014 Price) ✝ 3.95 € – ⇌ 2 € 🅴 2 € – 🔌 (16A) 3.95 €

Rental rates : (2014 Price) Permanent – 8 🛆. Per night from 55 to 65 € – Per week from 230 to 405 €

🚐 borne – ⛽🔌 9 €

There's a view of the lake from some pitches.

Surroundings : 🏞 ⛲ ⛱ ♨♨ ⚠ Leisure activities : 🛶 🏄 Facilities : ⚪⛟ (mid-July-mid-Aug) 🚿 🍴 🔲 Nearby : ✂ 🎣 🏊 (beach) 🛶 pedalos	**GPS** Longitude : 2.14772 Latitude : 45.20206

This guide is updated regularly, so buy your new copy every year!

BEAULIEU-SUR-DORDOGNE

19120 – Michelin map **329** M6 – pop. 1 283 – alt. 142
▶ Paris 513 – Aurillac 65 – Brive-la-Gaillarde 44 – Figeac 56

⚠⚠⚠ Flower Les Îles 👤👤

✆ 05 55 91 02 65. www.campingdesiles.com

Address : boulevard Rodolphe de Turenne (east of the town centre)

Opening times : from end April to end Sept.

7 ha (185 pitches) flat, grassy

Tariff : 30.50 € ✝✝ ⇌ 🅴 🔌 (10A) – Extra per person 7.70 € – Reservation fee 17 €

Rental rates : (from end April to end Sept.) – 24 🛆 – 11 canvas bungalows – 4 tent lodges – 2 tent lodges on stilts (with sanitary facilities). Per night from 45 to 138 € – Per week from 225 to 966 € – Reservation fee 17 €

🚐 borne

A picturesque site and setting on an island in the Dordogne river.

Surroundings : 🏞 ♨♨ ⚠ Leisure activities : 🍴 ✗ 🛶 🏑 🏄 🛶 🏊 🚣 Facilities : ⚠ ⛟ ▥ 🚿 🍴 launderette 🛒 Nearby : ✂	**GPS** Longitude : 1.84049 Latitude : 44.97968

BEYNAT

19190 – Michelin map **329** L5 – pop. 1 253 – alt. 420
▶ Paris 496 – Argentat 47 – Beaulieu-sur-Dordogne 23 – Brive-la-Gaillarde 21

⚠⚠⚠ Village Vacances Chalets en France Les Hameaux de Miel

(rental of chalets only)

✆ 05 55 84 34 48. www.chalets-en-france.com

Address : Miel, off the D921, 1.3km from the Etang de Miel (lake)

Opening times : Permanent

12 ha

Rental rates : ⚠ (3 chalets) – 98 🛆. Per week from 371 to 1,011 €
Reservation fee 13 €

Surroundings : 🏞 ⛱ ♀ Leisure activities : 🍴 🛶 ⛳ 🏃 🏄 🏊 🚣 multi-sports ground Facilities : ⚪⛟ 🍴 launderette Nearby : ✂ 🎣 🏊 🛶 pedalos	**GPS** Longitude : 1.76141 Latitude : 45.12932

⚠⚠⚠ Club Airotel Le Lac de Miel

✆ 05 55 85 50 66. www.camping-miel.com

Address : 4km east along the N 121, follow the signs for Argentat; beside a small lake

Opening times : from mid May to end Aug.

50 ha/9 for camping (140 pitches)

Tariff : 23.80 € ✝✝ ⇌ 🅴 🔌 (6A) – Extra per person 6.40 €

Rental rates : (from mid May to end Aug.) – 2 caravans – 40 🛆 – 6 🛆 – 3 canvas bungalows. Per night from 38 to 112 € – Per week from 150 to 784 € – Reservation fee 18 €

🚐 borne 12 € – ⛽🔌 12 €

Surroundings : 🏞 ⛱ ♀ ⚠ Leisure activities : 🍴 ✗ 🛶 🏄 ✂ 🎣 (open air in season) 🛶 Facilities : ⚠ ⛟ (July-Aug.) 🚿 🍴 🔲 Nearby : 🏊 (beach) pedalos	**GPS** Longitude : 1.77103 Latitude : 45.13332

BONNAC-LA-CÔTE

87270 – Michelin map **325** E5 – pop. 1 374 – alt. 428
▶ Paris 382 – Guéret 78 – Limoges 16 – Tulle 101

⚠⚠⚠ Les Castels Le Château de Leychoisier

Les Castels Le Château de Leychoisier

✆ 05 55 39 93 43. www.leychoisier.com

Address : 1km along the D 97, rte du 8 mai 1945

Opening times : from mid April to mid Sept.

47 ha/4 for camping (80 pitches) relatively flat, flat, grassy

Tariff : 34 € ✝✝ ⇌ 🅴 🔌 (10A) – Extra per person 9.50 €

Rental rates : (from mid April to mid Sept.) ✂ – 2 🛆. Per week from 400 to 600 €

🚐 borne

Situated in the grounds of the château.

Surroundings : 🏞 ♨♨ Leisure activities : 🍴 ✗ 🛶 🛶 Facilities : ⚠ ⛟ 🗑 ▥ 🚿 🛒 ⛟ 🍴 launderette 🛒	**GPS** Longitude : 1.28973 Latitude : 45.93337

To visit a town or region, use the MICHELIN Green Guides.

LE BOURG-D'HEM

23220 – Michelin map **325** H3 – pop. 225 – alt. 320
▶ Paris 333 – Aigurande 20 – Le Grand-Bourg 28 – Guéret 21

⚠ Municipal

✆ 05 55 62 84 36. www.paysdunois.fr

Address : to the west along the D 48, follow the signs for Bussière-Dunoise and take the road to the right

0.33 ha (36 pitches) open site

Basic sanitary facilities, but a pleasant site where the Creuse river broadens out into a lake.

Surroundings : 🐾 ⌂ ♨♨ ⚱
Leisure activities : 🐾
Facilities : ⅜ ⚲
Nearby : 🍴 ⚤ pedalos

G P S Longitude : 1.82412
Latitude : 46.29752

BOUSSAC-BOURG

23600 – Michelin map **325** K2 – pop. 787 – alt. 423
▶ Paris 334 – Aubusson 52 – La Châtre 37 – Guéret 43

⛰ Les Castels Le Château de Poinsouze ⛺⚐

𝒸 05 55 65 02 21. www.camping-de-poinsouze.com ✄ (from mid July to mid Aug.)

Address : route de La Châtre (2.8km north along the D 917)

Opening times : from mid May to mid Sept.

150 ha/22 for camping (145 pitches) relatively flat

Tariff : 28€ ⚤⚤ ⇔ 🔲 ⚡ (20A) – Extra per person 6€ – Reservation fee 15€

Rental rates : (from mid May to mid Sept.) ✄ – 2 caravans – 25 ⌸ – 2 ⌂ – 2 gîtes. Per night from 60 to 150€ – Per week from 220 to 700€ – Reservation fee 15€

⛽ borne – 15 🔲 12€ – ⛴12€

A spacious site laid out around a 16th-century château and its outbuildings, in a green setting with lots of flowers.

Surroundings : 🐾 ⩽ ⌂ ⚲
Leisure activities : 🍴 ✕ 🛶 ☀ ⚤ ⚤⚤ 🚴 🏊
🏊⚲ pedalos, farm or petting farm 🦋
Facilities : ⅜ ⚲⚲ ⚤ ⚲ ☂ ⚲ 🍴 launderette 🏊
⚲

G P S Longitude : 2.20472
Latitude : 46.3725

BUJALEUF

87460 – Michelin map **325** G6 – pop. 881 – alt. 380
▶ Paris 423 – Bourganeuf 28 – Eymoutiers 14 – Limoges 35

⛰ Municipal du Lac

𝒸 05 55 69 50 04. www.bujaleuf.fr

Address : located 1km north along the D 16 and take the turning to the left, near the lake

Opening times : from mid May to end Sept.

2 ha (110 pitches) very uneven, terraced, flat, grassy

Tariff : (2014 Price) 11.50€ ⚤⚤ ⇔ 🔲 ⚡ (10A) – Extra per person 2.50€

Rental rates : (2014 Price) Permanent – 15 ⌸ – 10 gîtes. Per night from 76 to 110€ – Per week from 170 to 380€

⛽ borne

The site is laid out across broad terraces overlooking a lake.

Surroundings : 🐾 ⚲
Leisure activities : 🚴
Facilities : ⅜ ⚲ 🍴 launderette
Nearby : 🍴 ✕ ⚤ (beach) 🐾

G P S Longitude : 1.6297
Latitude : 45.80166

Using the traditional Michelin classification method, the guide provides you with an easy, speedy reference for assessing the category of each site: 1 to 5 tents (see page 10).

BUSSIÈRE-GALANT

87230 – Michelin map **325** D7 – pop. 1 394 – alt. 410
▶ Paris 422 – Aixe-sur-Vienne 23 – Châlus 6 – Limoges 36

⛰ Municipal Espace Hermeline

𝒸 05 55 78 86 12. www.espace-hermeline.com

Address : avenue du Plan-d'eau (1.7km southwest along the D 20, follow the signs for La Coquille and take the road to the right, near the stadium and 100m from a small lake)

1 ha (23 pitches) terraced, relatively flat, grassy

Rentals : 2 yurts.

The site is based at a leisure and activity park.

Surroundings : 🐾 ⩽ ⌂ ♨♨
Facilities : ⅜ ⚤ 🍴 ⚲
Nearby : ✕ ⚤ m ⚤ (beach) 🐾 forest trail,
zip wiring , bike-rail, miniature railway

G P S Longitude : 1.03086
Latitude : 45.61364

A chambre d'hôte is a guesthouse or B & B-style accommodation.

CAMPS

19430 – Michelin map **329** M6 – pop. 246 – alt. 520
▶ Paris 520 – Argentat 17 – Aurillac 45 – Bretenoux 18

⛰ Municipal la Châtaigneraie

𝒸 05 55 28 53 15. www.correze-camping.fr

Address : in the town (to the west along the D 13 and take the road to the right)

Opening times : from beginning May to end Sept.

1 ha (23 pitches) gravelled

Tariff : ⚤ 2.50€ ⇔ 🔲 3€ – ⚡ (10A) 2.50€

Rental rates : Permanent – 9 ⌂. Per night from 34 to 80€ – Per week from 202 to 476€

Good-quality wooden chalets, with shaded pitches above a small lake.

Surroundings : 🐾 ⩽ ♨♨
Leisure activities : 🍴 ✕ ⚤⚤
Facilities : ⅜ ⚤ ☂ 🍴 🏊
Nearby : ⚤ ⚤ (beach) 🐾

G P S Longitude : 1.98756
Latitude : 44.98368

LA CELLE-DUNOISE

23800 – Michelin map **325** H3 – pop. 607 – alt. 230
▶ Paris 329 – Aigurande 16 – Aubusson 63 – Dun-le-Palestel 11

⛰ Municipal de la Baignade

𝒸 05 55 89 10 77. www.lacelledunoise.fr

Address : east, along the D 48a, follow the signs for Le Bourg d'Hem, near the Creuse river (direct access)

1.4 ha (30 pitches)

Rentals : 3 ⌂.

The site is based around a pretty stone building that houses the reception and sanitary facilities. A small, steep path leads down to the river.

Surroundings : ♨♨
Leisure activities : ⛱ ✕
Facilities : ⅜ ⚲ launderette
Nearby : 🍴 ✕ ⚤ 🐾

G P S Longitude : 1.77583
Latitude : 46.30913

CHAMBERET

19370 – Michelin map **329** L2 – pop. 1 318 – alt. 450
▶ Paris 453 – Guéret 84 – Limoges 66 – Tulle 45

⛰ Village Vacances Les Chalets du Bois Combet

(rental of chalets only)

𝒫 05 55 98 96 83. www.chamberet.net – traditional camp. spaces also available

Address : 1.3km southwest along the D 132, follow the signs for Meilhards and take the road to the right, 100m from a small lake and a lake

Opening times : from beginning April to end Oct.

1 ha flat, grassy

Rental rates : (2014 Price) ♿ (1 chalet) ⓟ – 3 🚐 – 10 🏠.
Per night from 42 to 109€ – Per week from 206 to 534€

🚐 borne 10.90€ – 10 🔲 10.90€

A small and pretty chalet village overlooking the water park.

Surroundings : 🐾 ⚲
Leisure activities : 🛋 🏄
Facilities : ⚷ 🏕 🍴 launderette
Nearby : 🏊 ⛷ ⛰ 🎣 forest trail

G P S | Longitude : 1.70994
Latitude : 45.57541

We have selected the best campsites in France with our usual care, listing those with the best facilities in the most pleasant surroundings.

CHÂTEAUNEUF-LA-FORÊT

87130 – Michelin map **325** G6 – pop. 1 641 – alt. 376
▶ Paris 424 – Eymoutiers 14 – Limoges 36 – St-Léonard-de-Noblat 19

⛰ Le Cheyenne

𝒫 05 55 69 39 29. www.camping-le-cheyenne.com

Address : avenue Michel Sinibaldi (800m west of the town centre, follow rte du Stade, 100m from a small lake)

Opening times : from beginning April to end Sept.

1 ha (45 pitches) flat, grassy

Tariff : (2014 Price) ★ 4€ 🚐 🔲 7€ – ⚡ (6A) 3.50€

Rental rates : (2014 Price) (from beginning April to end Sept.) – 9 🚐 – 1 tent lodge. Per night from 50€ – Per week from 200 to 450€

🚐 borne 4€

Surroundings : ☁ ⚲
Leisure activities : 🍽 🍴
Facilities : ♿ 🏕 🍴 launderette
Nearby : 🏄 🎿 🏊 (beach) 🎣

G P S | Longitude : 1.60127
Latitude : 45.71633

CHÂTEAUPONSAC

87290 – Michelin map **325** E4 – pop. 2 158 – alt. 290
▶ Paris 361 – Bélâbre 55 – Limoges 48 – Bellac 21

⛰ Aquadis Loisirs La Gartempe

𝒫 05 55 76 55 33. www.aquadis-loisirs.com

Address : avenue de Ventenat (take the southwestern exit along the D 711, follow the signs for Nantiat; 200m from the river)

Opening times : from beginning April to end Oct.

1.5 ha (56 pitches) terraced, relatively flat, flat, grassy

Tariff : 18.90€ ★★ 🚐 🔲 ⚡ (16A) – Extra per person 3.70€ – Reservation fee 9.90€

Rental rates : (from beginning April to end Oct.) – 2 🚐 – 11 🏠.
Per night from 55€ – Per week from 238 to 499€ – Reservation fee 19.90€

The site is close to the church, the town and the lush, green river bank.

Surroundings : ☁ ⚲⚲
Leisure activities : 🍽 🍴 🛋 🏄 ⛷
Facilities : ♿ 🏕 🍴 launderette
Nearby : 🏊 🏊 🎣

G P S | Longitude : 1.27046
Latitude : 46.1318

CHÂTELUS-MALVALEIX

23270 – Michelin map **325** J3 – pop. 563 – alt. 410
▶ Paris 333 – Aigurande 25 – Aubusson 46 – Boussac 19

⛰ Municipal La Roussille

Municipal La Roussille

𝒫 05 55 80 70 31. www.chatelusmalvaleix.fr

Address : 10 place de la Fontaine (to the west of the village)

Opening times : from beginning June to end Sept.

0.5 ha (26 pitches)

Tariff : ★ 🚐 🔲 6€ – ⚡ (16A) 4€

Rental rates : Permanent ♿ (1 chalet) – 8 🏠. Per night from 50 to 55€ – Per week from 180 to 450€

Basic sanitary facilities, but close to a good sports and leisure centre.

Surroundings : 🐾 ⚲⚲ ⛰
Leisure activities : 🛋 🚴 🎣
Facilities : 🏕 🍴
Nearby : 🍽 🏄 🎿

G P S | Longitude : 2.01818
Latitude : 46.3031

Some information or pricing may have changed since the guide went to press. We recommend you check the price list online in advance or at the entrance to the campsite and enquire about possible restrictions.

COGNAC-LA-FORET

87310 – Michelin map **325** D5 – pop. 1 022 – alt. 410
▶ Paris 417 – Guéret 113 – Limoges 27 – Périgueux 87

⛰ Les Alouettes

𝒫 05 55 03 26 93. www.camping-des-alouettes.com

Address : 1km west along the D 10, follow signs for Rochechouart

Opening times : from beginning April to end Sept.

5 ha (68 pitches) relatively flat, flat, grassy

Tariff : (2014 Price) 21.50€ ★★ 🚐 🔲 ⚡ (10A) – Extra per person 4.75€

Rental rates : (2014 Price) (from beginning April to end Sept.) – 6 🚐 – 3 tent lodges. Per night from 59 to 84€ – Per week from 410 to 585€

The site is in a green setting, with new and good-quality sanitary facilities.

Surroundings : 🐾 ☁
Leisure activities : 🛋 🏄 🏊
Facilities : ♿ 🏕 🍴 🔲

G P S | Longitude : 0.99678
Latitude : 45.82463

CORRÈZE

19800 – Michelin map **329** M3 – pop. 1 168 – alt. 455
▶ Paris 480 – Argentat 47 – Brive-la-Gaillarde 45 – Égletons 22

⚠ Municipal la Chapelle

🕿 05 55 21 25 21. http://www.mairie-correze.fr/

Address : La Chapelle (take the eastern exit along the D 143, follow the signs for Egletons and take a right turn, follow the signs for Bouysse – divided into two separate parts)

Opening times : from mid June to mid Sept.

3 ha (54 pitches)

Tariff : (2014 Price) ✶ 2.65€ ⇌ 1.40€ 🄴 2.50€ – 🅷 (10A) 2.30€
Rental rates : (2014 Price) (from beginning June to end Sept.) – 3 ⬚ – 1 gîte. Per week from 200 to 300€
🚐 borne – 8 🄴 8€ – 🕳 🄴 8€

The camping part of the site has a small road running through it; located beside the Corrèze river and near a small chapel.

Surroundings : 🐾 ♀♀ **Leisure activities :** 🏠 🚣 🎣 **Facilities :** ⛄ 🚱 📷 **Nearby :** 🛶	**GPS** Longitude : 1.8798 Latitude : 45.37191

The pitches of many campsites are marked out with low hedges of attractive bushes and shrubs.

CROMAC

87160 – Michelin map **325** E2 – pop. 266 – alt. 224
▶ Paris 339 – Argenton-sur-Creuse 41 – Limoges 68 – Magnac-Laval 22

⚠ Lac de Mondon

Lac de Mondon

🕿 05 55 76 93 34. www.campingdemondon.com

Address : Les Forges de Mondon (situated 2km south along the D 105, follow the signs for St-Sulpice-les-Feuilles and take the D 60 - recommended route via the D 912)

Opening times : from mid April to end Sept.

2.8 ha (100 pitches)

Tariff : 18€ ✶✶ ⇌ 🄴 🅷 (10A) – Extra per person 4€
🚐 borne 2€

In a green setting with some pitches adjacent to the leisure centre.

Surroundings : 🐾 ⌂ ♀♀ **Leisure activities :** ♀ ✗ 🏠 🚲 🎣 🛶 **Facilities :** ⛄ 🚱 🚻 📷 🍽 **Nearby :** 🚣 🐾 🛶 🏊 pedalos	**GPS** Longitude : 1.31153 Latitude : 46.3322

DONZENAC

19270 – Michelin map **329** K4 – pop. 2 492 – alt. 204
▶ Paris 469 – Brive-la-Gaillarde 11 – Limoges 81 – Tulle 27

⚠ La Rivière

🕿 05 55 85 63 95. http://campinglariviere.jimdo.com

Address : route d'Ussac (1.6km south of the town, following the signs for Brive; beside the Maumont river)

1.2 ha (60 pitches) flat, grassy

Rentals : 🚲 – 14 ⬚.

A pleasant and shaded grassy site, close to a small stream and the town's sports facilities.

Surroundings : ⌂ ♀♀ **Leisure activities :** 🏠 **Facilities :** ⛄ 🚱 🚻 **Nearby :** 🎣 🐾 🛶	**GPS** Longitude : 1.52149 Latitude : 45.21761

EYMOUTIERS

87120 – Michelin map **325** H6 – pop. 2 033 – alt. 417
▶ Paris 432 – Aubusson 55 – Guéret 62 – Limoges 44

⚠ Municipal

🕿 05 55 69 10 21. mairie-eymoutiers@wanadoo.fr

Address : at St-Pierre (situated 2km southeast along the D 940, follow the signs for Tulle and take road to the left)

1 ha (33 pitches) open site, terraced, relatively flat, flat, grassy

In an elevated location, this is a small, simple site with no services.

Surroundings : 🐾 ⌂ ♀♀ **Facilities :** ⛄	**GPS** Longitude : 1.75296 Latitude : 45.73161

GUÉRET

23000 – Michelin map **325** I3 – pop. 13 844 – alt. 457
▶ Paris 351 – Bourges 122 – Châteauroux 90 – Clermont-Ferrand 132

⚠ Courtille

🕿 05 55 81 92 24. www.camping-courtille.com

Address : route de Courtille (2.5km southwest along the D 914, follow the signs for Benevent and take road to the left)

Opening times : from beginning April to end Sept.

2.4 ha (70 pitches)

Tariff : ✶ 3.10€ ⇌ 2€ 🄴 8.30€ – 🅷 (10A) 2.80€
Rental rates : (from beginning April to end Sept.) – 4 ⬚ – 1 ⬚. Per week from 245 to 574 €– Reservation fee 10€

In a green and wooded location near a pretty lake and its activity centre.

Surroundings : 🐾 ⌂ ♀♀ **Leisure activities :** 🚣 **Facilities :** ⛄ 🚿 🍽 launderette **Nearby :** 🚲 ⛵ (beach) 🛶 ⚓ watersports centre	**GPS** Longitude : 1.85823 Latitude : 46.16093

LADIGNAC-LE-LONG

87500 – Michelin map **325** D7 – pop. 1 124 – alt. 334
▶ Paris 426 – Brive-la-Gaillarde 74 – Limoges 35 – Nontron 44

⚠ Bel Air

🕿 05 55 09 39 82. www.atouvert.com

Address : rue Bel'Air (located 1.5km north along the D 11, follow the signs for Nexon and take road to the left)

2.5 ha (100 pitches)

Rentals : 5 ⬚.

In a pleasant, wooded setting on the edge of a small lake.

Surroundings : 🐾 ⌂ ♀♀ **Leisure activities :** 🏠 🚲 **Facilities :** ⛄ 🚿 🍽 launderette **Nearby :** 🛶	**GPS** Longitude : 1.11185 Latitude : 45.59089

LAGUENNE

19150 – Michelin map **329** L4 – pop. 1 453 – alt. 205
▶ Paris 484 – Cahors 131 – Limoges 93 – Tulle 5

⚠ Le Pré du Moulin

✆ 05 55 26 21 96. www.lepredumoulin.com

Address : Chemin du Moulinot, off the D1120

Opening times : from beginning April to end Sept.

1.5 ha (22 pitches) terraced, flat, grassy

Tariff : ★ 9€ ⇦ 🖭 3.50€ – (½) (6A) 2.50€ – Reservation fee 15€
🚐 14 🖭 15€

Situated in a small clearing by the Corrèze river.

Surroundings : 🌲 🚃 ♨♨
Leisure activities : ⊿ (small swimming pool) 🏸
Facilities : ♿ ⌁ 🚽 🖼

Longitude : 1.78145
Latitude : 45.24657

This guide is not intended as a list of all the camping sites in France; its aim is to provide a selection of the best sites in each category.

LIGINIAC

19160 – Michelin map **329** P3 – pop. 641 – alt. 665
▶ Paris 464 – Aurillac 83 – Bort-les-Orgues 24 – Clermont-Ferrand 107

⚠ Municipal le Maury

✆ 05 55 95 92 28. www.camping-du-maury.com

Address : 4.6km southwest following signs for the beach; beside the Lac de Triouzoune - recommended route via the D 20, follow the signs for Neuvic

Opening times : from beginning May to end Sept.

2 ha (50 pitches) terraced, relatively flat, flat, grassy

Tariff : (2014 Price) 10.50€ ★★ ⇦ 🖭 (½) (16A) – Extra per person 3€
Rental rates : (2014 Price) (from mid April to mid Nov.) – 12 gîtes – 10 cabins. Per week from 140 to 882€
🚐 borne

The site is on a lovely undulating field that leads down to a lake.

Surroundings : 🌲 ♀
Leisure activities : 🖼 ⛵ ✂
Facilities : ⌁ 🚽 launderette
Nearby : 🍽 ✕ ⛴ 🏖 (beach) pedalos

Longitude : 2.30498
Latitude : 45.39143

LIMOGES

87000 – Michelin map **325** E6 – pop. 137 758 – alt. 300
▶ Paris 394 – Angoulême 104 – Guéret 90 – Tulle 90

⚠ Uzurat

✆ 05 55 38 49 43. www.campinglimoges.fr

Address : Z.I. (industrial zone) north of Uzurat, near the Leclerc shopping centre

Opening times : from mid March to end Oct.

2.5 ha (155 pitches) flat, grassy, gravelled

Tariff : (2014 Price) ★ 3.70€ ⇦ 🖭 7.60€ – (½) (10A) 3.60€
Rental rates : (2014 Price) (from mid March to end Oct.) – 16 🚐
Per night from 47 to 88€ – Per week from 235 to 505€
🚐 borne

A well-shaded site near a shopping centre.

Surroundings : ♨♨
Leisure activities : 🖼 ⛵
Facilities : ♿ ⌁ 🚽 🍽 launderette
Nearby : 🏖 🍽 ✕ ✂ 🚣 🌲 forest trail

Longitude : 1.27577
Latitude : 45.87056

LISSAC-SUR-COUZE

19600 – Michelin map **329** J5 – pop. 710 – alt. 170
▶ Paris 486 – Brive-la-Gaillarde 11 – Périgueux 68 – Sarlat-la-Canéda 42

⚠ La Prairie et gîtes de Lissac ♠♠

✆ 05 55 85 37 97. www.caussecorrezien.fr

Address : 1.4km southwest along the D 59 and take road to the left, near the Lac du Causse

Opening times : Permanent

5 ha (120 pitches) terraced, flat, grassy, fine gravel

Tariff : (2014 Price) 18.20€ ★★ ⇦ 🖭 (½) (6A) – Extra per person 5€
Rental rates : (2014 Price) Permanent – 20 🏠 – 25 gîtes. Per week from 142 to 545€
🚐 borne 4€ – 16 🖭 12.20€

The gîtes village is 500m from the main site.

Surroundings : 🌲 ← the Lac du Causse 🚃 ♨♨
Leisure activities : 🍽 ✕ 🖼 ⛵ 🏖 BMX track
Facilities : ♿ ⌁ ☑ 🚽 ⛱ 🏖 🍽 launderette 🚿
At the leisure/activities centre : 🚴 🏖 (beach) 🏊 ♀ 🐎 pedalos

Longitude : 1.45465
Latitude : 45.10125

⚠ Village Vacances Les Hameaux du Perrier

(rental of chalets only)

✆ 05 55 84 34 48. www.chalets-en-france.com

Address : Le Perrier

Opening times : Permanent

17 ha/10 for camping terraced

Rental rates : (2014 Price) – 94 🏠. Per week from 370 to 1,011€

A large chalet village offering different standards of comfort.

Surroundings : 🌲 ← ♨♨
Leisure activities : 🍽 ✕ ⛵ 🚣 ⊿
Facilities : ⌁ ☑ 🚽 🍽 launderette 🚿
Nearby : 🚴 ✂ 🏖 🏸 ♀

Longitude : 1.43848
Latitude : 45.10029

We value your opinion and welcome your feedback.
Do email us at campingfrance@tp.michelin.com

MAGNAC-LAVAL

87190 – Michelin map **325** D3 – pop. 1 850 – alt. 231
▶ Paris 366 – Limoges 64 – Poitiers 86 – Guéret 62

⚠ Village Vacances Le Hameau de Gîtes des Pouyades

(rental of gîtes only)

✆ 05 55 60 73 45. www.lelimousinsejoursvacances.com

Address : Les Pouyades

Opening times : from beginning Feb. to beginning Jan.

1.5 ha flat

Rental rates : – 12 gîtes. Per night from 72 to 184€ – Per week from 277 to 734€ – Reservation fee 16€

In a green setting beside a small, pretty lake.

Surroundings : ⌣ ≤ On the lake ⚲
Leisure activities : 🏠 🚲 🏊 🎣
Facilities : ♿ ▥ 🚰 launderette

GPS Longitude : 1.19236
Latitude : 46.20331

MASSERET

19510 – Michelin map **329** K2 – pop. 675 – alt. 380
▶ Paris 432 – Guéret 132 – Limoges 45 – Tulle 48

⛺ Domaine des Forges

✆ 05 55 73 44 57. www.camping-domainedesforges.com

Address : 3km east along the D 20, follow the signs for Les Meilhards, near the exit from Masseret-Gare

Opening times : from beginning April to end Sept.

100 ha/2 for camping (80 pitches) open site, undulating, relatively flat, flat, grassy, fine gravel

Tariff : 18€ ✶✶ 🚗 🔲 ⚡ (10A) – Extra per person 3€
Rental rates : (from beginning April to end Sept.) – 4 🚐. Per night from 50 to 70€ – Per week from 250 to 450€

In a pleasant wooded setting, looking out over a lake.

Surroundings : ⌣ ≤ the lake ⚿
Leisure activities : 🏠
Facilities : ♿ ⚯ 🚰
Nearby : 🍷 🍴 🏊 🚣 🎿 🎣 ≌ (beach) 🎣

GPS Longitude : 1.54908
Latitude : 45.54154

MEYSSAC

19500 – Michelin map **329** L5 – pop. 1 245 – alt. 220
▶ Paris 507 – Argentat 62 – Beaulieu-sur-Dordogne 21 – Brive-la-Gaillarde 23

⛰ Intercommunal Moulin de Valane

✆ 05 55 25 41 59. www.meyssac.fr

Address : located 1km to the northwest, follow the signs for Collonges-la-Rouge; beside a stream

Opening times : from beginning April to end Sept.

4 ha (115 pitches) terraced, relatively flat, flat, grassy

Tariff : (2014 Price) 22€ ✶✶ 🚗 🔲 ⚡ (10A) – Extra per person 4€
Rental rates : (2014 Price) (from beginning April to end Sept.) – 21 🚐. Per night from 50 to 60€ – Per week from 190 to 550€

Ageing sanitary facilities. The site welcomes groups and mini-camps for children.

Surroundings : 🏠 ⚿
Leisure activities : 🍴 🏠 🚣 🚲 🎿 🎣
🏊 🎣
Facilities : ♿ ⚯ (July–Aug.) 🚰
launderette 🛒

GPS Longitude : 1.66381
Latitude : 45.06102

Key to rentals symbols:

12 🚐   *Number of mobile homes*
20 🏠   *Number of chalets*
6 🛏   *Number of rooms to rent*
Per night   *Minimum/maximum rate per night*
30–50€
Per week   *Minimum/maximum rate per week*
300–1,000€

NEUVIC

19160 – Michelin map **329** O3 – pop. 1 868 – alt. 620
▶ Paris 465 – Aurillac 78 – Mauriac 25 – Tulle 56

⛰ Domaine de Mialaret

✆ 05 55 46 02 50. www.lemialaret.com

Address : 3km west along the D 991 and take a right turn

Opening times : from end April to mid Oct.

44 ha/3 for camping (170 pitches) undulating, sloping, relatively flat, flat, grassy

Tariff : (2014 Price) 34€ ✶✶ 🚗 🔲 ⚡ (10A) – Extra per person 9€
Rental rates : (2014 Price) Permanent – 31 🏠 – 25 tent lodges – 15 gîtes – hotel. Per night from 50 to 120€ – Per week from 350 to 840€

🚐 borne

Surroundings : ⌣ 🏠 ⚿⚿
Leisure activities : 🏊 🎣
Facilities : ♿ 🛒

GPS Longitude : 2.22922
Latitude : 45.38216

⛰ Municipal du Lac

✆ 05 55 95 85 48. www.campingdulac-neuvic-correze.com

Address : route de la Plage (2.3km east along the D 20, follow the signs for Bort-les-Orgues and turn left onto the beach road; beside the Lac de la Triouzoune)

Opening times : from beginning March to end Nov.

5 ha (93 pitches)

Tariff : ✶ 3.20€ 🚗 1.80€ 🔲 3.60€ – ⚡ (8A) 3.10€ – Reservation fee 8€
Rental rates : (2014 Price) (from beginning March to end Nov.) – 28 🏠. Per night from 42 to 49€ – Per week from 200 to 530€ Reservation fee 8€

🚐 borne 3.20€ – 40 🔲 8.60€ – 🛒 ⚡8.60€

Some pitches for tents and caravans have a view of the Lac de la Triouzoune.

Surroundings : ⌣ 🏠 ⚿⚿
Leisure activities : 🏠 🚣 🎣
Facilities : ⚯ 🚰 launderette
Nearby : 🍷 🍴 ≌ (beach) 🚤 ⚓ pedalos

GPS Longitude : 2.29207
Latitude : 45.3841

NEXON

87800 – Michelin map **325** E6 – pop. 2 457 – alt. 359
▶ Paris 412 – Châlus 20 – Limoges 22 – Nontron 53

⛺ Municipal de la Lande

✆ 05 55 58 35 44. www.camping-nexon.fr

Address : located 1km south following signs for St-Hilaire, access near the pl. de l'Hôtel-de-Ville

Opening times : from beginning June to end Sept.

2 ha (60 pitches) terraced, relatively flat, grassy

Tariff : 10€ ✶✶ 🚗 🔲 ⚡ (10A) – Extra per person 3.20€
Rental rates : (2014 Price) (from mid April to mid Nov.) – 9 🏠. Per night from 40 to 99€ – Per week from 196 to 485€

🚐 borne

A well-shaded, green site with a view over the lake from some pitches.

Surroundings : 🏠 ⚿⚿
Leisure activities : 🏠 🚲
Facilities : ♿ ⚯ 🛒 🚰
Nearby : 🚣 ≌ (beach) pedalos

GPS Longitude : 1.17997
Latitude : 45.67078

OBJAT

19130 – Michelin map **329** J4 – pop. 3 605 – alt. 131
▶ Paris 495 – Limoges 106 – Tulle 46 – Brive-la-Gaillarde 20

🏔 Village Vacances Les Grands Prés

(rental of chalets only)

🕿 05 55 24 08 80. www.brive-tourisme.com

Address : Espace Loisirs Les Grands Prés (Grands Prés leisure park)

Opening times : Permanent

18 ha/4 for camping flat

Rental rates : – 20 🏠. Per night from 49 to 149€ – Per week from 245 to 505€ – Reservation fee 16€

🚐 borne 7€

A large site with lots of activities.

Surroundings : 🦌 ◁	G
Leisure activities : ▣ 🏃	P
Facilities : ⚲ ▥ launderette	S
Nearby : 🍷 🗶 🚴 🏊 🛶 pedalos	

Longitude : 1.41069
Latitude : 45.26687

REYGADES

19430 – Michelin map **329** M5 – pop. 193 – alt. 460
▶ Paris 516 – Aurillac 56 – Brive-la-Gaillarde 56 – St-Céré 26

🏔 La Belle Étoile

🕿 05 55 28 50 08. www.campingbelle-etoile.fr

Address : Lestrade (located 1km north off the D 41, follow the signs for Beaulieu-sur-Dordogne)

Opening times : from beginning June to end Sept.

5 ha/3 for camping (25 pitches)

Tariff : 👤 4.15€ 🚗 ▣ 5.30€ – (⚡) (6A) 3.10€

Rental rates : Permanent – 6 🏠 – 6 🏠 – 4 canvas bungalows. Per week from 195 to 640€

A peaceful setting with shaded pitches and a variety of rental options

Surroundings : 🦌 ◁ ▭ ♨♨	G
Leisure activities : ▣ 🚣 🏊 (small swimming pool)	P
Facilities : ⚲ ⌒ 🚽 ⛴ launderette ▤	S

Longitude : 1.90538
Latitude : 45.02405

ROYÈRE-DE-VASSIVIÈRE

23460 – Michelin map **325** I5 – pop. 563 – alt. 735
▶ Paris 412 – Bourganeuf 22 – Eymoutiers 25 – Felletin 29

🏔 Les Terrasses du Lac

🕿 05 55 64 76 77. www.campings.lelacdevassiviere.com

Address : Vauveix (10km southwest along the D 3 and D 35, follow the signs for Eymoutiers; by the marina (direct access)

4 ha (142 pitches) terraced, relatively flat, flat, grassy, gravelled

In a panoramic location overlooking the lake and the marina.

Surroundings : ◁ Lac de Vassivière ▭ ♨♨	G
Leisure activities : ▣ 🏖 (beach) 🎣	P
Facilities : ⌒ ▥ ⛴ launderette	S
Nearby : ▤ 🍷 🗶 🚣 ⚓ 🎿 water skiing	

Longitude : 1.89526
Latitude : 45.78979

The information in the guide may have changed since going to press.

ST-GERMAIN-LES-BELLES

87380 – Michelin map **325** F7 – pop. 1 151 – alt. 432
▶ Paris 422 – Eymoutiers 33 – Limoges 34 – St-Léonard-de-Noblat 31

🏔 Le Montréal

🕿 05 55 71 86 20. www.campingdemontreal.com

Address : rue du Petit Moulin (take the southeastern exit, follow the signs for La Porcherie; beside a small lake)

1 ha (60 pitches) terrace, relatively flat, flat, grassy

Rentals : 2 🚐 – 5 🏠 – 6 canvas bungalows.

🚐 borne

Well marked-out pitches with a view of the lake.

Surroundings : 🦌 ◁ ▭ 🎣	G
Leisure activities : 🏊	P
Facilities : ⚲ ⌒ ▥ 🕈 launderette	S
Nearby : 🗶 🚴 🚣 🎿 🏖 (beach) 🎣	

Longitude : 1.5011
Latitude : 45.61143

The guide covers all 22 regions of France – see the map and list of regions on pages 4–5.

ST-LÉONARD-DE-NOBLAT

87400 – Michelin map **325** F5 – pop. 4 665 – alt. 347
▶ Paris 407 – Aubusson 68 – Brive-la-Gaillarde 99 – Guéret 62

🏔 Municipal de Beaufort

🕿 05 55 56 02 79. www.campingdebeaufort.fr

Address : Beaufort (1.7km along the N 141, follow signs for Limoges, then 1.5km to the left following signs for Masleon)

2 ha (98 pitches)

Rentals : 10 🚐 – 2 cabins.

The pitches are marked out and shaded, beside the Vienne river.

Surroundings : ▭ ♨♨	G
Leisure activities : ▣ 🎣	P
Facilities : ⚲ ⌒ 🚽 ⛴ 🕈 launderette	S
Nearby : 🚣	

Longitude : 1.49211
Latitude : 45.82276

ST-PARDOUX

87250 – Michelin map **325** E4 – pop. 536 – alt. 370
▶ Paris 366 – Bellac 25 – Limoges 33 – St-Junien 39

🏔 Aquadis Loisirs Le Freaudour

🕿 05 55 76 57 22. www.aquadis-loisirs.com

Address : leisure centre, Lac de St-Pardoux

Opening times : from beginning March to beginning Nov.

4.5 ha (107 pitches) relatively flat, flat, grassy

Tariff : 18.90€ 👤👤 🚗 ▣ (⚡) (10A) – Extra per person 5.15€ – Reservation fee 9.90€

Rental rates : (from beginning March to beginning Nov.) – 20 🚐 – 10 🏠. Per night from 68 to 89€ – Per week from 186 to 599€ Reservation fee 19.90€

In a green and shady setting, beside the lake.

Surroundings : 🦌 ▭ ♨♨	G
Leisure activities : 🍷 ▣ 🏊 fitness trail, water skiing	P
Facilities : ⚲ ⌒ ▣ 🚽 ⛴ 🕈 launderette	S
Nearby : 🚣 🏖 (beach)	

Longitude : 1.2788
Latitude : 46.04931

ST-PARDOUX-CORBIER

19210 – Michelin map **329** J3 – pop. 360 – alt. 404
▶ Paris 448 – Arnac-Pompadour 8 – Brive-la-Gaillarde 44 – St-Yrieix-la-Perche 27

⚠ Le Domaine Bleu

☎ 05 55 73 59 89. www.ledomainebleu.eu

Address : take the eastern exit along the D 50, follow the signs for Vigeois and take the road to the right, near a lake

Opening times : from end June to beginning Sept.

1 ha (40 pitches) terraced, relatively flat, flat, grassy

Tariff : 16€ ✳✳ ⚗ 🅴 (½) (16A) – Extra per person 4€

Pitches on shaded terraces, overlooking a lake.

Surroundings : 🐾 🏕 ♋♋	**G** Longitude : 1.45449
Leisure activities : 🐾	**P**
Facilities : ⚫🔑⚫ 🚻🚽🏛 🚿 ⚰ ⚱ 🏕 launderette	**S** Latitude : 45.42973
Nearby : 🍴	

ST-SORNIN-LAVOLPS

19230 – Michelin map **329** J3 – pop. 911 – alt. 400
▶ Paris 454 – Cahors 126 – Limoges 63 – Tulle 47

⚠ Les Étoiles

☎ 05 55 73 01 27. www.camping-pompadour.com

Address : in the village

Opening times : from end March to end Oct.

1 ha (40 pitches) terraced, flat, grassy

Tariff : (2014 Price) 23.50€ ✳✳ ⚗ 🅴 (½) (6A)

Rental rates : (2014 Price) (from end March to end Oct.) ⚫ (1 chalet) – 1 🏠. Per night from 70 to 80€ – Per week from 300 to 600€

🚐 borne – 🅱 11€

Located between the church and a small lake.

Surroundings : 🐾 ♋♋	**G** Longitude : 1.38333
Leisure activities : 🏊	**P**
Facilities : ⚫🔑⚫ 🏛 🚿🏠	**S** Latitude : 45.377
Nearby : 🐾	

ST-YRIEIX-LA-PERCHE

87500 – Michelin map **325** E7 – pop. 6 932 – alt. 360
▶ Paris 430 – Brive-la-Gaillarde 63 – Limoges 40 – Périgueux 63

⚠ Municipal d'Arfeuille

☎ 05 55 75 08 75. camping@saint-yrieix.fr

Address : route du Viaduc (2.5km north following signs for Limoges and take the road to the left; beside a small lake)

Opening times : from beginning April to mid Sept.

2 ha (76 pitches) terraced, flat, grassy

Tariff : 14.60€ ✳✳ ⚗ 🅴 (½) (10A) – Extra per person 4.30€

Rental rates : (from beginning March to end Oct.) ⚫ (1 chalet) – 11 🏠. Per night from 84 to 134€ – Per week from 230 to 460€

🚐 borne – 75 🅴 11.60€

A well-shaded green site with a panoramic view over the lake and simple sanitary facilities, somewhat ageing but well maintained.

Surroundings : 🐾 ⟨ 🏕 ♋♋	**G** Longitude : 1.20009
Leisure activities : 🏛 🏊	**P**
Facilities : ⚫🔑 🏕 launderette	**S** Latitude : 45.52791
Nearby : 🍷🍴 🚤 🏖 (beach) 🐾 pedalos	

SEILHAC

19700 – Michelin map **329** L3 – pop. 1 721 – alt. 500
▶ Paris 461 – Aubusson 97 – Brive-la-Gaillarde 33 – Limoges 73

⚞⚞⚞ Le Lac de Bournazel

☎ 05 55 27 05 65. www.camping-lac-bournazel.com

Address : located 1.5km northwest along the N 120, follow the signs for Uzerche then turn right after 1km

Opening times : from beginning April to end Sept.

6.5 ha (120 pitches) terraced, flat, grassy, gravelled

Tariff : (2014 Price) 18.40€ ✳✳ ⚗ 🅴 (½) (12A) – Extra per person 4.70€ – Reservation fee 9€

Rental rates : (2014 Price) (from beginning April to end Sept.) – 2 caravans – 10 🏠 – 2 tipis. Per night from 25 to 91€ – Per week from 175 to 637€ – Reservation fee 9€

🚐 borne 4€ – 🅱 (½)11.90€

In a pleasant leafy setting with plenty of shade; some pitches under lime trees.

Surroundings : 🐾 🏕 ♋♋	**G** Longitude : 1.7022
Leisure activities : 🍷🍴 🏕 🚤 🚴	**P**
Facilities : ⚫ 🔑 🏛 🏕 launderette 🐾	**S** Latitude : 45.37838
Nearby : 🍴 🏖 🐾 🐴 fitness trail	

Michelin classification:

⚞⚞⚞⚞	*Extremely comfortable, equipped to a very high standard*
⚞⚞⚞	*Very comfortable, equipped to a high standard*
⚞⚞⚞	*Comfortable and well equipped*
⚞⚞	*Reasonably comfortable*
⚞	*Satisfactory*

TREIGNAC

19260 – Michelin map **329** L2 – pop. 1 383 – alt. 500
▶ Paris 463 – Égletons 32 – Eymoutiers 33 – Limoges 75

⚞⚞⚞ Flower La Plage

☎ 05 55 98 08 54. www.camping-correze.com

Address : Lac des Barriousses (4.5km north along the D 940, follow the signs for Eymoutiers)

Opening times : from beginning April to end Sept.

3.5 ha (146 pitches) very uneven, terraced, flat and relatively flat, grassy, stony, adjacent wood

Tariff : (2014 Price) 24.90€ ✳✳ ⚗ 🅴 (½) (6A) – Extra per person 4.50€ Reservation fee 15€

Rental rates : (2014 Price) (from beginning April to end Sept.) ⚫ (1 mobile home) – 40 🏠 – 6 canvas bungalows – 4 tent lodges. Per night from 36 to 99€ – Per week from 180 to 693€ Reservation fee 20€

🚐 borne – 🅱 (½)12€

Situated on terraces overlooking the lake and, unfortunately, also the road.

Surroundings : ⟨ 🏕 ♋♋	**G** Longitude : 1.81373
Leisure activities : 🏛 🏕 🏊 (open air in season)	**P**
Facilities : ⚫ 🔑 🏛 🏕 launderette	**S** Latitude : 45.55992
Nearby : 🍴 🚤 🚴🏊 🏖 (beach) 🐾 pedalos	

VIDEIX

87600 – Michelin map **325** B6 – pop. 234 – alt. 260
▶ Paris 443 – Angoulême 53 – Limoges 53 – Nontron 36

⚞ Village Vacances Le Hameau de gîtes de Chassagne

(rental of chalets only)

✆ 05 55 48 83 39. www.tourisme-meteorite.com

Address : Plage de La Chassagne (head 1.7km north along the D 87, follow the signs for Pressignac; the area is known as La Chassagne)

Opening times : Permanent

3 ha flat, grassy
Rental rates : **Ⓟ** – 16 ⌂ – 16 gîtes. Per night from 70 to 90€
Per week from 245 to 480€

Surroundings : ⛰ ≤ lake ⛺ Leisure activities : ⌂ ⛵ Facilities : ♿ ⚷ ⤳ ▥ ⚎ launderette Nearby : ⛾ ✕ ⤢ ⚓ ◊ pedalos	**G P S**	Longitude : 0.71585 Latitude : 45.80106

VIGEOIS

19410 – Michelin map **329** K3 – pop. 1 194 – alt. 390
▶ Paris 457 – Limoges 68 – Tulle 32 – Brive-la-Gaillarde 41

⛺ Municipal du Lac de Pontcharal

✆ 05 55 98 90 86. www.vigeois.com

Address : Pontcharal (situated 2km southeast along the D 7, follow the signs for Brive, near the lake at Pontcharal)

Opening times : from beginning June to mid Sept.

32 ha/1.7 (85 pitches) terrace, undulating, relatively flat, flat, grassy
Tariff : ⚚ 3.80€ ⇔ ▣ 4.70€ – ⚡ (15A) 4.20€
Rental rates : (from end March to end Oct.) – 7 ⛟. Per night from 70€ – Per week from 290 to 423€
⚞ borne 3€
A pleasant campsite situated beside a leisure centre.

Surroundings : ⛰ ♨ ⛺ Leisure activities : ⛾ ✕ ⚓ (beach) ⚓ Facilities : ♿ ⚷ (July–Aug.) ⤳ ⚎ ▥ ⚎ Nearby : pedalos	**G P S**	Longitude : 1.53806 Latitude : 45.36873

LORRAINE

Christian Legay / Mairie de Metz

If you want to do justice to the collage of stunning sights of Lorraine, a region that shares borders with Luxembourg, Germany and Belgium, don't forget to pack your walking boots. But before you head for the hills, make sure you leave enough time to discover the artistic heritage of Nancy and admire the lights and contemporary art gallery of historic Metz. Then embark upon the trail of tiny spa resorts and the famous centres of craftsmanship that produce the legendary Baccarat crystal, Longwy enamels and Lunéville porcelain. From there head to historic Domrémy and Colombey. The water, forests and wildlife of the Vosges regional park, nestling in the 'Valley of Lakes', will keep you entranced as you make your way down hillsides dotted with orchards bursting with plums. Stop for a little light refreshment in a *marcairerie* (traditional farmhouse inn) and sample the famous *quiche Lorraine* tarts, a slab of Munster cheese and a delicious kirsch-flavoured dessert.

DEUTSCHLAND

LUXEMBOURG

●	Locality with campsite
■	Locality with campsite and rental option
<u>Vannes</u>	Locality with campsite and campervan area
<u>Moyaux</u>	Locality with at least one pleasant campsite
🚐	Motorway service area for campervans

Semois

Semois

Meuse

LUXEMBOURG

D 8043

D 643

D 618

Lo...

D 618

N 52

A 31

Moselle

Thionville

A 6

Buzancy

Meuse

D 603

A 30

Briey

Boulay-Moselle

Sarre

Ste-Menehould

Aire

N 5

Verdun

A 4

METZ

St-Avold

A 320

A 4

Sarreguemines

Oberbr...

MEUSE

Lac de Madine

Jaulny

MOSELLE

Château-Salins

Sarrebourg

A 4

Saverne

BAS-RHIN

Revigny-s-Ornain

D 635

Bar-le-Duc

Commercy

Toul

A 31

NANCY

Seille

N 4

Dabo

Wasselonne

STRASBOUR...

Moisheim

Ste-Mennould

N 4

A 31

Villey-le-Sec

MEURTHE-ET-MOSELLE

Lunéville

A 33

N 333

N 59

Meurthe

Sarre

N 4

Obernai

A 35

Éclaron

Braucourt

Aisne

N 67

Magnières

Celles-s-Plaine

le Hohwald

ffaumont-ampaubert

Thonnance-les-Moulins

Charmes

Bassemberg

Rombach-le-Franc

Dambach-la-Ville

Liépvre

Sélestat

Neufchâteau

D 674

ANDAUCOURT-LA-TRELLE

LORRAINE-SANDAUCOURT-LES-RAPPES

Moselle

N 57

la Chapelle-devant-Bruyères

Corcieux

Anould

Gemaingoutte

N 59

HAUT-

Aube

Bourg-Ste-Marie

Bulgnéville

VOSGES

Vittel

Épinal

Herpelmont

Xonrupt-Longemer

D 415

Ribeauvillé

Kaysersberg

HAUTE-MARNE

CHÂTEAUVILLAIN-ORGES

Chaumont

A 5

D 619

Contrexéville

Sanchey

le Tholy

Gérardmer

D 417

Turckheim

Wihr-au-Val

COLMAR

Éguisheim

Ste-Croix-e...

Bie...

Montigny-le-Roi

VAL-DE-MEUSE

Remiremont

Plombières-les-Bains

Saulxures-s-Moselotte

la Bresse

Mittlach

Munster

N 83

MONTIGNY-LE-ROI

A 31

Bourbonne-les-Bains

Bussang

Kruth

Geishouse

Guebwiller

A 35

Langres

Bannes

Le-Val-d'Ajol

Fresse-s-M

Moosch

HAUT-RHIN

Wattwiller

BA...

n-s-Seine

LANGRES-PERROGNEY

LANGRES-NOIDANT

Aube

Luxeuil-les-Bains

St-Maurice-s-M.

Masevaux

Thann

Cernay

A 36

MULHOUSE

A 31

Mélisey

Fresse

Guewenheim

Heimsbrunn

Saône

N 19

Champagney

Lachapelle-s/s-Rougemont

Burnhaupt-le-Haut

LA PORTE D'ALSACE

A 35

DIJON-BROGNON

N 57

N 19

N 19

BELFORT

Altkirch

Vesoul

HAUTE-SAÔNE

D 438

Seppois-le-Bas

Villersexel

Montbéliard

A 36

Bonnal

Mandeure

DIJON

Ognon

BESANÇON-CHAMPOUX

Huanne-Montmartin

Doubs

TE-D'OR

A 38

Pesmes

A 36

BESANÇON-MARCHAUX

Maîche

PONT VAL-DE-SAÔNE

GEVREY-CHAMBERTIN

A 39

Saône

Chalezeule

BESANÇON

St-Hippolyte

ANOULD

88650 – Michelin map **314** J3 – pop. 3 336 – alt. 457
▶ Paris 430 – Colmar 43 – Épinal 45 – Gérardmer 15

ᴍ Les Acacias

☏ 03 29 57 11 06. www.acaciascamp.com
Address : 191 rue Léonard de Vinci (take the western exit along the N 415, follow the signs for Colmar and take the road to the right)
Opening times : from mid Dec. to end Sept.
2.5 ha (84 pitches) terraced, flat, grassy
Tariff : (2014 Price) 15.50€ ♣♣ ⇔ 🖭 ⚡ (6A) – Extra per person 3.90€
Rental rates : (2014 Price) (from beginning Dec. to end Sept.) – 2 caravans – 8 🚐 – 8 🏠. Per week from 250 to 550€
🚐 borne – 6 🖭 10€ – 🚰 10€
Surroundings : 🗺 🌳
Leisure activities : 🍴 🏓 🎣 (small swimming pool)
Facilities : 🚿 🍴 (Jun-Sept) 🏪 🔥 🍴 launderette
Nearby : walking trails
GPS Longitude : 6.95786 Latitude : 48.18437

Using the traditional Michelin classification method, the guide provides you with an easy, speedy reference for assessing the category of each site: 1 to 5 tents (see page 10).

LA BRESSE

88250 – Michelin map **314** J4 – pop. 4 732 – alt. 636 – Winter sports : 650/1 350 m
▶ Paris 437 – Colmar 52 – Épinal 52 – Gérardmer 13

ᴍ Municipal le Haut des Bluches

☏ 03 29 25 64 80. www.hautdesbluches.com – alt. 708
Address : 5 route des Planches (head 3.2km east along the D 34, follow the signs for Le Col de la Schlucht; beside the Moselotte river)
Opening times : from mid Dec. to mid Nov.
4 ha (140 pitches) terraced, relatively flat, flat, grassy, rocks
Tariff : 25€ ♣♣ ⇔ 🖭 ⚡ (13A) – Extra per person 3.40€ – Reservation fee 2€
Rental rates : (from end Dec. to mid Nov.) 🚿 (2 chalets) – 7 🏠 – 13 🛏. Per night from 39 to 108€ – Per week from 267 to 646€ Reservation fee 2€
🚐 borne 3.30€ – 17 🖭 6.10€ – 🚰 ⚡11.80€
In a picturesque setting crossed by a stream.
Surroundings : 🌼 ⛰
Leisure activities : 🍴 🍽 🏓 🎣 adventure park, multi-sports ground
Facilities : 🚿 🏪 🔥 🍴 launderette
Nearby : sports trail
GPS Longitude : 6.91831 Latitude : 47.99878

ᴍ Belle Hutte

☏ 03 29 25 49 75. www.camping-belle-hutte.com – alt. 900
Address : 1bis Vouille de Belle Hutte (head 9km northeast along the D 34, follow the signs for Le Col de la Schlucht; beside the Moselotte river)
Opening times : from mid Dec. to mid Nov.
5 ha (125 pitches)
Tariff : 30.60€ ♣♣ ⇔ 🖭 ⚡ (10A) – Extra per person 8.30€ – Reservation fee 50€

Rental rates : (from mid Dec. to mid Nov.) 🚿 (2 chalets) – 15 🏠. Per night from 85 to 130€ – Per week from 266 to 910€ – Reservation fee 20€
On a pleasant, wooded site.
Surroundings : 🌼 ⛰ 🗺
Leisure activities : 🍴 🍽 🏓 🎣 🎿
Facilities : 🚿 🍴 🏪 🔥 🍴 launderette
Nearby : 🍽
GPS Longitude : 6.96254 Latitude : 48.0349

BULGNÉVILLE

88140 – Michelin map **314** D3 – pop. 1 400 – alt. 350
▶ Paris 331 – Contrexéville 6 – Épinal 53 – Neufchâteau 22

ᴍ Porte des Vosges

☏ 03 29 09 12 00. www.Camping-Portedesvosges.com
Address : at La Grande Tranchée (head 1.3km southeast along the D 164, follow the signs for Contrexéville and take D 14, follow the signs for Suriauville to the right)
Opening times : from beginning April to end Oct.
3.2 ha (100 pitches)
Tariff : 19€ ♣♣ ⇔ 🖭 ⚡ (6A) – Extra per person 4.60€
Rental rates : (from beginning April to end Oct.) – 1 🏠 – 2 tent lodges. Per night from 25 to 45 € – Per week from 175 to 315€
🚐 borne 7.20€
The site is in a rural setting.
Surroundings : 🌳
Facilities : 🚿 🔥 🎣 🍴
GPS Longitude : 5.84514 Latitude : 48.19529

*The classification (1 to 5 tents, **black** or red) that we award to selected sites in this guide is our own system. It should not be confused with the classification (1 to 5 stars) of official organisations.*

BUSSANG

88540 – Michelin map **314** J5 – pop. 1 604 – alt. 605
▶ Paris 444 – Belfort 44 – Épinal 59 – Gérardmer 38

ᴍ Sunêlia Domaine de Champé

☏ 03 29 61 61 51. www.domaine-de-champe.com
Address : 14 rue des Champs-Navets (located to the northeast, access via the turning to the left of the church)
Opening times : from mid March to end Nov.
3.5 ha (100 pitches) flat, grassy
Tariff : (2014 Price) 34€ ♣♣ ⇔ 🖭 ⚡ (6A) – Extra per person 6.50€ Reservation fee 19€
Rental rates : (2014 Price) Permanent – 22 🚐 – 8 🏠. Per night from 70 to 170€ – Per week from 490 to 1,190€ – Reservation fee 19€
🚐 borne
Situated beside the Moselle river and a stream.
Surroundings : ⛰
Leisure activities : 🍴 🍽 🏓 daytime 🏋 hammam 🎣 🎯 🎮 🏊 multi-sports ground
Facilities : 🚿 🔥 🏪 🍴 launderette
Nearby : 🚣
GPS Longitude : 6.85748 Latitude : 47.8889

CELLES-SUR-PLAINE

88110 – Michelin map **314** J2 – pop. 857 – alt. 318
▶ Paris 391 – Baccarat 23 – Blâmont 23 – Lunéville 49

⚞ Les Lacs ⚎

📞 03 29 41 28 00. www.camping-paysdeslacs.com

Address : 6 place de la gare (in the southwest of the village)

Opening times : from mid April to end Sept.

15 ha/4 for camping (135 pitches)

Tariff : 24€ ✷✷ ⬌ 🅔 🄗 (10A) – Extra per person 6.50€ – Reservation fee 10€

Rental rates : (2014 Price) (from mid April to end Sept.) – 6 canvas bungalows – 20 gîtes. Per night from 90 to 130€ – Per week from 300 to 440€ – Reservation fee 10€

🚐 30 🅔 18€

Beside the river and close to the lake.

Surroundings : ⬔ 🏕
Leisure activities : ⛲ 🛖 ⚲ ⚲ ✂ 🎣 🛶 ☐
Facilities : & ⛗ ⊞ 🛁 🚿 🚾 🍴 launderette 🧺
At the lake : 🚲 ⛵ ⚓

GPS Longitude : 6.94756
Latitude : 48.4557

LA CHAPELLE-DEVANT-BRUYÈRES

88600 – Michelin map **314** I3 – pop. 621 – alt. 457
▶ Paris 416 – Épinal 31 – Gérardmer 22 – Rambervillers 26

⚞ Les Pinasses

📞 03 29 58 51 10. www.camping-les-pinasses.fr

Address : 215 route de Bruyères (located 1.2km to the northwest on the D 60)

Opening times : from beginning April to end Sept.

3 ha (139 pitches) small lake

Tariff : 24€ ✷✷ ⬌ 🅔 🄗 (6A) – Extra per person 6€

Rental rates : (from beginning April to end Sept.) – 4 🛏 – 12 🏠. Per night from 43 to 79€ – Per week from 260 to 650€

🚐 borne 3€ – 7 🅔 24.40€

Surroundings : 🏕 ⚲⚲
Leisure activities : ✗ 🏖 ⚲ ⚲ 🛶 ☐
Facilities : ⛗ 🅔 🛁 🚾 🍴 launderette

GPS Longitude : 6.77411
Latitude : 48.18974

CHARMES

88130 – Michelin map **314** F2 – pop. 4 613 – alt. 282
▶ Paris 381 – Mirecourt 17 – Nancy 43 – Neufchâteau 58

⚞ Les Îles

📞 03 29 38 87 71. www.campinglesiles.blogspot.fr

Address : 20 rue de l'Écluse (located 1km to the southwest along the D 157 and take the road to the right; near the stadium)

Opening times : from beginning April to end Sept.

3.5 ha (67 pitches) flat, grassy

Tariff : (2014 Price) 14.70€ ✷✷ ⬌ 🅔 🄗 (10A) –
Extra per person 3.35€

In a pleasant setting between the Canal de l'Est and the Moselle river.

Leisure activities : 🏖 🚲 🛶
Facilities : & ⛗ 🚐🅔 🍴
Nearby : ✂ 🎣

GPS Longitude : 6.28668
Latitude : 48.37583

CONTREXÉVILLE

88140 – Michelin map **314** D3 – pop. 3 440 – alt. 342 – ♨
▶ Paris 337 – Épinal 47 – Langres 75 – Luxeuil 73

⚞ Le Tir aux Pigeons

📞 03 29 08 15 06. www.camping-letirauxpigeons.fr

Address : rue du 11 Septembre (located 1km southwest along the D 13, follow the signs for Suriauville)

Opening times : from mid March to end Oct.

1.8 ha (80 pitches)

Tariff : (2014 Price) 19.50€ ✷✷ ⬌ 🅔 🄗 (6A) – Extra per person 5€ Reservation fee 15€

Rental rates : (2014 Price) (from mid March to end Oct.) – 6 🛏 – 4 🏠 – 4 canvas bungalows. Per night from 45 to 70€ – Per week from 270 to 480 €– Reservation fee 15€

🚐 borne – 20 🅔 19.50€

Located at the edge of a wood.

Surroundings : 🌲 ⚲⚲
Leisure activities : 🍴 🛖
Facilities : & ⛗ ⊞ 🛁 🚿 🚾 🍴 🧺

GPS Longitude : 5.88517
Latitude : 48.18022

We have selected the best campsites in France with our usual care, listing those with the best facilities in the most pleasant surroundings.

CORCIEUX

88430 – Michelin map **314** J3 – pop. 1 668 – alt. 534
▶ Paris 424 – Épinal 39 – Gérardmer 15 – Remiremont 43

⚞ Yelloh! Village Le Domaine des Bans

📞 03 29 51 64 67. www.domaine-des-bans.fr

Address : 6 rue James Wiese (near the pl. Notre-Dame)

Opening times : Permanent

15.7 ha (634 pitches)

Tariff : 44€ ✷✷ ⬌ 🅔 🄗 (6A) – Extra per person 8€

Rental rates : Permanent – 250 🛏 – 60 gîtes. Per night from 28 to 259€ – Per week from 196 to 1,813€

🚐 borne 4€ – 10 🅔 12€

In a pleasant setting, in two separate sections (the des Bans site has 600 pitches, the la Tour site has 34 pitches); beside a small lake.

Surroundings : ⬔ 🏕 ⚲
Leisure activities : 🍴 ✗ 🛖 ⚲ ⚲ 🚲 ✂ ☐ 🛶 ☐ ☐ disco
Facilities : & ⛗ 🚐 🛁 🚾 🍴 launderette 🧺
Nearby : 🐴

GPS Longitude : 6.87985
Latitude : 48.16867

⚞ Sites et paysages Au Clos de la Chaume

📞 03 29 50 76 76. www.camping-closdelachaume.com

Address : 21 rue d'Alsace

Opening times : from mid April to end Sept.

4 ha (90 pitches) flat, grassy

Tariff : 25.40€ ✷✷ ⬌ 🅔 🄗 (6A) – Extra per person 6.30€ – Reservation fee 10€

Au Clos de la Chaume (vertical caption)

Rental rates : (from beginning April to end Sept.) – 10 🚐 – 5 🏠 – 2 tent lodges. Per night from 46 to 114€ – Per week from 326 to 798€ – Reservation fee 15€

🚐 borne 6€ – 5 🔲 12€ – 🚌 🕍11€

Surroundings : ♀
Leisure activities : 🏖 🚴 🎯 🐎
Facilities : 🚿 ⚷ 🛖 🏕 🌳 🍴 launderette

G P S Longitude : 6.88383
Latitude : 48.17026

DABO

57850 – Michelin map **307** O7 – pop. 2 636 – alt. 500
▶ Paris 453 – Baccarat 63 – Metz 127 – Phalsbourg 18

⛰ Le Rocher

📞 03 87 07 47 51. www.ot-dabo.fr

Address : route du Rocher (located 1.5km southeast along the D 45, at the junction with the road for Le Rocher)

Opening times : from beginning April to end Sept.

0.5 ha (42 pitches)

Tariff : (2014 Price) 🧍 3.40€ 🚗 1.30€ 🔲 4.20€ – 🕍 (10A) 3.90€

Located in a pleasant forest of fir trees.

Surroundings : ♀
Leisure activities : 🚴
Facilities : 🏕 🏛

G P S Longitude : 7.25267
Latitude : 48.64844

FRESSE-SUR-MOSELLE

88160 – Michelin map **314** I5 – pop. 1 868 – alt. 515
▶ Paris 447 – Metz 178 – Épinal 54 – Mulhouse 56

⛰ Municipal Bon Accueil

📞 03 29 25 08 98. camping.bonaccueil@orange.fr

Address : 36ter rue de Lorraine (take northwestern exit along the N 66, follow the signs for LeThillot; 80m from the Moselle river)

Opening times : from beginning April to mid Nov.

0.6 ha (50 pitches) flat, grassy

Tariff : 🧍 2.65€ 🚗 🔲 1.55€ – 🕍 (16A) 2.76€

🚐 borne 3.32€

Surroundings : ≼
Leisure activities : 🚴
Facilities : 🏕
Nearby : 🛒 🍴

G P S Longitude : 6.78023
Latitude : 47.878

GEMAINGOUTTE

88520 – Michelin map **314** K3 – pop. 119 – alt. 446
▶ Paris 411 – Colmar 59 – Ribeauvillé 31 – St-Dié 14

⛰ Municipal le Violu

📞 03 29 57 70 70. www.gemaingoutte.fr

Address : take the western exit along the RD 59, follow the signs for St-Dié; beside a stream

Opening times : from beginning May to end Oct.

1 ha (48 pitches) flat, grassy

Tariff : (2014 Price) 🧍 2.50€ 🚗 1.70€ 🔲 1.80€ – 🕍 (6A) 2.20€
Rental rates : (2014 Price) Permanent – 2 🏠. Per night from 55€ – Per week from 220 to 425€

🚐 borne 2€ – 10 🔲 6€

Leisure activities : 🚴
Facilities : 🚿 🏕 🛖 🗑

G P S Longitude : 7.08584
Latitude : 48.25361

GÉRARDMER

88400 – Michelin map **314** J4 – pop. 8 757 – alt. 669 – Winter sports : 660/1 350 m
▶ Paris 425 – Belfort 78 – Colmar 52 – Épinal 40

⛰ Les Sapins

📞 03 29 63 15 01. www.camping-gerardmer.com

Address : 18 chemin de Sapois (located 1.5km southwest, 200m from the lake)

Opening times : from beginning April to mid Oct.

1.3 ha (70 pitches)

Tariff : 20.20€ 🧍🧍 🚗 🔲 🕍 (10A) – Extra per person 4.50€ – Reservation fee 8€
Rental rates : (from beginning March to mid Nov.) – 3 🚐 – 1 apartment. Per night from 70 to 80€ – Per week from 300 to 550€ – Reservation fee 10€

🚐 borne 2€ – 🚌 9€

Surroundings : 🏞 ♀
Leisure activities : 🍴
Facilities : ⚷ 🏕 🍴
Nearby : 💧 🐎

G P S Longitude : 6.85614
Latitude : 48.0635

⛰ Les Granges-Bas

📞 03 29 63 12 03. www.lesgrangesbas.fr

Address : 116 chemin des Granges Bas (4km west along the D 417 then turn left at Costet-Beillard, follow road for 1km)

Opening times : from mid Dec. to mid Oct.

2 ha (100 pitches)

Tariff : 17€ 🧍🧍 🚗 🔲 🕍 (6A) – Extra per person 3.95€
Rental rates : (from mid Dec. to mid Oct.) 🏕 – 11 🚐 – 2 apartments – 1 tent lodge. Per night from 38 to 104€ – Per week from 245 to 637€ – Reservation fee 10€

🚐 2 🔲 13€

Surroundings : 🏔 ≼ 🏞
Leisure activities : 🏖 🚴 🍴
Facilities : ⚷ 🍴 launderette

G P S Longitude : 6.80653
Latitude : 48.06927

To visit a town or region, use the MICHELIN Green Guides.

HERPELMONT

88600 – Michelin map **314** I3 – pop. 247 – alt. 480
▶ Paris 413 – Épinal 28 – Gérardmer 20 – Remiremont 33

⛰⛰ Domaine des Messires

📞 03 29 58 56 29. www.domainedesmessires.com

Address : rue des Messires (located 1.5km to the north)

Opening times : from end April to end Sept.

11 ha/2 for camping (100 pitches) flat, grassy

Tariff : 28.70€ 🧍🧍 🚗 🔲 🕍 (10A) – Extra per person 6.50€ – Reservation fee 12€
Rental rates : (from end April to end Sept.) 🏕 – 22 🚐 – 8 canvas bungalows – 5 tent lodges. Per night from 42 to 100€ – Per week from 252 to 700€ – Reservation fee 12€

A pleasant site and setting beside a lake.

Surroundings : 🏞 ≼ lake and mountain 🏞
🎣 ♨
Leisure activities : 🍴 ✕ 🏖 🚴 🎣 🛶
Facilities : 🚿 ⚷ 🏕 🛖 🌳 🍴 launderette
🛏 🚲

G P S Longitude : 6.74278
Latitude : 48.17854

JAULNY

54470 – Michelin map **307** G5 – pop. 262 – alt. 230
▶ Paris 310 – Commercy 41 – Metz 33 – Nancy 51

⚠ La Pelouse

🖉 03 83 81 91 67. www.campingdelapelouse.com – limited spaces for one-night stay

Address : chemin de Fey (500m south of the town, access located near the bridge)

Opening times : from beginning April to end Sept.

2.9 ha (100 pitches)

Tariff : (2014 Price) 21.75€ ✸✸ ⟺ 🔲 🔌 (6A) – Extra per person 4.10€
Rental rates : (2014 Price) Permanent ♿ (2 chalets) – 5 🏠.
Per night 120€ – Per week from 340 to 432€

🚐 borne 15€ – 🚐11€

Situated on a small, wooded hill overlooking the river.

Surroundings : 🌿 ⟺ ♉♉		
Leisure activities : ✕ 🏓 🚣 🎣	**G**	Longitude : 5.88658
Facilities : ♿ ⚬━ 🔲	**P**	Latitude : 48.9705
Nearby : 🎣	**S**	

LUNÉVILLE

54300 – Michelin map **307** J7 – pop. 19 937 – alt. 224
▶ Paris 347 – Épinal 69 – Metz 95 – Nancy 36

⚠ Les Bosquets

🖉 06 74 72 49 73. www.cc-lunevillois.fr

Address : chemin de la Ménagerie (head north towards Château-Salins and take a right turn; after the bridge over the Vézouze)

1 ha (36 pitches)

Rentals : 4 🚐.

Close to the château grounds and gardens

Surroundings : ♉		
Leisure activities : 🏓	**G**	Longitude : 6.49886
Facilities : ♿ ⚬━ 🚿 ⚡ launderette	**P**	Latitude : 48.59647
Nearby : 🚣 ✕ 🏓 🔲	**S**	

MAGNIÈRES

54129 – Michelin map **307** K8 – pop. 341 – alt. 250
▶ Paris 365 – Baccarat 16 – Épinal 40 – Lunéville 22

⚠ Le Pré Fleury

🖉 03 83 73 82 21. www.magnieres.fr

Address : 18 rue de la Barre (500m west along the D 22, follow the signs for Bayon, 200m from the Mortagne river)

Opening times : from beginning April to end Oct.

1 ha (34 pitches)

Tariff : (2014 Price) 11€ ✸✸ ⟺ 🔲 🔌 (10A) – Extra per person 3€

By the old railway station and beside a lake.

Surroundings : 🌿 🚣		
Leisure activities : 🏓 🚣 🚲 🎣 draisines (handcars/rail cycling)	**G**	Longitude : 6.55735
Facilities : ♿ 🚿 ⚡ ⚬ 🖼	**P**	Latitude : 48.44653
Nearby : ✕	**S**	

METZ

57000 – Michelin map **307** I4 – pop. 121 841 – alt. 173
▶ Paris 330 – Longuyon 80 – Pont-à-Mousson 31 – St-Avold 44

⚠ Municipal Metz-Plage

🖉 03 87 68 26 48. www.tourisme.mairie-metz.fr

Address : allée de Metz-Plage (to the north, between the Les Morts bridge and the bridge at Thionville; beside the Moselle – from A 31: take the exit for Metz-Nord Pontiffroy)

2.5 ha (150 pitches)

🚐 borne

Surroundings : ♉♉		
Leisure activities : ✕ 🚣 🚲 🎣	**G**	Longitude : 6.17058
Facilities : ♿ ⚬━ 🔲 🚿 ⚡ 🍽 launderette 🏧	**P**	Latitude : 49.12569
Nearby : 🔲	**S**	

NEUFCHÂTEAU

88300 – Michelin map **314** C2 – pop. 7 040 – alt. 300
▶ Paris 321 – Chaumont 57 – Contrexéville 28 – Épinal 75

⚠ Intercommunal

🖉 03 29 94 19 03. contact@bassin-neufchateau.fr

Address : rue Georges Joecker (take the western exit, follow the signs for Chaumont and take a right turn, near the sports centre)

Opening times : Permanent

0.8 ha (50 pitches) flat, grassy

Tariff : (2014 Price) ✸ 3€ ⟺ 2.80€ 🔲 3€ – 🔌 (10A) 4€

🚐 borne

Surroundings : ♉♉		
Facilities : ♿ ⚬━ 🚿 🖼 ⚡ 🚿	**G**	Longitude : 5.68605
Nearby : ✕ 🏓 🔲 skateboarding	**P**	Latitude : 48.35725
	S	

PLOMBIÈRES-LES-BAINS

88370 – Michelin map **314** G5 – pop. 1 869 – alt. 429 – ⚕
▶ Paris 378 – Belfort 79 – Épinal 38 – Gérardmer 43

⚠ L'Hermitage

🖉 03 29 30 01 87. www.hermitage-camping.com

Address : 54 rue du Boulot (located 1.5km northwest along the D 63, follow the signs for Xertigny then take the D 20, follow the signs for Ruaux)

Opening times : from mid April to mid Oct.

1.4 ha (55 pitches) terraced, relatively flat, flat, grassy, gravelled

Tariff : 18.50€ ✸✸ ⟺ 🔲 🔌 (10A) – Extra per person 4.70€ – Reservation fee 10€

Rental rates : Permanent – 3 🚐 – 4 🏠. Per night from 70 to 120€ – Per week from 260 to 445€ – Reservation fee 10€

🚐 borne 4€ – 38 🔲 5.10€ – 🚐 🔌16.65€

Surroundings : ⟺ ♉		
Leisure activities : 🏓 🚣 🎣	**G**	Longitude : 6.4431
Facilities : ♿ ⚬━ 🍽 🖼 🚿	**P**	Latitude : 47.96859
	S	

⛺ Le Fraiteux

🖉 03 29 66 00 71. www.campingdufraiteux.fr

Address : 81 rue du Camping (4km west along the D 20 and D 20e)

0.8 ha (35 pitches)

Rentals : 2 🚐 – 3 🏠.

Surroundings : 🐾 �︎
Leisure activities : 🏊
Facilities : ⚤ 🎵 launderette

GPS Longitude : 6.41647
Latitude : 47.96573

Some information or pricing may have changed since the guide went to press. We recommend you check the price list online in advance or at the entrance to the campsite and enquire about possible restrictions.

REVIGNY-SUR-ORNAIN

55800 – Michelin map **307** A6 – pop. 3 145 – alt. 144

▶ Paris 239 – Bar-le-Duc 18 – St-Dizier 30 – Vitry-le-François 36

⛺ Municipal du Moulin des Gravières

🖉 03 29 78 73 34. www.ot-revigny-ornain.fr

Address : 1 rue du Stade (in the town towards southern exit, follow the signs for Vitry-le-François and turn right; 100m from the Ornain)

Opening times : from mid April to end Sept.

1 ha (27 pitches) flat, grassy

Tariff : (2014 Price) 🚶 2.50€ 🚐 回 7.10€ – [½] (6A) 3.20€

Rental rates : (2014 Price) Permanent 🚐 – 3 🚐. Per night from 42 to 65€ – Per week from 193 to 224€

🚐 borne

In a pleasant setting beside a stream.

Surroundings : �︎ ♀
Leisure activities : 🛶
Facilities : ⚤ ⚬ 🎵 ⚘ 🔲
Nearby : 🍴 🎣 🛶

GPS Longitude : 4.98373
Latitude : 48.82669

ST-AVOLD

57500 – Michelin map **307** L4 – pop. 16 298 – alt. 260

▶ Paris 372 – Haguenau 117 – Lunéville 77 – Metz 46

⛺ Le Felsberg

🖉 03 87 92 75 05. www.mairie-saint-avold.fr

Address : rue en Verrerie (to the north; near D 603, opposite the Record service station – from A 4: take the exit for St-Avold Carling)

Opening times : Permanent

1.2 ha (33 pitches) terraced, relatively flat, flat, grassy, stony

Tariff : (2014 Price) 🚶 4€ 🚐 回 6€ – [½] (10A) 5€

Rental rates : (2014 Price) Permanent 🚐 – 3 🏠 – 11 🛏. Per night from 55 to 65€ – Per week from 280 to 350€

🚐 borne – 15 回 19€

On the pleasantly wooded slopes of the town.

Surroundings : 🐾 �︎ ♀♀
Leisure activities : 🍴 🗙 🛶 🏊 🚲
Facilities : ⚤ ⚬ 🎵 ⚘ 🚯 🚰

GPS Longitude : 6.71579
Latitude : 49.11102

ST-MAURICE-SUR-MOSELLE

88560 – Michelin map **314** I5 – pop. 1 486 – alt. 560 – Winter sports : 550/1 250 m

▶ Paris 441 – Belfort 41 – Bussang 4 – Épinal 56

🏔 Les Deux Ballons

🖉 03 29 25 17 14. www.camping-deux-ballons.fr

Address : 17 Rue du Stade (take the southwestern exit along the N 66, follow the signs for Le Thillot; beside a stream)

Opening times : from mid April to end Sept.

4 ha (160 pitches)

Tariff : 36.50€ 🚶🚶 🚐 回 [½] (16A) – Extra per person 7.20€ – Reservation fee 15€

Rental rates : (from mid April to mid Sept.) 🚐 – 7 🏠. Per week from 390 to 800€

🚐 borne 7.50€

Surroundings : ♤ ♀♀
Leisure activities : 🍴 🗙 🛶 🏊 🚲 🎣 🗙 🏊 🏊
Facilities : ⚤ ⚬ 🎵 ⚘ 🚰 🚰 launderette 🚯
Nearby : 🚶 walking trails

GPS Longitude : 6.81124
Latitude : 47.8554

For more information on visiting particular towns or regions, consult the relevant regional MICHELIN Green Guide. We also recommend you use the appropriate Michelin regional map to locate your selected campsite, to calculate distances and to work out the best route.

SANCHEY

88390 – Michelin map **314** G3 – pop. 789 – alt. 368

▶ Paris 390 – Metz 129 – Épinal 8 – Nancy 69

🏔 Kawan Village Club Lac de Bouzey

🖉 03 29 82 49 41. www.lacdebouzey.com

Address : 19 rue du Lac (to the south along the D 41)

Opening times : Permanent

3 ha (160 pitches) terraced, relatively flat, flat, grassy

Tariff : 30€ 🚶🚶 🚐 回 [½] (10A) – Extra per person 11€ – Reservation fee 25€

Rental rates : Permanent – 34 🚐. Per week from 840 to 1,260€ Reservation fee 25€

🚐 borne – 10 回 30€ – 🚐 [½]28.50€

Situated opposite the lake; a pleasant reception area and lesiure facillities.

Surroundings : 🐾 🚫 ♀♀
Leisure activities : 🍴 🗙 🦉 🏊 🚲 🏊 disco 🚣 multi-sports ground, entertainment room
Facilities : ⚤ ⚬ 🔲 🎵 ⚘ ⚘ 🚰 🚰 launderette 🚯 🚰

GPS Longitude : 6.3602
Latitude : 48.1667

Key to rentals symbols:

12 🚐	*Number of mobile homes*
20 🏠	*Number of chalets*
6 🛏	*Number of rooms to rent*
Per night 30–50€	*Minimum/maximum rate per night*
Per week 300–1,000€	*Minimum/maximum rate per week*

SAULXURES-SUR-MOSELOTTE

88290 – Michelin map **314** I5 – pop. 2 782 – alt. 464
▶ Paris 431 – Épinal 46 – Gérardmer 24 – Luxeuil-les-Bains 53

⚤ Lac de la Moselotte

℘ 03 29 24 56 56. www.lac-moselotte.fr

Address : 336 route des Amias (located 1.5km west on the old D 43)

Opening times : Permanent

23 ha/3 for camping (75 pitches)

Tariff : 18.80 € ✹✹ ⇔ 🔲 ⚡ (10A) – Extra per person 5 €
Rental rates : Permanent – 7 🚐 – 30 🏠. Per night from 50 to 109 € – Per week from 278 to 736 € – Reservation fee 18 €

On a wooded site beside a lake and near a leisure and activity park.

Surroundings : ⟨ ⇆ △ ⛰
Leisure activities : ▼ 🏠 🏃 🔫 🚴 entertainment room
Facilities : ⅙ ⊶ 🏢 ⚖ ⤵ 🍴 🚿
At the leisure/activities centre : ⛵ ⤏ climbing

GPS Longitude : 6.75236
Latitude : 47.95264

LE THOLY

88530 – Michelin map **314** I4 – pop. 1 589 – alt. 628
▶ Paris 414 – Bruyères 21 – Épinal 30 – Gérardmer 11

⚤ Noirrupt

℘ 03 29 61 81 27. www.jpvacances.com

Address : 15 chemin de l'Étang de Noirrupt (1.3km northwest along the D 11, follow the signs for Épinal and take road to the left)

Opening times : from beginning May to end Sept.

2.9 ha (70 pitches)

Tariff : ✹ 6.10 € ⇔ 🔲 9.90 € – ⚡ (6A) 5 € – Reservation fee 13 €
Rental rates : Permanent ⤸ (from beginning July to end Aug.) – 12 🏠. Per night from 52 to 103 € – Per week from 285 to 445 € Reservation fee 13 €

🚐 borne

Surroundings : ⟨ ⚲
Leisure activities : ▼ 🏠 ⇆ 🔫 🎿 ⤏
Facilities : ⅙ ⊶ ⚖ ⤵ 🍴 launderette
Nearby : ⤏

GPS Longitude : 6.72893
Latitude : 48.08881

LE VAL-D'AJOL

88340 – Michelin map **314** G5 – pop. 4 069 – alt. 380
▶ Paris 382 – Épinal 41 – Luxeuil-les-Bains 18 – Plombières-les-Bains 10

⚤ Municipal

℘ 03 29 66 55 17. mairie@valdajol.fr

Address : rue des Oeuvres (take the northwestern exit along the D 20, follow the signs for Plombières-les-Bains)

1 ha (46 pitches) flat, grassy
Rentals : ⅙ (1 chalet) – 2 🏠.

Surroundings : ⟨ ⇆
Leisure activities : 🏠
Facilities : ⅙ ⊶ 🏢 ⚖ ⤵ 🍴
Nearby : 🎿 🔲 ⤵ ⤏

GPS Longitude : 6.47586
Latitude : 47.92488

VERDUN

55100 – Michelin map **307** D4 – pop. 18 557 – alt. 198
▶ Paris 263 – Bar-le-Duc 56 – Châlons-en-Champagne 89 – Metz 78

⚤ Les Breuils

℘ 03 29 86 15 31. www.camping-lesbreuils.com

Address : 7 allée des Breuils (take the southwestern exit along the bypass (rocade) D S1 towards Paris and take road to the left)

Opening times : from mid March to mid Oct.

5.5 ha (162 pitches) terraced, relatively flat, flat, grassy, gravelled, wood

Tariff : 16.50 € ✹✹ ⇔ 🔲 ⚡ (6A) – Extra per person 4 €
Rental rates : (from mid March to mid Oct.) – 15 🚐. Per night from 60 to 85 € – Per week from 280 to 650 € – Reservation fee 10 € 🚐 borne 5 € – 162 🔲 16.50 € – 🔋 16.50 €

In a rural setting beside a lake.

Surroundings : ⊡ ⚲
Leisure activities : ▼ 🏠 🔫 🚴 🔫 🎿 ⤏ multi-sports ground
Facilities : ⅙ ⊶ 🏢 ⚖ 🍴 launderette ⤵

GPS Longitude : 5.36598
Latitude : 49.15428

VILLEY-LE-SEC

54840 – Michelin map **307** G7 – pop. 415 – alt. 324
▶ Paris 302 – Lunéville 49 – Nancy 20 – Pont-à-Mousson 51

⚤ Camping de Villey-le-Sec

℘ 03 83 63 64 28. www.campingvilleylesec.com

Address : 34 rue de la Gare (situated 2km south along the D 909, follow the signs for Maron and take turning to the right)

Opening times : from beginning April to mid Oct.

2.5 ha (100 pitches) flat, grassy

Tariff : (2014 Price) 22.26 € ✹✹ ⇔ 🔲 ⚡ (10A) – Extra per person 3.80 €
Rental rates : (from beginning April to mid Oct.) ⤸ – 4 🚐 – 1 🏠. Per night from 37 to 80 € – Per week from 255 to 575 €

In a pleasant setting beside the Moselle river.

Surroundings : ⤏
Leisure activities : ▼ 🔫 ⤏ volleyball
Facilities : ⅙ ⊶ 🏢 ⚖ 🍴 launderette ⤵ ⤐

GPS Longitude : 5.98559
Latitude : 48.6526

VITTEL

88800 – Michelin map **314** D3 – pop. 5 434 – alt. 347
▶ Paris 342 – Belfort 129 – Épinal 43 – Chaumont 84

⚤ Aquadis Loisirs de Vittel

℘ 03 29 08 02 71. www.aquadis-loisirs.com

Address : 270 rue Claude Bassot (take the northeastern exit along the D 68, follow the signs for They-sous-Montfort)

Opening times : from end March to end Oct.

3.5 ha (120 pitches)

Tariff : 17 € ✹✹ ⇔ 🔲 ⚡ (10A) – Extra per person 4.85 € – Reservation fee 9.90 €
Rental rates : (from end March to end Oct.) – 12 🚐. Per night from 65 to 70 € – Per week from 227 to 500 € – Reservation fee 19.90 €
🚐 borne 8.50 € – 5 🔲 16 € – 🔋 11 €

Surroundings : ⊡ ⚲
Leisure activities : 🏠 🔫
Facilities : ⅙ ⊶ 🔲 🏢 🍴 launderette

GPS Longitude : 5.95605
Latitude : 48.2082

XONRUPT-LONGEMER

88400 – Michelin map **314** J4 – pop. 1 580 – alt. 714 – Winter sports : 750/1 300 m

▶ Paris 429 – Épinal 44 – Gérardmer 4 – Remiremont 32

⚠ La Vologne

🖉 03 29 60 87 23. www.lavologne.com

Address : 3030 route de Retournemer (4.5km southeast along the D 67a)

Opening times : from beginning May to end Sept.

2.5 ha (100 pitches) flat, grassy

Tariff : (2014 Price) 15.60€ ♣♣ ⇔ 🔲 🔌 (6A) – Extra per person 3.40€

Rental rates : (2014 Price) (from beginning May to end Sept.) – 3 🏠 – 1 yurt – 1 apartment – 2 canvas bungalows. Per night from 32 to 84€ – Per week from 192 to 588€ – Reservation fee 15€

On a wooded site beside the river.

Surroundings : ⩽
Leisure activities :
Facilities : ♿ ⌫ 🛁 🚿 🔲
Nearby : ⚓

GPS	Longitude : 6.96919
	Latitude : 48.06245

⚠ Les Jonquilles

🖉 03 29 63 34 01. www.camping-jonquilles.com

Address : 2586 route du Lac (2.5km southeast)

Opening times : from end April to beginning Oct.

4 ha (247 pitches)

Tariff : 20.94€ ♣♣ ⇔ 🔲 🔌 (10A) – Extra per person 3.80€ – Reservation fee 7€

🚐 borne – 5 🔲 14.80€

In a pleasant location beside the lake.

Surroundings : ⩽ Lac de Longemer and wooded mountains ⛰
Leisure activities : 🍸 🛖 ⚓ 🎣
Facilities : ♿ ⌫ 🛁 🚿 launderette 🚤 🛶

GPS	Longitude : 6.94871
	Latitude : 48.0677

The pitches of many campsites are marked out with low hedges of attractive bushes and shrubs.

G. Bertolissio / hemis.fr

Lourdes may be famous for its many miracles and is visited by millions of pilgrims every year, but some would say that the whole of the Midi-Pyrénées has been uniquely blessed. France's leading agricultural region – larger in size than Belgium or Switzerland – offers sanctuary to a host of exceptional fauna and flora, including the wild bears that still roam the high peaks of the Pyrenees. At sunset, the towers of medieval cities and fortresses are bathed in the evening light. Forbidding Cathar castles are stained with a blood red glow, Albi is veiled in crimson and Toulouse is tinged a romantic pink. This list of the marvels of the region would not be complete without a mention of the Garonne Valley's thriving and fertile 'Garden of France', famous for its vegetables, fruit and wine. This land of milk and honey is rich in culinary traditions, and it would be a crime not to experience the delights of *foie gras* or a *confit de canard* (duck confit) before leaving.

Legend:
- Locality with campsite
- Locality with campsite and rental option
- *Vannes* Locality with campsite and campervan area
- *Moyaux* Locality with at least one pleasant campsite
- Motorway service area for campervans

AGOS-VIDALOS

65400 – Michelin map **342** L4 – pop. 380 – alt. 450
▶ Paris 859 – Toulouse 185 – Tarbes 32 – Pau 51

▲▲▲ Flower Le Soleil du Pibeste ♛♣

✆ 05 62 97 53 23. www.campingpibeste.com

Address : 16 avenue Lavedan (take the southern exit, along the N 21)

1.5 ha (80 pitches) terraced, relatively flat, flat, grassy

Rentals : ♿ (2 mobile homes) – 29 🏠 – 11 🏠.
🚐 borne

*Situated opposite the Pyrenees, with a good range of leisure
facilities and services and a special area for camper vans.*

Surroundings : ⬅♀ Leisure activities : ▼✕ 🏠 ☺daytime 🏃 jacuzzi ⚡ ⛷ multi-sports ground Facilities : ♿ ⊶ 🏢 ⛲ ♨ ☂ ™ launderette ⚓	**G P S** Longitude : -0.07081 Latitude : 43.03562

▲▲▲ Club Airotel La Châtaigneraie

✆ 05 62 97 07 40. www.camping-chataigneraie.com

Address : 46 avenue du Lavedan (along the N 21; at Vidalos)

Opening times : from beginning Dec. to end Sept.

1.5 ha (80 pitches)

Tariff : 29.80€ ♛♣ ⬅ 🔲 ⚡ (6A) – Extra per person 6.20€ –
Reservation fee 17€

Rental rates : (from beginning Dec. to end Sept.) – 17 🏠 –
3 studios – 1 apartment. Per night from 30 to 100€ – Per week
from 285 to 695€

*Looking out towards the Pyrenees, with good quality sanitary
facilities and a variety of rental options.*

Surroundings : ⬅♀♀ Leisure activities : 🏠 ⚡ ⛷ ⛷ Facilities : ♿ ⊶ 🏢 ⛲™ launderette	**G P S** Longitude : -0.07534 Latitude : 43.03201

AGUESSAC

12520 – Michelin map **338** K6 – pop. 872 – alt. 375
▶ Paris 635 – Toulouse 198 – Rodez 62 – Montpellier 129

▲ La Via Natura Les Cerisiers

✆ 05 65 59 87 96. www.campinglescerisiers.com

Address : at Pailhas (3km north along the D 907, follow the signs for
Gorges du Tarn – from the A 75 take exit 44-1)

Opening times : from end April to mid Sept.

2.5 ha (80 pitches) flat, grassy

Tariff : 21€ ♛♣ ⬅ 🔲 ⚡ (6A) – Extra per person 5€
Rental rates : (from end April to mid Sept.) 🦅 – 5 🏠 – 2 tent
lodges. Per night from 30 to 50€ – Per week from 190 to 545€
🚐 borne 5€

*LPO (French bird protection organization) sanctuary on the
banks of the Tarn river.*

Surroundings : 🐟 ⬅♀ Leisure activities : 🏠 ⚓ 🛶 Facilities : ♿ ⊶™ 🔲 Nearby : 🚴	**G P S** Longitude : 3.12053 Latitude : 44.16745

*We value your opinion and welcome your feedback.
Do email us at campingfrance@tp.michelin.com*

AIGUES VIVES

09600 – Michelin map **343** J7 – pop. 559 – alt. 425
▶ Paris 776 – Carcassonne 63 – Castelnaudary 46 – Foix 36

▲▲ La Via Natura La Serre

✆ 05 61 03 06 16. www.camping-la-serre.com

Address : 5 chemin de La Serre (to the west of the town)

Opening times : from beginning April to end Sept.

6.5 ha (40 pitches) undulating, terraced, flat, grassy, fine gravel

Tariff : (2014 Price) 28€ ♛♣ ⬅ 🔲 ⚡ (5A) – Extra per person 5€

Rental rates : (2014 Price) (from beginning April to end Sept.) –
6 🏠 – 8 🏠 – 1 cabin in the trees. Per night from 110 to 180€ –
Per week from 330 to 830€
🚐 borne 4€

*A spacious, undulating site with trees; some pitches have a
view of the Pyrenées.*

Surroundings : 🐟 ▭ ♀♀ Leisure activities : 🏠 ⚡ 🚴 ⛷ Facilities : ♿ ⊶ 🔲 ♨™ 🔲	**G P S** Longitude : 1.87199 Latitude : 42.99741

ALBI

81000 – Michelin map **338** E7 – pop. 48 858 – alt. 174
▶ Paris 699 – Toulouse 77 – Montpellier 261 – Rodez 71

▲▲▲ Albirondack Park

✆ 05 63 60 37 06. www.albirondack.fr

Address : 1 allée de la Piscine

Opening times : Permanent

1.8 ha (84 pitches) terraced, flat, grassy, stony

Tariff : 35.70€ ♛♣ ⬅ 🔲 ⚡ (10A) – Extra per person 7.50€ –
Reservation fee 10€

Rental rates : Permanent ♿ (1 chalet) 🦅 – 10 🏠 – 27 🏠 –
2 cabins in the trees. Per night from 100 to 240€ – Per week
from 350 to 1,000€ – Reservation fee 25€
🚐 borne – 5 🔲 30€

There's a bus for the town centre.

Surroundings : ▭ ♀♀ Leisure activities : ▼✕ ☕ hammam, jacuzzi ⛷ spa centre Facilities : ♿ ⊶ ☂ ™ launderette ⚓	**G P S** Longitude : 2.16397 Latitude : 43.93445

ALRANCE

12430 – Michelin map **338** I6 – pop. 404 – alt. 750
▶ Paris 664 – Albi 63 – Millau 52 – Rodez 37

▲▲▲ Les Cantarelles

✆ 05 65 46 40 35. www.lescantarelles.com

Address : 3km south along the D 25; beside the Lac du Villefranche-
de-Panat

Opening times : from beginning May to end Sept.

3.5 ha (165 pitches) relatively flat, flat, grassy

Tariff : 22€ ♛♣ ⬅ 🔲 ⚡ (6A) – Extra per person 4.80€
Rental rates : (from beginning May to end Sept.) – 15 🏠.
Per night from 50 to 65€ – Per week from 350 to 680€

Surroundings : ⬅ ▭ ♀ ⛰ Leisure activities : ▼✕ 🏠 ⚡ 🚴 ⛷ ⚓ 🦅 pedalos 🏊 Facilities : ♿ ⊶ 🔲 ☂ ™ launderette	**G P S** Longitude : 2.68933 Latitude : 44.10669

ANGLARS-JUILLAC

46140 – Michelin map **337** D5 – pop. 331 – alt. 98
▶ Paris 590 – Cahors 26 – Gourdon 41 – Sarlat-la-Canéda 53

⚠ Base Nautique de Floiras

🔗 05 65 36 27 39. www.campingfloiras.com

Address : in the village, beside the river

Opening times : from beginning April to mid Oct.

1 ha (25 pitches) open site, flat, grassy

Tariff : 🛉 6€ ⇦ 🔲 12.50€ – ⚡ (10A) 4.25€ – Reservation fee 12€

Rental rates : (from beginning May to end Sept.) – 2 canvas bungalows. Per week from 375 to 750€ – Reservation fee 12€

All the pitches are opposite the Lot river.

Surroundings : 🏞 ♨♨
Leisure activities : 🛐 ✕ 🎣 🛶
Facilities : 🛁 ⊶ 🍴 launderette

ARAGNOUET

65170 – Michelin map **342** N8 – pop. 244 – alt. 1 100
▶ Paris 842 – Arreau 24 – Bagnères-de-Luchon 56 – Lannemezan 51

⚠ Fouga Pic de Bern

🔗 06 84 72 47 24. fouga.marc@orange.fr

Address : at Fabian (2.8km northeast along the D 118, follow the signs for St-Lary-Soulan, near the Neste-d'Avre)

Opening times : from beginning June to end Sept.

3 ha (80 pitches) open site, terraced, flat, grassy

Tariff : 🛉 3.60€ ⇦ 🔲 3.40€ – ⚡ (13A) 6.90€
🚐 borne – 🅿 12.50€

Choose the meadow part of the site, with both sun and shade, furthest away from the road.

Surroundings : 🏞 ♨♨
Leisure activities : 🛐 ✕ 🏠
Facilities : 🛁 ⊶ 🍴 🐴

ARCIZANS-AVANT

65400 – Michelin map **342** L5 – pop. 360 – alt. 640
▶ Paris 868 – Toulouse 194 – Tarbes 41 – Pau 61

⚠ Le Lac

🔗 05 62 97 01 88. www.camping-du-lac-pyrenees.com

Address : 29 chemin d'Azun (take the western exit, not far from the lake)

Opening times : from mid May to mid Sept.

2 ha (97 pitches) relatively flat

Tariff : 34.40€ 🛉🛉 ⇦ 🔲 ⚡ (10A) – Extra per person 8.20€ – Reservation fee 25€

Rental rates : Permanent – 14 🏠. Per night from 77 to 92€ – Per week from 315 to 810€
🚐 borne – 🅿 17.90€

Many pitches have an uninterrupted view of the Pyrenees, the village and church.

Surroundings : 🏞 ♨♨
Leisure activities : 🏠 🚣 🚲 ⛵
Facilities : 🛁 ⊶ 🄶 🍴 launderette 🐴
Nearby : 🎣

🏔 Les Châtaigniers

🔗 05 62 97 94 77. www.camping-les-chataigniers.com

Address : 6 rue Cap Deth Vilatge

Opening times : from end May to mid Sept.

3 ha (51 pitches) terraced, relatively flat, flat, grassy, wood

Tariff : (2014 Price) 24.60€ 🛉🛉 ⇦ 🔲 ⚡ (6A) – Extra per person 6.60€

Rental rates : (2014 Price) (from beginning April to mid Nov.) – 2 🏠. Per night from 30 to 85€ – Per week from 200 to 580€

Shaded pitches with a view of the valley and the village.

Surroundings : 🏞 ♨♨
Leisure activities : 🏠 🚣
Facilities : 🛁 ⊶ 🄰 launderette
Nearby : 🎣

Longitude : -0.10488
Latitude : 42.98505

ARGELÈS-GAZOST

65400 – Michelin map **342** L6 – pop. 3 297 – alt. 462 – ♨
▶ Paris 863 – Lourdes 13 – Pau 58 – Tarbes 32

🏔 Sunêlia Les Trois Vallées 🎪

🔗 05 62 90 35 47. www.L3v.fr

Address : avenue des Pyrénées (take the northern exit)

Opening times : from mid April to mid Oct.

11 ha (438 pitches) flat, grassy

Tariff : 48€ 🛉🛉 ⇦ 🔲 ⚡ (10A) – Extra per person 13.50€ – Reservation fee 30€

Rental rates : (from mid April to mid Oct.) 🛁 (2 mobile homes) – 250 🚐 – 2 tent lodges. Per night from 45 to 102€ – Per week from 420 to 1,596€ – Reservation fee 30€
🚐 borne

A water park and shops with beautiful floral decoration and very well-appointed sanitary facilities.

Surroundings : 🚄 ♨♨
Leisure activities : 🛐 ✕ 🏠 🎮 🛀 jacuzzi 🚣 🎣 ⛵ disco, multi-sports ground, entertainment room
Facilities : 🛁 ⊶ 🚿 🐴 🍴 launderette 🐴
Nearby : 🛒 🎿 🏇

Longitude : -0.09718
Latitude : 43.0121

ARRAS-EN-LAVEDAN

65400 – Michelin map **342** L5 – pop. 527 – alt. 700
▶ Paris 868 – Toulouse 193 – Tarbes 40 – Pau 60

🏔 L'Idéal

🔗 05 62 97 03 13. www.camping-ideal-pyrenees.com – alt. 600

Address : route du Val d'Azun (300m northwest along the D 918, follow the signs for Argelès-Gazost)

Opening times : from beginning June to mid Sept.

2 ha (60 pitches) terraced, flat, grassy

Tariff : (2014 Price) 🛉 4.50€ ⇦ 🔲 4.50€ – ⚡ (10A) 9.50€

Rental rates : (2014 Price) Permanent 🦮 – 2 🏠. Per night from 60€ – Per week from 280 to 550€
🚐 borne 3€

A pleasant site, but choose the pitches the furthest away from the road.

Surroundings : ♨♨
Leisure activities : 🏠 🚣 ⛵
Facilities : 🛁 ⊶ 🄰 🍴 launderette

Longitude : -0.11954
Latitude : 42.99483

ARRENS-MARSOUS

65400 – Michelin map **342** K7 – pop. 741 – alt. 885
▶ Paris 875 – Argelès-Gazost 13 – Cauterets 29 – Laruns 37

▲ La Hèche

📞 05 62 97 02 64. www.campinglaheche.com – 🏕

Address : 54 route d'Azun (800m east along the D 918, follow the signs for Argelès-Gazost and take the road to the right; beside the Gave d'Arrens (river)

Opening times : from beginning June to end Sept.

5 ha (166 pitches) flat, grassy

Tariff : (2014 Price) 13.34€ 🚶🚶 🚗 🔲 🔌 (4A) – Extra per person 3.60€
Rental rates : (2014 Price) (from beginning Feb. to end Nov.) ⚡ – 3 🚐. Per week from 350 to 500€ – Reservation fee 99€

Surroundings : 🌳 ≤ 🏡	**G**	Longitude : -0.20534
Leisure activities : 🏛 🏊	**P**	Latitude : 42.95847
Facilities : 🚿 🛒 🏛 🧺 launderette	**S**	
Nearby : 🏊 🍴 🎿 🏸 🛶		

▲ Le Moulian

📞 05 62 97 41 18. jean-guy.domec@wanadoo.fr

Address : 42 rue du Bourg (500m southeast of the village of Marsous)

Opening times : from beginning June to end Dec.

12 ha/4 for camping(75 pitches) flat, grassy

Tariff : 🚶 4.50€ 🚗 🔲 4.50€ – 🔌 (6A) 5€
Rental rates : (from beginning June to end Dec.) – 10 🚐 – 2 🏠 – 2 gîtes. Per night from 50 to 75€ – Per week from 350 to 497€
🚐 borne 6€ – 2 🔲 9€ – 🚰 8€
The site is near a large equestrian centre with donkeys, ponies and horses.

Surroundings : 🌳 ≤ 🏡	**G**	Longitude : -0.19638
Leisure activities : 🍴 🍴 🏛 🏊 🐴	**P**	Latitude : 42.96232
Facilities : 🚿 🛒 🚿 🧺 launderette 🚰	**S**	
Nearby : 🏊 🍴 🎿 🛶 🏊		

ARVIEU

12120 – Michelin map **338** H5 – pop. 861 – alt. 730
▶ Paris 663 – Albi 66 – Millau 59 – Rodez 31

▲ Le Doumergal

📞 05 65 74 24 92. www.camping-doumergal-aveyron.fr

Address : rue de la Rivière (to the west of the town; beside a stream)

1.5 ha (27 pitches) relatively flat, flat, grassy

Surroundings : 🌳 🏡 🌳	**G**	Longitude : 2.66014
Leisure activities : 🏊	**P**	Latitude : 44.19066
Facilities : 🚿 🛒 🚿 🚰	**S**	
Nearby : 🍴		

These symbols are used for a campsite that is exceptional in its category:

🔺🔺🔺...🔺 *Particularly pleasant setting, quality and range of services available*

🌳🌳 *Tranquil, isolated site – quiet site, particularly at night*

≤ ≤ *Exceptional view – interesting or panoramic view*

ASTON

09310 – Michelin map **343** I8 – pop. 219 – alt. 563
▶ Paris 788 – Andorra-la-Vella 78 – Ax-les-Thermes 20 – Foix 59

▲▲▲ Le Pas de l'Ours

📞 05 61 64 90 33. www.lepasdelours.fr

Address : at Les Gesquis (south of the town, near the rapids)

Opening times : from beginning June to beginning Sept.

3.5 ha (50 pitches)

Tariff : 🚶 7€ 🚗 🔲 9€ – 🔌 (6A) 4€ – Reservation fee 7€
Rental rates : (from mid Oct. to mid Sept.) – 27 🏠 – 4 gîtes. Per night from 70 to 85€ – Per week from 310 to 662€ – Reservation fee 7€

A pleasant site with rental options of a high standard.

Surroundings : 🌳 ≤ 🏡 🌳	**G**	Longitude : 1.67181
Leisure activities : 🏛 🏊 🚴 🍴 🦎 entertainment room	**P**	Latitude : 42.77245
Facilities : 🚿 🛒 (July–Aug.) 🍴 launderette	**S**	
Nearby : 🛶 🏊		

In order for the guide to remain wholly objective, the selection of campsites is made on an entirely independent basis.

AUCH

32000 – Michelin map **336** F8 – pop. 21 792 – alt. 169
▶ Paris 713 – Agen 74 – Bordeaux 205 – Tarbes 74

▲▲▲ Le Castagné

📞 06 07 97 40 37. www.domainelecastagne.com

Address : chemin de Naréoux (4km east along the D 924, follow the signs for Toulouse and take a right turn.)

Opening times : from mid June to end Sept.

70 ha/2 for camping(24 pitches)

Tariff : 🚶 5€ 🚗 🔲 5€ – 🔌 (15A) 4€
Rental rates : Permanent – 4 🚐 – 9 🏠 – 4 🏠 – 1 apartment. Per night from 80 to 130€ – Per week from 360 to 630€ – Reservation fee 20€

The accommodation includes 4 B&B rooms.

Surroundings : 🌳 ≤ 🌳	**G**	Longitude : 0.6337
Leisure activities : 🏛 🏊 🏊 🎿 🛶 pedalos	**P**	Latitude : 43.6483
Facilities : 🚿 🛒 🍴 🔲	**S**	

AUCUN

65400 – Michelin map **342** K7 – pop. 261 – alt. 853
▶ Paris 872 – Argelès-Gazost 10 – Cauterets 26 – Lourdes 22

▲ Azun Nature

📞 05 62 97 45 05. www.camping-azun-nature.com

Address : 1 route des Poueyes (700m east along the D 918, follow the signs for Argeles-Gazost and take turning to the right, 300m from the Gave d'Azun (river)

Opening times : from beginning May to end Sept.

1 ha (43 pitches) flat, grassy

Tariff : 21.50€ 🚶🚶 🚗 🔲 🔌 (10A) – Extra per person 4.50€

Rental rates : Permanent – 10 🏠. Per week from 200 to 520€

A well-kept site with good quality rental options, open summer and winter.

Surroundings : 🦢 ⬚ 🌳
Leisure activities : 🏠 ⛹
Facilities : 🚿 ⚙ 🍳 🍴 launderette
Nearby : 🚴 🥾 walking trails

| G P S | Longitude : -0.18796 |
| | Latitude : 42.97399 |

⚠ Lascrouts

𝄞 05 62 97 42 62. www.camping-lascrouts.com – limited spaces for one-night stay

Address : 2 route de Las Poueyes (700m east along the D 918, follow the signs for Argelès-Gazost and take turning to the right, 300m from the Gave d'Azun (river)

Opening times : Permanent

4 ha (72 pitches) terrace, relatively flat, flat, grassy

Tariff : 14.50€ 👫 🚗 🔲 ⚡ (6A) – Extra per person 3.50€ – Reservation fee 10€

Rental rates : Permanent – 2 🚐 – 13 🏠. Per night from 80 to 90€ – Per week from 240 to 510€ – Reservation fee 20€

A good choice of mobile homes and owner-occupied chalets, but very few pitches for tents or caravans.

Surroundings : 🦢 ⬚
Leisure activities : 🏠 ⛹
Facilities : 🚿 ⚙ 🍳 🍴 🔲
Nearby : paragliding

| G P S | Longitude : -0.18612 |
| | Latitude : 42.97361 |

09800 – Michelin map **343** D7 – pop. 63 – alt. 629
▶ Paris 788 – Aspet 22 – Castillon-en-Couserans 12 – St-Béat 30

⚠ La Vie en Vert

𝄞 05 61 96 82 66. www.lavieenvert.com

Address : east of the town; beside the Bouigane river

0.3 ha (15 pitches) flat, grassy

Rentals : 🚿 – 1 🛏 – 2 tipis.

The site is based around an old farmhouse made of local stone that has been painstakingly restored.

Surroundings : 🦢 ⬚ 🌳
Leisure activities : 🏠 🎣
Facilities : 🚿 ⚙ 🔲
Nearby : 🍴 ✗

| G P S | Longitude : 0.91978 |
| | Latitude : 42.93161 |

09140 – Michelin map **343** G8 – pop. 221 – alt. 750 – ⚓
▶ Paris 807 – Foix 76 – Oust 17 – St-Girons 34

⚠ Le Coulédous

𝄞 05 61 66 43 56. www.camping-aulus-couledous.com

Address : route de Saint-Girons (take northwestern exit along the D 32, near the Garbet)

Opening times : Permanent

1.6 ha (70 pitches)

Tariff : (2014 Price) 21.50€ 👫 🚗 🔲 ⚡ (10A) – Extra per person 4.70€

Rental rates : (2014 Price) Permanent – 18 🏠. Per night from 40 to 73€ – Per week from 220 to 510€
🚐 borne – 10 🔲 13€

In the middle of a park boasting some ancient trees, but the chalets and sanitary facilities are also rather old.

Surroundings : ⬚ 🌳
Leisure activities : 🏠 ⛹
Facilities : 🚿 ⚙ 🔲 🍴 launderette
Nearby : ✗ 🐎 🥾 forest trail

| G P S | Longitude : 1.33215 |
| | Latitude : 42.79394 |

31420 – Michelin map **343** D5 – pop. 1 187 – alt. 430
▶ Paris 750 – Auch 71 – Bagnères-de-Luchon 69 – Pamiers 92

⚠ Les Petites Pyrénées

𝄞 05 61 87 06 91. fabrice.ramalingom@orange.fr

Address : route de Boussens (take the southeastern exit along the D 635, to the right, near the stadium – A64 take exit 21)

0.9 ha (38 pitches) flat, grassy

Rentals : 2 🚐.

A small, simple site, rather old sanitary facilities, free use of the municipal pool. Groups welcome.

Surroundings : ⬚ 🌳
Leisure activities : 🏠
Facilities : ⚙ 🍴 launderette
Nearby : ✗ 🏊 🐎

| G P S | Longitude : 0.89132 |
| | Latitude : 43.21389 |

Key to rentals symbols :

12 🚐	*Number of mobile homes*
20 🏠	*Number of chalets*
6 🛏	*Number of rooms to rent*
Per night 30–50€	*Minimum/maximum rate per night*
Per week 300–1,000€	*Minimum/maximum rate per week*

09110 – Michelin map **343** J8 – pop. 1 384 – alt. 720 – ⚓
▶ Paris 805 – Toulouse 129 – Foix 43 – Pamiers 62

⚠ Sunêlia Le Malazeou ♨

𝄞 05 61 64 69 14. www.campingmalazeou.com

Address : road RN 20, route de l'Espagne (situated at Savignac-les-Ormeaux, 1km to the northwest, follow the signs for Foix)

Opening times : from beginning Dec. to mid Nov.

6.5 ha (244 pitches) terraced, flat, grassy, stony

Tariff : 29.50€ 👫 🚗 🔲 ⚡ (10A) – Extra per person 7.50€ – Reservation fee 30€

Rental rates : (from beginning Dec. to mid Nov.) – 21 🚐 – 46 🏠. Per night from 48 to 128€ – Per week from 336 to 896€ Reservation fee 30€
🚐 borne 11€

Plenty of shade, beside the Ariège river, but choose the pitches away from the road in preference.

Surroundings : 🌳
Leisure activities : 🍴 ✗ 🏠 🌙nighttime 🥾
🎯 ⛱ ⛹ 🏊 🎣
Facilities : 🚿 🔲 🍳 🍴 launderette 🐕

| G P S | Longitude : 1.82538 |
| | Latitude : 42.72852 |

AYZAC-OST

65400 – Michelin map **342** L4 – pop. 399 – alt. 430
▶ Paris 862 – Toulouse 188 – Tarbes 35 – Pau 54

⚠ La Bergerie

✆ 05 62 97 59 99. www.camping-labergerie.com

Address : 8 chemin de la Bergerie (take the southern exit along the N 21 and take road to the left)

Opening times : Permanent

2 ha (105 pitches) flat, grassy

Tariff : (2014 Price) 30.70€ ✿✿ ⚙ 🔲 🔌 (6A) – Extra per person 7.60€
Reservation fee 15€
Rental rates : (2014 Price) Permanent ⚡ – 13 🚐. Per night from 50 to 120€ – Per week from 325 to 820€

A pleasant, small, landscaped water park surrounded by a number of owner-occupied mobile homes.

Surroundings : ⬡ 🎣
Leisure activities : 🍷 🏠 ⚓ 🏊 ⛷
Facilities : 🚿 ⚬ 🍴 🍽 📺
Nearby : 🎯 ✕ ⛵

GPS Longitude : -0.0961
Latitude : 43.01824

BAGNAC-SUR-CÉLÉ

46270 – Michelin map **337** I3 – pop. 1 562 – alt. 234
▶ Paris 593 – Cahors 83 – Decazeville 16 – Figeac 15

⚠ Les Berges du Célé

✆ 06 64 99 82 33. www.camping-sudouest.com

Address : at La Plaine (to the southeast of the town, behind the station; beside the Célé river)

1 ha (44 pitches) flat, grassy
Rentals : 5 🚐 – 2 canvas bungalows.

Surroundings : 🎣
Leisure activities : ⚓ 🏊 🛶
Facilities : ⚬ 🍽 📺
Nearby : 🍴

GPS Longitude : 2.16009
Latitude : 44.66461

BAGNÈRES-DE-BIGORRE

65200 – Michelin map **342** M6 – pop. 8 040 – alt. 551 – ⚘
▶ Paris 829 – Lourdes 24 – Pau 66 – St-Gaudens 65

⚠ Le Monlôo

Le Monlôo

✆ 05 62 95 19 65. www.lemonloo.com

Address : 5 chemin de Monlôo (take the northeastern exit, along the D 938, follow the signs for Toulouse then take left turn 1.4km along the D 8, follow the signs for Tarbes and take the road to the right)

Opening times : Permanent

4 ha (199 pitches)

Tariff : (2014 Price) 25.30€ ✿✿ ⚙ 🔲
🔌 (16A) – Extra per person 5€
Rental rates : (2014 Price) Permanent – 16 🚐 – 9 🏠. Per night from 57 to 110€ – Per week from 275 to 775€
🚐 borne 14€ – 5 🔲 14€

A range of good quality rental options with a small eco lake (no chemicals) and a pretty beach.

Surroundings : 🏞 ⬡ 🎣
Leisure activities : 🏠 ⚓ 🏊 ≈ (lake) ⛷
Facilities : 🚿 ⚬ 🍽 🍴 launderette

GPS Longitude : 0.15107
Latitude : 43.0817

⚠ Les Fruitiers

✆ 05 62 95 25 97. www.camping-les-fruitiers.com

Address : 8 rue Pierre Latécoère (rte de Toulouse)

Opening times : from mid April to end Oct.

1.5 ha (88 pitches) flat, grassy

Tariff : (2014 Price) ✿ 4.50€ ⚙ 🔲 4.50€ – 🔌 (6A) 5€
Rental rates : (2014 Price) (from mid April to end Oct.) ⚡ – 2 🚐 – 3 apartments. Per night from 50€ – Per week from 250 to 400€
🚐 borne 5.50€

Lovely shaded grass areas, but choose the pitches away from the road.

Surroundings : ⬡ Pic du Midi (peak) 🎣
Leisure activities : 🏠 ⚓
Facilities : ⚬ 🍽 🍴 launderette
Nearby : 🎿

GPS Longitude : 0.15746
Latitude : 43.07108

BAGNÈRES-DE-LUCHON

31110 – Michelin map **343** B8 – pop. 2 600 – alt. 630 – ⚘ – Winter sports : at Superbagnères : 1 440/2 260 m
▶ Paris 814 – Bagnères-de-Bigorre 96 – St-Gaudens 48 – Tarbes 98

⚠ Pradelongue

Pradelongue

✆ 05 61 79 86 44. www.camping-pradelongue.com

Address : at Moustajon (2km north along the D 125, near the Intermarché supermarket)

Opening times : from beginning April to end Sept.

4 ha (142 pitches) flat, grassy

Tariff : 26.60€ ✿✿ ⚙ 🔲 🔌 (10A) – Extra per person 6.95€ – Reservation fee 13€
Rental rates : Permanent ⚡ – 18 🚐. Per week from 275 to 660€
Reservation fee 13€
🚐 borne – 7 🔲 14€

Plenty of green spaces, perfect for team sports or just relaxing

Surroundings : ⬡ 🏕 🎣
Leisure activities : 🏠 ⚓ 🎿
Facilities : 🚿 ⚬ 🍽 🍴 ⛷ 🍴 launderette
Nearby : 🎯 🐎

GPS Longitude : 0.5981
Latitude : 42.81667

⚠ Les Myrtilles 👥

✆ 05 61 79 89 89. www.camping-myrtilles.com

Address : at Moustajon (2.5km north along the D 125, beside a stream.)

Opening times : from mid Dec. to mid Nov.

2 ha (100 pitches) flat, grassy

Tariff : 22.70€ ✿✿ ⚙ 🔲 🔌 (10A) – Extra per person 4.90€ – Reservation fee 14€
Rental rates : Permanent – 17 🚐 – 24 🛏 – 4 canvas bungalows – 1 gîte. Per night from 33 to 65€ – Per week from 227 to 623€
Reservation fee 14€
🚐 3 🔲 10.90€

A free shuttle to the thermal baths.

Surroundings : ⬡ 🏕 🎣
Leisure activities : 🍷 ✕ 🏠 🏃 ⚓ 🎿
Facilities : 🚿 ⚬ 🍽 🍴 ⛷ 🍴 launderette 🐕
Nearby : 🐎

GPS Longitude : 0.59975
Latitude : 42.81663

⛰ Domaine Arôme Vanille ▲▴

℘ 05 61 79 00 38. www.camping-aromevanille.com

Address : at Montauban-de-Luchon, route de Subercarrère, (located 1.5km east along the D 27)

Opening times :

5 ha (194 pitches) flat and relatively flat, grassy

Tariff : (2014 Price) 20.50€ ♛♙ ⇔ 🅴 (10A) – Extra per person 4.50€

Rental rates : (2014 Price) Permanent – 8 ⛺ – 21 🏠. Per night from 60 to 75€ – Per week from 319 to 639 € – Reservation fee 10€

🚐 borne

Pitches in both the shade and the sun.

Surroundings : 🐾 🏕 ♀
Leisure activities : 🍸 ✕ 🏓 🏊 🚲
Facilities : ♿ ⚷ 🍴 🚿 📷 ⚱

GPS Longitude : 0.60814
Latitude : 42.79496

⛺ Au Fil de l'Oô

℘ 05 61 79 30 74. www.campingaufildeloo.com

Address : 37 avenue de Vénasque (1.5km south along the D 618)

Opening times : from mid March to beginning Nov.

2.5 ha (104 pitches) flat, grassy

Tariff : 18.10€ ♛♙ ⇔ 🅴 (10A) – Extra per person 5€ – Reservation fee 15€

Rental rates : (from mid Feb. to beginning Nov.) – 8 ⛺. Per week from 265 to 1,090€ – Reservation fee 15€

🚐 borne

Located by a stream with plenty of shade, but choose those pitches furthest away from the road.

Surroundings : 🏕 ♀♀
Leisure activities : 🛶
Facilities : ♿ ⚷ launderette ⚱

GPS Longitude : 0.6003
Latitude : 42.77777

BARBOTAN-LES-THERMES

32150 – Michelin map **336** B6 – ♨
▶ Paris 703 – Aire-sur-l'Adour 37 – Auch 75 – Condom 37

⛰ Club Airotel Le Lac de l'Uby ▲▴

℘ 05 62 09 53 91. www.camping-uby.com

Address : avenue du Lac (located 1.5km southwest, follow the signs for Cazaubon and take the turning to the left, at the leisure and activity park (beside the lake)

Opening times : from beginning April to end Oct.

6 ha (274 pitches)

Tariff : (2014 Price) 26€ ♛♙ ⇔ 🅴 (10A) – Extra per person 7€ – Reservation fee 8€

Rental rates : (2014 Price) (from beginning April to end Oct.) – 50 ⛺ – 7 🏠. Per night from 35 to 106€ – Per week from 240 to 740€ – Reservation fee 8€

🚐 borne – 26 🅴 30€

A pleasant parking spot for campervans is 300m away.

Surroundings : 🐾 ⚓ ♀♀ ⛰
Leisure activities : ✕ 🛶 🏓 🏊 🚲 ♪ 🏊 ⛵ multi-sports ground skate park
Facilities : ♿ ⚷ 🍴 🚿 launderette, refrigerators
Nearby : ✕ 🏖 (beach) pedalos

GPS Longitude : -0.04431
Latitude : 43.93971

LA BASTIDE DE SÉROU

09240 – Michelin map **343** G6 – pop. 959 – alt. 410
▶ Paris 779 – Foix 18 – Le Mas-d'Azil 17 – Pamiers 38

⛰ L'Arize

℘ 05 61 65 81 51. www.camping-arize.com

Address : take the eastern exit along the D 117, follow the signs for Foix then continue 1.5km along the D 15, follow signs to Nescus to the right; beside the river

Opening times : from beginning April to beginning Nov.

7.5 ha/1.5 (90 pitches) flat, grassy

Tariff : 28.60€ ♛♙ ⇔ 🅴 (6A) – Extra per person 6.40€

Rental rates : (from beginning April to beginning Nov.) – 16 ⛺ – 4 🏠. Per night from 33.60 to 104€ – Per week from 235 to 728€

🚐 borne 4.50€ – 9 🅴 18.50€ –

A small stream runs through the site, separating the shady side from the sunny side.

Surroundings : 🐾 🏕 ♀♀
Leisure activities : 🛶 🏓 🚲 🏊 ♪
Facilities : ♿ ⚷ 🚐📷 🍴 ⚱ 🚿 launderette
Nearby : ✕ 🐴

GPS Longitude : 1.44509
Latitude : 43.00168

⛺ Village Vacances Les Lambrilles (rental of chalets only)

℘ 05 61 64 53 53. www.seronais.com

Address : in the town; beside the Arize river

1 ha flat, grassy

Rentals : 24 🏠.

Semi-detached chalets in pairs near a stream and a small fishing lake.

Surroundings : 🐾
Leisure activities : 🛶 🏓 🏊 ♪
Facilities : ⚷ 🎮 🍴 📷
Nearby : ✕ 🎣

GPS Longitude : 1.42958
Latitude : 43.00974

BEAUMONT-DE-LOMAGNE

82500 – Michelin map **337** B8 – pop. 3 809 – alt. 400
▶ Paris 662 – Agen 60 – Auch 51 – Castelsarrasin 27

⛰ Municipal Le Lomagnol ▲▴

℘ 05 63 26 12 00. www.village-de-loisirs.com

Address : avenue du Lac (800m east, access via the diversion and a road; beside a small lake)

Opening times : from beginning April to end Oct.

6 ha/1.5 (100 pitches) flat, grassy

Tariff : (2014 Price) 17.50€ ♛♙ ⇔ 🅴 (10A) – Extra per person 3.90€ – Reservation fee 15€

Rental rates : (2014 Price) Permanent ♿ (1 mobile home) 🅿 – 4 ⛺ – 24 🏠 – 24 gîtes. Per night from 60 to 80€ – Per week from 210 to 549€ – Reservation fee 15€

🚐 borne

The site is spread out beside the lake; there's the opportunity to take part in different water sports, but bathing is not permitted.

Surroundings : 🏕 ♀♀
Leisure activities : 🛶 🌙nighttime 🏓 ⛵ jacuzzi 🏊 🚲 ✕ 🏖 🏊 ♪ pedalos 🛶
Facilities : ♿ ⚷ 🍴 🚿 📷 ⚱
Nearby : ✕ fitness trail

GPS Longitude : 0.99864
Latitude : 43.88295

BÉDUER

46100 – Michelin map **337** H4 – pop. 730 – alt. 260
▶ Paris 572 – Cahors 63 – Figeac 9 – Villefranche-de-Rouergue 36

⛰ Pech Ibert

✆ 05 65 40 05 85. www.camping-pech-ibert.com

Address : at Pech Ibert (located 1km northwest along the D 19, follow the signs for Cajarc and take turning to the right)

Opening times : from mid March to end Oct.

1 ha (37 pitches) flat, grassy, stony, fine gravel

Tariff : ♣ 3.30€ ⇌ 1.20€ 📧 3.50€ 🔌 (6A) 3.50€
Rental rates : (from mid March to end Oct.) – 1 caravan – 3 🚐 – 3 🏠 – 2 canvas bungalows. Per night from 11 to 80€ – Per week from 280 to 420€ – Reservation fee 20€
🚐 borne 6€ – 2 📧 9€ – 🚐 9€
Some pitches are well shaded.

Surroundings : 🌿 🗭 ♀
Leisure activities : 🍸 🖼 ⛵ 🎣
Facilities : ⚹ ☎ 🏛 🚿 🍴 📷 refrigerators
Nearby : ✖️

G P S Longitude : 1.9375
Latitude : 44.57833

LE BEZ

81260 – Michelin map **338** G9 – pop. 803 – alt. 644
▶ Paris 745 – Albi 63 – Anglès 12 – Brassac 5

⛰ Le Plô

✆ 05 63 74 00 82. www.leplo.com

Address : the village (900m west along the D 30, follow the signs for Castres and take road to the left)

2.5 ha (60 pitches) terraced, relatively flat, grassy, wood

Rentals : 🚐 – 9 tent lodges.

Surroundings : 🌿 ♀♀
Leisure activities : 🖼 ⛵ 🚲 🎣
Facilities : ⚹ ☎ 🍴 launderette

G P S Longitude : 2.47064
Latitude : 43.60815

BOISSE-PENCHOT

12300 – Michelin map **338** F3 – pop. 539 – alt. 169
▶ Paris 594 – Toulouse 193 – Rodez 46 – Aurillac 65

⛰ Le Roquelongue

✆ 05 65 63 39 67. www.camping-roquelongue.com

Address : 4.5km northwest along the D 963, D 21 and take the D 42, follow the signs for Boisse-Penchot, near the Lot (direct access)

Opening times : Permanent

3.5 ha (66 pitches) flat, grassy

Tariff : ♣ 4.65€ ⇌ 📧 8.90€ – 🔌 (10A) 4.75€
Rental rates : Permanent – 9 🚐 – 7 🏠. Per night from 57 to 101€ – Per week from 300 to 560€

Surroundings : ≤ 🗭 ♀♀
Leisure activities : 🍸 ✖️ ⛵ 🎣 🐟 pedalos 🚣
Facilities : ⚹ ☎ 🚐 🚿 🍴 📷

G P S Longitude : 2.22179
Latitude : 44.58224

There are several different types of sani-station ('borne' in French) – sanitation points providing fresh water and disposal points for grey water. See page 12 for further details.

BOR-ET-BAR

12270 – Michelin map **338** E5 – pop. 194 – alt. 250
▶ Paris 631 – Toulouse 109 – Rodez 61 – Albi 47

⛰ Le Gourpassou

✆ 05 65 65 76 98. www.camping-legourpassou.com

Address : Ferme de Cessetière

2.5 ha (39 pitches) flat, grassy

Rentals : 7 🚐 – 2 🏠.
The campsite is based at a farm.

Surroundings : ≤ ♀
Leisure activities : 🖼 🐟
Facilities : ☎ 🚿 🍴

G P S Longitude : 5.01096
Latitude : 47.32128

Routes nationales are main roads and their identifying numbers begin with N or RN. Routes départementales are generally quieter roads and begin with D or DN.

BOULOGNE-SUR-GESSE

31350 – Michelin map **343** B5 – pop. 1 612 – alt. 320
▶ Paris 735 – Auch 47 – Aurignac 24 – Castelnau-Magnoac 13

⛰ Village Vacances Le Lac (rental of chalets only)

✆ 05 61 88 20 54. www.ville-boulogne-sur-gesse.fr

Address : route du Lac (1.3km southeast along the D 633, follow the signs for Montréjeau and take turning to the left, 300m from the lake)

Opening times : Permanent

2 ha terraced

Rental rates : (2014 Price) 🅿 – 24 🏠. Per night from 70€ – Per week from 275 to 580€

Surroundings : 🌿 ≤ on the lake ♀
Leisure activities : 🖼 🐟
Facilities : ☎ 🚐 🏛 🍴 📷
Nearby : 🍷 🍸 ✖️ ⛷ ⛵ ✂ 🎣 🛶 pedalos

G P S Longitude : 0.65712
Latitude : 43.28328

BOURISP

65170 – Michelin map **342** O6 – pop. 147 – alt. 790
▶ Paris 828 – Toulouse 155 – Tarbes 70 – Lourdes 66

⛰ Le Rioumajou ♣♣

✆ 05 62 39 48 32. www.camping-le-rioumajou.com

Address : 1.3km northwest along the D 929, follow the signs for Arreau and take road to the left; beside the Neste d'Aure river

Opening times : Permanent

5 ha (192 pitches) flat, grassy, fine gravel

Tariff : ♣ 6.80€ ⇌ 📧 6.80€ – 🔌 (10A) 6€ – Reservation fee 14€
Rental rates : Permanent 🚐 – 5 🚐 – 9 canvas bungalows. Per night from 50 to 82€ – Per week from 350 to 570€ – Reservation fee 14€
🚐 borne 4.20€ – 🚐 🔌 14€
Plenty of green space in which to unwind, beside a stream.

Surroundings : ❄ 🌿 ≤ 🗭 ♀♀
Leisure activities : 🍸 ✖️ 🖼 🎮 ⛷ 🛷 jacuzzi ⛵ 🎣 🐟
Facilities : ⚹ ☎ 🏛 🛏 launderette 🚐

G P S Longitude : 0.33943
Latitude : 42.83786

BRASSAC

81260 – Michelin map **338** G9 – pop. 1 396 – alt. 487
▶ Paris 747 – Albi 65 – Anglès 14 – Castres 26

⛰ Municipal de la Lande

📞 05 63 74 09 11. www.camping.brassac.fr

Address : by the sports centre (take the southwestern exit towards Castres and take a right turn after the bridge; near the Agout river and crossed by a stream)

Opening times : from mid June to end Sept.

1 ha (50 pitches) flat, grassy

Tariff : (2014 Price) 🚶 2€ 🚙 1.30€ 🔲 1.70€ – 🔌 (2A) 1.70€

Surroundings : 🏞 ♨♨		
Leisure activities : 🛶	**G**	Longitude : 2.4952
Facilities : 🚮🚐	**P**	Latitude : 43.63067
Nearby : 🚲 ✂ ⛵ 🛶 🚣	**S**	

BRETENOUX

46130 – Michelin map **337** H2 – pop. 1 342 – alt. 136
▶ Paris 521 – Brive-la-Gaillarde 44 – Cahors 83 – Figeac 48

⛰⛰ La Bourgnatelle

📞 05 65 10 89 04. www.dordogne-vacances.fr

Address : take the northwestern exit, turn left after the bridge

Opening times : from end April to beginning Oct.

2.3 ha (135 pitches) flat, grassy

Tariff : 25€ 🚶🚶 🚙 🔲 🔌 (6A) – Reservation fee 15€

Rental rates : (from beginning April to end Oct.) – 76 🛖 – 5 canvas bungalows. Per night from 65 to 100€ – Per week from 240 to 750€ – Reservation fee 25€

🚐 borne – 🔌🔌10€

Pitches beside the river. The sanitary facilities leave something to be desired.

Surroundings : 🏞 ♨♨ ⛰		
Leisure activities : 🛶 🏊 🛶 🚣 ✈	**G**	Longitude : 1.83772
Facilities : 🚻 ☕ (July–Aug.) 🚽	**P**	Latitude : 44.91679
launderette 🧺	**S**	
Nearby : ✂ 🛶		

BRUSQUE

12360 – Michelin map **338** J8 – pop. 309 – alt. 465
▶ Paris 698 – Albi 91 – Béziers 75 – Lacaune 30

⛰⛰⛰ Village Vacances Val-VVF Le Domaine de Céras

📞 05 65 49 50 66. www.vvfvillages.fr

Address : 1.6km south along the D 92, follow the signs for Arnac; beside the Dourdou river and a small lake

Opening times : from mid June to mid Sept.

14 ha (160 pitches) undulating, flat, grassy

Tariff : 40€ 🚶🚶 🚙 🔲 🔌 (16A) – Extra per person 23€ – Reservation fee 32€

Rental rates : (from mid April to end Sept.) 🚻 (3 apartments) – 19 🛖 – 48 apartments – 27 canvas bungalows. Per night from 39 to 150€ – Per week from 280 to 1,200€ – Reservation fee 32€

Situated in a peaceful and secluded small, green valley.

Surroundings : 🏞 ≤ ♨♨ ⛰		
Leisure activities : 🍴 🍽 🛶 📷 🏊 🚣 ✂	**G**	Longitude : 2.95742
🏊 (fresh water) 🎣 fitness trail, multi-sports	**P**	Latitude : 43.75666
ground	**S**	
Facilities : 🚻🚐 🚽 launderette 🧺		

LES CABANNES

81170 – Michelin map **338** D6 – pop. 353 – alt. 200
▶ Paris 653 – Albi 27 – Montauban 57 – Rodez 80

⛰⛰⛰ Le Garissou

Le Garissou

📞 05 63 56 27 14. www.legarissou.fr

Address : 500m to the west along the D 600, follow the signs for Vindrac and take road to the left

Opening times : from mid March to beginning Nov.

7 ha/4 for camping (72 pitches) terraced, flat, grassy, stony

Tariff : 20€ 🚶🚶 🚙 🔲 🔌 (10A) – Extra per person 4€ – Reservation fee 9.90€

Rental rates : (from mid March to beginning Nov.) 🅿 – 30 🛖. Per night from 84 € – Per week from 271 to 655€ – Reservation fee 19.50€

🚐 borne – 🔌11€

Situated in an attractive, elevated location.

Surroundings : 🏞 ≤ Cordes-sur-Ciel and		
valley 🏕 ♨	**G**	Longitude : 1.94247
Leisure activities : 🛶 🏊 ⛰ 🚣 🛶	**P**	Latitude : 44.06767
multi-sports ground	**S**	
Facilities : 🚻 ☕ 🅲🅴 🧺 🚽 launderette		

CAHORS

46000 – Michelin map **337** E5 – pop. 19 948 – alt. 135
▶ Paris 575 – Agen 85 – Albi 110 – Bergerac 108

⛰⛰⛰ Rivière de Cabessut

📞 05 65 30 06 30. www.cabessut.com

Address : rue de la Rivière (3km south along the D 911 towards Rodez then take the road to the left, take quai Ludo-Rolles; beside the Lot river)

Opening times : from beginning April to mid Sept.

2 ha (113 pitches) flat, grassy

Tariff : 🚶 5.50€ 🚙 🔲 9€ – 🔌 (10A) 2€

Rental rates : (from beginning April to end Sept.) 🚣 – 8 🛖. Per night from 60 to 95€ – Per week from 310 to 590€

🚐 borne 4€ – 9 🔲 18€

Pitches that are well shaded in part, beside the Lot river.

Surroundings : 🏕 ♨♨		
Leisure activities : 🛶 🏊 ⛰ 🚣 ✂	**G**	Longitude : 1.44192
Facilities : 🚻 ☕ 🚮🏛 🏊 🚽 launderette	**P**	Latitude : 44.46364
Nearby : 🏊	**S**	

Michelin classification:

⛰⛰⛰⛰⛰ *Extremely comfortable, equipped to a very high standard*

⛰⛰⛰⛰ *Very comfortable, equipped to a high standard*

⛰⛰⛰ *Comfortable and well equipped*

⛰⛰ *Reasonably comfortable*

⛰ *Satisfactory*

CALMONT

31560 – Michelin map **343** H5 – pop. 2 177 – alt. 220
▶ Paris 724 – Toulouse 48 – Ordino 144 – Canillo 127

⚠ Le Mercier

📞 0534488131. www.camping-mercier.com

Address : 2.4km south along the D 11, follow the signs for Pamiers

Opening times : Permanent

0.6 ha (22 pitches) flat, grassy

Tariff : 20.50€ ✚✚ ⬅ 🔲 🔌 (5A) – Extra per person 5.50€

Rental rates : Permanent – 4 🚐. Per night from 35 to 75€ – Per week from 210 to 450€

🚰 borne 4€ – 🚐8€

A friendly welcome in a well-kept setting, with a variety of rental options.

Surroundings : 🏊 🛏 ♀
Leisure activities : 🛝
Facilities : 🚿 ⛟ 🚽 🖥

GPS Longitude : 1.6334
Latitude : 43.2819

The information in the guide may have changed since going to press.

LES CAMMAZES

81540 – Michelin map **338** E10 – pop. 309 – alt. 610
▶ Paris 736 – Aurillac 241 – Castres 35 – Figeac 183

⚠ La Rigole

📞 0563732899. www.campingdelarigole.com

Address : route du Barrage (take the southern exit from the D 629 and road to the left)

Opening times : from beginning May to end Sept.

3 ha (66 pitches)

Tariff : (2014 Price) 27€ ✚✚ ⬅ 🔲 🔌 (13A) – Extra per person 6€

Rental rates : (2014 Price) (from beginning May to end Sept.) – 10 🚐 – 9 🏠. Per night from 44 to 54€ – Per week from 280 to 777€

🚰 4 🔲 12.50€ – 🚐11€

Surroundings : 🏊 🛏 🛝
Leisure activities : 🍴✕ 🏓 🚴 🛝
Facilities : 🚿 ⛟ 🚽 🖥 launderette 🏊

GPS Longitude : 2.08625
Latitude : 43.40787

CANET-DE-SALARS

12290 – Michelin map **338** I5 – pop. 416 – alt. 850
▶ Paris 654 – Pont-de-Salars 9 – Rodez 33 – St-Beauzély 28

⚠ Les Castels Le Caussanel 👥

📞 0565468519. www.lecaussanel.com

Address : at the lake Pareloup (2.7km southeast along the D 538 and take a right turn)

Opening times : from mid May to beginning Sept.

10 ha (228 pitches) terraced, flat, grassy

Tariff : 36.60€ ✚✚ ⬅ 🔲 🔌 (6A) – Extra per person 7.90€ – Reservation fee 30€

Le Caussanel

Rental rates : (from mid May to beginning Sept.) – 80 🚐 – 40 🏠. Per night from 54 to 141€ – Per week from 321 to 987€ Reservation fee 30€

🚰 borne 3€

Surroundings : 🏊 ≤ on the lake ♀ 🌲
Leisure activities : 🍴✕ 🏓 🎯 🏊 🚴 🎾 🛝 🏹 treetop adventure trail, pedalos multi-sports ground, entertainment room
Facilities : 🚿 ⛟ 🖥 🚽 🍴 launderette 🏊

GPS Longitude : 2.76651
Latitude : 44.21426

⚠ Soleil Levant

📞 0565460365. www.camping-soleil-levant.com

Address : at Lac de Pareloup (3.7km southeast along the D 538 and D 993, follow the signs for Salles-Curan, to the left, before the bridge)

Opening times : from beginning May to end Sept.

11 ha (206 pitches) terraced, flat, grassy

Tariff : 28.90€ ✚✚ ⬅ 🔲 🔌 (6A) – Extra per person 7.20€ – Reservation fee 19.50€

Rental rates : (from beginning May to end Sept.) – 16 🚐. Per week from 185 to 705€ – Reservation fee 19.50€

In a pleasant location beside the Lac de Pareloup.

Surroundings : 🏊 ≤ ♀♀ 🌲
Leisure activities : 🍴 🎯 🏊 🎾 🛝
Facilities : 🚿 ⛟ 🚽 🍴 launderette
Nearby : 🚴 ⚓

GPS Longitude : 2.77795
Latitude : 44.21551

CAPDENAC-GARE

12700 – Michelin map **338** E3 – pop. 4 492 – alt. 175
▶ Paris 587 – Decazeville 20 – Figeac 9 – Maurs 24

⚠ Municipal les Rives d'Olt

📞 0565808887. www.campingcapdenac.fr

Address : 8 boulevard Paul Ramadier (take the western exit along the D 994, follow the signs for Figeac and take the turning to the left before the bridge, near the Lot river)

Opening times : from end May to mid Sept.

1.3 ha (60 pitches) flat, grassy

Tariff : ✚ 4.55€ ⬅ 🔲 5.10€ – 🔌 (16A) 3.15€

🚰 borne 2€

In a pleasant setting, green and leafy with good shade.

Surroundings : 🛏 🌿🌿
Leisure activities : 🏹
Facilities : 🚿 ⛟ 🚽 🍴 🖥
Nearby : 🛒 🍴✕ 🎯 🏊 🏞 sports trail

GPS Longitude : 2.07294
Latitude : 44.57209

These symbols are used for a campsite that is exceptional in its category:

🏕...⚠ *Particularly pleasant setting, quality and range of services available*

🏊🏊 *Tranquil, isolated site – quiet site, particularly at night*

≤≤ *Exceptional view – interesting or panoramic view*

CARLUCET

46500 – Michelin map **337** F3 – pop. 228 – alt. 322
▶ Paris 542 – Cahors 47 – Gourdon 26 – Labastide-Murat 11

🏔 Château de Lacomté

🖉 05 65 38 75 46. www.chateaulacomte.com

Address : at Lacomté (located 1.8km northwest of the town, by the castle)

Opening times : from beginning May to mid Sept.

12 ha/4 for camping(96 pitches) undulating, relatively flat, flat, grassy, wooded

Tariff : 38€ ♣♣ ⟵ 🔲 ⌀ (10A) – Extra per person 10€ – Reservation fee 15€

Rental rates : (from beginning May to mid Sept.) 🛌 – 4 🚐 – 5 🏠 – 1 gîte. Per week from 199 to 895€ – Reservation fee 15€

For adults only (18 years +). Pitches among trees and bushes or more in the sun, in a large area of parkland.

Surroundings : 🐾 ⟷ ♨		G
Leisure activities : ⛾ ✕ 🏠 🎣 🛶		P Longitude : 1.59692
Facilities : ⅙ ⟜ 🏢 🚿 🗑 🕯 launderette 🏖		S Latitude : 44.72881

The Michelin classification (🔺🔺🔺 ... 🔺) is totally independent of the official star classification system awarded by the local prefecture or other official organisation.

CARENNAC

46110 – Michelin map **337** G2 – pop. 389 – alt. 123
▶ Paris 528 – Toulouse 183 – Cahors 81 – Limoges 139

🏔 L'Eau vive ♣♣

🖉 05 65 10 97 39. www.camping-lot-eauvive.com

Address : 1.3km southwest along the D 30

Opening times : from mid May to mid Oct.

2 ha (80 pitches) terraced, flat, grassy

Tariff : 23.80€ ♣♣ ⟵ 🔲 ⌀ (6A) – Extra per person 6.40€

Rental rates : (from mid May to mid Oct.) – 20 🚐 – 3 canvas bungalows. Per night from 38 to 99€ – Per week from 150 to 693€ – Reservation fee 18€

🚐 borne – 🔌 ⌀12€

Choose the pitches beside the Dordogne river, furthest away from the road.

Surroundings : ⟷ ♨		G
Leisure activities : ⛾ ✕ 🏠 🎣 🛶 🐎 🛷 🌊		P Longitude : 1.74105
Facilities : ⅙ ⟜ 🚿 🕯 🗑 🏖		S Latitude : 44.9102

CASSAGNABÈRE-TOURNAS

31420 – Michelin map **343** C5 – pop. 415 – alt. 380
▶ Paris 758 – Auch 78 – Bagnères-de-Luchon 65 – Pamiers 101

🏔 Pré Fixe

🖉 05 61 98 71 00. www.camping-pre-fixe.com

Address : route de St-Gaudens (situated southwest of the town)

Opening times : from mid April to end Sept.

1.2 ha (40 pitches)

Tariff : 24€ ♣♣ ⟵ 🔲 ⌀ (10A) – Extra per person 6€

Rental rates : (from beginning April to mid Oct.) 🛌 – 6 🏠 – 2 tent lodges. Per night from 59 to 119€ – Per week from 245 to 790€

A pleasant site laid out in terraces, with a variety of upmarket rental options and a small wine bar run by the owner.

Surroundings : 🐾 ⟷ ♨		G
Leisure activities : ⛾ 🏠 🐎 🌊		P Longitude : 0.79
Facilities : ⅙ ⟜ 🕯 🗑 🏖		S Latitude : 43.22889
Nearby : 🛷		

CASSAGNES

46700 – Michelin map **337** C4 – pop. 209 – alt. 185
▶ Paris 577 – Cahors 34 – Cazals 15 – Fumel 19

🏔 Le Carbet

🖉 05 65 36 61 79. www.camping-carbet.fr

Address : at La Barte (located 1.5km northwest along the D 673, follow the signs for Fumel; near a lake)

Opening times : from mid April to mid Sept.

3 ha (29 pitches) open site, terraced, flat, grassy, stony

Tariff : 18€ ♣♣ ⟵ 🔲 ⌀ (6A) – Extra per person 6.20€ – Reservation fee 10€

Rental rates : (from mid April to mid Sept.) – 10 🚐 – 2 tent lodges. Per week from 190 to 545€ – Reservation fee 10€

The pitches are among trees and shrubs, with a variety of rental options of differing standards of quality.

Surroundings : ⟷ ♨		G
Leisure activities : ⛾ ✕ 🐎 🌊		P Longitude : 1.13102
Facilities : ⟜ 🚿 🕯 launderette 🏖		S Latitude : 44.56338
Nearby : 🛷		

In order for the guide to remain wholly objective, the selection of campsites is made on an entirely independent basis.

CASTELNAU-DE-MONTMIRAL

81140 – Michelin map **338** C7 – pop. 950 – alt. 287
▶ Paris 645 – Albi 31 – Bruniquel 22 – Cordes-sur-Ciel 22

🏔 Le Chêne Vert

🖉 05 63 33 16 10. www.camping-du-chene-vert.com

Address : at Travers du Rieutort (head 3.5km northwest along the D 964, follow the signs for Caussade, take D 1 and D 87, follow the signs for Penne; on the left)

Opening times : Permanent

10 ha/2 for camping(130 pitches)

Tariff : 24€ ♣♣ ⟵ 🔲 ⌀ (10A) – Extra per person 8€ – Reservation fee 20€

Rental rates : Permanent – 20 🚐 – 37 🏠 – 4 canvas bungalows. Per night from 30 to 94€ – Per week from 168 to 714€ – Reservation fee 20€

🚐 borne 9.50€ – 🔌 ⌀9.50€

Surroundings : 🐾 < ⟷ ♨		G
Leisure activities : ⛾ ✕ 🏠 🐎 🌊		P Longitude : 1.78947
Facilities : ⅙ ⟜ 🗑 🏊 🏖		S Latitude : 43.97702
At the leisure/activities centre (800m) : 🛷 🐎 (beach) ⛷		

CASTÉRA-VERDUZAN

32410 – Michelin map **336** E7 – pop. 937 – alt. 114
▶ Paris 720 – Agen 61 – Auch 40 – Condom 20

⛰ La Plage de Verduzan

✆ 05 62 68 12 23. www.camping-castera.com

Address : 30 rue du Lac (north of the town; beside the Aulone river)

Opening times : from beginning May to end Sept.

2 ha (100 pitches) flat, grassy

Tariff : (2014 Price) 24€ ✝✝ ⛺ ▣ ⟨⟩ (10A) – Extra per person 5€
Rental rates : (2014 Price) (from beginning May to end Sept.) –
18 ⟨⟩. Per week from 180 to 545€

Situated beside a lake; the pitches are well kept.

Surroundings : ▱ 00	
Leisure activities : 🖼 🏃	**G P S** Longitude : 0.43116
Facilities : ♿ ⛲ 🚿 🍴 🔥	Latitude : 43.80817
Nearby : 🍴 🏖 (beach) ⟨⟩ pedalos	

To visit a town or region, use the MICHELIN Green Guides.

CAUSSADE

82300 – Michelin map **337** F7 – pop. 6 586 – alt. 109
▶ Paris 606 – Albi 70 – Cahors 38 – Montauban 28

⛰ Municipal la Piboulette

✆ 05 63 93 09 07. www.mairie-caussade.fr

Address : located 1km northeast along the D 17, follow the signs for
Puylaroque and take the turning to the left, by the stadium, 200m
from a lake

Opening times : from beginning May to end Sept.

1.5 ha (72 pitches) flat, grassy

Tariff : (2014 Price) ✝ 2.75€ ⛺ ▣ 1.95€ – ⟨⟩ (6A) 1.95€
🚐 borne 4.10€ – 6 ▣ 4.10€
*The shaded pitches are situated between the municipal sports
grounds.*

Surroundings : ▱ 00	**G P S** Longitude : 1.54624
Facilities : ♿ ⛲ 🚿 🍴 🔥	Latitude : 44.16877
Nearby : 🏃 🍴 ⟨⟩ fitness trail	

CAUTERETS

65110 – Michelin map **342** L7 – pop. 1 118 – alt. 932 – ⚒ – Winter
sports : 1 000/2 350 m
▶ Paris 880 – Argelès-Gazost 17 – Lourdes 30 – Pau 75

⛰ Les Glères

✆ 05 62 92 55 34. www.gleres.com

Address : 19 route de Pierrefitte (take the northern exit along the
D 920; beside the Gave de Cauterets (river)

Opening times : from beginning Dec. to end Oct.

1.2 ha (80 pitches)

Tariff : 20.25€ ✝✝ ⛺ ▣ ⟨⟩ (6A) – Extra per person 4.85€ –
Reservation fee 10.45€
Rental rates : (from beginning Dec. to end Oct.) 🏠 – 16 ⟨⟩ –
5 🏡 – 1 apartment. Per night from 57 to 92€ – Per week
from 274 to 635€
🚐 41 ▣ 16€

---

*Good sanitary facilities, but slightly antiquated rental options
for a location so close to the town centre.*

Surroundings : ❄ ⟨ ▱ 00	
Leisure activities : 🖼 🏃 ⟨⟩	**G P S** Longitude : -0.11275
Facilities : ♿ ⛲ 🚿 🍴 🔥 launderette	Latitude : 42.89625
Nearby : 🍴 skating rink	

⛰ Le Cabaliros

✆ 05 62 92 55 36. www.camping-cabaliros.com

Address : 93 avenue du Mamelon Vert (1.6 km north following signs
for Lourdes, left across the bridge)

Opening times : from end May to beginning Oct.

2 ha (100 pitches) relatively flat to hilly, grassy

Tariff : 19.20€ ✝✝ ⛺ ▣ ⟨⟩ (6A) – Extra per person 5.30€
Rental rates : Permanent – 6 ⟨⟩. Per night from 70 to 75€ –
Per week from 270 to 570€
🚐 borne 3€
*Pitches in the shade or the sun, on a gentle slope leading down
to the Gave de Pau river.*

Surroundings : 🌿 ⟨ 00	
Leisure activities : 🖼 🏃 ⟨⟩	**G P S** Longitude : -0.10735
Facilities : ♿ ⛲ 🚿 🍴 launderette	Latitude : 42.90406

⛰ GR 10

GR 10

✆ 06 20 30 25 85. www.gr10camping.
com

Address : at Concé (2.8 km north along
the D 920, follow the signs for Lourdes,
near the Gave de Pau (river)

Opening times : from beginning June
to mid Sept.

1.5 ha (69 pitches) relatively flat, flat,
grassy, rocks

Tariff : 23€ ✝✝ ⛺ ▣ ⟨⟩ (8A) –
Extra per person 7€
Rental rates : Permanent – 1 ⟨⟩ – 2 🏡 – 5 🛏 – 2 apartments –
2 gîtes. Per night from 50 to 70 € – Per week from 530 to 690€
🚐 borne 5€
A good departure point for many mountain activities.

Surroundings : 🌿 ⟨ ▱ ⟨⟩	
Leisure activities : 🖼 🏃 🏊 forest trail,	**G P S** Longitude : -0.09892
rafting and canyoning, climbing	Latitude : 42.91107
Facilities : ♿ ⛲ 🚿 🔥 launderette	

⛰ Le Péguère

✆ 05 62 92 52 91. www.campingpeguere.com

Address : 31 route de Pierrefitte (located 1.5km north following
signs for Lourdes; beside the Gave de Pau (river)

Opening times : from beginning April to end Sept.

3.5 ha (160 pitches)

Tariff : 15€ ✝✝ ⛺ ▣ ⟨⟩ (10A) – Extra per person 4.35€
Rental rates : (from beginning April to end Sept.) 🏠 – 3 ⟨⟩ –
2 🏡. Per night from 31 to 52€ – Per week from 155 to 443€
🚐 borne 2€
*A site that lies between the road heading north from the town
and the Gave de Cauterets river.*

Surroundings : ⟨ ⟨⟩	
Leisure activities : 🖼 ⟨⟩	**G P S** Longitude : -0.10683
Facilities : ♿ ⛲ 🚿 🍴 launderette	Latitude : 42.9024

CAYLUS

82160 – Michelin map **337** G6 – pop. 1 536 – alt. 228
▶ Paris 628 – Albi 60 – Cahors 59 – Montauban 50

🏕 La Bonnette

𝒫 05 63 65 70 20. www.campingbonnette.com

Address : at Les Condamines (take the northeastern exit along the D 926, follow the signs for Villefranche-de-Rouergue and turn right onto the D 97, follow the signs for St-Antonin-Noble-Val)

Opening times : from mid March to beginning Oct.

1.5 ha (51 pitches) flat, grassy

Tariff : 23.50€ ✝✝ � 🔲 🔌 (10A) – Extra per person 6.50€
Rental rates : (from mid March to beginning Oct.) – 4 🚐 – 2 tent lodges. Per night from 45 to 90€ – Per week from 300 to 795€
🚰 borne

Situated beside the Bonnette river and near a lake.

Surroundings : 🛏 🌳🌳		
Leisure activities : 🍴 ✗ 🛶 🏊	**G**	Longitude : 1.77629
Facilities : 🚿 ⚡ 🚮 🗑 🚱 ♒ launderette	**P**	Latitude : 44.23375
Nearby : 🎣	**S**	

This guide is updated regularly, so buy your new copy every year!

CAYRIECH

82240 – Michelin map **337** F6 – pop. 264 – alt. 140
▶ Paris 608 – Cahors 39 – Caussade 11 – Caylus 17

🏕 Le Clos de la Lère 👥

𝒫 05 63 31 20 41. www.camping-leclosdelalere.com

Address : at Clergue (take the southeastern exit along the D 9, follow the signs for Septfonds)

Opening times : from beginning April to mid Nov.

1 ha (55 pitches) flat, grassy

Tariff : 23.50€ ✝✝ 🚗 🔲 🔌 (10A) – Extra per person 5.70€
Rental rates : (from beginning April to mid Nov.) – 7 🚐 – 6 🏠. Per night from 35 to 107€ – Per week from 245 to 751€
Reservation fee 8€
🚰 borne 3€ – 4 🔲 8€ – 🔋 🔌10€

Attractive shrubs and flowers decorate the site.

Surroundings : 🏞 🛏 🌳🌳		
Leisure activities : 🍴 ✗ 🎯 🛶 🏊	**G**	Longitude : 1.61291
Facilities : 🚿 ⚡ 🚿 🗑 ♒ launderette	**P**	Latitude : 44.21735
Nearby : 🍴	**S**	

CONDOM

32100 – Michelin map **336** E6 – pop. 7 099 – alt. 81
▶ Paris 729 – Agen 41 – Auch 46 – Mont-de-Marsan 80

⚠ Municipal

𝒫 05 62 28 17 32. www.condom.org/index.php/camping-municipal

Address : chemin de l'Argenté (2 km, southern exit from the D 931, follow the signs for Eauze; near the Baïse river)

Opening times : from beginning April to end Sept.

2 ha (75 pitches) flat, grassy

Tariff : (2014 Price) ✝ 3.60€ 🚗 🔲 5.14€ – 🔌 (10A) 3.80€

Rental rates : (2014 Price) (from beginning April to mid Oct.) ♿ ♒ – 10 🏠. Per week from 297 to 473€
🚰 borne

Surroundings : 🛏 🌳🌳		
Leisure activities : 🏊	**G**	Longitude : 0.36436
Facilities : 🚿 ⚡ 🚮 🗑 🚱 ♒ 🗑	**P**	Latitude : 43.94802
Nearby : 🍴 ✗ jacuzzi 🎯 🛶 🏊 🎣	**S**	

CONQUES

12320 – Michelin map **338** G3 – pop. 280 – alt. 350
▶ Paris 601 – Aurillac 53 – Decazeville 26 – Espalion 42

⚠ Beau Rivage

𝒫 05 65 69 82 23. www.campingconques.com

Address : at Molinols (to the west of the town, along the D 901; beside the Dourdou river)

Opening times : from beginning April to end Sept.

1 ha (60 pitches) flat, grassy

Tariff : ✝ 5€ 🚗 4€ 🔲 7.50€ – 🔌 (10A) 4.50€
Rental rates : (from beginning April to end Sept.) – 12 🚐. Per week from 280 to 560€
🚰 borne 5€

Situated on the river bank, just below the medieval village.

Surroundings : 🛏 🌳🌳		
Leisure activities : ✗ 🛶 🏊	**G**	Longitude : 2.39285
Facilities : 🚿 ⚡ (season) ♒ launderette 🛒	**P**	Latitude : 44.59891
	S	

CORDES-SUR-CIEL

81170 – Michelin map **338** D6 – pop. 1 006 – alt. 279
▶ Paris 655 – Albi 25 – Montauban 59 – Rodez 78

🏕 Moulin de Julien

𝒫 05 63 56 11 10. www.campingmoulindejulien.com

Address : 1.5 km southeast along the D 922, follow the signs for Gaillac; beside a stream

Opening times : from beginning May to mid Sept.

9 ha (130 pitches)

Tariff : 24.90€ ✝✝ 🚗 🔲 🔌 (5A) – Extra per person 7€ – Reservation fee 10€
Rental rates : (from beginning May to mid Sept.) ♒ – 3 🚐 – 5 🏠. Per night from 90 to 150€ – Per week from 290 to 600€
Reservation fee 10€

Surroundings : 🌳🌳		
Leisure activities : 🍴 🏛 🛶 🎣 🏊 🎿 🎣	**G**	Longitude : 1.97628
Facilities : 🚿 ⚡ 🗑 ♒ 🗑	**P**	Latitude : 44.05036
Nearby : 🍴	**S**	

⚠ Camp Redon

𝒫 05 63 56 14 64. www.campredon.com

Address : at Livers Cazelles (5km southeast along the D 600, follow the signs for Albi then continue 800m along the D 107, follow the signs for Virac to the left)

2 ha (40 pitches)

Rentals : ♒ – 2 🚐 – 3 canvas bungalows – 4 tent lodges.

Surroundings : 🏞 ⛰ 🛏 🌳		
Leisure activities : 🏛 🛶 🏊	**G**	Longitude : 2.01767
Facilities : ⚡ ♒ 🗑	**P**	Latitude : 44.04318
	S	

COS

09000 – Michelin map **343** H7 – pop. 369 – alt. 486
▶ Paris 766 – La Bastide-de-Sérou 14 – Foix 5 – Pamiers 25

⛺ Municipal

🕾 0671181038. www.camping-municipal-cos09.fr

Address : Le Rieutort (700m southwest on the D 61; beside a stream)

Opening times : Permanent

0.7 ha (32 pitches) open site, flat, grassy

Tariff : 13 € ♦♦ ⇔ ▣ (10A) – Extra per person 2 €

Rental rates : Permanent ⌇ – 3 🏠. Per week from 200 to 400 €

A small, shady site with basic and rather old sanitary facilities.

Surroundings : ⅍ ♀♀
Leisure activities : ⌂ ✕
Facilities : ⅍ ⚬⟷ ⊟ ⊞ ⚲ ⚱ ▣
Nearby : ⚞ ⅃
GPS Longitude : 1.57332 Latitude : 42.97102

CRAYSSAC

46150 – Michelin map **337** D4 – pop. 695 – alt. 300
▶ Paris 582 – Agen 81 – Cahors 16 – Toulouse 129

⚏ Campéole Les Reflets du Quercy

🕾 0565300027. www.camping-lot.info

Opening times : from beginning April to end Sept.

4.5 ha (136 pitches) very uneven, terraced, relatively flat, flat, grassy, stony

Tariff : (2014 Price) 27.50 € ♦♦ ⇔ ▣ (10A) – Extra per person 6.90 € – Reservation fee 25 €

Rental rates : (2014 Price) (from beginning April to end Sept.) – 28 🚍 – 26 🏠 – 27 canvas bungalows. Per night from 35 to 120 € – Per week from 245 to 840 € – Reservation fee 25 €

🚐 borne – ⚡⚡ 15.70 €

Surroundings : ⅍ ⊏ ♀♀
Facilities : ⅍ ⚬⟷ ⚲ ⚱
GPS Longitude : 1.32227 Latitude : 44.5099

CREISSELS

12100 – Michelin map **338** K6 – pop. 1 487 – alt. 330
▶ Paris 646 – Toulouse 184 – Rodez 69 – Montpellier 115

⛺ St-Martin

🕾 0565603183. www.campingsaintmartin.fr

Opening times : from beginning April to end Oct.

3 ha (90 pitches) flat, grassy

Tariff : 17.50 € ♦♦ ⇔ ▣ (10A) – Extra per person 3.50 € – Reservation fee 10 €

Rental rates : (from beginning April to end Oct.) ⌇ – 8 🚍. Per night from 35 to 70 € – Per week from 280 to 460 € – Reservation fee 10 €

Surroundings : ⅍ ← ⊏ ♀
Leisure activities : ⌂ ⚐ ⅃
Facilities : ⅍ ⚬⟷ ⊟ ⚱ launderette
Nearby : ✕
GPS Longitude : 3.04907 Latitude : 44.07461

CREYSSE

46600 – Michelin map **337** F2 – pop. 296 – alt. 110
▶ Paris 517 – Brive-la-Gaillarde 40 – Cahors 79 – Gourdon 40

⚏ Le Port

🕾 0565322082. www.campingduport.com

Address : south of the town, near the château; beside the Dordogne river

3.5 ha (100 pitches) open site, flat, grassy

Rentals : 5 🚍 – 5 tent lodges – 4 mobile homes (without sanitary facilities).

Close to a pleasant beach beside the Dordogne river; farm produce for sale – honey and nuts.

Surroundings : ⅍ ♀♀ ⚘
Leisure activities : ▾ ⌂ ⚐ ⚞ ⅃ ⚲ climbing, rafting and canyoning ⚲
Facilities : ⚬⟷ ⚱ launderette
GPS Longitude : 1.59895 Latitude : 44.88545

DAMIATTE

81220 – Michelin map **338** D9 – pop. 931 – alt. 148
▶ Paris 698 – Castres 26 – Graulhet 16 – Lautrec 18

⚏ Sites et Paysages Le Plan d'Eau St-Charles 👥

🕾 0563706607. www.campingplandeau.com

Address : la Cahuziere (take the exit following signs for Graulhet then continue 1.2km along the turning to the left before the level crossing)

Opening times : from mid May to mid Sept.

7.5 ha/2 for camping (82 pitches)

Tariff : 25.50 € ♦♦ ⇔ ▣ (6A) – Extra per person 6.50 € – Reservation fee 17 €

Rental rates : (from beginning April to end Oct.) – 20 🚍 – 15 🏠 – 9 canvas bungalows. Per night from 60 to 85 € – Per week from 200 to 810 € – Reservation fee 17 €

In an attractive location situated around a small but pretty lake.

Surroundings : ⅍ ← ⊏ ♀♀ ⚘
Leisure activities : ✕ ⌂ ⚞ ⚐ ⚞ ⅃
Facilities : ⅍ ⚬⟷ ⚐ ⚲ ⚱ ⚱ ▣ ⚞
Nearby : ⚞
GPS Longitude : 1.97011 Latitude : 43.66289

DURAVEL

46700 – Michelin map **337** C4 – pop. 957 – alt. 110
▶ Paris 610 – Toulouse 153 – Cahors 39 – Villeneuve-sur-Lot 37

⚏ FranceLoc Le Domaine Duravel 👥

🕾 0565246506. www.franceloc.fr

Address : route du Port-de-Vire (2.3km south along the D 58; beside the Lot)

Opening times : from beginning May to mid Sept.

9 ha (290 pitches) flat, grassy

Tariff : (2014 Price) 39 € ♦♦ ⇔ ▣ (10A) – Extra per person 7 € – Reservation fee 27 €

Rental rates : (2014 Price) (from beginning May to mid Sept.) – 157 🚍 – 8 canvas bungalows. Per night from 35 to 158 € – Per week from 140 to 1,260 € – Reservation fee 27 €

In a wooded setting, with a variety of rental options and private sanitary facilities for some VIP pitches.

Surroundings : ⅍ ⊏ ♀♀
Leisure activities : ▾ ✕ ⌂ ⚐ ⚞ ⚞ ⚲ ✕ ⅃ ⚞ ⚲
Facilities : ⅍ ⚬⟷ ⚐ – 36 private sanitary facilities (⚲ ⚱ ⚱ wc) ⚱ launderette ⚱ ⚞
GPS Longitude : 1.08201 Latitude : 44.49633

ENTRAYGUES-SUR-TRUYÈRE

12140 – Michelin map **338** H3 – pop. 1 224 – alt. 236
▶ Paris 600 – Aurillac 45 – Figeac 58 – Mende 128

⛰ Le Val de Saures

🗺 05 65 44 56 92. www.camping-valdesaures.com

Address : chemin de Saures (1.6km south along the D 904, follow the signs for Espeyrac, on the banks of the Lot river (direct access)

Opening times : from beginning May to end Sept.

4 ha (126 pitches) terraced, flat, grassy

Tariff : (2014 Price) 23.30€ ✳✳ ⇔ 🔲 🔌 (10A) –
Extra per person 4.20€ – Reservation fee 20€

Rental rates : (2014 Price) (from mid April to end Sept.) – 11 🏠 –
5 tent lodges. Per week from 203 to 721€ – Reservation fee 30€

Surroundings : 🌊 ⇆ 🔲 ♨
Leisure activities : 🏠 🚣 🎣
Facilities : ♿ ⛽ ♨ 🍽 launderette
Nearby : 🏊

GPS Longitude : 2.56352
Latitude : 44.64248

⛰ Le Lauradiol

🗺 05 65 44 53 95. www.camping-lelauradiol.com

Address : at Campouriez (5km northeast along the D 34, follow the signs for St-Amans-des-Cots; beside the Selves river)

Opening times : from end June to end Aug.

1 ha (31 pitches) flat, grassy

Tariff : (2014 Price) 17.50€ ✳✳ ⇔ 🔲 🔌 (6A) – Extra per person 4€
Reservation fee 20€

Rental rates : (2014 Price) (from end June to end Aug.) – 2 🚐.
Per week from 217 to 609€ – Reservation fee 30€

In a pleasant location at the bottom of a small valley, on the banks of the river.

Surroundings : 🌊 ⇆ ♨
Leisure activities : 🏠 🚣 🎿 🎣
Facilities : ♿ ⛽ (July-Aug.) ♨ 🍽 🔲

GPS Longitude : 2.58289
Latitude : 44.67768

ESPALION

12500 – Michelin map **338** I3 – pop. 4 409 – alt. 342
▶ Paris 592 – Aurillac 72 – Figeac 93 – Mende 101

⛰ Le Roc de l'Arche

Le Roc de l'Arche

🗺 05 65 44 06 79. www.rocdelarche.com

Address : Le Foirail (to the east, Rue du Foirail via Ave. de la Gare, turn off to the left, after the sports grounds, beside the Lot river)

Opening times : from mid May to beginning Sept.

2.5 ha (95 pitches) flat, grassy

Tariff : 24.80€ ✳✳ ⇔ 🔲 (10A) –
Extra per person 5.70€ – Reservation fee 15€

Rental rates : (from mid May to beginning Sept.) – 20 🚐.
Per night from 48 to 103€ – Per week from 286 to 721€ –
Reservation fee 15€

🚐 borne 3€

Surroundings : ⇆ ♨
Leisure activities : 🏠 🚣 🚲 🎣
Facilities : ♿ ⛽ 🔲 ♨ 🍽 🔲
Nearby : 🎿 🎿 🎣

GPS Longitude : 2.76959
Latitude : 44.52244

ESTAING

65400 – Michelin map **342** K7 – pop. 77 – alt. 970
▶ Paris 874 – Argelès-Gazost 12 – Arrens 7 – Laruns 43

⛰ La Via Natura Pyrénées Natura

🗺 05 62 97 45 44. www.camping-pyrenees-natura.com – alt. 1 000

Address : route du Lac (north of the town)

Opening times : from mid April to beginning Oct.

3 ha (65 pitches)

Tariff : 31.80€ ✳✳ ⇔ 🔲 🔌 (10A) – Extra per person 6€

Rental rates : (from mid April to beginning Oct.) – 19 🚐.
Per night from 48€ – Per week from 294 to 660€

🚐 borne – 4 🔲 17.60€ – 🛒 10€

A beautiful 19th-century barn building, good quality rental options and good sanitary facilities.

Surroundings : 🌊 ⇆ 🔲 ♨
Leisure activities : 🍽 🍴 🏠 🌊 jacuzzi
🚣 🎣
Facilities : ♿ ⛽ ♨ ♨ 🍽 launderette 🔲

GPS Longitude : -0.17725
Latitude : 42.94145

---

*For more information on visiting particular towns or regions, consult the relevant regional **MICHELIN Green Guide**. We also recommend you use the appropriate Michelin regional map to locate your selected campsite, to calculate distances and to work out the best route.*

ESTANG

32240 – Michelin map **336** B6 – pop. 643 – alt. 120
▶ Paris 712 – Aire-sur-l'Adour 25 – Eauze 17 – Mont-de-Marsan 35

⛰ Les Lacs de Courtès 🏷🏷

🗺 05 62 09 61 98. www.lacsdecourtes.com

Address : south of the town along the D 152, behind the church and beside a lake

Opening times : Permanent

7 ha (136 pitches) terraced, relatively flat, flat, grassy

Tariff : (2014 Price) 27.50€ ✳✳ ⇔ 🔲 🔌 (6A) – Extra per person 5.25€
Reservation fee 20€

Rental rates : (2014 Price) Permanent – 2 🚐 – 40 🏠 – 2 canvas bungalows – 22 gîtes. Per night from 46 to 105€ – Per week from 220 to 945€ – Reservation fee 20€

🚐 borne – 4 🔲 13€ – 🛒 13€

Surroundings : 🌊 ♨
Leisure activities : 🍽 🍴 🏠 🏓 jacuzzi
🚣 🏇 🎿 🌊 🎣
Facilities : ♿ ⛽ 🔲 ♨ 🍽 launderette 🔲

GPS Longitude : -0.10254
Latitude : 43.8891

Michelin classification:

⛰⛰⛰⛰ *Extremely comfortable, equipped to a very high standard*
⛰⛰⛰ *Very comfortable, equipped to a high standard*
⛰⛰⛰ *Comfortable and well equipped*
⛰⛰ *Reasonably comfortable*
⛰ *Satisfactory*

FIGEAC

46100 – Michelin map **337** I4 – pop. 9 847 – alt. 214
▶ Paris 578 – Aurillac 64 – Rodez 66 – Villefranche-de-Rouergue 36

⚠ Le Domaine du Surgié

☎ 05 61 64 88 54. www.domainedusurgie.com

Address : at the Domaine du Surgié (1.2km to the east along the N 140, follow the signs for Rodez, beside the river and a small lake)

Opening times : from end March to end Sept.

2 ha (159 pitches) gravelled

Tariff : 26€ ✯✯ ⇌ 回 ⁅ (10A) – Extra per person 7.50€ – Reservation fee 10€

Rental rates : (from end March to end Oct.) ⚡ – 20 ⌷ – 30 ⛺ – 6 canvas bungalows. Per night from 29 to 70€ – Per week from 200 to 795€ – Reservation fee 21€

⛽ borne – 10 回 19€

This campsite, bordered by the river, is in a leisure complex.

Surroundings : ⌿⌿
Leisure activities : ⌸ ⚿ ⚶ ⚲
Facilities : ⅙ ⚬⇀ ⌷launderette
Nearby : ⍾ ⚔ ⚓ ⚵ ⚲ ⚇ ⚲ pedalos

G P S Longitude : 2.05037
Latitude : 44.61031

FLAGNAC

12300 – Michelin map **338** F3 – pop. 972 – alt. 220
▶ Paris 603 – Conques 19 – Decazeville 5 – Figeac 25

⚠ Flower Le Port de Lacombe

☎ 05 65 64 10 08. www.campingleportdelacombe.fr

Address : located 1km north along the D 963 and take road to the left; near a small lake and the Lot river (direct access)

Opening times : from beginning April to end Sept.

4 ha (97 pitches) flat, grassy

Tariff : 29.90€ ✯✯ ⇌ 回 ⁅ (10A) – Extra per person 5.50€ – Reservation fee 20€

Rental rates : Permanent – 36 ⌷ – 6 canvas bungalows – 4 tent lodges. Per night from 25 to 124€ – Per week from 175 to 868€ Reservation fee 20€ ⛽ borne 5€

Surroundings : ⚲ ⌷ ⌿⌿
Leisure activities : ⍾ ⚔ ⌸ ⚶ ⚵ ⚲ ⚲
Facilities : ⅙ ⚬⇀ ⚲ launderette
Nearby : ⚲ ⚶ pedalos

G P S Longitude : 2.23533
Latitude : 44.60819

LA FOUILLADE

12270 – Michelin map **338** E5 – pop. 1 113 – alt. 420
▶ Paris 624 – Toulouse 109 – Rodez 61 – Albi 52

⚠ Le Bosquet

☎ 06 63 95 30 65. www.campinglafouillade.fr

Address : rue Genêts

Opening times : from mid April to mid Oct.

5 ha (76 pitches) terraced, flat, grassy

Tariff : (2014 Price) 22€ ✯✯ ⇌ 回 ⁅ (12A) – Extra per person 4€ – Reservation fee 4€

Rental rates : (2014 Price) (from mid April to mid Oct.) – 12 ⌷ – 8 canvas bungalows – 1 gîte. Per week from 80 to 720€ – Reservation fee 4€

⛽ borne 8€ – 8 回 12€ – ⚲12€

Surroundings : ⚲ ⚴ ⌿⌿
Leisure activities : ⚔ ⚵ ⚲ ⚲
Facilities : ⅙ ⚬⇀ ⚲ ⚲ launderette
Nearby : ⚲ ⚶

G P S Longitude : 2.03717
Latitude : 44.22635

GARIN

31110 – Michelin map **343** B8 – pop. 133 – alt. 1 100
▶ Paris 827 – Toulouse 153 – Tarbes 85 – Lourdes 84

⚠ Les Frênes   (rental of chalets only)

☎ 05 61 79 88 44. www.chalets-luchon-peyragudes.com – traditional camp. spaces also available

Address : east of the town along the D 618, follow the signs for Bagnères-de-Luchon and take the turning to the left, D 76e towards Billière

Opening times : Permanent

0.8 ha terraced

Rental rates : ℗ – 9 ⛺. Per night from 70 to 86€ – Per week from 202 to 729€

Rentals available on a nightly basis outside school holidays.

Surroundings : ⚲ ⚴ ⚲
Leisure activities : ⌸
Facilities : ⚬⇀ ⚲ ⚲ ⚲ launderette
Nearby : ⚲ ⚔

G P S Longitude : 0.51976
Latitude : 42.80933

GAVARNIE

65120 – Michelin map **342** L8 – pop. 140 – alt. 1 350 – Winter sports : 1 350/2 400 m
▶ Paris 901 – Lourdes 52 – Luz-St-Sauveur 20 – Pau 96

⚠ Le Pain de Sucre

☎ 05 62 92 47 55. www.camping-gavarnie.com – alt. 1 273

Address : Couret district (3km north along the D 921, follow the signs for Luz-St-Sauveur; beside the Gave de Gavarnie river)

Opening times : from beginning June to mid April

1.5 ha (54 pitches) open site, flat, grassy

Tariff : (2014 Price) ✯ 4.70€ ⇌ 回 4.90€ – ⁅ (10A) 6.70€ – Reservation fee 5€

Rental rates : (2014 Price) (from beginning June to mid April) ⚡ – 4 ⌷ – 4 ⛺. Per night from 33 to 41€ – Per week from 210 to 535€

A mountain setting beside a stream, with good-quality sanitary facilities.

Surroundings : ⚘ ⚴ ⌿⌿
Leisure activities : ⍾ ⚔ ⚵ ⚲
Facilities : ⅙ ⚬⇀ ⚲ ⚲ launderette

G P S Longitude : 0.00137
Latitude : 42.75983

GIRAC

46130 – Michelin map **337** G2 – pop. 379 – alt. 123
▶ Paris 522 – Beaulieu-sur-Dordogne 11 – Brive-la-Gaillarde 42 – Gramat 27

⚠ Les Chalets sur la Dordogne

☎ 05 65 10 93 33. www.camping-chalet-sur-dordogne.com

Address : at the Port (located 1km northwest along the D 803, follow the signs for Vayrac and take road to the left; beside the Dordogne river)

Opening times : from end April to end Sept.

2 ha (39 pitches) open site, flat, grassy, sandy

Tariff : (2014 Price) 21.50€ ✯✯ ⇌ 回 ⁅ (10A) – Extra per person 5.50€ – Reservation fee 8€

Rental rates : (2014 Price) (from beginning March to end Sept.) – 7 ⌷ – 3 ⛺. Per night from 30 to 65€ – Per week from 169 to 609€ – Reservation fee 12€

⛽ borne – 4 回 6€ – ⚲8€

There are shaded pitches beside the river. Welcomes groups and children.

Surroundings : 🌳 🏕 ♨ �‖
Leisure activities : 🍸 ✕ 🚣 🛷 🎿
Facilities : 🚿 ⚬🔌 (June–Aug) 🍴
launderette 🧺

G P S Longitude : 1.80501
Latitude : 44.91809

GONDRIN

32330 – Michelin map **336** D6 – pop. 1 180 – alt. 174
▶ Paris 745 – Agen 58 – Auch 42 – Condom 17

⛰ Le Pardaillan ⚐⚐

℘ 05 62 29 16 69. www.camping-le-pardaillan.com
Address : 27 rue Pardaillan (situated east of the town)
Opening times : from mid April to mid Oct.
2.5 ha (115 pitches)
Tariff : (2014 Price) 26 € ⚘ ⚘ 🚗 🔋 🔌 (10A) – Extra per person 6.20 €
Reservation fee 15 €
Rental rates : (2014 Price) (from mid April to beginning Oct.) –
23 🛖 – 27 🏠 – 5 canvas bungalows. Per night from 44 to 80 € –
Per week from 245 to 790 € – Reservation fee 15 €
🚐 borne – 2 🔲 26 €

Surroundings : 🌳 🏕 ♨
Leisure activities : 🍸 ✕ 🚣 🏃 🚴 🏊 🎣
Facilities : 🚿 ⚬🔌 🚲 🚿 🍴 launderette 🧺
Nearby : ✕ 🚣

G P S Longitude : 0.23873
Latitude : 43.88165

GOUAUX

65240 – Michelin map **342** O5 – pop. 73 – alt. 923
▶ Paris 824 – Toulouse 151 – Tarbes 65 – Foix 149

⛰ Le Ruisseau

℘ 05 62 39 95 49. www.camping-aure-pyrenees.com
Address : in the village
Opening times : Permanent
2 ha (115 pitches) terraced, flat, grassy
Tariff : (2014 Price) ⚘ 4.60 € 🚗 🔲 5.20 € – 🔋 🔌 (6A) 4.90 € – Reservation fee 5 €
Rental rates : (2014 Price) (from mid April to mid Oct.) – 12 🛖.
Per night from 50 to 82 € – Per week from 199 to 575 € –
Reservation fee 15 €
🚐 borne 2 €
Half of the pitches are occupied by rental or owner-occupier mobile homes.

Surroundings : ❮
Leisure activities : ✕
Facilities : 🚿 🚲 🏛 🚿 🍴 launderette 🧺

G P S Longitude : 0.36085
Latitude : 42.86423

These symbols are used for a campsite that is exceptional in its category:

⛰⛰⛰...⛰ *Particularly pleasant setting, quality and range of services available*

🦢🦢 *Tranquil, isolated site – quiet site, particularly at night*

❮❮ *Exceptional view – interesting or panoramic view*

GOURDON

46300 – Michelin map **337** E3 – pop. 4 622 – alt. 250
▶ Paris 543 – Bergerac 91 – Brive-la-Gaillarde 66 – Cahors 44

⛰ Le Paradis

℘ 05 65 41 65 01. www.campingleparadis.com
Address : at La Peyrugue (situated 2km southwest along the D 673, follow the signs for Fumel and take road to the left, near the Intermarché car park)
Opening times : from beginning May to beginning Sept.
1 ha (25 pitches) open site, terraced, flat, grassy, wooded
Tariff : 16.50 € ⚘ ⚘ 🚗 🔲 🔌 (6A) – Extra per person 4.75 €
Rental rates : (from beginning May to beginning Sept.) – 6 🛖 –
1 🏠. Per night from 40 to 60 € – Per week from 220 to 440 €
🚐 4 🔲 16.50 € – 🚐 14 €
Some pitches lie among trees and shrubs, others are more in the sun.

Surroundings : 🌳 ♨
Leisure activities : 🚣 🎿
Facilities : 🚿 ⚬🔌 🚲 🍴 🏛

G P S Longitude : 1.37397
Latitude : 44.72323

We have selected the best campsites in France with our usual care, listing those with the best facilities in the most pleasant surroundings.

GRAND-VABRE

12320 – Michelin map **338** G3 – pop. 406 – alt. 213
▶ Paris 615 – Aurillac 47 – Decazeville 18 – Espalion 50

⛰ Village Vacances Grand-Vabre Aventures et Nature

(rental of chalets only)
℘ 05 65 72 85 67. www.grand-vabre.com
Address : at Les Passes (located 1km southeast along the D 901, follow the signs for Conques; besides the Dourdou river)
Opening times : Permanent
1.5 ha flat, grassy
Rental rates : 🚿 – 20 🏠. Per night from 42 to 85 € – Per week from 260 to 675 €

Surroundings : ♨
Leisure activities : 🚣 🏃 🚴 🏊 🎣
Facilities : ⚬🔌 🚲 🏛 🍴 launderette

G P S Longitude : 2.36297
Latitude : 44.62473

HÈCHES

65250 – Michelin map **342** O6 – pop. 631 – alt. 690
▶ Paris 805 – Arreau 14 – Bagnères-de-Bigorre 35 – Bagnères-de-Luchon 47

⛰ La Bourie

℘ 05 62 98 73 19. www.camping-labourie.com
Address : at Rebouc (2km south along the D 929, follow the signs for Arreau and turn left onto the D 26, beside the Neste d'Aure river)
2 ha (122 pitches) flat, grassy
Rentals : 🚿 – 15 🛖.
On the site of an former factory, with many owner-occupiers.

Surroundings : ❮ 🏕 ♨
Leisure activities : ✕ 🚣 🎿 🎣
Facilities : 🚿 ⚬🔌 🏛 🍴 🏛

G P S Longitude : 0.37887
Latitude : 43.03815

L'HOSPITALET-PRÈS-L'ANDORRE

09390 – Michelin map **343** I9 – pop. 91 – alt. 1 446
▶ Paris 822 – Andorra-la-Vella 40 – Ax-les-Thermes 19 – Bourg-Madame 26

⚠ Municipal La Porte des Cimes

📞 05 61 05 21 10. www.laportedescimes.com – alt. 1 500

Address : 600m north along the N 20, follow the signs for Ax-les-Thermes and take turning to the right.

Opening times : from beginning June to end Oct.

1.5 ha (62 pitches)

Tariff : (2014 Price) 🚶 3.50 € 🚗 1 € 🔲 4 € – 🔌 (10A) 6 €

Choose the pitches furthest away from the road in preference.

Surroundings : ≤ ♀
Leisure activities : ✂
Facilities : ⅊ ⌕ (July–Aug.) 🚮 ▥ ⚞ ▾ 🍴
launderette
Nearby : ⚓ ⚲

GPS Longitude : 1.80343
Latitude : 42.59135

LACAM-D'OURCET

46190 – Michelin map **337** I2 – pop. 129 – alt. 520
▶ Paris 544 – Aurillac 51 – Cahors 92 – Figeac 38

⚠ Les Teuillères

📞 05 65 11 90 55. www.lesteuilleres.com

Address : 4.8km southeast along the D 25, follow the signs for Sousceyrac and then Sénaillac-Latronquière, towards the Lac du Tolerme

Opening times : from beginning April to end Oct.

3 ha (30 pitches)

Tariff : 🚶 5.75 € 🚗 🔲 6.75 € – 🔌 (6A) 2.95 €

Rental rates : (from beginning April to end Oct.) – 3 🛏 – 5 tent lodges – 2 gîtes. Per week from 400 to 800 €

The site is based around a pretty former farm in local stone.

Surroundings : ⚲ ≤ ⌂ ♀♀
Leisure activities : ⚞
Facilities : ⅊ ⌕ 🚮 ▥ 🍴 ▤

GPS Longitude : 2.04086
Latitude : 44.8342

LACAVE

46200 – Michelin map **337** F2 – pop. 284 – alt. 130
▶ Paris 528 – Brive-la-Gaillarde 51 – Cahors 58 – Gourdon 26

⚠ La Rivière ♟

📞 05 65 37 02 04. www.campinglariviere.com

Address : at Le Bougayrou (2.5km northeast along the D 23, follow the signs for Martel and take road to the left; beside the Dordogne river)

Opening times : from mid April to mid Sept.

2.5 ha (110 pitches) open site

Tariff : (2014 Price) 23.80 € 🚶🚶 🚗 🔲 🔌 (10A) – Extra per person 6 €
Reservation fee 9.50 €

Rental rates : (2014 Price) (from mid April to mid Sept.) – 17 🚐. Per night from 79 to 109 € – Per week from 260 to 630 € – Reservation fee 9.50 €

This is a family-friendly site, with pitches overlooking the river.

Surroundings : ⚲ ♀♀
Leisure activities : 🍴 ✗ ⚞ ⚞ ▤ ⚅ ▾ ⚓
Facilities : ⅊ ⌕ 🍴 launderette ▤

GPS Longitude : 1.559
Latitude : 44.8613

LAFRANÇAISE

82130 – Michelin map **337** D7 – pop. 2 828 – alt. 183
▶ Paris 621 – Castelsarrasin 17 – Caussade 41 – Lauzerte 23

⚑ Le Lac

📞 05 63 65 89 69. www.campings82.fr

Address : rue Jean Moulin (take the southeastern exit along the D 40, follow the signs for Montastruc and take the turning to the left, 250m from a small lake (direct access)

Opening times : from end April to end Sept.

0.9 ha (41 pitches) terraced, relatively flat, flat, grassy, stony

Tariff : 19.80 € 🚶🚶 🚗 🔲 🔌 (8A) – Extra per person 8 €

Rental rates : Permanent ⅊ (1 gîte) – 19 🚐 – 1 🏠 – 11 gîtes. Per night from 70 to 85 € – Per week from 495 to 585 €

🚐 borne 9 € – 4 🔲 19.80 €

The campsite is situated among trees and shrubs, overlooking the small leisure activity park.

Surroundings : ⚲ ⌂ ♨
Leisure activities : 🎣 ▤
Facilities : ⅊ ⌕ 🚮 ▵ 🍴 ▤
Nearby : ✗ ⚞ ⚞ ✂ ▤ ⚅ ▵ ⚲ pedalos

GPS Longitude : 1.24675
Latitude : 44.1246

LAGUIOLE

12210 – Michelin map **338** J2 – pop. 1 267 – alt. 1 004 – Winter sports : 1 100/1 400 m
▶ Paris 571 – Aurillac 79 – Espalion 22 – Mende 83

⚠ Municipal les Monts d'Aubrac

📞 05 65 44 39 72. http://www.campinglesmontsdaubraclaguiole.jimdo.com – alt. 1 050

Address : take the southern exit along the D 921, follow the signs for Rodez then continue 600m along the turning to the left; by the stadium

Opening times : from mid May to mid Sept.

1.2 ha (57 pitches) relatively flat, flat, grassy

Tariff : (2014 Price) 10 € 🚶🚶 🚗 🔲 🔌 (10A) – Extra per person 3 €

🚐 borne 2 € – 🚐 🔌 10 €

Surroundings : ⚲ ≤ ♀
Facilities : ⅊ ⌕ ▥ ⚞ ▤
Nearby : ✂ skateboarding

GPS Longitude : 2.85501
Latitude : 44.6815

LAMONTÉLARIÉ

81260 – Michelin map **338** H9 – pop. 62 – alt. 847
▶ Paris 736 – Toulouse 116 – Albi 83 – Castres 44

⚑ Rouquié

📞 05 63 70 98 06. www.campingrouquie.fr

Address : at the Lac de la Raviège, on the D14E

Opening times : from beginning May to end Oct.

3 ha (97 pitches)

Tariff : (2014 Price) 24.20 € 🚶🚶 🚗 🔲 🔌 (6A) – Extra per person 4.80 €
Reservation fee 15 €

Rental rates : (2014 Price) (from beginning April to end Oct.) – 9 🚐 – 5 🏠. Per night from 57 to 67 € – Per week from 285 to 722 € – Reservation fee 15 €

Surroundings : ⚲ ≤ ♀♀ ⚠
Leisure activities : 🍴 ✗ ⚞ pedalos ⚲
Facilities : ⅊ ⌕ ▵ 🍴 launderette ▤
Nearby : ⚓

GPS Longitude : 2.60663
Latitude : 43.60038

LAU-BALAGNAS

65400 – Michelin map **342** L5 – pop. 499 – alt. 430
▶ Paris 864 – Toulouse 188 – Tarbes 36 – Pau 70

▲▲▲ Kawan Village Le Lavedan

✆ 05 62 97 18 84. www.lavedan.com

Address : 44 route des Vallées (located 1km southeast)

Opening times : from mid March to end Oct.

2 ha (108 pitches) flat, grassy

Tariff : 38.35€ ✶✶ ⇌ 🅴 🕎 (10A) – Extra per person 10.25€ –
Reservation fee 25€

Rental rates : Permanent – 36 🛖. Per night from 50 to 97€ –
Per week from 306 to 930 € – Reservation fee 25€

Rental and owner-occupied mobile homes and pitches for tents and caravans, best chosen away from the road.

Surroundings : ♨♨
Leisure activities : ♟ ✗ 🎣 🖥 ☀ 🖼 (open air in season), entertainment room
Facilities : 🚿 ⚡ 🆒 ▥ 🐕 ☂ ♨ 🏴 launderette 🚱

Longitude : -0.08896
Latitude : 42.98818

LECTOURE

32700 – Michelin map **336** F6 – pop. 3 766 – alt. 155
▶ Paris 708 – Agen 39 – Auch 35 – Condom 26

▲▲▲▲ Yelloh! Village Le Lac des 3 Vallées ⛱⛱

✆ 05 62 68 82 33. www.lacdes3vallees.fr

Address : 2.4km southeast along the N 21, follow the signs for Auch, then continue 2.3km along the turning to the left beside the lake

Opening times : from beginning June to mid Sept.

40 ha (600 pitches)

Tariff : 50€ ✶✶ ⇌ 🅴 🕎 (10A) – Extra per person 9€

Rental rates : (from beginning June to mid Sept.) – 250 🛖 –
23 canvas bungalows – 19 tent lodges. Per night from 37 to
195€ – Per week from 259 to 1,365€

🚐 borne

Surroundings : ♨ ≤ 🌊 ♨♨
Leisure activities : ♟ ✗ 🎣 🖥 🏖 ☀ 🛶 🏃 jacuzzi ☀ ☀ 🐎 ♨ 🏊 ⛵ (beach) ☀ 🐟 disco, pedalos 🚣 multi-sports ground, skate park
Facilities : 🚿 ⚡ 🐕 ☂ ♨ 🏴 launderette 🛒 🚱 refrigerators

Longitude : 0.64533
Latitude : 43.91252

LOUDENVIELLE

65510 – Michelin map **342** O8 – pop. 308 – alt. 987
▶ Paris 833 – Arreau 15 – Bagnères-de-Luchon 27 – La Mongie 54

▲ Pène Blanche

Pène Blanche

✆ 05 62 99 68 85. www.peneblanche.com

Address : take the northwestern exit along the D 25, follow the signs for Génos; near the Neste de Louron (stream) and not far from a small lake

Opening times : Permanent

4 ha (120 pitches) terraced, relatively flat, flat, grassy

Tariff : 26.90€ ✶✶ ⇌ 🅴 🕎 (10A) – Extra per person 6€

Rental rates : Permanent – 19 🛖 – 3 tent lodges. Per night
from 43 to 102€ – Per week from 225 to 714€

A good choice of entertainment and water parks nearby.

Surroundings : ♨ ≤ ♀
Facilities : ⚡ (July–Aug.) ▥ launderette
Nearby : ♟ ✗ ☀ ☀ 🐎 🛶 🐟 🐎 fitness centre, paragliding

Longitude : 0.40722
Latitude : 42.79611

LOUPIAC

46350 – Michelin map **337** E3 – pop. 274 – alt. 230
▶ Paris 527 – Brive-la-Gaillarde 51 – Cahors 51 – Gourdon 16

▲ Sites et Paysages Les Hirondelles ⛱⛱

✆ 05 65 37 66 25. www.camping-leshirondelles.com

Address : at Al Pech (3km north following signs for Souillac and take road to the left; 200m from the N 20)

Opening times : from beginning April to mid Sept.

2.5 ha (60 pitches) relatively flat, flat, grassy, stony

Tariff : 23€ ✶✶ ⇌ 🅴 🕎 (6A) – Extra per person 5.70€ – Reservation fee 15€

Rental rates : (from beginning April to mid Sept.) 🚿 (1 mobile home) ☀ ☀ – 22 🛖 – 4 🏠 – 5 tent lodges. Per night from 60€ – Per week from 180 to 630€ – Reservation fee 15€

Pitches surrounded by greenery with a variety of different quality rental options.

Surroundings : 🌲 ♨♨
Leisure activities : ♟ ✗ 🎣 🏃 ☀ ☀ 🏊
Facilities : 🚿 ⚡ ▥ 🐕 ♨ launderette 🚱

Longitude : 1.46455
Latitude : 44.82934

LOURDES

65100 – Michelin map **342** L6 – pop. 15 127 – alt. 420
▶ Paris 850 – Bayonne 147 – Pau 45 – St-Gaudens 86

▲ Plein Soleil

✆ 05 62 94 40 93. www.camping-pleinsoleil.com

Address : 11 avenue du Monge (located 1km to the north)

Opening times : from beginning April to mid Oct.

0.5 ha (35 pitches) terraced, flat, grassy, fine gravel

Tariff : 23.20€ ✶✶ ⇌ 🅴 🕎 (13A) – Extra per person 5.20€

Rental rates : (from beginning April to mid Oct.) – 2 🛖 – 7 🏡.
Per night from 53 to 90€ – Per week from 56 to 95€

🚐 borne 5€ – 10 🅴 18.30€ – 🚽 🕎 18.30€

The pitches are laid out across terraces, with good-quality sanitary facilities.

Surroundings : ♨♨
Leisure activities : 🎣 ☀ ☀ 🖼 (open air in season)
Facilities : ⚡ ▥ 🐕 ☂ ♨ 🏴 launderette
Nearby : 🛒

Longitude : -0.03646
Latitude : 43.11438

The Michelin classification (▲▲▲ ... ▲) is totally independent of the official star classification system awarded by the local prefecture or other official organisation.

⛰ Sarsan

𝄞 05 62 94 43 09. www.lourdes-camping.com

Address : 4 avenue Jean Moulin (located 1.5km east via a diversion)

Opening times : from beginning April to mid Oct.

1.8 ha (67 pitches)

Tariff : (2014 Price) 19.80€ ✚✚ ⛺ 🔲 (⌁) (10A) – Extra per person 5€
Rental rates : (2014 Price) (from beginning April to mid Oct.) –
8 🚐. Per night from 50 to 80€ – Per week from 250 to 560€
🚾 borne 3€
The site is on a shady meadow, beside the swimming pool;
choose the pitches furthest away from the road.

Surroundings : 🔅🔅	
Leisure activities : 🏊 ⛹ 🔲 (open air in season)	**G** **P** **S** Longitude : -0.02744 Latitude : 43.10226
Facilities : ♿ ⛽ ⛺ ⛲ 🖼	

⛰ Le Moulin du Monge

𝄞 05 62 94 28 15. www.camping-lourdes.com

Address : 28 avenue Jean Moulin (1.3km to the north)

Opening times : from beginning April to beginning Oct.

1 ha (67 pitches) terrace, relatively flat, flat, grassy

Tariff : 22.70€ ✚✚ ⛺ 🔲 (⌁) (6A) – Extra per person 6€
Rental rates : (from beginning April to beginning Oct.) – 12 🚐 –
1 gîte. Per night from 58 to 104€ – Per week from 406 to 728€
🚾 borne 4€ – 10 🔲 18€
Lovely shady grass areas, but bear in mind the proximity of the
road and the railway line.

Surroundings : 🔅🔅	
Leisure activities : 🏊 🏊 ⛹ ⛲	**G** **P** **S** Longitude : -0.03148 Latitude : 43.11575
Facilities : ♿ ⛽ 🍴 ⛲ launderette ⛲	

⛰ Le Ruisseau Blanc

𝄞 05 62 42 94 83. www.camping-lourdes-ruisseau-blanc.com

Address : at Anclades, route de Bagnères-de-Bigorre (1.5km
east along the D 97, follow the signs for Jarret. Caravans are
recommended to take the D 937 towards Bagnère-de-Bigorre)

1.8 ha (102 pitches) flat, grassy

Rentals : ✂ – 3 🚐.

🚾 borne – 10 🔲

The site is on pleasant fields with shade, but the sanitary faci-
lities are very old.

Surroundings : 🌿 🔅🔅	
Leisure activities : 🏊 ⛹	**G** **P** **S** Longitude : -0.01816 Latitude : 43.09531
Facilities : ♿ ⛽ launderette	

LUZ-ST-SAUVEUR

65120 – Michelin map **342** L7 – pop. 1 014 – alt. 710 – ⚕ – Winter
sports : 1 800/2 450 m
▶ Paris 882 – Argelès-Gazost 19 – Cauterets 24 – Lourdes 32

⛰ Club Airotel Pyrénées 🏊👤

𝄞 05 62 92 89 18. www.airotel-pyrenees.com

Address : at Esquièze-Sère, 46 avenue du Barège (located 1km
northwest along the D 921, follow the signs for Lourdes)

Opening times : from beginning Dec. to end Sept.

2.5 ha (146 pitches) terraced, relatively flat, flat, grassy

Tariff : (2014 Price) 35.50€ ✚✚ ⛺ 🔲 (⌁) (10A) – Extra per person 8€
Reservation fee 25€

Rental rates : (2014 Price) (from beginning Dec. to end Sept.) ✂ –
50 🚐 – 12 🏠 – 10 apartments. Per week from 205 to 1,125€
Reservation fee 25€
🚾 borne 9€
A small, pretty, well-equipped chalet village and several swim-
ming pools, but choose pitches away from the road.

Surroundings : ❄ ≤ 🔅🔅	
Leisure activities : 🏊 ⛹ 🛶 🏊 hammam, jacuzzi ⛹ 🔲 🏊 ⛰ climbing wall, multi-sports ground, spa centre	**G** **P** **S** Longitude : -0.01152 Latitude : 42.88014
Facilities : ♿ ⛽ 🍴 ⛺ 🍴 launderette ⛲ 🛒	

⛰ International

𝄞 05 62 92 82 02. www.international-camping.fr

Address : at Esquièze-Sère, 50 avenue du Barège (1.3km northwest
along the D 921, follow the signs for Lourdes)

Opening times : from mid May to end Sept.

4 ha (180 pitches) very uneven, terraced, flat, grassy

Tariff : 35€ ✚✚ ⛺ 🔲 (⌁) (10A) – Extra per person 6.80€ – Reservation
fee 20€
Rental rates : (from mid May to end Sept.) ✂ – 22 🚐. Per week
from 210 to 750€ – Reservation fee 20€
Varied, good-quality rental options; good-quality sanitary faci-
lities for tents and caravans, but choose pitches away from the
road if possible.

Surroundings : ❄ ≤ 🔅🔅	
Leisure activities : 🍴 🏊 jacuzzi ⛹ 🏊 🔲 (open air in season) ⛰ multi-sports ground	**G** **P** **S** Longitude : -0.01388 Latitude : 42.88322
Facilities : ♿ ⛽ 🍴 🍴 ⛺ 🍴 launderette ⛲	

⛰ Sites et Paysages Pyrénévasion

𝄞 05 62 92 91 54. www.campingpyrenevasion.com – alt. 834

Address : at Sazos, route de Luz-Ardiden (3.4km northwest along the
D 921, follow the signs for Gavarnie and the D 12)

Opening times : from end Nov. to end Oct.

3.5 ha (99 pitches) terraced, flat, grassy, rocks

Tariff : 29€ ✚✚ ⛺ 🔲 (⌁) (10A) – Extra per person 6.20€ – Reservation
fee 10€
Rental rates : (from end Nov. to end Oct.) – 10 🚐 – 8 🏠 –
3 apartments. Per night from 45 to 95€ – Per week from
299 to 845€ – Reservation fee 12€
🚾 borne 6€ – 🔌 (⌁)14€
A pleasant indoor pool with a panoramic view over the Vallée
de Luz from some pitches.

Surroundings : 🌿 ≤ 🔅🔅	
Leisure activities : 🍴 🍴 🏊 🏊 jacuzzi ⛹ 🔲 🏊 multi-sports ground	**G** **P** **S** Longitude : -0.02417 Latitude : 42.8831
Facilities : ♿ ⛽ 🍴 ⛺ ⛲ 🍴 launderette 🛒	

⛰ Les Cascades

𝄞 05 62 92 85 85. www.camping-luz.com

Address : rue Ste-Barbe (south of the town; beside rapids,
recommended route via Gavarnie road)

Opening times : from beginning Dec. to end Sept.

1.5 ha (77 pitches) terraced, relatively flat, flat, grassy, rocks

Tariff : (2014 Price) 29€ ✚✚ ⛺ 🔲 (⌁) (10A) – Extra per person 6.50€

Rental rates : (2014 Price) (from beginning Dec. to end Sept.) – 18 📷. Per night from 60 to 75€ – Per week from 280 to 680€

A good standard of sanitary facilities for tents and caravans.

Surroundings : 🌊 ≤ ♤♤
Leisure activities : 🍴 ✕ 🔲 🛁 jacuzzi 🚣 ⛵
Facilities : ♿ ☛ ▥ ⅋ launderette 🦮

| G P S | Longitude : -0.00292 |
| | Latitude : 42.86973 |

⛺ Le Bergons

🔗 05 62 92 90 77. www.camping-bergons.com

Address : route de Barèges (500m east along the D 918)

1 ha (74 pitches) terraced, flat, grassy

Rentals : 4 📷 – 1 🏠 – 1 studio – 1 apartment.

Choose those pitches the furthest away from the road in preference.

Surroundings : ❄ ≤ ♤♤
Leisure activities : 🔲 🚣
Facilities : ♿ ☛ ▥ ⅋ launderette

| G P S | Longitude : 0.00281 |
| | Latitude : 42.87334 |

⛺ Toy

🔗 05 62 92 86 85. www.camping-toy.com

Address : 17 place du 8-Mai (town centre; beside the Bastan river)

Opening times : from beginning Dec. to mid April from beginning May to end Sept.

1.2 ha (83 pitches) terraced, flat, grassy, stony

Tariff : ♦ 4.50€ 🚐 🔲 4.50€ – ⚡ (10A) 7€

🚐 borne

Beside a mountain stream, but in the centre of Luz, with shops close by.

Surroundings : 🌊 ≤ ♤♤
Leisure activities : 🚣
Facilities : ☛ 🔲 ▥ ⅋ launderette
Nearby : 🍴 ✕ 🛁

| G P S | Longitude : -0.00312 |
| | Latitude : 42.87328 |

MANE

31260 – Michelin map **343** D6 – pop. 998 – alt. 297
▶ Paris 753 – Aspet 19 – St-Gaudens 22 – St-Girons 22

⛺ Village Vacances de la Justale

🔗 05 61 90 68 18. www.village-vacances-mane.fr

Address : 2 allée de la Justale (500m southwest of the village, along the road near the town hall)

3 ha (43 pitches) flat, grassy

Tariff : (2014 Price) ♦ 2.90€ 🚐 2.60€ 🔲 3.80€ – ⚡ (10A) 3.70€

Rental rates : (2014 Price) Permanent – 19 gîtes. Per week from 250 to 390€

A pleasant, leafy setting beside the Arbas river, with some basic, slightly old rental options.

Surroundings : 🌊 🚂 ♤♤
Leisure activities : 🔲 🚣 🎣 🛁
Facilities : ♿ ☛ 🔲 ⅋ launderette
Nearby : 🏌 🐎

| G P S | Longitude : 0.94716 |
| | Latitude : 43.07621 |

MARTRES-TOLOSANE

31220 – Michelin map **343** E5 – pop. 2 236 – alt. 268
▶ Paris 735 – Auch 80 – Auterive 48 – Bagnères-de-Luchon 81

〽 Sites et Paysages Le Moulin 👥

Sites et Paysages Le Moulin

🔗 05 61 98 86 40. www.CampingLeMoulin.com

Address : at Le Moulin (head 1.5km southeast along the rte du Stade, take av. de St-Vidian and then the road to the left after the bridge; beside a stream and a canal, near the Garonne river (direct access)

Opening times : from beginning April to end Sept.

6 ha/3 for camping(99 pitches)

Tariff : (2014 Price) 31.90€ ♦♦ 🚐 🔲 ⚡ (10A) – Extra per person 7€ Reservation fee 9€

Rental rates : (2014 Price) (from mid Jan. to mid Dec.) ♿ (1 chalet) – 2 caravans – 4 📷 – 17 🏠 – 2 canvas bungalows – 2 tent lodges. Per night from 29 to 119€ – Per week from 231 to 952€ Reservation fee 18€

🚐 borne – 🛒 14€

In a spacious green setting near the Garonne river and an old mill, with a range of good-quality rental options.

Surroundings : 🌊 🚂 ♤♤
Leisure activities : 🍴 ✕ 🔲 🛁 🎣 🚣 🏓 🚣 🦢 entertainment room
Facilities : ♿ ☛ 🛁 🦮 ⅋ launderette 🦮

| G P S | Longitude : 1.0181 |
| | Latitude : 43.1905 |

Key to rentals symbols:

12 📷 *Number of mobile homes*

20 🏠 *Number of chalets*

6 🛏 *Number of rooms to rent*

Per night *Minimum/maximum rate per night*
30–50€

Per week *Minimum/maximum rate per week*
300–1,000€

MAZAMET

81200 – Michelin map **338** G10 – pop. 9 975 – alt. 241
▶ Paris 739 – Albi 64 – Béziers 90 – Carcassonne 50

⛺ Municipal la Lauze

🔗 05 63 61 24 69. www.camping-mazamet.com

Address : chemin de la Lauze (take the eastern exit along the N 112, follow the signs for Béziers and take a right turn)

Opening times : from beginning May to end Sept.

1.7 ha (53 pitches)

Tariff : 19.50€ ♦♦ 🚐 🔲 ⚡ (16A)

Rental rates : Permanent 🦢 – 5 📷. Per week from 300 to 500€

🚐 borne – 11 🔲 11€

The Mazamet–Bédarieux Voie Verte (cycle path, 80km) is near the camp site.

Surroundings : 🚂 ♤♤
Leisure activities : 🔲 🚣
Facilities : ♿ ☛ ▥ 🛁 🦮 ⅋ 🖼
Nearby : 🏌 🎿 🐎 sports trail

| G P S | Longitude : 2.39148 |
| | Latitude : 43.49692 |

MERCUS-GARRABET

09400 – Michelin map **343** H7 – pop. 1 153 – alt. 480
▶ Paris 772 – Ax-les-Thermes 32 – Foix 12 – Lavelanet 25

⚠ Le Lac

𝒫 05 61 05 90 61. www.campingdulacmercus.com
Address : 1 promenade du Camping (800m south along the D 618, follow the signs for Tarascon and take a right turn at the level crossing)
Opening times : from beginning May to end Sept.
1.2 ha (50 pitches)
Tariff : (2014 Price) 30€ ★★ ⇔ 回 ⚡ (10A) – Extra per person 7.20€ Reservation fee 15€
Rental rates : (2014 Price) (from beginning April to end Sept.) – 16 ⬛ – 7 🏠. Per night from 50 to 115€ – Per week from 290 to 710€ – Reservation fee 15€
🚰 borne
Pitches and rental options with plenty of shade along the Ariège river.

Surroundings : 🞰🞰 ⚠	**G** Longitude : 1.62252
Leisure activities : 🖼 🛶 (small swimming pool) 🞦 🞧	**P** Latitude : 42.87154
Facilities : 🚻 🔑 🚿 🍴 🞕	**S**

MÉRENS-LES-VALS

09110 – Michelin map **343** J9 – pop. 185 – alt. 1 055
▶ Paris 812 – Ax-les-Thermes 10 – Axat 61 – Belcaire 36

⚠ Municipal de Ville de Bau

𝒫 05 61 02 85 40. http://camping.merenslesvals.fr – alt. 1 100
Address : at Ville de Bau (located 1.5km southwest along the N 20, follow the signs for Andorra and take the road to the right; beside the Ariège)
Opening times : Permanent
2 ha (70 pitches)
Tariff : (2014 Price) 15.70€ ★★ ⇔ 回 ⚡ (10A) – Extra per person 3.20€
Rental rates : (2014 Price) Permanent – 3 🏠. Per night from 70 to 100€ – Per week from 350 to 480€
Beside the Ariège river. Choose the pitches further away from the road in preference.

Surroundings : ≼ 🞤 🞰🞰	**G** Longitude : 1.83104
Leisure activities : 🖼 🞧	**P** Latitude : 42.64622
Facilities : 🚻 🔑 🞖 🞛 🞦 🞨 🍴 launderette 🞧	**S**

MEYRONNE

46200 – Michelin map **337** F2 – pop. 300 – alt. 130
▶ Paris 520 – Cahors 77 – Toulouse 180 – Tulle 74

⚠ La Plage

𝒫 05 65 32 23 26. www.camping-laplage.com
Address : 1km south along the D 15 and D 23
Opening times : from beginning June to mid Sept.
1.8 ha (80 pitches) flat, grassy
Tariff : ★ 4.50€ ⇔ 回 5.50€ – ⚡ (10A) 4.50€
Rental rates : (from beginning June to mid Sept.) – 10 canvas bungalows. Per night from 49 to 69€ – Per week from 200 to 520€
The shaded pitches lie near the Dordogne river, with a canoeing and kayaking centre.

Surroundings : 🞦 🞰🞰	**G** Longitude : 1.57732
Leisure activities : 🞢🞢 🞦 🞧 🞣	**P** Latitude : 44.87625
Facilities : 🚻 🔑 🚿 🍴 🞕 🞥 refrigerators	**S**

MIERS

46500 – Michelin map **337** G2 – pop. 435 – alt. 302
▶ Paris 526 – Brive-la-Gaillarde 49 – Cahors 69 – Rocamadour 12

⚠ Le Pigeonnier

𝒫 05 65 33 71 95. www.campinglepigeonnier.com
Address : 700m east along the D 91, follow the signs for Padirac and take the road to the right behind the cemetery
Opening times : from beginning April to beginning Oct.
1 ha (45 pitches) terraced, relatively flat, flat, grassy
Tariff : ★ 5.60€ ⇔ 回 6€ – ⚡ (16A) 3.70€ – Reservation fee 13€
Rental rates : (from beginning April to beginning Oct.) – 14 ⬛. Per night from 50 to 75€ – Per week from 215 to 729€ – Reservation fee 13€
🚰 borne 6€ – 6 回 17.20€
Good-quality rental options with a view of the village from some pitches.

Surroundings : 🞥 🞤 🞰🞰	**G** Longitude : 1.71028
Leisure activities : 🖼 🞢🞢 🞣	**P** Latitude : 44.85289
Facilities : 🚻 🔑 🚿 🍴 launderette	**S**

The prices listed were supplied by the campsite owners in 2014 (if prices were not available, those from the previous year are given). The fees should be regarded as basic charges and may fluctuate with inflation.

MILLAU

12100 – Michelin map **338** K6 – pop. 22 013 – alt. 372
▶ Paris 636 – Albi 106 – Alès 138 – Béziers 122

⚠ Club Airotel Les Rivages 🞵

𝒫 05 65 61 01 07. www.campinglesrivages.com
Address : 860 avenue de l'Aigoual (1.7km east along the D 991, follow the signs for Nant; beside the Dourbie river)
Opening times : from mid April to end Sept.
7 ha (314 pitches) flat, grassy
Tariff : 37€ ★★ ⇔ 回 ⚡ (10A) – Extra per person 8€ – Reservation fee 17€
Rental rates : (2014 Price) (from mid April to end Sept.) – 42 ⬛ – 12 canvas bungalows. Per night from 37 to 135€ – Per week from 240 to 945€ – Reservation fee 17€
🚰 borne 5€ – 35 回 14€ – 🞣 ⚡ 8€
A pretty view over the wooded massif (mountains).

Surroundings : 🞰🞰 ⚠	**G** Longitude : 3.09616
Leisure activities : 🍴 🞩 🖼 🞤 🞢🞢 jacuzzi 🞢🞢 🞦 🞣 🞤 🞧	**P** Latitude : 44.10161
Facilities : 🚻 🔑 🞤 🞥 🞨 🍴 launderette 🞧 🞥	**S**
Nearby : hang-gliding	

⚠ Viaduc 🞵

𝒫 05 65 60 15 75. www.camping-du-viaduc.com
Address : 121 avenue de Millau-Plage (800m northeast along the D 991, follow the signs for Nant and turn left onto the D 187 following signs for Paulhe)
Opening times : from beginning April to end Sept.
5 ha (237 pitches) flat, grassy
Tariff : 36€ ★★ ⇔ 回 ⚡ (6A) – Extra per person 8€ – Reservation fee 17€

Rental rates : (from beginning April to end Sept.) – 39 🚐 –
7 canvas bungalows. Per night from 35 to 124€ – Per week
from 228 to 868€ – Reservation fee 17€

Situated beside the Tarn river

Surroundings : ⌂ 00 ⚠
Leisure activities : ♈ ✗ ⌂ ⚡ ⛵ ⟋ ⟍ ⟍
Facilities : ⚐ ⌐ 🏢 ⛏ ⚓ ⚓ ⚑ launderette
⚡ ⚓
Nearby : ⚡🚲⚔ 🏇 paragliding

GPS Longitude : 3.08853
Latitude : 44.10578

⚠ Les Érables

📞 0565591513. www.campingleserables.fr

Address : avenue de Millau-Plage (900m northeast along the D 991,
following signs for Nant and turn left onto D 187, follow the signs for
Paulhe; beside the Tarn river)

Opening times : from beginning April to end Sept.

1.4 ha (78 pitches) flat, grassy

Tariff : (2014 Price) 15€ ★★ 🚗 ▣ (⚡) (10A) – Extra per person 4€
Rental rates : (2014 Price) (from beginning April to end Sept.) ⚡ –
6 🚐. Per night from 41 to 53€ – Per week from 246 to 560€
Reservation fee 16€

Surroundings : ⟍ ⌂ 00
Leisure activities : ⌂
Facilities : ⚐ ⌐ ⚑ launderette
Nearby : ⚡⚔ m ⚓

GPS Longitude : 3.08704
Latitude : 44.11022

MIRANDE

32300 – Michelin map **336** E8 – pop. 3 705 – alt. 173
▶ Paris 737 – Auch 25 – Mont-de-Marsan 98 – Tarbes 49

🏔 L'Île du Pont

📞 0562666411. www.groupevla.fr

Address : at Le Batardeau (east of the town, on an island in the
Grande Baïse river)

Opening times : from mid April to end Oct.

10 ha/5 for camping(164 pitches)

Tariff : 18.80€ ★★ 🚗 ▣ (⚡) (16A) – Extra per person 6.20€
Rental rates : (from mid April to end Oct.) ⚐ (3 mobile homes) –
35 🚐 – 10 🏠. Per week from 239 to 968€ – Reservation
fee 22€

🚐 borne 3€ – 5 ▣ 18.80€

A pleasant location on an island in the Baïse river.

Surroundings : ⚡ 00
Leisure activities : ♈ ✗ ⌂ ⚡ ⚓ ⚓ ⚓
Facilities : ⚐ ⌐ ⚑ launderette ⚓
Nearby : ⚡ ⚡fitness trail

GPS Longitude : 0.40932
Latitude : 43.51376

MIRANDOL-BOURGNOUNAC

81190 – Michelin map **338** E6 – pop. 1 077 – alt. 393
▶ Paris 653 – Albi 29 – Rodez 51 – St-Affrique 79

⚠ Les Clots

📞 0563769278. www.domainelesclots.com

Address : at Les Clots (5.5km north along the D 905, follow the signs
for Rieupeyroux and take road on the left; 500m from the Viaur river
(direct access)

Opening times : from beginning June to end Aug.

7 ha/4 for camping(62 pitches) very uneven, terraced, flat, grassy, stony

Tariff : 33€ ★★ 🚗 ▣ (⚡) (6A) – Extra per person 6.50€

Rental rates : (from beginning June to end Aug.) – 6 🏠 –
3 canvas bungalows – 1 gîte. Per week from 325 to 935€

Surroundings : ⚡ 000
Leisure activities : ⌂ ⚓ m ⚓
Facilities : ⌐ 🏢 ⚑ ▣
Nearby : ⚓

GPS Longitude : 2.17881
Latitude : 44.17713

MIREPOIX

32390 – Michelin map **336** G7 – pop. 204 – alt. 150
▶ Paris 696 – Auch 17 – Fleurance 13 – Gimont 25

🏔 Village Vacances Les Chalets des Mousquetaires

(rental of chalets only)

📞 0562643366. www.chalets-mousquetaires.com

Address : at En Luquet (situated 2km southeast of the town)

Opening times : Permanent

1 ha

Rental rates : ⚐ – 1 caravan – 11 🏠. Per night from 49 to 89€ –
Per week from 343 to 623€

*Near a farm, the site looks out over the undulating coutryside
of the Gers.*

Surroundings : ⚡ ⟍ ⌂ 00
Leisure activities : ⌂ ⚡ ⚓ m ⚓
Facilities : ⚐ ⌐ 🏢 ⚑ ▣
Nearby : ⚓

GPS Longitude : 0.69271
Latitude : 43.73682

MOISSAC

82200 – Michelin map **337** C7 – pop. 12 244 – alt. 76
▶ Paris 632 – Agen 57 – Auch 120 – Cahors 63

🏔 L'Île de Bidounet ⚲⚲

📞 0563325252. www.camping-moissac.com

Address : St-Benoît (located 1km south along the N 113, follow the
signs for Castelsarrasin and turn left onto D 72)

Opening times : from beginning April to end Sept.

4.5 ha/2.5 for camping(109 pitches) flat, grassy

Tariff : (2014 Price) 17€ ★★ 🚗 ▣ (⚡) (6A) – Extra per person 4.20€
Reservation fee 10€
Rental rates : (2014 Price) (from mid May to mid Sept.) ⚡ –
12 canvas bungalows. Per night from 35 to 50€ – Per week
from 200 to 350€ – Reservation fee 10€

🚐 borne – 6 ▣ 17€

In an attractive location on an island in the Tarn river.

Surroundings : ⚡ ⌂ 00
Leisure activities : ♈ ⌂ ⚡ ⚓ ⚓ ⚓
Facilities : ⚐ ⌐ ⚐ ⚑ launderette
Nearby : watersports centre

GPS Longitude : 1.09005
Latitude : 44.09671

---

*The Michelin classification (🏔🏔🏔 ... ⚠) is totally
independent of the official star classification system
awarded by the local prefecture or other official
organisation.*

MONCLAR-DE-QUERCY

82230 – Michelin map **337** F8 – pop. 1 692 – alt. 178
▶ Paris 644 – Toulouse 73 – Montauban 22 – Albi 58

⚹⚹⚹ Village Vacances Les Hameaux des Lacs

(rental of chalets only)

✆ 05 55 84 34 48. www.terresdefrance.com

Address : by the lakeside leisure centre

Opening times : Permanent

5 ha very uneven, vallonné, bois

Rental rates : 110 🏠. Per night from 45 to 120€ – Per week from 149 to 795€

🚐 borne – 25 ▣ 15€ – 💧 🚰15€

The site is in two sections, one overlooking an extensive activity park and the other among trees and shrubs.

Surroundings : 🌳 ⬙ 🌲🌲 Leisure activities : 🏠 🤾 🛷🏊 🎯 🎣 multi-sports ground Facilities : 🛒 launderette Nearby : 🔲 🏊 ⛵ ⛷ 🚣 🛶 pedalos	**G P S** Longitude : 1.59544 Latitude : 43.96957

MONTCABRIER

46700 – Michelin map **337** C4 – pop. 367 – alt. 191
▶ Paris 584 – Cahors 39 – Fumel 12 – Tournon-d'Agenais 24

⚹⚹⚹ Moulin de Laborde

✆ 05 65 24 62 06. www.moulindelaborde.eu ⚹

Address : situated 2km northeast along the D 673, follow the signs for Gourdon; beside the Thèze river

Opening times : from beginning May to beginning Sept.

4 ha (90 pitches) flat, grassy, small lake

Tariff : (2014 Price) ♦ 7.50€ 🚗 ▣ 10.80€ – 🔌 (6A) 3.50€

The camping area is laid out around the buildings of an old mill; attractive, shaded pitches.

Surroundings : 🌲🌲 Leisure activities : ♈ ✗ 🏠 🛷🏊 🏊 small boating lake Facilities : 🚿 🛒 🍽 🚰 🍽 launderette 🚗	**G P S** Longitude : 1.08247 Latitude : 44.54819

MONTESQUIOU

32320 – Michelin map **336** D8 – pop. 603 – alt. 214
▶ Paris 741 – Auch 32 – Mirande 12 – Mont-de-Marsan 87

⚹ Le Haget

✆ 05 62 70 95 80. www.lehaget.com

Address : route de Miélan (600m west along the D 943, follow the signs for Marciac then take left turn, 1.5km along the D 34 following signs for Miélan)

Opening times : from beginning May to end Sept.

10 ha (70 pitches)

Tariff : 27€ ♦♦ 🚗 ▣ 🔌 (3A) – Extra per person 6.50€ – Reservation fee 15€

Rental rates : (from beginning April to end Sept.) ⚹ – 5 🚐 – 18 🏠 – 10 🏚. Per week from 195 to 875€ – Reservation fee 15€

The campsite is in the grounds of the château.

Surroundings : 🌳 🌲🌲 Leisure activities : ♈ ✗ 🏠 🏊 Facilities : 🚿 🛒 🍽 🚰	**G P S** Longitude : 0.32002 Latitude : 43.56579

MONTLAUR

12400 – Michelin map **338** I7 – pop. 664 – alt. 320
▶ Paris 686 – Toulouse 145 – Rodez 88 – Montpellier 138

⚹⚹⚹ Le Hameau des Genêts   (rental of chalets only)

✆ 05 65 99 86 06. www.hameaudesgenets.com

Address : in the village

Opening times : from beginning April to mid Oct.

2 ha flat

Rental rates : 🔥 (1 gîte) – 32 🏠. Per night from 33 to 99€ – Per week from 231 to 693€ – Reservation fee 10€

Free entry to see the farm animals (goats, rabbits, ponies, etc.).

Surroundings : ⬙ 🎣 Leisure activities : 🏠 🚲 ⚹ 🔲 (open air in season) 🎣 farm or petting farm Facilities : 🛒 🚰 launderette Nearby : 🏊 🛷🏊	**G P S** Longitude : 2.83404 Latitude : 43.87653

There are several different types of sani-station ('borne' in French) – sanitation points providing fresh water and disposal points for grey water. See page 12 for further details.

MONTPEZAT-DE-QUERCY

82270 – Michelin map **337** E6 – pop. 1 461 – alt. 275
▶ Paris 598 – Cahors 28 – Caussade 12 – Castelnau-Montratier 13

⚹ Révéa Le Faillal

✆ 05 63 02 07 08. http://www.revea-camping.fr/fr/accueil-camping-le-faillal.html

Address : at the Le Faillal leisure centre (take the northern exit along the D 20, follow the signs for Cahors and take the turning to the left)

Opening times : from mid April to end Sept.

0.9 ha (69 pitches)

Tariff : 20.80€ ♦♦ 🚗 ▣ 🔌 (6A) – Extra per person 4.20€ – Reservation fee 10€

Rental rates : Permanent 🅿 – 24 🏠. Per night from 60 to 85€ – Per week from 195 to 665€ – Reservation fee 25€

🚐 3 ▣ 17.10€

Attractive pitches for tents and caravans; some gîtes that are a little old.

Surroundings : 🌳 🛏 🌲🌲 Leisure activities : 🏠 🛷🏊 🚲🎣 Facilities : 🛒 🍽 🎣 🚰 🍽 🍽 Nearby : ⚹ 🏊	**G P S** Longitude : 1.47725 Latitude : 44.24318

NAGES

81320 – Michelin map **338** I8 – pop. 340 – alt. 800
▶ Paris 717 – Brassac 36 – Lacaune 14 – Lamalou-les-Bains 45

⚹⚹⚹ Village Center Rieu-Montagné 🧍🧍

✆ 05 63 37 24 71. www.village-center.fr

Address : at the Lac du Laouzas leisure centre (4.5km south along the D 62 and take turning to the left; 50m from the lake)

Opening times : from end April to end Sept.

8.5 ha (179 pitches)

Tariff : 24€ ♦♦ 🚗 ▣ 🔌 (10A) – Extra per person 6€ – Reservation fee 10€

Rental rates : (from end April to end Sept.) – 31 – 13 🏠 – 20 tent lodges. Per night from 20 to 41€ – Per week from 280 to 861€ – Reservation fee 10€

Attractive elevated location.

Surroundings : 🐟 ≤ Lac du Laouzas and wooded mountains 🌳🌳
Leisure activities : ♟ ✕ ⛱ ♨ daytime 🏃
🏄 🏊
Facilities : ⚓ 🆒 ♿ 🚿 🚰 ♈ launderette
🧺 🔧
Nearby : 🚲 ✂ 📍 ≋ (beach) 💧 🐴 pedalos

NAILLOUX

31560 – Michelin map **343** H4 – pop. 2 717 – alt. 285
▶ Paris 711 – Auterive 15 – Castelnaudary 42 – Foix 50

⚠ Le Lac de la Thésauque

🖉 05 61 81 34 67. www.campingthesauque.com

Address : 3.4km east along the D 622, follow the signs for Villefranche-de-Lauragais, turn left onto D 25 and take road; 100m from the lake

Opening times : Permanent

6 ha (57 pitches) terraced, flat, grassy, stony

Tariff : (2014 Price) 14.80€ ✶✶ 🚗 🔌 (6A) – Extra per person 3.10€ – Reservation fee 13€

Rental rates : (2014 Price) Permanent ♿ (1 mobile home) – 5 – 14 🏠. Per night from 47 to 105€ – Per week from 240 to 595€ – Reservation fee 13€

🚐 borne 2€ – 15 🔌 6€ – 🚱 6€

Situated near a lake with water activities.

Surroundings : 🐟 🌳🌳
Leisure activities : ♟ ✕ ⛱ 🏄 ✂ 📍 🏊
🐟 pedalos
Facilities : ♿ ⚓ 🆒 🚿 ♈ 🧺 🔧

Longitude : 1.64834
Latitude : 43.3554

NANT

12230 – Michelin map **338** L6 – pop. 919 – alt. 490
▶ Paris 669 – Le Caylar 21 – Millau 33 – Montpellier 92

⚠ RCN Le Val de Cantobre 👥

🖉 05 65 58 43 00. www.rcn.fr

Address : Domaine de Vellas (4.5km north along the D 991, follow the signs for Millau and take the road to the right; beside the Dourbie river)

Opening times : from beginning April to end Sept.

6 ha (216 pitches) very uneven, terraced, flat, grassy, stony, rocky

Tariff : 51.50€ ✶✶ 🚗 🔌 (6A) – Extra per person 6.50€ – Reservation fee 19.95€

Rental rates : (from beginning April to end Sept.) – 28 – 9 🏠. Per night from 36 to 176 € – Per week from 219 to 1,232 € – Reservation fee 19.95€

🚐 borne

Based around an old 15th-century Caussenarde farmhouse.

Surroundings : 🐟 ≤ 🌳🌳
Leisure activities : ♟ ✕ ⛱ ♨ 🏃 🏄 📍 🏊
▵ multi-sports ground
Facilities : ♿ ⚓ 🆒 🚿 ♈ launderette
🧺 🔧 refrigerated food storage facilities

Longitude : 3.30177
Latitude : 44.04554

⚠ Sites et Paysages Les 2 Vallées

Les 2 Vallées

🖉 05 65 62 26 89. www.lesdeuxvallees.com

Address : route de l'Estrade Basse

Opening times : from mid April to mid Oct.

2 ha (80 pitches) flat, grassy

Tariff : 21€ ✶✶ 🚗 🔌 (6A) – Extra per person 4€

Rental rates : (from mid April to mid Oct.) – 14 – 1 🏠 – 1 canvas bungalow. Per night from 24 to 62€ – Per week from 168 to 637€

🚐 borne 5€ – 20 🔌 8€ – 🚱 8€

Surroundings : 🐟 🚐 🌳🌳
Leisure activities : ✕ ⛱ 🏄 🚲 🏊 🐟
Facilities : ♿ ⚓ 🚿 ♈ launderette, refrigerators
Nearby : 🐴

Longitude : 3.35457
Latitude : 44.0241

NAUCELLE

12800 – Michelin map **338** G5 – pop. 2 049 – alt. 490
▶ Paris 652 – Albi 46 – Millau 90 – Rodez 32

⚠ Flower Le Lac de Bonnefon

🖉 05 65 69 33 20. www.camping-du-lac-de-bonnefon.com

Address : take the southeastern exit along the D 997, follow the signs for Naucelle-Gare then continue 1.5km following signs for Crespin and turn left towards St-Just; 100m from the lake (direct access)

Opening times : from beginning April to mid Oct.

4.5 ha (112 pitches) terraced, flat, grassy

Tariff : 27.90€ ✶✶ 🚗 🔌 (10A) – Extra per person 6€ – Reservation fee 10€

Rental rates : Permanent ♿ (1) – 8 – 18 🏠 – 15 canvas bungalows – 2 tent lodges. Per night from 27 to 118€ – Per week from 190 to 826€ – Reservation fee 15€

🚐 borne 16.50€ – 4 🔌 16.50€

Surroundings : 🐟 🚐 🌳🌳
Leisure activities : ♟ ✕ 🏄 📍 🏊 🐟
Facilities : ♿ ⚓ 🚿 ♈ 🔧
Nearby : ✂ 🐴

Longitude : 2.34867
Latitude : 44.18902

To visit a town or region, use the MICHELIN Green Guides.

NÈGREPELISSE

82800 – Michelin map **337** F7 – pop. 5 056 – alt. 87
▶ Paris 614 – Bruniquel 13 – Caussade 11 – Gaillac 46

⚠ Municipal le Colombier

🖉 05 63 64 20 34. www.ville-negrepelisse.fr

Address : to the southwest, near the D 115

Opening times : from mid June to mid Sept.

1 ha (53 pitches) terraced, flat, grassy

Tariff : (2014 Price) 10.50€ ✶✶ 🚗 🔌 (10A) – Extra per person 2€

🚐 borne 10.50€ – 🚱 🔌 9.45€

Surroundings : 🌳🌳
Facilities : ⚓ 🚮 🆒 ♈ 🔧
Nearby : 🏄 🏊

Longitude : 1.51843
Latitude : 44.07286

OUST

09140 – Michelin map **343** F7 – pop. 545 – alt. 500
▶ Paris 792 – Aulus-les-Bains 17 – Castillon-en-Couserans 31 – Foix 61

⛰ Les Quatre Saisons

✆ 05 61 96 55 55. www.camping4saisons.com

Address : route d'Aulus-les-Bains (take southeastern exit along the D 32, near the Garbet)

Opening times : Permanent

3 ha (108 pitches) flat, grassy

Tariff : (2014 Price) 21.60€ ✶ ✶ ⇔ 回 ⚡ (10A) – Extra per person 5.70€

Rental rates : (2014 Price) Permanent – 21 ⌂ – 3 ⌂ – 6 ⊨ – 3 gîtes. Per week from 280 to 690€

⚙ borne –

Behind the hotel restaurant, a very pleasant well-kept camp-site with lots of shade.

Surroundings : ⌂ ₰₰
Leisure activities : ▾ ✗ ⌂ ⚡ ⤏ ⅃
Facilities : ⅋ ⊶ ▥ ⚐ launderette ⤻
Nearby : ✂ ⛖

OUZOUS

65400 – Michelin map **342** L4 – pop. 202 – alt. 550
▶ Paris 862 – Toulouse 188 – Tarbes 35 – Pau 55

⛺ La Ferme du Plantier

✆ 05 62 97 58 01. b.capdevielle@laposte.net

Address : rue de l'Oulet (in the village, D 102)

0.6 ha (15 pitches) terraced, flat, grassy

Surroundings : ⟡ ≤ mountains ₰
Leisure activities : ⤏
Facilities : ⅋ ⊶ ⚐ ▦

PADIRAC

46500 – Michelin map **337** G2 – pop. 194 – alt. 360
▶ Paris 531 – Brive-la-Gaillarde 50 – Cahors 68 – Figeac 41

⛰ FranceLoc Roca D'Amour ♟♦

✆ 05 65 33 65 54. www.camping.franceloc.fr

Address : route du Gouffre (located 1.5km northeast along the D 90)

6 ha (248 pitches) terraced, relatively flat, flat, grassy, stony

Rentals : ⅋ (2 mobile homes) ⤢ – 180 ⌂ – 10 canvas bungalows – 2 tent lodges.

The site is in two sections, partly linked by a footpath (800 m).

Surroundings : ⟡ ⌂ ₰₰
Leisure activities : ▾ ✗ ⌂ ⚡⤏⤏ ⅃ ⟰ ⅃ ⟰ 2 water parks, entertainment room
Facilities : ⅋ ⊶ ⚐ ⚐ launderette ⤻ ⤻

---

*The classification (1 to 5 tents, **black** or red) that we
award to selected sites in this guide is our own system.
It should not be confused with the classification
(1 to 5 stars) of official organisations.*

PAMIERS

09100 – Michelin map **343** H6 – pop. 15 383 – alt. 280
▶ Paris 746 – Toulouse 70 – Carcassonne 77 – Castres 105

⛰ Kawan Village L' Apamée

✆ 05 61 60 06 89. http://camping-apamee-ariege-pyrenees.fr

Address : route de St-Girons (0.8km northwest along the D119)

2 ha (80 pitches) flat, grassy

Rentals : 20 ⌂ – 10 ⌂ – 8 canvas bungalows.

*A shaded grassy area with a range of rental options, but choose
the pitches away from the road in preference.*

Surroundings : ₰₰
Leisure activities : ▾ ✗ ⤏⚡⤏ ⅃ ⤏
Facilities : ⅋ ⊶ ⚐ ⚐ launderette

Longitude : 1.60205
Latitude : 43.1249

---

*Some information or pricing may have changed since
the guide went to press. We recommend you check the
price list online in advance or at the entrance to the
campsite and enquire about possible restrictions.*

PAYRAC

46350 – Michelin map **337** E3 – pop. 670 – alt. 320
▶ Paris 530 – Bergerac 103 – Brive-la-Gaillarde 53 – Cahors 48

⛰ Les Pins ♟♦

✆ 05 65 37 96 32. www.les-pins-camping.com

Address : at Les Pins, off the D 820 (take the exit south of Payrac)

Opening times : from mid April to mid Sept.

4 ha (137 pitches) terraced, relatively flat, flat, grassy

Tariff : 33.50€ ✶ ✶ ⇔ 回 ⚡ (10A) – Extra per person 6.90€ – Reservation fee 10€

Rental rates : (from mid April to mid Sept.) – 48 ⌂ – 3 ⌂ – 5 canvas bungalows – 6 tent lodges. Per night from 14 to 134€ – Per week from 98 to 938€ – Reservation fee 10€

⚙ borne 6€

*The campsite is in two separate parts. Choose those pitches
furthest away from the road.*

Surroundings : ₰₰₰
Leisure activities : ▾ ✗ ⌂ ⚡ ⇶s jacuzzi ⤏ ⅃ ⅃ multi-sports ground
Facilities : ⅋ ⊶ ㏄ ▥ ⤻ ⚐ ⚐ ⚐ launderette ⤻

Longitude : 1.47214
Latitude : 44.78952

PONS

12140 – Michelin map **338** H2 – alt. 293
▶ Paris 588 – Aurillac 34 – Entraygues-sur-Truyère 11 – Montsalvy 12

⛺ Municipal de la Rivière

✆ 05 65 66 18 16. www.sainthippolyte.fr

Address : located 1km southeast of the town, along the D 526, follow the signs for Entraygues-sur-Truyère; beside the Goul river

0.9 ha (46 pitches) flat, grassy

Rentals : 11 ⌂.

Surroundings : ⟡ ⌂ ₰₰
Leisure activities : ⌂ ⤏ ✂ ⅃ ⤏
Facilities : ⅋ ⊶ ⤻ ⚐ ▦

Longitude : 2.56363
Latitude : 44.71119

PONT-DE-SALARS

12290 – Michelin map **338** I5 – pop. 1 606 – alt. 700
▶ Paris 651 – Albi 86 – Millau 47 – Rodez 25

⚘ Flower Les Terrasses du Lac ▲▲

✆ 05 65 46 88 18. www.campinglesterrasses.com

Address : route du Vibal (4km north along the D 523)

Opening times : from beginning April to end Sept.

6 ha (180 pitches) very uneven, terraced, flat, grassy

Tariff : 30.90€ ✱✱ ⛺ 🔲 [2] (6A) – Extra per person 6€ – Reservation fee 15€

Rental rates : (from beginning April to end Sept.) – 47 ▭ – 5 canvas bungalows. Per night from 46 to 129€ – Per week from 196 to 903€ – Reservation fee 15€

🚐 borne 20.50€ – 3 🔲 30.90€
In an attractive location overlooking the lake.

Surroundings : 🐟 ← ▭ ♨
Leisure activities : ♟ ✗ ▭ ☺ ✷ ⛵ ⊿
🏊 water park
Facilities : ♿ ⛽ (July-Aug.) ♨ ♻ ⚲ ♟
launderette ⚲,
Nearby : ✂ ⚓ ◗ ♞

G P S	Longitude : 2.73478
	Latitude : 44.30473

Using the traditional Michelin classification method, the guide provides you with an easy, speedy reference for assessing the category of each site: 1 to 5 tents (see page 10).

POUZAC

65200 – Michelin map **342** M4 – pop. 1 101 – alt. 505
▶ Paris 823 – Toulouse 149 – Tarbes 19 – Pau 60

⛺ Bigourdan

✆ 05 62 95 13 57. www.camping-bigourdan.com

Address : 79 avenue de la Mongie (on the D 935, between the Renault garage and the Intermarché supermarket)

1 ha (48 pitches) flat, grassy
Rentals : 8 ▭.
Choose the pitches away from the road if possible.

Surroundings : ♨
Leisure activities : ▭ ⛵ ⊿
Facilities : ♿ ⛽ ♟ launderette
Nearby : ⛽

G P S	Longitude : 0.13977
	Latitude : 43.08036

PUYBRUN

46130 – Michelin map **337** G2 – pop. 906 – alt. 146
▶ Paris 520 – Beaulieu-sur-Dordogne 12 – Brive-la-Gaillarde 39 Cahors 86

⚘ La Sole ▲▲

✆ 05 65 38 52 37. www.la-sole.com

Address : take the eastern exit, follow the signs for Bretenoux and take the road to the right after the service station

Opening times : Permanent

2.3 ha (72 pitches) flat, grassy

Tariff : (2014 Price) ✱ 5.40€ ⛺ 🔲 5.70€ [2] (10A) 4€ – Reservation fee 15€

Rental rates : (2014 Price) Permanent – 9 ▭ – 17 canvas bungalows – 5 gîtes. Per night from 50 to 70€ – Per week from 189 to 629 € – Reservation fee 15€

Surroundings : 🐟 ▭ ♨
Leisure activities : ✗ ▭ ✷ jacuzzi ⛵ ⊿
multi-sports ground
Facilities : ♿ ⛽ ♨ ♻ ⚲ ♟ 🖼

G P S	Longitude : 1.79432
	Latitude : 44.91457

PUY-L'ÉVÊQUE

46700 – Michelin map **337** C4 – pop. 2 159 – alt. 130
▶ Paris 601 – Cahors 31 – Gourdon 41 – Sarlat-la-Canéda 52

⚘ Sites et Paysages L'Évasion

✆ 05 65 30 80 09. www.lotevasion.com

Address : at Martignac (3km northwest along the D 28, follow the signs for Villefranche-du-Périgord and take the road to the right)

Opening times : from beginning April to end Oct.

8 ha/2 for camping(95 pitches) terraced, flat, grassy, stony

Tariff : ✱ 11€ ⛺ – [2] (10A) 3.20€ – Reservation fee 10€

Rental rates : (from beginning April to end Oct.) ♿ (1 chalet) – 8 ▭ – 31 ▭ – 3 tent lodges. Per night from 25€ – Per week from 330 to 955€ – Reservation fee 10€

A pretty water park and chalets set among trees, shrubs and bushes, with varying levels of comfort.

Surroundings : 🐟 ♨♨
Leisure activities : ♟ ✗ ▭ ✷ ⛷ ⛵ ✂
🏊 multi-sports ground
Facilities : ♿ ⛽ ♨ ♟ launderette ⚲

G P S	Longitude : 1.12704
	Latitude : 44.52546

We have selected the best campsites in France with our usual care, listing those with the best facilities in the most pleasant surroundings.

PUYSSÉGUR

31480 – Michelin map **343** E2 – pop. 119 – alt. 265
▶ Paris 669 – Agen 83 – Auch 51 – Castelsarrasin 48

⚘ Namasté

✆ 05 61 85 77 84. http://www.camping-namaste.com

Address : take the northern exit along the D 1, follow the signs for Cox and take the road to the right

Opening times : from beginning May to end Sept.

10 ha/2 for camping(60 pitches) terraced, relatively flat, flat, grassy, pond, adjacent wood

Tariff : 31€ ✱✱ ⛺ 🔲 [2] (10A) – Extra per person 7€ – Reservation fee 10€

Rental rates : (from end April to beginning Oct.) – 6 ▭ – 15 ▭. Per night from 95 to 120€ – Per week from 300 to 730€ – Reservation fee 15€

🚐 borne 5€ – 5 🔲 20€
The site also holds photographic exhibitions, sometimes in the open, around the pitches.

Surroundings : 🐟 ▭ ♨♨♨
Leisure activities : ▭ ⛱ ⛵ ⊿ ✎
fitness trail
Facilities : ♿ ⛽ ♺ ♨ ♻ ⚲ ♟
launderette ⚲

G P S	Longitude : 1.06134
	Latitude : 43.75082

REVEL

31250 – Michelin map **343** K4 – pop. 9 253 – alt. 210
▶ Paris 727 – Carcassonne 46 – Castelnaudary 21 – Castres 28

⚠ Municipal du Moulin du Roy

✆ 05 61 83 32 47. www.mairie-revel.fr

Address : chemin de la Pergue (take southeastern exit along the D 1, follow the signs for Dourgne and take a right turn)

Opening times : from end May to beginning Sept.

1.2 ha (50 pitches) flat, grassy

Tariff : (2014 Price) ✤ 3.20€ ⇐ 2.30€ 🅴 2.70€ – (½) (6A) 3.50€
🚐 45 🅴 11.50€

In a green setting, but choose pitches furthest away from the road if possible.

Surroundings : 🗁 ⚈⚈ Facilities : ⚒ ⊶ 🚿 🚾 ▽ ☂ 🔲 Nearby : ✗ 🏞 🏊	**G P S** Longitude : 2.01519 Latitude : 43.45464

RIEUX-DE-PELLEPORT

09120 – Michelin map **343** H6 – pop. 1 209 – alt. 333
▶ Paris 752 – Foix 13 – Pamiers 8 – St-Girons 47

⚠ Les Mijeannes

✆ 05 61 60 82 23. www.campinglesmijeannes.com

Address : route de Ferries (1.4km to the northeast, access via the D 311; beside a canal and near the Ariège river)

Opening times : Permanent

10 ha/5 for camping(152 pitches)

Tariff : ✤ 5.60€ ⇐ 🅴 9.90€ – (½) (10A) 4.80€
Rental rates : Permanent – 13 🚍 – 2 🏠. Per night from 42 to 105€ – Per week from 279 to 737€
🚐 borne 4€ – 🚐 11€

A spacious, pleasant site with good shade, near the river.

Surroundings : 🏊 ⟨ 🗁 ⚈⚈ Leisure activities : ♟ 🏠 ♒ 🏊 🚣 ✈ Facilities : ⚒ ⊶ 🚿 ☂ launderette	**G P S** Longitude : 1.62134 Latitude : 43.06293

RIGNAC

12390 – Michelin map **338** F4 – pop. 1 918 – alt. 500
▶ Paris 618 – Aurillac 86 – Figeac 40 – Rodez 27

⚠ La Peyrade

✆ 09 51 53 21 13. www.campinglapeyrade.fr

Address : south of the town, near a little lake

0.7 ha (36 pitches) terraced, flat, grassy
Rentals : 5 🚍.

Surroundings : 🏊 🗁 ⚈⚈ Facilities : ⚒ ⊶ 🚿 ☂ ▽ ☂ launderette Nearby : 🍴 🏠 ♒ ✗ 🏊	**G P S** Longitude : 2.28956 Latitude : 44.4058

For more information on visiting particular towns or regions, consult the relevant regional MICHELIN Green Guide. We also recommend you use the appropriate Michelin regional map to locate your selected campsite, to calculate distances and to work out the best route.

RIVIÈRE-SUR-TARN

12640 – Michelin map **338** K5 – pop. 1 042 – alt. 380
▶ Paris 627 – Mende 70 – Millau 14 – Rodez 65

⚠ Flower Le Peyrelade ⚐⚐

✆ 05 65 62 62 54. www.campingpeyrelade.com

Address : route des Gorgers du Tarn (situated 2km east along the D 907, follow the signs for Florac; beside the Tarn river)

Opening times : from mid May to mid Sept.

4 ha (190 pitches) terraced, flat, grassy

Tariff : 38€ ✤✤ ⇐ 🅴 (½) (10A) – Extra per person 8€ – Reservation fee 19€
Rental rates : (from mid May to mid Sept.) ⚔ – 45 🚍 – 8 canvas bungalows. Per night from 43 to 144€ – Per week from 196 to 1,008€ – Reservation fee 19€
🚐 borne

A pleasant site and setting at the entrance to the Tarn river gorges.

Surroundings : ⟨ ⚈ Leisure activities : ♟ ✗ 🏠 ☯ ⚘ ♒ 🏊 🚣 ⚘ ✈ Facilities : ⚒ ⊶ 🚿 ☂ ▽ ☂ 🔲 🏊 ♒ Nearby : 🚲 ✗ forest trail	**G P S** Longitude : 3.15807 Latitude : 44.18929

⚠ Kawan Village Les Peupliers

✆ 05 65 59 85 17. www.campinglespeupliers.fr

Address : 11 rue de la Combe (take the southwestern exit follow the signs for Millau and take road to the left; beside the Tarn river)

Opening times : from beginning April to end Sept.

1.5 ha (115 pitches) flat, grassy

Tariff : 34€ ✤✤ ⇐ 🅴 (½) (10A) – Extra per person 8€ – Reservation fee 20€
Rental rates : (from beginning April to end Sept.) – 17 🚍 – 3 apartments. Per week from 300 to 880 € – Reservation fee 20€
🚐 borne 5€

Surroundings : ⟨ 🗁 ⚈ Leisure activities : ♟ ✗ ☯ ♒ 🚲 🏊 ⚘ 🚣 ⚘ Facilities : ⚒ ⊶ 🅴 ☂ ▽ ☂ launderette	**G P S** Longitude : 3.12985 Latitude : 44.18747

ROCAMADOUR

46500 – Michelin map **337** F3 – pop. 689 – alt. 279
▶ Paris 531 – Brive-la-Gaillarde 54 – Cahors 60 – Figeac 47

⚠ Padimadour ⚐⚐

✆ 05 65 33 72 11. www.padimadour.fr

Address : 7.7km northeast along the D 36, follow signs for Martel on the D 840 and take a right turn

Opening times : from end April to mid Oct.

3.5 ha (52 pitches) terraced, relatively flat to hilly, flat, grassy

Tariff : 33.50€ ✤✤ ⇐ 🅴 (½) (10A) – Extra per person 9€ – Reservation fee 14€
Rental rates : (from mid April to beginning Nov.) ⚒ (1 mobile home) – 27 🚍. Per night from 59 to 133€ – Per week from 295 to 931€ – Reservation fee 14€
🚐 borne 4€ – 5 🅴 16€ – 🚐 (½)16€

Good quality rentals with new santitation facilities.

Surroundings : 🏊 🗁 ⚈⚈ Leisure activities : ✗ 🏠 ⚘ ♒ ⚘ Facilities : ⚒ ⊶ 🔲 ☂ ▽ launderette ⚘	**G P S** Longitude : 1.68617 Latitude : 44.81765

⛰ Les Cigales

📞 05 65 33 64 44. www.camping-cigales.com

Address : route de Gramat (take the eastern exit along the D 36 to Gramat)

Opening times : from mid June to mid Sept.

3 ha (100 pitches)

Tariff : 27 € ♥♥ 🚗 ▣ ⚡ (10A) – Extra per person 9 €
Rental rates : (from mid April to end Sept.) – 2 caravans – 48 🚐 – 12 🏠. Per night from 55 € – Per week from 229 to 835 €
🚰 borne 5 €

Pitches that are well shaded and good quality rental options.

Surroundings : 🌿 🞧🞧	**G** Longitude : 1.63221
Leisure activities : ♈ ✕ 🏠 🚣 🛝	**P** Latitude : 44.80549
Facilities : 🚻 ☎ 🞧 🛒 🞔 launderette 🞔	**S**
refrigerators	
Nearby : 🏊	

⛰ Le Roc

📞 05 65 33 68 50. www.camping-leroc.com

Address : at Pech-Alis (3km northeast along the D 673, follow the signs for Alvignac, 200m from the station)

Opening times : from beginning April to end Oct.

2 ha/0.5 (49 pitches)

Tariff : ♥ 6.20 € 🚗 ▣ 6.20 € – ⚡ (20A) 3.70 € – Reservation fee 10 €
Rental rates : (from beginning April to mid Nov.) – 4 🚐 – 8 🏠. Per week from 190 to 695 € – Reservation fee 14 €
🚰 borne 5 € – 4 ▣ 6.20 €

Choose those pitches furthest away from the road.

Surroundings : 🞧🞧	**G** Longitude : 1.65379
Leisure activities : ✕ 🚣 🛝	**P** Latitude : 44.81947
Facilities : 🚻 ☎ 🞔 🞔 🛒 🞔 🞔	**S**
Nearby : 🏊	

⛰ Le Paradis du Campeur

📞 05 65 33 63 28. www.leparadisducampeur.com

Address : l'Hospitalet (in the town)

Opening times : Permanent

1.7 ha (100 pitches)

Tariff : 17 € ♥♥ 🚗 ▣ ⚡ (10A) – Extra per person 6 €
🚰 borne 5 €

Choose those pitches furthest away from the road.

Surroundings : 🞧🞧	**G** Longitude : 1.62763
Leisure activities : 🛝	**P** Latitude : 44.80442
Facilities : ☎ 🛒 launderette	**S**
Nearby : 🏊 ♈ ✕	

Michelin classification:

⛰⛰⛰⛰⛰ *Extremely comfortable, equipped to a very high standard*

⛰⛰⛰⛰ *Very comfortable, equipped to a high standard*

⛰⛰⛰ *Comfortable and well equipped*

⛰⛰ *Reasonably comfortable*

⛰ *Satisfactory*

RODEZ

12000 – Michelin map **338** H4 – pop. 24 358 – alt. 635
▶ Paris 623 – Albi 76 – Alès 187 – Aurillac 87

⛰ Village Vacances Campéole Domaine de Combelles ♠♣

(rental of mobile homes, chalets and canvas bungalows only)

📞 05 65 78 29 53. www.camping-rodez.info

Address : at Le Monastère, at the domaine de Combelles (situated 2km southeast along the D 12, follow the signs for Ste-Radegonde, D 62, turn right towards Flavin and take road to the left)

Opening times : from beginning May to mid Oct.

120 ha/20 for camping undulating

Rental rates : (2014 Price) ♿ (2 chalets) – 30 🚐 – 35 🏠 – 27 canvas bungalows. Per night from 45 to 108 € – Per week from 210 to 756 € – Reservation fee 25 €

Plenty of activities for both young and old on this site based beside a large horse riding centre.

Surroundings : 🌿 < 🞗 🞧🞧	**G** Longitude : 2.59147
Leisure activities : ♈ 🏠 🞔 🚴 🚣 🚲 ✕ 🛝 🐎 entertainment room	**P** Latitude : 44.33086
Facilities : ☎ Ⓟ 🞔🛒 launderette 🞔	**S**

⛰ Municipal de Layoule

📞 05 65 67 09 52. www.ville-rodez.com

Address : rue de la Chapelle (to the northeast of the town)

Opening times : from beginning May to end Sept.

2 ha (79 pitches) terraced, flat, grassy

Tariff : 18 € ♥♥ 🚗 ▣ ⚡ (6A) – Extra per person 4 €
🚰 borne

In a pleasant, leafy setting with plenty of shade, near the Aveyron river.

Surroundings : < 🞗 🞧🞧	**G** Longitude : 2.58532
Leisure activities : 🏠 🚣	**P** Latitude : 44.35367
Facilities : 🚻 ☎ 🛒 🞔 🞔	**S**
Nearby : 🞔 walking trails	

To make the best possible use of this guide, please read pages 2–15 carefully.

LA ROMIEU

32480 – Michelin map **336** E6 – pop. 551 – alt. 188
▶ Paris 694 – Agen 32 – Auch 48 – Condom 12

⛰ Le Camp de Florence ♠♣

📞 05 62 28 15 58. www.lecampdeflorence.com

Address : route Astaffort (take the eastern exit from the town along the D 41)

Opening times : from beginning April to mid Oct.

10 ha/4 for camping (183 pitches) terraced, flat, grassy

Tariff : 36 € ♥♥ 🚗 ▣ ⚡ (10A) – Extra per person 8 €
Rental rates : (from beginning April to mid May) ♿ (3 chalets) – 30 🚐 – 1 🏠 – 6 canvas bungalows. Per night from 50 to 160 € – Per week from 350 to 1,120 €
🚰 borne 4 € – 20 ▣ 18 €

Surroundings : 🌿 < 🞗 🞧🞧	**G** Longitude : 0.50155
Leisure activities : ♈ ✕ 🏠 🞔 🚴 🞔 🚣 🚲 🞔 🛝 wildlife park	**P** Latitude : 43.98303
Facilities : 🚻 ☎ 🞔 🛒 🞔 launderette 🞔	**S**

ROQUELAURE

32810 – Michelin map **336** F7 – pop. 558 – alt. 206
▶ Paris 711 – Agen 67 – Auch 10 – Condom 39

⛰ **Yelloh! Village Le Talouch** ♣♠

✆ 05 62 65 52 43. www.camping-talouch.eu

Address : at Cassou (3.5km north along the D 272, follow the signs for Mérens then take left turn D 148, follow the signs for Auch)

Opening times : from mid April to mid Sept.

9 ha/5 for camping(147 pitches)

Tariff : 40€ ♣♠ ⬅ 🔲 🔌 (10A) – Extra per person 8€

Rental rates : Permanent – 17 🛖 – 32 🏠. Per night from 39 to 177€ – Per week from 273 to 1,239€

🚐 borne 12€

Surroundings : 🏞 🗂 ♨♨
Leisure activities : ⛵ 🎯 🎱 🎣 🚴 🛶 hammam jacuzzi ⚡🏊🚲 ✗ 🎿 ⛴
Facilities : ♿ ⛽ 🚿 🍴 launderette ⚒
G P S Longitude : 0.56437 Latitude : 43.71284

ST-AMANS-DES-COTS

12460 – Michelin map **338** H2 – pop. 775 – alt. 735
▶ Paris 585 – Aurillac 54 – Entraygues-sur-Truyère 16 – Espalion 31

⛰ **Tohapi Les Tours** ♣♠

✆ 0825 00 20 30. www.village-center.fr – alt. 600 – ⛽

Address : at Les Tours (6km southeast along the D 97 and turn left onto D 599; at the Lac de la Selves)

Opening times : from mid May to mid Sept.

15 ha (290 pitches) very uneven, terraced, flat, grassy

Tariff : (2014 Price) 16€ ♣♠ ⬅ 🔲 🔌 (16A) – Extra per person 6€ – Reservation fee 27€

Rental rates : (2014 Price) – 174 🛖 – 40 tent lodges. Per night from 28 to 105€ – Per week from 196 to 735€ – Reservation fee 27€

🚐 borne 5€ – 🚐 🔌16€

A pleasant site overlooking the lake.

Surroundings : 🏞 ⬅ 🗂 ♨♨ ⛰
Leisure activities : ⛵ ✗ 🎱 🎯 🎣 🚴 🛶 🚲 ✗ 🎿 🏊 watersports centre
Facilities : ♿ ⛽ 🔲 🚿 ⚒ 🍴 launderette ⚒⚒
G P S Longitude : 2.68056 Latitude : 44.66803

⛰ La Romiguière

✆ 05 65 44 44 64. www.laromiguiere.com – alt. 600

Address : beside the Lac de la Selves (aka Lac de Maury; 8.5km southeast along the D 97 and turn left onto D 599)

2 ha (62 pitches) terrace, flat, grassy
Rentals : 19 🛖.

In a peaceful location beside a lake.

Surroundings : 🏞 ⬅ 🗂 ♨♨ ⛰
Leisure activities : ⛵ ✗ 🎿 🎣 pedalos, scuba diving ✗
Facilities : ♿ ⛽ 🚿 ⚒ 🍴 launderette ⚒
Nearby : ⚓ water skiing
G P S Longitude : 2.70639 Latitude : 44.65528

The information in the guide may have changed since going to press.

ST-ANTONIN-NOBLE-VAL

82140 – Michelin map **337** G7 – pop. 1 829 – alt. 125
▶ Paris 624 – Cahors 55 – Caussade 18 – Caylus 11

⛰ **Sites et Paysages Les Trois Cantons** ♣♠

✆ 05 63 31 98 57. www.3cantons.fr

Address : 7.7km northwest along the D 19, follow the signs for Caylus and take road to the left, after the little bridge over the Bonnette, between Tarau and the D 926, between Septfonds (6km) and Caylus (9km)

Opening times : from mid April to mid Sept.

15 ha/4 for camping(99 pitches)

Tariff : (2014 Price) ♣ 6.60€ ⬅ 🔲 9.60€ – 🔌 (10A) 6€

Rental rates : (2014 Price) (from mid April to mid Sept.) – 17 🛖. Per night from 44 to 82€ – Per week from 595 to 770€

In a natural setting among trees, shrubs and bushes.

Surroundings : 🏞 🗂 ♨♨
Leisure activities : ⛵ ✗ 🎱 🎣 🚴 🛶 🚲 ✗ 🎿 climbing wall
Facilities : ♿ ⛽ 🚿 🔲 ⚒ refrigerators
G P S Longitude : 1.69612 Latitude : 44.1933

⛰ **Flower Les Gorges de l'Aveyron** ♣♠

✆ 05 63 30 69 76. www.camping-gorges-aveyron.com

Address : at Marsac Bas

Opening times : from beginning May to end Sept.

3.8 ha (80 pitches) flat, grassy

Tariff : (2014 Price) 18€ ♣♠ ⬅ 🔲 🔌 (10A) – Extra per person 3€ – Reservation fee 5€

Rental rates : (2014 Price) (from beginning May to end Sept.) – 23 🛖 – 9 tent lodges – 1 gîte. Per night from 37 to 119€ – Per week from 185 to 833€ – Reservation fee 15€

Pretty, well-shaded pitches, some beside the Aveyron river, with a variety of rental options.

Surroundings : 🏞 ♨♨
Leisure activities : ⛵ 🎱 🎣 🚴 🛶 🎿 🏊
Facilities : ♿ ⛽ 🔲 🚿 🍴 launderette ⚒⚒
G P S Longitude : 1.77256 Latitude : 44.15211

The guide covers all 22 regions of France – see the map and list of regions on pages 4–5.

ST-BERTRAND-DE-COMMINGES

31510 – Michelin map **343** B6 – pop. 259 – alt. 581
▶ Paris 783 – Bagnères-de-Luchon 33 – Lannemezan 23 – St-Gaudens 17

⛰ Es Pibous

✆ 05 61 88 31 42. www.es-pibous.fr

Address : chemin de St-Just (800m southeast along the D 26a, follow the signs for St-Béat and take road to the left)

2 ha (80 pitches) flat, grassy

🚐 borne

Some pitches have a view over the Sainte-Marie cathedral.

Surroundings : 🏞 ⬅ Cathédrale de St-Bertrand-de-Comminges 🗂 ♨♨
Leisure activities : 🎱 🎣 🎿
Facilities : ♿ ⛽ ▥ 🚿 🔲
Nearby : 🏞
G P S Longitude : 0.57799 Latitude : 43.02868

ST-CÉRÉ

46400 – Michelin map **337** H2 – pop. 3 563 – alt. 152
▶ Paris 531 – Aurillac 62 – Brive-la-Gaillarde 51 – Cahors 80

⚠ Le Soulhol

✆ 05 65 38 12 37. www.campinglesoulhol.com

Address : quai Salesses (take southeastern exit along the D 48; beside the Bave river)

Opening times : from beginning April to end Sept.

3.5 ha (120 pitches) flat, grassy, gravelled

Tariff : 21.40€ ✯✯ ⇔ 🔲 🔌 (10A) – Extra per person 5.40€

Rental rates : (from beginning April to end Sept.) ⌇ – 5 🚐 – 10 🏠 – 10 gîtes. Per week from 217 to 525€ – Reservation fee 10€

🚰 borne

Encircled by a stream, with a view of the château. Gîtes or somewhat ageing mobile homes to rent.

Surroundings : ≼ ♧♧
Leisure activities : 🎪 ⛹ 🚴 ⛲ ↝
Facilities : ♿ ⚷ 🍴 👕 launderette
Nearby : 🍸 ✗ 🍴

Longitude : 1.89747
Latitude : 44.85791

ST-CIRQ-LAPOPIE

46330 – Michelin map **337** G5 – pop. 217 – alt. 320
▶ Paris 574 – Cahors 26 – Figeac 44 – Villefranche-de-Rouergue 37

⚠ La Truffière 👥

La Truffière

✆ 05 65 30 20 22. www.camping-truffiere.com

Address : at Pradines (3km south along the D 42, follow the signs for Concots)

Opening times : from mid April to mid Sept.

6 ha (96 pitches) terraced, flat, grassy, stony, natural setting among trees and bushes

Tariff : 21.50€ ✯✯ ⇔ 🔲 🔌 (6A) – Extra per person 6.20€

Rental rates : (from mid April to mid Sept.) – 13 🏠. Per night from 67 to 100€ – Per week from 287 to 784€ – Reservation fee 12€

🚰 borne 3€ – 10 🔲 6.20€

A small and pretty chalet village among trees and shrubs, with some pitches offering a panoramic view of the Causse de Limogne (limestone plateau).

Surroundings : 🌲 ≼ ♧♧
Leisure activities : 🍸 ✗ 🎪 ⛹ ⛲ ↝
Facilities : ♿ ⚷ 🍴 👕 launderette 🚿

Longitude : 1.6746
Latitude : 44.44842

⚠ La Plage 👥

✆ 05 65 30 29 51. www.campingplage.com

Address : at Poroute Roques (1.4km northeast along the D 8, follow the signs for Tour-de-Faure, turn left before the bridge)

Opening times : from beginning April to end Sept.

3 ha (120 pitches)

Tariff : ✯ 7.21€ ⇔ 🔲 14.42€ – 🔌 (10A) 5.25€ – Reservation fee 10€

Rental rates : (from beginning April to end Sept.) ♿ (1 mobile home) – 10 🚐 – 12 🏠 – 5 tent lodges. Per night from 50 to 111€ – Per week from 240 to 780 € – Reservation fee 10€

🚰 borne – 9 🔲 11€ – 🛒 🔌 21€

Situated on the banks of the Lot river, at the foot of one of the prettiest villages in France

Surroundings : 🌲 🚏 ♧♧
Leisure activities : 🍸 ✗ ⛹ ⛲ ⛱ (beach) ↝
Facilities : ♿ ⚷ 🍴 🔲 👕 🚿 launderette 🚿

Longitude : 1.6812
Latitude : 44.46914

ST-GAUDENS

31800 – Michelin map **343** C6 – pop. 11 225 – alt. 405
▶ Paris 766 – Bagnères-de-Luchon 48 – Tarbes 68 – Toulouse 94

⚠ Municipal Belvédère des Pyrénées

✆ 05 62 00 16 03. www.st-gaudens.com

Address : rue des Chanteurs du Comminges (located 1km west along the N 117, towards Tarbes)

1 ha (83 pitches) flat, grassy, fine gravel

Rentals : 2 🚐.

There's a panoramic view over the Pyrenees, but some pitches also look down on the road.

Surroundings : ≼ Pyrénées 🚏 ♧♧
Facilities : ♿ ⚷ 👕 👕 launderette
Nearby : 🛒 🍸 ✗

Longitude : 0.70814
Latitude : 43.11

ST-GENIEZ-D'OLT

12130 – Michelin map **338** J4 – pop. 2 068 – alt. 410
▶ Paris 612 – Espalion 28 – Florac 80 – Mende 68

⚠ Village Center La Boissière 👥

✆ 05 65 70 40 43. www.village-center.fr

Address : route de la Cascade (1.2km northeast along the D 988, follow the signs for St-Laurent-d'Olt and turn left following signs for Pomayrols; beside the Lot river)

Opening times : from beginning April to end Sept.

5 ha (220 pitches) terraced, flat, grassy

Tariff : (2014 Price) 27.50€ ✯✯ ⇔ 🔲 🔌 (10A) – Extra per person 6.90€ – Reservation fee 10€

Rental rates : (2014 Price) (from beginning April to end Sept.) ♿ (1 mobile home) – 28 🚐 – 19 🏠 – 20 canvas bungalows – (with and without sanitary facilities). Per night from 21 to 120€ – Per week from 147 to 840€ – Reservation fee 10€

In a pleasant wooded setting beside the Lot river.

Surroundings : 🌲 🚏 ♧♧
Leisure activities : 🍸 🎪 ⛹ ⛲ 🚴 ✂ ↝
Facilities : ♿ ⚷ 🔲 🚿 👕 launderette, refrigerators
Nearby : 🐎

⚠ Résidence Le Colombier - L'Aveyronnais du Nord

(rental of gîtes only)

✆ 05 65 71 52 88. http://location-chalet-aveyron.over-blog.com

Address : rue Rivié (located 1km northeast via the D 988, follow the signs for St-Laurent-d'Olt and turn left following signs for Pomayrols; near the Lot river)

Opening times : Permanent

3 ha flat

Rental rates : (2014 Price) – 42 gîtes. Per week from 199 to 599€

Surroundings : 🌲
Leisure activities : ⛹ 🚴 ⛲
Facilities : ⚷ 👕 👕
Nearby : ↝

Longitude : 2.97809
Latitude : 44.46893

Longitude : 2.98366
Latitude : 44.47011

⛰ Kawan Village Marmotel ♟♦

📞 0565704651. www.marmotel.com

Opening times : from end April to end Sept.

4 ha (173 pitches) flat, grassy

Tariff : 27€ ♦♦ ⬛ 🅟 (10A) – Extra per person 6.50€ – Reservation fee 25€

Rental rates : (from end April to end Sept.) – 69 🚐 – 15 🏠. Per night from 35 to 50€ – Per week from 120 to 980€ – Reservation fee 25€

🚰 borne 5€ – 🔌16€

Surroundings : 🌳 ⬚ ♨
Leisure activities : 🍴✕ 🎣 ⛷ 🏊 🛶 ⛵
multi-sports ground entertainment room
Facilities : ♿ 🚿 ♨ – 42 private sanitary facilities 🚽 🧺 wc 🚰 ♨
launderette 🧺
Nearby : 🛒

G P S — Longitude : 2.9644 — Latitude : 44.462

ST-GERMAIN-DU-BEL-AIR

46310 – Michelin map **337** E4 – pop. 518 – alt. 215
▶ Paris 551 – Cahors 28 – Cazals 20 – Fumel 52

⛰ Le Moulin Vieux

📞 0565310071. www.camping-moulin-vieux-lot.com

Address : to the northwest of the town; beside the Céou river

Opening times : from beginning June to end Sept.

2 ha (90 pitches) flat, grassy

Tariff : 18€ ♦♦ ⬛ 🅟 (16A) – Extra per person 4€

Rental rates : (from beginning April to end Sept.) – 15 🏠. Per night from 50 to 60€ – Per week from 350 to 420 € – Reservation fee 50€

The shaded pitches lie between the swimming pool and a small lake.

Surroundings : 🌳 ♨
Leisure activities : 🏠 🏊 🛶
Facilities : 🚿 🧺 ♨ launderette
Nearby : 🛶

G P S — Longitude : 1.43476 — Latitude : 44.64986

ST-GIRONS

09200 – Michelin map **343** E7 – pop. 6 608 – alt. 398
▶ Paris 774 – Auch 123 – Foix 45 – St-Gaudens 43

⛰ Audinac ♟♦

📞 0561664450. www.camping-audinaclesbains.com

Address : at Audinac-les-Bains, near the lake (head 4.5km northeast along the D 117, follow the signs for Foix and take the D 627, follow the signs for Ste-Croix-Volvestre)

Opening times : from beginning April to mid Oct.

15 ha/6 for camping(115 pitches) small lake

Tariff : (2014 Price) 14€ ♦♦ ⬛ 🅟 (16A) – Extra per person 5€

Rental rates : (from beginning April to mid Oct.) ♿ (1 mobile home) – 22 🚐 – 12 🏠 – 20 canvas bungalows. Per night from 30 to 80€ – Per week from 180 to 760€ – Reservation fee 10€

🚰 borne 3€

A spacious site with 3 small springs, a lake and a swimming pool in front of an old 19th-century spa building.

Surroundings : 🌳 ♨
Leisure activities : 🍴✕ 🏠 nighttime 🎿
🚴 🏊 🛶 multi-sports ground
Facilities : ♿ 🚿 🧺 ♨ launderette 🧺
refrigerators

G P S — Longitude : 1.18407 — Latitude : 43.00705

ST-JEAN-DU-BRUEL

12230 – Michelin map **338** M6 – pop. 695 – alt. 520
▶ Paris 687 – Toulouse 295 – Rodez 128 – Millau 41

⛰ La Dourbie

📞 0565460640. www.camping-la-dourbie.com

Address : route de Nant

Opening times : from mid April to end Sept.

2.5 ha (78 pitches) flat, grassy

Tariff : 19€ ♦♦ ⬛ 🅟 (10A) – Extra per person 5€

Rental rates : (from mid April to end Sept.) – 6 🚐. Per night from 40 to 45€ – Per week from 230 to 570€

🚰 borne 4€ – 15 ⬛ 14€

A magnificent view over wooded hills.

Surroundings : ⬚ ♨
Leisure activities : 🍴✕ 🏊 🛶 ⛵
Facilities : ♿ 🚿 🧺 ♨ 🚰 ♨ 🧺

G P S — Longitude : 3.3466 — Latitude : 44.02004

ST-LARY-SOULAN

65170 – Michelin map **342** N8 – pop. 946 – alt. 820 – Winter sports : 1 680/2 450 m
▶ Paris 830 – Arreau 12 – Auch 103 – Bagnères-de-Luchon 44

⛰ Municipal

📞 0562394158. www.saintlary-vacances.com ♻

Address : rue Lalanne (in the village)

Opening times : from beginning Dec. to mid Sept.

1 ha (77 pitches) relatively flat, flat, grassy, stony

Tariff : (2014 Price) ♦ 5.70€ ⬛ 5.70€ – 🅟 (10A) 7€

🚰 10 ⬛ 10€

A pleasant oasis of greenery in the centre of the village.

Surroundings : ❄ 🌳 ⛰ ♨
Leisure activities : 🏠 🏊
Facilities : ♿ 🚿 🧺 ♨ 🚰 ♨ launderette
Nearby : 🍴 🛶

G P S — Longitude : 0.32282 — Latitude : 42.81548

ST-PANTALÉON

46800 – Michelin map **337** D5 – pop. 239 – alt. 269
▶ Paris 597 – Cahors 22 – Castelnau-Montratier 18 – Montaigu-de-Quercy 28

⛰ Les Arcades

📞 0565229227. www.des-arcades.com

Address : at Le Moulin de St. Martial (4.5km east on the D 653, follow the signs for Cahors; beside the Barguelonnette river)

Opening times : from mid May to mid Sept.

12 ha/2.6 for camping(80 pitches) open site, small lake

Tariff : 28.80€ ♦♦ ⬛ 🅟 (6A) – Extra per person 6.70€ – Reservation fee 17€

Rental rates : (from mid May to mid Sept.) ♻ – 11 🚐 – 2 tent lodges. Per night from 45 to 145€ – Per week from 300 to 995€ Reservation fee 17€

There's a clubroom and small pub in a restored mill. Choose the pitches furthest from the road.

Surroundings : ⬚ ♨
Leisure activities : 🍴✕ 🏠 🎣 🏊 🛶
Facilities : ♿ 🚿 🚰 ♨ 🧺

G P S — Longitude : 1.30667 — Latitude : 44.36918

ST-PIERRE-LAFEUILLE

46090 – Michelin map **337** E4 – pop. 352 – alt. 350
▶ Paris 566 – Cahors 10 – Catus 14 – Labastide-Murat 23

⚞ Quercy-Vacances

⌖ 05 65 36 87 15. www.quercy-vacances.com

Address : at Mas de la Combe (located 1.5km northeast along the N 20, follow the signs for Brive and take road to the left)

Opening times : from beginning April to end Sept.

3 ha (80 pitches)

Tariff : 23.40€ ✶✶ ⇌ 回 ⒣ (10A) – Extra per person 5€

Rental rates : (from beginning April to end Sept.) – 14 ⸦⸧ – 6 ⌂ – 2 cabins in the trees – 3 canvas bungalows. Per week from 210 to 630€

There's a variety of rental options, some of good quality.

Surroundings : ⚞ ♤♤
Leisure activities : ♈ ✗ ⌂ ⏢ jacuzzi ⛲
multi-sports ground
Facilities : ⚲ ⚮ ⛺ ⛻ 回 ⚱

| GPS | Longitude : 1.45925 Latitude : 44.53165 |

To make the best possible use of this guide, please read pages 2–15 carefully.

ST-ROME-DE-TARN

12490 – Michelin map **338** J6 – pop. 853 – alt. 360
▶ Paris 655 – Millau 18 – Pont-de-Salars 42 – Rodez 66

⚞ La Cascade

⌖ 05 65 62 56 59. www.camping-cascade-aveyron.com – pitches accessed via steep slope, help moving caravans onto and off pitches avilable on request

Address : route du Pont (300m north along the D 993, follow the signs for Rodez; beside the Tarn river)

Opening times : Permanent

4 ha (99 pitches) terraced, flat, grassy

Tariff : (2014 Price) 33€ ✶✶ ⇌ 回 ⒣ (6A) – Extra per person 8€ – Reservation fee 16€

Rental rates : (2014 Price) Permanent – 28 ⸦⸧ – 14 ⌂ – 9 canvas bungalows. Per night from 60 to 139€ – Per week from 200 to 890€ – Reservation fee 16€

🚐 borne 6€

A terraced site on the side of a hill overlooking the Tarn river.

Surroundings : ⚞ ⋖ ⛫ ♤ ⚱
Leisure activities : ✗ ⌂ ⚲ ⛖ ⚲ ⛲ ⛲ ⛲
Facilities : ⚲ ⚮ ⛺ ⚱ ⚐ ♈ launderette
⚱ ⚱
Nearby : pedalos

| GPS | Longitude : 2.89947 Latitude : 44.05336 |

ST-SALVADOU

12200 – Michelin map **338** E5 – pop. 410 – alt. 450
▶ Paris 619 – Toulouse 120 – Rodez 54 – Albi 63

⚞ Le Muret

⌖ 05 65 81 80 69. www.campinglemuret.fr

Address : at le Muret, 3 km south-east, beside a lake

Opening times : from end May to beginning Sept.

3 ha (44 pitches) flat, grassy

Tariff : ✶ 4€ ⇌ 回 10.50€ – ⒣ (16A) 4.50€

Rental rates : (from end May to beginning Sept.) – 4 ⸦⸧ – 5 ⛏ – 4 tent lodges – 1 gîte. Per night from 38 to 110€ – Per week from 221 to 610€

Situated on the Le Muret estate with its 18th-century farm buildings.

Surroundings : ⚞ ⋖ ⛫ ♤♤
Leisure activities : ⌂ ⛖ ⛖ ⚲ ⛲ ⚲
multi-sports ground
Facilities : ⚲ ⚮ ⛺ ♈ 回 ⚱
Nearby : ⚱ ⚲ ♞

| GPS | Longitude : 2.11563 Latitude : 44.26712 |

STE-MARIE-DE-CAMPAN

65710 – Michelin map **342** N5
▶ Paris 841 – Arreau 26 – Bagnères-de-Bigorre 13 – Luz-St-Sauveur 37

⚞ L'Orée des Monts

⌖ 05 62 91 83 98. www.camping-oree-des-monts.com – alt. 950

Address : at La Séoube (3km southeast along the D 918, follow the signs for Le Col d'Aspin ; beside the Adour de Payolle river)

Opening times : Permanent

1.8 ha (99 pitches)

Tariff : (2014 Price) 16.40€ ✶✶ ⇌ 回 ⒣ (10A) – Extra per person 5€ Reservation fee 10€

Rental rates : (2014 Price) Permanent – 9 ⸦⸧. Per night from 45 to 63€ – Per week from 175 to 630€ – Reservation fee 10€

🚐 5 回 16.40€

A mountain campsite beside a stream.

Surroundings : ⋖ ♤
Leisure activities : ♈ ✗ ⌂ ⛖ ⛲ ⚲
Facilities : ⚮ 𝄞 ⛺ ♈ 回 ⚱

| GPS | Longitude : 0.24522 Latitude : 42.96664 |

Some campsites benefit from proximity to a municipal leisure centre.

SALLES-CURAN

12410 – Michelin map **338** I5 – pop. 1 067 – alt. 887
▶ Paris 650 – Albi 77 – Millau 39 – Rodez 40

⚞ Kawan Village Les Genêts ⚑⚑

⌖ 05 65 46 35 34. www.camping-les-genets.fr – alt. 1 000

Address : at the Lac de Pareloup (5km northwest along the D 993 then take left turning along the D 577, follow the signs for Arvieu and continue 2km along the road to the right)

Opening times : from mid May to mid Sept.

3 ha (163 pitches) terraced, flat, grassy

Tariff : 42€ ✶✶ ⇌ 回 ⒣ (10A) – Extra per person 8.30€ – Reservation fee 30€

Rental rates : (from mid May to mid Sept.) – 43 ⸦⸧ – 11 ⌂ – 7 canvas bungalows. Per night from 36 to 66€ – Per week from 252 to 910€ – Reservation fee 30€

🚐 borne

Situated beside the Lac de Pareloup.

Surroundings : ⚞ ⋖ ⛫ ♤ ⚱
Leisure activities : ♈ ✗ ⛖ ♈ ⛖ ⛖ ⚲ ⛲
⚲ entertainment room
Facilities : ⚲ ⚮ (from mid June to beg Sept) 回 ⛺ ⚱ ⚐ ♈ launderette ⚱

| GPS | Longitude : 2.76776 Latitude : 44.18963 |

⛰ Sites et Paysages Beau Rivage

Beau Rivage

📞 05 65 46 33 32. www.beau-rivage.fr
alt. 800

Address : route des Vernhes – Lac du Pareloup (3.5km north along the D 993, follow the signs for Pont-de-Salars and turn left onto the D 243)

Opening times : from beginning May to end Sept.

2 ha (80 pitches) terraced, flat, grassy

Tariff : 35.90€ ★★ ⇔ 🗐 (10A) – Extra per person 5€ – Reservation fee 20€

Rental rates : (from beginning April to end Oct.) – 16 🏚 – 6 🏠. Per night from 42 to 149€ – Per week from 198 to 1,064€ – Reservation fee 30€

🚐 borne – 🛒 ⚡14€

In a pleasant location beside the Lac de Pareloup.

Surroundings : ⟨ ⌂ ♀ ⌂	G P S	Longitude : 2.77585
Leisure activities : 🍴 ✗ 🏠 ⛵ 🚲 🎣 🚤		Latitude : 44.20081
Facilities : ⛐ ⚬ 🚿 🅿 launderette 🌊		
Nearby : 🦆 forest trail		

⚠ Parc du Charrouzech

📞 06 83 95 04 42. www.parcducharouzech.fr

Address : 5km northwest along the D 993 then take left turning along the D 577, follow the signs for Arvieu and continue 3.4km along the road to the right; near the Lac de Pareloup (direct access)

Opening times : from beginning July to end Aug.

3 ha (104 pitches) terraced, relatively flat, flat, grassy

Tariff : 28€ ★★ ⇔ 🗐 (5A) – Extra per person 4€

Rental rates : (from beginning July to end Aug.) – 25 🏚 – 35 canvas bungalows. Per night from 40 to 80€ – Per week from 250 to 780€ – Reservation fee 30€

Situated with a view looking out over the lake.

Surroundings : 🏞 ⟨ ⌂ ♀♀	G P S	Longitude : 2.75659
Leisure activities : 🏠 🏃 ⛵ 🎣 ≋ 🎣 ✈		Latitude : 44.1968
Facilities : ⛐ ⚬ 🚿 🚿 🚿 launderette		

SALLES-ET-PRATVIEL

31110 – Michelin map **343** B8 – pop. 136 – alt. 625

▶ Paris 814 – Toulouse 141 – Tarbes 86 – Lourdes 105

⚠ Le Pyrénéen

📞 05 61 79 59 19. www.campingdepyreneen-luchon.com

Address : Les Sept Molles (600m south along the D 27; beside the Pique river)

Opening times : from beginning Dec. to end Oct.

1.1 ha (75 pitches) flat, grassy

Tariff : 19.50€ ★★ ⇔ 🗐 (10A) – Extra per person 5€ – Reservation fee 15€

Rental rates : (from beginning Dec. to end Oct.) ⛐ (1 mobile home) – 12 🏚. Per night from 42 to 75€ – Per week from 290 to 525€ – Reservation fee 15€

🚐 borne 5€

A free shuttle to the Bagnères-de-Luchon thermal baths.

Surroundings : ❄ 🏂 ⟨ ♀♀	G P S	Longitude : 0.60637
Leisure activities : 🍴 ✗ 🏠 ⛵ 🎣		Latitude : 42.8224
Facilities : ⛐ ⚬ 🚿 🚿 🚿 launderette		
Nearby : 🐎		

SASSIS

65120 – Michelin map **342** L5 – pop. 92 – alt. 700

▶ Paris 879 – Toulouse 206 – Tarbes 53 – Pau 72

⚠ Le Hounta

📞 05 62 92 95 90. www.campinglehounta.com

Address : 600m south along the D 12

Opening times : Permanent

2 ha (125 pitches) relatively flat, flat, grassy

Tariff : (2014 Price) 18.80€ ★★ ⇔ 🗐 (6A) – Extra per person 4.10€ Reservation fee 4.20€

Rental rates : (2014 Price) (from mid Dec. to mid Oct.) – 16 🏚 – 1 🏠. Per night from 39 to 76€ – Per week from 195 to 580€ Reservation fee 7.20€

🚐 borne 5€

Choose those pitches near the small canal, further away from the road.

Surroundings : ❄ 🏂 ⟨ ♀	G P S	Longitude : -0.01491
Leisure activities : ⛵		Latitude : 42.87252
Facilities : ⛐ ⚬ 🏛 🚿 🚿 launderette		
Nearby : 🎣		

SÉNERGUES

12320 – Michelin map **338** G3 – pop. 481 – alt. 525

▶ Paris 630 – Toulouse 197 – Rodez 50 – Aurillac 62

⚠ L'Étang du Camp

📞 05 65 46 01 95. www.etangducamp.fr

Address : L'Etang du Camp (6km southwest along the D 242, follow the signs for St-Cyprien-sur-Dourdou; beside a lake)

Opening times : from beginning April to end Sept.

5 ha (60 pitches) flat and relatively flat, grassy

Tariff : 19.50€ ★★ ⇔ 🗐 (6A) – Extra per person 3.50€

Rental rates : (from beginning April to end Sept.) 🏕 – 1 🏚 – 4 tipis. Per night from 34 to 62€ – Per week from 227 to 490€

Pretty flowers and shrubs decorate the site.

Surroundings : 🏂 ⌂ ♀♀	G P S	Longitude : 2.46391
Leisure activities : 🍴 ✗ 🏠 🚲 🎣		Latitude : 44.55837
Facilities : ⛐ ⚬ 🚿 🚿 🖼		

SÉNIERGUES

46240 – Michelin map **337** F3 – pop. 136 – alt. 390

▶ Paris 540 – Cahors 45 – Figeac 46 – Fumel 69

⛰ Domaine de la Faurie

📞 05 65 21 14 36. www.camping-lafaurie.com

Address : at La Faurie (6km south along the D 10, follow the signs for Montfaucon then take the D 2, follow the signs for St-Germain-du-Bel-Air and take the road to the right; from the A 20. take exit 56)

Opening times : from beginning April to end Sept.

27 ha/5 for camping(84 pitches) relatively flat, flat, grassy, stony

Tariff : ★ 7€ ⇔ 🗐 11.30€ – (6A) 4.70€

Rental rates : (from beginning April to end Sept.) 🅿 – 8 🏚 – 17 🏠 – 5 canvas bungalows. Per night from 30 to 117€ – Per week from 210 to 819€

🚐 borne – 🛒 15€

On a 27-hectare wooded estate that looks out over the valley, with a shop selling local produce.

Surroundings : ⚲ ⛰ ♨♨
Leisure activities : ♟ ✗ 🏛 🏊 🚴 ⛷
Facilities : ♿ ⛟ cc 🗑 🏕 ♨ ♨
launderette 🚿

G P S Longitude : 1.53444
Latitude : 44.69175

SEPTFONDS

Michelin map **337** F6
▶ Paris 616 – Toulouse 87 – Montauban 33 – Cahors 44

⛰ Bois Redon

✆ 05 63 64 92 49. www.campingdeboisredon.com

Address : 10 chemin de Bonnet, Septfonds, off the D926

Opening times : Permanent

8 ha/2.5 for camping(40 pitches) sloping, relatively flat, grassy, stony

Tariff : (2014 Price) 23.50 € ✷✷ 🚐 🔲 (½) (10A) –
Extra per person 5.50 € – Reservation fee 10 €

Rental rates : (2014 Price) Permanent – 4 🏠 – 4 tent lodges –
(with and without sanitary facilities). Per night from 50 to 65 € –
Per week from 325 to 700 € – Reservation fee 10 €

This campsite with a family atmosphere is set among trees and shrubs.

Surroundings : ⚲ ♨♨
Leisure activities : ✗ 🏛 🏊 ⛷
Facilities : ♿ ⛟ 🗑🏕 ♨ 🖾

G P S Longitude : 1.60492
Latitude : 44.18285

SÉVÉRAC-L'ÉGLISE

12310 – Michelin map **338** J4 – pop. 412 – alt. 630
▶ Paris 625 – Espalion 26 – Mende 84 – Millau 58

⛰ Flower La Grange de Monteillac 🔗

✆ 05 65 70 21 00. www.la-grange-de-monteillac.com

Address : chemin de Monteillac (take the northeastern exit along the
D 28, follow the signs for Laissac, opposite the cemetery)

Opening times : from mid May to mid Sept.

4.5 ha (59 pitches) terraced, flat, grassy

Tariff : 37.40 € ✷✷ 🚐 🔲 (½) (16A) – Extra per person 6.80 € –
Reservation fee 15 €

Rental rates : (from beginning April to end Sept.) Ⓟ – 15 🚐 –
22 🏠 – 9 canvas bungalows – 4 tent lodges – Per night
from 38 to 148 € – Per week from 190 to 1,036 € – Reservation fee
15 €

Pretty decorative flowers and shrubs.

Surroundings : 🗺 ♨
Leisure activities : ♟ ✗ 🏛 🎣 🏊 🚴
🍴 ⛷
Facilities : ♿ ⛟ (July–Aug.) 🏕 ♨
launderette 🚿

G P S Longitude : 2.85101
Latitude : 44.36434

Key to rentals symbols:

12 🚐	*Number of mobile homes*
20 🏠	*Number of chalets*
6 🛏	*Number of rooms to rent*
Per night 30–50 €	*Minimum/maximum rate per night*
Per week 300–1,000 €	*Minimum/maximum rate per week*

SORÈZE

81540 – Michelin map **338** E10 – pop. 2 564 – alt. 272
▶ Paris 732 – Castelnaudary 26 – Castres 27 – Puylaurens 19

⛰ St-Martin

✆ 05 63 50 20 19. www.campingsaintmartin.com

Address : rue du 19 Mars 1962 at Les Vigariés (north of the town,
access via the r. de la Mairie; by the stadium)

1 ha (54 pitches)

Rentals : 3 🚐 – 6 🏠.

Surroundings : ⚲ 🗺 ♨♨
Leisure activities : 🏊 ⛷
Facilities : ♿ ⛟ ♨ 🖾
Nearby : 🍴

G P S Longitude : 2.06594
Latitude : 43.45337

SORGEAT

09110 – Michelin map **343** J8 – pop. 95 – alt. 1 050
▶ Paris 808 – Ax-les-Thermes 6 – Axat 50 – Belcaire 23

⛰ Municipal La Prade

✆ 05 61 64 36 34. www.camping-ariege-sorgeat.fr – alt. 1 000 – limited
spaces for one-night stay

Address : above the village (signposted from the village)

Opening times : Permanent

2 ha (40 pitches)

Tariff : (2014 Price) 17 € ✷✷ 🚐 🔲 (½) (10A) – Extra per person 3.40 €

Rental rates : (2014 Price) Permanent – 2 🚐. Per night
from 45 to 52 € – Per week from 260 to 360 € 🚐 1 🔲 17 €

*A pleasant location, not far from the Bonascre Ax 3 Domaines
ski resort.*

Surroundings : ⚲ ⛰ Vallée d'Ax-les-
Thermes 🗺 ♨♨
Leisure activities : 🏛
Facilities : ♿ ⛟ (July–Aug.) 🏕 ♨ 🖾

G P S Longitude : 1.85378
Latitude : 42.73322

SOUILLAC

46200 – Michelin map **337** E2 – pop. 3 864 – alt. 104
▶ Paris 516 – Brive-la-Gaillarde 39 – Cahors 68 – Figeac 74

⛰ Les Castels Le Domaine de la Paille Basse 🔗

✆ 05 65 37 85 48. www.lapaillebasse.com

Address : 6.5 km northwest along the D 15, follow the signs for
Salignac-Eyvignes then continue 2km along a road to the right

Opening times : from mid May to mid Sept.

80 ha/12 for camping(288 pitches) undulating, terraced, flat, grassy,
stony

Tariff : (2014 Price) 35.90 € ✷✷ 🚐 🔲 (½) (16A) –
Extra per person 9.50 € – Reservation fee 20 €

Rental rates : (2014 Price) (from mid May to mid Sept.) ♿
(1 mobile home) – 83 🚐 – 2 tent lodges. Per night 120 € –
Per week from 250 to 1,170 € – Reservation fee 20 €
🚐 borne – 🛒

*A spacious, undulating site with trees and bushes, set around a
pretty restored hamlet built of local stone.*

Surroundings : ⚲ 🗺 ♨♨
Leisure activities : ♟ ✗ 🏛 🎣 🏃 🏊
🚴 🍴 ⛷ 🏔 disco, farm or petting farm,
entertainment room
Facilities : ♿ ⛟ cc🏕 🗑 🏕 ♨ 🍴 launderette
🚿 🚿

G P S Longitude : 1.44175
Latitude : 44.94482

⚠ Flower les Ondines 🚻

📞 05 65 37 86 44. www.camping-lesondines.com

Address : at Les Ondines (located 1km southwest following signs for Sarlat and take road to the left; near the Dordogne river)

Opening times : from beginning May to end Sept.

5 ha (219 pitches) flat, grassy

Tariff : (2014 Price) 27.50€ ★★ ⇔ 🔲 🚿 (6A) – Extra per person 5€
Reservation fee 15€

Rental rates : (2014 Price) (from beginning May to end Sept.)
♿ (1 mobile home) – 40 🚐 – 8 cabins in the trees – 12 canvas bungalows – 25 tent lodges. Per night from 37 to 113€ – Per week from 223 to 811€ – Reservation fee 20€

🚾 borne – 🔋 🚿 14.50€

A variety of good quality rental options, on shaded or sunny pitches.

Surroundings : 🏊 〰
Leisure activities : 🍹✕ 🎣 🏓 🛶 〰
Facilities : ♿ ⚡ 🧺 launderette 🎣
Nearby : 🚴 ✂ 🎿 🛶 🏕 🏇 forest trail

GPS Longitude : 1.47604
Latitude : 44.89001

The prices listed were supplied by the campsite owners in 2014 (if prices were not available, those from the previous year are given). The fees should be regarded as basic charges and may fluctuate with inflation.

TARASCON-SUR-ARIÈGE

09400 – Michelin map **343** H7 – pop. 3 515 – alt. 474
▶ Paris 777 – Ax-les-Thermes 27 – Foix 18 – Lavelanet 30

⚠ Yelloh! Village Le Pré Lombard 🚻

interaview productions

📞 05 61 05 61 94. www.prelombard.com

Address : located 1.5km southeast along the D 23; beside the Ariège

Opening times : from beginning March to beginning Oct.

4 ha (210 pitches) flat, grassy

Tariff : 39€ ★★ ⇔ 🔲 🚿 (10A) – Extra per person 8€

Rental rates : (from beginning March to beginning Oct.) – 46 🚐 – 19 🏡 – 14 canvas bungalows. Per night from 31 to 175€ – Per week from 217 to 1,225€

🚾 borne 3€ – 🔋 🚿 18€

Situated alongside the Ariège river; plenty of shade, with a range of quality rental options.

Surroundings : 🏊 〰
Leisure activities : 🍹✕ 🏊 🎣 🏓 🛶 🚴 〰 multi-sports ground
Facilities : ♿ ⚡ 🧺 🚿 launderette 🎣
Nearby : 🛒

GPS Longitude : 1.61227
Latitude : 42.83984

In order for the guide to remain wholly objective, the selection of campsites is made on an entirely independent basis.

TEILLET

81120 – Michelin map **338** G7 – pop. 462 – alt. 475
▶ Paris 717 – Albi 23 – Castres 43 – Lacaune 49

⚠ L'Entre Deux Lacs

📞 05 63 55 74 45. www.campingdutarn.com

Address : 29 rue du Baron de Solignac (take the southern exit along the D 81, follow the signs for Lacaune)

Opening times : from beginning April to end Sept.

4 ha (65 pitches)

Tariff : (2014 Price) 21.80€ ★★ ⇔ 🔲 🚿 (10A) – Extra per person 4.70€ – Reservation fee 10€

Rental rates : (2014 Price) (from beginning April to end Nov.)
🅿 – 17 🏡 – 2 canvas bungalows. Per night from 41 to 93€ – Per week from 270 to 650€ – Reservation fee 10€

🚾 borne 5€ – 🔋 11€

Surroundings : 🏊 🌄 〰
Leisure activities : 🍹✕ 🎣 🛶
Facilities : ♿ ⚡ 🚿 🔲 🎣

GPS Longitude : 2.34
Latitude : 43.83

These symbols are used for a campsite that is exceptional in its category:

⚠⚠ … ⚠ **Particularly pleasant setting, quality and range of services available**

🏊🏊 **Tranquil, isolated site – quiet site, particularly at night**

≪≪ **Exceptional view – interesting or panoramic view**

THÉGRA

46500 – Michelin map **337** G3 – pop. 492 – alt. 330
▶ Paris 535 – Brive-la-Gaillarde 58 – Cahors 64 – Rocamadour 15

⚠ Sites et Paysages Le Ventoulou 🚻

Le Ventoulou

📞 05 65 33 67 01. www.camping-leventoulou.com

Address : 2.8km northeast along the D 14, follow the signs for Loubressac and take D 60, follow the signs for Mayrinhac-Lentour to the right

Opening times : from beginning April to beginning Nov.

2 ha (66 pitches) terraced, flat, grassy

Tariff : 31€ ★★ ⇔ 🔲 🚿 (10A) – Extra per person 7€ – Reservation fee 18€

Rental rates : (from beginning April to beginning Nov.) – 18 🚐 – 4 🏡 – 6 canvas bungalows – 1 tent lodge. Per night from 42 to 129€ – Per week from 210 to 903€ – Reservation fee 18€

🚾 borne 5€ – 🔋 12€

Situated beside a pretty building of local stone, with a range of different quality rental options.

Surroundings : 🏊 〰
Leisure activities : 🍹✕ 🏊 🎣 🏓 🛶 🖼 (open air in season)
Facilities : ♿ ⚡ 🚿 🎣 🧺 launderette 🎣

GPS Longitude : 1.77778
Latitude : 44.82603

THÉRONDELS

12600 – Michelin map **338** I1 – pop. 486 – alt. 965
▶ Paris 565 – Toulouse 234 – Rodez 87 – Aurillac 45

▲▲▲ Flower La Source

🖉 05 65 66 27 10. www.camping-la-source.com

Address : Presqu'Île de Laussac (peninsula in the Lac de Sarrans)

4.5 ha (62 pitches) terraced, flat, grassy

Rentals : 20 🛏 – 11 🏠 – 8 canvas bungalows.

A pleasant site situated beside the Lac de Sarrans.

Surroundings : 🛁 ← 🛋 ⁰⁰		
Leisure activities : 🍴 ✗ 🎱 🛝 🚣 ✂ m 🛶 🏊 🛥 🌊 pedalos 🚲 multi-sports ground	**G**	Longitude : 2.77143
Facilities : 🖓 ☕ launderette	**P** **S**	Latitude : 44.85381

*Routes nationales are main roads and their identifying
numbers begin with N or RN. Routes départementales are
generally quieter roads and begin with D or DN.*

THOUX

32430 – Michelin map **336** H7 – pop. 223 – alt. 145
▶ Paris 681 – Auch 40 – Cadours 13 – Gimont 14

▲▲▲ Lac de Thoux - Saint Cricq

🖉 05 62 65 71 29. www.camping-lacdethoux.com

Address : Lannes (to the northeast along the D 654; beside the lake)

Opening times : from beginning May to mid Sept.

3.5 ha (130 pitches)

Tariff : 33€ ✶✶ 🚗 🔲 🔌 (10A) – Extra per person 8€ – Reservation fee 15€

Rental rates : (from end March to end Sept.) – 42 🛏 – 12 tent lodges. Per night from 51 to 134€ – Per week from 196 to 938€ Reservation fee 15€

🚐 borne 5€ – 5 🔲 14€

Surroundings : ⁰⁰ ⏚		
Leisure activities : 🛝 🚲 🛶	**G**	Longitude : 1.00234
Facilities : 🖓 ☕ 🎣 🛶 🌊 🍴 launderette	**P** **S**	Latitude : 43.68587
Nearby : 🏖 🍴 ✗ 🎣 jacuzzi 🚣 ✂ m 🛶 (beach) 🌊 🚣 pedalos		

TOUZAC

46700 – Michelin map **337** C5 – pop. 352 – alt. 75
▶ Paris 603 – Cahors 39 – Gourdon 51 – Sarlat-la-Canéda 63

▲▲▲ Le Ch'Timi

🖉 05 65 36 52 36. www.campinglechtimi.com

Address : La Roque (direct access to the Lot river (via steep steps)

Opening times : from beginning April to end Sept.

3.5 ha (79 pitches)

Tariff : ✶ 6.55€ 🚗 🔲 9.95€ – 🔌 (6A) 4.20€ – Reservation fee 10€

Rental rates : (from beginning April to end Sept.) – 1 caravan – 1 🛏 – 6 🏠. Per week from 154 to 695€ – Reservation fee 10€

🚐 borne

There's a variety of rental options, some of high quality. Choose the pitches furthest away from the road.

Surroundings : ⁰⁰		
Leisure activities : ✗ 🚣 🚲 ✂ 🛶 🏊	**G**	Longitude : 1.06533
Facilities : ☕ 🎣 🍴 🔲	**P** **S**	Latitude : 44.49889

LE TREIN D'USTOU

09140 – Michelin map **334** F8 – pop. 351 – alt. 739
▶ Paris 804 – Aulus-les-Bains 13 – Foix 73 – St-Girons 31

▲ Le Montagnou

🖉 05 61 66 94 97. www.lemontagnou.com

Address : route de Guzet (take northwestern exit along the D 8, follow the signs for Seix, near the Alet)

Opening times : Permanent

1.2 ha (40 pitches) flat, grassy

Tariff : 23.20€ ✶✶ 🚗 🔲 🔌 (10A) – Extra per person 5.50€

Rental rates : Permanent – 2 caravans – 8 🛏 – 2 tent lodges. Per night from 30 to 75€ – Per week from 210 to 630€

Pleasant pine grove with pitches near the stream.

Surroundings : ⁰⁰		
Leisure activities : 🎱 🛶	**G**	Longitude : 1.25618
Facilities : 🖓 ☕ 🔲 🎣 🛶 🍴 launderette 🛒	**P** **S**	Latitude : 42.81178
Nearby : ✂		

LE TRUEL

12430 – Michelin map **338** I6 – pop. 348 – alt. 290
▶ Paris 677 – Millau 40 – Pont-de-Salars 37 – Rodez 52

▲ Municipal la Prade

🖉 05 65 46 41 46

Address : head east of the town along the D 31, turn left after the bridge; beside the Tarn river

Opening times : from mid June to mid Sept.

0.6 ha (28 pitches) flat, grassy

Tariff : (2014 Price) ✶ 2€ 🚗 🔲 4€ – 🔌 (6A) 2€

Rental rates : (2014 Price) (from mid June to mid Sept.) – 3 🛏 – 5 🏡 – 1 gîte. Per week from 230€

The site is situated beneath the poplars beside the Tarn river.

Surroundings : ← 🛋 ⁰⁰		
Leisure activities : 🎱 🚲 🛶	**G**	Longitude : 2.76317
Facilities : 🎣 🔲	**P** **S**	Latitude : 44.04937
Nearby : ✂ 🛶 🚣 pedalos		

VAYRAC

46110 – Michelin map **337** G2 – pop. 1 330 – alt. 139
▶ Paris 512 – Beaulieu-sur-Dordogne 17 – Brive-la-Gaillarde 32 – Cahors 89

▲▲▲ Chalets Mirandol Dordogne (rental of chalets only)

🖉 05 65 32 57 12. www.mirandol-dordogne.com

Address : at Vormes (2.3km south along the D 116, towards the leisure and activity park)

Opening times : from beginning April to end Sept.

2.6 ha undulating

Rental rates : (2014 Price) 🅿 – 22 🏠. Per night from €40 to 70 – Per week from 180 to 700€

A small village of chalets of various sizes, in a wooded setting.

Surroundings : 🛁 ⁰⁰		
Leisure activities : 🛶	**G**	Longitude : 1.69771
Facilities : ☕ 🎣 🔲 🍴	**P** **S**	Latitude : 44.93657
Nearby : 🍴 ✗ 🎣 🛥 🚣		

⚠ Municipal la Palanquière

📞 05 65 32 43 67. www.vayrac.fr

Address : at La Palanquière (located 1km south along the D 116, towards the leisure and activity park)

Opening times : from beginning May to mid Sept.

1 ha (33 pitches) flat, grassy

Tariff : 👤 3.60€ ⚗ 🔲 3.50€ – (⚡) (10A) 3.60€

Set in a grassy area, with shade from trees; campers have key access to the sanitary facilities.

Surroundings : 🦢 ♨♨
Facilities : ⅙ 🚻 🚿 🛁 🏠

GPS	Longitude : 1.70389
	Latitude : 44.94464

Routes nationales are main roads and their identifying numbers begin with N or RN. Routes départementales are generally quieter roads and begin with D or DN.

VERS

46090 – Michelin map **337** F5 – pop. 415 – alt. 132
▶ Paris 565 – Cahors 15 – Villefranche-de-Rouergue 55

🏕 Village Vacances Domaine du Mas de Saboth

(rental of chalets and mobile homes only)

📞 05 65 31 41 74. www.masdesaboth.com

Address : 1km west along the D 49

Opening times : from end June to end Aug.

20 ha terraced, grassy, stony

Rental rates : ⅙ (3 chalets) – 33 🚐 – 60 🏠. Per week from 670 to 1 105€

A chalet and mobile home village surrounded by greenery, some of which enjoy a panoramic view over Le Causse (limestone plateau).

Surroundings : 🦢 ♨♨
Leisure activities : 🍸 ✕ 🛶 🎣 🏃 ⛷ 🚣 🚴
🍴 ⛳ 🏊 disco, ponies entertainment room
Facilities : ⚡ launderette 🚿

GPS	Longitude : 1.54407
	Latitude : 44.47792

🏕 La Chêneraie

📞 05 65 31 40 29. www.cheneraie.com – limited spaces for one-night stay

Address : at Le Cuzoul (2.5km southwest along the D 653, follow the signs for Cahors and take the road to the right after the level crossing)

Opening times : from beginning April to end Sept.

2.6 ha (58 pitches) flat, grassy

Tariff : (2014 Price) 27€ 👤👤 ⚗ 🔲 (⚡) (16A) – Extra per person 4€ – Reservation fee 9€

Rental rates : (2014 Price) (from beginning April to end Sept.) – 11 🚐 – 19 gîtes. Per night from €35 to 100 – Per week from €195 to 1 150 – Reservation fee 9€

🚐 borne 3€

In a wooded setting with one section of the site for rentals and another for tents and caravans.

Surroundings : 🦢 �︎ ♨♨
Leisure activities : 🍸 ✕ 🛶 🚣 🎣 ⛳ 🏊
Facilities : ⅙ ⚡ 🚿 🛁 🏠 🚿

GPS	Longitude : 1.54593
	Latitude : 44.47154

VIELLE-AURE

65170 – Michelin map **342** N6 – pop. 355 – alt. 800
▶ Paris 828 – Toulouse 155 – Tarbes 70 – Lourdes 66

🏕 Le Lustou

📞 05 62 39 40 64. www.lustou.com

Address : Agos (situated 2km northeast along the D 19, near the Neste-d'Aure and a lake)

Opening times : Permanent

2.8 ha (65 pitches) flat, grassy

Tariff : 22€ 👤👤 ⚗ 🔲 (⚡) (10A) – Extra per person 4.90€

Rental rates : (from mid Dec. to end Sept.) 🚐 – 6 🚐 – 5 🛏 – 1 gîte. Per night from €50 to 55 – Per week from €260 to 440

In 2 separate sections on either side of a small road; the site's owner organises hiking trips.

Surroundings : ❄ ⩽ ♨♨
Leisure activities : 🍸 🛶 🚣
Facilities : ⅙ ⚡ 🏚 🛁 🚿 🍴 launderette
Nearby : 🚣 rafting and canyoning

GPS	Longitude : 0.33841
	Latitude : 42.84492

For more information on visiting particular towns or regions, consult the relevant regional MICHELIN Green Guide. We also recommend you use the appropriate Michelin regional map to locate your selected campsite, to calculate distances and to work out the best route.

LE VIGAN

46300 – Michelin map **337** E3 – pop. 1 457 – alt. 224
▶ Paris 537 – Cahors 43 – Gourdon 6 – Labastide-Murat 20

🏕 Le Rêve

📞 05 65 41 25 20. www.campinglereve.com

Address : at Revers (3.2km north along the D 673, follow the signs for Souillac then continue 2.8km along the road to the left)

Opening times : from mid May to mid Sept.

8 ha/2.5 for camping (60 pitches) relatively flat, flat, grassy, wooded

Tariff : 23.60€ 👤👤 ⚗ 🔲 (⚡) (10A) – Extra per person 5.80€ – Reservation fee 5€

Rental rates : (from mid May to mid Sept.) – 4 🏠. Per week from €265 to 580

🚐 borne

Some pitches lie among trees and shrubs, others are more in the sun.

Surroundings : 🦢 �︎ ♨♨
Leisure activities : 🍸 ✕ 🚣 🏊
Facilities : ⅙ ⚡ 🚿 🛁 🍴 launderette 🚿

GPS	Longitude : 1.44183
	Latitude : 44.77274

Michelin classification:

🏕🏕🏕🏕 *Extremely comfortable, equipped to a very high standard*

🏕🏕🏕 *Very comfortable, equipped to a high standard*

🏕🏕🏕 *Comfortable and well equipped*

🏕🏕 *Reasonably comfortable*

🏕 *Satisfactory*

VILLEFRANCHE-DE-PANAT

12430 – Michelin map **338** I6 – pop. 771 – alt. 710
▶ Paris 676 – Toulouse 177 – Rodez 45 – Millau 46

Le Hameau des Lacs (rental of chalets only)

✆ 05 65 65 81 81. www.le-hameau-des-lacs.fr

Address : route de Rodez

Opening times : from mid June to mid Sept.

1 ha terraced, flat, grassy

Rental rates : Ⓟ – 22 🏠. Per night from 40 to 93€ – Per week from 280 to 650€ – Reservation fee 30€

Set in a large green meadow beside a lake.

Surroundings : 🐾 ≼ ⚬
Leisure activities : 🎦 🏃 🚣 🛶
multi-sports ground
Facilities : ♿ ⚬🔫 🏛 launderette
Nearby : ≊ (beach)

G P S Longitude : 2.69457
Latitude : 44.09654

VILLEFRANCHE-DE-ROUERGUE

12200 – Michelin map **338** E4 – pop. 12 213 – alt. 230
▶ Paris 614 – Albi 68 – Cahors 61 – Montauban 80

Le Rouergue

✆ 05 65 45 16 24. www.campingdurouergue.com

Address : 35bis avenue de Fondies (located 1.5km southwest along the D 47, follow the signs for Monteils)

Opening times : from mid April to end Sept.

1.8 ha (93 pitches) flat, grassy

Tariff : 19.70€ ✷✷ ⇔ 🔲 ⒥ (16A) – Extra per person 3€ – Reservation fee 3€

Rental rates : Permanent – 7 🚐 – 6 canvas bungalows. Per night from 50 to 85€ – Per week from 200 to 470€ – Reservation fee 3€
🚐 borne 3€ – 🐦 ⒥18.70€

Surroundings : 🏕 ⚬⚬
Leisure activities : 🎦 🚣
Facilities : ♿ ⚬🔫 🛁 🚿 ♨ 🍴 🏛
Nearby : ⇶ jacuzzi 🍴 🎳 🛶 🛶

G P S Longitude : 2.02615
Latitude : 44.3423

P. Cheuve / Photononstop

A local saying claims that the hearts of the men of the north are warm enough to thaw the chilly climate. They certainly throw themselves body and soul into the traditional 'dance of the giants' at local fairs and carnivals. Giants are huge in this part of France, as are the street markets: several tonnes of *moules-frites* (mussels and chips) and countless litres of beer sustain around a million visitors to the Braderie, Lille's annual giant street market where people turn out their attics and sell their goods on the streets of the town. The influence of Flanders can be heard in the names of towns and people, seen in the wealth of Gothic architecture and tasted in such delicious regional dishes as beef in amber beer and *potjevleesch*, a terrine made with rabbit, chicken and veal. The sound of bells ringing from tall, slender belfries, neat rows of miners' houses and the distant silhouettes of windmills, all remind visitors that they are on the border with Belgium and within sight of the white cliffs of Dover.

BUYSSCHEURE

59285 – Michelin map **302** B3 – pop. 510 – alt. 25
▶ Paris 269 – Béthune 44 – Calais 47 – Dunkerque 31

⚠ La Chaumière

✆ 03 28 43 03 57, www.campinglachaumiere.com

Address : 529 Langhemast Straete (in the village)

Opening times : from beginning April to end Oct.

1 ha (29 pitches) small lake

Tariff : 20€ ♣♥ ⊞ ⊡ 🚿 (6A) – Extra per person 8€

🚲 borne – 20 ⊡ 20€

Surroundings : 🌳 🛏 ♉♉
Leisure activities : ⛄✗ 🛶 ♏ 🐟 🛝
Facilities : 🔌 🚽 🏖 🚿 🍴 🖼

GPS · Longitude : 2.33942
Latitude : 50.80166

CAMBRAI

59400 – Michelin map **302** H6 – pop. 32 518 – alt. 53
▶ Paris 183 – Lille 67 – Amiens 100 – Namur 139

⚠ Municipal Les 3 Clochers

✆ 03 27 70 91 64, camping@mairie-cambrai.fr

Address : 77 rue Jean

1 ha (50 pitches) flat, grassy

The pitches are on grass, marked out by hedges.

Surroundings : 🛏 ♉
Facilities : 🔌 🚽 🖼 🏖 🚿
Nearby : 🍴⛄✗

GPS · Longitude : 3.21476
Latitude : 50.17533

CONDETTE

62360 – Michelin map **301** C4 – pop. 2 575 – alt. 35
▶ Paris 254 – Boulogne-sur-Mer 10 – Calais 47 – Desvres 19

⚠ Caravaning du Château 🅿🔒

✆ 03 21 87 59 59, www.camping-caravaning-du-chateau.com

Address : 21 rue Nouvelle (take the southern exit along the D 119)

Opening times : from beginning April to end Oct.

1.2 ha (70 pitches)

Tariff : (2014 Price) 27.50€ ♣♥ ⊞ ⊡ 🚿 (10A) –
Extra per person 6.25€

Rental rates : (2014 Price) Permanent – 2 🚐. Per week
from 385 to 670€

🚲 borne 5€

Surroundings : 🛏 ♉♉
Leisure activities : ♏ 🛝
Facilities : 🔌 🚽 🖼 🏖 🍴 launderette,
refrigerators
Nearby : ✗✂

GPS · Longitude : 1.62557
Latitude : 50.64649

These symbols are used for a campsite that is exceptional
in its category:

🏕🏕...⚠ *Particularly pleasant setting, quality
and range of services available*

🌳🌳 *Tranquil, isolated site – quiet site,
particularly at night*

≪≪ *Exceptional view – interesting or panoramic
view*

DANNES

62187 – Michelin map **301** C4 – pop. 1 303 – alt. 30
▶ Paris 242 – Lille 136 – Arras 133 – Amiens 114

⚠ Municipal Le Mont-St-Frieux

✆ 03 21 33 24 76, www.mairiededannes.fr

Address : 21 rue de la Mer

1.5 ha (52 pitches) flat, grassy

Surroundings : 🛏 ♉
Leisure activities : 🎿 ♏ 🐎
Facilities : 🔌 🚽 🍴 launderette

GPS · Longitude : 1.60997
Latitude : 50.58924

ÉPERLECQUES

62910 – Michelin map **301** G3 – pop. 3 162 – alt. 42
▶ Paris 271 – Lille 78 – Arras 86 – St-Omer 14

🏕🏕🏕 Kawan Village Château du Gandspette

✆ 03 21 93 43 93, www.chateau-gandspette.com

Address : 133 rue du Gandspette

Opening times : from beginning April to end Sept.

11 ha/4 for camping (167 pitches)

Tariff : (2014 Price) 25.80€ ♣♥ ⊞ ⊡ – Extra per person 6.20€

Rental rates : (2014 Price) (from beginning April to end Sept.) 🚿 –
8 🚐. Per week from 278 to 625€

The site is in the wooded grounds of the château.

Surroundings : 🌳 ♉
Leisure activities : ⛄✗ 🛶 ♏ ✂ 🛝
multi-sports ground
Facilities : 🔌 🚽 📺 🏖 🍴 launderette 🌿

GPS · Longitude : 2.1789
Latitude : 50.81894

*For more information on visiting particular towns or
regions, consult the relevant regional MICHELIN Green
Guide. We also recommend you use the appropriate
Michelin regional map to locate your selected campsite,
to calculate distances and to work out the best route.*

FILLIÈVRES

62770 – Michelin map **301** F6 – pop. 523 – alt. 46
▶ Paris 206 – Arras 52 – Béthune 46 – Hesdin 13

🏕🏕 Les Trois Tilleuls

✆ 03 21 47 94 15, www.camping3tilleuls.com – limited spaces for
one-night stay

Address : 28 rue de Frévent (take the southeastern exit along the
D 340)

Opening times : from beginning April to mid Oct.

4.5 ha (120 pitches)

Tariff : (2014 Price) ♣ 4.50€ ⇔ 3€ ⊡ 3€ – 🚿 (10A) 3.50€

Rental rates : (2014 Price) (from beginning April to mid Oct.) 🔌
(1 mobile home) – 1 caravan – 9 🚐. Per week from 219 to 692€

In the heart of the Vallée de la Canche.

Surroundings : 🛏 ♉♉
Leisure activities : 🛶 🎣 ♏ 🛝
multi-sports ground, entertainment room
Facilities : 🔌 🚽 🏖 🍴 launderette
Nearby : 🐟

GPS · Longitude : 2.15952
Latitude : 50.31417

GRAND-FORT-PHILIPPE

59153 – Michelin map **302** A2 – pop. 5 491 – alt. 5
▶ Paris 289 – Calais 28 – Cassel 40 – Dunkerque 24

⚠ La Plage

✆ 03 28 65 31 95, www.camping-de-la-plage.info

Address : 115 rue du Maréchal Foch (to the northwest)

Opening times : from beginning April to end Oct.

1.5 ha (84 pitches) flat, grassy

Tariff : ♣ 2.80€ ⬌ 1.30€ 🅴 2.30€ – 🔌 (10A) 3.90€

Rental rates : (from beginning April to end Oct.) – 5 🏠 – 2 tent lodges. Per night from 46 to 116€ – Per week from 153 to 376€

🚐 borne

Surroundings : ♤♤	**G** Longitude : 2.09746
Leisure activities : ⛵	**P** Latitude : 51.00264
Facilities : ♿ ⚓ 🏢 🍴 launderette	**S**

GRAVELINES

59820 – Michelin map **302** A2 – pop. 11 499
▶ Paris 309 – Lille 94 – Arras 125 – Brugge 100

⚠ Les Dunes

✆ 03 28 23 09 80, www.camping-des-dunes.com

Address : at Petit-Fort-Philippe, rue Victor-Hugo (beside the beach)

Opening times : from beginning April to end Oct.

8 ha (304 pitches)

Tariff : ♣ 6.30€ ⬌ 2.54€ 🅴 4.82€ – 🔌 (10A) 4.55€

Rental rates : (from beginning April to end Oct.) – 20 🏠 – 14 🏠 – 5 tent lodges. Per night from 48 to 155€ – Per week from 280 to 795€

🚐 borne – 🔋🔌19.65€

Surroundings : ⛱ ⬅	**G** Longitude : 2.11802
Facilities : ♿ ⚓ 🏢 🍴 launderette	**P** Latitude : 51.00754
	S

GUÎNES

62340 – Michelin map **301** E2 – pop. 5 501 – alt. 5
▶ Paris 282 – Arras 102 – Boulogne-sur-Mer 29 – Calais 11

⛰ Les Castels La Bien Assise ♣♣

✆ 03 21 35 20 77, www.camping-bien-assise.fr

Address : take the southwestern exit along the D 231, follow the signs for Marquise

Opening times : from beginning April to end Sept.

20 ha/12 for camping (198 pitches) small lake

Tariff : 36.10€ ♣♣ ⬌ 🅴 🔌 (10A) – Extra per person 6.50€

Rental rates : (2014 Price) (from beginning April to mid Sept.) – 10 🏠 – 4 🏠. Per night from 74€ – Per week from 380 to 800€ – Reservation fee 10€

🚐 borne 7€ – 5 🅴 36,10€

There's a hotel and haute cuisine restaurant in the outbuildings of the château.

Surroundings : ⛱ ♤♤	**G** Longitude : 1.85815
Leisure activities : 🍴 ✗ 🏠 🏃 ⛵ 🚲 🍴 🎿 🎱 (open air in season) ⛷	**P** Latitude : 50.86631
Facilities : ♿ ⚓ 🏢 🍴 launderette 🚿	**S**

ISQUES

62360 – Michelin map **301** C3 – pop. 1 173 – alt. 15
▶ Paris 247 – Lille 125 – Arras 122 – Calais 44

⚠ Les Cytises

✆ 03 21 31 11 10, www.campinglescytises.fr

Address : chemin Geoges Ducrocq (access via the N 1, near the stadium; from the A 16 take exit 28)

Opening times : from beginning April to end Oct.

2.5 ha (100 pitches) terrace, flat, grassy

Tariff : (2014 Price) 19.50€ ♣♣ ⬌ 🅴 – Extra per person 4.60€

Rental rates : (2014 Price) (from beginning April to end Oct.) – 2 🏠. Per night from 60 to 80€ – Per week from 450 to 500€

🚐 borne 3€ – 3 🅴 18.80€

Surroundings : ⬅ ♤♤	**G** Longitude : 1.64932
Leisure activities : 🏠 ⛵	**P** Latitude : 50.67749
Facilities : ♿ ⚓ 🍴 launderette	**S**
Nearby : ✗	

The Michelin classification (⛰⛰⛰... ⚠) is totally independent of the official star classification system awarded by the local prefecture or other official organisation.

LICQUES

62850 – Michelin map **301** E3 – pop. 1 563 – alt. 81
▶ Paris 276 – Arras 97 – Boulogne-sur-Mer 31 – Calais 25

⛰ Pommiers des Trois Pays

✆ 03 21 35 02 02, www.pommiers-3pays.com

Address : 273 rue du Breuil

Opening times : from beginning April to end Oct.

2 ha (58 pitches) flat, grassy

Tariff : 25€ ♣♣ ⬌ 🅴 🔌 (16A) – Extra per person 5€

Rental rates : (from beginning April to end Oct.) ♿ (1 chalet) – 5 🏠 – 5 🏠. Per night from 70 to 100€ – Per week from 350 to 660€

🚐 6 🅴 25€

Surroundings : ⛱ ⬅ ♤	**G** Longitude : 1.94776
Leisure activities : 🍴 ✗ 🏠 ⛵ 🎿 (covered off season)	**P** Latitude : 50.77991
Facilities : ♿ ⚓ 🚿 🎿 🍴 launderette	**S**

MAUBEUGE

59600 – Michelin map **302** L6 – pop. 31 970 – alt. 134
▶ Paris 242 – Charleville-Mézières 95 – Mons 21 – St-Quentin 114

⚠ Municipal du Clair de Lune

✆ 03 27 62 25 48, www.ville-maubeuge.fr

Address : 212 route de Mons (located 1.5km north along the N 2)

2 ha (92 pitches) flat, grassy

The site is decorated with flowers and shrubs.

Surroundings : ⬅ ♨	**G** Longitude : 3.9766
Leisure activities : ⛵	**P** Latitude : 50.29573
Facilities : ♿ ⚓ 🏢 🍴	**S**

WILLIES

59740 – Michelin map **302** M7 – pop. 165 – alt. 167
▶ Paris 225 – Avesnes-sur-Helpe 16 – Cambrai 69 – Charleroi 48

⛰ ValJoly

✆ 03 27 61 83 76, www.valjoly.com

Address : at Eppé Sauvage, the ValJoly activity centre (located 1.5km east along the D 133, 300m from the lake)

Opening times : from mid April to end Sept.

4 ha (180 pitches)

Tariff : (2014 Price) ★ 4.95€ ⇔ 🅿 7.50€ ⚡ (6A)

Rental rates : (2014 Price) (and school holidays) – 30 🏠. Per week from 256 to 1,050€

Located 1.5km from the ValJoly tourist resort and activity park.

Surroundings : 🦌 ⛳
Leisure activities : 🏛 🛶 ✂
Facilities : ⚷ 🚗 CC 🏧 launderette 🚿
Nearby : 🎣 🛶

G P S Longitude : 4.11518
Latitude : 50.12245

NORMANDY

B. Rieger / hemis.fr

Normandy has inspired many poets and artists, including Baudelaire, Turner and Monet. Today, it also offers rural relaxation and coastal rejuvenation. Take a walk along the coast to fill your lungs with sea air and admire the elegant resorts. You may need to catch your breath when you first see the medieval Benedictine abbey of Mont Saint-Michel rising up from the sands or glimpse the view over Étretat's white cliffs. No visitor could fail to be moved by the memory of the brave men who gave their lives on the Normandy beaches in World War II. Further inland, you will discover acres of neat, hedge-lined fields. Drink in the scent of apple blossom, admire the pretty half-timbered cottages and follow the River Seine as it meanders past medieval cities, impressive castles and venerable abbeys. No experience would be complete without savouring the region's culinary classics, including a plate of boat-fresh seafood, creamy Camembert, cider and Calvados, the famous apple brandy.

Legend:
- Locality with campsite
- Locality with campsite and rental option
- Vannes — Locality with campsite and campervan area
- Moyaux — Locality with at least one pleasant campsite
- Motorway service area for campervans

ALDERNEY

Omonville-la-Rogue
CHERBOURG-OCTEVILLE
Maupertus-s-M.

St-Vaast-la-Hougue

les Pieux
N 13
le Rozel
D 2
Ravenoville
Surtainville
Barneville-Carteret
St-Sauveur-le-Vicomte
Ste-Marie-du-Mont
Baubigny
Colleville-s-M.
Courseulles-s-M.
Port-en-Bessin
Bernières-s-M.
Arromanches-les-B^s
St-Aubin-s-M.
Villers-s-M.
St-Jean-de-la-Rivière
Isigny-s-M.
Surrain
Luc-s-M.
Houlgate
Denneville
Ste-Mère-Église
Dives-s-M.
St-Symphorien-le-Valois
Carentan
Trévières
Bayeux
JERSEY
St-Germain-s-Ay
Merville-Franceville-Pl.
Gonneville-en-A.
Martragny
N 13
A 13
St-Lô
CAEN
N 158
D 613

MANCHE
Agon-Coutainville
Coutances
CALVADOS
D 999
Vire
Annoville
LA VALLÉE DE LA VIRE-GOUVET
Thury-Harcourt
le Vey
Bréville-s-M.
D 971
Falaise
Bréhal
Pont-Farcy
Donville-les-B.
A 88
Îles Chausey
Granville
D 924
Vire
St-Pair-s-Mer
D 973
Villedieu-les-Poêles
Orne
A 84
Flers
Genêts
Brécey
Argentan
St-Malo
Cancale
Sée
D 924
le-Guildo
St-Lunaire
Roz-sur-Couesnon
Avranches
ORNE
A 88
St-Briac-s-M.
St-Coulomb
Courtils
Ducey
urien
St-Père
Beauvoir
St-Hilaire-du-Harcouët
ignon
Cherrueix
Sélune
Plancoët
St-Jouan-des-Guérets
N 176
St-Marcan
Les Biards
Bagnoles-de-l'O.
LA DENTELLE D'ALENÇON
Pléven
St-Samson-s-R.
Dol-de-Bretagne
Pontorson
D 976
Taden
N 176
Dinan
N 12
Jugon-les-Lacs
la Chapelle-aux-Filtzméens
Alençon
D 766
Rance
Tinténiac
Ambrières-les-Vallées
drignac
Feins
Fougères
Fresnay-s-Sarthe
Ille
D 175
N 12
N 12
D 137
A 84
Mayenne
Sillé-le-Guillaume
D 766
Châtillon-en-Vendelais
MAYENNE
Mézières-s/s-Lavardin
RENNES
Andouillé
Évron
Tennie
Paimpont
Vilaine
Évron
A 81
N 24
Châteaugiron
N 157
St-Berthevin
Laval
ILLE-ET-VILAINE
Mayenne
D 21
A 81
Marcillé-Robert
Meslay-du-Maine
Loué
N 137
D 771
N 162
Vilaine
la Selle-Craonnaise
Villiers-Charlemagne
Bouère
Avoise
A 11
Martigné-Ferchaud
LE M

AGON-COUTAINVILLE

50230 – Michelin map **303** C5 – pop. 2 826 – alt. 36
▶ Paris 348 – Barneville-Carteret 48 – Carentan 43 – Cherbourg 80

⚠ Municipal le Marais

✆ 02 33 47 05 20. http://www.agoncoutainville.fr

Address : boulevard Lebel-Jéhenne (take the northeastern exit, near the racecourse)

Opening times : from beginning July to end Aug.

2 ha (104 pitches) flat, grassy

Tariff : (2014 Price) ★ 4€ ⚐ 回 5.70€ – ⚡ (5A) 3.50€

🚐 borne – 34 回 6.30€

Surroundings : ⚓
Leisure activities : 🏊
Facilities : ♿ ⛟
Nearby : 🍴 ✗ 🔭 ⛵

GPS Longitude : -1.59283
Latitude : 49.04975

⚠ Municipal le Martinet

✆ 02 33 47 05 20. www.agoncoutainville.fr

Address : boulevard Lebel-Jéhenne (take the northeastern exit, near the racecourse (hippodrome)

Opening times : from beginning April to end Oct.

1.5 ha (122 pitches) flat, grassy

Tariff : (2014 Price) ★ 4€ ⚐ 回 5.70€ – ⚡ (5A) 3.50€

🚐 borne – 34 回 6.30€

Surroundings : 🏠 ⚲
Leisure activities : 🏊
Facilities : ♿ ⛟ launderette
Nearby : 🍴 ✗ 🔭 ⛵ 🐎

GPS Longitude : -1.59283
Latitude : 49.04958

ALENÇON

61000 – Michelin map **310** J4 – pop. 27 325 – alt. 135
▶ Paris 190 – Chartres 119 – Évreux 119 – Laval 90

⚠ Municipal de Guéramé

✆ 02 33 26 34 95. camping.guerame@orange.fr

Address : 65 route de Guéramé (to the southwest along the ring road (périphérique)

1.5 ha (54 pitches)

In a pleasant setting beside the Sarthe river.

Surroundings : 🏠 ⚲
Leisure activities : 🏠 🏊 ✗
Facilities : ♿ ⛟ 🏢 🌊 launderette
Nearby : 🍴 🍴 🔭 🌊 ⚓ 🐎

GPS Longitude : 0.0728
Latitude : 48.4259

ANNOVILLE

50660 – Michelin map **303** C6 – pop. 619 – alt. 28
▶ Paris 348 – Barneville-Carteret 57 – Carentan 48 – Coutances 14

⚠ Municipal les Peupliers

✆ 02 33 47 67 73. www.camping-annoville.fr

Address : rue des Peupliers (3km southwest along the D 20 and take the road to the right, 500m from the beach)

Opening times : from mid June to beginning Sept.

2 ha (100 pitches)

Tariff : (2014 Price) ★ 3€ ⚐ 回 3.40€ – ⚡ (6A) 3.20€

Rental rates : (2014 Price) (from mid April to end Sept.) – 5 🚍.
Per night from 57 to 83€ – Per week from 257 to 463€

Surroundings : 🏖
Leisure activities : 🏊 🚴 🔭
Facilities : ⛟ ⛟ 🏢 🌊

GPS Longitude : -1.55309
Latitude : 48.95767

ARGENTAN

61200 – Michelin map **310** I2 – pop. 14 356 – alt. 160
▶ Paris 191 – Alençon 46 – Caen 59 – Dreux 115

⚠ Municipal de la Noë

✆ 02 33 36 05 69. www.argentan.fr/tourisme

Address : rue de la Noë

Opening times : from beginning April to beginning Oct.

0.3 ha (23 pitches) flat, grassy

Tariff : (2014 Price) ★ 2.60€ ⚐ 2€ 回 2.60€ – ⚡ 2.60€

🚐 borne 2.30€

In a pleasant location near a park and a lake.

Surroundings : 🏠
Leisure activities : 🏠
Facilities : ♿ ⛟ 🏢 launderette
Nearby : 🔭 🌊 ⚓ fitness trail

GPS Longitude : -0.01687
Latitude : 48.73995

To visit a town or region, use the MICHELIN Green Guides.

ARROMANCHES-LES-BAINS

14117 – Michelin map **303** I3 – pop. 608 – alt. 15
▶ Paris 266 – Bayeux 11 – Caen 34 – St-Lô 46

⚠ Municipal

✆ 02 31 22 36 78. camping.arromanches@wanadoo.fr

Address : 9 avenue de Verdun

Opening times : from beginning April to beginning Nov.

1.5 ha (126 pitches) terraced, relatively flat, flat, grassy

Tariff : (2014 Price) 17.90€ ★★ ⚐ 回 ⚡ (10A) –
Extra per person 4.30€

Rental rates : (2014 Price) (from beginning April to beginning Nov.)
– 6 🚍. Per week from 365 to 420€

🚐 borne – 14 回

Surroundings : ⚲
Leisure activities : 🏊
Facilities : ♿ ⛟ (from mid June to mid Sept) launderette
Nearby : ✗ 🔭 🔭 ⚓ 🐎

GPS Longitude : -0.62642
Latitude : 49.3381

AUMALE

76390 – Michelin map **304** K3 – pop. 2 405 – alt. 130
▶ Paris 136 – Amiens 48 – Beauvais 49 – Dieppe 69

⚠ Municipal le Grand Mail

✆ 02 35 93 40 50. www.aumale.com – ⛩

Address : 6 Le Grand Mail

Opening times : from mid March to end Sept.

0.6 ha (40 pitches) flat, grassy

Tariff : (2014 Price) ★ 2.70€ ⚐ 2.70€ 回 2.70€ – ⚡ (7A) 2.70€

🚐 borne 2€

On the side of a hill on the slopes above the town.

Surroundings : 🦌 ♀
Facilities : 🔥 🚐⊘🎖

G P S Longitude : 1.74202
Latitude : 49.76566

BAGNOLES-DE-L'ORNE

61140 – Michelin map **310** G3 – pop. 2 454 – alt. 140 – ♨
▶ Paris 236 – Alençon 48 – Argentan 39 – Domfront 19

⚠ Municipal la Vée

📞 0233378745. www.campingbagnolesdelorne.com

Address : avenue du Président Coty (1.3km southwest, near Tessé-la-Madeleine, 30m from the river)

Opening times : from beginning March to mid Nov.

2.8 ha (250 pitches)

Tariff : (2014 Price) 17.80€ ✶✶ ⬳ 🔲 🔌 (10A) –
Extra per person 4.30€

Rental rates : (2014 Price) (from beginning March to mid Nov.) –
14 🛖. Per week from 342 to 420€

🚐 borne – 51 🔲 17.80€ – 🚌 🔌 8.70€

Surroundings : 🦌 🚐
Leisure activities : 🏊 🐎
Facilities : 🔥 ⚏ 🎖 🚿🛁🚾 🍴
launderette 🧺
Nearby : 🍴 🏊 🛶 🐎 fitness trail

G P S Longitude : -0.41982
Latitude : 48.54787

BARNEVILLE-CARTERET

50270 – Michelin map **303** B3 – pop. 2 282 – alt. 47
▶ Paris 356 – Caen 123 – Carentan 43 – Cherbourg 39

⚠ Les Bosquets

📞 0233047362. www.camping-lesbosquets.com

Address : rue du Capitaine Quenault (2.5km southwest following signs for Barneville-Plage and take turning to the left, 450m from the beach)

15 ha/6 for camping (331 pitches) very uneven, flat, grassy, sandy

In an unspoilt and natural setting among pine trees and sand dunes.

Surroundings : 🦌 🚐 ♀
Leisure activities : ♟ 🏊 🐎 🛶
Facilities : ⚏ 🧺 launderette
Nearby : 🏊 🐎 sand yachting

G P S Longitude : -1.76081
Latitude : 49.36587

⚠ La Gerfleur

📞 0233043841. www.lagerfleur.fr 🏊

Address : rue Guillaume-le-Conquérant (800m west along the D 903e, follow the signs for Carteret)

Opening times : from beginning April to end Oct.

2.3 ha (93 pitches)

Tariff : 22.64€ ✶✶ ⬳ 🔲 🔌 (6A) – Extra per person 5.50€

Rental rates : (from beginning April to end Oct.) 🏊 – 11 🛖.
Per night from 50€ – Per week from 310 to 580€

🚐 borne

The campsite is beside a small lake.

Surroundings : 🚐 ♀
Leisure activities : ♟ 🏊 🐎 🛶 🏊
Facilities : 🔥 ⚏ 🎖 launderette
Nearby : 🛒 🍴 🎣 🛶 🐎

G P S Longitude : -1.76435
Latitude : 49.38346

BAUBIGNY

50270 – Michelin map **303** B3 – pop. 154 – alt. 30
▶ Paris 361 – Barneville-Carteret 9 – Cherbourg 33 – Valognes 28

⚠ Bel Sito

📞 0233043274. www.bel-sito.com

Address : at L'Eglise, just off the D131, on the left, heading west towards the sea

6 ha/4 for camping (85 pitches) relatively flat to hilly, flat, grassy, sandy, dunes

Rentals : 1 🛖 – 7 🏠.

In a natural and unspoilt setting among sand dunes.

Surroundings : 🦌 ⛵
Leisure activities : 🏊 🐎
Facilities : ⚏ 🧺 🎖 launderette

G P S Longitude : -1.80513
Latitude : 49.42954

This guide is updated regularly, so buy your new copy every year!

BAYEUX

14400 – Michelin map **303** H4 – pop. 13 348 – alt. 50
▶ Paris 265 – Caen 31 – Cherbourg 95 – Flers 69

⚠ Municipal

📞 0231920843. www.camping-bayeux.fr

Address : boulevard Eindhoven (north of the town)

2.5 ha (140 pitches) flat, grassy

Rentals : 5 🛖.

Attractive shrubs and bushes decorate the site.

Surroundings : ♀♀
Leisure activities : 🏊 🐎
Facilities : 🔥 ⚏ 🎖 launderette
Nearby : 🛒 🍴 🔲 (open air in season)

G P S Longitude : -0.69774
Latitude : 49.28422

BAZINVAL

76340 – Michelin map **304** J2 – pop. 350 – alt. 120
▶ Paris 165 – Abbeville 33 – Amiens 62 – Blangy-sur-Bresle 9

⚠ Municipal de la Forêt

📞 0232970401. bazinval2@wanadoo.fr

Address : 10 rue de Saulx (take the southwestern exit along the D 115 and take turning to the left, near the town hall)

Opening times : from beginning April to end Oct.

0.4 ha (20 pitches) open site, relatively flat, grassy

Tariff : (2014 Price) ✶ 2€ ⬳ 2€ 🔲 2€ – 🔌 (16A) 4€

🚐 borne 5€ – 3 🔲 5€

Shrubs and bushes surround the pitches.

Surroundings : 🚐 ♀
Facilities : 🚐⊘🎖

G P S Longitude : 1.55136
Latitude : 49.95487

Some information or pricing may have changed since the guide went to press. We recommend you check the price list online in advance or at the entrance to the campsite and enquire about possible restrictions.

BEAUVOIR

50170 – Michelin map **303** C8 – pop. 419
▶ Paris 358 – Caen 125 – St-Lô 91 – Rennes 63

⚠ Aux Pommiers

🖉 02 33 60 11 36. www.camping-auxpommiers.com

Address : 28 route du Mont Saint Michel

Opening times : from end March to mid Nov.

1.79 ha (107 pitches) flat, grassy

Tariff : (2014 Price) 20.64€ ♦♦ ⟶ 🔲 🔌 (10A) –
Extra per person 4.70€

Rental rates : (2014 Price) (from end March to mid Nov.) –
1 caravan – 18 🚐 – 7 🏠 – 4 🛏 – 4 canvas bungalows.
Per night from 48 to 103€ – Per week from 310 to 495€
🚙 borne – 15 🔲 6.50€ – 🛥 18.62€

Surroundings : 🌳
Leisure activities : 🎯 🛶 🚴 🎣 🏓 🏊
Facilities : ⟶ 2 private sanitary facilities (🚿
🚽 wc) 🍴 launderette
Nearby : 🍴 🎿 🐴

| | G P S | Longitude : -1.51264 Latitude : 48.59618 |

We have selected the best campsites in France with our usual care, listing those with the best facilities in the most pleasant surroundings.

LE BEC-HELLOUIN

27800 – Michelin map **304** E6 – pop. 419 – alt. 101
▶ Paris 153 – Bernay 22 – Évreux 46 – Lisieux 46

⚠ Municipal St-Nicolas

🖉 02 32 44 83 55. www.campingstnicolas.fr

Address : 15 rue St-Nicolas (situated 2km east, along the D 39 and D 581, follow the signs for Malleville-sur-le-Bec and take road to the left)

Opening times : from mid March to mid Oct.

3 ha (90 pitches) flat, grassy

Tariff : (2014 Price) 16.10€ ♦♦ ⟶ 🔲 🔌 (10A) –
Extra per person 4.30€

Rental rates : (2014 Price) (from mid March to mid Oct.) – 5 🚐.
Per night from 52 to 93€ – Reservation fee 8€
🚙 borne 5€
A well-kept site with flowers.

Surroundings : 🌿 🌳
Leisure activities : 🛶 🎿 library
Facilities : ⟶ 🚿 🍴 launderette
Nearby : 🐴

| | G P S | Longitude : 0.72268 Latitude : 49.23586 |

BELLÊME

61130 – Michelin map **310** M4 – pop. 1 547 – alt. 241
▶ Paris 168 – Alençon 42 – Chartres 76 – La Ferté-Bernard 23

⚠ Le Val

🖉 06 24 70 55 17. www.campingduperchebellemois.com

Address : take the western exit along the D 955, follow the signs for Mamers and take road to the left, near the swimming pool

Opening times : Permanent

1.5 ha (50 pitches) terraced, relatively flat, flat, grassy

Tariff : 19.50€ ♦♦ ⟶ 🔲 🔌 (16A) – Extra per person 3.50€

Rental rates : Permanent – 6 🚐 – 1 cabin in the trees. Per night from 70 to 160€ – Per week from 390 to 490€
🚙 borne 4€ – 8 🔲 11€ – 🛥 11€

Surroundings : 🌿 🌳
Facilities : ⟶ 🚿
Nearby : 🛒 🍴 🏖 🏊

| | G P S | Longitude : 0.555 Latitude : 48.3747 |

BERNAY

27300 – Michelin map **304** D7 – pop. 10 285 – alt. 105
▶ Paris 155 – Argentan 69 – Évreux 49 – Le Havre 72

⚠ Municipal

🖉 02 32 43 30 47. www.bernay-tourisme.fr

Address : rue des Canadiens (situated 2km southwest along the N 138, follow the signs for Alençon and take turning to the left - recommended route via the diversion (déviation) and ZI Malouve)

Opening times : from beginning May to end Sept.

1 ha (50 pitches) flat, grassy

Tariff : (2014 Price) ♦ 3.20€ ⟶ 3.30€ 🔲 3.30€ – 🔌 (8A) 3.65€

Rental rates : (2014 Price) (from beginning May to end Sept.) – 2 🚐. Per night from 46€ – Per week from 290 to 367€
🚙 borne 8.60€
A well-kept, lush green campsite.

Surroundings : 🌳
Leisure activities : 🛶 🎿
Facilities : 🚿 ⟶ 🍴 launderette
Nearby : 🍴 🎿 🏊

| | G P S | Longitude : 0.58683 Latitude : 49.07879 |

BERNIÈRES-SUR-MER

14990 – Michelin map **303** J4 – pop. 2 351
▶ Paris 253 – Caen 20 – Le Havre 114 – Hérouville-Saint-Clair 21

⚠ Le Havre de Bernières

🖉 02 31 96 67 09. www.camping-normandie.com

Address : chemin de Quintefeuille

6.5 ha (240 pitches) flat, grassy

Rentals : 32 🚐.

Surroundings : 🌳🌳
Leisure activities : 🍴 🍽 🎿 🎯 🏊 🛶 🏊
Facilities : 🚿 ⟶ 🚿 🍴 launderette 🚿
Nearby : 🛒 🍴 🏖 (beach) 🐴 bowling

| | G P S | Longitude : -0.42795 Latitude : 49.33245 |

Some campsites benefit from proximity to a municipal leisure centre.

LES BIARDS

50540 – Michelin map **303** E8 – alt. 495
▶ Paris 358 – Alençon 108 – Avranches 22 – Caen 126

⚠ Municipal La Mazure

🖉 02 33 89 19 50. www.lamazure.com

Address : Mazure leisure centre (2.3km southwest along the D 85e, on the banks of the Lac de Vezins)

Opening times : from mid June to beginning Sept.

3.5 ha/0.4 (28 pitches)

Tariff : (2014 Price) ♦ 3.50€ ⟶ 🔲 6€ – 🔌 (6A) 3€

Rental rates : (2014 Price) (from mid June to mid Sept.) – 12 🏠 – 4 tipis. Per week from 310 to 500€

Surroundings : 🦢 ⛴
Leisure activities : 🎣 ☕ ⛳ ⛵ 🚴 ✂
Facilities : ♿ 🔌 ♨ 💧 🍽 launderette 🧺
At the leisure/activities centre : 🎣 electric boats

G P S Longitude : -1.2047
Latitude : 48.5734

BLANGY-LE-CHÂTEAU

14130 – Michelin map **303** N4 – pop. 678 – alt. 60
▶ Paris 197 – Caen 56 – Deauville 22 – Lisieux 16

⛰ Les Castels Le Brévedent 👫

🕿 02 31 64 72 88. www.campinglebrevedent.com
Address : route du Pin (3km southeast along the D 51, by the château; beside a lake)
6 ha/3.5 for camping (140 pitches)
Rentals : 8 🚐.

In the grounds of a 14th-century château with a lake.

Surroundings : 🦢 ⛲
Leisure activities : 🎣 ☕ 🌙nighttime 🏃
⛵ 🚴 🏊 🎣 🛶
Facilities : ♿ 🔌 🍽 launderette 🧺
Nearby : ✂ 🐴 🏇

G P S Longitude : 0.3045
Latitude : 49.2253

BLANGY-SUR-BRESLE

76340 – Michelin map **304** J2 – pop. 3 000 – alt. 70
▶ Paris 156 – Abbeville 29 – Amiens 56 – Dieppe 55

⛰ Aux Cygnes d'Opale

🕿 02 35 94 55 65. www.auxcygnesdopale.fr
Address : rue du Marais (southeast, between two lakes and 200m from the Bresle river; access via the r. du Maréchal-Leclerc, near the church)
Opening times : from beginning April to beginning Nov.
0.8 ha (57 pitches) flat, grassy
Tariff : (2014 Price) 20€ 👫 🚗 💻 📺 (10A) – Extra per person 3.50€
Rental rates : (2014 Price) (from beginning April to beginning Nov.) – 10 🚐. Per night from 75 to 85€ – Per week from 370 to 580€
🚐 borne 2€ – 6 📺 4€

Surroundings : ⛲
Leisure activities : 📺 🛶
Facilities : ♿ 🔌 🍽
Nearby : ⛵ ✂ 🎣

G P S Longitude : 1.63638
Latitude : 49.93096

BOURG-ACHARD

27310 – Michelin map **304** E5 – pop. 2 948 – alt. 124
▶ Paris 141 – Bernay 39 – Évreux 62 – Le Havre 62

⛰ Le Clos Normand

🕿 02 32 56 34 84. www.leclosnormand.eu
Address : 235 route de Pont-Audemer (take the western exit)
Opening times : from mid April to end Sept.
1.4 ha (75 pitches)
Tariff : (2014 Price) 👤 5€ 🚗 2.50€ 📺 4.20€ – (6A) 3.80€

Rental rates : (2014 Price) (from mid April to end Sept.) – 6 🚐. Per night from 50 to 70€ – Per week from 250 to 470€
🚐 borne – 🔌 💧20.50€

In a green setting with lots of flowers.

Surroundings : ⛴ ⛲
Leisure activities : 🎣 ☕ ⛵ 🛶
Facilities : 🔌 🍽 📺 🧺

G P S Longitude : 0.80765
Latitude : 49.35371

BRÉCEY

50370 – Michelin map **303** F7 – pop. 2 165 – alt. 75
▶ Paris 328 – Avranches 17 – Granville 42 – St-Hilaire-du-Harcouët 20

⛰ Intercommunal le Pont Roulland

🕿 02 33 48 60 60. www.camping-brecey.com
Address : 1.1km east along the D 911, follow the signs for Cuves
Opening times : from beginning April to end Sept.
1 ha (52 pitches)
Tariff : 👤 2.90€ 🚗 📺 3.90€ – (10A) 2.90€
Rental rates : (from beginning March to end Sept.) – 4 🚐. Per night from 39 to 57€ – Per week from 273 to 399€
🚐 borne 4.70€

In a rural setting near a small lake.

Surroundings : 🦢 ⛲
Leisure activities : ⛵ 🛶 🎣
Facilities : 🚿 🍽 📺
Nearby : ✂

G P S Longitude : -1.15235
Latitude : 48.72184

Key to rentals symbols:

12 🚐	*Number of mobile homes*
20 🏠	*Number of chalets*
6 🛏	*Number of rooms to rent*
Per night 30–50€	*Minimum/maximum rate per night*
Per week 300–1,000€	*Minimum/maximum rate per week*

BRÉHAL

50290 – Michelin map **303** C6 – pop. 3 017 – alt. 69
▶ Paris 345 – Caen 113 – St-Lô 48 – St-Malo 101

⛰ La Vanlée

🕿 02 33 61 63 80. www.camping-vanlee.com
Address : rue des Gabions
Opening times : from beginning May to mid Sept.
11 ha (466 pitches)
Tariff : 25.90€ 👫 🚗 📺 (10A) – Extra per person 5.80€ –
Reservation fee 9€
🚐 borne – 🔌 💧18€

A pleasant campsite in an unspoilt setting beside the sea.

Surroundings : 🦢 🏖
Leisure activities : 🎣 ☕ 🛶 multi-sports ground
Facilities : ♿ 🍽 launderette 🛒

G P S Longitude : -1.56474
Latitude : 48.90913

BRÉVILLE-SUR-MER

50290 – Michelin map **303** K4 – pop. 803 – alt. 70
▶ Paris 341 – Caen 108 – St-Lô 50 – St-Malo 95

🏕 Kawan Village La Route Blanche 👥

🖉 02 33 50 23 31. www.camping-breville.com

Address : 6 rue de La Route Blanche (located 1km northwest following signs for the beach, near the golf course)

Opening times : from beginning April to end Sept.

5.5 ha (273 pitches)

Tariff : 37.50€ ✱✱ 🚗 🔲 (10A) – Extra per person 7.50€ – Reservation fee 8€

Rental rates : (from beginning April to end Sept.) 🛖 – 40 🚐.
Per night from 50 to 102€ – Per week from 350 to 714€ – Reservation fee 8€

🚐 borne – 🛢14€

Surroundings : 🖵
Leisure activities : ✗ 🏠 🎣 🏇 🛶 🏊 🏄 multi-sports ground
Facilities : 🚿 ⚬━ 🔲▥ 🛢 🚰 launderette 🏧
Nearby : 🍴 🛶 🐴 sports trail

Longitude : -1.56376
Latitude : 48.86966

CANY-BARVILLE

76450 – Michelin map **304** D3 – pop. 3 080 – alt. 25
▶ Paris 187 – Bolbec 34 – Dieppe 45 – Fécamp 21

⚠ Municipal

🖉 02 35 97 70 37. www.cany-barville.fr

Address : route de Barville (take the southern exit along the D 268, follow the signs for Yvetot, after the stadium)

Opening times : from beginning April to end Sept.

2.9 ha (100 pitches) flat, grassy, concrete surface areas

Tariff : (2014 Price) 12.45€ ✱✱ 🚗 🔲 (10A) – Extra per person 3.55€

Rentals : (2014 Price) Permanent 🚿 (2 mobile homes) – 15 🚐
🚐 borne 2.75€ – 25 🔲 5.35€
There are numerous pitches, some on a hard standing and some on grass.

Surroundings : 🖵 🌳
Leisure activities : 🏠 🎣
Facilities : 🚿 ⚬━ ▥ 🛢 🚰 launderette

Longitude : 0.64231
Latitude : 49.7834

CARENTAN

50500 – Michelin map **303** E4 – pop. 6 056 – alt. 18
▶ Paris 308 – Avranches 89 – Caen 74 – Cherbourg 52

🏕 Flower Le Haut Dick

🖉 02 33 42 16 89. www.camping-lehautdick.com

Address : 30 chemin du Grand Bas Pays (beside the canal, near the swimming pool)

Opening times : from end March to end Sept.

2.5 ha (130 pitches)

Tariff : (2014 Price) 27.50€ ✱✱ 🚗 🔲 (10A) – Extra per person 5€

Rental rates : (2014 Price) (from end March to end Sept.) – 10 🚐 – 4 tent lodges. Per night from 45 to 107€ – Per week from 315 to 749€

🚐 borne – 2 🔲 14€ – 🛢 11€

In a pleasant, green setting.

Surroundings : 🏞 🖵 🌿
Leisure activities : 🍴 ✗ 🏠 🎣 🛶
Facilities : 🚿 ⚬━ 🚰
Nearby : 🍴 🎣 🛶

Longitude : -1.23917
Latitude : 49.3087

COLLEVILLE-SUR-MER

14710 – Michelin map **303** G3 – pop. 171 – alt. 42
▶ Paris 281 – Bayeux 18 – Caen 48 – Carentan 36

⚠ Le Robinson

🖉 02 31 22 45 19. www.campinglerobinson.com

Address : at Cabourg hamlet (800m northeast along the D 514, follow the signs for Port-en-Bessin)

Opening times : from beginning April to end Sept.

1 ha (67 pitches) flat, grassy

Tariff : ✱ 6.20€ 🚗 2.75€ 🔲 6€ – (10A) 4.75€ – Reservation fee 18€

Rental rates : (from beginning April to end Sept.) 🛖 – 13 🚐 – 2 🏠 – 1 canvas bungalow. Per night from 53 to 74€ – Per week from 298 to 696€ – Reservation fee 18€

🚐 borne

Surroundings : 🖵
Leisure activities : 🍴 ✗ 🎣 🔲 🛶
Facilities : 🚿 ⚬━ 🚰 launderette
Nearby : 🍴 🐴

Longitude : -0.83497
Latitude : 49.34968

A chambre d'hôte is a guesthouse or B & B-style accommodation.

COURSEULLES-SUR-MER

14470 – Michelin map **303** J4 – pop. 4 185
▶ Paris 252 – Arromanches-les-Bains 14 – Bayeux 24 – Cabourg 41

🏕 Municipal le Champ de Course

🖉 02 31 37 99 26. www.campingcourseulles.com

Address : avenue de la Libération (to the north)

7.5 ha (381 pitches) flat, grassy

Rentals : 26 🚐 – 4 🏠 – 2 tent lodges.
Situated close to the beach.

Surroundings : 🖵
Leisure activities : 🏠 🎣
Facilities : 🚿 ⚬━ 🛢 🚰 launderette
Nearby : ✗ 🍴 🛶 🏊 🐴

Longitude : -0.44606
Latitude : 49.33289

COURTILS

50220 – Michelin map **303** D8 – pop. 245 – alt. 35
▶ Paris 349 – Avranches 13 – Fougères 43 – Pontorson 15

🏕 St-Michel

🖉 02 33 70 96 90. www.campingsaintmichel.com

Address : 35 route du Mont Saint Michel (take the western exit along the D 43)

Opening times : from beginning April to mid Nov.

2.5 ha (100 pitches)

Tariff : 27€ ✱✱ 🚗 🔲 (6A) – Extra per person 7€

Rental rates : (from beginning April to mid Nov.) – 50 .
Per night from 48 to 115€ – Per week from 280 to 805€
borne 5€ – 6 ▤ – 15€

Surroundings : 🏡 ♀
Leisure activities : ✕ 🏠 🚣 ⛳ 🎿
wildlife park
Facilities : ♿ ⚬⇥ cc 🏛 🍴 launderette 🚿
Nearby : ✗ 🐴 🏹

G P S   Longitude : -1.41611
   Latitude : 48.62829

DENNEVILLE

50580 – Michelin map **303** C4 – pop. 539 – alt. 5
▶ Paris 347 – Barneville-Carteret 12 – Carentan 34 – St-Lô 53

🏔 L'Espérance

📞 02 33 07 12 71. www.camping-esperance.fr – limited spaces for one-night stay

Address : 36 rue de la Gamburie (3.5km west along the D 137, 500m from the beach)

Opening times : from beginning April to end Sept.

3 ha (134 pitches)

Tariff : 31.70€ ★★ 🚗 ▤ (6A) – Extra per person 7€
Rental rates : (from beginning April to end Sept.) – 12 .
Per week from 330 to 710€

Surroundings : 🏞 ♀
Leisure activities : 🍴 ✕ 🌙 nighttime 🚣 ✂
🏊 🛶
Facilities : ⚬⇥ 🍴 launderette 🚿 🚿

G P S   Longitude : -1.68832
   Latitude : 49.30332

DIEPPE

76200 – Michelin map **304** G2 – pop. 32 670 – alt. 6
▶ Paris 197 – Abbeville 68 – Beauvais 107 – Caen 176

🏔 Vitamin'

📞 02 35 82 11 11. www.camping-vitamin.com – limited spaces for one-night stay

Address : 865 chemin des Vertus (3km south along the N 27, follow the signs for Rouen and take a right turn)

Opening times : from beginning April to mid Oct.

5.3 ha (180 pitches) flat, grassy

Tariff : 26.40€ ★★ 🚗 ▤ (10A) – Extra per person 5.90€ –
Reservation fee 5€
Rental rates : (from beginning April to mid Nov.) ♿ (1 mobile home) – 1 caravan – 34 – 4 🏠. Per night from 59 to 69€ – Per week from 349 to 719€ – Reservation fee 5€
3 ▤ 26.40€ – 16€
There's an attractive indoor water park.

Surroundings : 🏡
Leisure activities : 🍴 🏠 🛶 🚥 jacuzzi 🚣
🏊 🛶 ⛷ multi-sports ground
Facilities : ♿ ⚬⇥ 🍴 launderette 🚿
Nearby : ✕ ✗ 🎰, squash

G P S   Longitude : 1.07481
   Latitude : 49.90054

---

*For more information on visiting particular towns or regions, consult the relevant regional **MICHELIN Green Guide**. We also recommend you use the appropriate Michelin regional map to locate your selected campsite, to calculate distances and to work out the best route.*

🏔 La Source

📞 02 35 84 27 04. www.camping-la-source.fr – limited spaces for one-night stay

Address : 63 rue des Tisserands (3km southwest along the D 925, follow the signs for Le Havre then turn left onto D 153; at Petit-Appeville)

Opening times : from mid March to mid Oct.

2.5 ha (120 pitches) flat, grassy

Tariff : ★ 6.70€ 🚗 2€ ▤ 9€ – (10A) 4.50€ – Reservation fee 7€
Rental rates : (from mid March to mid Oct.) – 6 . Per night from 100 to 140€ – Per week from 360 to 550€ – Reservation fee 15€
borne 2€ – 14 ▤ 9.90€
There are pitches are beside the Scie river.

Leisure activities : 🍴 🏠 🚣 ⛳ 🛶
Facilities : ♿ ⚬⇥ cc 🏛 🍴 launderette

G P S   Longitude : 1.05732
   Latitude : 49.89824

DIVES-SUR-MER

14160 – Michelin map **303** L4 – pop. 5 935 – alt. 3
▶ Paris 219 – Cabourg 2 – Caen 27 – Deauville 22

🏔 Le Golf

📞 02 31 24 73 09. www.campingdugolf.com – limited spaces for one-night stay

Address : route de Lisieux (take the eastern exit, D 45 for 3.5km)

Opening times : from beginning April to end Sept.

2.8 ha (155 pitches) flat, grassy

Tariff : (2014 Price) ★ 3.90€ 🚗 3€ ▤ 3€ – (6A) 3.30€
Rental rates : (2014 Price) (from beginning April to end Sept.) – 18 – 2 🏠 – 1 canvas bungalow. Per night from 54 to 84€ – Per week from 279 to 559€ – Reservation fee 15€

Surroundings : 🏡 ♀
Leisure activities : 🍴 🚣 🛶
Facilities : ♿ ⚬⇥ 🍴 launderette

G P S   Longitude : -0.0701
   Latitude : 49.2792

---

*We value your opinion and welcome your feedback.
Do email us at campingfrance@tp.michelin.com*

DONVILLE-LES-BAINS

50350 – Michelin map **303** C6 – pop. 3 269 – alt. 40
▶ Paris 341 – Caen 112 – St-Lô 77

🏔 L'Ermitage

📞 02 33 50 09 01. www.camping-ermitage.com

Address : rue de l'Ermitage (located 1km north along the r. du Champ de Courses)

Opening times : from mid April to mid Oct.

5 ha (298 pitches)

Tariff : (2014 Price) ★ 5.90€ 🚗 2.15€ ▤ 8.42€ – (10A) 8.42€
borne
Near a beautiful beach of fine sand.

Surroundings : 🏡
Leisure activities : 🏠 🌙 daytime 🚣
Facilities : ♿ ⚬⇥ 🚿 🚿 launderette
Nearby : 🏊 🍴 ✕ 🚿 ✗ 🎰 (open air in season) 🚣 🐴 bowling

G P S   Longitude : -1.58075
   Latitude : 48.85212

DUCEY

50220 – Michelin map **303** E8 – pop. 2 465 – alt. 15
▶ Paris 348 – Avranches 11 – Fougères 41 – Rennes 80

⚠ Municipal la Sélune

📞 02 33 48 46 49. www.ducey-tourisme.com

Address : rue de Boishue (take the western exit along the N 176 and take the D 178, follow the signs for St-Aubin-de-Terregatte to the left; by the stadium)

0.42 ha (40 pitches) flat, grassy

The pitches are well marked out with hedges of thuja.

Surroundings : ⌑	**G** Longitude : -1.29452
Facilities : 🚿 🍴	**P** Latitude : 48.61686
Nearby : ✂ 🏊 🛶	**S**

ÉTRETAT

76790 – Michelin map **304** B3 – pop. 1 502 – alt. 8
▶ Paris 206 – Bolbec 30 – Fécamp 16 – Le Havre 29

⚠ Municipal

📞 02 35 27 07 67. www.etretat.fr – 🏠

Address : 69 rue Guy de Maupassant (located 1km southeast along the D 39, follow the signs for Criquetot-l'Esneval)

Opening times : from beginning April to mid Oct.

1.2 ha (73 pitches)

Tariff : (2014 Price) 🚶 3.75 € 🚗 2 € 🔲 2 € – 🔌 (6A) 6 €
🚐 borne 8 € – 30 🔲 8 €

Flowers surround the entrance and the whole site is very well kept; there's an adjacent service area for campervans.

Surroundings : ♀	**G** Longitude : 0.21557
Leisure activities : 🏠 🏃	**P** Latitude : 49.70063
Facilities : 🚿 🍴 launderette	**S**
Nearby : ✂ 🎣	

FALAISE

14700 – Michelin map **303** K6 – pop. 8 333 – alt. 132
▶ Paris 264 – Argentan 23 – Caen 36 – Flers 37

⚠ Municipal du Château

📞 02 31 90 16 55. www.camping.falaise.fr

Address : rue du Val d'Ante (to the west of the town, in the Val d'Ante)

Opening times : from beginning May to end Sept.

2 ha (66 pitches)

Tariff : 🚶 4.50 € 🚗 🔲 5.30 € – 🔌 (10A) 4.20 €

In a green setting in the grounds of the château.

Surroundings : ≼ Château Val de Meuse ♀	**G** Longitude : -0.2052
Leisure activities : 🏠 🏃 ✂ library	**P** Latitude : 48.89563
Facilities : 🚿 🍴	**S**
Nearby : 🛶 climbing wall	

Routes nationales are main roads and their identifying numbers begin with N or RN. Routes départementales are generally quieter roads and begin with D or DN.

FIQUEFLEUR-ÉQUAINVILLE

27210 – Michelin map **304** B5 – pop. 642 – alt. 17
▶ Paris 189 – Deauville 24 – Honfleur 7 – Lisieux 40

🏕 Sites et Paysagères La Catinière

📞 02 32 57 63 51. www.camping-honfleur.com

Address : route de Honfleur (1km south of Fiquefleur along the D 22)

Opening times : from beginning April to mid Oct.

3.8 ha (130 pitches) flat, grassy

Tariff : 34.50 € 🚶🚶 🚗 🔲 🔌 (13A) – Extra per person 6 €

Rental rates : (from beginning April to mid Oct.) – 23 🚐 – 1 gîte. Per week from 290 to 838 €

🚐 borne – 🚰 🔌 14 €

A long site in a green setting, between two streams.

Surroundings : ⌑ ♀	**G** Longitude : 0.30382
Leisure activities : 🍽 ✗ 🏠 🏃 🏊 🛶	**P** Latitude : 49.40161
Facilities : 🚿 🔑 🛁 🍴 launderette	**S**

FLERS

61100 – Michelin map **310** F2 – pop. 15 592 – alt. 270
▶ Paris 234 – Alençon 73 – Argentan 42 – Caen 60

⚠ Le Pays de Flers

📞 02 33 65 35 00. http://www.flers-agglomeration.fr/culture-sports-et-loisirs/heberg

Address : La Fouquerie (1.7km east along the D 924, follow the signs for Argentan and take road to the left)

Opening times : from beginning April to end Oct.

1.5 ha (50 pitches)

Tariff : (2014 Price) 🚶 3 € 🚗 2 € 🔲 3 € – 🔌 (10A) 5 €

Rental rates : (2014 Price) Permanent 🚿 (1 mobile home) – 3 🚐. Per night from 52 € – Per week from 258 to 361 €

Surroundings : 🌿 ⌑ ♀	**G** Longitude : -0.54311
Leisure activities : 🏠 🏃 🚲	**P** Latitude : 48.75463
Facilities : 🚿 🔑 🛁 🍴	**S**
Nearby : 🛶	

GENÊTS

50530 – Michelin map **303** D7 – pop. 427 – alt. 2
▶ Paris 345 – Avranches 11 – Granville 24 – Le Mont-St-Michel 33

🏕 Les Coques d'Or

📞 02 33 70 82 57. www.campinglescoquesdor.com

Address : 14 Le Bec d'Andaine (700m northwest along the D 35e1, follow the signs for Le Bec d'Andaine)

Opening times : from beginning April to end Sept.

4.7 ha (225 pitches) flat, grassy

Tariff : (2014 Price) 🚶 6.80 € 🚗 3.30 € 🔲 3.50 € – 🔌 (10A) 4.50 €

Rental rates : (from beginning April to end Sept.) – 34 🚐 – 2 🏠. Per night from 65 to 85 € – Per week from 329 to 750 €

There's a pleasant indoor pool with a spa area.

Surroundings : 🌿 ⌑ ♀	**G** Longitude : -1.48444
Leisure activities : 🍽 ✗ 🎰 🏊 hammam, jacuzzi 🏃 🚲 🛶 spa centre	**P** Latitude : 48.68778
Facilities : 🚿 🔑 🛁 🍴 launderette 🚿	**S**
Nearby : 🚶 walking and horse-riding trail	

Les Coques d'Or

GONNEVILLE-EN-AUGE

14810 – Michelin map **303** K4 – pop. 419 – alt. 16
▶ Paris 223 – Caen 20 – Le Havre 84 – Hérouville-St-Clair 16

⚠ Le Clos Tranquille

℘ 02 31 24 21 36. www.campingleclostranquille.fr

Address : 17 route de Troarn (800m south along the D 95a)

Opening times : from beginning April to end Sept.

1.3 ha (78 pitches) flat, grassy

Tariff : ☀ 5€ ⟷ 🅴 6€ – (12) (10A) 5€

Rental rates : (from beginning March to end Dec.) – 6 🚐 – 3 🏠 – 3 🛏 – 3 gîtes. Per night from 80 to 100€ – Per week from 300 to 550€

Surroundings : ≫ ⟷ ⚲	**G**	Longitude : -0.17771
Leisure activities : ⟷ ⚲🏇	**P**	Latitude : 49.23853
Facilities : ⟷ ♨ launderette	**S**	
Nearby : ✂ ♞ ♘		

GRANVILLE

50400 – Michelin map **303** C6 – pop. 12 847 – alt. 10
▶ Paris 342 – Avranches 27 – Caen 109 – Cherbourg 105

⚠ Les Castels Le Château de Lez-Eaux

℘ 02 33 51 66 09. www.lez-eaux.com

Address : at St-Aubin-des-Préaux (7km southeast along the D 973, follow the signs for Avranches)

Opening times : from beginning April to mid Sept.

12 ha/8 for camping (229 pitches)

Tariff : 43.50€ ☀☀ ⟷ 🅴 (12) (10A) – Extra per person 8€ – Reservation fee 8€

Rental rates : (from beginning April to mid Sept.) ⚲ (1 chalet) – 14 🚐 – 45 🏠 – 2 cabins in the trees. Per night from 99 to 238€ – Per week from 448 to 1,666€ – Reservation fee 8€

🚐 8 🅴 40€

In the grounds of the château; an attractive swimming area.

Surroundings : ≫ ⚲	**G**	Longitude : -1.52461
Leisure activities : 🍸 ⟷ ♨🏇 ⚲🚴 ✂ ⬜	**P**	Latitude : 48.79774
⬜🏊		
Facilities : ⚲ ⟷ ▦ ♨ ⚲ ⟆ ♨ launderette ⚲	**S**	
Nearby : ⚲ ♘ ♞		

⚠ La Vague

℘ 02 33 50 29 97. www.camping-la-vague.com

Address : 126 route de Voudrelin (2.5km southeast along the D 911, follow the signs for St-Pair and take the D 572 to the left; at St Nicolas-Plage)

2 ha (145 pitches)

Rentals : 7 🚐.

In a green setting that is pleasant and well kept.

Surroundings : ⟷ ⚲	**G**	Longitude : -1.57317
Leisure activities : 🚗 ♨🏇 ⚲	**P**	Latitude : 48.82146
Facilities : ⚲ ⟷ 🖥	**S**	
Nearby : ⬜ (open air in season) ⚲ ♞		

LE GROS-THEIL

27370 – Michelin map **304** F6 – pop. 931 – alt. 145
▶ Paris 136 – Bernay 30 – Elbeuf 16 – Évreux 34

⚠ Salverte

℘ 02 32 35 51 34. www.camping-salverte.com – limited spaces for one-night stay

Address : 3km southwest along the D 26, follow the signs for Brionne and take road to the left

Opening times : Permanent

17 ha/10 for camping (300 pitches) flat, grassy

Tariff : 21€ ☀☀ ⟷ 🅴 (12) (10A) – Extra per person 7€

Rental rates : (from beginning April to mid Oct.) – 4 🚐. Per night from 65 to 80€ – Per week from 390 to 510€

A pleasant wooded site.

Surroundings : ≫ ⚲⚲	**G**	Longitude : 0.84149
Leisure activities : 🍸 ✂ 🚗 ⚲♨ 🎣 ♨🏇 ⬜	**P**	Latitude : 49.22619
⬜ ⬜🏊 library, entertainment room		
Facilities : ⟷ ▦ ⚲ ⟆ ♨ launderette ⚲	**S**	

HONFLEUR

14600 – Michelin map **303** N3 – pop. 8 163 – alt. 5
▶ Paris 195 – Caen 69 – Le Havre 27 – Lisieux 38

⚠ La Briquerie

℘ 02 31 89 28 32. www.campinglabriquerie.com – limited spaces for one-night stay

Address : at Equemauville (follow the signs for Trouville, 3.5km southwest following signs for Pont-l'Évêque and right onto the D 62)

Opening times : from beginning April to end Sept.

11 ha (430 pitches) flat, grassy

Tariff : 34.70€ ☀☀ ⟷ 🅴 (12) (10A) – Extra per person 9.30€

Rental rates : (from beginning April to end Sept.) – 13 🚐 – 11 🏠. Per week 690€

🚐 30 🅴 34.70€ – 🚐 14€

The sanitary facilities are good quality, but a lot of the mobile homes belong to owner-occupiers.

Surroundings : ⟷ ⚲	**G**	Longitude : 0.20826
Leisure activities : 🍸 ✂ 🚗 ⚲♨ 🎣 jacuzzi	**P**	Latitude : 49.39675
♨🏇 ⬜ ⬜🏊 multi-sports ground		
Facilities : ⚲ ⟷ ⚲▦ ⚲ ⟆ ♨	**S**	
launderette ⚲		
Nearby : ⚲ ✂ ♞		

These symbols are used for a campsite that is exceptional in its category:

⚠⚠ ....⚠ *Particularly pleasant setting, quality and range of services available*

≫≫ *Tranquil, isolated site – quiet site, particularly at night*

≪≪ *Exceptional view – interesting or panoramic view*

HOULGATE

14510 – Michelin map **303** L4 – pop. 1 988 – alt. 11
▶ Paris 214 – Caen 29 – Deauville 14 – Lisieux 33

⛰ Yelloh! Village La Vallée 👥

🕿 02 31 24 40 69. www.campinglavallee.com

Address : 88 route de la Vallée (located 1km south along the D 24a, follow the signs for Lisieux and turn right onto the D 24)

Opening times : from beginning April to beginning Nov.

11 ha (350 pitches) terraced, relatively flat, flat, grassy

Tariff : 46€ ✹ ✹ ⇔ 🔲 (6A) – Extra per person 8€

Rental rates : (from beginning April to beginning Nov.) – 72 🚐. Per night from 39 to 195€ – Per week from 273 to 1,365€

🚐 borne 2€ – 12 🔲 18€

In a pleasant setting near some old Norman-style buildings.

Surroundings : ≤ 🗆 ⚲
Leisure activities : 🏆 ✗ 🎦 ⚄ 🏇 🏊 🚴 🍴 🔲 🎱 🎣
Facilities : 🚿 ⊙━ ⚖ ⚄ 🏴 launderette ⚒ 🚿
Nearby : 🎿 ⚲

Longitude : -0.06733
Latitude : 49.29422

To visit a town or region, use the MICHELIN Green Guides.

INCHEVILLE

76117 – Michelin map **304** I1 – pop. 1 357 – alt. 19
▶ Paris 169 – Abbeville 32 – Amiens 65 – Blangy-sur-Bresle 16

⛺ Municipal de l'Etang

🕿 02 35 50 30 17. campingdeletang@orange.fr – limited spaces for one-night stay 🅁

Address : rue Mozart (take the northeastern exit, follow the signs for Beauchamps and take right turn)

Opening times : from beginning March to end Oct.

2 ha (190 pitches) flat, grassy

Tariff : (2014 Price) ✹ 2.75€ ⇔ 3.55€ 🔲 3.55€ – (10A) 3.75€

🚐 borne 6€ – 2 🔲 12.80€

The campsite is near a fishing lake.

Surroundings : ⚲
Leisure activities : 🎦 ⚄
Facilities : 🚿 ⊙━ ⚄ ⚖ 🔲
Nearby : 🍴 🎣

Longitude : 1.50788
Latitude : 50.01238

ISIGNY-SUR-MER

14230 – Michelin map **303** F4 – pop. 2 782 – alt. 4
▶ Paris 298 – Bayeux 35 – Caen 64 – Carentan 14

⛰ Le Fanal

🕿 02 31 21 33 20. www.camping-normandie-fanal.fr

Address : rue du Fanal (to the west, access via the town centre, near the sports field)

Opening times : from beginning April to end Sept.

6.5 ha/5.5 for camping (240 pitches) flat, grassy

Tariff : 33€ ✹ ✹ ⇔ 🔲 – Extra per person 7.50€ – Reservation fee 5€

Rental rates : (from beginning April to end Sept.) – 96 🚐 – 4 🏠 – 4 tent lodges. Per night from 30 to 129€ – Per week from 210 to 903€ – Reservation fee 11€

🚐 borne 5€

In a pleasant, well-kept setting, beside a small lake.

Surroundings : 🌊 ⚲
Leisure activities : 🎦 🎣 ⚄ 🏴 🔲
Facilities : 🚿 ⊙━ 🔲 ⚄ ⚒ 🏴 launderette
Nearby : 🎿 🦆 ⚄ sports trail

Longitude : -1.10872
Latitude : 49.31923

JUMIEGES

76480 – Michelin map **304** E5 – pop. 1 719 – alt. 25
▶ Paris 161 – Rouen 29 – Le Havre 82 – Caen 132

⛰ La Forêt

🕿 02 35 37 93 43. www.campinglaforet.com

Address : rue Mainberte

Opening times : from beginning April to end Oct.

2 ha (111 pitches) flat, grassy

Tariff : 28€ ✹ ✹ ⇔ 🔲 (10A) – Extra per person 5.50€ – Reservation fee 5€

Rental rates : (from beginning April to end Oct.) 🏊 – 18 🚐 – 5 🏠. Per night from 62 to 90€ – Per week from 372 to 630€ Reservation fee 5€

🚐 borne 6€

Situated in the Brotonne Regional Park.

Surroundings : 🌊 🗆 ⚲
Leisure activities : 🎦 🎣 🔲 🎱
Facilities : 🚿 ⊙━ 🔲 ⚄ 🏴 launderette
Nearby : 🍴

Longitude : 0.82883
Latitude : 49.43485

LISIEUX

14100 – Michelin map **303** N5 – pop. 21 826 – alt. 51
▶ Paris 169 – Caen 54 – Le Havre 66 – Hérouville-St-Clair 53

⛺ La Vallée

🕿 02 31 62 00 40. www.lisieux-tourisme.com

Address : 9 rue de la Vallée (take the northern exit along the D 48, follow the signs for Pont-l'Évêque)

Opening times : from beginning April to beginning Oct.

1 ha (75 pitches)

Rentals : 5 🚐.

Surroundings : ⚲⚲
Facilities : 🚿 ⊙━ ⚄ launderette
Nearby : 🍴

Longitude : 0.22068
Latitude : 49.16423

LES LOGES

76790 – Michelin map **304** B3 – pop. 1 155 – alt. 92
▶ Paris 205 – Rouen 83 – Le Havre 34 – Fécamp 10

⛰ Club Airotel L'Aiguille Creuse

🕿 02 35 29 52 10. www.campingaiguillecreuse.com

Address : 24 residence de l'Aiguille Creuse

Opening times : from beginning April to end Sept.

3 ha (105 pitches)

Tariff : 28€ ✹ ✹ ⇔ 🔲 (10A) – Extra per person 5.80€ – Reservation fee 7€

Rental rates : (2014 Price) (from beginning April to end Sept.) 🏊 – 18 🚐. Per night from 55 to 100€ – Per week from 255 to 700€ Reservation fee 15€

🚐 borne

Pleasant pitches with good-quality rentals.

Surroundings : 🗔
Leisure activities : 🍸 ⚓🛶 🎿 (open air in season)
Facilities : 🔥 ⛗ 📧🏧 🌳🍴 launderette
Nearby : 🍴

GPS Longitude : 0.27575 Latitude : 49.69884

LOUVIERS

27400 – Michelin map **304** H6 – pop. 17 943 – alt. 15
▶ Paris 104 – Les Andelys 22 – Bernay 52 – Lisieux 75

🏕 Le Bel Air

📞 02 32 40 10 77. www.camping-lebelair.fr – limited spaces for one-night stay

Address : route de la-Haye-Malherbe (3km west along the D 81)

Opening times : from mid March to mid Oct.

2.5 ha (92 pitches) flat, grassy

Tariff : (2014 Price) 🚶 5.70€ ⚗ 📧 6.90€ – 🔌 (6A) 4.90€
Rental rates : (2014 Price) (from mid Feb. to mid Oct.) 🍴 – 2 🚐 – 3 🏠. Per night from 65 to 75€ – Per week from 472 to 582€
🚱 2 📧 24€

Set among trees with plenty of shade.

Surroundings : 🗔 🌳🌳
Leisure activities : 🖼 ⚓🛶 🎿
Facilities : ⛗ 🏧 🍴 launderette
Nearby : 🍴 🖼

GPS Longitude : 1.1332 Latitude : 49.2152

LUC-SUR-MER

14530 – Michelin map **303** J4 – pop. 3 133
▶ Paris 249 – Arromanches-les-Bains 23 – Bayeux 29 – Cabourg 28

🏕 Municipal la Capricieuse

📞 02 31 97 34 43. www.campinglacapricieuse.com

Address : 2 rue Brummel (to the west, allée Brummel; 200m from the beach)

Opening times : from beginning April to end Sept.

4.6 ha (226 pitches)

Tariff : 🚶 5.30€ ⚗ 📧 6.25€ – 🔌 (10A) 6.65€
Rental rates : (from beginning April to end Oct.) 🔥 (1 mobile home) 🍴 – 18 🚐 – 10 🏠. Per week from 332 to 779€
🚱 borne 5.20€

Surroundings : ⟨ 🗔 🌳🌳
Leisure activities : 🖼 ⚓🛶 🍴 🏖 (beach) multi-sports ground
Facilities : 🔥 ⛗ 🌳🌳 🍴 launderette
Nearby : 🛒🚲🏕 🎿 🎣

GPS Longitude : -0.35781 Latitude : 49.3179

Michelin classification:
🏕🏕🏕🏕 *Extremely comfortable, equipped to a very high standard*
🏕🏕🏕 *Very comfortable, equipped to a high standard*
🏕🏕 *Comfortable and well equipped*
🏕 *Reasonably comfortable*
🏕 *Satisfactory*

LYONS-LA-FORÊT

27480 – Michelin map **304** I5 – pop. 751 – alt. 88
▶ Paris 104 – Les Andelys 21 – Forges-les-Eaux 30 – Gisors 30

🏕 Municipal St-Paul

📞 02 32 49 42 02. www.camping-saint-paul.fr – limited spaces for one-night stay

Address : 2 route Saint-Paul (to the northeast along the D 321, by the stadium; beside the Lieure river)

Opening times : from beginning April to end Oct.

3 ha (100 pitches) flat, grassy

Tariff : (2014 Price) 20.50€ 🚶🚶 ⚗ 📧 🔌 (6A) – Extra per person 5.20€
Rental rates : (2014 Price) (from beginning April to end Oct.) – 7 🏠. Per night from 60 to 85€ – Per week from 210 to 430€
🚱 borne – 5 📧 16.50€ – 🚐 🔌8€

Surroundings : 🗔 🌳
Leisure activities : 🖼 ⚓🛶
Facilities : 🔥 ⛗ 🌳🏧 🌳🎿🍴 🏧
Nearby : 🍴🏕 🎿 🐴 🎣

GPS Longitude : 1.47657 Latitude : 49.39869

There are several different types of sani-station ('borne' in French) – sanitation points providing fresh water and disposal points for grey water. See page 12 for further details.

MARCHAINVILLE

61290 – Michelin map **310** N3 – pop. 207 – alt. 235
▶ Paris 124 – L'Aigle 28 – Alençon 65 – Mortagne-au-Perche 28

🏕 Municipal les Fossés

📞 02 33 73 65 80. mairiemarchainville@wanadoo.fr

Address : the north along the D 243, in the village

1 ha (17 pitches)

Surroundings : 🐕 🗔
Leisure activities : 🍴
Facilities : 🔥 🌳

GPS Longitude : 0.8135 Latitude : 48.5861

MARTIGNY

76880 – Michelin map **304** G2 – pop. 481 – alt. 24
▶ Paris 196 – Dieppe 10 – Fontaine-le-Dun 29 – Rouen 64

🏕 Les Deux Rivières

📞 02 35 85 60 82. www.camping-2-rivieres.com – limited spaces for one-night stay

Address : off the D 154 (700m to the northwest, off the rte de Dieppe, 8km south-east of Dieppe)

Opening times : from end March to beginning Oct.

3 ha (110 pitches) flat, grassy

Tariff : (2014 Price) 20.60€ 🚶🚶 ⚗ 📧 🔌 (10A) – Extra per person 4.20€
Rental rates : (2014 Price) (from end March to beginning Oct.) – 6 🚐. Per night from 170€ – Per week from 368 to 609€

In a pleasant location beside a river and lakes.

Surroundings : ⟨ extensive lakeland and the Château d'Arques 🌳
Leisure activities : 🖼 ⚓🛶 🎣
Facilities : 🔥 ⛗ 🌳🍴 launderette
Nearby : 🏖 🎣

GPS Longitude : 1.14417 Latitude : 49.87059

MARTRAGNY

14740 – Michelin map **303** I4 – pop. 367 – alt. 70
▶ Paris 257 – Bayeux 11 – Caen 23 – St-Lô 47

⚠ Les Castels Le Château de Martragny

☎ 02 31 80 21 40. www.chateau-martragny.com

Address : 52 St Léger hamlet (on the old N 13, access via the village centre)

Opening times : from end May to end Aug.

13 ha/4 for camping (160 pitches) flat, grassy

Tariff : ✴ 8.50€ ⇔ 国 16.50€ – (2) (15A) 5€ – Reservation fee 10€
Rental rates : (from end May to end Aug.) – 5 ⨅ – 4 tent lodges – 1 gîte. Per week from 420 to 550€ – Reservation fee 10€
⛽ borne – 5 国 38.50€

B&B accommodation in an 18th-century château.

Surroundings : ⌇ ♤♤
Leisure activities : ⍭ ⌂ ⇆ ✗ ⑅ ⌇
Facilities : ⅚ ⚬�om 匣 ♨⑂ launderette ⚏ ⍚
Nearby : ⌖

GPS Longitude : -0.60532
Latitude : 49.24406

MAUPERTUS-SUR-MER

50330 – Michelin map **303** D2 – pop. 256 – alt. 119
▶ Paris 359 – Barfleur 21 – Cherbourg 13 – St-Lô 80

⚠ Les Castels l'Anse du Brick 🏊♨

l'Anse du Brick

☎ 02 33 54 33 57. www.anse-du-brick.com

Address : 18 Anse du Brick (to the northwest along the D 116, 200m from the beach, direct access via a walkway)

Opening times : from beginning April to mid Sept.

17 ha/7 for camping(189 pitches) very uneven, terraced, flat, grassy, stony, wood

Tariff : 43€ ✴✴ ⇔ 国 (2) (10A) – Extra per person 8.50€ – Reservation fee 8€
Rental rates : (from beginning April to mid Sept.) – 36 ⌷⌷⌷ – 6 ⌂ – 3 gîtes. Per week from 406 to 1,309€ – Reservation fee 8€
⛽ borne 8€

In a pleasantly leafy setting with plenty of shade on an unspoilt site.

Surroundings : ⌇ ⟨ ⍩ ♤♤
Leisure activities : ⍭ ⌂ ⍟ ⨁ ⇆ ⧖ ⨂ ✗
⌇ ⌇ ⚏
Facilities : ⅚ ⚬⟶ ♨⑂ launderette ⚏
Nearby : ✗ ⌖ watersports centre

GPS Longitude : -1.49
Latitude : 49.66722

Key to rentals symbols:

12 ⌷⌷⌷	*Number of mobile homes*
20 ⌂	*Number of chalets*
6 ⨅	*Number of rooms to rent*
Per night 30–50€	*Minimum/maximum rate per night*
Per week 300–1,000€	*Minimum/maximum rate per week*

MERVILLE-FRANCEVILLE-PLAGE

14810 – Michelin map **303** K4 – pop. 1 991 – alt. 2
▶ Paris 225 – Arromanches-les-Bains 42 – Cabourg 7 – Caen 20

⚠ Les Peupliers

☎ 02 31 24 05 07. www.camping-peupliers.com

Address : allée des Pins (2.5km east, a right turn off the D514 rte de Cabourg)

Opening times : from beginning April to end Oct.

3.6 ha (164 pitches) flat, grassy

Tariff : (2014 Price) 31.20€ ✴✴ ⇔ 国 (2) (10A) – Extra per person 8.10€
Rental rates : (2014 Price) (from beginning April to end Oct.) – 1 caravan – 44 ⌷⌷⌷ – 10 ⌂. Per night from 90 to 145€ – Per week from 310 to 990€
⛽ borne

Leisure activities : ⍭ ⌂ ⍟ ⇆ ⧖
Facilities : ⅚ ⚬⟶ 匣 ♨⑂ launderette
Nearby : ⨂ ⌖ ⌇ ⍩ ⌖

GPS Longitude : -0.17011
Latitude : 49.2829

⚠ Seasonova Le Point du Jour

☎ 02 31 24 23 34. www.vacances-seasonova.com

Address : route de Cabourg (take the eastern exit along the D 514)

Opening times : from beginning April to beginning Nov.

2.7 ha (140 pitches)

Tariff : (2014 Price) 39€ ✴✴ ⇔ 国 – Extra per person 8.60€ – Reservation fee 12€
Rental rates : (2014 Price) (from beginning April to beginning Nov.) ⌇ – 32 ⌷⌷⌷. Per week from 350 to 975€ – Reservation fee 12€
⛽ borne – 7 国 23€ – ⛽ (2)20.70€

In an attractive location close to the beach.

Surroundings : ⌇ ⍚
Leisure activities : ✗ ⌂ ⍾ jacuzzi ⇆
⍜ (open air in season)
Facilities : ⅚ ⚬⟶ 匣 ♨⑂ launderette
Nearby : ⨂ ⌖ ⍩ ⌖

GPS Longitude : -0.19392
Latitude : 49.2833

MOYAUX

14590 – Michelin map **303** O4 – pop. 1 356 – alt. 160
▶ Paris 173 – Caen 64 – Deauville 31 – Lisieux 13

⚠ Le Colombier

Le Colombier

☎ 02 31 63 63 08. www.camping-lecolombier.com

Address : 3km northeast along the D 143, follow the signs for Lieurey

Opening times : from beginning May to mid Sept.

15 ha/6 for camping(180 pitches) flat, grassy

Tariff : (2014 Price) 38.70€ ✴✴ ⇔ 国 (2) (12A) – Extra per person 8€

There's a swimming pool in the château's formal garden.

Surroundings : ⌇ ♤
Leisure activities : ⍭ ✗ ⌂ ⍟ ⇆ ⧖ ⨂ ⌖
⌇ library
Facilities : ⅚ ⚬⟶ 匣 ♨ ⚏ ♨⑂ launderette
⚏ ⍚

GPS Longitude : 0.3897
Latitude : 49.2097

OMONVILLE-LA-ROGUE

50440 – Michelin map **303** A1 – pop. 534 – alt. 25
▶ Paris 377 – Caen 144 – St-Lô 99 – Cherbourg 24

⚠ Municipal du Hable

𝒫 0233528615. www.omonvillelarogue.fr – ᵮ

Address : 4 route de la Hague

Opening times : from end April to beginning Sept.

1 ha (60 pitches)

Tariff : (2014 Price) 🛉 3€ ⏤ 2.35€ 🅴 2.35€ – 🔌 (10A) 6€

Rental rates : (2014 Price) Permanent – 5 🏠. Per night from 41 to 45€ – Per week from 254 to 350€

🚐 borne 3.45€

Surroundings : ⟋
Facilities : 🍴 launderette
Nearby : ☷ ✕ 𝄢

Longitude : -1.84087
Latitude : 49.70439

ORBEC

14290 – Michelin map **303** O5 – pop. 2 381 – alt. 110
▶ Paris 173 – L'Aigle 38 – Alençon 80 – Argentan 53

⚠ Les Capucins

𝒫 0962579600. camping.sivom@orange.fr

Address : 13 avenue du Bois (located 1.5km northeast along the D 4, follow the signs for Bernay and take road to the left, by the stadium)

Opening times : from mid May to beginning Sept.

0.9 ha (35 pitches) flat, grassy

Tariff : (2014 Price) 12€ 🛉🛉 ⏤ 🅴 🔌 (3A) – Extra per person 2.50€
🚐 25 🅴 12€

In a green setting, a very well-kept site.

Surroundings : ♀
Leisure activities : 🎱 🚣
Facilities : ⚍ 🧺 🛁 🚿 🍴
Nearby : ✕ 🎯 🐎

Longitude : 0.40875
Latitude : 49.02982

LES PIEUX

50340 – Michelin map **303** B2 – pop. 3 588 – alt. 104
▶ Paris 366 – Barneville-Carteret 18 – Cherbourg 22 – St-Lô 48

🏔 Le Grand Large

𝒫 0233524075. www.legrandlarge.com

Address : 11 route du Grand Large (3km southwest along the D 117 and turn right onto the D 517 then continue 1km along the road to the left)

3.7 ha (236 pitches)

Rentals : 50 🚎.

In an attractive location among the dunes, near the Plage de Sciottot (beach).

Surroundings : ⟋ ⟨ ⌂ ⚓
Leisure activities : 🍽 🎱 🛁jacuzzi 🚣 ✕
🏊 🏊 paddling pool
Facilities : 🍴 ⚍ 🏛 🛁 🚿 🍴 launderette

Longitude : -1.8425
Latitude : 49.49361

In order for the guide to remain wholly objective, the selection of campsites is made on an entirely independent basis.

PONT-AUDEMER

27500 – Michelin map **304** D5 – pop. 8 599 – alt. 15
▶ Paris 165 – Rouen 58 – Évreux 91 – Le Havre 44

⚠ Flower Risle-Seine - Les Étangs

𝒫 0232424665. http://www.camping-risle-seine.com

Address : 19 route des Étangs at Toutainville (2.5km east, turn left under the motorway bridge, near the water sports centre)

Opening times : from beginning April to end Oct.

2 ha (71 pitches) flat, grassy

Tariff : 16.90€ 🛉🛉 ⏤ 🅴 🔌 (10A) – Extra per person 4.20€ – Reservation fee 7€

Rental rates : (from mid Feb. to end Dec.) ♿ (1 mobile home) – 6 🚎 – 10 🏠 – 2 canvas bungalows. Per night from 50 to 88€ – Per week from 250 to 616 € – Reservation fee 15€

A small chalet village on stilts overlooking the lake.

Surroundings : ⌂ ♞♞
Leisure activities : 🎱 🚣 🚲
Facilities : ♿ ⚍ 🛁 🚿 🍴 launderette
Nearby : ⟋ 𝄢 golf practice

Longitude : 0.48739
Latitude : 49.3666

PONT-AUTHOU

27290 – Michelin map **304** E6 – pop. 711 – alt. 49
▶ Paris 152 – Bernay 22 – Elbeuf 26 – Évreux 45

⚠ Municipal les Marronniers

𝒫 0232427506. campingmunicipaldesmarronniers@orange.fr – limited spaces for one-night stay

Address : 8 rue Louise Givon (south of the town, along the D 130, follow the signs for Brionne; beside a stream)

Opening times : Permanent

2.5 ha (64 pitches) flat, grassy

Tariff : (2014 Price) 🛉 2.70€ ⏤ 1.95€ 🅴 2.70€ – 🔌 (10A) 3.40€

Rental rates : (2014 Price) Permanent – 5 🚎. Per night from 41 to 45€ – Per week from 210 to 220€

🚐 borne 4.35€ – 5 🅴 13.35€

Leisure activities : 🚣
Facilities : ♿ ⚍ 🧺 🏛
Nearby : 🚲

Longitude : 0.70332
Latitude : 49.24193

PONT-FARCY

14380 – Michelin map **303** F6 – pop. 527 – alt. 72
▶ Paris 296 – Caen 63 – St-Lô 30 – Villedieu-les-Poêles 22

⚠ Municipal

𝒫 0231683206. www.pont.farcy.fr – ᵮ

Address : route de Tessy (take the northern exit along the D 21, follow the signs for Tessy-sur-Vire)

Opening times : from mid May to end Sept.

1.5 ha (60 pitches) flat, grassy

Tariff : (2014 Price) 12€ 🛉🛉 ⏤ 🅴 🔌 (10A) – Extra per person 2.50€

Rental rates : (2014 Price) (from mid May to end Sept.) – 1 🚎. Per week from 200€

Beside the Vire river.

Leisure activities : 🎱 🚣 ✕ ⟋ 🚣
Facilities : ♿ 🧺 🍴

Longitude : -1.0349
Latitude : 48.93899

PONTORSON

50170 – Michelin map **303** C8 – pop. 4 080 – alt. 15
▶ Paris 359 – Avranches 23 – Dinan 50 – Fougères 39

⚠ **Haliotis** ♣♦

📞 02 33 68 11 59. www.camping-haliotis-mont-saint-michel.com

Address : chemin des Soupirs (situated to the northwest along the D 19, follow the signs for Dol-de-Bretagne; near the Couesnon river)

Opening times : from beginning April to mid Nov.

8 ha/3.5 for camping(170 pitches) flat, grassy

Tariff : 20.50€ ♣♦ ⬅ 🅴 🅷 (16A) – Extra per person 6€ – Reservation fee 4€

Rental rates : (from beginning April to mid Nov.) – 37 🚐 – 1 🏠. Per night from 35 to 85€ – Per week from 224 to 770€ Reservation fee 4€

🚐 borne 4.50€

Surroundings : ⬍ 🏞
Leisure activities : 🍴 🎱 🎣 daytime ⛹ 🏊 jacuzzi ⛵ 🚴 🛶 fitness trail, multi-sports ground
Facilities : 🅶 🚿 🛁 – 12 private sanitary facilities (🚿 wc) 🛁 🚰 🧺 launderette
Nearby : 🏊 🚣 🎣 🐎

GPS Longitude : -1.5145
Latitude : 48.55798

PORT-EN-BESSIN

14520 – Michelin map **303** H3 – pop. 2 141 – alt. 10
▶ Paris 277 – Caen 43 – Hérouville-St-Clair 45 – St-Lô 47

⚠ **Port'Land** ♣♦

📞 02 31 51 07 06. www.camping-portland.com

Address : chemin du Castel; not far from Omaha Beach

Opening times : from beginning April to beginning Nov.

8.5 ha (256 pitches) flat, grassy

Tariff : (2014 Price) 43€ ♣♦ ⬅ 🅴 🅷 (16A) – Extra per person 10€

Rental rates : (2014 Price) (from beginning April to beginning Nov.) – 98 🚐. Per night from 57 to 195€ – Per week from 399 to 1,365€

🚐 borne 5€ – 5 🅴 43€

Pretty flowers and shrubs and several ponds where you can fish.

Surroundings : 🏊 🏞
Leisure activities : 🍴 🍽 🎱 🎮 ⛹ ⛵ 🎣 🚴 🛶 fitness trail, multi-sports ground
Facilities : 🅶 🚿 🛁 🚰 🧺 launderette 🚣 🛁
Nearby : 🎣 🛶

GPS Longitude : -0.77044
Latitude : 49.34716

QUIBERVILLE

76860 – Michelin map **304** F2 – pop. 535 – alt. 50
▶ Paris 199 – Dieppe 18 – Fécamp 50 – Rouen 67

⚠ **Municipal de la Plage**

📞 02 35 83 01 04. www.campingplagequiberville.fr – limited spaces for one-night stay

Address : 123 rue de la Saane (at Quiberville-Plage, access via the D 127, follow the signs for Ouville-la-Rivière)

Opening times : from beginning April to end Oct.

2.5 ha (202 pitches) flat, grassy

Tariff : (2014 Price) ♣ 5.90€ ⬅ 🅴 11.25€ – 🅷 (10A) 5.50€

🚐 borne 3.90€
Situated 100m from the sea, on the other side of the road.

Surroundings : 🏊 ⬍ 🏞
Leisure activities : 🎱 ⛵
Facilities : 🅶 🚿 🛁 🚰 launderette
Nearby : 🍴 🍽 🚣 🎣 🛶

GPS Longitude : 0.92878
Latitude : 49.90507

RADON

61250 – Michelin map **310** J3 – pop. 1 042 – alt. 175
▶ Paris 200 – Caen 106 – Alençon 11 – Le Mans 67

⚠ **Ferme des Noyers**

📞 02 33 28 75 02. www.ecouves.net

Address : Ferme des Noyers; east of Radon, off the D 26

Opening times : from beg. April to end Oct

2 ha (43 pitches) flat, grassy

Tariff : 16.10€ ♣♦ ⬅ 🅴 🅷 (16A) – Extra per person 3.20€
Rental rates : Permanent – 1 caravan – 4 🏠 – 2 🛏 – 1 gîte. Per night from 58 to 100€ – Per week from 210 to 380€

🚐 borne 3€ – 8 🅴 16.10€ – 🔌14.70€

Surroundings : 🌿
Leisure activities : 🎱 ⛵ 🎣
Facilities : 🅶 🚿 🚰 🧺 📺
Nearby : 🍽 🚤 (pond)

GPS Longitude : 0.0684
Latitude : 48.4957

RAVENOVILLE

50480 – Michelin map **303** E3 – pop. 261 – alt. 6
▶ Paris 328 – Barfleur 27 – Carentan 21 – Cherbourg 40

⚠ **Kawan Village Le Cormoran** ♣♦

📞 02 33 41 33 94. www.lecormoran.com – limited spaces for one-night stay

Address : 2 rue du Cormoran (3.5km northeast along the D 421, follow the signs for Utah Beach; near the beach)

8 ha (256 pitches)

Rentals : 🅿 – 40 🚐 – 46 🏠.

Lovely flowers and shrubs decorate the site.

Surroundings : 🏞
Leisure activities : 🍴 🎱 🎮 ⛹ 🏊 jacuzzi 🚴 🚲 🎣 ⛵ 🛶 farm or petting farm, radio control boats, multi-sports ground
Facilities : 🅶 🚿 🛁 🚰 🧺 launderette 🚣 🛁
Nearby : 🐎

GPS Longitude : -1.23527
Latitude : 49.46658

LE ROZEL

50340 – Michelin map **303** B3 – pop. 281 – alt. 21
▶ Paris 369 – Caen 135 – Cherbourg 26 – Rennes 197

⚠ **Le Ranch**

📞 02 33 10 07 10. www.camping-leranch.com

Address : at La Mielle (situated 2km southwest along the D 117 and take the D 62 to the right)

Opening times : from beginning April to end Sept.

4 ha (130 pitches) undulating, terrace, flat, grassy, sandy

Tariff : (2014 Price) ♣ ⬅ 🅴 35.50€ – 🅷 (10A) 4.70€

Rental rates : (2014 Price) (from beginning April to end Sept.) – 17 🚐. Per night from 130 to 187€ – Per week from 340 to 1,030€

Situated close to the beach.

Surroundings : 🐾 ⛰
Leisure activities : ♀ ✕ 🏠 ⚓ 🛶 🏄
🏊 🎯 🛝
Facilities : 🚿 ⚓ (July-Aug.) 🏛 🍴 🚰 ♿ 🍽
launderette
Nearby : ⛷ ♨ sand yachting

Longitude : -1.84199
Latitude : 49.48013

ST-ARNOULT

14800 – Michelin map **303** M3 – pop. 1 193 – alt. 4
▶ Paris 198 – Caen 43 – Le Havre 41 – Rouen 90

▲▲▲ La Vallée de Deauville 🔞

𝒮 02 31 88 58 17. www.camping-deauville.com – limited spaces for one-night stay

Address : avenue de la Vallée (located 1km south along the D 27, follow the signs for Varaville and take the D 275 following signs for Beaumont-en-Auge to the left; beside a stream and near a small lake)

Opening times : from end March to end Oct.

10 ha (411 pitches) flat, grassy

Tariff : 35.70€ ✹✹ 🚐 🔲 ⚡ (10A) – Extra per person 9.50€
Rental rates : (from end March to end Oct.) – 60 🚐 – 6 mobile homes (without sanitary facilities). Per night from 75 to 140€ – Per week from 240 to 1,150€

The site is laid out beside a pleasant lake.

Surroundings : 🏞 ♀
Leisure activities : ♀ 🏠 🎮 ⚓ ⚓
hammam, jacuzzi 🛶 🏊 🎯 🛝 🚣
multi-sports ground
Facilities : 🚿 ⚓ 🏛 🚰 ♿ 🍽 launderette 🚮 🚿
Nearby : 🍴 ✕ 🎣 ⛷ ♨ 🐎

Longitude : 0.0862
Latitude : 49.3287

ST-AUBIN-SUR-MER

14750 – Michelin map **303** J4 – pop. 2 048
▶ Paris 252 – Arromanches-les-Bains 19 – Bayeux 29 – Cabourg 32

▲▲▲ Yelloh! Village Sandaya Côte de Nacre 🔞

𝒮 02 31 97 14 45. www.camping-cote-de-nacre.com – limited spaces for one-night stay

Address : 17 rue du Général Moulton (south of the town along the D 7b)

Opening times : from beginning April to mid Sept.

10 ha (350 pitches) flat, grassy

Tariff : (2014 Price) 47€ ✹✹ 🚐 🔲 ⚡ (10A) – Extra per person 9€
Rental rates : (2014 Price) (from beginning April to mid Sept.) – 291 🚐. Per night from 39 to 190€ – Per week from 273 to 1,330€

There's a partially covered water park.

Leisure activities : ♀ 🏠 🎮 ⚓ hammam, jacuzzi 🛶 🚲 🏊 🎯 🛝 multi-sports ground, spa centre
Facilities : 🚿 ⚓ 🏛 🚰 ♿ 🍽 launderette 🚮 🚿
Nearby : ✕

Longitude : -0.3946
Latitude : 49.3324

*To visit a town or region, use the **MICHELIN Green Guides**.*

ST-AUBIN-SUR-MER

76740 – Michelin map **304** F2 – pop. 267 – alt. 15
▶ Paris 191 – Dieppe 21 – Fécamp 46 – Rouen 59

▲ Municipal le Mesnil

𝒮 02 35 83 02 83. www.campinglemesnil.com

Address : route de Sotteville (situated 2km west along the D 68, follow the signs for Veules-les-Roses)

2.2 ha (117 pitches)

🚏 borne

The site is based around a former Norman farmhouse and its outbuildings with thatched roofs. Lots of old owner-occupier mobile homes.

Surroundings : 🐾 🏞
Leisure activities : ✕ 🏠 🛶
Facilities : 🚿 ⚓ 🏛 ♿ 🍽 launderette 🚿

Longitude : 0.85204
Latitude : 49.88353

ST-ÉVROULT-NOTRE-DAME-DU-BOIS

61550 – Michelin map **310** L2 – pop. 452 – alt. 355
▶ Paris 153 – L'Aigle 14 – Alençon 56 – Argentan 42

▲ Municipal des Saints-Pères

𝒮 06 78 33 04 94. catherine-motte@orange.fr – 🏴

Address : to the southeast of the village

Opening times : from beginning April to end Sept.

0.6 ha (27 pitches) terrace, flat, grassy, fine gravel, wood

Tariff : ✹ 3€ 🚐 1.50€ – ⚡ (10A) 2.50€
Rental rates : (from mid April to mid Oct.) 🚲 (from mid April to mid Sept.) – 1 🚐 – 14 🛏 – 1 gîte. Per night from 40 to 70€ – Per week from 250 to 350€
🚏 borne 6€ – 5 🔲 6€

Situated in a pleasant location, beside a lake.

Surroundings : ♀
Leisure activities : 🛶 ⛷ 🎣 pedalos
Facilities : 🚿 ⚓ 🚮 🏴 🚿
Nearby : 🚮 ✕ 🐎

Longitude : 0.4663
Latitude : 48.7888

Do not confuse:
▲ *to* ▲▲▲ *: MICHELIN classification with*
★ *to* ★★★★★ *: official classification*

ST-GEORGES-DU-VIÈVRE

27450 – Michelin map **304** D6 – pop. 720 – alt. 138
▶ Paris 161 – Bernay 21 – Évreux 54 – Lisieux 36

▲ Municipal du Vièvre

𝒮 02 32 42 76 79. www.camping-eure-normandie.fr

Address : route de Noards (take the southwestern exit along the D 38)

Opening times : from beginning April to end Sept.

1.1 ha (50 pitches) flat, grassy

Tariff : (2014 Price) ✹ 2.30€ 🚐 1.30€ 🔲 2.20€ – ⚡ (5A) 2.20€
Rental rates : (2014 Price) (from beginning April to end Sept.) – 2 🚐. Per week from 200 to 300€

Surroundings : 🐾 🏞
Leisure activities : 🚲
Facilities : 🚿 🏴 🚿 🍽
Nearby : ✕ 🏊

Longitude : 0.58064
Latitude : 49.2427

ST-GERMAIN-SUR-AY

50430 – Michelin map **303** C4 – pop. 896 – alt. 5
▶ Paris 345 – Barneville-Carteret 26 – Carentan 35 – Coutances 27

⛰ Aux Grands Espaces

✆ 02 33 07 10 14. www.auxgrandsespaces.com – limited spaces for one-night stay

Address : 6 rue du Camping (4km west along the D 306; at St-Germain-Plage)

Opening times : from mid April to end Oct.

16 ha (580 pitches)

Tariff : 22.40€ ✶✶ 🚗 🔌 (10A) – Extra per person 5.50€
Rental rates : (from mid April to mid Sept.) 🛖 – 20 🚐 – 3 canvas bungalows. Per week from 280 to 730€

Surroundings : 🌲 ⛱ ♨
Leisure activities : 🍴 🛶 ⛵ 🎿 🏖 🏊
Facilities : ⚡ (July–Aug.) ♨ 🚿 launderette ♨
Nearby : 🏇 sand yachting

Longitude : -1.64089
Latitude : 49.23654

ST-HILAIRE-DU-HARCOUËT

50600 – Michelin map **303** F8 – pop. 4 036 – alt. 70
▶ Paris 339 – Alençon 100 – Avranches 27 – Caen 102

⛺ Municipal de la Sélune

✆ 02 33 49 43 74. www.st-hilaire.fr

Address : 700m northwest along the N 176, follow the signs for Avranches and take a right turn, near the river

Opening times : from beginning April to end Sept.

1.9 ha (70 pitches) flat, grassy

Tariff : ✶ 2.35€ 🚗 1€ – 🔌 (12A) 1.95€
Rental rates : (from beginning April to end Sept.) 🛖 – 2 caravans. Per night from 63 to 88€ – Per week from 251 to 451€

🚐 borne 3€ – 5 🔲 3€

Leisure activities : 🛶 🛶
Facilities : & ⚡ 🚿 launderette
Nearby : 🍴 ⛵ 🏊 🎿

Longitude : -1.09765
Latitude : 48.58127

ST-JEAN-DE-LA-RIVIÈRE

50270 – Michelin map **303** B3 – pop. 355 – alt. 20
▶ Paris 351 – Caen 119 – St-Lô 63 – Cherbourg 40

⛰ Yelloh! Village Les Vikings

✆ 02 33 53 84 13. www.camping-lesvikings.com

Address : 4 rue des Vikings (along the D 166 and take the road to the right)

Opening times : from beginning April to end Sept.

6 ha (250 pitches)

Tariff : 46€ ✶✶ 🚗 🔲 🔌 (10A) – Extra per person 8€
Rental rates : (from beginning April to end Sept.) & (1 mobile home) – 82 🚐. Per night from 45 to 179€ – Per week from 315 to 1,253€

🚐 borne
The entrance is decorated with flowers and small palm trees.

Surroundings : 🌲 ⛱
Leisure activities : 🍴 🛶 ⛵ 🏖 🎿 🏊
multi-sports ground, entertainment room
Facilities : & ⚡ 🚿 launderette ♨
Nearby : ⛵ 🐎 🏇 sand yachting

Longitude : -1.75293
Latitude : 49.36335

ST-MARTIN-EN-CAMPAGNE

76370 – Michelin map **304** H2 – pop. 1 319 – alt. 118
▶ Paris 209 – Dieppe 13 – Rouen 78 – Le Tréport 18

⛰ Municipal les Goélands

✆ 02 35 83 82 90. www.camping-les-goelands.fr – limited spaces for one-night stay

Address : rue des Grèbes (situated 2km to the northwest, at St-Martin-Plage)

Opening times : from mid March to beginning Nov.

3 ha (140 pitches) terraced, flat and relatively flat, grassy

Tariff : (2014 Price) ✶ 4.20€ 🚗 🔲 14.50€ – 🔌 (16A) 4.10€
Rental rates : (2014 Price) (from mid March to beginning Nov.) – 8 🚐. Per night from 129€ – Per week from 400 to 630€

🚐 5 🔲 12.50€
Some pitches enjoy a view of he sea; there's also a good-quality restaurant.

Surroundings : ⟨ ⛱
Leisure activities : 🍴 ✗ 🛶 🛶 multi-sports ground
Facilities : & ⚡ 🎱 ♨ 🎿 🚿 🍴 launderette ♨ 🎿

Some campsites benefit from proximity to a municipal leisure centre.

Longitude : 1.20425
Latitude : 49.96632

ST-PAIR-SUR-MER

50380 – Michelin map **303** C7 – pop. 3 788 – alt. 30
▶ Paris 342 – Avranches 24 – Granville 4 – Villedieu-les-Poêles 29

⛺ Angomesnil

✆ 02 33 61 85 87. www.angomesnil.com 🛖

Address : 891 route du Guigeois (head 4.9km southeast along the D 21, follow the signs for St-Michel-des-Loups and turn left onto D 154, following signs for St-Aubin-des-Préaux)

Opening times : from mid June to mid Sept.

1.2 ha (45 pitches) flat, grassy

Tariff : (2014 Price) ✶ 4.80€ 🚗 3.60€ 🔲 3.90€ – 🔌 (6A) 3.60€ – Reservation fee 15€

🚐 borne 11.10€

Surroundings : 🌲 ♨
Leisure activities : 🛶 🛶
Facilities : & ⚡ 🚿 🎱 🔲
Nearby : ⛵ 🎿 🔲 (open air in season) ♨ 🐎 sports trail

Longitude : -1.5261
Latitude : 48.79065

ST-SAUVEUR-LE-VICOMTE

50390 – Michelin map **303** C3 – pop. 2 053 – alt. 30
▶ Paris 336 – Barneville-Carteret 20 – Cherbourg 37 – St-Lô 56

⛺ Municipal du Vieux Château

✆ 02 33 41 72 04. www.saintsauveurlevicomte.stationverte.com

Address : avenue Division Leclerc (in the town; beside the Douve)

1 ha (57 pitches) flat, grassy
Situated in the grounds of the medieval château.

Leisure activities : 🛶
Facilities : & ⚡ launderette
Nearby : 🛶 ⛵

Longitude : -1.52779
Latitude : 49.38748

ST-SYMPHORIEN-LE-VALOIS

50250 – Michelin map **303** C4 – pop. 822 – alt. 35
▶ Paris 335 – Barneville-Carteret 19 – Carentan 25 – Cherbourg 47

🏕 Club Airotel L'Étang des Haizes ♣♨

𝒫 02 33 46 01 16. www.campingetangdeshaizes.com

Address : rue Cauticote (take the northern exit along the D 900, follow the signs for Valognes and turn left onto D 136 towards the town)

Opening times : from beginning April to beginning Oct.

4.5 ha (160 pitches)

Tariff : 37€ ♣♣ ⟵ 🗐 🗲 (10A) – Extra per person 8€
Rental rates : (from mid April to end Sept.) 👍 (1 mobile home) ⚿ – 24 ⫘ – 4 🏠 – 1 tipi – 2 tent lodges. Per night from 55 to 128€ – Per week from 327 to 896€ ⟲ borne

In a charming leafy setting around a pretty lake.

Surroundings : ⟆
Leisure activities : 🍷 🏠 🕯 ⚑ ⚡ 🚲 ⚓ 🛶
Facilities : 👍 ⚷ 🚿🍴 launderette

GPS	Longitude : -1.54482 Latitude : 49.29992

ST-VAAST-LA-HOUGUE

50550 – Michelin map **303** E2 – pop. 2 091 – alt. 4
▶ Paris 347 – Carentan 41 – Cherbourg 31 – St-Lô 68

🏕 La Gallouette

𝒫 02 33 54 20 57. www.lagallouette.com

Address : 10bis rue de la Gallouette (South of the town, 500m from the beach)

Opening times : from beginning April to end Sept.

2.3 ha (183 pitches) flat, grassy

Tariff : ♣ 6.80€ ⟵ 🗐 11.45€ – 🗲 (10A) 5€
Rental rates : (from beginning April to end Sept.) – 15 ⫘ – 10 🏠. Per night from 80 to 109€ – Per week from 323 to 859€
⟲ borne – 15 🗐 14.60€

Surroundings : ⟆
Leisure activities : 🍷 🍴 🏠 ⚡ 🛶
multi-sports ground
Facilities : 👍 ⚷ 🚿🍴 launderette
Nearby : 🍴 🎣 fitness trail

GPS	Longitude : -1.26873 Latitude : 49.5846

ST-VALERY-EN-CAUX

76460 – Michelin map **304** E2 – pop. 4 463 – alt. 5
▶ Paris 190 – Bolbec 46 – Dieppe 35 – Fécamp 33

🏕 Seasonova Etennemare

𝒫 02 35 97 15 79. www.seasonova.com – limited spaces for one-night stay

Address : 21 rue du Hameau d'Etennemare (located to the southwest, towards the hamlet of Le Bois d'Entennemare)

Opening times : from beg. April to beg. Nov.

4 ha (116 pitches)

Tariff : (2014 Price) 25€ ♣♣ ⟵ 🗐 🗲 (10A) – Extra per person 4.50€
Rental rates : (2014 Price) Permanent – 7 ⫘ – 10 🏠. Per week from 345 to 690€ – Reservation fee 12€

Some owner-occupier mobile homes, with good-quality rental options.

Surroundings : 🐟 ⟆
Leisure activities : 🏠 🖼 (open air in season) ⚑
Facilities : 👍 ⚷ ⫘ 🚿 🗑 launderette

GPS	Longitude : 0.70378 Latitude : 49.85878

STE-MARIE-DU-MONT

50480 – Michelin map **303** E3 – pop. 761 – alt. 31
▶ Paris 318 – Barfleur 38 – Carentan 11 – Cherbourg 47

🏕 Flower Utah-Beach

𝒫 02 33 71 53 69. www.camping-utahbeach.com – limited spaces for one-night stay

Address : 6km northeast along the D 913 and take D 421; 150m from the beach

Opening times : from beginning April to end Sept.

5.5 ha (149 pitches)

Tariff : 29.50€ ♣♣ ⟵ 🗐 🗲 (6A) – Extra per person 6€
Rental rates : (2014 Price) (from beginning April to end Sept.) – 9 ⫘ – 14 🏠 – 2 canvas bungalows. Per night from 44 to 129€ – Per week from 220 to 903€
⟲ borne 16€ – 40 🗐 9.80€ – 🛒 🗲16€

Surroundings : 🐟
Leisure activities : 🍷 🍴 🏠 🛁 jacuzzi
⚡ ⚓ 🛶 multi-sports ground,
entertainment room
Facilities : 👍 ⚷ 🗐 🚿🍴 launderette ⚘
Nearby : 🚲sand yachting

GPS	Longitude : -1.18028 Latitude : 49.42001

STE-MÈRE-ÉGLISE

50480 – Michelin map **303** E3 – pop. 1 643 – alt. 28
▶ Paris 321 – Bayeux 57 – Cherbourg 39 – St-Lô 42

🏕 Municipal

𝒫 02 33 41 35 22. mairie-sme@wanadoo.fr

Address : 6 rue Airborne (take the eastern exit along the D 17 and take a right turn; near the sports field)

Opening times : from beginning March to beginning Nov.

1.3 ha (70 pitches) flat, grassy

Tariff : (2014 Price) 20€ ♣♣ ⟵ 🗐 🗲 (6A) – Extra per person 5€
Rental rates : (2014 Price) (from beginning April to end Oct.) – 5 ⫘. Per night from 65 to 80€ – Per week from 350 to 550€

Surroundings : 🐟
Leisure activities : 🏠 ⚡ 🚲🍴 🖼
multi-sports ground
Facilities : ⚷ 🗑 launderette

GPS	Longitude : -1.31018 Latitude : 49.41003

SURRAIN

14710 – Michelin map **303** G4 – pop. 159 – alt. 40
▶ Paris 278 – Cherbourg 83 – Rennes 187 – Rouen 167

🏕 La Roseraie d'Omaha

𝒫 02 31 21 17 71. www.camping-calvados-normandie.fr

Address : rue de l'église (take the southern exit along the D 208, follow the signs for Mandeville-en-Bessin)

Opening times : from beginning April to end Sept.

3 ha (66 pitches)

Tariff : 19.10€ ♣♣ ⟵ 🗐 🗲 (10A) – Extra per person 5€
Rental rates : (from beginning April to end Sept.) ⚿ – 12 ⫘ – 15 🏠 – 1 gîte. Per night from 56 to 92€ – Per week from 290 to 760€
⟲ borne – 🛒 🗲14€

Surroundings : ⟆ 🌳
Leisure activities : 🍴 🏠 ⚡ 🚲 🍴 🎯 🖼 ⚑
Facilities : 👍 ⚷ 🚿 🍴 launderette
Nearby : 🐴

GPS	Longitude : -0.86443 Latitude : 49.32574

SURTAINVILLE

50270 – Michelin map **303** B3 – pop. 1 255 – alt. 12
▶ Paris 367 – Barneville-Carteret 12 – Cherbourg 29 – St-Lô 42

⚠ Municipal les Mielles

🖉 02 33 04 31 04. www.camping-municipal-normandie.com

Address : 80 route des Laguettes (head 1.5km west along the D 66 and follow the signs for the sea, 80m from the beach, direct access)

Opening times : Permanent

25 ha (151 pitches)

Tariff : 🛉 3.39€ 🚗 回 3.39€ – ⚡ (16A) 3.26€ – Reservation fee 5€
Rental rates : Permanent – 2 🛏. Per night from 56€ – Per week from 238 to 403€ – Reservation fee 5€

🚐 borne 4.16€ – 6 回

Surroundings : 🔊 ♨
Leisure activities : 🏠 🏇
Facilities : ♿ ⌐ 🚿 🛁 🚰 🍴 launderette
Nearby : 🏄 sand yachting

Longitude : -1.82881
Latitude : 49.46386

THURY-HARCOURT

14220 – Michelin map **303** J6 – pop. 1 968 – alt. 45
▶ Paris 257 – Caen 28 – Condé-sur-Noireau 20 – Falaise 27

⚠ Le Traspy

🖉 02 31 79 61 80. www.campingdutraspy.com

Address : rue du Pont Benoît (head east of the town along the bd du 30-Juin-1944 and take road to the left)

1.5 ha (78 pitches) terraced, flat, grassy

Rentals : 12 🛏 – 1 🛖.

🚐 borne – 6 回

Situated beside the Traspy river and near a small lake.

Surroundings : 🗀 ♨
Leisure activities : ✗ 🏠 ⛵ 🏇
Facilities : ♿ ⌐ 🛁 🚰 🍴 launderette 🍽 🧺
Nearby : 🚲 🦌 🏠 🛶 🎣 paragliding

Longitude : -0.46913
Latitude : 48.98896

TOUFFREVILLE-SUR-EU

76910 – Michelin map **304** H2 – pop. 201 – alt. 45
▶ Paris 171 – Abbeville 46 – Amiens 101 – Blangy-sur-Nesle 35

⚠ Municipal Les Acacias

🖉 02 35 50 06 33. www.camping-acacias.fr

Address : at Les Prés du Thil (head 1km to the southeast along the D 226 and take the D 454, following the signs for Guilmecourt)

Opening times : Permanent

1 ha (50 pitches) flat, grassy

Tariff : (2014 Price) 🛉 2.40€ 🚗 1€ 回 2.70€ – ⚡ (10A) 5€

Near the old station buildings of Touffreville-Criel.

Surroundings : 🔊 🗀 ♨
Facilities : ♿ 🛁 🍴

Longitude : 1.33537
Latitude : 49.99531

---

*The classification (1 to 5 tents, **black** or red) that we award to selected sites in this guide is our own system. It should not be confused with the classification (1 to 5 stars) of official organisations.*

TOUSSAINT

76400 – Michelin map **304** C3 – pop. 743 – alt. 105
▶ Paris 196 – Bolbec 24 – Fécamp 5 – Rouen 69

⚠ Municipal du Canada

🖉 02 35 29 78 34. www.commune-de-toussaint.fr – limited spaces for one-night stay

Address : rue de Rouen (500m northwest along the D 926, follow the signs for Fécamp and take road to the left)

Opening times : from mid March to mid Oct.

2.5 ha (100 pitches)

Tariff : 14€ 🛉🛉 🚗 回 ⚡ (6A) – Extra per person 3.80€
Rental rates : (from mid March to mid Oct.) – 2 🛏 – 2 🛖. Per night from 53 to 62€ – Per week from 340 to 450€

🚐 borne 2.50€ – 3 回 14€

Choose the pitches furthest from the road. Lots of old owner-occupier mobile homes.

Surroundings : 🗀 ♨
Facilities : ♿ ⌐ 🍴 🛁
Nearby : 🏇 🏄

Longitude : 0.417
Latitude : 49.74008

LE TRÉPORT

76470 – Michelin map **304** I1 – pop. 5 416 – alt. 12
▶ Paris 180 – Abbeville 37 – Amiens 92 – Blangy-sur-Bresle 26

⚠⚠ Municipal les Boucaniers

🖉 02 35 86 35 47. www.ville-le-treport.fr/camping

Address : rue Pierre Mendès-France (take the av. des Canadiens; near the stadium)

Opening times : from beginning April to end Sept.

5.5 ha (243 pitches) flat, grassy

Tariff : (2014 Price) 23.10€ 🛉🛉 🚗 回 ⚡ (6A) – Extra per person 5€
Rental rates : (2014 Price) Permanent ♿ (1 chalet) – 50 🛖. Per night from 40 to 86€ – Per week from 230 to 560€ – Reservation fee 5€

🚐 27 回 18.50€

A pretty chalet village. Choose the pitches close to the entrance and furthest away from the nearby factory.

Surroundings : ♨
Leisure activities : 🍴 🏠 🏇
Facilities : ♿ ⌐ 🍴 🛁 🚰 launderette 🧺
Nearby : 🍴

Longitude : 1.38882
Latitude : 50.0577

TRÉVIÈRES

14710 – Michelin map **303** G4 – pop. 938 – alt. 14
▶ Paris 283 – Bayeux 19 – Caen 49 – Carentan 31

⚠ Municipal Sous les Pommiers

🖉 02 31 92 89 24. www.ville-trevieres.fr

Address : rue du Pont de la Barre (take the northern exit along the D 30, follow the signs for Formigny; near a stream)

1.2 ha (75 pitches) flat, grassy

Pitches in the shade of apple trees.

Surroundings : 🗀 ♨
Leisure activities : 🏇
Facilities : ♿ 🛁 🧺 🛁
Nearby : 🎣 🏇

Longitude : -0.90637
Latitude : 49.3132

VEULES-LES-ROSES

76980 – Michelin map **304** E2 – pop. 561 – alt. 15
▶ Paris 188 – Dieppe 27 – Fontaine-le-Dun 8 – Rouen 57

🏚 Seasonova Les Mouettes

✆ 02 35 97 61 98. www.camping-lesmouettes-normandie.com

Address : avenue Jean-Moulin (take the eastern exit along the D 68, follow the signs for Sotteville-sur-Mer, 500m from the beach)

Opening times : from beginning April to beginning Nov.

3.6 ha (160 pitches) flat, grassy

Tariff : (2014 Price) 28.30€ ★★ ⇔ 🔲 (6A) – Extra per person 5.60€
Rental rates : (2014 Price) (from beginning April to beginning Nov.)
⚘ – 24 🚐 – 2 tent lodges. Per week from 330 to 860€
🚐 borne 10€

Attractive, marked-out pitches, 200m from the cliffs.

Surroundings : 🏞 🗔 ♀
Leisure activities : 🏛 🎣 ⇌ jacuzzi ⛺
🚲 🔲
Facilities : & ⚲ ⟲ ⛺ launderette

GPS Longitude : 0.80335
Latitude : 49.87579

LE VEY

14570 – Michelin map **303** J6 – pop. 87 – alt. 50
▶ Paris 269 – Caen 47 – Hérouville-St-Clair 46 – Flers 23

🏚 Les Rochers des Parcs

✆ 02 31 69 70 36. www.camping-normandie-clecy.fr

Address : at La Cour, near Le Pont du Vey (picturesque old bridge)

Opening times : from beginning April to end Sept.

1.5 ha (90 pitches)

Tariff : (2014 Price) ★ 5.80€ ⇔ 🔲 6.50€ – (10A) 3.90€ –
Reservation fee 5€
Rental rates : (2014 Price) (from beginning April to end Sept.) –
10 🚐 – 5 canvas bungalows. Per night from 52 to 78€ –
Per week from 225 to 565€ – Reservation fee 5€
🚐 borne 2.50€ – 4 🔲 11€ – 🚐 11€

Surroundings : ♀ ⛰
Leisure activities : 🏛 🎣 🚲 ⚘
Facilities : & ⚲ ⟲ ⛺ launderette
Nearby : ✗ 🐎 adventure park

VILLEDIEU-LES-POÊLES

50800 – Michelin map **303** E6 – pop. 3 882 – alt. 105
▶ Paris 314 – Alençon 122 – Avranches 26 – Caen 82

🏚 Les Chevaliers

✆ 02 33 61 02 44. www.camping-deschevaliers.com

Address : 2 impasse Pré-de-la-Rose (access via the town centre, take r. des Costils to the left of the post office)

Opening times : from beginning April to end Sept.

1.4 ha (82 pitches)

Tariff : (2014 Price) 26.70€ ★★ ⇔ 🔲 – Extra per person 4.70€
Rental rates : (2014 Price) (from beginning April to end Sept.) –
21 🚐. Per night from 41 to 105€ – Per week from 287 to 735€
🚐 borne – 10 🔲 14€ – 🚐 14€

This guide is updated regularly, so buy your new copy every year!

A pleasant, well-kept setting, beside the Sienne river.

Surroundings : 🏞 🗔 ♀
Leisure activities : ✗ 🏛 🎣 🚲 ✗ ⚘
multi-sports ground
Facilities : & ⚲ ⛺ launderette ⚘
Nearby : 🔲 🏊

GPS Longitude : -1.21694
Latitude : 48.83639

VILLERS-SUR-MER

14640 – Michelin map **303** L4 – pop. 2 707 – alt. 10
▶ Paris 208 – Caen 35 – Deauville 8 – Le Havre 52

🏚 Bellevue

✆ 02 31 87 05 21. www.camping-bellevue.com – limited spaces for one-night stay

Address : route de Dives (situated 2km southwest along the D 513, follow the signs for Cabourg)

Opening times : from beginning April to end Oct.

5.5 ha (257 pitches) terraced, relatively flat, flat, grassy

Tariff : 31€ ★★ ⇔ 🔲 (10A) – Extra per person 8.50€ – Reservation fee 10€
Rental rates : (from beginning April to end Sept.) ⚘ – 40 🚐.
Per night from 60 to 95€ – Per week from 280 to 760€ –
Reservation fee 10€

Situated overlooking the bay at Deauville.

Surroundings : ⇐ 🗔
Leisure activities : ♈ 🏛 🌙 nighttime 🎣
🎣 🔲 🏊
Facilities : & ⚲ ⟲ ⛺ ✗ ⚲ ⛺ launderette
Nearby : 🛒 🚲 ✗ 🏛 🔲 🐎

GPS Longitude : -0.0195
Latitude : 49.3097

*For more information on visiting particular towns or regions, consult the relevant regional **MICHELIN Green Guide**. We also recommend you use the appropriate Michelin regional map to locate your selected campsite, to calculate distances and to work out the best route.*

VIMOUTIERS

61120 – Michelin map **310** K1 – pop. 3 828 – alt. 95
▶ Paris 185 – L'Aigle 46 – Alençon 66 – Argentan 31

🏚 Municipal la Campière

✆ 02 33 39 18 86. www.mairie-vimoutiers.fr

Address : 14 boulevard Dentu (700m north, in the direction of Lisieux, by the stadium; beside La Vie river)

Opening times : from beginning April to end Oct.

1 ha (40 pitches) flat, grassy

Tariff : (2014 Price) ★ 3.50€ ⇔ 2.55€ 🔲 2.55€ – (6A) 2.70€
Rental rates : (2014 Price) (from beginning April to end Oct.) –
4 🚐. Per night from 58 to 63€ – Per week from 268 to 320€

Norman-style buildings in a lush, green setting surrounded by flowers.

Surroundings : 🗔 ♀
Leisure activities : 🏛 🎣 ✗
Facilities : & ⚲ ⛺ ⟲ 🏛
Nearby : 🛒

GPS Longitude : 0.1966
Latitude : 48.9326

PAYS-DE-LA-LOIRE

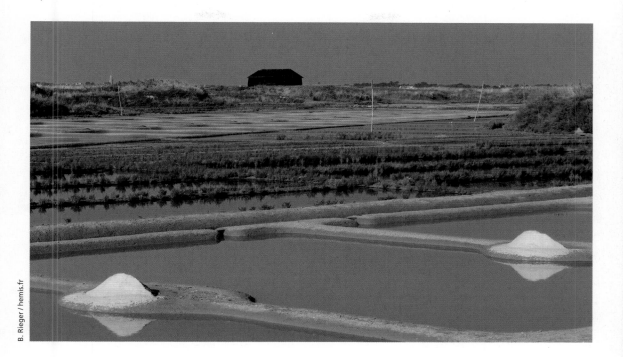

B. Rieger / hemis.fr

The 'Garden of France' is renowned for its tranquil atmosphere, glorious châteaux, magnificent floral gardens and acres of orchards and vineyards. Enjoy a glass of light Loire wine accompanied by a plate of rillettes (pork pâté), *matelote d'anguilles* (eel stew) or a slice of goat's cheese, perfect partners in the gastronomic experience offered by the region. Continue downriver to Nantes, redolent today of the scent of spices first brought back from the New World. This is the home of the famous dry Muscadet wines. Further south, the Vendée region still echoes with the cries of 18th-century Royalists' before revolutionary fervour took hold. Explore the secrets of its salt marshes, relax in balmy seaside resorts or head for the spectacular attractions of the Puy du Fou amusement park. Simple country fare is the order of the day here, so make sure you sample a piping-hot plate of *chaudrée* (fish chowder) or a mouth-watering slice of fresh brioche.

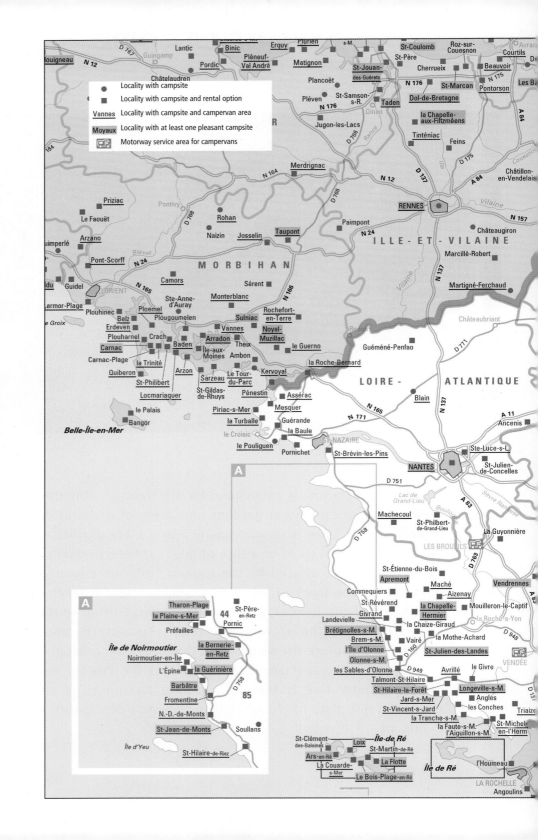

Lantic
Binic
Pordic
Pléneuf-
Val André
Plurien
Erquy
s-M.
St-Coulomb
St-Père
Roz-sur-
Couesnon
Courtils
N 12
Rouigneau
D 787
Guingamp
Matignon
Cherrueix
Beauvoir
Avrar.
N 176
St-Marcan
Pontorson
Les Ba
Châtelaudren
Plancoët
St-Jouan-
des-Guérets
Dol-de-Bretagne
N 175
N 175
A 84
Pléven
St-Samson-
s-R.
la Chapelle-
aux-Filtzméens
Pléhon
N 176
Taden
Tinténiac
Feins
Jugon-les-Lacs
Dinan
N 175
D 175
Châtillon-
en-Vendelais

Merdrignac
RENNES
Vilaine
N 157
Priziac
Rohan
Paimpont
Châteaugiron
Le Faouët
Josselin
Taupont
ILLE-ET-VILAINE
Arzano
Naizin
Marcillé-Robert
Pont-Scorff
N 24
MORBIHAN
Martigné-Ferchaud
du
Guidel
Camors
Sérent
LORIENT
N 165
Ste-Anne-
d'Auray
Monterblanc
Châteaubriant
Larmor-Plage
Plouhinec
Ploemel
Monterblanc
Rochefort-
en-Terre
D 771
Belz
Plougoumelen
Sulniac
Erdeven
Vannes
Noyal-
Muzillac
Guéméné-Penfao
Plouharnel
Crach
Arradon
Theix
le Guerno
Carnac
Baden
Île-aux-
Moines
Ambon
la Roche-Bernard
LOIRE-
ATLANTIQUE
Carnac-Plage
la Trinité
Arzon
Kervoyal
Quiberon
St-Philibert
Sarzeau
Le Tour-
du-Parc
Blain
N 137
Ancenis
Locmariaquer
St-Gildas-
de-Rhuys
Pénestin
Assérac
N 171
A 11
le Palais
Piriac-s-Mer
Mesquer
N 165
Ste-Luce-s-L
Bangor
la Turballe
Guérande
St-Julien-
de-Concelles
Belle-Île-en-Mer
le Croisic
la Baule
St-NAZAIRE
NANTES
le Pouliguen
Pornichet
St-Brévin-les-Pins
D 751
Lac de
Grand-Lieu
A 83
La Guyonnière

A

Machecoul
St-Philbert-
de-Grand-Lieu
LES BROUILS
D 763
D 758

St-Étienne-du-Bois
Vendrennes
Commequiers
Apremont
Maché
Aizenay
Mouilleron-le-Captif
St-Révérend
Givrand
la Chapelle-
Hermier
la Roche-s-Yon
Landevielle
la Chaize-Giraud
Brétignolles-s-M.
Brem-s-M.
Vairé
la Mothe-Achard
D 948
l'Île d'Olonne
Olonne-s-M.
St-Julien-des-Landes
VENDÉE
les Sables-d'Olonne
D 949
Avrillé
le Givre
Talmont-St-Hilaire
Longeville-s-M.
D 131
St-Hilaire-la-Forêt
Angles
Jard-s-Mer
les Conches
St-Vincent-s-Jard
Triaize
la Tranche-s-M.
la Faute-s-M.
St-Michel-
en-l'Herm
l'Aiguillon-s-M.

A

Tharon-Plage
St-Père-
en-Retz
44
la Plaine-s-Mer
Pornic
Préfailles
Île de Noirmoutier
la Bernerie-
en-Retz
Noirmoutier-en-Île
L'Épine
la Guérinière
85
Barbâtre
D 758
Fromentine
N.-D.-de-Monts
St-Jean-de-Monts
Soullans
St-Clément-
des-Baleines
Loix
Île-de-Ré
Île d'Yeu
Ars-en-Ré
St-Martin-de-Ré
St-Hilaire-de-Riez
La Couarde-
s-Mer
La Flotte
Île de Ré
l'Houmeau
Le Bois-Plage-en-Ré
LA ROCHELLE
Angoulins

Legend:
• Locality with campsite
■ Locality with campsite and rental option
Vannes Locality with campsite and campervan area
Moyaux Locality with at least one pleasant campsite
Motorway service area for campervans

L'AIGUILLON-SUR-MER

85460 – Michelin map **316** I10 – pop. 2 310 – alt. 4
▶ Paris 458 – Luçon 20 – Niort 83 – La Rochelle 51

⚠ La Cléroca

📞 02 51 27 19 92. www.camping-la-cleroca.com

Address : 2.2km northwest along the D 44, follow the signs for Grues

Opening times : from end May to beginning Sept.

1.5 ha (66 pitches) flat, grassy

Tariff : 27 € ✱✱ 🚗 🔲 🔌 (10A) – Extra per person 5 €

Rental rates : (from end May to beginning Sept.) – 1 yurt – 2 tent lodges – 1 gîte. Per night from 50 to 70€ – Per week from 200 to 460€

🔁 borne – 6 🔲 9 € – 🚐 🔌 13 €

In a lush, green setting and plenty of shade.

Surroundings : 🞊🞊	G
Leisure activities : 🛶 🛥 🚣 🏊 multi-sports ground	Longitude : -1.31513
Facilities : 🚻 ⛲ 🍽 🔥 🖥 launderette	Latitude : 46.35003

AIZENAY

85190 – Michelin map **316** G7 – pop. 7 930 – alt. 62
▶ Paris 435 – Challans 26 – Nantes 60 – La Roche-sur-Yon 18

⚠ La Forêt

📞 02 51 34 78 12. www.camping-laforet.com

Address : 1 rue de la Clairière (located 1.5km southeast along the D 948, follow the signs for la Roche-sur-Yon and take road to the left, behind the commercial centre)

Opening times : from beginning April to beginning Oct.

2.5 ha (96 pitches)

Tariff : 21.70 € ✱✱ 🚗 🔲 🔌 (6A) – Extra per person 3.40 €

Rental rates : Permanent – 16 🏕 – 1 🏠. Per night from 56 to 102 € – Per week from 290 to 788 €

🔁 borne 3 € – 2 🔲 – 🚐 13 €

A pleasant site with plenty of shade.

Surroundings : 🞊🞊	G
Leisure activities : 🛥 🏐 🏊	Longitude : -1.58947
Facilities : 🚻 ⛲ 🔥 🍽 launderette	Latitude : 46.73427
Nearby : 🛒 🍹 🍴 🎣 fitness trail	

ALLONNES

49650 – Michelin map **317** J5 – pop. 2 979 – alt. 28
▶ Paris 292 – Angers 64 – Azay-le-Rideau 43 – Chinon 28

⚠ Club Airotel Le Pô Doré

📞 02 41 38 78 80. www.camping-lepodore.com

Address : 51 route du Pô (3.2km northwest along the D 10, follow the signs for Saumur and take road to the left)

Opening times : from mid March to mid Nov.

2 ha (90 pitches) flat, grassy

Tariff : (2014 Price) 24.80 € ✱✱ 🚗 🔲 🔌 (10A) – Extra per person 5.30 €

Rental rates : (2014 Price) (from mid March to mid Nov.) – 20 🏕. Per night from 50 to 120€ – Per week from 330 to 745€ Reservation fee 15€

Surroundings : 🞊 🗖	G
Leisure activities : 🍹 🍴 🛶 🛥 🏊	Longitude : -0.01244
Facilities : 🚻 ⛲ 🔥 🚿 🍽 🔲 🚐	Latitude : 47.29923

AMBRIÈRES-LES-VALLÉES

53300 – Michelin map **310** F4 – pop. 2 778 – alt. 144
▶ Paris 248 – Alençon 60 – Domfront 22 – Fougères 46

⚠ Municipal de Vaux

📞 02 43 04 90 25. www.parcdevaux.com

Address : situated 2km southeast along the D 23, follow the signs for Mayenne and take the turning to the left; by the swimming pool

Opening times : from beginning April to mid Oct.

1.5 ha (61 pitches)

Tariff : (2014 Price) 18.30 € ✱✱ 🚗 🔲 🔌 (10A) – Extra per person 4.70 € – Reservation fee 10€

Rental rates : (2014 Price) (from mid April to end Sept.) – 13 🏕 – 20 🏠 – 5 canvas bungalows. Per night from 35 to 97€ – Per week from 195 to 721€ – Reservation fee 10€

🔁 borne

A pleasant wooded park beside the Varenne (small lake).

Surroundings : 🞆 🗖 🞊🞊	G
Leisure activities : 🛶 🚲	Longitude : -0.6171
Facilities : 🚻 ⛲ 🚐 🚿 🍽 launderette	Latitude : 48.39175
Nearby : 🛥 🏓 🍴 🏊 🛶 🚣 🐎	

ANCENIS

44150 – Michelin map **316** I3 – pop. 7 543 – alt. 13
▶ Paris 347 – Angers 55 – Châteaubriant 48 – Cholet 49

⚠ L'Île Mouchet

📞 02 40 83 08 43. www.camping-estivance.com

Address : impasse de l'Île Mouchet (take the western exit along the bd Joubert and take the turning to the left, behind the municipal sports centre)

3.5 ha (105 pitches) flat, grassy

Rentals : 11 🏕 – 5 canvas bungalows.

A site on lovely fields with plenty of shade, situated near the municipal stadium and the Loire river.

Surroundings : 🞊🞊	G
Leisure activities : 🛶 🛥 🏊 🚣	Longitude : -1.18707
Facilities : 🚻 ⛲ 🍽 launderette	Latitude : 47.36095
Nearby : 🏓 🎿 🎣 sports trail	

ANDOUILLÉ

53240 – Michelin map **310** E5 – pop. 2 300 – alt. 103
▶ Paris 282 – Fougères 42 – Laval 15 – Mayenne 23

⚠ Municipal le Pont

📞 02 43 01 18 10. www.ville-andouille.fr

Address : 5 allée des Isles (along the D 104, follow the signs for St-Germain-le-Fouilloux, right next to municipal gardens; beside the Ernée river)

Opening times : from mid April to mid Oct.

0.8 ha (31 pitches) flat, grassy

Tariff : (2014 Price) ✱ 1.55 € 🚗 🔲 1.53 € – 🔌 (6A) 1.45 €

Rental rates : (2014 Price) Permanent 🎿 – 4 🏕. Per week from 187 to 371 €

Surroundings : 🗖 🞆	G
Facilities : 🚻 🔥 🍽 🔲	Longitude : -0.78697
Nearby : 🛥 fitness trail	Latitude : 48.17604

ANGERS

49000 – Michelin map **317** F4 – pop. 147 305 – alt. 41
▶ Paris 294 – Caen 249 – Laval 79 – Le Mans 97

▲▲▲ Lac de Maine ▲▲

✆ 02 41 73 05 03. www.lacdemaine.fr

Address : avenue du Lac de Maine (4km southwest along the D 111, follow the signs for Pruniers, near the lake (direct access) and near the leisure and activity park)

Opening times : from end March to mid Oct.

4 ha (163 pitches)

Tariff : (2014 Price) 27€ ♣♣ ⟚ 🗐 🔌 (6A) – Extra per person 3.40€

Rental rates : (2014 Price) (from end March to mid Oct.) ⟳ (2 mobile homes) – 17 🚐. Per week from 293 to 690€ – Reservation fee 30€

Public transport for the centre of Angers is just 300m away.

Surroundings : 🏞 ⚲
Leisure activities : 🍴 🗡 🖼 🏊 ⚓ 🚴 ⛵
spa facilities
Facilities : ⟳ ⟲ 🚻 🛁 🚿 ♨ 🍴 📷 🛒
Nearby : 🍴 ⚓ 🎣 🦢 pedalos

GPS Longitude : -0.59654
Latitude : 47.45551

*The classification (1 to 5 tents, **black** or red) that we award to selected sites in this guide is our own system. It should not be confused with the classification (1 to 5 stars) of official organisations.*

ANGLES

85750 – Michelin map **316** H9 – pop. 2 329 – alt. 10
▶ Paris 450 – Luçon 23 – La Mothe-Achard 38 – Niort 86

▲▲▲ L'Atlantique ▲▲

✆ 02 51 27 03 19. www.camping-atlantique.com

Address : 5bis rue du Chemin de Fer (in the town, take the exit for la Tranche-sur-Mer and take turning to the left)

Opening times : from end March to end Oct.

6.9 ha (363 pitches)

Tariff : (2014 Price) 31.90€ ♣♣ ⟚ 🗐 🔌 (10A) – Extra per person 7.80€ – Reservation fee 25€

Rental rates : (2014 Price) (from end March to end Oct.) – 150 🚐 – 15 🏠. Per week from 149 to 795€ – Reservation fee 25€

A well laid-out site, although the sanitary facilities and some rental options are rather old. There's a free shuttle service to the beaches.

Surroundings : 🏞 ⚲⚲
Leisure activities : 🍴 🗡 🖼 🏊 ⚓ 🎣 🦢 ⚓ 🚴 🍴 🖼 🏊 🌊 entertainment room
Facilities : ⟳ ⟲ 🛁 🚿 ♨ 🍴 launderette 🛒 refrigerators

GPS Longitude : -1.40552
Latitude : 46.40465

▲▲▲ APV Moncalm ▲▲

(rental of mobile homes and chalets only)

✆ 02 51 97 55 50. www.camping-apv.com

Address : rue du Chemin de Fer (in the town, take the exit for La Tranche-sur-Mer and take turning to the left)

Opening times : from mid April to end Sept.

3 ha (200 pitches)

Rental rates : (2014 Price) – 27 🚐 – 84 🏠 – 1 canvas bungalow. Per night from 40 to 77€ – Per week from 252 to 938€ Reservation fee 28€

A mobile home park and chalets, with an open-air play and paddling pool area; free shuttle service to the beaches.

Surroundings : 🏞 ⚲⚲
Leisure activities : 🍴 🗡 🖼 🏊 ⚓ 🦢 ⚓ 🚴 🌊 multi-sports ground
Facilities : ⟳ ⟲ 🛁 🍴 launderette 🛒

GPS Longitude : -1.40548
Latitude : 46.40467

▲▲▲ Le Clos Cottet ▲▲

✆ 02 51 28 90 72. www.camping-clos-cottet.com

Address : route de La Tranche-sur-Mer (2.2km to the south, near the D 747)

Opening times : from beginning April to end Sept.

4.5 ha (196 pitches) flat, grassy, small lake

Tariff : (2014 Price) 20€ ♣♣ ⟚ 🗐 🔌 (10A) – Extra per person 5€ – Reservation fee 25€

Rental rates : (2014 Price) Permanent – 80 🚐 – 20 🏠 – 5 canvas bungalows. Per night from 71 to 109 € – Per week from 99 to 839€ – Reservation fee 25€

Based around a renovated farmhouse with some animals; free shuttle service to the beaches.

Surroundings : 🏞 ⚲⚲
Leisure activities : 🍴 🗡 🖼 🏊 ⚓ 🎣 🦢 hammam ⚓ 🏊 🌊 🦢 quad biking, multi-sports ground, entertainment room
Facilities : ⟳ ⟲ 🍴 launderette

GPS Longitude : -1.40345
Latitude : 46.39248

APREMONT

85220 – Michelin map **316** F7 – pop. 1 546 – alt. 19
▶ Paris 448 – Challans 17 – Nantes 64 – La Roche-sur-Yon 30

▲▲▲ Les Charmes

✆ 02 51 54 48 08. www.campinglescharmes.com

Address : at Les Lilas (3.6km north along the D 21, follow the signs for Challans and take turning to the right, towards La Roussière)

Opening times : from beginning April to mid Sept.

1 ha (55 pitches) flat, grassy

Tariff : 19.90€ ♣♣ ⟚ 🗐 🔌 (10A) – Extra per person 5.20€ – Reservation fee 16€

Rental rates : Permanent ⟳ (1 mobile home) – 12 🚐 – 5 🏠. Per night from 65 to 105€ – Per week from 189 to 705€ – Reservation fee 16€

A pleasant site with upmarket rental options and a small wellness centre.

Surroundings : 🦢 🏞 ⚲⚲
Leisure activities : 🍴 🖼 🦢 jacuzzi ⚓ 🏊 entertainment room
Facilities : ⟳ ⟲ 🍴 launderette

GPS Longitude : -1.73397
Latitude : 46.77827

The prices listed were supplied by the campsite owners in 2014 (if prices were not available, those from the previous year are given). The fees should be regarded as basic charges and may fluctuate with inflation.

ASSÉRAC

44410 – Michelin map **316** B3 – pop. 1 773 – alt. 12
▶ Paris 454 – Nantes 79 – Rennes 108 – Vannes 48

▲▲▲ Moulin de Leclis

🖉 02 40 01 76 69. www.camping-leclis.com

Address : at Pont Mahé (situated 4km west along the D 82)

Opening times : from beginning April to mid Nov.

3.8 ha (180 pitches)

Tariff : (2014 Price) ⇔🔲 16.10€ – [⚡] (10A) 4.50€ – Reservation fee 20€

Rental rates : (2014 Price) (from beginning April to mid Nov.)
♿ (1 mobile home) – 31 🚐 – 31 🏠 – 1 canvas bungalow.
Per night from 88 to 220€ – Per week from 238 to 1,204€ –
Reservation fee 20€

🚐 borne 4.70€ – 🛒 6.90€

In the bay at Pont-Mahé, with a view of La Pointe du Bile (headland).

Surroundings : 🏖 🗖 ♨♨ ⚠
Leisure activities : ▼ ✗ 🚣 🗙 (open air in season) 🎱
Facilities : ♿ ⊶ 🏛 🛁 ↑ launderette 🧺
Nearby : skate surfing

Longitude : -2.44795
Latitude : 47.44576

AVOISE

72430 – Michelin map **310** H7 – pop. 539 – alt. 112
▶ Paris 242 – La Flèche 28 – Le Mans 41 – Sablé-sur-Sarthe 11

▲ L'Oeil dans le Rétro

🖉 02 43 92 76 12. http://www.campingloeildansleretro.fr

Address : place des 2 Fonds (in the town, along the D 57)

Opening times : from beginning April to end Oct.

1.8 ha (54 pitches) flat, grassy

Tariff : (2014 Price) 11.70€ ♦♦ ⇔ 🔲 [⚡] (16A) –
Extra per person 2.20€

Rental rates : (2014 Price) (from beginning April to end Oct.)
🚐 – 6 vintage caravans. Per night from 50 to 60€ – Per week
from 315 to 378€

🚐 borne 3.50€

Situated beside the Sarthe river.

Surroundings : 🗖 ♨♨
Leisure activities : ▼ 🚣 🐾
Facilities : ♿ ⊶ 🛁 ↑ 🧺
Nearby : ⚓

AVRILLÉ

85440 – Michelin map **316** H9 – pop. 1 194 – alt. 45
▶ Paris 445 – Luçon 27 – La Rochelle 70 – La Roche-sur-Yon 27

▲▲▲ FranceLoc Le Domaine Des Forges 👥

🖉 02 51 22 38 85. www.campingdomainedesforges.com

Address : rue des Forges (take the northeastern exit along the D 19,
follow the signs for Moutiers-les-Mauxfaits and take the turning to
the left, 0.7km along the rue des Forges)

Opening times : from beginning April to end Sept.

12 ha (295 pitches) flat, grassy, pond

Tariff : (2014 Price) 34€ ♦♦ ⇔ 🔲 [⚡] (16A) – Extra per person 7€ –
Reservation fee 27€

Rental rates : (2014 Price) (from beginning April to end Sept.)
♿ (2 mobile homes) – 150 🚐 – 2 🏠 – 15 tent
lodges. Per night from 33 to 126€ – Per week from 161 to 1,183€ –
Reservation fee 27€

🚐 borne – 20 🔲 15€

The site is beside a small, pretty château and a lake.

Surroundings : 🏖 🗖 ♀
Leisure activities : ▼ ✗ 🏠 🗙 🏃 ⛷ 🚣
🚴 ✂ 🎱 🗙 ⛱ 🎱 🎱 launderette
🛁 🧺

Longitude : -1.49467
Latitude : 46.47587

▲▲▲ Les Mancellières

🖉 02 51 90 35 97. www.lesmancellieres.com

Address : 1300 route de Longeville (1.7km south along the D 105)

Opening times : from beginning April to mid Sept.

2.6 ha (133 pitches)

Tariff : (2014 Price) 26.40€ ♦♦ ⇔ 🔲 [⚡] (6A) – Extra per person 4.40€
Reservation fee 20€

Rental rates : (2014 Price) (from beginning April to mid Sept.) –
60 🚐 – 4 🏠. Per night from 22 to 42€ – Per week
from 172 to 755€ – Reservation fee 20€

A pleasant, shady site with lots of green space.

Surroundings : 🗖 ♨♨
Leisure activities : ✗ 🏠 jacuzzi 🚣 🗙 ⛱
multi-sports ground
Facilities : ♿ ⊶ 🛁 ↑ launderette

Longitude : -1.48509
Latitude : 46.45608

LA BAULE

44500 – Michelin map **316** B4 – pop. 16 235 – alt. 31
▶ Paris 450 – Nantes 76 – Rennes 120 – St-Nazaire 19

▲▲▲ Club Airotel La Roseraie 👥

🖉 02 40 60 46 66. www.laroseraie.com

Address : 20 avenue Jean Sohier (take the northeastern exit for La
Baule-Escoublac)

Opening times : from beginning April to end Sept.

5 ha (220 pitches)

Tariff : (2014 Price) 33€ ♦♦ ⇔ 🔲 [⚡] (10A) – Extra per person 7.30€
Reservation fee 30€

Rental rates : (2014 Price) (from beginning April to end Sept.) ♿
(1 mobile home) – 75 🚐 – 3 🏠. Per night from 67 to 140€ –
Per week from 315 to 980€ – Reservation fee 30€

🚐 borne

*In a pleasant, green setting, but choose the pitches away from
the road.*

Surroundings : 🗖 ♀
Leisure activities : ▼ ✗ 🏠 🗙 🏃 🚣 jacuzzi
🚣 🚴 ✂ 🗙 (open air in season) ⛱
multi-sports ground, entertainment room
Facilities : ♿ ⊶ 🛁 🛁 ↑ launderette 🧺

Longitude : -2.35776
Latitude : 47.29828

Key to rentals symbols:

12 🚐	*Number of mobile homes*
20 🏠	*Number of chalets*
6 🛏	*Number of rooms to rent*
Per night 30–50€	*Minimum/maximum rate per night*
Per week 300–1,000€	*Minimum/maximum rate per week*

BEAUMONT-SUR-SARTHE

72170 – Michelin map **310** J5 – pop. 2 094 – alt. 76
▶ Paris 223 – Alençon 24 – La Ferté-Bernard 70 – Le Mans 29

⛰ Municipal du Val de Sarthe

✆ 02 43 97 01 93. www.ville-beaumont-sur-sarthe.fr

Address : located to the southeast of the town

Opening times : from beginning May to end Sept.

1 ha (73 pitches) flat, grassy

Tariff : ✝ 2.50€ ⬅ 2€ 🅴 2€ – [⚡] (6A) 3.60€

Rental rates : (from beginning May to end Sept.) – 2 canvas bungalows. Per night from 43 to 78€ – Per week from 165 to 305€

🚐 borne 4.85€

A pleasant site and setting beside the Sarthe river.

Surroundings : 🌳 🚂 ♀		
Leisure activities : 🎯 🏊 fitness trail	**G**	Longitude : 0.13384
Facilities : ☕ 🚿 🚽 🔌	**P**	Latitude : 48.2261
Nearby : 🎣 🏊	**S**	

*To visit a town or region, use the **MICHELIN Green Guides**.*

LA BERNERIE-EN-RETZ

44760 – Michelin map **316** D5 – pop. 2 541 – alt. 24
▶ Paris 426 – Challans 40 – Nantes 46 – St-Nazaire 36

⛰ Les Écureuils 👥

✆ 02 40 82 76 95. www.camping-les-ecureuils.com

Address : 24 avenue Gilbert Burlot (take northeastern exit, follow the signs for Nantes and take the turning to the left after the level crossing, 350m from the sea)

Opening times : from beginning April to mid Sept.

5.3 ha (312 pitches)

Tariff : 44€ ✝✝ ⬅ 🅴 [⚡] (10A) – Extra per person 8€ – Reservation fee 20€

Rental rates : (from beginning April to end Sept.) 🏠 – 80 🚐 – 19 🏡. Per night from 85 to 115€ – Per week from 231 to 945 € Reservation fee 20€

🚐 borne

A pretty site with upmarket rental options based around the swimming and play area.

Surroundings : 🌳 🚂 ♀		
Leisure activities : 🍹 🎯 🌙 nighttime 🏃	**G**	Longitude : -2.03558
🏊 🛶 multi-sports ground	**P**	Latitude : 47.08375
Facilities : ☕ 🚿 🚽 🍽 launderette	**S**	
refrigerators		
Nearby : 💧		

BESSÉ-SUR-BRAYE

72310 – Michelin map **310** N7 – pop. 2 363 – alt. 72
▶ Paris 198 – La Ferté-Bernard 43 – Le Mans 57 – Tours 56

⛰ Municipal du Val de Braye

✆ 02 43 35 31 13. www.campingmunicipal-duvaldebraye.jimdo.com

Address : head southeast along the D 303, follow the signs for Pont de Braye

Opening times : from beginning April to end Oct.

2 ha (120 pitches) flat, grassy

Tariff : (2014 Price) 13.20€ ✝✝ ⬅ 🅴 [⚡] (13A) – Extra per person 3.10€

Rental rates : Permanent ♿ (1 mobile home) – 6 🚐 – 4 tipis – 1 canvas bungalow. Per night from 29 to 52€ – Per week from 113 to 309€

🚐 borne 3.10€ – 30 🅴 11.30€

Beautiful trees and shrubs decorate this site beside the Braye river.

Surroundings : ♀		
Leisure activities : 🎯 🏊 🎣	**G**	Longitude : 0.75427
Facilities : ☕ 🚿 (July-Aug.) 🍽 🔌	**P**	Latitude : 47.83119
Nearby : 🍴 🍽 🏊 🛶	**S**	

BLAIN

44130 – Michelin map **316** F3 – pop. 9 284 – alt. 23
▶ Paris 411 – Nantes 41 – Nort-sur-Erdre 22 – Nozay 16

⛰ Municipal le Château

✆ 02 40 79 11 00. www.ville-blain.fr

Address : rue Henri II de Rohan, Le Gravier (take the southwestern exit along the N 171, follow the signs for St-Nazaire and take the road to the left, 250m from the Nantes-Brest canal)

Opening times : from beginning May to end Sept.

1 ha (44 pitches) flat, grassy

Tariff : (2014 Price) 14€ ✝✝ ⬅ 🅴 [⚡] (16A) – Extra per person 2.70€

🚐 borne – 4 🅴 9€ – 🏠 12.20€

In a well-kept, green setting, near a 14th-century château.

Surroundings : ♀♀ ♀		
Leisure activities : 🎯 🏊	**G**	Longitude : -1.76763
Facilities : ☕ 🚿 (July-Aug.) 🍽 🔌 🍽	**P**	Latitude : 47.46772
Nearby : 🍹 🍴 🐴 ⚓	**S**	

*For more information on visiting particular towns or regions, consult the relevant regional **MICHELIN Green Guide**. We also recommend you use the appropriate Michelin regional map to locate your selected campsite, to calculate distances and to work out the best route.*

BOUÈRE

53290 – Michelin map **310** G7 – pop. 1 027 – alt. 81
▶ Paris 273 – Nantes 146 – Laval 39 – Angers 70

⛰ Village Vacances Nature et Jardin

(rental of chalets only)

✆ 02 43 06 08 56. www.vacances-nature-jardin.fr

Address : rue Vierge Vacances (to the south, follow r. des Sencies and take the road to the left)

Opening times : Permanent

3 ha

Rental rates : 11 🏡. Per night from 77 to 92€ – Per week from 219 to 428€ – Reservation fee 15€

🚐 borne 2€

The Nature et Jardin (Nature and Gardening) workshops are open throughout the year.

Surroundings : 🌳 🚂		
Leisure activities : 🎯 🚲 ⛷ 🎣	**G**	Longitude : -0.47506
Facilities : 🍽 🍽 refrigerators	**P**	Latitude : 47.86306
Nearby : 🏊 🍽	**S**	

BRAIN-SUR-L'AUTHION

49800 – Michelin map **317** G4 – pop. 3 330 – alt. 22

▶ Paris 291 – Angers 16 – Baugé 28 – Doué-la-Fontaine 38

⚠ Kawan Village du Port Caroline

℘ 02 41 80 42 18. www.campingduportcaroline.fr

Address : rue du Pont Caroline (take the southern exit along the D 113, 100m from L'Authion)

Opening times : from beginning April to mid Oct.

3.2 ha (121 pitches) flat, grassy

Tariff : (2014 Price) 21€ ★★ ⊸ 🅴 🄷 (10A) – Extra per person 4.50€

Rental rates : (2014 Price) (from beginning April to mid Oct.) – 12 🚐 – 2 🏠 – 2 canvas bungalows – 4 tent lodges. Per night from 36 to 112€ – Per week from 226 to 784€

🚐 borne

Surroundings :
Leisure activities : ✗ 🏛 ⚓ 🛶
Facilities : ♿ ⊸ CC 🍴 🖫 🏖
Nearby : 🛹 skateboarding

G P S Longitude : -0.40855
Latitude : 47.44386

BREM-SUR-MER

85470 – Michelin map **316** F8 – pop. 2 565 – alt. 13

▶ Paris 454 – Aizenay 26 – Challans 29 – La Roche-sur-Yon 34

⛰ Le Chaponnet ⚐⚑

℘ 02 51 90 55 56. www.le-chaponnet.com

Address : 16 rue du Chaponnet (to the west of the town)

Opening times : from beginning April to end Sept.

6 ha (357 pitches) flat, grassy

Tariff : 37.95€ ★★ ⊸ 🅴 🄷 (6A) – Extra per person 7.80€ – Reservation fee 25€

Rental rates : (2014 Price) (from beginning April to end Sept.) ♿ (1 mobile home) – 100 🚐 – 20 🏠. Per night from 35 to 149€ – Per week from 182 to 1,045€ – Reservation fee 25€

🚐 borne

In a green setting with flowers, with shade in places. A free shuttle service to the beaches.

Surroundings : 🏖 ▭ 🎣
Leisure activities : 🍴 ✗ 🏛 🛖 ⚓ 🎠 🏊
⚓ 🏐 🛶 🏊 multi-sports ground
Facilities : ♿ ⊸ 🏖 🍴 launderette 🏖

G P S Longitude : -1.83225
Latitude : 46.6043

⛰ Cybele Vacances L'Océan ⚐⚑

℘ 02 51 90 59 16. www.campingdelocean.fr

Address : rue des Gabelous (located 1km west, 600 from the beach)

Opening times : from mid April to end Sept.

13 ha (566 pitches)

Tariff : (2014 Price) 28€ ★★ ⊸ 🅴 🄷 (16A) – Extra per person 6€ – Reservation fee 25€

Rental rates : (2014 Price) (from mid April to end Sept.) ♿ (2 mobile homes) – 175 🚐 – 3 tent lodges. Per night from 40 to 150€ – Per week from 190 to 989€ – Reservation fee 25€

Surroundings : 🏖 ▭
Leisure activities : 🍴 ✗ 🏛 🛖 🎠 🏊
🚴 🏐 🛶 🏊 multi-sports ground
Facilities : ♿ ⊸ 🏖 🍴 launderette 🏖
Nearby : 🍴

G P S Longitude : -1.83225
Latitude : 46.6043

⛰ Le Brandais ⚐⚑

℘ 02 51 90 55 87. www.lebrandais.com – limited spaces for one-night stay

Address : rue du Sablais (take the northwestern exit along the D 38 and take turning to the left)

Opening times : from end April to beginning Oct.

2.3 ha (165 pitches)

Tariff : 30.30€ ★★ ⊸ 🅴 🄷 (10A) – Extra per person 5€ – Reservation fee 10€

Rental rates : (from beginning April to end Oct.) ♿ (1 mobile home) – 2 caravans – 20 🚐 – 5 🏠. Per night from 60 to 70€ – Per week from 139 to 960€ – Reservation fee 18€

In a residential area, with a range of rental options and some pitches for tents and caravans. Free shuttle service to the beaches.

Surroundings : 🏖 ▭ 🎣
Leisure activities : 🍴 🏛 🎠 ⚓ 🚴 🏊 🛶
Facilities : ♿ ⊸ 🏖 🍴 launderette 🏖
Nearby : 🍴

G P S Longitude : -1.83949
Latitude : 46.60486

BRÉTIGNOLLES-SUR-MER

85470 – Michelin map **316** E8 – pop. 4 127 – alt. 14

▶ Paris 459 – Challans 30 – La Roche-sur-Yon 36 – Les Sables-d'Olonne 18

⛰ Les Vagues ⚐⚑

℘ 02 51 90 19 48. www.campinglesvagues.fr – limited spaces for one-night stay

Address : 20 boulevard du Nord (to the north along the D 38 towards St-Gilles-Croix-de-Vie)

Opening times : from beginning April to end Sept.

4.5 ha (252 pitches) relatively flat, flat, grassy

Tariff : 32€ ★★ ⊸ 🅴 🄷 (10A) – Extra per person 7.50€ – Reservation fee 20€

Rental rates : (from mid April to end Sept.) – 40 🚐 – 2 🏠. Per week from 300 to 800€ – Reservation fee 20€

A pleasant site with shade and plenty of pitches for tents and caravans.

Surroundings : ▭ 🎣
Leisure activities : 🍴 ✗ 🏛 🎠 ⚓ 🏐 🛶
🏊 multi-sports ground
Facilities : ♿ ⊸ 🏖 🍴 🖫

G P S Longitude : -1.85935
Latitude : 46.63012

⛰ Chadotel La Trevillière

℘ 02 51 90 09 65. http://www.chadotel.com/fr/camping/vendee/bretignolles-sur-mer/cam

Address : rue de Bellevue (take the northern exit along the rte du Stade and take the turning to the left)

Opening times : from beginning April to end Sept.

3 ha (204 pitches) relatively flat, flat, grassy

Tariff : 31€ ★★ ⊸ 🅴 🄷 (10A) – Extra per person 6€ – Reservation fee 25€

Rental rates : (from beginning April to end Sept.) ♿ (1 mobile home) – 1 🚐 – 1 🏠. Per night from 25 to 129€ – Per week from 175 to 903€ – Reservation fee 25€

🚐 1 🅴 31€

In a green setting, with good shade in places.

Surroundings : 🏖 ▭ 🎣
Leisure activities : 🍴 ✗ ⚓ 🛝 🏐 🛶 🏊
Facilities : ♿ ⊸ 🏖 🏖 🍴 launderette 🏖

G P S Longitude : -1.85822
Latitude : 46.63627

⚠ Le Marina

☎ 02 51 33 83 17. www.le-marina.com

Address : rue de La Martinière (take the northwestern exit along the D 38, follow the signs for St-Gilles-Croix-de-Vie then take left turn 1km along the r. de la Martignière)

2.7 ha (131 pitches) flat, grassy

Rentals : 6 🛏.

In a green setting in a residential area, but choose the pitches away from the road in preference.

Surroundings : ⌂ ♤♤
Leisure activities : 🏖 🛝
Facilities : ♿ ⚲ ♨ ⚐ ▽ 🖼

G P S Longitude : -1.87185
Latitude : 46.63582

⚠ La Motine

☎ 02 51 90 04 42. www.lamotine.com

Address : 4 rue des Morinières (continue along the av. de la Plage and take a right turn)

Opening times : from beginning April to end Sept.

1.8 ha (103 pitches)

Tariff : 29 € ♦♦ ⚗ 🖥 ⚡ (10A) – Extra per person 6 € – Reservation fee 15 €

Rental rates : (from beginning April to end Sept.) – 10 🛏 – 1 apartment. Per night from 98 to 156 € – Per week from 327 to 653 € – Reservation fee 15 €

🚐 borne 8 €

Ornamental trees and shrubs surround the pitches; situated in a residential area.

Surroundings : ⌂ ♤
Leisure activities : 🖼
Facilities : ♿ ⚲ ♨ ⚐ ▽ ⚐ launderette
Nearby : 🔥

G P S Longitude : -1.8644
Latitude : 46.62745

⚠ Le Bon Accueil

☎ 02 51 90 15 92. https://sites.google.com/site/campinglebonaccueil

Address : 24 route de St-Gilles (1.2km northwest along the D 38)

Opening times : from beginning May to mid Sept.

3 ha (146 pitches) relatively flat, flat, grassy

Tariff : (2014 Price) 24.50 € ♦♦ ⚗ 🖥 ⚡ (10A) – Extra per person 4.70 € – Reservation fee 15 €

Rental rates : (2014 Price) (from beginning May to mid Sept.) – 7 🛏. Per night from 50 € – Per week from 220 to 500 €

There is some rental accommodation and rather old but well-maintained sanitary facilities.

Surroundings : ♤♤
Leisure activities : 🏖 🛝
Facilities : ♿ ⚲ ⚐ ⚐ 🖼

G P S Longitude : -1.86605
Latitude : 46.63625

Michelin classification:

⛰⛰⛰⛰ *Extremely comfortable, equipped to a very high standard*
⛰⛰⛰ *Very comfortable, equipped to a high standard*
⛰⛰ *Comfortable and well equipped*
⛰ *Reasonably comfortable*
⚠ *Satisfactory*

BRISSAC-QUINCÉ

49320 – Michelin map **317** G4 – pop. 2 898 – alt. 65
▶ Paris 307 – Angers 18 – Cholet 62 – Doué-la-Fontaine 23

⛰⛰ Sites et Paysages Domaine de l'Étang

☎ 02 41 91 70 61. www.campingetang.com

Address : route de St-Mathurin (situated 2km northeast along the D 55, and take the road to the right; beside the Aubance river and near a lake)

Opening times : from end April to mid Sept.

3.5 ha (150 pitches) flat, grassy, small lake

Tariff : 35 € ♦♦ ⚗ 🖥 ⚡ (16A) – Extra per person 6.60 € – Reservation fee 14 €

Rental rates : (from mid April to end Sept.) 🦮 – 17 🛏 – 4 canvas bungalows – 4 tent lodges – 3 gîtes. Per night from 36 to 139 € – Per week from 216 to 834 € – Reservation fee 14 €

🚐 borne 14 € – 🚐 ⚡16 €

Spacious and comfortable pitches in the grounds of an old farmhouse.

Surroundings : 🌿 ⌂
Leisure activities : ✕ 🚣 🚲🖼 (open air in season)
Facilities : ♿ ⚲ ⚏ ♨ ⚐ launderette
Nearby : 🚤 🛶 leisure park

G P S Longitude : -0.43529
Latitude : 47.36082

Some information or pricing may have changed since the guide went to press. We recommend you check the price list online in advance or at the entrance to the campsite and enquire about possible restrictions.

CHAILLÉ-LES-MARAIS

85450 – Michelin map **316** J9 – pop. 1 902 – alt. 16
▶ Paris 446 – Fontenay-le-Comte 23 – Niort 57 – La Rochelle 34

⛰⛰ L'Île Cariot

☎ 02 51 56 75 27. www.camping-chaille-les-marais.com

Address : rue du 8 Mai (south of the town; beside small streams and near the stadium)

Opening times : from beginning April to end Sept.

1.2 ha (50 pitches) flat, grassy

Tariff : (2014 Price) 17.80 € ♦♦ ⚗ 🖥 ⚡ (10A) – Extra per person 4.55 € – Reservation fee 8 €

Rental rates : (2014 Price) (from beginning April to end Sept.) – 5 🛏 – 5 🏠 – 2 canvas bungalows. Per night from 35 to 51 € – Per week from 170 to 526 € – Reservation fee 8 €

🚐 borne 3 € – 🚐 8 €

A very lush and leafy site beside some canals, ideal for canoeing.

Surroundings : ⌂ ♤♤
Leisure activities : 🚣 🚤 🚲🛝 🏊
Facilities : ♿ ⚲ ⚏ ⚐ launderette
Nearby : ✕

G P S Longitude : -1.0209
Latitude : 46.3927

LA CHAIZE-GIRAUD

85220 – Michelin map **316** F8 – pop. 878 – alt. 15
▶ Paris 453 – Challans 24 – La Roche-sur-Yon 32 – Les Sables-d'Olonne 21

⚠ Les Alouettes

𝒫 0251229621. www.lesalouettes.com – limited spaces for one-night stay

Address : route de Saint-Gilles (located 1km west along the D 12, follow the signs for St-Gilles-Croix-de-Vie)

3 ha (130 pitches) terraced, relatively flat, flat, grassy

Rentals : 66 🏠 – 19 🏠 – 5 canvas bungalows.

A mobile home and chalet park, with some pitches for tents and caravans.

Surroundings : 🖵 ♀	G
Leisure activities : ♟ ✕ 🖼 ⇌ jacuzzi	P Longitude : -1.83342
🏊🦆 🖼 ⚞	S Latitude : 46.64832
Facilities : ㅎ ⚡ 🚿 ⑂ launderette	

CHALONNES-SUR-LOIRE

49290 – Michelin map **317** E4 – pop. 6 421 – alt. 25
▶ Paris 322 – Nantes 82 – Angers 26 – Cholet 40

⚠ Le Candais

𝒫 0241780227. www.camping-portesdelaloire.com

Address : route de Rochefort (located 1km east along the D 751, follow the signs for Les Ponts-de-Cé; beside the Loire river and near a small lake)

3 ha (210 pitches) flat, grassy

Rentals : 2 caravans.

Surroundings : ♀	G
Leisure activities : 🖼 ⚞	P Longitude : -0.74813
Facilities : ㅎ ⚡ ⑂ 🖼	S Latitude : 47.35132
Nearby : 🛒 🚲 ✕ ♏ ⚞	

CHAMBRETAUD

85500 – Michelin map **316** K6 – pop. 1 460 – alt. 214
▶ Paris 377 – Nantes 83 – La Roche-sur-Yon 56 – Cholet 21

⚠ Au Bois du Cé

𝒫 0251915432. www.camping-auboisduce.com ⚡

Address : route du Puy-du-Fou (located 1km to the south, on the D 27)

Opening times : from beginning April to end Sept.

5 ha (110 pitches)

Tariff : (2014 Price) 27.50€ ⭐⭐ ⇌ 🔲 ⚡ (16A) – Extra per person 4.90€ – Reservation fee 10€

Rental rates : (2014 Price) (from beginning April to end Sept.) ⚡ – 30 🏠 – 10 🏠 – 2 studios. Per night from 57 to 143€ – Per week from 300 to 780€ – Reservation fee 10€

🚐 borne

In a green setting, with pitches laid out around swimming pools, with a range of upmarket rental options.

Surroundings : ⚞ 🖵	G
Leisure activities : ♟ 🖼 jacuzzi 🖼 ⚞	P Longitude : -0.95
Facilities : ㅎ ⚡ 🖼 ⑂ launderette	S Latitude : 46.915

LA CHAPELLE-HERMIER

85220 – Michelin map **316** F7 – pop. 796 – alt. 58
▶ Paris 447 – Aizenay 13 – Challans 25 – La Roche-sur-Yon 29

⚠⚠ Pin Parasol 👥

𝒫 0251346472. http://www.campingpinparasol.fr

Address : at Chateaulong (3.3km southwest along the D 42, follow the signs for L'Aiguillon-sur-Vie then continue 1km along the turning to the left)

Opening times : from end April to mid Sept.

12 ha (379 pitches) terraced, relatively flat, flat, grassy

Tariff : 35.75€ ⭐⭐ ⇌ 🔲 (10A) – Extra per person 8.10€ – Reservation fee 25€

Rental rates : (from end April to end Sept.) ㅎ (1 chalet) ⚡ – 81 🏠 – 21 🏠 – 6 tent lodges. Per night from 110 to 324€ – Per week from 212 to 1,264€ – Reservation fee 25€

🚐 borne 5€

The swimming pool has a colourful play and paddling pool area; near the Lac de Jaunay (direct access).

Surroundings : 🏊 ⚞ 🖼 ♀	
Leisure activities : ♟ 🖼 🖼 daytime 🏇 ♗	G
⇌ hammam 🏊🚲 ✕ 🖼 🖼 ⚞ multi-	P Longitude : -1.75502
sports ground	S Latitude : 46.66647
Facilities : ㅎ ⚡ ⑂ 🖼 ⑂ launderette 🚗 🚙	
Nearby : 🦢 pedalos	

⚠⚠ Village Vacances Le Domaine du Pré 👥

(rental of chalets only)

𝒫 0251080707. www.domainedupre.com

Address : Bellevue (5km southwest along the D 42, follow the signs for L'Aiguillon-sur-Vie then continue along the turning to the left)

Opening times : from beginning March to mid Nov.

11 ha

Rental rates : ㅎ (4 chalets) – 82 🏠. Per night from 43 to 190€ – Reservation fee 10€

A chalet village beside a large spa and wellness centre.

Surroundings : 🏊 ⚞	
Leisure activities : 🖼 🏇 ⇌ hammam,	G
jacuzzi 🏊🚲 🖼 (small swimming pool) ⚞	P Longitude : -1.76769
multi-sports ground, spa centre	S Latitude : 46.66485
Facilities : ㅎ ⚡ 🔲 ⑂ ⑂ launderette 🚗 🚙	
Nearby : 🦢 pedalos	

*We value your opinion and welcome your feedback.
Do email us at campingfrance@tp.michelin.com*

CHÂTEAU-GONTIER

53200 – Michelin map **310** E8 – pop. 11 532 – alt. 33
▶ Paris 288 – Angers 50 – Châteaubriant 56 – Laval 30

⚠⚠ Le Parc

𝒫 0243073560. www.campingchateaugontier.fr

Address : 15 route de Laval (800m north along the N 162 follow the signs for Laval; near the sports centre)

Opening times : Permanent

2 ha (55 pitches)

Tariff : (2014 Price) 12€ ⭐⭐ ⇌ 🔲 ⚡ (10A) – Extra per person 4€

Rental rates : Permanent – 12 🏠. Per night from 105 to 205€ – Per week from 195 to 380€

🚐 borne

The pitches are shaded by all kinds of tree varieties, on the banks of the Mayenne river.

Leisure activities : 🏊 🎣
Facilities : ☕ 🚰
Nearby : climbing wall

| G P S | Longitude : -0.6995 |
| | Latitude : 47.83866 |

CHÂTEAUNEUF-SUR-SARTHE

49330 – Michelin map **317** G2 – pop. 2 972 – alt. 20
▶ Paris 278 – Angers 31 – Château-Gontier 25 – La Flèche 33

🏕 Municipal du Port

🖉 02 41 69 82 02. www.chateauneufsursarthe.fr

Address : 14 place R. Le Fort (take the southeastern exit along the D 859, follow the signs for Durtal and take second road to the right after the bridge; beside the Sarthe river (mooring point)

Opening times : from beginning April to end Sept.

1 ha (60 pitches) flat, grassy

Tariff : (2014 Price) 8€ ✱ ✱ 🚗 🔌 (16A) – Extra per person 2.47€
🚐 borne 5€ – 8 🔌 5€

Surroundings : 🏞 ♀
Facilities : ♿ 🚿🚽🚮

| G P S | Longitude : -0.48695 |
| | Latitude : 47.67749 |

CHEMILLÉ

49120 – Michelin map **317** E5 – pop. 6 967 – alt. 84
▶ Paris 331 – Angers 43 – Cholet 22 – Saumur 60

🏕 La Via Natura La Coulvée

🖉 02 41 30 39 97. www.camping-coulvee-chemille.com

Address : route de Cholet (take the southern exit along the N 160, follow the signs for Cholet and take the road to the right; near a small lake)

Opening times : from beginning May to mid Sept.

2 ha (42 pitches) flat, grassy

Tariff : 11.70€ ✱ ✱ 🚗 🔌 (9A) – Extra per person 3.50€
Rental rates : Permanent – 12 🚐. Per night from 52 to 70€ – Per week from 360 to 470€
🚐 borne 3€ – 🔌8€

Surroundings : 🏞 ♀♀
Leisure activities : 🚴
Facilities : ♿ 🚿 🚮🚽 🚰 🧺

Nearby : 🚣 🏊

| G P S | Longitude : -0.7359 |
| | Latitude : 47.20308 |

CHOLET

49300 – Michelin map **317** D6 – pop. 54 121 – alt. 91
▶ Paris 353 – Ancenis 49 – Angers 64 – Nantes 60

🏕 Centre Touristique Lac de Ribou 👥

🖉 02 41 49 74 30. www.lacderibou.com

Address : 5km southeast along the D 20, follow the signs for Maulevrier and turn right onto D 600

Opening times : from end April to mid Sept.

5 ha (162 pitches)

Tariff : (2014 Price) 27€ ✱ ✱ 🚗 🔌 (10A) – Extra per person 6€
Rental rates : (2014 Price) Permanent – 19 🚐 – 8 🛖 – 19 gîtes.
Per night from 52 to 113€ – Per week from 196 to 889€
🚐 borne 6€ – 🔌17€

The site isocated 100m from the lake (direct access).

Surroundings : 🏞 🏡
Leisure activities : 🍽 ✗ 🏊 🌙nighttime 🏃
🚴 ✗ 🎣 🛶
Facilities : ♿ ☕ 🏛 🖐 🛝 🚰 launderette 🧺
Nearby : 🎠 🐎

| G P S | Longitude : -0.84017 |
| | Latitude : 47.03621 |

COMMEQUIERS

85220 – Michelin map **316** E7 – pop. 2 910 – alt. 19
▶ Paris 441 – Challans 13 – Nantes 63 – La Roche-sur-Yon 38

🏕 La Vie

🖉 02 51 54 90 04. www.campinglavie.com

Address : at Le Motteau (1.3km southeast along the D 82, follow the signs for Coëx and take road to the left)

Opening times : from beginning April to end Sept.

6 ha (110 pitches) flat, grassy, small lake

Tariff : (2014 Price) 16€ ✱ ✱ 🚗 🔌 (6A) – Extra per person 4€ – Reservation fee 10€
Rental rates : (2014 Price) (from mid April to mid Sept.) – 20 🚐. Per night from 16 to 21€ – Per week from 310 to 608€ – Reservation fee 10€

A peaceful, country setting, able to accommodate groups and summer camps.

Surroundings : 🏞 ♀
Leisure activities : 🍽 ✗ 🏊 🛶 🎣
Facilities : ♿ ☕ 🖐 🚰 launderette

| G P S | Longitude : -1.824 |
| | Latitude : 46.75902 |

🏕 Le Trèfle à 4 feuilles

🖉 02 51 54 87 54. www.campingletreflea4feuilles.com

Address : at La Jouère (3.3km southeast along the D 82, follow the signs for Coëx et 1.4km along the road to the left)

Opening times : from mid April to end Sept.

1.8 ha (50 pitches)

Tariff : (2014 Price) 16€ ✱ ✱ 🚗 🔌 (6A) – Extra per person 5.10€ Reservation fee 7.50€
Rental rates : (from mid April to end Sept.) – 12 🚐. Per night from 50 to 120€ – Per week from 260 to 580€ – Reservation fee 7.50€

A farm campsite in the grounds of a grain farm with chickens, sheep, goats, a donkey....

Surroundings : 🏞 ♀♀
Leisure activities : 🍽 🏊 🚴 🎮
Facilities : ♿ ☕ 🚰 launderette

| G P S | Longitude : -1.78507 |
| | Latitude : 46.75935 |

LES CONCHES

85560 – Michelin map **316** H9
▶ Paris 465 – Nantes 109 – La Roche 37 – La Rochelle 63

🏕 Le Clos des Pins

🖉 02 51 90 31 69. www.campingclosdespins.com

Address : 1336 avenue du Dct Joussemet

1.6 ha (94 pitches)

Rentals : 36 🚐 – 13 🛖.

Some of the rental accommodation is rather old, but there are also some luxury mobile homes.

Surroundings : 🏞 🏘
Leisure activities : 🍽 🏊 🚣 🚴 🛶 🎣
Facilities : ♿ ☕ 🖐 🚰 launderette
Nearby : 🎿

| G P S | Longitude : -1.48842 |
| | Latitude : 46.38856 |

⚠ Le Sous-Bois

🔗 02 51 33 36 90. lesousbois85@gmail.com

Address : at La Haute-Saligotière

Opening times : from beginning June to mid Sept.

1.7 ha (140 pitches)

Tariff : 23 € ♠♠ ⊕ 回 ⚡ (10A) – Extra per person 4 €
Rental rates : (from beginning June to end Sept.) – 4 🚐.
Per week from 150 to 495 €

*A simple, shady site with well-maintained but rather old
facilities.*

Surroundings : ⌂ ⌐ ♀♀		G
Leisure activities : 🎱 🏇 ✂		P
Facilities : ⅄ ⊶ 🗐 🛁 🕁 🚰 🗑		S

Longitude : -1.48727
Latitude : 46.3956

CONCOURSON-SUR-LAYON

49700 – Michelin map **317** G5 – pop. 544 – alt. 55
▶ Paris 332 – Angers 44 – Cholet 45 – Saumur 25

⚠⚠ La Vallée des Vignes

🔗 02 41 59 86 35. www.campingvdv.com

Address : at La Croix Patron (900m west along the D 960, follow the
signs for Vihiers and take turning to the right after the bridge; beside
the Layon river)

Opening times : from beginning May to end Sept.

3.5 ha (63 pitches) flat, grassy

Tariff : 31 € ♠♠ ⊕ 回 ⚡ (10A) – Extra per person 6 € – Reservation
fee 13 €
Rental rates : (from beginning May to end Sept.) ✂ – 2 🚐.
Per week from 330 to 680 € – Reservation fee 13 €

In a rural setting.

Surroundings : ⌐		G
Leisure activities : ♀ 🏇 🏇 ⚲ 🛶 🎣		P
Facilities : ⅄ ⊶ 🛁 🕁 🚰 🗑 🛒		S

Longitude : -0.34766
Latitude : 47.17394

*The pitches of many campsites are marked out with low
hedges of attractive bushes and shrubs.*

COUTURES

49320 – Michelin map **317** G4 – pop. 530 – alt. 81
▶ Paris 303 – Angers 25 – Baugé 35 – Doué-la-Fontaine 23

⚠⚠⚠ Yelloh! Village Parc de Montsabert

🔗 02 41 57 91 63. www.parcdemontsabert.com

Address : route de Montsabert (located 1.5km to the northeast, near
the château at Montsabert)

Opening times : from mid April to beginning Sept.

5 ha (150 pitches)

Tariff : 31 € ♠♠ ⊕ 回 ⚡ (10A) – Extra per person 7 €
Rental rates : (from mid April to beginning Sept.) – 3 caravans –
43 🚐 – 14 🏠. Per night from 45 to 147 € – Per week
from 315 to 1,029 €
🚐 borne 5 € – 1 回 16 € – ⚡⚡17.10 €

A pleasant wooded park.

Surroundings : ⌂ ⌐ ♀♀		G
Leisure activities : ✗ 🎱 🏇 ✂ 🛶 🎣		P
(open air in season)		S
Facilities : ⅄ ⊶ 🎫 🛁 🕁 🚰 launderette		

Longitude : -0.34679
Latitude : 47.37448

CRAON

53400 – Michelin map **310** D7 – pop. 4 590 – alt. 75
▶ Paris 309 – Fougères 70 – Laval 29 – Mayenne 60

⚠ Municipal du Mûrier

🔗 02 43 06 96 33. www.ville-craon53.fr

Address : rue Alain Gerbault (800m east, follow the signs for
Château-Gontier and take road to the left)

Opening times : from beginning May to end Sept.

1 ha (51 pitches) flat, grassy

Tariff : ♠ 3.30 € ⊕ 回 4.20 € – ⚡ (10A) 2.70 €
Rental rates : (from end April to end Dec.) – 9 🏠. Per night
from 62 to 146 € – Per week from 173 to 409 € – Reservation
fee 15 €
🚐 borne 3 €

In a pleasant setting near a small lake.

Surroundings : ⌐ ♀♀		G
Leisure activities : 🎱 🏇		P
Facilities : ⅄ 🚰 🗑		S
Nearby : 🚲 ♀ ✗ ✂ 🎡 🛶 🛷 🎣 🏇		

Longitude : -0.94398
Latitude : 47.84837

To visit a town or region, use the MICHELIN Green Guides.

DAON

53200 – Michelin map **310** F8 – pop. 486 – alt. 42
▶ Paris 292 – Angers 46 – Château-Gontier 11 – Châteauneuf-sur-
Sarthe 15

⚠⚠ Les Rivières

🔗 02 43 06 94 78. www.campingdaon.fr

Address : 1 rue du Port (take the western exit along the D 213, follow
the signs for la Ricoullière and take a right turn before the bridge;
near the Mayenne river)

Opening times : from beginning April to end Sept.

1.8 ha (98 pitches) flat, grassy

Tariff : (2014 Price) 13 € ♠♠ ⊕ 回 ⚡ (10A) – Extra per person 4 €
Rental rates : (2014 Price) Permanent – 10 🏠. Per night
from 82 to 178 € – Per week from 166 to 356 €

Surroundings : ⌂ ⌐ ♀		G
Leisure activities : 🎱		P
Facilities : ⅄ ⊶ 🚰 🗑		S
Nearby : ♀ ✗ 🏇 🎡 🛶 🎣 ⚓ pedalos		

Longitude : -0.64059
Latitude : 47.74996

DURTAL

49430 – Michelin map **317** H2 – pop. 3 337 – alt. 39
▶ Paris 261 – Angers 38 – La Flèche 14 – Laval 66

⚠⚠ Les Portes de l'Anjou

🔗 02 41 76 31 80. www.lesportesdelanjou.com

Address : 9 rue du Camping (take northeastern exit following signs
for la Flèche and take right turn)

Opening times : from beginning April to mid Oct.

3.5 ha (127 pitches) flat, grassy

Tariff : 18.40 € ♠♠ ⊕ 回 ⚡ (10A) – Extra per person 4.70 € –
Reservation fee 5 €
Rental rates : (from beginning April to mid Oct.) – 11 🚐 –
8 canvas bungalows – 1 gîte. Per night from 25 to 88 € – Per week
from 310 to 616 € – Reservation fee 10 €
🚐 borne

A pleasant site and setting beside the Loir river.

Surroundings : 🌿 🖵 ♀
Leisure activities : 🍴 ✕ 🏛 🚣 ⛵ 🎣
Facilities : 🔥 ⚬⟳ 🆑 ⚑ 🏖
Nearby : 🏊

LES ÉPESSES

85590 – Michelin map **316** K6 – pop. 2 575 – alt. 214
▶ Paris 375 – Bressuire 38 – Chantonnay 29 – Cholet 24

🔺 La Bretèche

✆ 02 51 57 33 34. www.campinglabreteche.com

Address : by the leisure centre, just north of Les Epesses (take the northern exit along the D 752, follow the signs for Cholet and take the road to the right)

Opening times : from beginning April to end Sept.

3 ha (164 pitches)

Tariff : 23.60€ ⚤ 🚗 🅿 (10A) – Extra per person 4.80€ – Reservation fee 10€

Rental rates : (2014 Price) (from beginning April to end Sept.) – 24 🏠 – 12 canvas bungalows. Per night from 35 to 85€ – Per week from 204 to 739€ – Reservation fee 10€

🚐 borne

Ornamental trees and shrubs decorate the site, 3km from Le Puy du Fou.

Surroundings : 🌿 🖵 ♀♀
Leisure activities : 🍴 ✕ 🏛 🚣 🏊
Facilities : 🔥 ⚬⟳ ⚑ launderette
Nearby : 🎣 amusement park

Longitude : -0.89925
Latitude : 46.88986

ÉVRON

53600 – Michelin map **310** G6 – pop. 7 099 – alt. 114
▶ Paris 250 – Alençon 58 – La Ferté-Bernard 98 – La Flèche 69

🔺 Municipal de la Zone Verte

✆ 02 43 01 65 36. www.camping-evron.fr

Address : boulevard du Maréchal Juin (take the western exit)

Opening times : Permanent

3 ha (92 pitches)

Tariff : (2014 Price) 11.20€ ⚤ 🚗 🅿 (10A) – Extra per person 2.20€

Rental rates : (2014 Price) Permanent – 11 🏠. Per night from 46 to 61€ – Per week from 155 to 280€

🚐 borne 2€ – 8 🅿 9.80€

Surroundings : 🖵 ♀
Leisure activities : 🏛 🚣 🗻 sports trail
Facilities : ⚬⟳ 🏖 launderette
Nearby : ✂ 🎯 🏊 🏖

Longitude : -0.41321
Latitude : 48.15073

LA FAUTE-SUR-MER

85460 – Michelin map **316** I9 – pop. 916 – alt. 4
▶ Paris 465 – Luçon 37 – Niort 106 – La Rochelle 71

🔺 APV Les Flots Bleus

✆ 02 51 27 11 11. www.camping-lesflotsbleus.com – limited spaces for one-night stay

Address : av. des Chardons (located 1km southeast following signs for La Pointe d'Arçay (headland)

1.5 ha (104 pitches)

Rentals : 77 🚚 – 2 tent lodges.
Situated in a residential area, 200m from the beach.

Surroundings : 🖵 ♀
Leisure activities : ✕ 🚣 🏛 (open air in season)
Facilities : 🔥 ⚬⟳ 🏖 ⚑ launderette
Nearby : 🍸

Longitude : -1.31842
Latitude : 46.32508

Key to rentals symbols:

12 🚚	**Number of mobile homes**
20 🏠	**Number of chalets**
6 🛏	**Number of rooms to rent**
Per night 30–50€	**Minimum/maximum rate per night**
Per week 300–1,000€	**Minimum/maximum rate per week**

LA FLÈCHE

72200 – Michelin map **310** I8 – pop. 15 228 – alt. 33
▶ Paris 244 – Angers 52 – Châteaubriant 106 – Laval 70

🔺 Municipal de la Route d'Or

✆ 02 43 94 55 90. www.camping-laroutedor.com

Address : allée du Camping (take the southern exit towards Saumur and take a right turn; beside the Loir river)

4 ha (250 pitches) flat, grassy
Rentals : 10 🚚.

Surroundings : 🖵 ♀
Leisure activities : 🏛 🚴 ✂ 🏊
Facilities : 🔥 ⚬⟳ 🏛 🏖 ⚑ 🏊
Nearby : 🎣

Longitude : -0.07779
Latitude : 47.69509

FRESNAY-SUR-SARTHE

72130 – Michelin map **310** J5 – pop. 2 198 – alt. 95
▶ Paris 235 – Alençon 22 – Laval 73 – Mamers 30

🔺 Municipal Sans Souci 👥

✆ 02 43 97 32 87. www.camping-fresnaysursarthe.fr

Address : rue du Haut Ary (located 1km west along the D 310, follow the signs for Sillé-le-Guillaume)

Opening times : from beginning April to end Sept.

2 ha (90 pitches)

Tariff : (2014 Price) 12.65€ ⚤ 🚗 🅿 (10A) – Extra per person 2.50€

Rental rates : (2014 Price) 🚵 – 5 🏠. Per week from 171 to 491€

🚐 borne 3.15€

Attractive, marked-out pitches beside the Sarthe river.

Surroundings : 🌿 🖵
Leisure activities : 🏛 🚣 🚴 ✂
Facilities : 🔥 ⚬⟳ 🏖 ⚑ 🏊 🏖 🏊
Nearby : 🗻 🏊 🎣

Longitude : 0.01589
Latitude : 48.28252

The prices listed were supplied by the campsite owners in 2014 (if prices were not available, those from the previous year are given). The fees should be regarded as basic charges and may fluctuate with inflation.

FROMENTINE

85550 – Michelin map **316** D6
▶ Paris 455 – Nantes 69 – La Roche 72 – St-Nazaire 70

⚠ **Campéole La Grande Côte** ♠♦

✆ 02 51 68 51 89. www.campeole.com

Address : route de la Grande Côte (situated 2km along the D 38b)

Opening times : from beginning April to mid Sept.

21 ha (810 pitches) terraced, flat, sandy

Tariff : (2014 Price) 30€ ♣♦ ➔ 🗏 [ǧ] (10A) – Extra per person 8€ – Reservation fee 25€

Rental rates : (2014 Price) Permanent ♿ (1 mobile home) – 95 ⬚ – 36 ⬚ – 68 canvas bungalows – 47 tent lodges. Per night from 37 to 140€ – Per week from 259 to 980€ –Reservation fee 25€

⬚ borne

Situated in the Forêt des Pays de Monts, near the Île de Noirmoutier bridge; close to the beach.

Surroundings : 🌳🌊⛰
Leisure activities : ♈ 🏛 🎣🏊🚣🚴 🎿 multi-sports ground
Facilities : ♿ ➔ ⬚ 🍴 launderette 🚿🚽
Nearby : 🍴 🎣

	G	Longitude : -2.14732
	P	Latitude : 46.88553
	S	

GIVRAND

85800 – Michelin map **316** E7 – pop. 1 946 – alt. 10
▶ Paris 460 – Nantes 79 – La Roche-sur-Yon 39

⚠ **FranceLoc Domaine Les Dauphins Bleus** ♠♦

(rental of mobile homes and chalets only)

✆ 02 51 55 59 34. www.camping-franceloc.fr

Address : 16 rue du Rocher

Opening times : from mid April to mid Sept.

7 ha flat, grassy

Rental rates : (2014 Price) ♿ (2 mobile homes) – 301 ⬚ – 12 ⬚. Per night from 37 to 133€ – Per week from 147 to 1,239€

A mobile home village and chalets set around a water park.

Surroundings : 🌊🌊
Leisure activities : ♈ 🍴🏛 🎣🏊🚣🚴 🎿 🎣 🏊 🎿 ⛹ cinema, multi-sports ground
Facilities : ♿ ➔ 🏛 🍴 launderette 🚿🚽

	G	Longitude : -1.89497
	P	Latitude : 46.67292
	S	

⚠ **Chadotel Le Domaine de Beaulieu**

✆ 02 51 55 59 46. www.chadotel.com/fr/camping/vendee – limited spaces for one-night stay

Address : rue du Parc (take turning off the roundabout where the D 42 joins the D 38)

Opening times : from beginning April to end Sept.

8 ha (340 pitches) flat, grassy

Tariff : 31€ ♣♦ ➔ 🗏 [ǧ] (10A) – Extra per person 6€ – Reservation fee 25€

Rental rates : (from beginning April to end Sept.) –1 ⬚ –1 ⬚. Per night from 28 to 150€ – Per week from 196 to 1,050€ – Reservation fee 25€

⬚ borne – 1 🗏 31€

In a partially shaded setting; ageing sanitary facilities.

Surroundings : 🌊🌊
Leisure activities : ♈ 🍴 🏛 🎣 nighttime, jacuzzi 🚴 🎿 ⛹ multi-sports ground, entertainment room
Facilities : ♿ ➔ 🚿🚽🍴

	G	Longitude : -1.90389
	P	Latitude : 46.67056
	S	

LE GIVRE

85540 – Michelin map **316** H9 – pop. 424 – alt. 20
▶ Paris 446 – Luçon 20 – La Mothe-Achard 33 – Niort 88

⚠ **La Grisse**

✆ 02 51 30 83 03. www.campinglagrisse.com

Address : at Le Givre (continue 2.5km south towards La Jonchère along the D 85)

Opening times : Permanent

1 ha (79 pitches) flat, grassy

Tariff : ♣ 7.70€ ➔ 🗏 8.80€ – [ǧ] (16A) 4.30€

Rental rates : Permanent – 6 ⬚ – 1 gîte. Per week from 198 to 674€

In the grounds of a farm (visits possible); one part of the site has plenty of shade.

Surroundings : 🌳🌊
Leisure activities : 🎣
Facilities : ♿ ➔ 🍴 launderette

	G	Longitude : -1.39815
	P	Latitude : 46.44484
	S	

GUÉMENÉ-PENFAO

44290 – Michelin map **316** F2 – pop. 4 951 – alt. 37
▶ Paris 408 – Bain-de-Bretagne 35 – Châteaubriant 39 – Nantes 59

⚠ **Flower L'Hermitage**

✆ 02 40 79 23 48. www.campinglhermitage.com

Address : 46 avenue du Paradis (1.2km east following signs for Châteaubriant and take the road to the right, near the municipal swimming pool)

Opening times : from beginning April to end Oct.

2.5 ha (83 pitches) relatively flat, flat, grassy

Tariff : 22.50€ ♣♦ ➔ 🗏 [ǧ] (6A) – Extra per person 5€

Rental rates : Permanent – 8 ⬚ – 3 canvas bungalows – 2 tent lodges – 1 gîte. Per night from 39 to 96€ – Per week from 273 to 672€ – Reservation fee 13€

A pleasant, wooded campsite.

Surroundings : 🌊🌊
Leisure activities : 🏛 🎣 🚴 🎿 (small swimming pool) ⛹
Facilities : ♿ ➔ 🚽 🍴 🚿🚽
Nearby : 🏊 🍴 🎿 🐎

	G	Longitude : -1.81838
	P	Latitude : 47.62572
	S	

GUÉRANDE

44350 – Michelin map **316** B4 – pop. 15 446 – alt. 54
▶ Paris 450 – La Baule 6 – Nantes 77 – St-Nazaire 20

⚠ **Trémondec**

✆ 02 40 60 00 07. www.camping-tremondec.com

Address : 48 rue du Château Careil

Opening times : from beginning May to mid Sept.

2 ha (107 pitches) terraced, relatively flat, grassy

Tariff : (2014 Price) ♣ 6€ ➔ 🗏 18€ [ǧ] (10A)

Rental rates : (2014 Price) (from beginning May to mid Sept.) – 20 ⬚ – 23 ⬚. Per night from 38 to 130€ – Per week from 264 to 880€

Surroundings : 🌊🌊
Leisure activities : ♈ 🏛 🎣 🚴 🎿
Facilities : ♿ ➔ 🍴 launderette 🚿
Nearby : 🚲

	G	Longitude : -2.40155
	P	Latitude : 47.29792
	S	

LA GUYONNIÈRE

85600 – Michelin map **316** I6 – pop. 2 674 – alt. 63
▶ Paris 395 – Nantes 47 – La Roche-sur-Yon 48 – Angers 105

⚠️ La Chausselière

La Chausselière

📞 02 51 41 98 40. www.chausseliere.fr

Address : route des Herbiers (1.2km to the south; beside the Lac de La Chausselière)

Opening times : from beginning April to end Sept.

1 ha (51 pitches) flat, grassy

Tariff : 20.50€ ♀♀ ⇔ 🔲 🔌 (16A) – Extra per person 4€

Rental rates : Permanent ♿ (1 chalet) – 11 🛖 – 9 🏕️ – 3 tent lodges. Per night from 37 to 110€ – Per week from 185 to 721€

In a green setting beside the lake.

Surroundings : 🐟 🚣 ♀♀
Leisure activities : 🏇 🏊 multi-sports ground
Facilities : ♿ ⚡ 🔥 🛒 🍴 🖼️
Nearby : 🎣 🏊

G P S Longitude : -1.2457
Latitude : 46.95735

ÎLE DE NOIRMOUTIER

85 – Michelin map **316** – alt. 8

Barbâtre 85630 – Michelin map **316** C6 – pop. 1 802 – alt. 5
▶ Paris 453 – Challans 32 – Nantes 70 – Noirmoutier-en-l'Île 11

⚠️ Original Camping Domaine Le Midi ♟️

📞 02 51 39 63 74. www.domaine-le-midi.com

Address : rue du Camping (continue 1km northwest along the D 948 and take road to the left)

Opening times : from beginning April to end Sept.

13 ha (419 pitches) undulating, flat and relatively flat, grassy, sandy

Tariff : (2014 Price) 34.90€ ♀♀ ⇔ 🔲 🔌 (16A) – Extra per person 7.90€ – Reservation fee 25€

Rental rates : (2014 Price) (from beginning April to end Sept.) – 42 🛖 – 105 🏕️ – 8 tipis – 30 canvas bungalows – 19 tent lodges. Per week from 199 to 1,349€ – Reservation fee 25€

🚐 borne – 🔌 13€

Close to the beach; a range of rental options in a well laid-out natural site.

Surroundings : 🐟 ♀ ⚓
Leisure activities : ✖️ 🎯 🏇 🎿 🏄 ⛳ 🎣 🏊 ♦ multi-sports ground, entertainment room
Facilities : ♿ ⚡ 🔥 🍴 launderette 🧺
Nearby : 🏊 🚴

G P S Longitude : -2.18447
Latitude : 46.94531

L'Épine 85740 – Michelin map **316** C6 – pop. 1 727 – alt. 2
▶ Paris 466 – Nantes 79 – La Roche-sur-Yon 81

⚠️ Original Camping La Bosse

📞 02 53 46 97 47. www.camping-de-la-bosse.com

Address : rue du Port

Opening times : from beginning April to end Sept.

10 ha (350 pitches)

Tariff : (2014 Price) 22.70€ ♀♀ ⇔ 🔲 🔌 (6A) – Extra per person 5.70€ Reservation fee 21€

Rental rates : (2014 Price) (from beginning April to end Sept.) – 8 tipis – 3 canvas bungalows. Per week from 155 to 449€ – Reservation fee 21€

Close to the beach in a natural, undulating setting.

Surroundings : ⇐ Port de Morin marina ♀ ⚓
Leisure activities : 🏇
Facilities : 🛒 launderette

G P S Longitude : -2.2833
Latitude : 46.98523

La Guérinière 85680 – Michelin map **316** C6 – pop. 1 488 – alt. 5
▶ Paris 460 – Challans 39 – Nantes 77 – Noirmoutier-en-l'Île 5

⚠️ Original Camping Domaine Les Moulins ♟️

📞 02 51 39 51 38. www.domaine-les-moulins.com

Address : rue des Moulins (take the eastern exit along the D948 and turn right at the roundabout)

Opening times : from beginning April to end Sept.

5.5 ha (175 pitches) dunes

Tariff : (2014 Price) 50€ ♀♀ ⇔ 🔲 🔌 (16A) – Extra per person 9€ – Reservation fee 30€

Rental rates : (2014 Price) (from beginning April to end Sept.) – 18 🛖 – 11 tipis – 32 canvas bungalows – 72 tent lodges. Per week from 250 to 3,499€ – Reservation fee 30€

🚐 borne

Close to the beach, with a viariety of original rental options – vehicles not permitted.

Surroundings : 🐟 🚣 ♀♀ ⚓
Leisure activities : ♀ ✖️ 🎰 ☕ daytime 🏇 💆 hammam, jacuzzi 🏇 🎯 🏊 multi-sports ground, entertainment room
Facilities : ♿ ⚡ ⊕ 🎰 🔥 🍴 launderette 🧺
Nearby : 🏊

G P S Longitude : -2.217
Latitude : 46.96675

⚠️ Le Caravan'île ♟️

📞 02 51 39 50 29. www.caravanile.com

Address : 1 rue de la Tresson (take the eastern exit along the D 948 and take a right turn before the roundabout)

Opening times : from mid March to mid Nov.

8.5 ha (385 pitches) relatively flat, flat, grassy, sandy

Tariff : (2014 Price) 33€ ♀♀ ⇔ 🔲 🔌 (8A) – Extra per person 7.50€ Reservation fee 20€

Rental rates : (2014 Price) (from mid March to mid Nov.) – 95 🛖. Per night from 57 to 124€ – Per week from 252 to 973€ Reservation fee 20€

🚐 borne 9€ – 49 🔲 – 🔌 13€

Close to the beach (direct access via the steps through the dunes).

Surroundings : 🐟 ⚓
Leisure activities : ♀ ✖️ 🎰 ☕ 🏇 💆 jacuzzi 🏇 ⛳ 🎣 🏊 multi-sports ground
Facilities : ♿ ⚡ 🔥 🍴 launderette 🏊 🧺

G P S Longitude : -2.21674
Latitude : 46.96569

These symbols are used for a campsite that is exceptional in its category:

⚠️ᴬ *Particularly pleasant setting, quality and range of services available*

🐟🐟 *Tranquil, isolated site – quiet site, particularly at night*

⇐⇐ *Exceptional view – interesting or panoramic view*

Noirmoutier-en-l'île 85330 – Michelin map **316** C5 – pop. 4 661 alt. 8

▶ Paris 468 – Nantes 80 – St-Nazaire 82 – Vannes 160

⚠ Indigo Noirmoutier

Campingindigo ©R.Etienne

✆ 02 51 39 06 24. www.camping-indigo.com

Address : 23 allée des Sableaux – Bois de la Chaize

Opening times : from beginning April to beginning Oct.

12 ha (530 pitches)

Tariff : (2014 Price) 29.20€ ♣♣ ⇔ ▣ ⬧ (10A) – Extra per person 5.60€ – Reservation fee 22€

Rental rates : (2014 Price) (from beginning April to beginning Oct.) – 100 tent lodges. Per night from 52 to 115€ – Per week from 255 to 805€ – Reservation fee 22€

🚐 borne 7€ – 40 ▣ 23.90€

In an attractive location, beside the La Plage des Sableaux (beach).

Surroundings : 🏞 ⬧ ♀ ▲
Leisure activities : ♟ ✗ 🏠 🚣 🚲
Facilities : ㋕ �ー 🏕 🍴 launderette 🧺
Nearby : 🏇

G P S Longitude : -2.2205
Latitude : 46.9966

⚠ Municipal le Clair Matin

✆ 02 51 39 05 56. www.noirmoutier-campings.fr

Address : Les Sableaux (at Les Bois de la Chaize) near the Reserve Naturelle de Mullembourg

Opening times : from end March to beginning Nov.

6.5 ha (276 pitches)

Tariff : (2014 Price) 24€ ♣♣ ⇔ ▣ ⬧ (10A) – Extra per person 5€ – Reservation fee 9€

A site with free access to many nearby natural areas.

Surroundings : 🏞 ♀♀
Leisure activities : 🚣 🚲
Facilities : ㋕ ー (summer) 🍴 📷
Nearby : ♟ ✗ 🏇

G P S Longitude : -2.2205
Latitude : 46.99567

L'ILE-D'OLONNE

85340 – Michelin map **316** F8 – pop. 2 668 – alt. 5

▶ Paris 455 – Nantes 100 – La Roche-sur-Yon 35 – Challans 37

⚠ Île aux Oiseaux ♣♣

✆ 02 51 90 89 96. www.ile-aux-oiseaux.fr – limited spaces for one-night stay

Address : rue du Pré Neuf (800m northeast along the D 87)

Opening times : from beginning April to end Oct.

5 ha (215 pitches) flat, grassy

Tariff : (2014 Price) 29€ ♣♣ ⇔ ▣ ⬧ (10A) – Extra per person 4.80€ – Reservation fee 17€

The Michelin classification (⚠⚠⚠ … ⚠) is totally independent of the official star classification system awarded by the local prefecture or other official organisation.

Rental rates : (2014 Price) (from beginning April to end Oct.) – 29 🚐. Per night from 43 to 68€ – Per week from 227 to 698€ – Reservation fee 17€

A pleasant setting, with few pitches for tents or caravans.

Surroundings : 🏞 🛖 ♀
Leisure activities : 🏠 🏃 🚣 🏊 🛝 multi-sports ground
Facilities : ㋕ ー (July–Aug.) 🏕 🧺 🍴 launderette

G P S Longitude : -1.77813
Latitude : 46.56624

There are several different types of sani-station ('borne' in French) – sanitation points providing fresh water and disposal points for grey water. See page 12 for further details.

JARD-SUR-MER

85520 – Michelin map **316** G9 – pop. 2 497 – alt. 14

▶ Paris 453 – Challans 62 – Luçon 36 – La Roche-sur-Yon 35

⚠⚠⚠ Chadotel L'Océano d'Or ♣♣

✆ 02 51 33 65 08. www.chadotel.com

Address : 58 rue Georges Clemenceau (to the northeast of Jard sur Mer, along the D 21)

Opening times : from beginning April to end Sept.

8 ha (450 pitches) flat, grassy

Tariff : 32€ ♣♣ ⇔ ▣ ⬧ (10A) – Extra per person 6€ – Reservation fee 25€

Rental rates : (from beginning April to end Sept.) ㋕ (1 chalet) – 1 🚐 – 1 🏠. Per night from 29 to 165€ – Per week from 203 to 1,155€ – Reservation fee 25€

🚐 borne – 1 ▣ 32€

A pretty site with classic and luxury rental accommodation in mobile homes and gîtes.

Surroundings : 🛖 ♀♀
Leisure activities : ♟ 🏠 🎮 🏃 🎣 🚣 🚲 🎿 🛝 🏊 multi-sports ground, entertainment room
Facilities : ㋕ ー 🚿 🏕 🧺 🍴 launderette 🛝 🧺

G P S Longitude : -1.57195
Latitude : 46.42032

⚠⚠⚠ Club Airotel Le Curty's ♣♣

(rental of mobile homes and chalets only)

✆ 02 51 33 06 55. www.campinglecurtys.com

Address : rue de la Perpoise (north of Jard sur Mer)

Opening times : from mid April to mid Sept.

8 ha (360 pitches) flat, grassy

Rental rates : (2014 Price) – 191 🚐 – 20 🏠. Per night from 40 to 125€ – Per week from 260 to 1,090€ – Reservation fee 25€

A mobile home park for both rentals and owner-occupiers.

Surroundings : 🛖 ♀
Leisure activities : ♟ ✗ 🏠 🎮 🏃 🚣 🚲 🎿 🛝 🏊 multi-sports ground, entertainment room
Facilities : ㋕ ー 🏕 🍴 launderette 🧺
Nearby : 🛒 🏇

G P S Longitude : -1.57825
Latitude : 46.42032

⚠ Chadotel La Pomme de Pin

☎ 02 51 33 05 05. www.chadotel.com – limited spaces for one-night stay

Address : rue Vincent Auriol (southeast, 150m from the beach at Boisvinet)

Opening times : from beginning April to mid Sept.

2 ha (150 pitches)

Tariff : 37€ ⚹⚹ ⇔ 🔲 🔌 (10A) – Extra per person 6€ – Reservation fee 25€

Rental rates : (from beginning April to mid Sept.) – 80 🚐 – 11 🏠. Per night from 39 to 135€ – Per week from 273 to 945€ Reservation fee 25€

Near the beach, numerous mobile homes beside a small (partially covered) water park.

Surroundings : 🗂 ♀		
Leisure activities : 🍴✕ 🏠 ⛵ 🚲🏊 🎿⛷	**G P S**	Longitude : -1.57264
Facilities : ♿ ⚏ 🏕🍴 launderette 🏊 🚰		Latitude : 46.41084

⚠ La Mouette Cendrée

☎ 02 51 33 59 04. www.mouettecendree.com

Address : chemin du Faux Prieur, Les Malecots (take the northeastern exit along the D 19, follow the signs for St-Hilaire-la-Forêt)

Opening times : Permanent

1.8 ha (101 pitches) flat, grassy

Tariff : 30€ ⚹⚹ ⇔ 🔲 🔌 (6A) – Extra per person 5€ – Reservation fee 17.50€

Rental rates : Permanent ♿ (1 mobile home) – 23 🚐 – 5 canvas bungalows. Per night from 40 to 115€ – Per week from 240 to 780€ – Reservation fee 17.50€

In a leafy, green setting with rental mobile homes that are mostly modern.

Surroundings : 🗂 ♀♀		
Leisure activities : ⛷ 🎿⛷	**G P S**	Longitude : -1.56702
Facilities : ♿ ⚏ 🍴 🏠		Latitude : 46.42767

85220 – Michelin map **316** F8 – pop. 1 185 – alt. 37
▶ Paris 452 – Challans 25 – Nantes 83 – La Roche-sur-Yon 32

⚠ L'Orée de l'Océan 👥

☎ 02 51 22 96 36. www.camping-oreedelocean.com

Address : rue du Capitaine de Mazenod (take the western exit, follow the signs for Brétignolles-sur-Mer)

Opening times : from beginning April to end Oct.

2.8 ha (240 pitches)

Tariff : (2014 Price) 26€ ⚹⚹ ⇔ 🔲 🔌 (10A) – Extra per person 6€ – Reservation fee 25€

Rental rates : (2014 Price) (from beginning April to end Oct.) ♿ (1 mobile home) – 23 canvas bungalows. Per week from 260 to 745€ – Reservation fee 25€

There's a pretty, colourful play and paddling pool area.

Surroundings : 🏊 🗂 ♀♀		
Leisure activities : 🍴✕ 🏠 🏊 🎿⛷ 🎣 ⛷ 🎿⛷ 🎿multi-sports ground, entertainment room	**G P S**	Longitude : -1.80635
Facilities : ♿ ⚏ 🏕🍴 launderette		Latitude : 46.64087
Nearby : ✂		

72390 – Michelin map **310** M6 – pop. 838 – alt. 122
▶ Paris 173 – Bonnétable 26 – Bouloire 14 – La Ferté-Bernard 19

⚠ Le Val de Braye

☎ 02 43 71 96 44. www.basedeloisirs-lavare.fr

Address : route de Vibraye (take the eastern exit along the D 302, at the leisure and activity park)

Opening times : Permanent

0.3 ha (20 pitches) flat, grassy

Tariff : ⚹ 2€ ⇔ 1€ – 🔌 (5A) 2€

Rental rates : Permanent – 11 🏠. Per night from 45 to 76€ – Per week from 250 to 470€

In an attractive location near a small lake.

Surroundings : ≪ 🗂 ♀		
Leisure activities : 🏠 ⛷ ✏	**G P S**	Longitude : 0.64522
Facilities : ⚏ 🏕 ⛷		Latitude : 48.05326
Nearby : ✂ 🚣 ♪ mountain biking		

*For more information on visiting particular towns or regions, consult the relevant regional **MICHELIN Green Guide**. We also recommend you use the appropriate Michelin regional map to locate your selected campsite, to calculate distances and to work out the best route.*

49220 – Michelin map **317** E3 – pop. 3 638 – alt. 45
▶ Paris 295 – Angers 27 – Candé 27 – Château-Gontier 22

⚠ Municipal les Frênes

☎ 06 46 02 58 37. www.camping-les-frenes.com

Address : route de Chateau Gontier (take the northeastern exit along the N 162, beside the Oudon river)

Opening times : from beginning April to end Oct.

2 ha (94 pitches) flat, grassy

Tariff : 12€ ⚹⚹ ⇔ 🔲 🔌 (10A) – Extra per person 3€ – Reservation fee 10€

Rental rates : (from beginning April to end Oct.) – 2 🚐 – 4 canvas bungalows – 3 tent lodges. Per night from 25 to 45€ – Per week from 100 to 390€ – Reservation fee 15€
🚐 borne 5€ – 🚐 8.50€

Set among majestic ash trees, beside the Oudon river.

Surroundings : ♀		
Leisure activities : 🏠 ⛷	**G P S**	Longitude : -0.71154
Facilities : ♿ ⚏ 🍴		Latitude : 47.63094
Nearby : 🏇 racecourse		

These symbols are used for a campsite that is exceptional in its category:

⚠⚠...⚠ *Particularly pleasant setting, quality and range of services available*

🦢🦢 *Tranquil, isolated site – quiet site, particularly at night*

≪≪ *Exceptional view – interesting or panoramic view*

LONGEVILLE-SUR-MER

85560 – Michelin map **316** H9 – pop. 2 356 – alt. 10
▶ Paris 448 – Challans 74 – Luçon 29 – La Roche-sur-Yon 31

🏕 MS Vacances Les Brunelles 👥👤

🕿 02 53 81 70 00. www.ms-vacances.com – limited spaces for one-night stay

Address : rue de La Parée (at Le Bouil, 1km to the south)

Opening times : from beginning April to mid Sept.

13 ha (600 pitches) relatively flat, flat, grassy

Tariff : 47 € ✶✶ 🚐 🔲 🔌 (10A) – Extra per person 12.40 € – Reservation fee 25 €

Rental rates : (from beginning April to mid Sept.) ♿ (1 mobile home) – 446 🚐 – 10 🏠. Per week from 180 to 1,510 € – Reservation fee 25 €

🚐 borne – 🔋30 €

Surroundings : 🏊 🏞 🎣
Leisure activities : 🍴 🍽 🏛 🎲 🎯 🏋 ⛸
hammam, jacuzzi 🚴 ⛳ 🏓 🎮 🎱
multi-sports ground
Facilities : ♿ 🔌 🏧 🍴 🚿 🚽 ⛲
launderette 🍴 🚿
Nearby : 🏇

Longitude : -1.52191
Latitude : 46.41326

🏕 Camp'Atlantique Le Petit Rocher 👥👤

🕿 02 51 20 41 94. www.camp-atlantique.com

Address : 1250 avenue du Dct Mathevet

Opening times : from beginning April to mid Sept.

5 ha (211 pitches) undulating, terraced, relatively flat, flat, grassy

Tariff : (2014 Price) 32 € ✶✶ 🚐 🔲 🔌 (10A) – Extra per person 9 € – Reservation fee 25 €

Rental rates : 2014 Price) (from beginning April to mid Sept.) ♿ (1 mobile home) – 5 caravans – 99 🚐 – 9 canvas bungalows – 5 tent lodges. Per week from 239 to 1,049 € – Reservation fee 25 €

An undulating site with lots of shade, 250m from the beach via a pedestrian path. 🎣 🏞

Surroundings : 🏞 🎣
Leisure activities : 🍴 🍽 🎲 🎯 ⛸ hammam,
jacuzzi 🚴 🎱 🏊 multi-sports ground
Facilities : ♿ 🔌 🚿 ⛲ launderette
Nearby : 🚿 🍴 🚿

Longitude : -1.50727
Latitude : 46.40344

LOUÉ

72540 – Michelin map **310** I7 – pop. 2 129 – alt. 112
▶ Paris 230 – Laval 59 – Le Mans 30

🏕 Village Loisirs

🕿 02 43 88 65 65. www.villageloisirs.com

Address : place Hector Vincent (head towards the northeastern exit along the D 21, rte du Mans; by the swimming pool)

Opening times : from beginning April to end Sept.

1 ha (16 pitches) flat, grassy

Tariff : (2014 Price) ✶ 8.50 € 🚐 – 🔌 (10A) 4.50 €

Rental rates : (2014 Price) Permanent – 10 🏠. Per night from 60 to 90 € – Per week from 280 to 450 €

In a pleasant location beside the Vègre river.

Leisure activities : 🍴 🍽 🏛 🚴 🏊
Facilities : ♿ 🔌 (June–Sept) 🏧 🚿
Nearby : 🏊 walking trails

Longitude : -0.14711
Latitude : 47.99734

LUCHÉ-PRINGÉ

72800 – Michelin map **310** J8 – pop. 1 658 – alt. 34
▶ Paris 242 – Château-du-Loir 31 – Écommoy 24 – La Flèche 14

🏕 Municipal la Chabotière

🕿 02 43 45 10 00. www.lachabotiere.com

Address : place des Tilleuls (to the west of the town)

3 ha (75 pitches)

Rentals : 10 🏠 – 10 canvas bungalows.

In a leisure and activity park, beside the Loir river.

Surroundings : 🏊 🚐 🎣
Leisure activities : 🍴 🚴 🏊
Facilities : ♿ 🔌 🅿 🚿 ⛲ launderette
Nearby : 🍴 🏊 🏊 🏊 🏇 boats to hire

Longitude : 0.07364
Latitude : 47.70252

The pitches of many campsites are marked out with low hedges of attractive bushes and shrubs.

LE LUDE

72800 – Michelin map **310** J9 – pop. 4 049 – alt. 48
▶ Paris 244 – Angers 63 – Chinon 63 – La Flèche 20

🏕 Municipal au Bord du Loir

🕿 02 43 94 67 70. www.campingmunicipallelude.fr

Address : route du Mans (0.8km northwest along the D 307, follow the signs for Le Mans)

Opening times : from mid April to beginning Oct.

2.5 ha (111 pitches) flat, grassy

Tariff : (2014 Price) 12 € ✶✶ 🚐 🔲 🔌 (10A) – Extra per person 3.80 €

Rental rates : (2014 Price) (from mid April to beginning Oct.) 🚐 – 4 🚐 – 5 🏠 – 4 canvas bungalows. Per night from 25 to 88 € – Per week from 130 to 466 €

🚐 borne 2 €

In a rural setting beside the Loir river.

Surroundings : 🎣
Leisure activities : 🍴 🚴 🚴 🏊
Facilities : ♿ 🔌 🚿 ⛲ 🚽 🖼
Nearby : 🍴 🍽 🎮 🏊 🏊 pedalos

Longitude : 0.16247
Latitude : 47.65119

MACHÉ

85190 – Michelin map **316** F7 – pop. 1 337 – alt. 42
▶ Paris 443 – Challans 22 – Nantes 59 – La Roche-sur-Yon 26

🏕 Le Val de Vie

🕿 02 51 60 21 02. www.campingvaldevie.fr

Address : 5 rue du Stade (take the exit for Apremont and take the road to the left; 400m from the lake)

Opening times : from beginning April to end Sept.

2.5 ha (93 pitches)

Tariff : (2014 Price) 20.90 € ✶✶ 🚐 🔲 🔌 (16A) – Extra per person 3.50 €

Rental rates : (2014 Price) Permanent – 3 🚐 – 2 🏠. Per night from 40 to 60 € – Per week from 150 to 680 €

🚐 borne 2.50 € – 🔋8.50 €

Surroundings : 🏊 🚐
Leisure activities : 🚴 🏊
Facilities : ♿ 🔌 🚿 🚽 🖼
Nearby : 🍽

Longitude : -1.68595
Latitude : 46.75305

MACHECOUL

44270 – Michelin map **316** F6 – pop. 5 872 – alt. 5
▶ Paris 420 – Beauvoir-sur-Mer 23 – Nantes 39 – La Roche-sur-Yon 56

⚠ La Rabine

✆ 02 40 02 30 48. www.camping-la-rabine.com

Address : allée de la Rabine (take the southern exit along the D 95, follow the signs for Challans; beside the Falleron river)

Opening times : from beginning April to end Sept.

2.8 ha (131 pitches) flat, grassy

Tariff : (2014 Price) 14.60€ ✲✲ ⬅ 🔲 (13A) – Extra per person 4.10€

Rental rates : (2014 Price) (from beginning April to end Sept.) – 1 caravan – 3 🏠 – 3 canvas bungalows. Per week from 319 to 504€ – Reservation fee 31€

🚐 borne 3.50€ – 4 🔲 11.20€
Very near the town centre, in the bend of a small river.

Surroundings : ♀		
Leisure activities : 🏌🏇 🎣	**G**	Longitude : -1.81555
Facilities : 🚿 ⚬🔌 ⚏ launderette	**P**	Latitude : 46.9887
Nearby : 🍴 🔲	**S**	

*We value your opinion and welcome your feedback.
Do email us at campingfrance@tp.michelin.com*

MAILLEZAIS

85420 – Michelin map **316** L9 – pop. 962 – alt. 6
▶ Paris 436 – Fontenay-le-Comte 15 – Niort 27 – La Rochelle 49

⚠ Municipal de l'Autize

✆ 06 43 19 19 49 0. www.maillezais.fr

Address : rue du Champ de foire (take the southern exit, follow the signs for Courçon)

Opening times : from beginning April to end Sept.

1 ha (40 pitches) flat, grassy

Tariff : (2014 Price) 14.60€ ✲✲ ⬅ 🔲 (13A) – Extra per person 2.60€

🚐 borne 2€
In a green setting at the exit from the town.

Surroundings : ▱ ♀♀		
Leisure activities : 🏌	**G**	Longitude : -0.73914
Facilities : 🚿 ⚬🔌 (July–Aug.) ⚏ ⚒ 🔲	**P**	Latitude : 46.37133
Nearby : 🏇 🍴	**S**	

MALICORNE-SUR-SARTHE

72270 – Michelin map **310** I8 – pop. 1 962 – alt. 39
▶ Paris 236 – Château-Gontier 52 – La Flèche 16 – Le Mans 32

⚠ Municipal Port Ste Marie

✆ 02 43 94 80 14. www.ville-malicorne.fr

Address : to the west of the town along the D 41

Opening times : from beginning April to end Sept.

1 ha (80 pitches) flat, grassy

Tariff : (2014 Price) 15.20€ ✲✲ ⬅ 🔲 (13A) – Extra per person 2.40€

Rental rates : (2014 Price) (from beginning April to end Sept.) – 4 🏠 – 4 canvas bungalows. Per night from 49 to 127€ – Per week from 149 to 396€

🚐 borne 4€

A pleasant site and setting near the Sarthe river.

Surroundings : ♀		
Leisure activities : 🏠 🏌🏇	**G**	Longitude : -0.0893
Facilities : 🚿 ⚬🔌 (July–Aug.) ⚏ ⚒ launderette	**P**	Latitude : 47.81763
Nearby : 🚴 🍴 🔲 🔲 🏇 pedalos	**S**	

MAMERS

72600 – Michelin map **310** L4 – pop. 5 545 – alt. 128
▶ Paris 185 – Alençon 25 – Le Mans 51 – Mortagne-au-Perche 25

⚠⚠ Municipal du Saosnois

✆ 02 43 97 68 30. www.mairie-mamers.fr

Address : continue 1km north following signs for Mortagne-au-Perche and take D 113 to the left, following signs for Contilly, near two lakes

Opening times : from beginning March to end Oct.

1.5 ha (50 pitches) terraced, relatively flat, flat, grassy

Tariff : (2014 Price) 15€ ✲✲ ⬅ 🔲 (10A) – Extra per person 3€

Rental rates : (2014 Price) (from beginning March to end Oct.) – 3 🏠 – 5 canvas bungalows. Per night from 25 to 55€ – Per week from 150 to 360€

🚐 borne 7€ – 8 🔲 7€

Surroundings : ▱ ♀		
Leisure activities : 🍹 🏊 (beach)	**G**	Longitude : 0.37303
Facilities : ⚬🔌 🔲 ⚏ ⚒ 🔲	**P**	Latitude : 48.35809
Nearby : 🏇 🍴 🎣 🔲 🏇 fitness trail	**S**	

Michelin classification:

⚠⚠⚠⚠ *Extremely comfortable, equipped to a very high standard*
⚠⚠⚠ *Very comfortable, equipped to a high standard*
⚠⚠⚠ *Comfortable and well equipped*
⚠⚠ *Reasonably comfortable*
⚠ *Satisfactory*

MANSIGNÉ

72510 – Michelin map **310** J8 – pop. 1 579 – alt. 80
▶ Paris 235 – Château-du-Loir 28 – La Flèche 21 – Le Lude 17

⚠⚠ La Plage - Base de Loisirs

✆ 02 43 46 14 17. www.basedeloisirsmansigne.fr

Address : rue du Plessis (take the northern exit along the D 31, follow the signs for La Suze-sur-Sarthe, 100m from a small lake)

Opening times : from beginning April to end Oct.

3 ha (175 pitches) flat, grassy

Tariff : (2014 Price) 15.80€ ✲✲ ⬅ 🔲 (10A) – Extra per person 3€ Reservation fee 19.50€

Rental rates : (2014 Price) Permanent – 8 🏠 – 20 🏠 – 8 canvas bungalows – 1 gîte. Per night from 40 to 90€ – Per week from 230 to 480€ – Reservation fee 19.50€

🚐 borne – 15 🔲 – 🚐 10.50€

Surroundings : ♀		
Leisure activities : 🍹 🏠 🚴 🍴 🔲 🏊	**G**	Longitude : 0.13284
Facilities : 🚿 ⚬🔌 (14 Jul–16 Aug) ⚒ launderette	**P**	Latitude : 47.75078
Nearby : 🏇 🔲 🏊 (beach) 🏇 pedalos	**S**	

MARÇON

72340 – Michelin map **310** M8 – pop. 1 028 – alt. 59
▶ Paris 245 – Château-du-Loir 10 – Le Grand-Lucé 51 – Le Mans 52

▲▲▲ Lac des Varennes

📞 02 43 44 13 72. www.lacdesvarennes.com

Address : route de Port Gauthier (located 1km west along the D 61, near the leisure park)

Opening times : from mid April to end Sept.

5.5 ha (250 pitches) flat, grassy

Tariff : 20€ ✶✶ ⇔ 🅴 (4) (10A) – Extra per person 5€

Rental rates : (from mid April to end Sept.) – 20 🚐 – 1 🏠 – 8 canvas bungalows. Per night from 35 to 110€ – Per week from 195 to 770€ – Reservation fee 10€

🚻 borne 5€ – 🚐 11€

In a pleasant setting beside a lake equipped for various leisure activities.

Surroundings : ♀
Leisure activities : 🍷 ✕ 🏕 🏖 ⛵ (beach) 🎣
Facilities : 🚿 ⚬━ 🆒 🛁 🚽 🏮 🏊 ⚓
Nearby : ✂ 🏹 🐴 pedalos

Longitude : 0.4993
Latitude : 47.7125

MAYENNE

53100 – Michelin map **310** F5 – pop. 13 350 – alt. 124
▶ Paris 283 – Alençon 61 – Flers 56 – Fougères 47

▲▲ Du Gué St-Léonard

📞 02 43 04 57 14. http://www.paysdemayenne-tourisme.fr

Address : rue du Gué St-Léonard (north of the town, via av. de Loré and turning to the right)

1.8 ha (70 pitches) flat, grassy
Rental rates : 5 🚐.

In a pleasant setting beside the Mayenne river.

Surroundings : ♀♀
Leisure activities : ✕ 🏕 🏊 🎣
Facilities : 🚿 ⚬━ 🏮 🚽 launderette
Nearby : 🛒 ✂

Longitude : -0.61387
Latitude : 48.3142

LE MAZEAU

85420 – Michelin map **316** L9 – pop. 427 – alt. 8
▶ Paris 435 – Fontenay-le-Comte 22 – Niort 21 – La Rochelle 53

▲ Municipal le Relais du Pêcheur

📞 02 51 52 93 23. www.mairielemazeau.fr

Address : route de la Sèvre (700m south of the town, near canals)

Opening times : from beginning April to end Sept.

1 ha (54 pitches) flat, grassy

Tariff : (2014 Price) ✶ 3.60€ ⇔ 🅴 4.70€ – (4) (10A) 10€

Rental rates : (2014 Price) (from beginning May to end Sept.) 🎣 – 3 canvas bungalows. Per night from 32 to 52€ – Per week from 131 to 292€

A pleasant site and setting in the heart of the Venise Verte ('Green Venice' marshland).

Surroundings : 🌳 🗗 ♀♀
Leisure activities : 🏕 🏖
Facilities : 🚿 (July–Aug.) 🏮 🏮
Nearby : 🎣

Longitude : -0.67535
Latitude : 46.33052

MÉNIL

53200 – Michelin map **310** E8 – pop. 965 – alt. 32
▶ Paris 297 – Angers 45 – Château-Gontier 7 – Châteauneuf-sur-Sarthe 21

▲ Municipal du Bac

📞 02 43 70 24 54. www.menil53.fr

Address : rue du Port (east of the village)

Opening times : from mid April to mid Sept.

0.5 ha (39 pitches) flat, grassy

Tariff : (2014 Price) 11.50€ ✶✶ ⇔ 🅴 (4) (10A) – Extra per person 4€

Rental rates : (2014 Price) Permanent – 5 🏠. Per week from 163 to 350€ – Reservation fee 13€

🚻 borne 2€

A pleasant site and setting near the Mayenne river.

Surroundings : 🌳 🗗 ♀
Leisure activities : ✕ 🏖 🚲 🎣
Facilities : 🚿 ⚬━ 🏮

Longitude : -0.67319
Latitude : 47.77494

To visit a town or region, use the MICHELIN Green Guides.

MERVENT

85200 – Michelin map **316** L8 – pop. 1 077 – alt. 85
▶ Paris 426 – Bressuire 52 – Fontenay-le-Comte 12 – Parthenay 50

▲▲ La Joletière

📞 02 51 00 26 87. www.campinglajoletiere.fr

Address : 700m west along the D 99

Opening times : from mid March to mid Nov.

1.3 ha (73 pitches)

Tariff : (2014 Price) 18€ ✶✶ ⇔ 🅴 (4) (16A) – Extra per person 4€ – Reservation fee 2€

Rental rates : (2014 Price) (from mid March to mid Nov.) – 1 caravan – 19 🚐 – 4 🏠 – 3 canvas bungalows. Per night from 45 to 93€ – Per week from 210 to 655€ – Reservation fee 2€

Plenty of green spaces on a gentle slope, with a range of rental options.

Surroundings : 🌳 🗗 ♀♀
Leisure activities : ✕ 🏕 🏖 🚲 🎮 🏊
Facilities : 🚿 ⚬━ 🏮 🚽 🏮
Nearby : 🍷

Longitude : -0.7691
Latitude : 46.5214

MESLAY-DU-MAINE

53170 – Michelin map **310** F7 – pop. 2 726 – alt. 90
▶ Paris 268 – Angers 60 – Château-Gontier 21 – Châteauneuf-sur-Sarthe 34

▲▲ La Chesnaie

📞 02 43 98 48 08. www.paysmeslaygrez.fr

Address : Plan d'eau de la Chesnaie (artificial lake Le Buru, 2.5km northeast along the D 152, follow the signs for St-Denis-du-Maine)

Opening times : from beginning May to end Sept.

7 ha/0.8 (60 pitches) flat, grassy

Tariff : (2014 Price) 9.70€ ✶✶ ⇔ 🅴 (4) (10A) – Extra per person 3.40€

Rental rates : (2014 Price) Permanent – 8 🚐 – 8 🏠. Per night from 75 to 120€ – Per week from 165 to 430€ – Reservation fee 15€

🚻 borne

The site is beside a small, beautiful lake.

Surroundings : ⛰ ← ⌂ ◊
Leisure activities : 🚲
Facilities : ⚐ ⊶ (July–Aug.) ⚑ ▦
At the leisure/activities centre : ⚑ ✕ ▱
⚓ ⛷ ≋ ◊ fitness trail

G P S Longitude : -0.53002
Latitude : 47.96415

MESQUER

44420 – Michelin map **316** B3 – pop. 1 710 – alt. 6
▶ Paris 460 – La Baule 16 – Muzillac 32 – Pontchâteau 35

⛰ Soir d'Été ♣♦

📞 02 40 42 57 26. www.camping-soirdete.com

Address : 401 rue de Bel Air (head 2km northwest along the D 352 and take turning to the left)

Opening times : from beginning April to end Sept.

1.5 ha (92 pitches)

Tariff : 33€ ✚✚ ⇔ ▣ ⚡ (6A) – Extra per person 6€

Rental rates : (from beginning April to end Sept.) – 20 ▥ – 4 ⌂. Per night from 60 to 80€ – Per week from 270 to 780€
▥ borne

In a shaded setting beside a salt marsh.

Surroundings : ⛰ ⌂ ◊◊
Leisure activities : ⚑ ✕ ▱ 🏃 ⚓ 🚲 ▱ (open air in season), multi-sports ground
Facilities : ⚐ ⊶ ⛷ ⚑ launderette ⌁
Nearby : ✕ ⛷

G P S Longitude : -2.47575
Latitude : 47.4064

⛰ Le Praderoi

📞 02 40 42 66 72. http://www.camping-praderoi.com

Address : at Quimiac, 14 allée des Barges (2.5km to the northwest, 100m from the beach)

Opening times : from beginning April to end Sept.

0.4 ha (32 pitches)

Tariff : 26.50€ ✚✚ ⇔ ▣ ⚡ (10A) – Extra per person 4.50€

Rental rates : (from beginning April to mid Sept.) ✕ – 2 caravans – 5 ▥. Per week from 220 to 620€

A small campsite, very peaceful and family-orientated.

Surroundings : ⛰ ◊
Leisure activities : ⚓
Facilities : ⚐ ⊶ ⇥ cc ⚑ launderette

G P S Longitude : -2.48895
Latitude : 47.40572

MÉZIÈRES-SOUS-LAVARDIN

72240 – Michelin map **310** J6 – pop. 634 – alt. 75
▶ Paris 221 – Alençon 38 – La Ferté-Bernard 69 – Le Mans 25

⛰ Parc des Braudières

📞 02 43 20 81 48. www.campinglesbraudieres.com – limited spaces for one-night stay

Address : 4.5km east along the back road to St-Jean

Opening times : Permanent

1.7 ha (52 pitches)

Tariff : 20€ ✚✚ ⇔ ▣ ⚡ (5A) – Extra per person 4.50€

Rental rates : Permanent – 6 ▥. Per night from 60 to 80€ – Per week from 400 to 500€
▥ 3 ▣ 16€

Situated beside a small fishing lake.

Surroundings : ⛰ ⌂ ◊
Leisure activities : jacuzzi ⚓ ⛷ ⤳
Facilities : ⚐ ⊶ ⚑

G P S Longitude : 0.06328
Latitude : 48.15758

MONTREUIL-BELLAY

49260 – Michelin map **317** I6 – pop. 4 041 – alt. 50
▶ Paris 335 – Angers 54 – Châtellerault 70 – Chinon 39

⛰ Les Nobis ♣♦

📞 02 41 52 33 66. www.campinglesnobis.com

Address : rue Georges Girouy (take the northwestern exit, follow the signs for Angers and take the road to the left before the bridge)

Opening times : from beginning April to end Sept.

4 ha (165 pitches) terraced, flat, grassy

Tariff : 28€ ✚✚ ⇔ ▣ ⚡ (16A) – Extra per person 4€ – Reservation fee 10€

Rental rates : (from mid March to mid Nov.) – 14 ▥ – 2 canvas bungalows. Per night from 58 to 86€ – Per week from 209 to 602€ Reservation fee 10€
▥ borne

A pleasant location on the banks of the Thouet river and beside a château.

Surroundings : ⌂ ◊◊
Leisure activities : ⚑ ✕ ▱ ⊙ daytime 🏃 ⚓ 🚲 ▱ ⤳
Facilities : ⚐ ⊶ ⛷ ⚑ launderette
Nearby : pedalos

G P S Longitude : -0.15897
Latitude : 47.13204

Key to rentals symbols :

12 ▥	*Number of mobile homes*	
20 ⌂	*Number of chalets*	
6 ⊨	*Number of rooms to rent*	
Per night 30–50€	*Minimum/maximum rate per night*	
Per week 300–1,000€	*Minimum/maximum rate per week*	

MONTSOREAU

49730 – Michelin map **317** J5 – pop. 485 – alt. 77
▶ Paris 292 – Angers 75 – Châtellerault 65 – Chinon 18

⛰ Kawan Village L'Isle Verte

📞 02 41 51 76 60. www.campingisleverte.com

Address : avenue de la Loire (take the northwestern exit along the D 947, follow the signs for Saumur; beside the Loire river)

Opening times : from beginning April to mid Oct.

2.5 ha (105 pitches) flat, grassy

Tariff : 28€ ✚✚ ⇔ ▣ ⚡ (16A) – Extra per person 6€ – Reservation fee 10€

Rental rates : Permanent – 18 ▥ – 7 tent lodges. Per night from 45 to 120€ – Per week from 250 to 840€ – Reservation fee 15€
▥ borne

Surroundings : ◊◊
Leisure activities : ✕ ▱ ⚓ ✕ ⤳
Facilities : ⚐ ⊶ cc ⛷ ⚑ ▣ ⌁

G P S Longitude : 0.05165
Latitude : 47.21861

LA MOTHE-ACHARD

85150 – Michelin map **316** G8 – pop. 2 524 – alt. 20
▶ Paris 439 – Aizenay 15 – Challans 40 – La Roche-sur-Yon 19

⚲ Le Pavillon

℘ 02 51 05 63 46. www.camping-le-pavillon.com

Address : 175 avenue Georges Clemenceau (located 1.5km southwest, follow the signs for Les Sables-d'Olonne)

3.6 ha (117 pitches)

Rentals : 16 ⌂ – 6 ⌂ – 6 canvas bungalows.

In a green setting, with a range of mostly modern rental accommodation.

Surroundings : ♤♤
Leisure activities : ♈ ⌂ ⤢ ⤢ ⤢ ⤢
multi-sports ground
Facilities : ⅍ ⊶ ⌂ ⌂ launderette

GPS Longitude : -1.66728
Latitude : 46.60653

MOUCHAMPS

85640 – Michelin map **316** J7 – pop. 2 600 – alt. 81
▶ Paris 394 – Cholet 40 – Fontenay-le-Comte 52 – Nantes 68

△ Le Hameau du Petit Lay

℘ 02 51 66 25 72. www.lehameaudupetitlay.com

Address : Chauvin (600m south along the D 113, follow the signs for St-Prouant)

Opening times : from mid June to mid Sept.

0.4 ha (39 pitches) flat, grassy

Tariff : (2014 Price) 13.90€ ★ ★ ⇌ 🔲 (½) (16A) – Extra per person 4€

Rental rates : (2014 Price) Permanent – 15 ⌂. Per night from 43 to 53€ – Per week from 197 to 497€ – Reservation fee 32€

The campsite and chalets are on both sides of the small wooden bridge crossing the Le Lay stream.

Surroundings : ⌂ ♤♤
Leisure activities : ⌂ ⤢ ⤢ ⤢ (small swimming pool)
Facilities : ⅍ ⌂ ⌂
Nearby : ⤢

GPS Longitude : -1.05483
Latitude : 46.77585

MOUILLERON-LE-CAPTIF

85000 – Michelin map **316** h7 – pop. 4 511 – alt. 70
▶ Paris 421 – Challans 40 – La Mothe-Achard 22 – Nantes 63

⚲ L'Ambois

℘ 02 51 37 29 15. www.campingambois.com – limited spaces for one-night stay

Address : take southeastern exit along the D 2, follow the signs for la Roche-sur-Yon, then continue 2.6km along the road to the right

Opening times : Permanent

1.75 ha (49 pitches) relatively flat, flat, grassy

Tariff : (2014 Price) 17.50€ ★ ★ ⇌ 🔲 (½) (10A) – Extra per person 4.50€

Rental rates : (2014 Price) Permanent – 40 ⌂ – 5 ⌂ – 3 gîtes. Per night from 35 to 70€ – Per week from 178 to 571€

In a rural setting with very few places for tents and caravans.

Surroundings : ⤢ ⌂ ♤
Leisure activities : ⌂ jacuzzi ⤢ ⤢ 🔲 (open air in season), farm or petting farm
Facilities : ⅍ ⊶ ⌂ ⌂ launderette ⤢

GPS Longitude : -1.46092
Latitude : 46.69647

NANTES

44000 – Michelin map **316** G4 – pop. 282 047 – alt. 8
▶ Paris 381 – Angers 88 – Bordeaux 325 – Lyon 660

⚲ Nantes Camping - Le Petit Port

℘ 02 40 74 47 94. www.nantes-camping.fr

Address : 21 boulevard du Petit Port (situated beside the Cens river)

Opening times : from beginning April to end Sept.

8 ha (151 pitches) relatively flat, flat, grassy, gravelled

Tariff : (2014 Price) 36.20€ ★ ★ ⇌ 🔲 (½) (16A) – Extra per person 6.20€ – Reservation fee 10€

Rental rates : (2014 Price) Permanent ⅍ (1 chalet) – 60 ⌂ – 6 ⌂ – 1 tent lodge. Per night from 41 to 114€ – Per week from 246 to 966€ – Reservation fee 25€

⤢ borne 2€ – 15 🔲 12€

High-end rentals, free use of the swimming pool and a tram stop for the town centre.

Surroundings : ⤢ ⌂ ♤♤
Leisure activities : ♈ ✕ ⤢ ⤢ ⤢
Facilities : ⅍ ⊶ ⌂ ⌂ ⤢ ⌂ launderette
Nearby : 🔲 ⤢ skating rink

GPS Longitude : -1.5567
Latitude : 47.24346

The Michelin classification (⚲⚲⚲... △) is totally independent of the official star classification system awarded by the local prefecture or other official organisation.

NOTRE-DAME-DE-MONTS

85690 – Michelin map **316** D6 – pop. 1 866 – alt. 6
▶ Paris 459 – Nantes 74 – La Roche-sur-Yon 72

⚲ L'Albizia

℘ 02 28 11 28 50. www.campinglalbizia.com – limited spaces for one-night stay

Address : 52 rue de la Rive (1.9km to the north)

3.6 ha (153 pitches)

Rentals : 35 ⌂.

A pleasant campsite, but numerous owner-occupied mobile homes.

Surroundings : ⌂
Leisure activities : ♈ ✕ nighttime ⤢ ⤢ ⤢ 🔲 ⤢ multi-sports ground
Facilities : ⅍ ⊶ ⌂ launderette

GPS Longitude : -2.12755
Latitude : 46.8503

△ Municipal de l'Orgatte

℘ 02 51 58 84 31. www.notre-dame-de-monts.fr

Address : avenue Abbé Thibaud (1.2km north along the D 38, turn off to the left, 300m from the beach)

Opening times : from beginning April to end Sept.

4.5 ha (315 pitches)

Tariff : (2014 Price) 19.10€ ★ ★ ⇌ 🔲 (½) (10A) – Extra per person 5.15€ – Reservation fee 10€

⤢ 1 🔲 19.10€

In a pleasant location among hills and shaded by pine trees.

Surroundings : ⤢ ♤♤
Leisure activities : ⤢ multi-sports ground
Facilities : ⌂ ⌂

GPS Longitude : -2.13882
Latitude : 46.83972

⛰ Le Pont d'Yeu

📞 0251588376. www.camping-pontdyeu.com

Address : rue du Pont d'Yeu (located 1km south along the D 38, follow the signs for St-Jean-de-Monts, and take turning to the left)

Opening times : from beginning April to end Sept.

1.3 ha (90 pitches)

Tariff : (2014 Price) 25.95€ ★★ ⛺ 🔲 🅿 (10A) – Extra per person 4.90€ – Reservation fee 10€

Rental rates : (2014 Price) (from beginning April to end Sept.) – 28 🛏 – 2 🏠. Per night from 70 to 95€ – Per week from 220 to 685€

A peaceful, family atmosphere; half the pitches are for owner-occupied mobile homes.

Surroundings : ⌂ ♀
Leisure activities : 🏄 🔲 (open air in season)
Facilities : ♿ ⌐ 🍴 launderette

Longitude : -2.13585
Latitude : 46.82052

NYOISEAU

49500 – Michelin map **317** D2 – pop. 1 305 – alt. 40
▶ Paris 316 – Ancenis 50 – Angers 47 – Châteaubriant 39

⛺ La Rivière

📞 0241922677. www.campinglariviere.fr

Address : 1.2km southeast along the D 71, follow the signs for Segré and take turning to the left; beside the Oudon river

Opening times : from mid June to mid Sept.

1 ha (25 pitches) flat, grassy

Tariff : (2014 Price) 12€ ★★ ⛺ 🔲 🅿 (10A) – Extra per person 3.30€

Rental rates : (2014 Price) (from mid June to mid Sept.) 🏄 – 1 🛏. Per week from 300€

🚐 borne 4.50€

Surroundings : 🌳 ♀♀
Leisure activities : 🔲 🏄
Facilities : ♿ ⌐ (Jul-15 Sept) 🍴
Nearby : 🚵 mountain biking

Longitude : -0.90981
Latitude : 47.71216

OLONNE-SUR-MER

85340 – Michelin map **316** F8 – pop. 13 279 – alt. 40
▶ Paris 458 – Nantes 102 – La Roche-sur-Yon 36 – La Rochelle 96

⛰ Sunêlia La Loubine ♨♨

📞 0251331292. www.la-loubine.fr – limited spaces for one-night stay 🏄 (from beginning July to end Aug.)

Address : 1 route de la Mer (3km to the west)

Opening times : from beginning April to mid Sept.

8 ha (401 pitches) flat, grassy

Tariff : 41€ ★★ ⛺ 🔲 🅿 (6A) – Extra per person 6.90€ – Reservation fee 22€
Rental rates : Permanent ♿ (1 mobile home) 🏄 (from beginning July to end Aug.) – 148 🛏 – 2 🏠. Per night from 39 to 150€ – Per week from 273 to 1,050€ – Reservation fee 22€

The site is based around a 16th-century Vendée farm, with a charming landscaped water and play park.

Surroundings : ⌂ ♀♀
Leisure activities : 🍴 ✕ 🔲 nighttime 🏋
🎿 🔥 jacuzzi 🏄 🚲 🎾 ⚽ 🔲 🏊 multi-sports ground
Facilities : ♿ ⌐ 🍴 launderette 🚿 🐾
Nearby : 🐴

Longitude : -1.80647
Latitude : 46.54595

⛰ Le Moulin de la Salle ♨♨

📞 0251959910. www.moulindelasalle.com – limited spaces for one-night stay

Address : rue du Moulin de la Salle (2.7km to the west)

Opening times : from beginning April to mid Sept.

2.7 ha (216 pitches) flat, grassy

Tariff : (2014 Price) 34.10€ ★★ ⛺ 🔲 🅿 (10A) – Extra per person 5.20€ – Reservation fee 25€

Rental rates : (2014 Price) (from beginning April to beginning Sept.) – 130 🛏 – 7 gîtes. Per night from 60 to 80€ – Per week from 220 to 850€ – Reservation fee 25€

Numerous mobile homes beside a pretty windmill, but with few pitches for tents and caravans.

Surroundings : ⌂ ♀
Leisure activities : 🍴 ✕ 🔲 🏋 🎿 🏄 🔲 🏊 multi-sports ground, entertainment room
Facilities : ♿ ⌐ ㏄ 🍴 🚿 launderette 🐾

Longitude : -1.79217
Latitude : 46.53183

⛰ Domaine de l'Orée ♨♨

📞 0251331059. www.l-oree.com

Address : 13 route des Amis de la Nature

Opening times : from beginning May to beginning Sept.

6 ha (320 pitches) flat, grassy

Tariff : (2014 Price) 20.50€ ★★ ⛺ 🔲 🅿 (10A) – Extra per person 4€ Reservation fee 26€

Rental rates : (2014 Price) (from mid April to mid Sept.) – 145 🛏 – 6 🏠. Per week from 290 to 855€ – Reservation fee 26€

The site is divided into two sections; some pitches have private sanitary facilities.

Surroundings : ⌂ ♀
Leisure activities : 🍴 ✕ 🔲 nighttime 🏋 🎿 jacuzzi 🏄 🚲 🎾 🏊 🔲 🏊 multi-sports ground
Facilities : ♿ ⌐ 🐾 10 individual sanitary facilities (🚿 🛁 wc) 🚿 🍴 launderette 🚿 🐾
Nearby : 🐴

Longitude : -1.80827
Latitude : 46.5494

⛰ Nid d'Été

📞 0251953438. www.leniddete.com

Address : 2 rue de la Vigne Verte (2.5km to the west)

Opening times : from beginning April to end Sept.

2 ha (199 pitches) flat, grassy

Tariff : 19.40€ ★★ ⛺ 🔲 🅿 (10A) – Extra per person 3.70€ – Reservation fee 15€

Rental rates : (from beginning April to end Sept.) – 32 🛏 – 1 🏠. Per week from 245 to 679€ – Reservation fee 15€

The site is divided into two sections; good sanitary facilities.

Surroundings : 🌳 ⌂ ♀♀
Leisure activities : 🍴 ✕ 🔲 jacuzzi 🏄 🔲 (open air in season)
Facilities : ♿ ⌐ 🍴 launderette 🐾

Longitude : -1.79393
Latitude : 46.53326

In order for the guide to remain wholly objective, the selection of campsites is made on an entirely independent basis.

⛰ Le Petit Paris ♙♙

⌖ 02 51 22 04 44. www.campingpetitparis.com

Address : 41 rue du Petit-Versailles (located 5.5km southeast)

Opening times : from beginning April to end Oct.

3 ha (154 pitches) flat, grassy

Tariff : (2014 Price) 18.50€ ♙♙ ⌂ ▣ ⚡ (10A) –
Extra per person 2.50€ – Reservation fee 18€

Rental rates : (2014 Price) (from beginning April to end Oct.) –
4 caravans – 28 ⏚ – 2 ⌂ – 4 canvas bungalows. Per night
from 40 to 100€ – Per week from 80 to 680€ – Reservation
fee 18€

*In a green setting with a range of rental options and one area
reserved for tents and caravans.*

Surroundings : ⛱ ⌑ ♒
Leisure activities : ♟ ⌂ ♟ ⚴ ▣ (open
air in season) ⚔ multi-sports ground
Facilities : ♿ ⚷ ⚐ ⚲ ♨ ♟ launderette ⚰
Nearby : parachuting

G P S	Longitude : -1.72041 Latitude : 46.47359

⛰ Les Fosses Rouges

⌖ 02 51 95 17 95. www.camping-lesfossesrouges.com

Address : 8 rue des Fosses Rouges, la Pironnière (3km southeast)

3.5 ha (248 pitches) flat, grassy

Rentals : 13 ⏚.

*Situated in a residential area. Choose those pitches furthest
away from the road.*

Surroundings : ⌑ ♒
Leisure activities : ♟ ⚴ ⚳ ⚺ ▣ (open air
in season)
Facilities : ♿ ⚷ ⚐ ♟ launderette ⚰ ⚲

G P S	Longitude : -1.74124 Latitude : 46.47956

⛺ Sauveterre

⌖ 02 51 33 10 58. www.campingsauveterre.com

Address : 3 route des Amis de la Nature (3km to the west)

3.2 ha (234 pitches) flat, grassy

Rentals : 23 ⏚.

Surroundings : ♒
Leisure activities : ✗ ⚔ ⚔
Facilities : ♿ ⚷ ♟ ▣ ⚰ ⚲
Nearby : ⚘

G P S	Longitude : -1.80547 Latitude : 46.54697

PIRIAC-SUR-MER

44420 – Michelin map **316** A3 – pop. 2 245 – alt. 7
▣ Paris 462 – La Baule 17 – Nantes 88 – La Roche-Bernard 33

⛰ Parc du Guibel ♙♙

⌖ 02 40 23 52 67. www.parcduguibel.com

Address : route de Kerdrien (3.5km east along the D 52, follow the
signs for Mesquer and take turning to the left)

Opening times : from beginning April to end Sept.

14 ha (450 pitches)

Tariff : ♟ 6.50€ ⌂ 4.25€ ▣ 6.50€ – ⚡ (10A) 4.60€ – Reservation
fee 18€

Rental rates : (from beginning April to end Sept.) – 90 ⏚ –
34 ⌂. Per night from 50 to 120€ – Per week from 266 to 840€
Reservation fee 18€

⏚ borne – 10 ▣ 14€ – ⚓ 11€

The site is divided into 2 distinct sections in a natural wooded
park. There is a partially open-air swimming area.

Surroundings : ⛱ ⌑ ♒
Leisure activities : ♟ ✗ ⌂ ♟ ⚴ ♂ ⚵ ▣
⚔ ⚔ multi-sports ground
Facilities : ♿ ⚷ ⚐ ⚲ ♨ ♟ launderette
⚰
Nearby : ⚘ ⚘

G P S	Longitude : -2.51024 Latitude : 47.3862

⛰ Armor Héol ♙♙

⌖ 02 40 23 57 80. www.camping-armor-heol.com

Address : at Kervin, route de Guérande (located 1km southeast along
the D 333)

Opening times : from beginning April to mid Sept.

4.5 ha (270 pitches) flat, grassy, small lake

Tariff : (2014 Price) ♟ 7.50€ ⌂ ▣ 14.50€ – ⚡ (6A) 4.50€ –
Reservation fee 18€

Rental rates : (2014 Price) (from beginning April to mid Sept.) –
1 caravan – 58 ⏚ – 22 ⌂. Per night from 55 to 83€ – Per week
from 275 to 835€ – Reservation fee 20€

*A partially open-air swimming area and the luxury of private
sanitary facilities for 20 pitches.*

Surroundings : ⌑ ♒
Leisure activities : ♟ ✗ ⌂ ⚳ ♟ ♓ ⚴ ⚵
▣ ⚔ ⚔ multi-sports ground
Facilities : ♿ ⚷ ⚐ – 20 individual sanitary
facilities (⚲ ⚯ wc) ♟ launderette

G P S	Longitude : -2.53563 Latitude : 47.3748

⛰ Mon Calme

⌖ 02 40 23 60 77. www.campingmoncalme.com

Address : rue de Norvoret (located 1km south following signs for La
Turballe and take the turning to the left, 450m from the ocean)

Opening times : from beginning April to end Sept.

1.2 ha (88 pitches) flat, grassy

Tariff : (2014 Price) 28.50€ ♙♙ ⌂ ▣ ⚡ (10A) –
Extra per person 6.80€ – Reservation fee 18€

Rental rates : (2014 Price) (from beginning April to end Sept.) –
20 ⏚ – 12 apartments. Per night from 48 to 68€ – Per week
from 260 to 640€ – Reservation fee 18€

⏚ borne 2.50€

*Mobile homes and camping pitches, as well as an upmarket
apart-hotel, open 11 months of the year.*

Surroundings : ♒
Leisure activities : ✗ ⚴ ♂ ⚳
Facilities : ♿ ⚷ ♟ ♟ ▣
Nearby : ⚘ ⚺ ⚗

G P S	Longitude : -2.54882 Latitude : 47.37208

LA PLAINE-SUR-MER

44770 – Michelin map **316** C5 – pop. 3 815 – alt. 26
▣ Paris 438 – Nantes 58 – Pornic 9 – St-Michel-Chef-Chef 7

⛰ Sites et Paysages La Tabardière ♙♙

⌖ 02 40 21 58 83. www.camping-la-tabardiere.com

Address : 2 route de la Tabardiere (3.5km east along the D 13, follow
the signs for Pornic and take turning to the left)

Opening times : from beginning April to end Sept.

6 ha (270 pitches)

Tariff : 39€ ♙♙ ⌂ ▣ ⚡ (10A) – Extra per person 8.50€ – Reservation
fee 20€

Rental rates : (from beginning April to end Sept.) ✈ – 10 ⛺ – 20 ⛺. Per night from 39 to 127€ – Per week from 273 to 889€ Reservation fee 20€

🚐 borne 15€ – 5 🔲 15€ – 🚽 15€

Surroundings : 🌳 ♉
Leisure activities : 🍸 🎣 🏃 🚣 🎣 🖼 (open air in season) ⛵ 🎣 multi-sports ground
Facilities : 🚻 ⚓ CC 🏕 🍴 launderette 🧺 🔧

GPS Longitude : -2.15313
Latitude : 47.14087

🏕 Le Ranch

📞 02 40 21 52 62. www.camping-le-ranch.com

Address : chemin des Hautes Raillères (3km northeast along the D 96)

Opening times : from beginning April to end Sept.

3 ha (183 pitches) flat, grassy

Tariff : (2014 Price) 33.70€ ✚✚ 🚐 🔲 ⚡ (10A) – Extra per person 6.50€ – Reservation fee 17.50€

Rental rates : (2014 Price) (from beginning April to end Sept.) ✈ – 12 ⛺ – 17 ⛺. Per night from 33 to 115€ – Per week from 199 to 805€ – Reservation fee 17.50€

🚐 borne – 4 🔲 14.50€

In a green setting with lots of flowers.

Surroundings : 🌳 ♉
Leisure activities : 🍸 🍽 🖼 🚣 🎣 🖼 multi-sports ground, entertainment room
Facilities : 🚻 ⚓ CC 🏕 🍴 launderette 🔧

GPS Longitude : -2.16292
Latitude : 47.15412

LES PONTS-DE-CÉ

49130 – Michelin map **317** F4 – pop. 11 575 – alt. 25
▶ Paris 302 – Nantes 92 – Angers 7 – Cholet 57

🏕 Île du Château ♣♣

📞 09 83 76 62 05. www.camping-ileduchateau.fr

Address : avenue de la Boire Salée (situated on the Île du Château)

2.3 ha (135 pitches) flat, grassy

Rentals : 1 ⛺ – 7 canvas bungalows.

In a wooded setting near the Loire river and municipal gardens.

Surroundings : 🗨 ♉♉
Leisure activities : 🍽 🖼 🏃 🚣 🚲 🎣
Facilities : 🚻 ⚓ 🏕 🔱 🍴 🔧
Nearby : 🎿 🎣 🚤 ⛵

GPS Longitude : -0.53055
Latitude : 47.4244

PORNIC

44210 – Michelin map **316** D5 – pop. 14 052 – alt. 20
▶ Paris 429 – Nantes 49 – La Roche-sur-Yon 89 – Les Sables-d'Olonne 93

🏕 Club Airotel La Boutinardière ♣♣

📞 02 40 82 05 68. www.camping-boutinardiere.com

Address : 23 rue de la Plage de la Boutinardiere (5km southeast along the D 13 and take turning to the right, 200m from the beach)

Opening times : from beginning April to end Sept.

7.5 ha (400 pitches) relatively flat, flat, grassy

Tariff : 49€ ✚✚ 🚐 🔲 ⚡ (10A) – Extra per person 7€ – Reservation fee 25€

Rental rates : (from beginning April to end Sept.) – 150 ⛺ – 37 ⛺ – 11 apartments. Per night from 65 to 127€ – Per week from 250 to 1,200€ – Reservation fee 25€

🚐 borne 8€ – 🚽 14€

A village club with a range of services, including a spa centre, and apartment rentals equipped to a good standard.

Surroundings : 🌳 🗨 ♉
Leisure activities : 🍸 🍽 🖼 🚣 🏃 🎣 hammam, jacuzzi 🚣 🚲 🎣 🖼 🎣 ⛵ multi-sports ground, spa centre
Facilities : 🚻 ⚓ 🏕 🍴 🔱 launderette 🧺 🔧

GPS Longitude : -2.05222
Latitude : 47.09747

🏕 Yelloh! Village La Chênaie ♣♣

La Chênaie

📞 02 40 82 07 31. www. campinglachenaie.com

Address : 36 bis rue du Pâtisseau (east along the D 751, follow the signs for Nantes and take turning to the left)

Opening times : from end April to mid Sept.

8 ha (305 pitches) terraced, relatively flat, flat, grassy

Tariff : 43€ ✚✚ 🚐 🔲 ⚡ (10A) –

Extra per person 8€

Rental rates : (from mid April to mid Sept.) – 86 ⛺. Per night from 39 to 185€ – Per week from 273 to 1,295€

🚐 borne

Extensive green areas for relaxation; there's an enclosure with farm animals for the kids.

Surroundings : 🌳 🗨 ♉
Leisure activities : 🍸 🍽 🎣 🏃 🎣 hammam, jacuzzi 🚣 🚲 🖼 🎣 ⛵ farm or petting farm, multi-sports ground, entertainment room
Facilities : 🚻 ⚓ 🏕 🍴 launderette 🔧

GPS Longitude : -2.07196
Latitude : 47.1187

PORNICHET

44380 – Michelin map **316** B4 – pop. 10 466 – alt. 12
▶ Paris 449 – Nantes 74 – Vannes 84 – La Roche-sur-Yon 143

🏕 Les Forges

📞 02 40 61 18 84. www.campinglesforges.com – limited spaces for one-night stay

Address : 98 route de la Villès-Blais, Les Forges district

2 ha (130 pitches)

Rentals : 23 ⛺.

There's a bus stop for the town centre.

Surroundings : 🗨 ♉
Leisure activities : 🖼 🚣 🖼 (open air in season), multi-sports ground
Facilities : 🚻 ⚓ 🍴 launderette

GPS Longitude : -2.29379
Latitude : 47.26917

Michelin classification:

🏕🏕🏕🏕🏕 *Extremely comfortable, equipped to a very high standard*
🏕🏕🏕🏕 *Very comfortable, equipped to a high standard*
🏕🏕🏕 *Comfortable and well equipped*
🏕🏕 *Reasonably comfortable*
🏕 *Satisfactory*

LE POULIGUEN

44510 – Michelin map **316** B4 – pop. 4 977 – alt. 4
▶ Paris 453 – Guérande 8 – La Baule 4 – Nantes 80

⚠ Municipal les Mouettes

✆ 02 40 42 43 98. www.tourisme-lepouliguen.fr – ⊞

Address : 45 boulevard de l'Atlantique (to the west Le Pouliguen, along the D 45, right next to the stadium)

Opening times : from end March to end Oct.

4.7 ha (220 pitches) small lake

Tariff : (2014 Price) 19.50€ ✶✶ ⇌ 🗐 (4A) – Extra per person 5.10€
Relatively near the town centre and the shops.

Surroundings : ⌁ ♀♀	**G**	Longitude : -2.43942
Leisure activities : 🖼 🎿	**P**	Latitude : 47.27385
Facilities : ♿ ⚬⟍ ▥ ♨ ♈ launderette	**S**	
Nearby : ♀		

⚠ Municipal le Clein

✆ 02 40 42 43 99. leclein@mairie-lepouliguen.fr – ⊞

Address : 22 avenue de Kerdun

Opening times : from mid March to end Sept.

1.5 ha (110 pitches)

Tariff : (2014 Price) 20€ ✶✶ ⇌ 🗐 (10A) – Extra per person 4.90€
🚐 borne 10.80€ – 26 🗐 10.80€
Near the town centre and the beach, with a good parking area for campervans.

Surroundings : ♀♀	**G**	Longitude : -2.4301
Leisure activities : 🎿	**P**	Latitude : 47.27135
Facilities : ♿ ⚬⟍ ▥ ♨ ♈ launderette	**S**	
Nearby : 🛒 ♀		

POUZAUGES

85700 – Michelin map **316** K7 – pop. 5 428 – alt. 225
▶ Paris 390 – Bressuire 30 – Chantonnay 22 – Cholet 42

⚠ Le Lac

✆ 02 51 91 37 55. www.campingpouzauges.com

Address : by the lake (located 1.5km west along the D 960 bis, follow the signs for Chantonnay and take the road to the right)

Opening times : Permanent

1 ha (54 pitches) terrace, relatively flat, flat, grassy

Tariff : (2014 Price) 19€ ✶✶ ⇌ 🗐 (10A) – Extra per person 5€ – Reservation fee 20€
🚐 2 🗐 19€
Shaded by plane trees, 50m from the lake.

Surroundings : ♒ ⛰	**G**	Longitude : -0.8532
Leisure activities : ✗ 🎿	**P**	Latitude : 46.78183
Facilities : ♿ ⚬⟍ ♈ launderette	**S**	
Nearby : 🍸 🍽 ⚓		

The Michelin classification (⚠⚠⚠... ⚠) is totally independent of the official star classification system awarded by the local prefecture or other official organisation.

PRÉFAILLES

44770 – Michelin map **316** C5 – pop. 1 255 – alt. 10
▶ Paris 440 – Challans 56 – Machecoul 38 – Nantes 60

⚠⚠ Éléovic

✆ 02 40 21 61 60. www.camping-eleovic.com

Address : route de la Pointe Saint-Gildas (located 1km west along the D 75)

3 ha (150 pitches) relatively flat, flat, grassy
Rentals : 60 🚍.
A site overlooking the ocean and picturesque creeks.

Surroundings : ♒ ≪ ocean and Île de Noir- moutier ⌁ ♀	**G**	Longitude : -2.23151
Leisure activities : ✗ 🖼 🌙nighttime 🎿 ♪ 🎿 🎠 🖳 (open air in season), multi-sports ground	**P**	Latitude : 47.13292
Facilities : ♿ ⚬⟍ ♈ launderette 🎿	**S**	

PRUILLÉ

49220 – Michelin map **317** F3 – pop. 630 – alt. 30
▶ Paris 308 – Angers 22 – Candé 34 – Château-Gontier 33

⚠ Municipal Le Port

✆ 02 41 32 67 29. www.pruille.mairie49.fr

Address : rue du Bac (north of the town; beside the Mayenne – mooring point)

Opening times : from beginning May to end Oct.

1.2 ha (41 pitches) flat, grassy

Tariff : (2014 Price) 9€ ✶✶ ⇌ 🗐 (6A) – Extra per person 2€
Rental rates : (2014 Price) Permanent – 5 🚍. Per night from 45 to 50€ – Per week from 205 to 420€

Surroundings : ♒ ♀	**G**	Longitude : -0.66474
Leisure activities : ✂	**P**	Latitude : 47.57897
Facilities : 🎿	**S**	

LES ROSIERS-SUR-LOIRE

49350 – Michelin map **317** H4 – pop. 2 348 – alt. 22
▶ Paris 304 – Angers 32 – Baugé 27 – Bressuire 66

⚠⚠ Flower Le Val de Loire

✆ 02 41 51 94 33. www.camping-valdeloire.com

Address : 6 rue Sainte-Baudruche (take the northern exit along the D 59, follow the signs for Beaufort-en-Vallée, near the junction with the D 79)

Opening times : from beginning April to end Sept.

3.5 ha (110 pitches) flat, grassy

Tariff : (2014 Price) 29€ ✶✶ ⇌ 🗐 (10A) – Extra per person 5.50€ – Reservation fee 7.50€

Rental rates : (2014 Price) (from beginning April to end Sept.) – 2 caravans – 29 🚍 – 4 tent lodges. Per night from 42 to 131€ – Per week from 206 to 917€ – Reservation fee 10€
🚐 borne
In a pleasant leafy setting.

Surroundings : ⌁ ♀	**G**	Longitude : -0.22599
Leisure activities : ✗ 🖼 🎿 🎠 🖳 🏊	**P**	Latitude : 47.35821
Facilities : ♿ ⚬⟍ ♨ 🎿 ♈ 🖳	**S**	
Nearby : ✗ 🎿 🎿		

LES SABLES-D'OLONNE

85100 – Michelin map **316** F8 – pop. 14 572 – alt. 4
▶ Paris 456 – Cholet 107 – Nantes 102 – Niort 115

⚠️ Chadotel La Dune des Sables 👥

𝒫 02 51 32 31 21. www.chadotel.com – limited spaces for one-night stay

Address : at Le Paracou – chemin de la Bernardière (4km to the northwest, follow the signs for l'Aubraie)

Opening times : from beginning April to end Sept.

7.5 ha (290 pitches) undulating, terraced, flat, grassy, sandy

Tariff : 37€ 👫 ➾ 🔲 (10A) – Extra per person 6€ – Reservation fee 25€

Rental rates : (from beginning April to end Sept.) – 1 🚐 – 2 tent lodges. Per night from 25 to 165€ – Per week from 175 to 1,155€ Reservation fee 25€

🚐 borne – 1 🔲 37€

A mobile home park near the beach, overlooking the ocean, but with few pitches for tents or caravans.

Surroundings : 🏖️ ← ◠
Leisure activities : 🍽️ 🍴 📺 ⛳ 🏃 🏋️ 🚴 ✂️ 🎣 🏊 ⛷️
Facilities : 🚿 ⚡ ♨️ 🔥 💧 🍴 launderette 🧺 🚗

GPS	Longitude : -1.81395
	Latitude : 46.51207

⚠️ Chadotel Les Roses

𝒫 02 51 95 10 42. www.chadotel.com

Address : 61 rue des Roses (400m from the beach)

Opening times : from beginning April to beginning Nov.

3.3 ha (200 pitches) terraced, relatively flat, flat, grassy

Tariff : 37€ 👫 ➾ 🔲 (10A) – Extra per person 6€ – Reservation fee 25€

Rental rates : (from beginning April to beginning Nov.) 🚿 (1 mobile home) – 1 🚐 – 1 🏠. Per night from 27 to 165€ – Per week from 189 to 1,155€ – Reservation fee 25€

🚐 borne – 1 🔲 37€

In a residential area, mobile homes to rent, some luxurious; pitches for tents and caravans are always available.

Surroundings : ◠ 🌳
Leisure activities : 📺 🏋️ 🚴 🏊 ⛷️ multi-sports ground
Facilities : 🚿 ⚡ 🔥 🍴 launderette
Nearby : 🍽️ 🚗

GPS	Longitude : -1.76482
	Latitude : 46.49166

SABLÉ-SUR-SARTHE

72300 – Michelin map **310** G7 – pop. 12 399 – alt. 29
▶ Paris 252 – Angers 64 – La Flèche 27 – Laval 44

⚠️ Municipal de l'Hippodrome 👥

𝒫 02 43 95 42 61. www.tourisme.sablesursarthe.fr

Address : allée du Québec (take the southern exit towards Angers and the turning to the left, next to racecourse (hippodrome)

Opening times : from end March to mid Oct.

2 ha (84 pitches) flat, grassy

Tariff : (2014 Price) 13.90€ 👫 ➾ 🔲 (16A) – Extra per person 3.15€ – Reservation fee 2€

Rental rates : (2014 Price) (from end March to mid Oct.) 🚿 (1 chalet) ✂️ – 2 🚐 – 5 🏠. Per night from 70 to 95€ – Per week from 290 to 485€ – Reservation fee 2€

🚐 borne 2€

The site has decorative trees and shrubs; located beside the Sarthe river.

Surroundings : 🏖️ ◠ 🌳
Leisure activities : 📺 🏃 🏋️ 🏊 🎣
Facilities : 🚿 ⚡ 🔥 🍴 launderette
Nearby : ✂️ 🎣 🏊 🏇

GPS	Longitude : -0.33193
	Latitude : 47.83136

ST-BERTHEVIN

53940 – Michelin map **310** E6 – pop. 7 097 – alt. 108
▶ Paris 289 – Nantes 128 – Laval 10 – Rennes 66

⚠️ Municipal de Coupeau

𝒫 02 43 68 30 70. www.laval-tourisme.com

Address : by the leisure centre (south of the town, 150m from the Vicoin river)

Opening times : from mid April to end Sept.

0.4 ha (32 pitches)

Tariff : (2014 Price) 🚶 3.50€ ➾ 2€ 🔲 2.50€ – (10A) 2.20€

Situated looking out over a green and restful valley.

Surroundings : 🏖️ ◠
Leisure activities : 📺
Facilities : 🚿 🍴
Nearby : ✂️ 🎣 🏊 fitness trail

GPS	Longitude : -0.83235
	Latitude : 48.06431

ST-BRÉVIN-LES-PINS

44250 – Michelin map **316** C4 – pop. 12 133 – alt. 9
▶ Paris 438 – Challans 62 – Nantes 64 – Noirmoutier-en-l'Île 70

⚠️ Sunêlia Le Fief 👥

𝒫 02 40 27 23 86. www.lefief.com

Address : 57 chemin du Fief (2.4km south following signs for Saint-Brévin-l'Océan and take the turning to the left)

Opening times : from mid April to end Sept.

7 ha (397 pitches) flat, grassy

Tariff : (2014 Price) 48€ 👫 ➾ 🔲 (8A) – Extra per person 11€ – Reservation fee 35€

Rental rates : (2014 Price) (from mid April to end Sept.) 🚿 (1 mobile home) – 205 🚐. Per night from 54 to 235€ – Per week from 381 to 1,645€ – Reservation fee 35€

🚐 borne

A superb spa centre and truly upmarket VIP rental village, all set within a green garden area.

Surroundings : ◠ 🌳
Leisure activities : 🍽️ 🍴 📺 ⛳ 🏃 🏋️ hammam, jacuzzi 🏋️ 🚴 ✂️ 🎣 🏊 ⛷️ multi-sports ground, spa centre, entertainment room
Facilities : 🚿 ⚡ 🔥 💧 🍴 launderette 🧺 🚗

GPS	Longitude : -2.16768
	Latitude : 47.23465

For more information on visiting particular towns or regions, consult the relevant regional MICHELIN Green Guide. We also recommend you use the appropriate Michelin regional map to locate your selected campsite, to calculate distances and to work out the best route.

⚠ La Courance

𝒫 02 40 27 22 91. www.campinglacourance.fr – limited spaces for one-night stay

Address : 110 avenue du Maréchal Foch

Opening times : Permanent

2.4 ha (156 pitches) terraced, flat, sandy

Tariff : (2014 Price) 27.50€ ♣♣ ⇌ 回 [½] (10A) – Extra per person 7.30€ – Reservation fee 25€

Rental rates : (2014 Price) Permanent ♿ (1 mobile home) – 1 caravan – 43 ⛺ – 10 🏠 – 13 canvas bungalows. Per night from 61 to 93€ – Per week from 255 to 810€ – Reservation fee 25€

🚐 borne 3€ – 20 回 17.50€ – 🔋11€

Beside the beach, with a view of the St-Nazaire bridge. There's a bathing spot 500m away.

Surroundings : ♀♀ Leisure activities : ♈✗☾nighttime ⛵ Facilities : ♿ ⊶ 🛏 ♨♍ launderette Nearby : ✗ ◲	**GPS** Longitude : -2.1703 Latitude : 47.23786

⚠ Le Mindin

𝒫 02 40 27 46 41. www.camping-de-mindin.com – limited spaces for one-night stay

Address : 32 avenue du Bois (situated 2km to the north, near the ocean (direct access)

Opening times : Permanent

1.7 ha (87 pitches)

Tariff : (2014 Price) 27.50€ ♣♣ ⇌ 回 [½] (16A) – Extra per person 7.30€ – Reservation fee 25€

Rental rates : (2014 Price) Permanent – 34 ⛺ – 3 canvas bungalows. Per night from 61 to 93 € – Per week from 215 to 810€ Reservation fee 25€

🚐 borne 3€ – 🔋11€

Set in a small pine wood close to the beach, with a view of the port and the bridge at St-Nazaire.

Surroundings : ♨♀⛰ Leisure activities : ♈✗🏠◲ Facilities : ♿ ⊶ 🛏 ♨♍ 回	**GPS** Longitude : -2.16915 Latitude : 47.2648

ST-CALAIS

72120 – Michelin map **310** N7 – pop. 3 482 – alt. 155
▶ Paris 188 – Blois 65 – Chartres 102 – Châteaudun 58

⚠ Le Lac

𝒫 02 43 35 04 81. www.saint-calais.fr

Address : rue du Lac (take the northern exit along the D 249, follow the signs for Montaillé)

Opening times : from beginning April to mid Oct.

2 ha (85 pitches) flat, grassy

Tariff : (2014 Price) 14.20€ ♣♣ ⇌ 回 [½] (10A) – Extra per person 3.65€

Rental rates : (2014 Price) (from beginning April to mid Oct.) – 3 ⛺ – 3 🏠. Per night from 42 to 68€ – Per week from 204 to 342€

The campsite is situated near a lake.

Surroundings : 🏠 Leisure activities : 🏠 Facilities : ♿ ⊶ ♿ ♍ 回 Nearby : ⚓✗🏊⚓	**GPS** Longitude : 0.74426 Latitude : 47.92688

ST-ÉTIENNE-DU-BOIS

85670 – Michelin map **316** G7 – pop. 1 901 – alt. 38
▶ Paris 427 – Aizenay 13 – Challans 26 – Nantes 49

⚠ Municipal la Petite Boulogne

𝒫 02 51 34 54 51. www.stetiennedubois-vendee.fr

Address : rue du Stade (south of the town along the D 81, follow the signs for Poiré-sur-Vie and take the road to the right; near the river and a lake)

1.5 ha (35 pitches) terrace, flat and relatively flat, grassy

Rentals : 6 🏠.

A footpath links the campsite to the town and a small chalet village set among shrubs and bushes.

Surroundings : ♨ ⊏ ♀♀ Leisure activities : 🏊 (small swimming pool) Facilities : ♿ ⊶ ♨ launderette Nearby : ⚓✗✗	**GPS** Longitude : -1.59293 Latitude : 46.82925

There are several different types of sani-station ('borne' in French) – sanitation points providing fresh water and disposal points for grey water. See page 12 for further details.

ST-GEORGES-SUR-LAYON

49700 – Michelin map **317** G5 – pop. 769 – alt. 65
▶ Paris 328 – Angers 39 – Cholet 45 – Saumur 27

⚠ Les Grésillons

𝒫 02 41 50 02 32. www.camping-gresillons.com

Address : chemin des Grésillons (800m south along the D 178, follow the signs for Concourson-sur-Layon and take the road to the right, near the river)

Opening times : from beginning April to mid Sept.

1.5 ha (43 pitches) terraced, relatively flat, grassy

Tariff : (2014 Price) 17.80€ ♣♣ ⇌ 回 [½] (10A) – Extra per person 4.20€

Rental rates : (2014 Price) (from beginning April to end Sept.) – 12 canvas bungalows. Per night from 54 to 154€ – Per week from 151 to 431€ – Reservation fee 15€

Surroundings : ♨ ≼ Leisure activities : 🚲 🏊 (small swimming pool) ⚲ Facilities : ♿ ⊷ (July–Aug.) ♍ 回	**GPS** Longitude : -0.37032 Latitude : 47.19324

ST-HILAIRE-DE-RIEZ

85270 – Michelin map **316** E7 – pop. 10 504 – alt. 8
▶ Paris 453 – Challans 18 – Noirmoutier-en-l'Île 48 – La Roche-sur-Yon 48

Le Pissot (4 km north)

⚠ Les Biches ♣♠

𝒫 02 51 54 38 82. www.campingdesbiches.com – limited spaces for one-night stay

Address : chemin de Petite Baisse (situated 2km to the north)

Opening times : from mid April to mid Sept.

13 ha/9 for camping (434 pitches)

Tariff : (2014 Price) 45€ ♣♣ ⇌ 回 [½] (10A) – Extra per person 8.50€ Reservation fee 20€

Rental rates : (2014 Price) (from mid April to mid Sept.) – 240 🚐 – 57 🏕 – 1 🛏 – 7 studios – 10 mobile homes (without sanitary facilities). Per week from 232 to 985€ – Reservation fee 20€

In a pleasant pine wood with a range of rental options, but with few pitches for tents and caravans.

Surroundings : 🐾 ⌂ ♨
Leisure activities : ⛵ ✕ 🚣 ⌂ 🏃 🎿 🚴 🏍
🎣 ♨ 🏊 🏊 🏊 disco, multi-sports ground
Facilities : 🚿 o━ 🏧 🚻 🚼 🧺 launderette
🛁 🚗 refrigerators

Longitude : -1.94445
Latitude : 46.74052

---

*For more information on visiting particular towns or regions, consult the relevant regional **MICHELIN Green Guide**. We also recommend you use the appropriate Michelin regional map to locate your selected campsite, to calculate distances and to work out the best route.*

Les Demoiselles (10 km northwest)

🏕 Odalys Vitalys Les Demoiselles

📞 02 51 58 10 71. www.odalys-vacances.com – limited spaces for one-night stay

Address : avenue des Becs (9.5km to the northwest, along the D 123 and 300m from the beach)

Opening times : from beginning April to end Sept.

13.7 ha (180 pitches) undulating, flat and relatively flat, grassy, sandy

Tariff : (2014 Price) 21€ ★★ 🚗 📺 🔌 (10A) – Extra per person 7€

Rental rates : (2014 Price) (from beginning April to end Sept.) 🚿 (4 mobile homes) – 154 🚐. Per night from 75 to 140€ – Per week from 250 to 1,050€ – Reservation fee 25€

A mobile home park with plenty of shade and some pitches for tents and caravans.

Surroundings : 🐾 ♨
Leisure activities : ⌂ 🏃 🎿 🚴 🏊 multi-sports ground
Facilities : 🚿 o━ 🧺 launderette
Nearby : ✕ 🚗

Longitude : -2.04086
Latitude : 46.76815

La Fradinière (7 km north-west)

🏕 La Puerta del Sol 👥

📞 02 51 49 10 10. www.campinglapuertadelsol.com

Address : 7 chemin des Hommeaux (4.5km to the north)

Opening times :

4 ha (207 pitches) flat, grassy

Tariff : (2014 Price) 35€ ★★ 🚗 📺 🔌 (10A) – Extra per person 6.90€

Rental rates : (2014 Price) (from beginning April to end Sept.) 🚿 (1 chalet) – 74 🚐 – 40 🏕. Per night from 80 to 130 € – Per week from 180 to 910€

In a green setting; a rental park with various standards of accommodation, but few pitches for tents and caravans.

Surroundings : 🐾 ⌂ ♨
Leisure activities : ⛵ ✕ 🚣 ⌂ nighttime 🏃
🎣 ♨ jacuzzi 🚣 🚴 🏊 🏊 🏊 multi-sports ground, entertainment room
Facilities : 🚿 o━ 🚻 🚼 🧺 launderette 🛁
🚗 refrigerators

La Pège (6 km north-west)

🏕 Les Écureuils 👥

📞 02 51 54 33 71. www.camping-aux-ecureuils.com – limited spaces for one-night stay

Address : 98 avenue de la Pège (5.5km to the northwest, 200m from the beach)

Opening times : from beginning April to end Sept.

4 ha (215 pitches)

Tariff : (2014 Price) 38.60€ ★★ 🚗 📺 🔌 (10A) – Extra per person 6.70€ – Reservation fee 25€

Rental rates : (2014 Price) (from end April to beginning Sept.) – 19 🚐 – 2 🏕. Per week from 330 to 985€ – Reservation fee 25€

In a pleasant setting; divided into 2 separate campsites, with some pitches for tents and caravans.

Surroundings : 🐾 ⌂ ♨
Leisure activities : 🐾 ✕ 🚣 nighttime 🏃
🎣 ♨ hammam 🚣 🚴 🏊 🏊 🏊 launderette 🚗
Nearby : 🚗 🏊

Longitude : -2.00897
Latitude : 46.74478

🏕 La Ningle

📞 02 51 54 07 11. www.campinglaningle.com

Address : 66 chemin des Roselières (situated 5.7km to the northwest)

Opening times : from beginning May to mid Sept.

3.2 ha (150 pitches) flat, grassy, small lake

Tariff : (2014 Price) 38.15€ ★★ 🚗 📺 🔌 (10A) – Extra per person 5.50€ – Reservation fee 16€

Rental rates : (2014 Price) (from mid April to mid Sept.) – 20 🚐. Per night from 50 to 116€ – Per week from 260 to 815€ – Reservation fee 16€

A pleasantly leafy setting and a well-kept site.

Surroundings : 🐾 ⌂ ♨
Leisure activities : ⛵ 🚣 🎣 🚣 🚴 🏊 🏊 🏊
Facilities : 🚿 o━ 🚻 🚼 🧺 launderette
Nearby : 🚗 ✕ 🚗 🏊

Longitude : -2.00473
Latitude : 46.7446

🏕 La Parée Préneau

📞 02 51 54 33 84. www.campinglapareepreneau.com

Address : 23 avenue de La Parée Préneau (3.5km to the northwest)

Opening times : from beginning April to end Sept.

3.6 ha (217 pitches)

Tariff : (2014 Price) 29.90€ ★★ 🚗 📺 🔌 (6A) – Extra per person 5.50€ Reservation fee 20€

Rental rates : (2014 Price) (from beginning April to end Sept.) – 55 🚐 – 7 🏕 – 5 canvas bungalows. Per night from 51 to 96€ – Per week from 199 to 789€ – Reservation fee 20€

In a pleasant setting, but choose the pitches away from the road in preference.

Surroundings : ⌂ ♨
Leisure activities : ⛵ 🚣 nighttime 🚣
🚴 🏊 🏊 multi-sports ground
Facilities : 🚿 o━ 🚻 🚼 🧺 launderette

Longitude : -1.98488
Latitude : 46.74034

Routes nationales are main roads and their identifying numbers begin with N or RN. Routes départementales are generally quieter roads and begin with D or DN.

⛰ Le Bosquet

📞 02 51 54 34 61. www.lebosquet.fr

Address : 62 avenue de la Pège (5km to the northwest)

2 ha (115 pitches)

Rentals : 40 🛏 – 3 apartments.

Situated relatively close to the beach (250m).

Surroundings : 🌳🌳 Leisure activities : 🍹✕ 🏠 🛶 🏊 Facilities : 🚿 ⚡ ♨ launderette 🎣 Nearby : 🍽 🚴	**G P S** Longitude : -2.00326 Latitude : 46.74073

⛰ Le Romarin

📞 02 51 54 43 82. www.leromarin.fr

Address : rue des Martinets (3.8km to the northwest)

Opening times : from beginning April to end Sept.

4 ha/1.5 (97 pitches)

Tariff : (2014 Price) 28€ ✸✸ 🚐 🔲 ⚡ (10A) – Extra per person 4.30€
Reservation fee 19€

Rental rates : (2014 Price) (from beginning April to mid Sept.) 🚫 –
5 🛏. Per night from 50 to 90€ – Per week from 200 to 625€
Reservation fee 19€

Mobile homes and some pitches for tents and caravans arranged around a small but pretty pine wood.

Surroundings : 🌳🌳 Leisure activities : ✕ 🛶 🏊 multi-sports ground Facilities : 🚿 ⚡ (July–Aug.) ♨ launderette 🎣	**G P S** Longitude : -1.98756 Latitude : 46.74243

⛰ La Pège

📞 02 51 54 34 52. www.campinglapege.com

Address : 67 avenue de la Pège (5km to the northwest)

1.8 ha (100 pitches)

Rentals : 20 🛏 – 1 🏠.

Access to the beach (100m) along a small road leading directly to the lifeguard's station. Choose the pitches away from the road in preference

Surroundings : 🌳🌳 Leisure activities : 🛶 🚴 🏊 Facilities : 🚿 ⚡ ♨ 🔲 Nearby : 🍽 🍹✕ 🎣	**G P S** Longitude : -2.00545 Latitude : 46.7411

Sion-sur-l'Océan (3 km west)

⛰ Municipal de la Plage de Riez

📞 02 51 54 36 59. www.campingsainthilairederiez.com

Address : avenue des Mimosas (3km west, 200m from the beach)

Opening times : from beginning April to end Oct.

9 ha (560 pitches)

Tariff : (2014 Price) 30€ ✸✸ 🚐 🔲 ⚡ (10A) – Extra per person 6.50€
Reservation fee 19€

Rental rates : (2014 Price) (from beginning April to end Oct.) –
66 🛏 – 1 🏠 – 10 canvas bungalows. Per night from 62 to 127€ –
Per week from 185 to 890€ – Reservation fee 19€

🚐 borne 4.50€ – 9 🔲 30€

We have selected the best campsites in France with our usual care, listing those with the best facilities in the most pleasant surroundings.

The campsite is shaded by beautiful pine trees; direct access to the beach.

Surroundings : 🏖 🚣 🌳🌳🌳 Leisure activities : 🍹✕ 🏠 🛶 🛶 🚴 🏊 multi-sports ground Facilities : 🚿 ⚡ ♨ 🔲 ♨ launderette 🎣 🎣	**G P S** Longitude : -1.97941 Latitude : 46.72298

⛰ Municipal de la Plage de Sion

📞 02 51 54 34 23. www.campingsainthilairederiez.com

Address : avenue de la Forêt (take the northern exit)

Opening times : from beginning April to end Oct.

3 ha (164 pitches) undulating, relatively flat, flat, grassy, sandy,
gravelled

Tariff : (2014 Price) 30€ ✸✸ 🚐 🔲 ⚡ (10A) – Extra per person 6.50€
Reservation fee 19€

Rental rates : (2014 Price) (from mid April to end Oct.) – 18 🛏 –
3 canvas bungalows. Per night from 62 to 105€ – Per week
from 185 to 731€ – Reservation fee 19€

🚐 borne 4.50€ – 6 🔲 19€

300m from the beach (direct access), surrounded by forest.

Surroundings : 🏖 🚣 🌳 Leisure activities : 🏠 🛶 🚴 Facilities : 🚿 ⚡ ♨ ♨ ♨ launderette	**G P S** Longitude : -1.97246 Latitude : 46.71695

ST-HILAIRE-LA-FORÊT

85440 – Michelin map **316** G9 – pop. 611 – alt. 23

▶ Paris 449 – Challans 66 – Luçon 31 – La Roche-sur-Yon 31

⛰ La Grand' Métairie

📞 02 51 33 32 38. www.la-grand-metairie.com – limited spaces for
one-night stay

Address : 8 rue de La Vineuse en Plaine (north of the town along the
D 70)

Opening times : from beginning April to end Sept.

3.8 ha (172 pitches) flat, grassy

Tariff : (2014 Price) 28€ ✸✸ 🚐 🔲 ⚡ (10A) – Extra per person 7€ –
Reservation fee 25€

Rental rates : (2014 Price) (from beginning April to end Sept.) –
116 🛏 – 11 🏠. Per night from 19 to 134€ – Per week
from 89 to 849€ – Reservation fee 25€

Numerous mobile homes on a lush, green site with lots of flowers.

Surroundings : 🏖 🚣 🌳🌳 Leisure activities : 🍹✕ 🏠 🎇 nighttime 🎿 🏊 🛶 🚴 ✂ 🔲 🏊 🚜 farm or petting farm Facilities : 🚿 ⚡ ♨ ♨ ♨ ♨ launderette 🎣	**G P S** Longitude : -1.52545 Latitude : 46.44776

⛰ Les Batardières

📞 02 51 33 33 85. www.batardieres.com

Address : 2 rue des Batardières (continue west along the D 70 and
take the turning to the left, following signs for Le Poteau)

Opening times : from beginning July to end Aug.

1.6 ha (75 pitches) flat, grassy

Tariff : (2014 Price) 25€ ✸✸ 🚐 🔲 ⚡ (10A) – Extra per person 4€

Pretty, clearly marked-out pitches with lots of shade.

Surroundings : 🏖 🚣 🌳 Leisure activities : 🏠 🛶 ✂ Facilities : ⚡ 🔲 ♨ ♨ 🔲	**G P S** Longitude : -1.52934 Latitude : 46.44807

ST-HILAIRE-ST-FLORENT

49400 – Michelin map **317** I5

▶ Paris 324 – Nantes 131 – Angers 45 – Tours 72

⛰ **Sites et Paysages Chantepie** 👥

✆ 02 41 67 95 34. www.campingchantepie.com

Address : route de Chantepie (5.5km northwest along the D 751, follow the signs for Gennes and take road to the left; at La Mimerolle)

Opening times : from end April to mid Sept.

10 ha/5 for camping (150 pitches) flat, grassy

Tariff : 22.60€ 👫 🚐 🔲 🔌 (16A) – Extra per person 4.40€ – Reservation fee 14€

Rental rates : (from end April to mid Sept.) – 21 🛖 – 10 canvas bungalows – 2 tent lodges. Per week from 55 to 144€ – Per week from 330 to 937€ – Reservation fee 14€

Children will like to see the farm animals .

Surroundings : 🐾 ≤ Loire Valley 🛋 ♨♨
Leisure activities : ¶ ✕ 🏛 ♣ 🚴 🌳
🔲 🏊
Facilities : ♿ ☛ cc 🛁 🚽 ¶ launderette 🏮 🚿

Longitude : -0.14305
Latitude : 47.2937

Routes nationales are main roads and their identifying numbers begin with N or RN. Routes départementales are generally quieter roads and begin with D or DN.

ST-JEAN-DE-MONTS

85160 – Michelin map **316** D7 – pop. 8 037 – alt. 16

▶ Paris 451 – Cholet 123 – Nantes 73 – Noirmoutier-en-l'Ile 34

Centre

⛰ Aux Coeurs Vendéens 👥

✆ 02 51 58 84 91. www.coeursvendeens.com

Address : 251 route de Notre-Dame-de-Monts (4km northwest on the D 38)

2 ha (117 pitches)

Rentals : 🏠 – 64 🛖 – 1 🏡.

Choose the pitches away from the road if possible.

Surroundings : 🛋 ♨♨
Leisure activities : ¶ ✕ 🏛 ♣ ♨ hammam, jacuzzi ♣ 🚴 🔲 🏊 spa centre
Facilities : ♿ ☛ 🛁 🚽 ¶ launderette 🏮
Nearby : 🏮

Longitude : -2.11008
Latitude : 46.80988

⛰ Les Pins

✆ 02 51 58 17 42. www.camping-despins.fr

Address : 166 avenue Valentine (2.5km southeast on the D 123)

Opening times : from end May to end Sept.

1.2 ha (118 pitches) undulating, terraced, flat, sandy

Tariff : (2014 Price) 30€ 👫 🚐 🔲 🔌 (10A) – Extra per person 7.95€ Reservation fee 20€

Rental rates : (2014 Price) (from end May to end Sept.) 🏠 – 15 🏡. Per week from 240 to 640€ – Reservation fee 20€

A very pleasant, undulating pine wood, but the rental chalets are a little old.

Surroundings : 🛋 ♨
Leisure activities : ¶ 🏛 ♣ 🚴
Facilities : ☛ 🚽 ¶ 🔲
Nearby : 🏮 🚿

Longitude : -2.03894
Latitude : 46.78081

North

⛰ Les Amiaux 👥

✆ 02 51 58 22 22. www.amiaux.fr

Address : 223 route de Notre-Dame (3.5km to the northwest, on the D 38)

Opening times : from beginning May to end Sept.

17 ha (543 pitches)

Tariff : 👤 5€ 🚐 🔲 27.50€ 🔌 (10A) – Reservation fee 16€

Rental rates : (from beginning May to end Sept.) 🏠 – 28 🛖 – 4 apartments. Per week from 322 to 972€ – Reservation fee 16€

Divided into 2 separate sections connected by a tunnel.

Surroundings : 🛋 ♨
Leisure activities : ¶ ✕ 🏛 ♣ ♣ 🚴 🏇 🎾
🔲 🏊 multi-sports ground
Facilities : ♿ ☛ 🛁 🚽 ¶ launderette
🏮

Longitude : -2.11517
Latitude : 46.81107

⛰ Le Bois Joly 👥

✆ 02 51 59 11 63. www.camping-lebois-joly.com

Address : 46 route de Notre-Dame-de-Monts (located 1km to the northwest; beside a brook)

Opening times : from beginning April to end Sept.

7.5 ha (356 pitches)

Tariff : 35€ 👫 🚐 🔲 🔌 (10A) – Extra per person 6€ – Reservation fee 25€

Rental rates : (from beginning April to end Sept.) ♿ (1 mobile home) 🏠 – 2 caravans – 102 🛖 – 22 🏡. Per week from 250 to 990€ – Reservation fee 25€

🛖 borne – 5 🔲 18€

An attractive swimming area.

Surroundings : 🛋 ♨
Leisure activities : ¶ ✕ 🏛 ♣ 🏍 🏄
jacuzzi ♣ 🔲 🏊 🛷 🎣 multi-sports ground
Facilities : ♿ ☛ 🔳 🛁 🚽 ¶
launderette 🏮
Nearby : 🏮

Longitude : -2.07417
Latitude : 46.79918

⛰ Club Airotel Les Places Dorées 👥

✆ 02 51 59 02 93. www.placesdorees.com – limited spaces for one-night stay 🏠

Address : route de Notre-Dame-de-Monts (4km northwest on the D 38)

Opening times : from mid April to mid Sept.

5 ha (288 pitches)

Tariff : (2014 Price) 38.80€ 👫 🚐 🔲 🔌 (10A) – Extra per person 7.20€ – Reservation fee 25€

Rental rates : (2014 Price) (from mid April to mid Sept.) 🏠 – 79 🛖. Per night from 35.60 to 146€ – Per week from 249 to 1,020€ – Reservation fee 25€

There's an attractive swimming area.

Surroundings : 🛋 ♨♨
Leisure activities : ¶ ✕ ♣ 🏍 🏄 hammam,
jacuzzi ♣ 🔲 🏊 🛷 multi-sports ground
Facilities : ♿ ☛ 🛁 ¶ launderette 🏮
Nearby : 🏮

Longitude : -2.10997
Latitude : 46.8097

The information in the guide may have changed since going to press.

APV Les Aventuriers de la Calypso ♠♠

0251597966. www.camping-apv.com – limited spaces for one-night stay

Address : route de Notre-Dame-de-Monts, Les Tonnelles (4.6km to the northwest)

Opening times : from mid April to end Sept.

4 ha (284 pitches)

Tariff : (2014 Price) 32.30€ ♦♦ ⇌ 回 ⚡ (10A) – Extra per person 9.20€ – Reservation fee 28€

Rental rates : (2014 Price) (from mid April to end Sept.) – 152 🏠 – 38 🏠. Per night from 41 to 84 € – Per week from 259 to 1,050€ 🚐 borne – 8 回 19.80€

There are a few pitches for tents or caravans and some of the rental accommodation is very old.

Surroundings : ⅍ ⌁ ♀
Leisure activities : ♈ ✗ 🎪 ⏾ nighttime ⚶ ⚘ jacuzzi ⚗ ⚲ ✂ ▥ ⚝ multi-sports ground
Facilities : ⅍ ⚬ ⚐ ⚱ ⚓ ⚖ launderette ⚘

Longitude : -2.11533
Latitude : 46.81232

Club Airotel l'Abri des Pins ♠♠

0251588386. www.abridespins.com – limited spaces for one-night stay ⚒

Address : route de Notre-Dame-de-Monts (4km northwest on the D 38)

Opening times : from beginning April to mid Sept.

3 ha (209 pitches)

Tariff : (2014 Price) 38.80€ ♦♦ ⇌ 回 ⚡ (10A) – Extra per person 7.20€ – Reservation fee 25€

Rental rates : (2014 Price) (from mid April to mid Sept.) ⚒ – 79 🏠. Per night from 39 to 146€ – Per week from 273 to 1,020€ Reservation fee 25€

A pretty play and paddling pool area. Choose pitches away from the road in preference.

Surroundings : ⌁ ♀♀
Leisure activities : ♈ ✗ 🎪 ⚶ ⚘ hammam, jacuzzi ⚗ ✂ ▥ ⚝ ⚓
Facilities : ⅍ ⚬ ⚐ ⚱ ⚓ ⚖ launderette ⚘
Nearby : ⚐

Longitude : -2.10997
Latitude : 46.8097

Le Vieux Ranch

0251588658. www.levieuxranch.com

Address : chemin de la Parée du Jonc (4.3km to the northwest)

Opening times : from beginning April to end Sept.

5 ha (242 pitches) undulating, flat, grassy, sandy

Tariff : (2014 Price) 32.95€ ♦♦ ⇌ 回 ⚡ (10A) – Extra per person 7€ Reservation fee 16€

Rental rates : (2014 Price) (from beginning April to end Sept.) ⚒ – 22 🏠 – 8 🏠. Per week from 230 to 880€ – Reservation fee 16€

A gently undulating, attractive location, 200m from the beach.

Surroundings : ⅍ ⌁ ♀♀
Leisure activities : ♈ 🎪 ⚓ ⚗ ⚲ ⚝ ⚓ entertainment room
Facilities : ⅍ ⚬ ⚐ ⚱ ⚓ ⚖ launderette
Nearby : ✗ ⚘

Longitude : -2.11351
Latitude : 46.80717

Flower Plein Sud ♠♠

0251591040. www.campingpleinsud.com

Address : 246 route de Notre-Dame-de-Monts (4km to the northwest, on the D 38)

Opening times : from mid April to mid Sept.

2 ha (110 pitches) flat, grassy, sandy

Tariff : (2014 Price) 32€ ♦♦ ⇌ 回 ⚡ (6A) – Extra per person 5€ – Reservation fee 20€

Rental rates : (2014 Price) (from mid April to mid Sept.) ⚒ – 30 🏠 – 2 canvas bungalows – 2 tent lodges. Per night from 25 to 113€ – Per week from 294 to 791€ – Reservation fee 20€

An elongated site with well marked-out pitches.

Surroundings : ⌁ ♀
Leisure activities : ♈ ⚶ ⚗ ⚲ ⚝ multi-sports ground
Facilities : ⅍ ⚬ ⚐ ⚱ ⚓ ♈ launderette

Longitude : -2.11093
Latitude : 46.8103

La Forêt

0251588463. www.hpa-laforet.com

Address : 190 chemin de la Rive (5.5km to the northwest, follow the signs for Notre-Dame-de-Monts and take turning to the left)

Opening times : from beginning April to mid Sept.

1 ha (61 pitches)

Tariff : 34.90€ ♦♦ ⇌ 回 ⚡ (10A) – Extra per person 5.20€ – Reservation fee 30€

Rental rates : (from beginning April to end Sept.) – 16 🏠. Per week from 309 to 779 € – Reservation fee 30€

🚐 borne

Attractive shrubs and bushes decorate this eco-friendly campsite.

Surroundings : ⌁ ♀♀
Leisure activities : 🎪 ⚗ ⚲ ⚝
Facilities : ⅍ ⚬ ⚐ ⚱ ⚓ ♈ ▦

Longitude : -2.12993
Latitude : 46.81828

La Davière-Plage

0251582799. www.daviereplage.com

Address : 197 route de Notre-Dame-de-Monts (3km to the northwest, on the D 38)

Opening times : from mid April to end Sept.

3 ha (174 pitches)

Tariff : 28€ ♦♦ ⇌ 回 ⚡ (10A) – Extra per person 6.10€ – Reservation fee 20€

Rental rates : (from mid March to end Sept.) ⚒ – 27 🏠 – 6 canvas bungalows – 2 gîtes. Per night from 50 to 110€ – Per week from 220 to 815€ – Reservation fee 20€

🚐 borne 16€ – ⚓ ⚡ 16€

The campsite is divided into 2 separate sections; choose the pitches away from the road in preference.

Surroundings : ⌁ ♀
Leisure activities : ✗ 🎪 ⚗ ⚲ ⚝
Facilities : ⅍ ⚬ (July–Aug.) ⚱ ♈ launderette ⚑
Nearby : ♈

Longitude : -2.10085
Latitude : 46.8054

South

🏔 La Yole ♣♣

📞 0251586717. www.vendee-camping.eu – limited spaces for one-night stay

Address : chemin des Bosses, at Orouet (7km southeast)

Opening times : from mid April to end Sept.

5 ha (369 pitches)

Tariff : (2014 Price) 38.50€ ♥♥ ⊕ 🔲 🔅 (10A) – Extra per person 7.20€ – Reservation fee 29€

Rental rates : (2014 Price) (from beginning April to end Sept.) 🚫 – 58 🚐. Per night from 50 to 136€ – Per week from 270 to 950€ Reservation fee 29€

In a green, well-kept setting, with lots of flowers and plenty of shade from the pine wood nearby.

Surroundings : 🌿 🚐 ♨♨
Leisure activities : ♈ ✗ 🏠 ⊕ 🏕 jacuzzi 🚣 🚲 ✗ 🔲 🏊 ♨ launderette 🏊 🚵

GPS Longitude : -2.00728
Latitude : 46.75664

🏔 Les Jardins de l'Atlantique

📞 0251580574. www.camping-jardins-atlantique.com – limited spaces for one-night stay

Address : 100 rue de la Caillauderie (5.5km to the northeast)

Opening times : from beginning April to end Sept.

5 ha (318 pitches) undulating, relatively flat, flat, sandy

Tariff : (2014 Price) 26€ ♥♥ ⊕ 🔲 🔅 (6A) – Extra per person 6€ – Reservation fee 20€

Rental rates : (2014 Price) (from beginning April to end Sept.) – 61 🚐. Per night from 47 to 59 € – Per week from 275 to 705€ Reservation fee 20€

Divided into 2 separate sections on both sides of the road, with a pretty covered paddling pool, perfect for young children.

Surroundings : 🚐 ♨♨
Leisure activities : ♈ ✗ 🏠 ⊕ ♒ hammam, jacuzzi 🚣 🚲 🏊 ♨ multi-sports ground
Facilities : 🚿 ♨ 🚵 ♨ launderette 🏊 🚵

GPS Longitude : -2.02751
Latitude : 46.76972

🏔 Le Both d'Orouet

📞 0251586037. http://www.camping-lebothdorouet.com

Address : 77 avenue d'Orouët (6.7km southeast on the D 38, follow the signs for St-Hilaire-de-Riez, near a stream)

Opening times : from beginning April to end Sept.

4.4 ha (200 pitches)

Tariff : (2014 Price) 27€ ♥♥ ⊕ 🔲 🔅 (6A) – Extra per person 5.20€ Reservation fee 15.50€

Rental rates : (2014 Price) (from beginning April to end Sept.) – 31 🚐 – 19 🏠 – 5 tent lodges. Per night from 29 to 102€ – Per week from 315 to 712€ – Reservation fee 15.50€

🚐 borne

In a green setting; there's a games room in an old barn attached to the farmhouse dating back to 1875.

Surroundings : 🚐 ♨♨
Leisure activities : 🏠 jacuzzi 🚣 ♨ multi-sports ground
Facilities : 🚿 ♨ 🚵 ♨ 🚵 ♨ launderette 🏊 🚵
Nearby : ♈ ✗

GPS Longitude : -1.99759
Latitude : 46.76495

🏔 Campéole les Sirènes

📞 0251580131. http://vendee-camping.info

Address : avenue des Demoiselles (to the southeast, 500m from the beach)

Opening times : from beginning April to mid Sept.

15 ha/5 for camping (470 pitches) undulating, flat, sandy

Tariff : (2014 Price) 30€ ♥♥ ⊕ 🔲 🔅 (10A) – Extra per person 8€ – Reservation fee 25€

Rental rates : (2014 Price) (from beginning April to mid Sept.) 🏠 (2 mobile homes) – 52 🚐 – 40 🏠 – 40 canvas bungalows. Per night from 25 to 140€ – Per week from 175 to 980 € – Reservation fee 25€

🚐 borne

A pleasant, natural setting in Les Pays de Monts (regional pine forest), although the sanitary facilities are rather old.

Surroundings : 🌿 ♨♨
Leisure activities : ♈ ⊕ 🏕 🚲 🏊 multi-sports ground
Facilities : 🚿 ♨ ♨ launderette
Nearby : ✗

GPS Longitude : -2.0548
Latitude : 46.7799

There are several different types of sani-station ('borne' in French) – sanitation points providing fresh water and disposal points for grey water. See page 12 for further details.

🏔 Le Logis

📞 0251586067. www.camping-saintjeandemonts.com – limited spaces for one-night stay 🚫

Address : 4 chemin du Logis (4.3km southeast on the D 38, follow the signs for St-Gilles-Croix-de-Vie)

Opening times : from beginning May to beginning Sept.

0.8 ha (44 pitches) terraced, flat, grassy

Tariff : 26.50€ ♥♥ ⊕ 🔲 🔅 (10A) – Extra per person 5€ – Reservation fee 16€

Rental rates : (from beginning April to beginning Sept.) 🚫 – 11 🚐 – 2 gîtes. Per week from 260 to 620€ – Reservation fee 16€

🚐 borne 23€ – 🚐 🔅 8€

Choose the pitches away from the road in preference.

Surroundings : 🚐
Leisure activities : 🏠 🚣 🏊 (small swimming pool)
Facilities : 🚿 ♨ 🚵
Nearby : ♈ ✗ ♨

GPS Longitude : -2.01308
Latitude : 46.77953

Key to rentals symbols:

12 🚐   *Number of mobile homes*

20 🏠   *Number of chalets*

6 🛏   *Number of rooms to rent*

Per night   *Minimum/maximum rate per night*
30–50€

Per week   *Minimum/maximum rate per week*
300–1,000€

ST-JULIEN-DE-CONCELLES

44450 – Michelin map **316** H4 – pop. 6 839 – alt. 24
▶ Paris 384 – Nantes 19 – Angers 89 – La Roche-sur-Yon 80

🏕 Le Chêne

✆ 02 40 54 12 00. www.campingduchene.fr

Address : 1 route du Lac (located 1.5km east along the D 37 (diversion), near the small lake)

Opening times : from beginning April to end Oct.

2 ha (100 pitches) flat, grassy

Tariff : (2014 Price) 19.70€ ★★ ⇌ ⊞ ⚡ (10A) – Extra per person 4.80€

Rental rates : (2014 Price) Permanent – 21 ▦ – 4 canvas bungalows. Per night from 38 to 98€ – Per week from 195 to 610€

▦ 2 ⊞ 18.10€

In an attractive location, lots of green space; beside a lake.

Surroundings : ▭ ⚓⚓	
Leisure activities : ♈ 🍴 ⚓⚓ ✂ ▣ (open air in season)	**G P S** Longitude : -1.37098
Facilities : ⚒ ⟲ ⚒ ♒ launderette ⚲	Latitude : 47.2492
Nearby : ⚓ ⚲ pedalos	

ST-JULIEN-DES-LANDES

85150 – Michelin map **316** F8 – pop. 1 331 – alt. 59
▶ Paris 445 – Aizenay 17 – Challans 32 – La Roche-sur-Yon 24

🏕 Les Castels La Garangeoire ♣♣

✆ 02 51 46 65 39. www.camping-la-garangeoire.com

Address : head 2.8km north along the D 21

Opening times : from mid April to end Sept.

200 ha/10 for camping (356 pitches) undulating, terraced, flat, grassy

Tariff : 41.50€ ★★ ⇌ ⊞ ⚡ (16A) – Extra per person 8.70€ – Reservation fee 25€

Rental rates : (from mid April to end Sept.) ⚒ (1 mobile home) – 22 ▦ – 28 ⌂. Per night from 39 to 188€ – Per week from 272 to 1,315€ – Reservation fee 25€

▦ borne

An extensive, charming site in the grounds of a château, with meadows, lakes and woods.

Surroundings : ▭ ⚓⚓	
Leisure activities : ♈ 🍴 ⚓ ⚒ ⚓s jacuzzi ⚓⚓ ⚒ ⚒ ▣ ⚲ pedalos multi-sports ground	**G P S** Longitude : -1.71359
Facilities : ⚒ ⟲ ⚒ ♒ launderette ⚲ ⚒ refrigerators	Latitude : 46.66229

🏕 Sunêlia Village de La Guyonnière ♣♣

✆ 02 51 46 62 59. www.camping-guyonniere.com

Address : head 2.4km northwest along the D 12, follow the signs for Landevieille then continue 1.2km along the road to the right not far from the lake at Le Jaunay

Opening times : from end April to mid Sept.

30 ha (294 pitches)

Tariff : 47€ ★★ ⇌ ⊞ ⚡ (10A) – Extra per person 10€ – Reservation fee 20€

Rental rates : (from end April to mid Sept.) ⚒ – 83 ▦ – 25 ⌂ – 9 tent lodges. Per night from 34 to 214€ – Per week from 238 to 1,498€ – Reservation fee 20€

▦ borne 5€ – 5 ⊞ 25€

A leafy, green location on several small islands, with farm animals nearby.

Surroundings : ⚒ ⚲	
Leisure activities : ♈ 🍴 ⚒ ⚒ ⚒ ⚓s hammam, jacuzzi ⚓⚓ ⚒ ✂ ▣ ⚒ ⚲ farm or petting farm, multi-sports ground, spa centre	**G P S** Longitude : -1.74963 Latitude : 46.65258
Facilities : ⚒ ⟲ ▣ ⚒ ♒ launderette ⚲	

🏕 Yelloh! Village Château La Forêt ♣♣

✆ 02 51 46 62 11. www.chateaulaforet.com

Address : located 0.5 km northeast along the D 55, follow the signs for Martinet

Opening times : from mid May to beginning Sept.

50 ha/5 for camping (209 pitches)

Tariff : 43€ ★★ ⇌ ⊞ ⚡ (10A) – Extra per person 7€

Rental rates : (from mid May to beginning Sept.) – 29 ▦ – 9 ⌂ – 1 cabin in the trees – 5 tent lodges. Per night from 29 to 209€ – Per week from 203 to 1,463€

In a wooded setting in the grounds of the château and its outbuildings.

Surroundings : ⚒ ▭ ⚲	
Leisure activities : ♈ 🍴 ⚒ ⚒ daytime ⚒ ⚓⚓ ⚒ ✂ ⚒ ▣ ⚒ ⚲ disco, zip wiring	**G P S** Longitude : -1.71135 Latitude : 46.64182
Facilities : ⚒ ⟲ ⚒ ⚲ ⚒ ♒ launderette ⚲	

ST-LAURENT-SUR-SÈVRE

85290 – Michelin map **316** K6 – pop. 3 442 – alt. 121
▶ Paris 365 – Angers 76 – Bressuire 36 – Cholet 14

🏕 Le Rouge Gorge

✆ 02 51 67 86 39. www.camping-lerougegorge-vendee.com

Address : route de La Verrie (located 1km west along the D 111)

Opening times : from mid April to mid Oct.

2 ha (93 pitches)

Tariff : (2014 Price) 23.30€ ★★ ⇌ ⊞ ⚡ (8A) – Extra per person 4.20€ Reservation fee 10€

Rental rates : (2014 Price) (from mid April to mid Oct.) ⚒ – 9 ▦ – 13 ⌂ – 4 tent lodges. Per night from 55 to 102€ – Per week from 228 to 715€ – Reservation fee 10€

▦ borne

A pleasant setting with lots of green space and plenty of shade.

Surroundings : ▭ ⚲	
Leisure activities : ⚒ ⚓⚓ ▣ zip wiring	**G P S** Longitude : -0.90307
Facilities : ⚒ ⟲ ⚒ ⚒ ♒ launderette ⚲	Latitude : 46.95788
Nearby : ⚓	

For more information on visiting particular towns or regions, consult the relevant regional MICHELIN Green Guide. We also recommend you use the appropriate Michelin regional map to locate your selected campsite, to calculate distances and to work out the best route.

ST-MICHEL-EN-L'HERM

85580 – Michelin map **316** I9 – pop. 2 129 – alt. 9
▶ Paris 453 – Luçon 15 – La Rochelle 46 – La Roche-sur-Yon 47

▲▲▲ Les Mizottes

℘ 02 51 30 23 63. www.
campinglesmizottes.fr

Address : 41 rue des Anciens Quais
(800m southwest along the D 746,
follow the signs for l'Aiguillon-sur-Mer)

Opening times : from beginning April
to end Sept.

3 ha (150 pitches) flat, grassy

Tariff : (2014 Price) 27 € ♣♣ ⇌ ▣
⚡ (6A) – Extra per person 5 € –

Reservation fee 20 €
Rental rates : (2014 Price) (from beginning April to end Sept.)
♿ (1 mobile home) – 40 ⟦⟧ – 3 canvas bungalows. Per night
from 42 to 80 € – Per week from 210 to 755 € – Reservation fee 20 €
⟦⟧ 2 ▣ 27 €

High-quality services and leisure facillities.

Surroundings : 🐟 ▭ ⚲
Leisure activities : ♈ ✕ 🏛 🚶🚴🏊 ⛱
multi-sports ground, entertainment room
Facilities : ♿ ⚬ ⛺🍴 launderette 🐾

G P S Longitude : -1.25482
Latitude : 46.34943

*The classification (1 to 5 tents, **black** or red) that we
award to selected sites in this guide is our own system.
It should not be confused with the classification
(1 to 5 stars) of official organisations.*

ST-PÈRE-EN-RETZ

44320 – Michelin map **316** D4 – pop. 4 113 – alt. 14
▶ Paris 425 – Challans 54 – Nantes 45 – Pornic 13

▲ Le Grand Fay

℘ 02 40 21 72 89. www.camping-grandfay.com

Address : rue du Grand Fay (take the eastern exit along the D 78,
follow the signs for Frossay then continue 500m down the turning
to the right)

Opening times : Permanent

1.2 ha (76 pitches)

Tariff : 25 € ♣♣ ⇌ ▣ ⚡ (6A) – Extra per person 5.50 € – Reservation
fee 15 €

Rental rates : Permanent – 5 ⟦⟧. Per night from 65 to 105 € –
Per week from 220 to 640 € – Reservation fee 15 €

*In a quiet residential area, behind the municipal sports centre
and near a lake.*

Surroundings : ⚲⚲
Leisure activities : ♈⛱⛱
Facilities : ♿ ⚬ 🍴 launderette
Nearby : ✂ 🐟

G P S Longitude : -2.03654
Latitude : 47.20266

*Some information or pricing may have changed since
the guide went to press. We recommend you check the
price list online in advance or at the entrance to the
campsite and enquire about possible restrictions.*

ST-PHILBERT-DE-GRAND-LIEU

44310 – pop. 7 806 – alt. 10
▶ Paris 407 – Nantes 27 – La Roche-sur-Yon 57 – Angers 112

▲ La Boulogne

℘ 02 40 78 88 79. www.camping-la-boulogne.com

Address : 1 avenue de Nantes

4.5 ha (180 pitches) flat, grassy

Rentals : 1 caravan – 10 ⟦⟧ – 10 canvas bungalows.

Beside the Boulogne river and near a pleasant lake.

Surroundings : ⚲⚲
Leisure activities : ♈⛱ 🐟
Facilities : ♿ ⚬ ▥ ⛺🍴 launderette
Nearby : jacuzzi 🏊 🏄 ⛱ ♪

G P S Longitude : -1.64027
Latitude : 47.0419

ST-RÉVÉREND

85220 – Michelin map **316** F7 – pop. 1 323 – alt. 19
▶ Paris 453 – Aizenay 20 – Challans 19 – La Roche-sur-Yon 36

▲▲▲ Le Pont Rouge

℘ 02 51 54 68 50. www.camping-lepontrouge.com

Address : rue Georges Clemenceau (take the southwestern exit along
the D 94 and take the road to the right; beside a stream)

Opening times : from beginning April to end Sept.

2.2 ha (73 pitches)

Tariff : 24.50 € ♣♣ ⇌ ▣ ⚡ (6A) – Extra per person 5 € – Reservation
fee 15 €

Rental rates : (2014 Price) (from beginning April to end Sept.) –
17 ⟦⟧ – 1 🏠 – 4 canvas bungalows. Per night from 40 to 60 € –
Per week from 180 to 731 € – Reservation fee 15 €

A green, well-kept setting, with a range of rental options.

Surroundings : 🐟 ▭ ⚲⚲
Leisure activities : ♈ ✕ ⊙ nighttime ⛱⛱ ⛱
Facilities : ♿ ⚬ ⛺🍴 launderette 🐾

G P S Longitude : -1.83448
Latitude : 46.69366

ST-VINCENT-SUR-JARD

85520 – Michelin map **316** G9 – pop. 1 205 – alt. 10
▶ Paris 454 – Challans 64 – Luçon 34 – La Rochelle 70

▲▲▲ Chadotel La Bolée d'Air

℘ 02 51 90 36 05. www.chadotel.com

Address : route du Bouil (situated 2km east along the D 21 follow the
signs for Longeville and take a right turn)

Opening times : from beginning April to end Sept.

5.7 ha (280 pitches) flat, grassy

Tariff : 31 € ♣♣ ⇌ ▣ ⚡ (10A) – Extra per person 6 € – Reservation
fee 25 €

Rental rates : (from beginning April to end Sept.) – 1 ⟦⟧ –
1 🏠. Per night from 28 to 129 € – Per week from 196 to 903 €
Reservation fee 25 €

⟦⟧ 1 ▣ 31 €

Choose the pitches away from the road in preference.

Surroundings : ▭ ⚲⚲
Leisure activities : ♈ 🍴 ⊙ 🍴 ⛱🚴✂ ♫
🏊⛱ multi-sports ground
Facilities : ♿ ⚬ ⛺🛁 ⟲ 🍴 launderette ⛱

G P S Longitude : -1.52622
Latitude : 46.41978

Les Mizottes

STE-LUCE-SUR-LOIRE

44980 – Michelin map **316** H4 – pop. 11 679 – alt. 9
▶ Paris 378 – Nantes 7 – Angers 82 – Cholet 58

⚠ Belle Rivière

🖉 02 40 25 85 81. www.camping-belleriviere.com

Address : route des Perrières (situated 2km northeast along the D 68, follow the signs for Thouaré; at La Gicquelière, take turning to the right for 1km; direct access to a branch of the Loire river)

Opening times : Permanent

3 ha (110 pitches) flat, grassy

Tariff : ﹡ 4.65€ ⬅ 2.20€ 圓 5.35€ – ⅊ (10A) 3.90€
Rental rates : (2014 Price) Permanent ⇝ – 7 ⌂. Per week from 265 to 540€ – Reservation fee 15€
🖭 borne – 20 圓 17.55€

A pleasant, leafy setting with a great variety of trees and shrubs. Bus stop for the town.

Surroundings : 🏞 ♤♤ Leisure activities : ⬆ ♠ Facilities : & ⌗ (June-Aug) 🏢 ♨ 🚾 launderette Nearby : 🐎 🏇	**G P S** Longitude : -1.45574 Latitude : 47.254

SAUMUR

49400 – Michelin map **317** I5 – pop. 28 070 – alt. 30
▶ Paris 300 – Angers 67 – Châtellerault 76 – Cholet 70

⚠ Flowers L'Île d'Offard ♣♣

🖉 02 41 40 30 00. www.cvtloisirs.com

Address : Bd de Verden (access via the town centre, on an island in the Loire river)

Opening times : from mid March to mid Nov.

4.5 ha (250 pitches) flat, grassy

Tariff : 31€ ﹡﹡ ⬅ 圓 ⅊ (10A) – Extra per person 7€ – Reservation fee 10€

Rental rates : (2014 Price) (from mid March to mid Nov.) ⇝ – 50 ⌂ – 10 tent lodges – 9 tents on stilts. Per night from 49 to 122€ – Per week from 190 to 854€ – Reservation fee 20€
🖭 borne

A pleasant location at the tip of the island, with a view of the château.

Surroundings : < 🏞 ♧ Leisure activities : ♟ ✗ 🏛 🕑daytime 🏃 ⬆ ♠ 🛝 🐟 Facilities : & ⌗ 🏢 ♨ 🚾 ♈ launderette ⚓ Nearby : ✗	**G P S** Longitude : -0.0656 Latitude : 47.26022

LA SELLE-CRAONNAISE

53800 – Michelin map **310** C7 – pop. 931 – alt. 71
▶ Paris 316 – Angers 68 – Châteaubriant 32 – Château-Gontier 29

⚠ Base de Loisirs de la Rincerie

🖉 02 43 06 17 52. http://www.la-rincerie.com

Address : 3.5km northwest along the D 111, D 150, follow the signs for Ballots and take turning to the left

Opening times : from mid March to mid Oct.

120 ha/5 for camping (50 pitches) relatively flat, flat, grassy

Tariff : 14.60€ ﹡﹡ ⬅ 圓 ⅊ (10A) – Extra per person 3.30€

Rental rates : (from mid March to mid Oct.) ⇝ –1 ⌂ –1 🏠 – 4 canvas bungalows. Per night from 50 to 65€ – Per week from 245 to 310€
🖭 borne 2€

Situated near a small lake with plenty of water-based activities.

Surroundings : 🏞 ≤ Leisure activities : 🕑daytime 🏊 🏇 Facilities : & ⌗ 🏢 ♨ 🚾 ♈ At the leisure/activities centre : ⬆ 🚲 🛶 ♨	**G P S** Longitude : -1.06528 Latitude : 47.86631

SILLÉ-LE-GUILLAUME

72140 – Michelin map **310** I5 – pop. 2 361 – alt. 161
▶ Paris 230 – Alençon 39 – Laval 55 – Le Mans 35

⚠ Indigo Les Molières

© Campingindigo

🖉 02 43 20 16 12. www.camping-indigo.com

Address : at Sillé-Plage (head 2.5km north along the D 5, D 105, D 203 and take the road to the right)

Opening times : from end April to end Sept.

3.5 ha (133 pitches) flat, grassy

Tariff : (2014 Price) 26.50€ ﹡﹡ ⬅ 圓 ⅊ (10A) – Extra per person 5.30€ – Reservation fee 22€

Rental rates : (2014 Price) (from end April to end Sept.) – 12 ⌂ – 25 tent lodges. Per night from 44 to 95€ – Per week from 216 to 665€ – Reservation fee 22€
🖭 borne 7€ – 40 圓 21.20€

The campsite is in the forest, near a small lake and two ponds.

Surroundings : 🏞 ♨♨♨ Leisure activities : 🏛 Facilities : & ⌗ 🚾 Nearby : ♟ ✗ ⛳ ♨ 🏇 pedalos	**G P S** Longitude : -0.12917 Latitude : 48.18333

We have selected the best campsites in France with our usual care, listing those with the best facilities in the most pleasant surroundings.

SILLÉ-LE-PHILIPPE

72460 – Michelin map **310** L6 – pop. 1 091 – alt. 35
▶ Paris 195 – Beaumont-sur-Sarthe 25 – Bonnétable 11 Connerré 15

⚠ Les Castels Le Château de Chanteloup

🖉 02 43 27 51 07. www.chateau-de-chanteloup.com

Address : at Chanteloup (situated 2km southwest along the D 301, follow the signs for Le Mans)

Opening times : from beginning June to end Aug.

20 ha (100 pitches) relatively flat, flat, grassy, sandy, pond, natural setting among trees and bushes

Tariff : ﹡ 9.50€ ⬅ 圓 16€ – ⅊ (10A) 4€

Rental rates : (from beginning June to end Aug.) – 3 apartments – 5 tent lodges – 2 gîtes. Per week from 610 to 750€

Surroundings : 🏞 ♨♨♨ Leisure activities : ♟ ✗ 🏛 ⬆ 🚲 🛶 Facilities : ⌗ 🏢 🚾 ♈ launderette ⚓	**G P S** Longitude : 0.34012 Latitude : 48.10461

SOULLANS

85300 – Michelin map **316** E7 – pop. 4 058 – alt. 12
▶ Paris 443 – Challans 7 – Noirmoutier-en-l'Île 46 – La Roche-sur-Yon 48

⚠ Municipal le Moulin Neuf

✆ 02 51 68 00 24. camping-soullans@orange.fr

Address : rue Saint-Christophe (take the northern exit along the D 69, follow the signs for Challans and take the turning to the right)

Opening times : from mid June to mid Sept.

1.2 ha (80 pitches) flat, grassy

Tariff : (2014 Price) 9.50€ ✷✷ ⛖ 回 ⚡ (10A) – Extra per person 2.50€

Near the town, a small and peaceful site with clearly marked-out pitches, but average sanitary facilities.

Surroundings : ⌂ ▭ ♀
Facilities : & ⚬▭ ▥
Nearby : ✕ ⚲

G P S Longitude : -1.89566
Latitude : 46.79817

TALMONT-ST-HILAIRE

85440 – Michelin map **316** G9 – pop. 6 829 – alt. 35
▶ Paris 448 – Challans 55 – Luçon 38 – La Roche-sur-Yon 30

⚠ Yelloh! Village Le Littoral

✆ 02 51 22 04 64. www.campinglelittoral.com

Address : at Le Porteau (9.5km southwest along the D 949, D 4a, after Querry-Pigeon, take right turn onto D 129, follow coast road to les Sables-d'Olonne; 100m from the ocean)

Opening times : from beginning April to mid Sept.

9 ha (483 pitches) relatively flat, flat, grassy, sandy

Tariff : 45€ ✷✷ ⛖ 回 ⚡ (10A) – Extra per person 7€

Rental rates : (from beginning April to mid Sept.) & (1 mobile home) Ⓟ – 194 ⛺ – 19 ⌂. Per night from 39 to 259 € – Per week from 273 to 1,813€

⛺ borne

An attractive site with upmarket rental accommodation and a pedestrian-only area. Free shuttle to the beaches.

Surroundings : ▭ ♀
Leisure activities : ▾ ✕ ⛩ ☺ ☀ ⅃ jacuzzi
⛆ ✼ ▣ ⅃ ⅄ multi-sports ground
Facilities : & ⚬▭ ▥ ♨ ⅄ ☂ ¶ launderette
⛲ ⅃

G P S Longitude : -1.70222
Latitude : 46.45195

⚠ Le Paradis

✆ 02 51 22 22 36. www.camping-leparadis85.com

Address : rue de la Source (3.7km west along the D 949, follow the signs for Les Sables-d'Olonne, turn left onto D 4a, follow the signs for Querry-Pigeon and take the road to the right)

4.9 ha (148 pitches) terraced, relatively flat, flat, grassy, sandy
Rentals : 60 ⛺ – 15 ⌂ – 8 canvas bungalows.

A sloping site, well shaded in places, with a range of rental accommodation.

Surroundings : ⌂ ▭ ♀♀
Leisure activities : ▾ ✕ ⊙ nighttime ⌂▲ ▣
(open air in season), multi-sports ground
Facilities : & ⚬▭ ⅄ ¶ launderette ⅃

G P S Longitude : -1.65491
Latitude : 46.46462

THARON-PLAGE

44730 – Michelin map **316** C5
▶ Paris 444 – Nantes 59 – St-Nazaire 25 – Vannes 94

⚠ La Riviera

✆ 02 28 53 54 88. www.campinglariviera.com – limited spaces for one-night stay

Address : rue des Gâtineaux (east of the resort, along the D 96, follow the signs for St-Michel-Chef-Chef)

6 ha (250 pitches)
Rentals : 2 ⛺ – 5 ⌂.

A mobile home village for owner-occupiers, but with some space for tents and caravans.

Surroundings : ▭
Leisure activities : ▾ ⛩ jacuzzi ⌂▲ ⅃
multi-sports ground
Facilities : & ⚬▭ ▥ ⅄ ☂ ¶ ▥

G P S Longitude : -2.15087
Latitude : 47.16492

TENNIE

72240 – Michelin map **310** I6 – pop. 1 023 – alt. 100
▶ Paris 224 – Alençon 49 – Laval 69 – Le Mans 26

⚠ Municipal de la Vègre

✆ 02 43 20 59 44. www.camping.tennie.fr – limited spaces for one-night stay

Address : rue Andrée Le Grou (take the western exit along the D 38, follow the signs for Ste-Suzanne)

Opening times : from beginning April to end Sept.

2 ha (83 pitches) flat, grassy ✷✷

Tariff : (2014 Price) 11.15€ ✷✷ ⛖ 回 ⚡ (6A) – Extra per person 2.25€
Rental rates : (2014 Price) Permanent & (1 chalet) ⅄ – 1 ⛺ –
5 ⌂. Per night from 70 to 83€ – Per week from 285 to 430€

In a pleasant setting beside a river and a lake.

Surroundings : ⌂ ▭ ⅃
Leisure activities : ⌂▲ ⌂▲ ✼ ☀ ⅃
Facilities : & ⚬▭ ⅃ ¶ ▥
Nearby : ✕ ⚲

G P S Longitude : -0.07874
Latitude : 48.10705

LA TRANCHE-SUR-MER

85360 – Michelin map **316** H9 – pop. 2 715 – alt. 4
▶ Paris 459 – Luçon 31 – Niort 100 – La Rochelle 64

⚠ Club Airotel Le Jard 👥

✆ 02 51 27 43 79. www.campingdujard.fr ⅄

Address : 123 boulevard de Lattre de Tassigny (at La Grière-Plage, 3.8km along the road to L'Aiguillon)

Opening times : from beginning May to mid Sept.

6 ha (350 pitches) flat, grassy

Tariff : 33€ ✷✷ ⛖ 回 ⚡ (10A) – Extra per person 7€ – Reservation fee 25€

Rental rates : (from beginning May to mid Sept.) ⅄ – 60 ⛺.
Per night from 48 to 124€ – Per week from 195 to 865€ –
Reservation fee 25€

A pleasant site with good sanitary facilities.

Surroundings : ▭ ♀♀
Leisure activities : ▾ ✕ ⛩ ☺ ☀ ⅃ ⛵
⌂▲ ⛆ ✼ ⅃ ▣ ⅃ ⅄
Facilities : & ⚬▭ ⌺ ⅄ ☂ ¶ launderette
⛲ ⅃

G P S Longitude : -1.38694
Latitude : 46.34788

To visit a town or region, use the MICHELIN Green Guides.

⚘ Les Préveils ♠♣

📞 0251303052. www.lespreveils.pep79.net

Address : avenue Sainte Anne (at La Grière-Plage, follow the signs for L'Aiguillon for 4.2km)

Opening times : from beginning April to end Sept.

4 ha (180 pitches) undulating

Tariff : 34€ ♦♦ ⇔ 🔲 (10A) – Extra per person 7€ – Reservation fee 18€

Rental rates : (2014 Price) (from beginning April to end Sept.) ♿ (1 mobile home) – 50 🚐 – 5 🏠 – 6 🛏 – 10 apartments. Per night from 55 to 128€ – Per week from 382 to 900€ – Reservation fee 18€

A pleasant site 200m from the beach.

Surroundings : ⌂ ♀♀
Leisure activities : ✗ 🖼 ⚡ 🎣 ⛵ jacuzzi ⚡ multi-sports ground, entertainment room
Facilities : ♿ ⚬ 🛁 🚿 ⚐ 🍴 launderette ♻

Longitude : -1.3936
Latitude : 46.34398

⚘ Baie d'Aunis

📞 0251274736. www.camping-baiedaunis.com ⚐ (from beginning July to end Aug.)

Address : 10 rue du Pertuis Breton (take the eastern exit, follow the signs for l'Aiguillon)

Opening times : from end April to mid Sept.

2.5 ha (149 pitches)

Tariff : (2014 Price) 35.40€ ♦♦ ⇔ 🔲 (10A) – Extra per person 7.80€ – Reservation fee 30€

Rental rates : (2014 Price) (from end April to mid Sept.) ⚐ 10 🚐 – 9 🏠. Per week from 350 to 870€ – Reservation fee 30€
🚐 borne

Situated 50m from the beach; choose the pitches away from the road.

Surroundings : ⌂ ♀♀
Leisure activities : 🍴 ✗ 🖼 ⚡ ⛵ multi-sports ground
Facilities : ♿ ⚬ 🕌 🚿 🍴 launderette ♻
Nearby : ✂ 🎣 ♦

Longitude : -1.4321
Latitude : 46.34602

⚘ TRIAIZE

85580 – Michelin map **316** I9 – pop. 1 011 – alt. 3
▶ Paris 446 – Fontenay-le-Comte 38 – Luçon 9 – Niort 71

⚘ Municipal

📞 0251561153. www.triaize.fr

Address : rue du Stade (in the village)

Opening times : from beginning July to end Aug.

2.7 ha (70 pitches) flat, grassy, stony, pond

Tariff : (2014 Price) ♦ 2.60€ ⇔ 1.80€ 🔲 2.30€ – 🔌 (10A) 2.80€

Rental rates : (2014 Price) (from beginning May to end Sept.) – 6 🚐. Per night from 125 to 260€ – Per week from 220 to 430€
🚐 5 🔲 14€

Surroundings : ⚐ ⌂
Leisure activities : ⚡ ⛵
Facilities : ♿ ⚐ 🖼
Nearby : ✂

Longitude : -1.20152
Latitude : 46.39515

⚘ LA TURBALLE

44420 – Michelin map **316** A3 – pop. 4 515 – alt. 6
▶ Paris 457 – La Baule 13 – Guérande 7 – Nantes 84

⚘ Municipal les Chardons Bleus

📞 0240628060. www.camping-laturballe.fr

Address : boulevard de La Grande Falaise (2.5km to the south)

Opening times : from end March to end Sept.

5 ha (300 pitches)

Tariff : (2014 Price) 23.30€ ♦♦ ⇔ 🔲 🔌 (10A) – Extra per person 5.10€ – Reservation fee 10€

Rental rates : (2014 Price) (from mid Jan. to mid Dec.) ♿ (2 chalets) – 10 🏠. Per week from 275 to 653€ – Reservation fee 10€

For lovers of wide, open spaces, near the beach.

Surroundings : ⚐ ⌂ ⛰
Leisure activities : 🍴 ✗ 🖼 ⚡ ⛵
Facilities : ♿ ⚬ 🚿 🍴 launderette ♻ ♻
Nearby : 🚴 ⚡ fitness trail

Longitude : -2.50048
Latitude : 47.32832

⚘ Parc Ste-Brigitte

📞 0240248891. www.campingsaintebrigitte.com

Address : chemin des Routes (3km southeast, follow the signs for Guérande)

Opening times : from beginning April to end Sept.

10 ha/4 for camping (150 pitches) relatively flat, flat, grassy, pond

Tariff : (2014 Price) ♦ 6.90€ ⇔ 3.55€ 🔲 7.90€ – 🔌 (10A) 6.80€ – Reservation fee 16€

Rental rates : (2014 Price) (from beginning April to end Sept.) – 19 🚐. Per night from 57 to 98€ – Per week from 380 to 783€ – Reservation fee 16€
🚐 borne

Pretty grounds and manor house; the ageing facilities are fortunately well maintained.

Surroundings : ⚐ 🎵
Leisure activities : ✗ 🖼 ⚡ 🚴 ⛵ (open air in season) ⚐
Facilities : ♿ ⚬ 🚿 ⚐ 🍴 launderette ♻

Longitude : -2.4717
Latitude : 47.34254

This guide is updated regularly, so buy your new copy every year!

⚘ VAIRÉ

85150 – Michelin map **316** F8 – pop. 1 474 – alt. 49
▶ Paris 448 – Challans 31 – La Mothe-Achard 9 – La Roche-sur-Yon 27

⚘ Le Roc

📞 0251337189. www.campingleroc.com

Address : route de Brem-sur-Mer (located 1.5km northwest along the D 32, follow the signs for Landevieille and turn left towards Brem-sur-Mer)

1.4 ha (100 pitches)

Rentals : 26 🚐 – 3 🏠 – 2 canvas bungalows.

A shaded setting, but choose the pitches away from the road.

Surroundings : ⌂ ♀
Leisure activities : 🍴 ✗ 🎣 ⚡ ⛵ (small swimming pool) ⚡
Facilities : ♿ ⚬ 🕌 🚿 🍴 launderette

Longitude : -1.76785
Latitude : 46.60815

VARENNES-SUR-LOIRE

49730 – Michelin map **317** J5 – pop. 1 898 – alt. 27
▶ Paris 292 – Bourgueil 15 – Chinon 22 – Loudun 30

⚏ Les Castels Domaine de la Brèche ♙♙

✆ 02 41 51 22 92. www.domainedelabreche.com

Address : 5 Impasse de la Brèche (6km west along the D 85. RD 952, follow the signs for Saumur, and take the road to the right; beside the lake)

Opening times : from mid April to mid Sept.

14 ha/7 for camping (201 pitches)

Tariff : 49€ ♛♛ ⇔ 🅿 ⚡ (16A) – Extra per person 9€ – Reservation fee 10€

Rental rates : (from mid April to mid Sept.) – 3 caravans – 39 ⌂ – 1 cabin in the trees – 2 canvas bungalows. Per night from 28 to 125€ – Per week from 142 to 1,364€ – Reservation fee 10€

⛺ borne
A pleasant site and setting beside a lake.

Surroundings : ⚲ ⌂ ♀
Leisure activities : ♟ ✗ ⚑ ♣ ⛵ 🏇 ⚐ ⚓ ⚒ ⚏ ⚌ ⚍ ⚎ farm or petting farm, pitch & putt (18 holes), multi-sports ground
Facilities : ⚒ ⚭ ⚙ ⚗ ⚖ ⚕ ⚔ ⚓ ⚒ ⚑
G P S Longitude : 0.00213
Latitude : 47.24837

The prices listed were supplied by the campsite owners in 2014 (if prices were not available, those from the previous year are given). The fees should be regarded as basic charges and may fluctuate with inflation.

VENDRENNES

85250 – Michelin map **316** J7 – pop. 1 447 – alt. 97
▶ Paris 392 – Nantes 65 – La Roche-sur-Yon 30 – Niort 95

⚏ La Motte

✆ 02 51 63 59 67. www.camping-lamotte.com

Address : La Motte (0.4km to the northeast)

Opening times : Permanent

3.5 ha (83 pitches) flat, grassy

Tariff : (2014 Price) 20.70€ ♛♛ ⇔ 🅿 ⚡ (16A) – Extra per person 3.60€

Rental rates : (2014 Price) Permanent – 33 ⌂ – 5 ⌂. Per night from 52 to 180€– Per week from 225 to 1,030€

Green, floral setting arranged around a small ornamental lake.

Surroundings : ⚲ ⌂
Leisure activities : ♟ ✗ ⚑ ⚘ daytime ⚓
⚒ bowling
Facilities : ⚒ ⚭ ⚙ ⚔ ⚖ launderette ⚓
G P S Longitude : -1.11854
Latitude : 46.82587

Michelin classification:

⚏ *Extremely comfortable, equipped to a very high standard*
⚏ *Very comfortable, equipped to a high standard*
⚏ *Comfortable and well equipped*
⚏ *Reasonably comfortable*
⚏ *Satisfactory*

VIHIERS

49310 – Michelin map **317** F6 – pop. 4 275 – alt. 100
▶ Paris 334 – Angers 45 – Cholet 29 – Saumur 40

⚏ Municipal de la Vallée du Lys

✆ 02 41 75 00 14. www.vihiers.fr – ⚑

Address : route du Voide (take the western exit along the D 960, follow the signs for Cholet then take the D 54 to the right, following signs for Valanjou; beside the Lys river)

Opening times : from mid June to mid Sept.

0.3 ha (30 pitches) flat, grassy

Tariff : (2014 Price) ♛ 2€ ⇔ 2.55€ 🅿 2.55€ – ⚡ (6A) 1.95€

Surroundings : ⚲ ♀
Leisure activities : ⚑ ⚓ ⚒
Facilities : ⚒ ⚗
G P S Longitude : -0.54034
Latitude : 47.1471

VILLIERS-CHARLEMAGNE

53170 – Michelin map **310** E7 – pop. 1 052 – alt. 105
▶ Paris 277 – Angers 61 – Châteaubriant 61 – Château-Gontier 12

⚏ Village Vacances Pêche

✆ 02 43 07 71 68. http://www.vacancesetpeche.fr

Address : Village des Haies (take the western exit along the D 4, follow the signs for Cossé-le-Vivien and take road to the left near the stadium)

Opening times : Permanent

9 ha/1 for camping (20 pitches) flat, grassy

Tariff : 17.70€ ♛♛ ⇔ 🅿 ⚡ (16A) – Extra per person 6.30€

Rental rates : Permanent – 12 ⌂. Per week from 200 to 595€ – Reservation fee 15€

⛺ borne – 10 🅿 8.30€
A pleasant site for angling, with chalets situated virtually on top of the water.

Surroundings : ⚲ ⚶ ⌂ ♀
Leisure activities : ⚑ ⚘ daytime ⚓ ⚒ ⚓
Facilities : ⚒ ⚭ ⚗ – 20 individual sanitary facilities (⚒ ⚙ ⚔ wc) ⚖ ⚕ ⚔ refrigerators
Nearby : ✗ ⚑
G P S Longitude : -0.68233
Latitude : 47.9208

YVRÉ-L'ÉVÊQUE

72530 – Michelin map **310** K6 – pop. 4 412 – alt. 57
▶ Paris 204 – Nantes 194 – Le Mans 8 – Alençon 66

⚏ Onlycamp Le Pont Romain

✆ 02 43 82 25 39. www.onlycamp.fr

Address : La Châtaigneraie (leave the village via the the Roman bridge, then take the road to the left, continue for 200m)

Opening times : from mid March to mid Nov.

2.5 ha (80 pitches) flat, grassy

Tariff : (2014 Price) 22€ ♛♛ ⇔ 🅿 ⚡ (16A) – Extra per person 5.60€

Rental rates : (2014 Price) (from mid March to mid Nov.) 🅿 – 5 ⌂ – 5 ⌂ – 2 canvas bungalows. Per night from 49 to 129€ – Per week from 80 to 369€

⛺ borne 5€ – 10 🅿 22€

Surroundings : ♀
Leisure activities : ⚑ ⚓ ⚒
Facilities : ⚭ 🅿 ⚙ ⚖ ⚕ ⚔ launderette
Nearby : ⚒ ♟ ✗
G P S Longitude : 0.27972
Latitude : 48.01944

PICARDY

H. Lenain / hemis.fr

Are you ready for an action-packed journey through Picardy's fair and historic lands? The region that gave Gaul – now France – her first Christian king, Clovis, is renowned for its wealthy Cistercian abbeys, splendid Gothic cathedrals and flamboyant town halls, along with deeply poignant reminders of two world wars. If you are in the mood to explore the countryside, take a boat trip through the floating gardens of Amiens or explore the botanical reserve of Marais de Cessière. Try a spot of birdwatching on the Somme estuary or at Marquenterre bird sanctuary. Spend time relaxing in unspoilt hills, woods, pastures and vineyards. Picardy has a rich culinary history, so where better to try *soupe aux hortillonages* (vegetable gardener's soup), the famous *agneau pré-salé* (lamb fattened on the salt marshes), a plate of smoked eel or duck pâté, or a dessert laced with Chantilly cream. 'Drink well, eat well and do nothing', to quote Lafleur, the famous 19th-century Amiens puppet.

Legend:
- Locality with campsite
- Locality with campsite and rental option
- Locality with campsite and campervan area
- Locality with at least one pleasant campsite
- Vannes
- Moyaux — Motorway service area for campervans

AMIENS

80000 – Michelin map **301** G8 – pop. 133 998 – alt. 34
▶ Paris 135 – Lille 122 – Beauvais 62 – Arras 74

⛰ Sites et Paysages Le Parc des Cygnes

℘ 03 22 43 29 28. www.parcdescygnes.com

Address : 111 avenue des Cygnes (to the northeast, rue du Grand-Marais – from the bypass (rocade), take exit 40 for Amiens Longpré)

Opening times : from beginning April to mid Oct.

3.2 ha (145 pitches)

Tariff : 27.70€ ♦♦ ⇔ 🔲 🔌 (10A) – Extra per person 6.70€ – Reservation fee 13.50€
Rental rates : (from beginning April to mid Oct.) ⌛ – 9 🚐. Per night from 47 to 107€ – Per week from 280 to 660€ – Reservation fee 13.50€
🚐 borne 4.20€ – 5 🔲 11.50€
There's a bus to the town centre.

Surroundings : ♀
Leisure activities : ▼ ✗ 🛆 ⇔ ⚲ 🚴 ♒
Facilities : ⅙ ⊶ 🎦 🖫 🛆 ⚗ ⚐ 🕆 launderette
Nearby : ⌇

GPS Longitude : 2.25918
Latitude : 49.92118

ATTICHY

Michelin map **305** J4
▶ Paris 109 – Amiens 103 – Beauvais 80 – Laon 59

⛰ L' Aigrette

℘ 03 44 42 15 97. www.campingdelaigrette.com

Address : 22 rue Fontaine Aubier

Opening times : from beginning March to end Nov.

1.3 ha (61 pitches) flat, grassy

Tariff : 20€ ♦♦ ⇔ 🔲 🔌 (10A) – Extra per person 4€
Rental rates : Permanent ⌛ – 1 🚐 – 4 tipis – 1 tent lodge. Per night from 60 to 155€ – Per week from 240 to 395€
🚐 borne 4€
Situated beside a large lake with swans and ducks.

Surroundings : ⌇ ⊏ ♀♀
Leisure activities : ⌇
Facilities : ⅙ ⊶ 🖫 🛆 ⚐ 🕆 launderette
Nearby : ✗ ♒ ⌇

GPS Longitude : 3.05295
Latitude : 49.40667

BERNY-RIVIÈRE

02290 – Michelin map **306** A6 – pop. 604 – alt. 49
▶ Paris 100 – Compiègne 24 – Laon 55 – Noyon 28

⛰ La Croix du Vieux Pont ♣♣

℘ 03 23 55 50 02. www.la-croix-du-vieux-pont.com – limited spaces for one-night stay

Address : rue de la Fabrique (located 1.5km south on the D 91, at the entrance to Vic-sur-Aisne; beside the Aisne river)

Opening times : Permanent

34 ha (660 pitches)

Tariff : 39€ ♦♦ ⇔ 🔲 🔌 (6A) – Extra per person 12.50€

There are several different types of sani-station ('borne' in French) – sanitation points providing fresh water and disposal points for grey water. See page 12 for further details.

Rental rates : (from beginning April to end Oct.) ⅙ (mobile homes & chalets) ⌛ – 11 🏠 – 1 cabin in the trees – 11 tent lodges – 11 gîtes. Per night from 100 to 200€ – Per week from 500 to 1,150€

A holiday village offering lots of activities, some indoor, in a pleasant setting by the Aisne river.

Surroundings : ⌇ ⊏ ♀
Leisure activities : ▼ ✗ 🛆 ⚲ ⚲♠ ⌸ ⛵ jacuzzi ⇔ 🚴 ✗ ♒ 🖾 🛆 ⚓ (fresh water) 🛆 ⌇ bowling , laser game, pedalos, multi-sports ground, water park
Facilities : ⅙ ⊶ 🎦 🖫 🛆 ⚐ ⚗ 🕆 launderette 🖳 ⌇

GPS Longitude : 3.1284
Latitude : 49.40495

BERTANGLES

80260 – Michelin map **301** G8 – pop. 591 – alt. 95
▶ Paris 154 – Abbeville 44 – Amiens 11 – Bapaume 49

⛰ Le Château

℘ 03 60 65 68 36. www.camping-bertangles.fr

Address : rue du Château (in the village)

Opening times : from mid April to mid Sept.

0.7 ha (33 pitches) flat, grassy

Tariff : ♦ 4.50€ ⇔ 2.80€ 🔲 4.50€ – 🔌 (5A) 4.20€

The campsite is set in an orchard near the château.

Surroundings : ⌇ ⊏ ♀
Leisure activities : ⇔
Facilities : ⅙ ⊶ 🎦 🖾 🕆

GPS Longitude : 2.30131
Latitude : 49.97167

Key to rentals symbols :

12 🚐	*Number of mobile homes*
20 🏠	*Number of chalets*
6 🛏	*Number of rooms to rent*
Per night 30–50€	*Minimum/maximum rate per night*
Per week 300–1,000€	*Minimum/maximum rate per week*

CARLEPONT

60170 – Michelin map **305** J3 – pop. 1 416 – alt. 59
▶ Paris 103 – Compiègne 19 – Ham 30 – Pierrefonds 21

⛰ Les Araucarias

℘ 03 44 75 27 39. www.camping-les-araucarias.com – limited spaces for one-night stay

Address : 870 rue du Général Leclerc (take the southwestern exit along the D 130, follow the signs for Compiègne)

Opening times : from beginning April to end Oct.

1.2 ha (60 pitches)

Tariff : ♦ 3€ ⇔ 2€ 🔲 3.30€ – 🔌 (10A) 3€
Rental rates : Permanent – 16 🚐 – 4 🏠. Per night from 60 to 70€ – Per week from 250 to 400€
🚐 borne 3€ – 2 🔲 14.80€
There's a wide variety of plants – including some rare trees – in and around the camping area.

Surroundings : ⌇ ⊏ ♀♀
Leisure activities : ⇔
Facilities : ⅙ ⊶ 🖫 🕆 launderette

GPS Longitude : 3.01836
Latitude : 49.50728

CAYEUX-SUR-MER

80410 – Michelin map **301** B6 – pop. 2 813 – alt. 2
▶ Paris 217 – Abbeville 29 – Amiens 82 – Le Crotoy 26

⛰ Les Galets de la Mollière 👥

📞 03 22 26 61 85. www.campinglesgaletsdelamolliere.com

Address : at Mollière, rue Faidherbe (3.3km northeast along the D 102, coastal road)

Opening times : from end March to beginning Nov.

6 ha (195 pitches)Tariff : (2014 Price) 33€ 🏕🏕 🚗 ▤ –
Extra per person 7€ – Reservation fee 12€

Rental rates : (2014 Price) (from end March to beginning Nov.) –
39 🚐. Per night from 74 to 106€ – Per week from 280 to 742€
Reservation fee 12€

🚐 borne – 40 ▤

Situated 100m from the beach and dunes.

Surroundings : 🏖 🚤 ♨		G
Leisure activities : 🍸 🍴 🏠 🎯 🚤 🎱 🛶		P
Facilities : 🚿 ⛽ 🍖 launderette 🚿	Longitude : 1.52608	S
	Latitude : 50.20275	

⛰ Le Bois de Pins

📞 03 22 26 71 04. www.campingleboisdepins.com – limited spaces for one-night stay

Address : at Brighton, avenue Guillaume-le-Conquérant (2km northeast along the D 102, coastal road)

Opening times : from end March to beginning Nov.

4 ha (163 pitches) flat, grassy

Tariff : (2014 Price) 27€ 🏕🏕 🚗 ▤ – Extra per person 7€

🚐 borne

Situated 400m from the beach and dunes, with numerous owner-occupier mobile homes.

Surroundings : 🏖 🚤 ♨		G
Leisure activities : 🏠	Longitude : 1.5169	P
Facilities : 🚿 ⛽ 🍖 launderette	Latitude : 50.1974	S

CHARLY-SUR-MARNE

02310 – Michelin map **306** B9 – pop. 2 741 – alt. 63
▶ Paris 82 – Château-Thierry 14 – Coulommiers 33 – La Ferté-sous-Jouarre 16

⛰ Municipal des Illettes

📞 03 23 82 12 11. www.charly-sur-marne.fr

Address : route de Pavant (south of the town, 200m from the D 82 (recommended route)

Opening times : from beginning April to end Sept.

1.2 ha (43 pitches)

Tariff : (2014 Price) 17.90€ 🏕🏕 🚗 ▤ 🔌 (10A) –
Extra per person 4.40€

🚐 borne

Surroundings : 🚤 ♨♨		G
Leisure activities : 🏠		P
Facilities : 🚿 ⛽ 🎯 🍖 launderette	Longitude : 3.28209	S
Nearby : 🛒 🍴 🎣	Latitude : 48.97369	

This guide is updated regularly, so buy your new copy every year!

LE CROTOY

80550 – Michelin map **301** C6 – pop. 2 265 – alt. 1
▶ Paris 210 – Abbeville 22 – Amiens 75 – Berck-sur-Mer 29

⛰ Kawan Village Le Ridin

📞 03 22 27 03 22. www.campingleridin.com – limited spaces for one-night stay

Address : Mayocq (3km north following signs for St-Quentin-en-Tourmont and take the road to the right)

Opening times : from beginning April to end Oct.

4.5 ha (162 pitches) flat, grassy

Tariff : 31€ 🏕🏕 🚗 ▤ 🔌 (10A) – Extra per person 5.50€ – Reservation fee 6€

Rental rates : (from beginning April to end Oct.) – 36 🚐.
Per night from 52 to 112€ – Per week from 260 to 784€ –
Reservation fee 6€

🚐 borne 16€ – 10 ▤ 16€

The swimming pool area and restaurant are on the other side of the small road.

Surroundings : 🏖 🚤 ♨		G
Leisure activities : 🍸 🍴 🏠 🛁 jacuzzi 🚤 🚲 🛶	Longitude : 1.63182	P
Facilities : 🚿 ⛽ ▣ 🍖 launderette 🚿	Latitude : 50.23905	S

⛰ Flower Les Aubépines

📞 03 22 27 01 34. www.camping-lesaubepines.com – limited spaces for one-night stay

Address : at St-Firmin, 800 rue de la Maye (4km to the north, follow the signs for St-Quentin-en-Tourmont and take road to the left)

Opening times : from beginning April to end Oct.

2.5 ha (196 pitches)

Tariff : 31€ 🏕🏕 🚗 ▤ 🔌 (10A) – Extra per person 6€ – Reservation fee 6€

Rental rates : (from beginning April to end Oct.) – 40 🚐 – 6 🏠.
Per night from 51 to 150€ – Per week from 255 to 1,050€ –
Reservation fee 6€

🚐 borne 16€ – 5 ▤ 16€

Part of the rental accommodation is of a high standard and car-free.

Surroundings : 🏖 🚤 ♨		G
Leisure activities : 🏠 🚤 🚲 🛶	Longitude : 1.61139	P
Facilities : 🚿 ⛽ 🍖 🚿 🛶 launderette	Latitude : 50.24955	S

⛰ Les Trois Sablières

📞 03 22 27 01 33. www.camping-les-trois-sablieres.com – limited spaces for one-night stay

Address : 1850 rue de la Maye (4km to the northwest, follow the signs for St-Quentin-en-Tourmont and take the road to the left, 400m from the beach)

Opening times : from beginning April to beginning Nov.

1.5 ha (97 pitches)

Tariff : (2014 Price) 29€ 🏕🏕 🚗 ▤ 🔌 (6A) – Extra per person 6.80€

Rental rates : (2014 Price) (from beginning April to beginning Nov.) 🚿 (1 mobile home) – 20 🚐 – 2 🏠. Per night from 62 to 103€ – Per week from 290 to 725€

🚐 borne 2€ – 🚐12€

In a green setting with flowers.

Surroundings : 🏖 🚤 ♨		G
Leisure activities : 🍸 🏠 🛁 🍴 🚤 🛶	Longitude : 1.59883	P
Facilities : 🚿 ⛽ 🍖 launderette	Latitude : 50.24825	S

LA FÈRE

02800 – Michelin map **306** C5 – pop. 3 012 – alt. 54
▶ Paris 137 – Compiègne 59 – Laon 24 – Noyon 31

△ Municipal du Marais de la Fontaine

📞 03 23 56 82 94

Address : rue Vauban (via the town centre towards Tergnier and take a right turn at the sports centre; near a branch of the Oise river)

0.7 ha (26 pitches) flat, grassy

Surroundings : 🔲 ♀	**GPS** Longitude : 3.36353
Facilities : ♿ ⊶	Latitude : 49.6654
Nearby : ✂	

*The classification (1 to 5 tents, **black** or red) that we award to selected sites in this guide is our own system. It should not be confused with the classification (1 to 5 stars) of official organisations.*

FORT-MAHON-PLAGE

80120 – Michelin map **301** C5 – pop. 1 311 – alt. 2
▶ Paris 225 – Abbeville 41 – Amiens 90 – Berck-sur-Mer 19

⚠ Club Airotel Le Royon 🏕👥

📞 03 22 23 40 30. www.campingleroyon.com – limited spaces for one-night stay

Address : 1271 route de Quend (located 1km to the south)

Opening times : from mid March to beginning Nov.

4 ha (376 pitches)

Tariff : 36€ 🏕🏕 🚐 📧 🔌 (6A) – Extra per person 7€ – Reservation fee 12€

Rental rates : (from mid March to beginning Nov.) ⚙ – 85 🛖. Per night from 79 to 112€ – Per week from 290 to 790 €

Reservation fee 12€

🛒 borne 3€

A pleasant campsite, but with numerous owner-occupier mobile homes.

Surroundings : 🔲 ♀	**GPS** Longitude : 1.57963
Leisure activities : 🍴 🎯 ⚓ ✂ 🎣 🔲 🏊 farm or petting farm, entertainment room	Latitude : 50.33263
Facilities : ♿ ⊶ ⛛ 🚿 🧺 ⚙ launderette	

⚠ Le Vert Gazon

📞 03 22 23 37 69. www.camping-levertgazon.com – limited spaces for one-night stay

Address : 741 route de Quend

Opening times : from beginning April to beginning Oct.

2.5 ha (130 pitches) flat, grassy

Tariff : (2014 Price) 26.90€ 🏕🏕 🚐 📧 🔌 (6A) – Extra per person 7€ Reservation fee 10€

Rental rates : (2014 Price) Permanent ♿ (1 mobile home) – 1 caravan – 15 🛖 – 5 🛖 – 5 gîtes. Per night from 99 to 129€ – Per week from 349 to 629€ – Reservation fee 10€

🛒 borne 5€ – 5 📧 26.90€

There are various rental options of a good standard.

Surroundings : 🔲	**GPS** Longitude : 1.57374
Leisure activities : 🍴 🛖 ⚓ 🚲 🏊	Latitude : 50.33438
Facilities : ♿ ⊶ 🚿 🚿 🧺 ⚙ launderette	

MERS-LES-BAINS

80350 – Michelin map **301** B7 – pop. 3 124 – alt. 3
▶ Paris 217 – Amiens 89 – Rouen 99 – Arras 130

⚠⚠ Flower Le Rompval

📞 02 35 84 43 21. www.campinglerompval.com

Address : Blengues (situated 2km to the northeast)

Opening times : from beginning April to beginning Nov.

3 ha (132 pitches) flat, grassy

Tariff : 30.50€ 🏕🏕 🚐 📧 🔌 (8A) – Extra per person 6€ – Reservation fee 15€

Rental rates : (from beginning April to beginning Nov.) – 29 🛖 – 6 studios – 2 canvas bungalows. Per night from 39 to 115€ – Per week from 196 to 805€ – Reservation fee 15€

🛒 borne

Rental options in some unusual and colourful styles. Choose those pitches the furthest away from the road in preference.

Surroundings : 🔲 ♀	**GPS** Longitude : 1.4154
Leisure activities : 🍴 🛖 ⚓ 🚲 🏊 (open air in season)	Latitude : 50.0773
Facilities : ♿ ⊶ 🅿 🚿 🧺 ⚙ launderette	

The prices listed were supplied by the campsite owners in 2014 (if prices were not available, those from the previous year are given). The fees should be regarded as basic charges and may fluctuate with inflation.

MIANNAY

80132 – Michelin map **301** D7 – pop. 568 – alt. 15
▶ Paris 191 – Amiens 63 – Arras 104 – Rouen 109

⚠⚠ Sites et Paysages Le Clos Cacheleux

📞 03 22 19 17 47. www.camping-lecloscacheleux.fr

Address : route de Bouillancourt-sous-Miannay

Opening times : from mid March to mid Oct.

8 ha (119 pitches)

Tariff : (2014 Price) 27.10€ 🏕🏕 🚐 📧 🔌 (10A) – Extra per person 5.60€ – Reservation fee 12€

Rental rates : (2014 Price) (from beginning April to end Oct.) ⚙ – 4 cabins in the trees – 1 gîte. Per night from 80 to 140€ – Per week from 560 to 800€ – Reservation fee 12€

🛒 borne – 10 📧 27.10€ – 🚐 🔌 13€

Situated in the grounds of a working farm (crops and cattle).

Surroundings : 🦢 🔲 ♀	**GPS** Longitude : 1.71536
Leisure activities : ⚓	Latitude : 50.08646
Facilities : ♿ ⊶ 🚿 ⚙ launderette	
Nearby : 🍴 ✕ 🛖 🎯 🏊 (open air in season) activities at the Le Val de Trie, opposite	

These symbols are used for a campsite that is exceptional in its category:

⚠⚠⚠ ... △ *Particularly pleasant setting, quality and range of services available*

🦢 🦢 *Tranquil, isolated site – quiet site, particularly at night*

≪ ≪ *Exceptional view – interesting or panoramic view*

MOYENNEVILLE

80870 – Michelin map **301** D7 – pop. 667 – alt. 92
▶ Paris 194 – Abbeville 9 – Amiens 59 – Blangy-sur-Bresle 22

⚠ Le Val de Trie ♣♣

✆ 03 22 31 48 88. www.camping-levaldetrie.fr

Address : 1 rue des Sources at Bouillancourt-sous-Miannay (3km northwest along the D 86; beside a stream)

Opening times : from beginning April to beginning Oct.

2 ha (100 pitches) flat, grassy, small lake

Tariff : (2014 Price) 27.10€ ✶✶ ⌂ 🅴 🄶 (10A) –
Extra per person 5.60€ – Reservation fee 12€

Rental rates : (2014 Price) (from beginning April to beginning Oct.)
⅃ (1 chalet) – 19 🛏 – 5 ⌂. Per night from 49 to 112€ –
Per week from 343 to 1,085€ – Reservation fee 12€

🚐 10 🅴 27.10€

Surroundings : 🐟 🗔 ♬♬ Leisure activities : 🍸 🍴 🛖 🚶 🚣 🏊 (open air in season) Facilities : ⅃ ⚬⌐ 🆑 ▦ 🛁 ♨ 🚰 launderette	**GPS** Longitude : 1.71508 Latitude : 50.08552

To visit a town or region, use the MICHELIN Green Guides.

NAMPONT-ST-MARTIN

80120 – Michelin map **301** D5 – pop. 260 – alt. 10
▶ Paris 214 – Abbeville 30 – Amiens 79 – Boulogne-sur-Mer 52

⚠ Kawan Village La Ferme des Aulnes

✆ 03 22 29 22 69. www.fermedesaulnes.com – limited spaces for one-night stay

Address : at Fresne, 1 rue du Marais (3km southwest along the D 85e, follow the signs for Villier-sur-Authie)

Opening times : from beginning April to beginning Nov.

4 ha (120 pitches)

Tariff : (2014 Price) 35€ ✶✶ ⌂ 🅴 🄶 (10A) – Extra per person 7€

Rental rates : (2014 Price) (from beginning April to beginning Nov.) – 18 🛏. Per week from 393 to 814€

🚐 borne – 12 🅴

The setting is a traditional Picardy farm.

Surroundings : 🐟 🗔 ♪ Leisure activities : 🍸 🍴 🛖 ⍟(piano bar) 🏋 ♨ jacuzzi 🚣 🏊 (open air in season), entertainment room Facilities : ⅃ ⚬⌐ 🆑 ▦ 🛁 ♨ 🚰 launderette 🐾	**GPS** Longitude : 1.71201 Latitude : 50.33631

LE NOUVION-EN-THIÉRACHE

02170 – Michelin map **306** E2 – pop. 2 809 – alt. 185
▶ Paris 198 – Avesnes-sur-Helpe 20 – Le Cateau-Cambrésis 19
Guise 21

⚠ Municipal du Lac de Condé

✆ 03 23 98 98 58. www.camping-thierache.com

Address : promenade Henri d'Orléans (situated 2km south along the D 26 and take the road to the left)

Opening times : from beginning April to mid Sept.

1.3 ha (56 pitches) flat and relatively flat

Tariff : 13.60€ ✶✶ ⌂ 🅴 🄶 (8A) – Extra per person 3.60€

🚐 borne 3€ – 5 🅴

On the edge of the forest, near a lake and a leisure park.

Surroundings : 🐟 🗔 Leisure activities : 🛖 Facilities : ⅃ ⚬⌐ 🛁 Nearby : 🍸 🍴 🚣 🚵 🏊 🎣 bowling, mountain biking	**GPS** Longitude : 3.78271 Latitude : 50.00561

PÉRONNE

80200 – Michelin map **301** K8 – pop. 7 981 – alt. 52
▶ Paris 141 – Amiens 58 – Arras 48 – Doullens 54

⚠ Port de Plaisance

✆ 03 22 84 19 31. www.camping-plaisance.com

Address : take the southern exit, following the signs for Paris, between the marina and the commercial port; beside the Canal de la Somme

Opening times : from beginning March to end Oct.

2 ha (90 pitches)

Tariff : 30.10€ ✶✶ ⌂ 🅴 🄶 (10A) – Extra per person 4€

Rental rates : (from beginning March to end Oct.) 🛖 – 4 ⌂.
Per night from 78 to 85€ – Per week from 287 to 513€

🚐 borne – 4 🅴 23.50€

Surroundings : 🗔 ♬♬ Leisure activities : 🍸 🛖 🚣 🚲 🏊 Facilities : ⅃ ⚬⌐ 🆑 ▦ 🛁 🚰 🚰 launderette Nearby : 🎣 ⚓	**GPS** Longitude : 2.93237 Latitude : 49.91786

PIERREFONDS

60350 – Michelin map **305** I4 – pop. 1 969 – alt. 81
▶ Paris 82 – Beauvais 78 – Compiègne 15 – Crépy-en-Valois 17

⚠ Municipal de Batigny

✆ 03 44 42 80 83. www.lecoeurdelaforet.fr

Address : rue de l'Armistice (take northwestern exit along the D 973, follow the signs for Compiègne)

1 ha (60 pitches)

Rentals : 🛖 – 2 ⌂.

Attractive trees and shrubs decorate the site.

Surroundings : 🗔 ♬♬ Leisure activities : 🚣 Facilities : ⚬⌐ 🛁 🚰 🚰 Nearby : 🍴	**GPS** Longitude : 2.97962 Latitude : 49.35194

POIX-DE-PICARDIE

80290 – Michelin map **301** E9 – pop. 2 388 – alt. 106
▶ Paris 133 – Abbeville 45 – Amiens 31 – Beauvais 46

⚠ Municipal le Bois des Pêcheurs

✆ 03 22 90 11 71. www.ville-poix-de-picardie.fr

Address : route de Verdun (take the western exit along the D 919, follow the signs for Formerie, beside a stream)

Opening times : from beginning April to end Sept.

2 ha (88 pitches) flat, grassy

Tariff : (2014 Price) 18€ ✶✶ ⌂ 🅴 🄶 (6A) – Extra per person 1.50€

Rental rates : (from beginning April to end Sept.) – 2 🛏.
Per night from 100€ – Per week from 250 to 300€

🚐 borne 2€ – 4 🅴 8€

The campsite has some lovely, well marked-out pitches.

Surroundings : ⌐ ♀
Leisure activities : 🛶 ♨ 🚲
Facilities : ♿ ⚬━ 🚿 ♨ 🕯 launderette
Nearby : ✂ 🏊

G P S	Longitude : 1.9743
	Latitude : 49.75

*We value your opinion and welcome your feedback.
Do email us at campingfrance@tp.michelin.com*

RESSONS-LE-LONG

02290 – Michelin map **306** A6 – pop. 756 – alt. 72
▶ Paris 97 – Compiègne 26 – Laon 53 – Noyon 31

🔺 La Halte de Mainville

🔗 03 23 74 26 69. www.lahaltedemainville.com
Address : 18 rue du Routy (take the northeastern exit)
Opening times : from mid Jan. to mid Dec.
5 ha (155 pitches) flat, grassy, small lake
Tariff : (2014 Price) 21.50€ ✹✹ ⌐ 🔲 ⚡ (8A) – Extra per person 4.50€
Rental rates : (2014 Price) (from beginning April to mid Oct.) – 2 🚐 – 2 🏠. Per night from 100 to 135€ – Per week from 325 to 465€
🚐 borne

Surroundings : ⌐ ♀
Leisure activities : 🛶 ♨ 🏊 🛶
Facilities : ♿ ⚬━ 🚿🔲🕯 ♨ 🕯 launderette

G P S	Longitude : 3.15186
	Latitude : 49.39277

RUE

80120 – Michelin map **301** D6 – pop. 3 095 – alt. 9
▶ Paris 212 – Abbeville 28 – Amiens 77 – Berck-Plage 22

🔺 Les Oiseaux

🔗 03 22 25 71 82. www.campingbaiesomme.com – limited spaces for one-night stay
Address : 3.2km south along the D 940, follow the signs for Le Crotoy and take the Chemin de Favières to the left; near a stream
1.2 ha (71 pitches) flat, grassy
Rentals : 2 🚐 – 5 gîtes.

Surroundings : ⌐ ♀
Leisure activities : 🛶
Facilities : ♿ ⚬━ 🕯 🕯 🔲

G P S	Longitude : 1.66872
	Latitude : 50.25264

ST-LEU-D'ESSERENT

60340 – Michelin map **305** F5 – pop. 4 708 – alt. 50
▶ Paris 57 – Beauvais 38 – Chantilly 7 – Creil 9

🔺 Campix

🔗 03 44 56 08 48. www.campingcampix.com
Address : rue Pasteur (take the northern exit along the D 12, follow the signs for Cramoisy then continue 1.5km along the turning to the right and then a road)
Opening times : Permanent
6 ha (160 pitches) undulating, terraced, flat, grassy, stony
Tariff : ✹ 7€ ⌐ 🔲 7€ – ⚡ (6A) 4€
Rental rates : Permanent – 4 caravans – 7 🚐 – 7 🏠. Per night from 85 to 115€ – Per week 75€
🚐 borne 6€

Situated in a shady former quarry overlooking the town and the Oise river.

Surroundings : 🌿 ⌐ 〰
Leisure activities : ✗ 🛶 ♨ 🚲 🛶
Facilities : ♿ ⚬━ 🔲🕯 ♨ 🕯 launderette 🛶

G P S	Longitude : 2.42722
	Latitude : 49.22492

ST-QUENTIN-EN-TOURMONT

80120 – Michelin map **301** C6 – pop. 305
▶ Paris 218 – Abbeville 29 – Amiens 83 – Berck-sur-Mer 24

🔺 Le Champ Neuf

🔗 03 22 25 07 94. www.camping-lechampneuf.com – limited spaces for one-night stay
Address : 8 rue du Champ Neuf
Opening times : from beginning April to end Oct.
8 ha/4.5 for camping (161 pitches)
Tariff : (2014 Price) 31.50€ ✹✹ ⌐ 🔲 ⚡ (10A) – Extra per person 6.50€ – Reservation fee 10€
Rental rates : (2014 Price) (from beginning April to end Oct.) – 34 🚐 – 1 gîte. Per night from 61 to 94€ – Per week from 250 to 720€ – Reservation fee 10€
🚐 borne
The site has a lovely indoor water park.

Surroundings : 🌿 ⌐ ♀
Leisure activities : 🍴 🛶 🎣 🏊 ♨ 🚲 🏊 🛶 fitness trail, multi-sports ground, entertainment room
Facilities : ♿ ⚬━ 🕯 ♨ 🕯 launderette
Nearby : ✗

G P S	Longitude : 1.60153
	Latitude : 50.26978

The Michelin classification (🔺🔺🔺 ... 🔺) is totally independent of the official star classification system awarded by the local prefecture or other official organisation.

ST-VALERY-SUR-SOMME

80230 – Michelin map **301** C6 – pop. 2 873 – alt. 27
▶ Paris 206 – Abbeville 18 – Amiens 71 – Blangy-sur-Bresle 45

🔺 Club Airotel Le Walric

🔗 03 22 26 81 97. www.campinglewalric.com – limited spaces for one-night stay
Address : route d'Eu (to the west along the D 3)
Opening times : from beginning April to beginning Nov.
5.8 ha (263 pitches)
Tariff : 36€ ✹✹ ⌐ 🔲 ⚡ (6A) – Extra per person 7€ – Reservation fee 12€
Rental rates : (from beginning April to beginning Nov.) – 80 🚐. Per night from 75 to 112€ – Per week from 287 to 784€ – Reservation fee 12€
🚐 borne
A pleasant site, but with numerous owner-occupier mobile homes and caravans.

Surroundings : ⌐ ♀
Leisure activities : 🍴 🛶 🎣 ♨ ✂ 🏊 (open air in season)
Facilities : ♿ ⚬━ 🕯 ♨ 🕯 launderette
Nearby : 🏊

G P S	Longitude : 1.61791
	Latitude : 50.1839

⋀⋀⋀ Les Castels Le Domaine de Drancourt ▲⋮

📞 03 22 26 93 45. www.chateau-drancourt.com

Address : 3.5km south along the D 48 and take a right turn after crossing the CD 940

Opening times : from mid April to mid Sept.

5 ha (326 pitches) flat and relatively flat, grassy

Tariff : (2014 Price) 40€ ⚹⚹ 🚐 🔲 ⚡ (10A) – Extra per person 8€ – Reservation fee 25€

Rental rates : (2014 Price) (from mid April to mid Sept.) – 42 🛏️ – 5 🏠. Per night from 40 to 165€ – Per week from 280 to 1,155€ Reservation fee 25€

🚐 borne

Situated in the pleasant grounds of the château, with a partially covered water park.

Surroundings : 🐎 🗐 ♀
Leisure activities : 🍴 ✗ 🏠 🏃 ⛷ 🚲 ♨
🖼️ 🎿 ⛏
Facilities : ⚹ ⊶ 🏛️ 🛁 launderette 🏊 🚿

	GPS	
	Longitude : 1.63598	
	Latitude : 50.15277	

SERAUCOURT-LE-GRAND

02790 – Michelin map **306** B4 – pop. 787 – alt. 102
▶ Paris 148 – Chauny 26 – Ham 16 – Péronne 28

⋀ Le Vivier aux Carpes

📞 03 23 60 50 10. www.camping-picardie.com

Address : 10 rue Charles Voyeux (to the north along the D 321, near the post office, 200m from the Somme)

Opening times : from beginning March to end Oct.

2 ha (60 pitches) flat, grassy

Tariff : 21€ ⚹⚹ 🚐 🔲 ⚡ (10A) – Extra per person 4.50€

Rental rates : (from beginning March to end Oct.) – 1 🛏️ – 2 🏠. Per night from 77 to 82€ – Per week from 462 to 492€

🚐 borne 4€

In a pleasant location beside a fishing lake.

Surroundings : 🐎 🗐 ♀♀
Leisure activities : 🖼️ 🐎
Facilities : ⚹ ⊶ 🏛️ launderette
Nearby : 🏊

	GPS	
	Longitude : 3.21435	
	Latitude : 49.78272	

VILLERS-SUR-AUTHIE

80120 – Michelin map **301** D6 – pop. 411 – alt. 5
▶ Paris 215 – Abbeville 31 – Amiens 80 – Berck-sur-Mer 16

⋀⋀⋀ Kawan Village Le Val d'Authie ▲⋮

📞 03 22 29 92 47. www.valdauthie.fr – limited spaces for one-night stay

Address : 20 route de Vercourt (take the southern exit of the town)

Opening times : from beginning April to beginning Oct.

7 ha/4 for camping (170 pitches) relatively flat, flat, grassy

Tariff : 34€ ⚹⚹ 🚐 🔲 ⚡ (10A) – Extra per person 6.50€

Rental rates : (from beginning April to beginning Oct.) – 24 🛏️. Per night from 54 to 120€ – Per week from 378 to 840€

🚐 borne – 6 🔲 20€

Attractive shrubs and bushes decorate the site.

Surroundings : 🐎 🗐 ♀♀
Leisure activities : 🍴 ✗ 🏠 🎱 🏃 ⛷ 🚿
hammam, jacuzzi ⛷ 🚲 ⚽ 🖼️ (open air in season), fitness trail, multi-sports ground, entertainment room
Facilities : ⚹ ⊶ 🔲🏛️ 🛁 🚿 ↻ 🍴 launderette

	GPS	
	Longitude : 1.69486	
	Latitude : 50.31356	

These symbols are used for a campsite that is exceptional in its category:

⋀⋀⋀ ... ⋀   *Particularly pleasant setting, quality and range of services available*

🐎 🐎   *Tranquil, isolated site – quiet site, particularly at night*

≤≤   *Exceptional view – interesting or panoramic view*

POITOU-CHARENTES

Spila Riccardo / Sime / Photononstop

Names such as Cognac, Angoulême or La Rochelle all echo through France's history, but there's just as much to appreciate in the Poitou-Charentes region today. Visit a thalassotherapy resort and allow the seawater to revive your spirits and tone aching muscles, or soak up the sun on the region's sandy beaches, where the scent of pine trees mingles with the fresh sea breezes. The best way to discover the region's attractive coastal islands is by bike; explore the country lanes lined with tiny blue and white cottages and colourful hollyhocks. Back on the mainland, take a trip on the canals of the marshy – and mercifully mosquito-free – Marais Poitevin, or 'Green Venice', with its poplar trees and green duckweed. You will have earned a drop of Cognac or a glass of the local apéritif, a fruity, ice-cold Pineau des Charentes. For a multimedia experience and a trip into the future of the moving image, head to Futuroscope, a hugely popular award-winning theme park located in Poitiers.

AIGREFEUILLE-D'AUNIS

17290 – Michelin map **324** E3 – pop. 3 682 – alt. 20
▶ Paris 457 – Niort 50 – Rochefort 22 – La Rochelle 25

⚠ La Taillée

✆ 05 46 35 50 88. www.lataillee.com

Address : 3 rue du Bois Gaillard (east of the town, near the swimming pool)

Opening times : from beginning April to mid Oct.

2 ha (80 pitches) flat, grassy

Tariff : (2014 Price) 18.60€ ✸✸ ⇐ 🗉 ⚡ (6A) – Extra per person 4€
Rental rates : (2014 Price) (from beginning April to mid Oct.) Ⓟ –
28 🚐 – 10 🏠 – 10 canvas bungalows. Per night from 50 to 95€ –
Per week from 310 to 690€
🚰 borne
A pleasant wooded setting among centuries-old ash and plane trees.

Surroundings : 🌲 ♤♤ Leisure activities : 🏠 🚣 🎣 Facilities : 🚿 ⚊ ▥ 🧺 launderette Nearby : 🏊	**G P S** Longitude : -0.92682 Latitude : 46.11514

ANGOULINS

17690 – Michelin map **324** D3 – pop. 3 720 – alt. 15
▶ Paris 481 – Poitiers 148 – La Rochelle 12 – Niort 73

⚠ Les Chirats - La Platère

✆ 05 46 56 94 16. www.campingleschirats.fr

Address : rue du Chay (1.7km west along the r. des Salines and follow the signs for the customs post, 100m from the beach)

Opening times : from beginning April to end Sept.

4 ha (232 pitches)

Tariff : 29.30€ ✸✸ ⇐ 🗉 ⚡ (12A) – Extra per person 5.50€ –
Reservation fee 20€
Rental rates : (from beginning April to end Sept.) – 35 🏠.
Per night from 51 to 89€ – Per week from 474 to 699€ –
Reservation fee 20€
The site is in 3 distinct sections with a covered swimming pool, used as a spa in season; rental chalets that are now a little old.

Surroundings : 🏡 ♤♤ Leisure activities : 🍴 🏠 ⚡ 🎿 🏊 jacuzzi 🚣 🎣 🛏 (small swimming pool) 🏊 ⛷ spa centre Facilities : 🚿 ⚊ 🛁 🧺 🍴 🗄 🗑 Nearby : 🐎	**G P S** Longitude : -1.13076 Latitude : 46.104

ARCHIAC

17520 – Michelin map **324** I6 – pop. 812 – alt. 111
▶ Paris 514 – Angoulême 49 – Barbezieux 15 – Cognac 22

⚠ Municipal

✆ 05 46 49 10 46. archiacmairie@free.fr

Address : 7 rue des Voituriers

1 ha (44 pitches) terraced, flat, grassy
Close to the municipal sports complex.

Surroundings : 🌲 🏡 ♤♤ Leisure activities : 🏠 Facilities : 🗑 Nearby : 🍴 🏊 ⛷	**G P S** Longitude : -0.30467 Latitude : 45.52322

ARGENTON-LES-VALLEES

79150 – Michelin map **322** D3 – pop. 1 588
▶ Paris 367 – Poitiers 100 – Niort 89 – Nantes 102

⚠ Municipal du lac d'Hautibus

✆ 05 49 65 95 08. campinghautibus@orange.fr

Address : rue de la Sablière (to the west of the town - access near the roundabout at the junction of the D 748 and D 759)

Opening times : from beginning April to end Sept.

1.5 ha (64 pitches) terraced, relatively flat, grassy

Tariff : (2014 Price) ✸ 2.40€ ⇐ 2.05€ 🗉 2.25€ – ⚡ (6A) 2.80€
🚰 borne 5.25€
Situated 150m from the lake, with direct access (picturesque site).

Surroundings : ⪡ 🏡 ♤ Leisure activities : 🏠 Facilities : 🚿 ⚊ 🧺 launderette Nearby : 🍴 🏊 🎣 boats to hire	**G P S** Longitude : -0.45164 Latitude : 46.98764

Michelin classification:

🏔🏔🏔🏔	*Extremely comfortable, equipped to a very high standard*
🏔🏔🏔	*Very comfortable, equipped to a high standard*
🏔🏔🏔	*Comfortable and well equipped*
🏔🏔	*Reasonably comfortable*
🏔	*Satisfactory*

ARVERT

17530 – Michelin map **324** D5 – pop. 3 100 – alt. 20
▶ Paris 513 – Marennes 16 – Rochefort 37 – La Rochelle 74

⚠ Le Presqu'Île

✆ 05 46 36 81 76. www.campinglepresquile.com

Address : 7 rue des Aigrettes (north of the town, 150m from the D 14)

Opening times : from beginning April to end Sept.

0.8 ha (60 pitches) flat, grassy

Tariff : 19€ ✸✸ ⇐ 🗉 ⚡ (10A) – Extra per person 4.50€
Rental rates : (from beginning April to end Sept.) 🚫 – 3 🚐.
Per week from 200 to 650€
🚰 borne
A pleasant site with good shade, but also many owner-occupied mobile homes.

Surroundings : ♤♤ Leisure activities : 🏠 🚣 Facilities : 🚿 ⚊ 🧺 🗑 Nearby : 🍴	**G P S** Longitude : -1.12725 Latitude : 45.74526

For more information on visiting particular towns or regions, consult the relevant regional MICHELIN Green Guide. We also recommend you use the appropriate Michelin regional map to locate your selected campsite, to calculate distances and to work out the best route.

AVAILLES-LIMOUZINE

86460 – Michelin map **322** J8 – pop. 1 314 – alt. 142
▶ Paris 410 – Confolens 14 – L'Isle-Jourdain 15 – Niort 100

🔺 le Parc

🖉 05 49 48 51 22. www.campingleparc.net

Address : at Les Places (take the eastern exit along the D 34, to the left after the bridge; beside the Vienne river)

Opening times : from mid April to end Oct.

2.7 ha (100 pitches) flat, grassy

Tariff : (2014 Price) 15.70€ ✦✦ 🚐 🗉 🔌 (6A) – Extra per person 3.30€

Rental rates : (2014 Price) (from mid April to end Oct.) ♿ (2 chalets) – 4 🛖 – 3 🏚. Per night from 42 to 63€ – Per week from 275 to 420€

🚉 borne – 🔋 12€

Surroundings : 🏊 🎣 〰️ Leisure activities : 🛶 🚣 🎣 ⛵ pedalos 🎿 Facilities : ♿ ⛽ 🏛 🚿 🔥 📷 Nearby : 🍴	**GPS** Longitude : 0.65829 Latitude : 46.12401

This guide is updated regularly, so buy your new copy every year!

AVANTON

86170 – Michelin map **322** H5 – pop. 1 819 – alt. 110
▶ Paris 337 – Poitiers 12 – Niort 84 – Châtellerault 37

🔺 Du Futur

🖉 05 49 54 09 67. www.camping-du-futur.com

Address : 9 rue des Bois (1.3km southwest along the D 757, follow the signs for Poitiers and take turning to the right after the level crossing)

Opening times : from beginning April to end Oct.

4 ha/1.5 (68 pitches) flat, grassy

Tariff : 23.70€ ✦✦ 🚐 🗉 🔌 (10A) – Extra per person 3.80€ – Reservation fee 10€

Rental rates : (from beginning April to end Oct.) ♾️ – 1 caravan – 15 🛖. Per night from 60 to 95 € – Per week from 385 to 574€ Reservation fee 15€

🚉 borne 4.50€ – 3 🗉 23.70€

Surroundings : �=🔲 🎣 Leisure activities : 🏓 🚣 🎣 🎿 Facilities : ♿ ⛽ 🚿 launderette	**GPS** Longitude : 0.30124 Latitude : 46.65638

BONNES

86300 – Michelin map **322** J5 – pop. 1 688 – alt. 70
▶ Paris 331 – Châtellerault 25 – Chauvigny 7 – Poitiers 25

🔺 Municipal

🖉 05 49 56 44 34. www.campingbonnes86.fr

Address : 13 rue de la Varenne (south of the town; beside the Vienne river)

1.2 ha (56 pitches) flat, grassy

Rentals : ♿ (1 mobile home) – 6 🛖.

Surroundings : �="🔲 🎣 Leisure activities : 🚣 🚴 🎿 Facilities : ♿ 🔥 launderette Nearby : 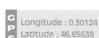	**GPS** Longitude : 0.59856 Latitude : 46.60182

CHÂTELAILLON-PLAGE

17340 – Michelin map **324** D3 – pop. 6 081 – alt. 3
▶ Paris 482 – Niort 74 – Rochefort 22 – La Rochelle 19

🔼 Port Punay 👥

🖉 05 17 81 00 00. www.camping-port-punay.com

Address : Les Boucholeurs district, allée Bernard Moreau

Opening times : from beginning May to end Sept.

3 ha (157 pitches) flat, grassy

Tariff : (2014 Price) 33.50€ ✦✦ 🚐 🗉 🔌 (10A) – Extra per person 6.50€ – Reservation fee 18€

Rental rates : (2014 Price) (from beginning May to end Sept.) ♿ (1 mobile home) ♾️ – 36 🛖 – 4 tent lodges. Per night from 43 to 105€ – Per week from 295 to 960€ – Reservation fee 18€

🚉 borne

Both shady and sunny pitches 200m from the beach and the port.

Surroundings : 🏊 🚐 🎣 Leisure activities : 🍴 🍽 🏠 🛶 🏊 🚣 🚴 🎿 Facilities : ♿ ⛽ 🚿 🔥 launderette 🗄 🚙	**GPS** Longitude : -1.0846 Latitude : 46.05352

🔼 Club Airotel 2 Plages - Village Corsaire

🖉 05 46 56 27 53. www.2plages.com

Address : avenue d'Angoulins (follow the signs for La Rochelle; 300 m. from the beach)

4.5 ha (265 pitches) flat, grassy

Rentals : ♿ (1 mobile home) – 115 🛖.

Choose the pitches away from the road and the railway line.

Surroundings : 🚐 🎣 Leisure activities : 🍴 🍽 🏠 🚣 🎿 multi-sports ground Facilities : ♿ ⛽ 🚿 🔥 launderette 🗄 🚙 Nearby : 🚴	**GPS** Longitude : -1.09344 Latitude : 46.08441

🔼 L'Océan

🖉 05 46 56 87 97. www.campingocean17.com

Address : avenue d'Angoulins (1.3km north along the D 202, follow the signs for La Rochelle and take a right turn)

Opening times : from mid May to end Sept.

3 ha (97 pitches) flat, grassy

Tariff : (2014 Price) 31.50€ ✦✦ 🚐 🗉 🔌 (10A) – Extra per person 6.50€ – Reservation fee 18€

🚉 borne

A pretty, naturally filtered, landscaped lake.

Surroundings : 🏊 🎣 Leisure activities : 🏠 🚣 🏊 (lake), entertainment room Facilities : ♿ ⛽ 🚿 🔥 launderette	**GPS** Longitude : -1.09412 Latitude : 46.08818

The Michelin classification (🔼🔼🔼 ... 🔺) is totally independent of the official star classification system awarded by the local prefecture or other official organisation.

CHAUVIGNY

86300 – Michelin map **322** J5 – pop. 6 848 – alt. 65
▶ Paris 333 – Bellac 64 – Le Blanc 36 – Châtellerault 30

⚠ Municipal de la Fontaine

𝄞 05 49 46 31 94. www.chauvigny.fr

Address : rue de la Fontaine (take the northern exit along the D 2, follow the signs for La Puye and take turning to the right; beside a stream)

Opening times : from beginning April to end Sept.

2.8 ha (102 pitches)

Tariff : ⚹ 2.70€ ➡ 2€ ▣ 2€ – ⚡ 3.20€
Rental rates : Permanent – 1 🚐 – 4 🏠 – 5 studios. Per night from 18 to 23€ – Per week from 126 to 570€
🚐 borne – 10 ▣ 7€
The site adjoins some public gardens with a water feature.

Surroundings : ≤ Medieval city, several castles ♀♀ Leisure activities : 🎪 🏊 Facilities : 🚿 ⚊ 🗑 🏖 🚻 launderette Nearby : 🎣	**G P S**	Longitude : 0.65349 Latitude : 46.57095

COGNAC

16100 – Michelin map **324** I5 – pop. 18 729 – alt. 25
▶ Paris 478 – Angoulême 45 – Bordeaux 120 – Libourne 116

⚠ Municipal

𝄞 05 45 32 13 32. www.campingdecognac.com

Address : boulevard de Châtenay (2.3km north along the D 24, follow the signs for Boutiers; between the Charente and the Solençon rivers)

2 ha (160 pitches) flat, grassy

Rentals : 🚿 (1 mobile home) – 8 🚐 – 2 canvas bungalows.
In an attractive parkland setting, well shaded in parts.

Surroundings : 🏕 ♀♀ Leisure activities : 🏊 🏊 🎣 Facilities : 🚿 ⚊ 🏖 🚻 ▣ Nearby : 🍽 ✖	**G P S**	Longitude : -0.30726 Latitude : 45.70926

COUHÉ

86700 – Michelin map **322** H7 – pop. 1 885 – alt. 140
▶ Paris 370 – Confolens 58 – Montmorillon 61 – Niort 65

⚠ Sites et Paysages Les Peupliers 👥

𝄞 05 49 59 21 16. www.lespeupliers.fr

Address : avenue de Paris (situated 1km north, follow the signs for Poitiers; at Valence)

Opening times : from beginning May to end Sept.

16 ha/6 for camping (160 pitches)

Tariff : ⚹ 8.30€ ➡ ▣ 14€ – ⚡ (10A) 5€
Rental rates : Permanent – 25 🚐 – 18 🏠. Per night from 100 to 170€ – Per week from 245 to 1,110€
🚐 borne – 6 ▣ 14€ – �️14€
In a wooded setting with a picturesque river running through it.

Les Peupliers

Surroundings : 🏞 🏕 ♀♀ Leisure activities : 🍽 ✖ 📺 🔦 🎿 🏊 🎿 🏊 🎿 🎣 Facilities : 🚿 ⚊ 🗑 🏖 – 2 private sanitary facilities (🚿 🚾 wc) 🏖 🚻 launderette 🏊 🏊	**G P S**	Longitude : 0.18222 Latitude : 46.31222

COULON

79510 – Michelin map **322** C7 – pop. 2 211 – alt. 6
▶ Paris 418 – Fontenay-le-Comte 25 – Niort 11 – La Rochelle 63

⚠ La Venise Verte 👥

𝄞 05 49 35 90 36. www.camping-laveniseverte.fr

Address : 178 route des Bords de Sèvre (2.2km southwest along the D 123, follow the signs for Vanneau; beside a canal and near the Sèvre Niortaise river)

Opening times : from beginning April to end Oct.

2.2 ha (140 pitches) flat, grassy

Tariff : 30€ ⚹⚹ ➡ ▣ ⚡ (10A) – Extra per person 7€
Rental rates : (from beginning April to end Oct.) – 23 🏠.
Per night from 58 to 105€ – Per week from 400 to 820€
🚐 borne
The campsite is making great efforts to be eco-friendly.

Surroundings : ♀♀ Leisure activities : 🍽 ✖ 🏛 🔦 🎿 🎿 🚲 🏊 🛶 Facilities : 🚿 ⚊ 🏖 🏖 🚻 🚻 ▣ 🏊 Nearby : 🛶	**G P S**	Longitude : -0.60889 Latitude : 46.31444

COZES

17120 – Michelin map **324** E6 – pop. 1 973 – alt. 43
▶ Paris 494 – Marennes 41 – Mirambeau 35 – Pons 26

⚠ Municipal le Sorlut

𝄞 05 46 90 75 99. www.villedecozes.fr

Address : rue des Chênes (to the north, near the old station, behind the Champion supermarket)

Opening times : from mid April to mid Oct.

1.4 ha (120 pitches) flat, grassy

Tariff : (2014 Price) ⚹ 2.68€ ➡ ▣ 2.83€ – ⚡ (10A) 2.78€
Rental rates : (2014 Price) (from mid March to mid Nov.) 🚿 (1 chalet) 🚿 – 8 🏠. Per night from 61 to 66€ – Per week from 453 to 566€
Pleasant, shady pitches and comfortable chalets; the municipal swimming pool is adjacent to the campsite.

Surroundings : 🏊 ♀♀ Leisure activities : 🏊 Facilities : 🚿 ⚊ (July-Aug.) 🚻 ▣ Nearby : ✂ 🎿 🏊 🎿	**G P S**	Longitude : -0.83728 Latitude : 45.58649

There are several different types of sani-station ('borne' in French) – sanitation points providing fresh water and disposal points for grey water. See page 12 for further details.

DIENNE

86410 – Michelin map **322** J6 – pop. 508 – alt. 112
▶ Paris 362 – Poitiers 26 – Niort 107 – Limoges 107

⚠ DéfiPlanet au Domaine de Dienné

𝄞 05 49 45 87 63. www.defiplanet.com – limited spaces for one-night stay

Address : at La Boquerie (RN 147)

Opening times : from beginning Feb. to beginning Jan.

47 ha/1 for camping (19 pitches) lake, forest

Tariff : 39€ ⚹⚹ ➡ ▣ ⚡ (16A) – Extra per person 7.50€

Rental rates : (from beginning Feb. to beginning Jan.) ♿ Ⓟ –
22 caravans – 7 🏠 – 8 yurts – 26 cabins in the trees – 2 gîtes.
Per night from 73 to 209 € – Per week from 365 to 1,045 €

*A vast wooded estate offering a number of activities, nearly a
dozen accommodation options of the more unusual kind and
some pitches for tents and caravans.*

Surroundings : 🐾 ♀
Leisure activities : ♟ ✕ 🏠 🗺 ⛹ ☗ ⛸
hammam, jacuzzi 🚣 🚴 ⊠ 🎣 🏊 🏇
horse riding centre, zip wire, spa centre,
entertainment room
Facilities : ♿ ⚷ Ⓟ 🏢 🚾 launderette 🧺

G P S	Longitude : 0.56024
	Latitude : 46.44614

DOMPIERRE-SUR-MER

17139 – Michelin map **324** H5 – pop. 5 337 – alt. 30
▶ Paris 465 – Poitiers 132 – La Rochelle 9 – La Roche-sur-Yon 84

⚠ Aire Naturelle Le Verger

Le Verger

📞 05 46 34 91 00, www.
campingleverger17.com

Address : 27 rue Jean-Pierre Pigot (2km
northwest along the D 107)

Opening times : from mid June to
end Aug.

1.5 ha (25 pitches) flat, grassy

Tariff : 🧍 5 € 🚗 🅴 5 € – ⚡ (5A) 5 €
Rental rates : (from mid June
to end Aug.) 🚳 – 2 caravans – 1 tent lodge. Per week
from 420 to 570 €

Pitches in the shade of young apricot, cherry and apple trees.

Surroundings : 🐾 ♀
Facilities : ♿ ⚷ 🚽 🚾

G P S	Longitude : -1.05428
	Latitude : 46.17787

*The guide covers all 22 regions of France – see the map
and list of regions on pages 4–5.*

FOURAS

17450 – Michelin map **324** D4 – pop. 4 092 – alt. 5
▶ Paris 485 – Châtelaillon-Plage 18 – Rochefort 15 – La Rochelle 34

⛰ Municipal le Cadoret 👥

📞 05 46 82 19 19. www.campings-fouras.com

Address : boulevard de Chaterny (North coast; beside the Anse de
Fouras, 100m from the beach)

Opening times : Permanent

7.5 ha (498 pitches)

Tariff : (2014 Price) 29 € 🧍🧍 🚗 🅴 ⚡ (10A) – Extra per person 6 € –
Reservation fee 25 €
Rental rates : (2014 Price) (from end March to beginning Nov.)
♿ (2 mobile homes) – 22 🏠. Per week from 280 to 650 € –
Reservation fee 25 €

*Beside the sea, near the sea fishing piers and the beautiful,
wide beach 50m away.*

Surroundings : 🗺 ♀♀
Leisure activities : ♟ ✕ 🏠 🗺 ☗ 🚣 🏊 ⛷
multi-sports ground
Facilities : ♿ 🏢 🚿 🧺 🚾 launderette 🧺
Nearby : ✂ 🎣 ♨

G P S	Longitude : -1.08714
	Latitude : 45.99296

L'HOUMEAU

17137 – Michelin map **324** C2 – pop. 2 073 – alt. 19
▶ Paris 478 – Poitiers 145 – La Rochelle 6 – Niort 83

⛰ Au Petit Port de l'Houmeau

📞 05 46 50 90 82. www.aupetitport.com

Address : rue des Sartières (take the northeastern exit along
the D 106, follow the signs for Nieul-sur-Mer, via the ring road
(périphérique) towards Île de Ré and take the exit for Lagord-
l'Houmeau)

2 ha (132 pitches)

Rentals : ♿ (1 chalet) – 55 🏠 – 15 🏠.

*Numerous rental options include some rather old chalets and
newer mobile homes equipped to a good standard, clad in
wood.*

Surroundings : 🗺 ♀♀
Leisure activities : ♟ ✕ 🏠 🚣 🚴
Facilities : ♿ ⚷ 🚿 🚾 launderette 🧺
Nearby : ✂ 🎣

G P S	Longitude : -1.1883
	Latitude : 46.19566

ÎLE-D'AIX

17123 – Michelin map **324** C3 – pop. 227 – alt. 10
▶ Paris 486 – Poitiers 152 – La Rochelle 31 – Niort 78

⚠ Le Fort de la Rade

📞 05 46 84 28 28. www.fortdelarade.ifrance.com

Address : situated at la Pointe Ste-Catherine, 300m from the beach
at L'Anse de la Croix

3 ha (73 pitches) flat, grassy

Rentals : 5 tent lodges.

*In the grounds of the Fort de la Rade, surrounded by fortified
walls; reserved for tents.*

Surroundings : 🐾
Leisure activities : ✕ 🏠 🏊 ♨
Facilities : ♿ ⚷ 🚾 🧺 no electrical hook-up
Nearby : 🏊 ♟ 🚴

G P S	Longitude : -1.17657
	Latitude : 46.00935

ÎLE DE RÉ

17 – Michelin map **324**

Ars-en-Ré 17590 – Michelin map **324** A2 – pop. 1 321 – alt. 4
▶ Paris 506 – Fontenay-le-Comte 85 – Luçon 75 – La Rochelle 34

⛰ Club Airotel le Cormoran 👥

📞 05 46 29 46 04. www.cormoran.com

Address : route de Radia (located 1km west)

Opening times : from beginning April to end Sept.

3 ha (142 pitches) flat, grassy

Tariff : 50.50 € 🧍🧍 🚗 🅴 ⚡ (10A) – Extra per person 11.80 € –
Reservation fee 25 €
Rental rates : (from beginning April to end Sept.) ♿ (1 mobile
home) – 97 🏠 – 5 tent lodges. Per night from 40 to 214 € –
Per week from 230 to 1,498 € – Reservation fee 35 €
🏠 borne 4 €

*An attractive site decorated with flowers, near vineyards, a
forest and salt marshes.*

Surroundings : 🐾 🗺 ♀
Leisure activities : ♟ ✕ 🏠 🗺 ☗ ⛹ 🏌 ⛸
🚣 🚴 ✂ 🏊 multi-sports ground
Facilities : ♿ ⚷ 🏢 🚿 🧺 🚾 🚾 launderette
🧺

G P S	Longitude : -1.53026
	Latitude : 46.21136

Le Bois-Plage-en-Ré 17580 – Michelin map **324** B2 – pop. 2 364 – alt. 5
▶ Paris 494 – Fontenay-le-Comte 74 – Luçon 64 – La Rochelle 23

⚴ Sunêlia Interlude ♣♣

℘ 05 46 09 18 22. www.interlude.fr

Address : 8 route de Gros Jonc (2.3km southeast)

Opening times : from mid April to end Sept.

7.5 ha (387 pitches) undulating, flat, grassy, sandy

Tariff : 49€ ♣♣ ⇖ ▣ ⚡ (6A) – Extra per person 10€ – Reservation fee 30€

Rental rates : (2014 Price) (from mid April to end Sept.) ♿ (1 mobile home) – 194 🚐 – 5 tent lodges. Per night from 59 to 235€ – Per week from 413 to 1,645€ – Reservation fee 30€

⛽ borne 11€ – 60 ▣ 26€ – ⚡11€

Situated 150m from the beach.

Surroundings : ⚲ ⊏⊐ ☌	
Leisure activities : 🍴 🍽 🏠 ☌ ⛹ 🎿 ⛲ hammam, jacuzzi 🚴 🏊 (small swimming pool) 🏄 ⛷ multi-sports ground, spa centre	**G P S** Longitude : -1.3793 Latitude : 46.17472
Facilities : ♿ ⚿ ▥ ☕ ☄ ⚘ 🚰 launderette ⚂ ⚘	
Nearby : ✂ ⚓	

⚴ Les Varennes

℘ 05 46 09 15 43. www.les-varennes.com

Address : at Raise Maritaise (1.7km southeast, 300m from the beach)

2.5 ha (145 pitches) flat, grassy

Rentals : 85 🚐.

Mobile homes and pitches in the shade of a charming pine wood.

Surroundings : ⚲ ☌	
Leisure activities : 🍴 🚴 🚲 🏄 (open air in season)	**G P S** Longitude : -1.38306 Latitude : 46.17829
Facilities : ♿ ⚿ ▥ ☕ 🚰 launderette ⚘	
Nearby : ✂	

La Couarde-sur-Mer 17670 – Michelin map **324** B2 – pop. 1 248 – alt. 1
▶ Paris 497 – Fontenay-le-Comte 76 – Luçon 66 – La Rochelle 26

⚴ L'Océan ♣♣

℘ 05 46 29 87 70. www.campingocean.com

Address : 50 rue d'Ars (at La Passe)

Opening times : from beginning April to end Sept.

9 ha (338 pitches) flat, grassy

Tariff : (2014 Price) 49€ ♣♣ ⇖ ▣ ⚡ (10A) – Extra per person 13€ Reservation fee 32€

Rental rates : (2014 Price) (from beginning April to end Sept.) ♿ (1 mobile home) ✂ – 170 🚐 – 10 🏠 – 10 tent lodges. Per night from 43 to 139€ – Per week from 336 to 1,484€ – Reservation fee 32€

⛽ borne

High-quality rental options surrounding a charming swimming area. At the bottom of the site there are 2 natural salt-water pools that are perfect for fishing.

Surroundings : ⚲ ⊏⊐ ☌	
Leisure activities : 🍴 🍽 🏠 ☌ ⛹ ⛲ hammam, jacuzzi 🚴 🚲 ✂ 🎣 🏊 multi-sports ground, spa centre, entertainment room	**G P S** Longitude : -1.46737 Latitude : 46.20447
Facilities : ♿ ⚿ ▣▥ ☕ ☄ ⚘ 🚰 launderette ⚂ ⚘	

⚴ La Tour des Prises

℘ 05 46 29 84 82. www.lesprises.com

Address : chemin de la Griffonerie (1.8km northwest along the D 735, turn off to the right)

Opening times : Permanent

2.5 ha (140 pitches) flat, grassy

Tariff : 16€ ♣♣ ⇖ ▣ ⚡ (16A) – Extra per person 3€ – Reservation fee 14€

Rental rates : Permanent – 58 🚐. Per night from 55 to 110€ – Per week from 315 to 795€ – Reservation fee 20€

⛽ borne 10€ – 60 ▣ 16€ – ⚡11€

The campsite is enclosed by a pretty wall of local stone and surrounded by vines.

Surroundings : ⚲ ⊏⊐ ☌	
Leisure activities : 🏠 🚴 🚲 🏄 (open air in season)	**G P S** Longitude : -1.4447 Latitude : 46.20473
Facilities : ♿ ⚿ ▥ ☕ ⚘ 🚰 launderette ⚂ ⚘	

La Flotte 17630 – Michelin map **324** C2 – pop. 2 918 – alt. 4
▶ Paris 489 – Fontenay-le-Comte 68 – Luçon 58 – La Rochelle 17

⚴ Camp'Atlantique Les Peupliers ♣♣

℘ 02 51 20 41 94. www.camp-atlantique.com – limited spaces for one-night stay

Address : RD 735, route de Rivedoux (1.3km southeast)

Opening times : from beginning April to end Sept.

4.5 ha (220 pitches) flat, grassy

Tariff : (2014 Price) 41€ ♣♣ ⇖ ▣ ⚡ (10A) – Extra per person 9€ – Reservation fee 25€

Rental rates : (2014 Price) (from beginning April to end Sept.) ♿ (2 mobile homes) – 144 🚐. Per week from 269 to 1,399€ Reservation fee 25€

Located at the entrance to the village of La Flotte, with lots of mobile homes, some of which are for owner-occupiers, and a few tent or caravan pitches.

Surroundings : ⚲ ⊏⊐ ☌	
Leisure activities : 🍴 🍽 🏠 ☌ ⛹ ⛲ hammam, jacuzzi 🚴 🚲 🏄 ⛷ multi-sports ground, entertainment room	**G P S** Longitude : -1.308 Latitude : 46.1846
Facilities : ♿ ⚿ ☕ 🚰 launderette ⚂	

⚴ La Grainetière ♣♣

℘ 05 46 09 68 86. www.la-grainetiere.com

Address : chemin des Essards (to the west of the town, follow the signs for Saint-Martin-de-Ré, recommended route via the D 735)

Opening times : from beginning April to end Sept.

2.3 ha (140 pitches) flat, sandy

Tariff : 41€ ♣♣ ⇖ ▣ ⚡ (10A) – Extra per person 9€

Rental rates : (from beginning April to end Sept.) – 3 caravans – 80 🚐. Per night from 85 to 95€ – Per week from 299 to 890€

⛽ borne

Choose the pitches furthest away from the road.

Surroundings : ☌	
Leisure activities : 🍽 🏠 ⛹ jacuzzi 🚴 🚲 🏄 (open air in season)	**G P S** Longitude : -1.34412 Latitude : 46.18747
Facilities : ♿ ⚿ ☕ 🚰 launderette ⚂ ⚘	

Loïx 17111 – Michelin map **324** B2 – pop. 731 – alt. 4
▶ Paris 505 – Fontenay-le-Comte 84 – Luçon 74 – La Rochelle 33

⚏ Flower Les Ilates ⚏

✆ 05 46 29 05 43. www.camping-loix.com

Address : at Le Petit Boucheau, route du Grouin (take the eastern exit, 500m from the ocean)

Opening times : from beginning April to end Sept.

4.5 ha (228 pitches) flat, grassy

Tariff : (2014 Price) 44€ ✲✲ ⇔ 回 ⚡ (10A) – Extra per person 9€ – Reservation fee 15€

Rental rates : (2014 Price) Permanent ♿ (2 chalets) – 78 ⌂ – 30 ⌂ – 10 canvas bungalows – 10 tent lodges. Per night 111€ – Per week 777€ – Reservation fee 20€

⛽ borne 4€

Rental options of varying degrees of comfort and design, sometimes unusual and suitable for large families.

Surroundings : ⚲ ⌂ ♀
Leisure activities : ▾ ✕ ⚘ jacuzzi ⚓ ⚲ ⚲
Facilities : ♿ ⚲ ⚲ ⚲ ⚲ ⚲ launderette ⚲
GPS Longitude : -1.42608 Latitude : 46.22756

St-Martin-de-Ré 17410 – Michelin map **324** B2 – pop. 2 585 – alt. 14
▶ Paris 493 – Fontenay-le-Comte 72 – Luçon 62 – La Rochelle 22

⚏ Municipal

✆ 05 46 09 21 96. www.saint-martin-de-re.fr

Address : rue du Rempart (situated in the town)

Opening times : from mid Feb. to mid Nov.

3 ha (200 pitches) terraced, flat, grassy

Tariff : (2014 Price) 25€ ✲✲ ⇔ 回 ⚡ (10A) – Extra per person 4.70€
Reservation fee 14.50€

Rental rates : (2014 Price) (from mid Feb. to mid Nov.) – 21 ⌂. Per night from 49 to 122€ – Per week from 260 to 740€ – Reservation fee 14.50€

⛽ borne 5€

Situated amid the town's fortifications and close to the centre.

Surroundings : ♀♀
Leisure activities : ✕ ⚲ ⚓
Facilities : ♿ ⚲ ⚲ launderette
GPS Longitude : -1.36758 Latitude : 46.19921

ÎLE D'OLÉRON

17 – Michelin map **324**

La Brée-les-Bains 17840 – Michelin map **324** B3 – pop. 758 – alt. 5
▶ Paris 531 – Marennes 32 – Rochefort 53 – La Rochelle 90

⚏ Antioche d'Oléron

✆ 05 46 47 92 00. www.camping-antiochedoleron.com

Address : route de Proires (located 1km northwest along the D 273 follow the signs for St Denis and take a right turn, 150m from the beach)

2.5 ha (129 pitches) flat, grassy

Rentals : 45 ⌂.

Pitches in both the shade and full sun and several luxurious mobile homes.

Surroundings : ⌂ ♀
Leisure activities : ✕ ⚲ jacuzzi ⚓ ⚲ ⚲
Facilities : ♿ ⚲ ⚲ ⚲ ⚲ launderette ⚲
Nearby : ✕
GPS Longitude : -1.35773 Latitude : 46.02033

Le Château-d'Oléron 17480 – Michelin map **324** C4 – pop. 3 930 alt. 9
▶ Paris 507 – Marennes 12 – Rochefort 33 – La Rochelle 70

⚏ La Brande ⚏

✆ 05 46 47 62 37. www.camping-labrande.com

Address : route des Huîtres (2.5km to the northwest, 250m from the sea)

Opening times : from end March to mid Nov.

4 ha (199 pitches) flat, grassy

Tariff : (2014 Price) 44€ ✲✲ ⇔ 回 ⚡ (10A) – Extra per person 8.50€
Reservation fee 20€

Rental rates : (from end March to mid Nov.) ♿ (4 chalets) – 30 ⌂ – 40 ⌂ – 1 tent lodge. Per night from 49 to 250€ – Per week from 255 to 1,250€ – Reservation fee 20€

⛽ borne 7.50€ – 20 ⧠ 16.90€

Both shaded and sunny pitches are available.

Surroundings : ♀♀
Leisure activities : ▾ ✕ ⚲ ⚲ ⚘ ⚲
hammam, jacuzzi ⚓ ⚲ ✕ ⚲ ⚲ (open air in season) ⚲ ⚲ multi-sports ground
Facilities : ♿ ⚲ ⚲ – 6 private sanitary facilities (⚲ wc) ⚲ ⚲ launderette ⚲ ⚲
GPS Longitude : -1.21607 Latitude : 45.90464

⚏ Fief-Melin

✆ 05 46 47 60 85. www.camping.fiefmelin.com

Address : rue des Alizés (1.7km west following signs for St-Pierre-d'Oléron then turn right and continue for 600m)

Opening times : from beginning May to end Sept.

2.2 ha (144 pitches) flat, grassy

Tariff : 32.40€ ✲✲ ⇔ 回 ⚡ (10A) – Extra per person 5.10€

Rental rates : (from beginning April to end Oct.) – 28 ⌂. Per night from 120 to 180€ – Per week from 255 to 740€

Surroundings : ⚲ ⌂ ♀
Leisure activities : ⚲ ⚲ ⚓ ⚲ ⚲ (open air in season), multi-sports ground
Facilities : ⚲ ⚲ ⚲
GPS Longitude : -1.21408 Latitude : 45.89371

Dolus-d'Oléron 17550 – Michelin map **324** C4 – pop. 3 176 – alt. 7
▶ Paris 511 – Marennes 17 – Rochefort 39 – La Rochelle 75

⚏ Ostréa

✆ 05 46 47 62 36. www.camping-ostrea.com

Address : route des Huitres (3.5km east)

Opening times : from beginning April to end Sept.

2 ha (110 pitches) flat, grassy

Tariff : 29.70€ ✲✲ ⇔ 回 ⚡ (6A) – Extra per person 8.30€ – Reservation fee 20€

Rental rates : (from beginning April to end Sept.) – 26 ⌂. Per week from 320 to 720€ – Reservation fee 20€

⛽ borne 5€

On the east coast, very close to the sea. Choose the pitches away from the road.

Surroundings : ⚲ ♀♀
Leisure activities : ⚲ ⚓ ⚲ (open air in season)
Facilities : ♿ ⚲ ⚲ ⚲ launderette ⚲ ⚲
GPS Longitude : -1.22402 Latitude : 45.91299

🏔 Indigo Oléron Les Chênes Verts 👥

Campingindigo ©R Etienne

📞 05 46 75 32 88. www.camping-indigo.com

Address : 9 Passe de l'Écuissière (Côte Ouest (west side of the island), 3.2km southwest along the D 126)

Opening times : from mid May to end Sept.

3 ha (120 pitches) undulating, flat, grassy

Tariff : (2014 Price) 31.70€ ★★ ⇌ 🅴 🅷 (10A) – Extra per person 6.10€ – Reservation fee 22€

Rental rates : (2014 Price) (from mid May to end Sept.) – 45 tent lodges. Per night from 50 to 104€ – Per week from 245 to 728€ Reservation fee 22€

🚐 borne 7€ – 40 🛏 26.40€

In a wooded and undulating setting near the sea.

Surroundings : 🐾 🎇		G
Leisure activities : ✗ 🌙 nighttime 🏃 🛷 🏹 archery		P
Facilities : 🚿 🔑 🏠 🍴 launderette 🐾		S

Longitude : -1.27575
Latitude : 45.88727

⛺ La Perroche Leitner

📞 05 46 75 37 33. www.oleron-camping.eu

Address : 18 rue du Renclos-de-la-Perroche (4km southwest, at La Perroche)

Opening times : from beginning April to beginning Oct.

1.5 ha (100 pitches) flat, grassy

Tariff : 29.20€ ★★ ⇌ 🅴 🅷 (6A) – Extra per person 7.50€

Rental rates : (from beginning April to beginning Oct.) – 28 🚐 2 canvas bungalows. Per night from 45 to 60€ – Per week from 150 to 740€ – Reservation fee 15€

🚐 borne 5.50€ – 15 🛏 15€ – 🚐 🅷14€

In an attractive location close to the sea, with a choice of shady or sunny pitches.

Surroundings : 🐾 🎇		G
Leisure activities : 🛷 🏹		P
Facilities : 🚿 🔑 🏠 🍴 🖼		S
Nearby : 🍴 ✗		

Longitude : -1.3031
Latitude : 45.9016

St-Denis-d'Oléron 17650 – Michelin map **324** B3 – pop. 1 336 – alt. 9

▶ Paris 527 – Marennes 33 – Rochefort 55 – La Rochelle 92

🏔 Village Vacances Les Hameaux des Marines

(rental of chalets only)

📞 05 55 84 34 48. www.terresdefrance.com

Address : rue de Seulières (situated 300m from the beach)

Opening times : Permanent

2.5 ha flat

Rental rates : 🚿 (1 chalet) – 48 🛏. Per night from 59 to 135€ – Per week from 199 to 1,099€

A pleasant, small chalet village, all equipped with lovely, large covered terraces.

Surroundings : 🐾 🎇		G
Leisure activities : 🍴 🏃 🛷 🖼 (open air in season)		P
Facilities : 🔑 🆔 🍴 launderette		S

Longitude : -1.39169
Latitude : 46.01354

⛺ Les Seulières

📞 05 46 47 90 51. www.campinglesseulieres.com

Address : 1371 route des Seulières - Les Huttes (3.5km southwest, follow the signs for Chaucre; 400m from the beach)

Opening times : from beginning April to end Oct.

2.4 ha (120 pitches) flat, grassy

Tariff : 23€ ★★ ⇌ 🅴 🅷 (10A) – Extra per person 4€ – Reservation fee 15€

Rental rates : Permanent – 9 🚐 – 8 🛏. Per night from 50 to 100€ – Per week from 300 to 700€ – Reservation fee 15€

Sunny or shaded pitches are available in a peaceful, family-friendly setting.

Surroundings : 🐾 🎇		G
Leisure activities : 🏆 🖼		P
Facilities : 🚿 🔑 🏠 🍴 launderette		S
Nearby : ✗ 🍴		

Longitude : -1.38512
Latitude : 46.0034

St-Georges-d'Oléron 17190 – Michelin map **324** C4 – pop. 3 497 alt. 10

▶ Paris 527 – Marennes 27 – Rochefort 49 – La Rochelle 85

🏔 Camping-Club Verébleu 👥

Camping-Club Verébleu

📞 05 46 76 57 70. www.verebleu.tm.fr 🐾

Address : La Jousselinière (1.7km southeast along the D 273 and turn left, following signs for Sauzelle)

Opening times : from beginning June to mid Sept.

7.5 ha (324 pitches) flat, grassy

Tariff : (2014 Price) 43€ ★★ ⇌ 🅴 🅷 (13A) – Extra per person 11€ – Reservation fee 25€

Rental rates : (2014 Price) (from beginning June to mid Sept.). 🚿 (1 chalet) 🐾 – 76 🚐 – 59 🛏. Per week from 350 to 1,340€ – Reservation fee 25€

🚐 borne 34€

Divided into 2 separate sections with tents, caravans and rental accommodation surrounding a swimming and play area themed around Fort Boyard.

Surroundings : 🐾 🚐 🎇		G
Leisure activities : 🎮 🏃 🛷 🚲 🎯 🎣 🏊 🛷 multi-sports ground		P
Facilities : 🚿 🔑 🏠 🚿 🍴 launderette 🚐 🐾		S

Longitude : -1.31759
Latitude : 45.97111

These symbols are used for a campsite that is exceptional in its category:

🏔🏔 ....⛺ *Particularly pleasant setting, quality and range of services available*

🐾🐾 *Tranquil, isolated site – quiet site, particularly at night*

≪≪ *Exceptional view – interesting or panoramic view*

Domaine des 4 Vents

📞 05 46 76 65 47. www.camping-oleron-4vents.com

Address : at La Jousselinière (2km southeast along the D 273 and turn left, following signs for Sauzelle)

Opening times : from mid April to mid Sept.

7 ha (300 pitches) flat, grassy

Tariff : (2014 Price) 32.60 € ★★ 🚐 🄴 🄿 (10A) – Extra per person 6.30 € – Reservation fee 20 €

Rental rates : (2014 Price) (from mid April to mid Sept.) – 90 🛏. Per night from 115 to 195 € – Per week from 250 to 950 € – Reservation fee 20 €

🚰 borne 4 € – 20 🄴 18.60 € – 🛒 🄿12 €

Sunny or shaded pitches with a large number of owner-occupied mobile homes.

Surroundings : 🏖 🗺 ♨
Leisure activities : ✗ 🏛 🏃 🚣 🛶 ⛷ multi-sports ground
Facilities : 🚿 ☕ 🧺 🚽 🍴 launderette 🍷

GPS Longitude : -1.31995
Latitude : 45.96973

Oléron Loisirs ♣♣

(rental of mobile homes, chalets and canvas bungalows only)

📞 05 46 76 50 20. www.oleron-loisirs.com – traditional camp. spaces also available

Address : at La Jousselinière (1.9km southeast along the D 273 and turn left, following signs for Sauzelle)

8 ha (321 pitches) flat, grassy

Rentals : 🚿 (1 mobile home) ⚡ – 200 🛏 – 10 🏠 – 13 canvas bungalows.

A mobile home park, many belonging to owner-occupiers.

Surroundings : 🏖 🗺 ♨♨
Leisure activities : 🍴 🏛 🎯 🏃 🚣 🚴 ⚽ 🔲 🏊 🛶 multi-sports ground, entertainment room
Facilities : 🚿 ☕ 🧺 🍴 launderette 🏊 🍷

GPS Longitude : -1.31435
Latitude : 45.97062

There are several different types of sani-station ('borne' in French) – sanitation points providing fresh water and disposal points for grey water. See page 12 for further details.

La Campière ♣♣

📞 05 46 76 72 25. www.la-campiere.com

Address : chemin de l'Achenau (5.4km southwest following signs for Chaucre and take road to the left)

Opening times : from mid April to end Sept.

1.7 ha (66 pitches) flat, grassy

Tariff : (2014 Price) 37 € ★★ 🚐 🄴 🄿 (10A) – Extra per person 8.50 € Reservation fee 17 €

Rental rates : (2014 Price) (from mid April to end Sept.) – 1 🛏 – 12 🏠 – 4 tent lodges. Per night from 45 to 70 € – Per week from 205 to 890 € – Reservation fee 19 €

🚰 borne

In a pleasant, leafy setting, with a small wine bar where you can taste the local produce.

Surroundings : 🏖 🍇
Leisure activities : 🍴 🏛 🏃 🚣 🚴 (small swimming pool)
Facilities : 🚿 ☕ 🧺 🚽 🍴 launderette

GPS Longitude : -1.38198
Latitude : 45.99108

West coast

Club Airotel Les Gros Joncs ♣♣

📞 05 46 76 52 29. www.camping-les-gros-joncs.com – limited spaces for one-night stay

Address : 850 route de Ponthezière – Les Sables Vignier (5km southwest, 300m from the sea)

Opening times : from mid March to mid Nov.

5 ha (253 pitches) terraced, flat, sandy

Tariff : 50.50 € ★★ 🚐 🄴 🄿 (10A) – Extra per person 13.30 € – Reservation fee 18 €

Rental rates : Permanent 🚿 (5 chalets) – 114 🛏 – 96 🏠. Per night from 73 to 212 € – Per week from 404 to 1,484 € – Reservation fee 18 €

🚰 borne

A partially covered swimming area, good-quality rental options and some pitches for tents and caravans, but with old sanitary facilities.

Surroundings : 🏖 🗺 ♨♨
Leisure activities : 🍴 ✗ 🏛 🎯 🏃 🛹 hammam, jacuzzi 🚣 🚴 🔲 🏊 🛶 spa centre, entertainment room
Facilities : 🚿 ☕ 🧺 🚽 🍴 launderette 🏊 🍷

GPS Longitude : -1.379
Latitude : 45.95342

St-Pierre-d'Oléron 17310 – Michelin map **324** C4 – pop. 6 532 – alt. 8
▶ Paris 522 – Marennes 22 – Rochefort 44 – La Rochelle 80

Aqua 3 Masses

📞 05 46 47 23 96. www.campingles3masses.com – limited spaces for one-night stay

Address : at Le Marais-Doux (4.3km southeast)

3 ha (130 pitches) flat, grassy

Rentals : 🚿 (1 chalet) – 35 🛏 – 12 🏠.

In a pleasant setting with flowers; good-quality rental options.

Surroundings : 🏖 🗺 ♨♨
Leisure activities : ✗ 🏛 🚣 🚴 🔲 (open air in season) 🛶
Facilities : 🚿 ☕ 🧺 🍴 launderette 🍷

GPS Longitude : -1.29226
Latitude : 45.91815

St-Trojan-les-Bains 17370 – Michelin map **324** C4 – pop. 1 471 – alt. 5
▶ Paris 509 – Marennes 16 – Rochefort 38 – La Rochelle 74

La Combinette ♣♣

📞 05 46 76 00 47. www.combinette-oleron.com

Address : 36 avenue des Bris (located 1.5km southwest)

Opening times : from beginning April to mid Oct.

4 ha (208 pitches) undulating, flat, grassy, sandy

Tariff : (2014 Price) 27.90 € ★★ 🚐 🄴 🄿 (10A) – Extra per person 9.50 € – Reservation fee 25 €

Rental rates : (2014 Price) (from beginning April to mid Oct.) – 22 🛏 – 19 🏠 – 9 studios. Per night from 40 to 112 € – Per week from 280 to 789 € – Reservation fee 25 €

🚰 borne 17 €

An undulating site with shade and good quality services.

Surroundings : 🏖 🍇
Leisure activities : 🍴 ✗ 🏛 🏃 🛹 🚡 hammam, jacuzzi 🚣 🚴 🏊 multi-sports ground
Facilities : 🚿 ☕ 🧺 🚽 🍴 🖼 🏊 🍷
Nearby : ✗

GPS Longitude : -1.2159
Latitude : 45.82958

⛰ Indigo Oléron Les Pins ♣♣

© Campingindigo

📞 05 46 76 02 39. www.camping-indigo.com

Address : 11 avenue des Bris (to the southwest)

Opening times : from end April to mid Sept.

5 ha (160 pitches) undulating, flat, grassy, sandy

Tariff : (2014 Price) 29.20€ ♥♥ ⟵ 🖪 (10A) – Extra per person 5.70€ – Reservation fee 22€

Rental rates : (2014 Price) (from end April to mid Sept.) – 56 tent lodges. Per night from 49 to 109€ – Per week from 241 to 763€ Reservation fee 22€

🚐 borne 7€ – 40 🖪 23.90€

A natural setting, but choose the pitches away from the road.

Surroundings : 🌳 🍃
Leisure activities : 🏃 🛶 🏊
Facilities : 🕭 ⟿ 🛁 ¶ launderette 🍴

G P S Longitude : -1.21413
Latitude : 45.83128

INGRANDES

86220 – Michelin map **322** J3 – pop. 1 784 – alt. 50
▶ Paris 305 – Châtellerault 7 – Descartes 18 – Poitiers 41

⛰ Les Castels Le Petit Trianon de Saint Ustre

📞 05 49 02 61 47. www.petit-trianon.com

Address : 1 rue du Moulin de St-Ustre (3km to the northeast; at St-Ustre)

Opening times : from mid April to mid Sept.

4 ha (95 pitches)

Tariff : 33.80€ ♥♥ ⟵ 🖪 (10A) – Extra per person 8.60€

Rental rates : (from mid April to mid Sept.) – 23 🚐 – 2 🛏 – 1 studio – 1 cabin in the trees – 6 tent lodges – 1 gîte. Per night from 40 to 170€ – Per week from 224 to 1,190 € – Reservation fee 10€

🚐 borne 10€

A pleasant setting around a small château, with a range of rental options.

Surroundings : 🌳 ⟨ 🍃
Leisure activities : 🏛 🛶 🏊
Facilities : 🕭 ⟿ 🖂 🛁 ¶ 🖩 🍴

G P S Longitude : 0.58653
Latitude : 46.88779

JONZAC

17500 – Michelin map **324** H7 – pop. 3 488 – alt. 40 – ⚓
▶ Paris 512 – Angoulême 59 – Bordeaux 84 – Cognac 36

⛰ Les Castors

📞 05 46 48 25 65. www.campingcastors.com

Address : 8 rue de Clavelaud (located 1.5km southwest along the D 19, follow the signs for Montendre and take the road to the right)

Opening times : from mid March to mid Nov.

3 ha (120 pitches) relatively flat, flat, grassy

Tariff : (2014 Price) 22€ ♥♥ ⟵ 🖪 (6A) – Extra per person 5.50€ Reservation fee 8€

Rental rates : (from mid March to mid Nov.) – 61 🚐 – 6 🏠 – 1 canvas bungalow. Per night from 43 to 121€ – Per week from 245 to 663 € – Reservation fee 8€

🚐 borne 3.20€

The part of the site near the swimming pools is well shaded; another part is in the sun, with good-quality mobile homes.

Surroundings : 🌳 🍃
Leisure activities : ¶ 🏛 jacuzzi 🛶 🚲 🏊 🏊 multi-sports ground
Facilities : 🕭 ⟿ 🛁 ¶ launderette 🍴

G P S Longitude : -0.44712
Latitude : 45.43009

LANDRAIS

17290 – Michelin map **324** E3 – pop. 680 – alt. 12
▶ Paris 455 – Niort 48 – Rochefort 23 – La Rochelle 32

⛰ le Pré Maréchat

📞 05 46 27 73 69. www.cc-plaine-aunis.fr

Address : take northwestern exit along the D 112, follow the signs for Aigrefeuille-d'Aunis and take road to the left, 120m from a lake

Opening times : from mid June to mid Sept.

0.6 ha (37 pitches) flat, grassy

Tariff : (2014 Price) ♥ 2.50€ ⟵ 1.50€ 🖪 3€ – (30A) 2€

Surroundings : 🌿 🌳 🍃
Leisure activities : 🛶
Facilities : 🕭 🖃
Nearby : 🚿

G P S Longitude : -0.86536
Latitude : 46.06963

LE LINDOIS

16310 – Michelin map **324** N5 – pop. 343 – alt. 270
▶ Paris 453 – Angoulême 41 – Confolens 34 – Montbron 12

⛰ L'Étang

📞 05 45 65 02 67. www.campingdeletang.com

Address : route de Rouzède (500m southwest along the D 112)

Opening times :

10 ha/1.5 (29 pitches) relatively flat, grassy

Tariff : (2014 Price) 23.50€ ♥♥ ⟵ 🖪 (16A) – Extra per person 5€

Rental rates : (from beginning April to end Oct.) – 4 chalets (without sanitary facilities). Per night from 45 to 55€

In a pleasant unspoilt and natural setting with trees beside a lake.

Surroundings : 🌿 🌳 🍃
Leisure activities : ¶ ✕ 🏖 (beach) 🏊 boats for hire
Facilities : 🕭 ⟿ 🖂 🖩 🖩

G P S Longitude : 0.58555
Latitude : 45.73974

LOUDUN

86200 – Michelin map **322** G2 – pop. 7 089 – alt. 120
▶ Paris 311 – Angers 79 – Châtellerault 47 – Poitiers 55

⛰ Municipal de Beausoleil

📞 05 49 98 15 38. www.ville-loudun.fr

Address : chemin de l'Étang (2.5km take the northern exit along the D 347, towards Angers and take road to the left after the level crossing; beside a stream and near a lake)

0.6 ha (33 pitches)

Surroundings : 🌳 🍃
Leisure activities :
Facilities : 🕭 🖩

G P S Longitude : 0.06175
Latitude : 47.00334

MARANS

17230 – Michelin map **324** E2 – pop. 4 623 – alt. 1
▶ Paris 461 – Fontenay-le-Comte 28 – Niort 56 – La Rochelle 24

⚠ Municipal du Bois Dinot

✆ 05 46 01 10 51. www.ville-marans.fr

Address : route de Nantes (500m north along the N 137, 80m from the Marans-La Rochelle canal)

Opening times : from end March to end Sept.

7 ha/3 for camping (170 pitches) flat, grassy

Tariff : (2014 Price) ☂ 3.75€ ⟷ 2.40€ ▣ 3€ – ⚡ (10A) 3€
Rental rates : (2014 Price) (from end March to end Sept.) ♿ (1 chalet) – 12 ⟐ – 5 tent lodges. Per night from 40 to 64€ – Per week from 190 to 562€
⟐ borne 4€ – 10 ▣ 11€ – ⟐ 11€

In the heart of a wooded park with a former velodrome for lovers of 2-wheeled transport.

Surroundings : ⟐ 0 0	
Leisure activities : ⟐	**G**
Facilities : ♿ ⟐ ⟐ ⟐ launderette	**P** Longitude : -0.98945
Nearby : ⟐ ⟐ pedalos	**S** Latitude : 46.31583

To visit a town or region, use the MICHELIN Green Guides.

MARENNES

17320 – Michelin map **324** D5 – pop. 5 608 – alt. 10
▶ Paris 494 – Pons 61 – Rochefort 22 – Royan 31

⚠ Au Bon Air

✆ 05 46 85 02 40. www.aubonair.com

Address : 9 avenue Pierre Voyer (2.5km to the west; at Marennes-Plage)

Opening times : from beginning April to end Sept.

2.4 ha (126 pitches) flat, grassy, sandy

Tariff : (2014 Price) 22.90€ ☂☂ ⟷ ▣ ⚡ (16A) –
Extra per person 6.20€ – Reservation fee 18€
Rental rates : (from beginning April to end Sept.) – 25 ⟐ – 5 ⟐. Per night from 42 to 77€ – Per week from 259 to 819 € Reservation fee 18€
⟐ borne 2€ – ⟐ 11€

Close to the beach (200m); pitches in the shade with some owner-occupier mobile homes.

Surroundings : ⟐ 0 0	
Leisure activities : ⟐ ⟐ ⟐ ⟐	**G** Longitude : -1.13442
Facilities : ♿ ⟐ ⟐ ⟐ ⟐ launderette	**P** Latitude : 45.81882
	S

LES MATHES

17570 – Michelin map **324** D5 – pop. 1 719 – alt. 10
▶ Paris 514 – Marennes 18 – Rochefort 40 – La Rochelle 76

⚠ La Pinède ♨

✆ 05 46 22 45 13. www.campinglapinede.com – limited spaces for one-night stay

Address : 2103 route de la Fouasse (3km to the northwest)

Opening times : from beginning April to end Sept.

8 ha (372 pitches) flat and relatively flat, grassy

Tariff : (2014 Price) 48€ ☂☂ ⟷ ▣ ⚡ (10A) – Extra per person 9€ – Reservation fee 9€

Rental rates : (2014 Price) (from beginning April to end Sept.) ♿ – 201 ⟐ – 10 ⟐. Per night from 28 to 154€ – Per week from 196 to 1,078€ – Reservation fee 9€

A large swimming area, partially covered, with several pitches for tents and caravans, but choose those furthest away from the road.

Surroundings : ⟐ ⟐ 0 0	
Leisure activities : ⟐ ⟐ ⟐ ⟐ ⟐ ⟐ ⟐ ⟐ ⟐ ⟐ ⟐ ⟐ ⟐ archery, multi-sports ground	**G**
Facilities : ♿ ⟐ ⟐ – 4 private sanitary facilities (⟐ ⟐ ⟐ wc) ⟐ ⟐ ⟐ launderette ⟐ ⟐	**P** Longitude : -1.17568
Nearby : amusement park	**S** Latitude : 45.72784

⚠ L'Estanquet ♨

✆ 05 46 22 47 32. www.campinglestanquet.com

Address : route de la Fouasse (3.5km to the northwest)

Opening times : from beginning April to end Sept.

6 ha (387 pitches)

Tariff : (2014 Price) 21€ ☂☂ ⟷ ▣ ⚡ (10A) – Extra per person 6.50€ Reservation fee 20€
Rental rates : (2014 Price) (from beginning April to end Sept.) – 234 ⟐ – 10 ⟐ – 20 canvas bungalows. Per night from 79 to 119€ – Per week from 159 to 1,085€ – Reservation fee 20€

A good choice of mobile homes at a water park, with free use of the covered swimming pool and play area at the Les Sables de Cordouan campsite 200m away.

Surroundings : ⟐ 0 0	
Leisure activities : ⟐ ⟐ ⟐ ⟐ ⟐ ⟐ ⟐ ⟐ ⟐ multi-sports ground	**G** Longitude : -1.17661
Facilities : ♿ ⟐ ⟐ ⟐ ⟐ ⟐ launderette ⟐ ⟐	**P** Latitude : 45.73214
Nearby : ⟐ amusement park	**S**

⚠ L'Orée du Bois ♨

✆ 05 46 22 42 43. www.camping-oree-du-bois.fr – limited spaces for one-night stay

Address : 225 route de la Bouverie (3.5km to the northwest, at La Fouasse)

6 ha (429 pitches) flat, grassy

Rentals : 170 ⟐.

Tent and caravan pitches with refurbished private sanitary facilities; some luxury mobile homes.

Surroundings : ⟐ 0 0	
Leisure activities : ⟐ ⟐ ⟐ ⟐ ⟐ ⟐ ⟐ ⟐ ⟐ ⟐ multi-sports ground	**G** Longitude : -1.17905
Facilities : ♿ ⟐ ⟐ – 40 private sanitary facilities (⟐ ⟐ ⟐ wc) ⟐ launderette ⟐ ⟐	**P** Latitude : 45.72998
	S

Key to rentals symbols:

12 ⟐	*Number of mobile homes*
20 ⟐	*Number of chalets*
6 ⟐	*Number of rooms to rent*
Per night 30–50€	*Minimum/maximum rate per night*
Per week 300–1,000€	*Minimum/maximum rate per week*

⚲ Les Sables de Cordouan

☏ 05 32 09 04 08. www.campingsablesdecordouan.com – limited spaces for one-night stay

Address : route de la Fouasse (situated 3.6km northwest)

3 ha (150 pitches) flat, grassy
Rentals : 30 🚐.

Campers can also make use of all the services and entertainment provided at the the Estanquet campsite (200m). Not many pitches for tents and caravans.

Surroundings : 🗺 ⌂⌂	
Leisure activities : 🏊 🔲	**G** Longitude : -1.17563
Facilities : ₳ ⚬⟷ launderette	**P** Latitude : 45.73022
Nearby : 🛥 ⛏ ✕ 🚣 ⛵ amusement park	

⚠ Monplaisir

☏ 05 46 22 50 31. www.campingmonplaisirlesmathes.fr

Address : 26 avenue de La Palmyre (southwestern exit)

Opening times : from beginning April to end Sept.

2 ha (114 pitches) flat, grassy

Tariff : (2014 Price) 24.50€ ✶✶ � 🔲 ⚡ (10A) – Extra per person 7€ 🚐 borne 4€
Only pitches for tents and caravans – no rental options.

Surroundings : ⌂⌂	
Leisure activities : 🏛 🏊 🔲	**G** Longitude : -1.15563
Facilities : ₳ ⚬⟷ ⛺⛟ launderette	**P** Latitude : 45.71541
Nearby : 🍴 ⛏ ✕ 🚴 🎿 🐟	

MAUZÉ-SUR-LE-MIGNON

79210 – Michelin map **322** B7 – pop. 2 758 – alt. 30
▶ Paris 430 – Niort 23 – Rochefort 40 – La Rochelle 43

⚠ Municipal le Gué de la Rivière

☏ 05 49 26 30 35. www.ville-mauze-mignon.fr – ⛯

Address : rue du Port (located 1km northwest along the D 101, follow the signs for St-Hilaire-la-Palud and take the turning to the left; between the Mignon river and the canal)

Opening times : from mid May to beginning Sept.

1.5 ha (75 pitches) flat, grassy

Tariff : (2014 Price) ✶ 2.60€ 🚗 🔲 2.70€ – ⚡ (10A) 3.60€ 🚐 borne 4€

Surroundings : 🛥 🗺 ⌂⌂	
Leisure activities : 🏛	**G** Longitude : -0.67959
Facilities : ⚬⟷	**P** Latitude : 46.19968

MÉDIS

17600 – Michelin map **324** E6 – pop. 2 698 – alt. 29
▶ Paris 498 – Marennes 28 – Mirambeau 48 – Pons 39

⚲ Sites et Paysages Le Clos Fleuri

☏ 05 46 05 62 17. www.le-clos-fleuri.com

Address : 8 impasse du Clos Fleuri (situated 2km southeast along the D 117e 3)

Opening times : from beginning June to mid Sept.

3 ha (120 pitches) flat and relatively flat, grassy

Tariff : 39.50€ ✶✶ 🚗 🔲 ⚡ (10A) – Extra per person 9.50€ – Reservation fee 20€

Rental rates : (from beginning June to mid Sept.) 🚫 – 4 🚐 – 10 🏠. Per week from 290 to 790€ – Reservation fee 20€

A pleasant rural setting with ample shade from a great variety of trees.

Surroundings : 🛥 🗺 ⌂⌂	
Leisure activities : ⛏ ✕ 🏛 🛶 🏊 🎿 🏐	**G** Longitude : -0.94633
Facilities : ₳ ⚬⟷ ⛺⛟ launderette 🚿 🚱	**P** Latitude : 45.63003

MONTBRON

16220 – Michelin map **324** N5 – pop. 2 161 – alt. 141
▶ Paris 460 – Angoulême 29 – Nontron 25 – Rochechouart 38

⚲ Les Castels Les Gorges du Chambon ▲▲

☏ 05 45 70 71 70. www.camping-gorgesduchambon.com 🚫

Address : at Le Chambon (4.4km east along the D 6, follow the signs for Piégut-Pluviers, then take left turn for 3.2km along the D 163, follow the signs for Écuras and take the road to the right; 80m from the Tardoir river (direct access)

Opening times : from end April to mid Sept.

28 ha/7 for camping (132 pitches) flat, grassy

Tariff : 34.10€ ✶✶ 🚗 🔲 ⚡ (10A) – Extra per person 9.10€ – Reservation fee 12€

Rental rates : (from end April to mid Sept.) ₳ (1 mobile home) 🚫 – 12 🚐 – 8 🏠 – 5 canvas bungalows – 4 tent lodges – 1 gîte. Per night from 35 to 105 € – Per week from 240 to 735€ Reservation fee 20€

In a pretty, wooded green setting based on an old landscaped and renovated farmhouse.

Surroundings : 🛥 ⌂⌂	
Leisure activities : ⛏ ✕ 🏛 🎯 🏃 🏊 🚴 🏐 🛶 🎿 🐟 🚣	**G** Longitude : 0.5593
Facilities : ₳ ⚬⟷ ⛺ ⛟ launderette 🚿 🚱	**P** Latitude : 45.65945
Nearby : 🐎	

*For more information on visiting particular towns or regions, consult the relevant regional **MICHELIN Green Guide**. We also recommend you use the appropriate Michelin regional map to locate your selected campsite, to calculate distances and to work out the best route.*

MONTIGNAC-CHARENTE

16330 – Michelin map **324** K5 – pop. 731 – alt. 50
▶ Paris 432 – Angoulême 17 – Cognac 42 – Rochechouart 66

⚠ Municipal les Platanes

☏ 05 45 39 70 09. www.montignac-charente.fr

Address : 25 avenue de la Boixe (200m northwest along the D 115, follow the signs for Aigré)

Opening times : from beginning June to end Aug.

1.5 ha (100 pitches) flat, grassy

Tariff : (2014 Price) ✶ 🚗 🔲 5.35€ – ⚡ (12A) 6.20€
Choose the shady pitches furthest away from the road.

Surroundings : ⌂⌂	
Leisure activities : 🏛	**G** Longitude : 0.11797
Facilities : ₳ 🚿 🚱	**P** Latitude : 45.78189
Nearby : 🏊 🐟	

MONTMORILLON

86500 – Michelin map **322** L6 – pop. 6 410 – alt. 100
▶ Paris 354 – Bellac 43 – Le Blanc 32 – Chauvigny 27

🛆 Municipal de l'Allochon

𝒫 05 49 91 02 33. www.ville-montmorillon.fr

Address : 31 avenue Fernad-Tribot (take the southeastern exit along the D 54, follow the signs for Le Dorat; 50m from the Gartempe river, beside a stream)

Opening times : from beginning March to end Oct.

2 ha (80 pitches) terraced, flat, grassy

Tariff : (2014 Price) ⭑ 1.78€ 🚗 1€ 🔲 1€ – ⚡ (10A) 3.63€
🚐 borne – 2 🔲 1€

Surroundings : 🌣🌣
Leisure activities : 🏠 🏌
Facilities : 🔥 🔒 🏛 🍴 📷
Nearby : 🎣 🚣 🏊

Longitude : 0.87526
Latitude : 46.42038

MORTAGNE-SUR-GIRONDE

17120 – Michelin map **324** F7 – pop. 1 027 – alt. 51
▶ Paris 509 – Blaye 59 – Jonzac 30 – Pons 26

🛆 Municipal Bel Air

𝒫 06 42 01 17 62. www.mortagne-sur-gironde

Address : towards the port

Opening times : from beginning May to end Sept.

1 ha (20 pitches) terraced, flat, grassy

Tariff : (2014 Price) 11.90€ ⭑⭑ 🚗 🔲 ⚡ (10A) –
Extra per person 3.10€

Several pitches have a panoramic view of the estuary and the marina.

Surroundings : 🚣 ← 🏕 🌣🌣
Leisure activities : 🏌
Facilities : 🔥 🚲 🍴 🍴

Longitude : -0.79147
Latitude : 45.47974

MOSNAC

17240 – Michelin map **324** G6 – pop. 476 – alt. 23
▶ Paris 501 – Cognac 34 – Gémozac 20 – Jonzac 11

🛆 Municipal les Bords de la Seugne

𝒫 05 46 70 48 45. mosnac@mairie17.com

Address : 34 rue de la Seugne (in the village; beside the river)

0.9 ha (33 pitches) flat, grassy

A small campsite in the village, beside the pretty little church; very simple but very pleasant.

Surroundings : 🚣 ← the church 🏕 🌣🌣
Leisure activities : 🎣
Facilities : 🏛 📷

Longitude : -0.52293
Latitude : 45.5058

In order for the guide to remain wholly objective, the selection of campsites is made on an entirely independent basis.

LA PALMYRE

17570 – Michelin map **324** C5
▶ Paris 524 – Poitiers 191 – La Rochelle 77 – Rochefort 46

🏔 Village Siblu Bonne Anse Plage

(rental of mobile homes only)

𝒫 05 46 22 40 90. www.siblu.fr/bonneanse

Address : avenue de la Coubre (situated 2km west along the D 25, 400m from the beach)

Opening times : from end May to mid Sept.

18 ha (613 pitches) undulating

Rental rates : (2014 Price) 🏠 – 200 🚐. Per night from 59 to 227 € – Per week from 413 to 1,589€ – Reservation fee 15€
🚐 6 🔲 31€

A mobile home park, most of which belong to owner-occupiers.

Surroundings : 🏕 🌣🌣
Leisure activities : 🍸 🍽 🎣 🏌 🏄 🏌 🚴 🚣 climbing wall, multi-sports ground
Facilities : 🔥 🔒 🍴 launderette 🚰 🚗

Longitude : -1.19983
Latitude : 45.69843

🏔 Yelloh! Village Parc de la Côte Sauvage 👥

𝒫 05 46 22 40 18. www.yellohvillage-parcdelacotesauvage.com 🏠

Address : la Coubre (3km west along the D 25)

Opening times : from mid April to mid Sept.

14 ha (400 pitches) undulating, flat, relatively flat, grassy, sandy

Tariff : 18€ ⭑⭑ 🚗 🔲 ⚡ (10A) – Extra per person 7€
Rental rates : (from mid April to mid Sept.) 🏠 – 120 🚐 – 120 🏠. Per night from 39 to 225€ – Per week from 273 to 1,575€
🚐 borne – 15 🔲 18€ – 🚐 ⚡18€

In a wooded setting very near the beach and the la Coubre lighthouse.

Surroundings : 🚣 🏕 🌣🌣
Leisure activities : 🍸 🍽 🏠 🎣 🏌 🏄 🏌 🚴 🎣 🚣 multi-sports ground
Facilities : 🔥 🔒 🏛 🍴 launderette 🚰 🚗

Longitude : -1.22769
Latitude : 45.69584

🏔 Beausoleil

𝒫 05 46 22 30 03. www.campingbeausoleil.com

Address : 20 avenue de la Coubre (take the northwestern exit, 500m from the beach)

Opening times : from beginning April to mid Sept.

4 ha (244 pitches) undulating, flat, grassy, sandy

Tariff : (2014 Price) 35€ ⭑⭑ 🚗 🔲 ⚡ (10A) – Extra per person 5.10€
Reservation fee 18.50€
Rental rates : (2014 Price) (from beginning April to mid Sept.) – 20 🚐 – 2 canvas bungalows. Per week from 210 to 805€ – Reservation fee 18.50€

A tranquil, family-oriented site, with owner-occupiers and a further hundred or so pitches for tents or caravans.

Surroundings : 🌣🌣
Leisure activities : 🏠 🏌 🏊 (small swimming pool)
Facilities : 🔥 🔒 🍴 launderette 🚰 🚗

Longitude : -1.18301
Latitude : 45.69242

PARTHENAY

79200 – Michelin map **322** E5 – pop. 10 338 – alt. 175
▶ Paris 377 – Bressuire 32 – Châtellerault 79 – Fontenay-le-Comte 69

⛰ Le Bois Vert

✆ 05 49 64 78 43. www.camping-boisvert.com

Address : 14 rue Boisseau (take the southwestern exit follow the signs for La Roche-sur-Yon and take a right turn after the bridge over the Thouet; near a lake)

Opening times : from mid April to end Oct.

2 ha (86 pitches) flat, grassy

Tariff : 28.50€ �star �star 🚐 ▣ (½) (10A) – Extra per person 6.50€ – Reservation fee 10€

Rental rates : (from mid April to end Oct.) & (1 mobile home) – 14 🛏 – 4 canvas bungalows. Per night from 36 to 93€ – Per week from 252 to 651€ – Reservation fee 10€

🚐 borne 9€ – 3 ▣ 28.50€

Surroundings : ▭ ♀
Leisure activities : ♟ 🛖 🎯 🚴 🛶
Facilities : & ⚡ ▥ 🚿 ☁ 🍴 launderette 🧺
Nearby : ✗ 🛶 🎣 ✂ 🔥 ⌇

GPS Longitude : -0.2675 Latitude : 46.64194

PONS

17800 – Michelin map **324** G6 – pop. 4 446 – alt. 39
▶ Paris 493 – Blaye 64 – Bordeaux 97 – Cognac 24

⛰ Les Moulins de la Vergne

Les Moulins de la Vergne

✆ 05 46 90 02 80. www.lesmoulinsdelavergne.com|

Address : 9 impasse du Moulin de la Vergne (situated 2km north along the D 234, towards Colombiers)

Opening times : Permanent

3 ha/1 for camping (51 pitches) flat, grassy

Tariff : 21€ ✦ ✦ 🚐 ▣ (½) (10A) – Extra per person 4€

🚐 20 ▣ 21€
The bar-restaurant at the mill has an attractive terrace.

Surroundings : 🌿 ♀
Leisure activities : ♟ ✗ 🛖 🛶 🎣
Facilities : ⚡ ▥ 🍴 launderette 🧺

GPS Longitude : -0.53906 Latitude : 45.59444

⛺ Municipal le Paradis

✆ 05 46 91 36 72. campingmunicipalpons@voila.fr

Address : avenue du Paradis (to the west near the swimming pool)

Opening times : from beginning May to end Sept.

1 ha (60 pitches) flat, grassy

Tariff : (2014 Price) ✦ 8€ 🚐 ▣ 8€ (½) (6A)

🚐 borne 6€
A good expanse of grass and plenty of shade in a simple but very pleasant site.

Surroundings : ♀♀
Leisure activities : 🛖
Facilities : & ⚡ ☁ 🍴 🚿 ▣
Nearby : 🛶 ⌇

GPS Longitude : -0.5553 Latitude : 45.57793

PONT-L'ABBÉ-D'ARNOULT

17250 – Michelin map **324** E5 – pop. 1 716 – alt. 20
▶ Paris 474 – Marennes 23 – Rochefort 19 – La Rochelle 59

⛰ Parc de la Garenne

✆ 05 46 97 01 46. www.lagarenne.net

Address : 24 avenue Bernard Chambenoit (take the southeastern exit along the D 125, follow the signs for Soulignonne)

2.7 ha (111 pitches) flat, grassy

Rentals : 30 🛏 – 2 canvas bungalows.

Well shaded in part, some leisure activities and very simple sanitary facilities.

Surroundings : 🌿 ▭ ♀
Leisure activities : 🛖 🎣 🚴 ✂ multi-sports ground
Facilities : & ⚡ ☁ 🚿 🍴 launderette 🧺
Nearby : 🛶

GPS Longitude : -0.87096 Latitude : 45.82729

The pitches of many campsites are marked out with low hedges of attractive bushes and shrubs.

PRAILLES

79370 – Michelin map **322** E7 – pop. 666 – alt. 150
▶ Paris 394 – Melle 15 – Niort 23 – St-Maixent-l'École 13

⛰ Le Lambon

✆ 05 49 32 85 11. www.lelambon.com

Address : at Le Lambon lake (2.8km southeast)

Opening times : from beginning April to end Sept.

1 ha (50 pitches) terraced, relatively flat, flat, grassy

Tariff : 13.30€ ✦ ✦ 🚐 ▣ (½) (10A) – Extra per person 4.50€

Rental rates : (from mid March to end Oct.) – 7 🛏 – 39 gîtes. Per night from 67 to 87€ – Per week from 186 to 378€

🚐 borne
Situated 200m from the boating centre where a number of activities are offered.

Surroundings : 🌿 ♀♀
Facilities : & 🚿 🍴 launderette
Nearby : ♟ ✗ 🛖 🎣 ✂ 🔥 🏊 (beach) 🛶 sports trail

GPS Longitude : -0.20753 Latitude : 46.30055

RIVIÈRES

16110 – Michelin map **324** M5 – pop. 1 833 – alt. 75
▶ Paris 445 – Poitiers 108 – Angoulême 26 – Limoges 84

⛰ des Flots

✆ 06 48 51 18 90. www.campinglesflots.16.hebergratuit.com

Address : 714 rue des Flots

Opening times : from mid April to mid Oct.

1 ha (25 pitches) flat, grassy, stony

Tariff : (2014 Price) ✦ 3.50€ 🚐 2€ ▣ 6€ – (½) 3.60€

Rental rates : (2014 Price) – 2 🛏. Per week from 250 to 380€

🚐 borne 2€ – 5 ▣ 16.60€
Beside the river and close to the Château de La Rochefoucauld.

Surroundings : 🌿 ▭ ♀
Leisure activities : 🎣
Facilities : & 🚿 ▣ 🍴
Nearby : 🛶

GPS Longitude : 0.3809 Latitude : 45.74507

ROCHEFORT

17300 – Michelin map **324** E4 – pop. 25 317 – alt. 12 – ♨
▶ Paris 475 – Limoges 221 – Niort 62 – La Rochelle 38

⋀⋀ Le Bateau

✆ 05 46 99 41 00. www.campinglebateau.com

Address : rue des Pêcheurs D'Islande (near the Charente river, along the western bypass (bd Bignon) and follow the signs for Port Neuf, near the aquatic centre)

Opening times : from beginning April to mid Nov.

5 ha/1.5 (133 pitches)

Tariff : (2014 Price) 16€ ★★ ⇔ 🔲 🔌 (10A) – Extra per person 4.70€ – Reservation fee 15€

Rental rates : (2014 Price) (from beginning April to mid Nov.) – 39 🚐. Per night from 57 to 111€ – Per week from 299 to 649 € – Reservation fee 15€

🚐 40 🔲 16€

Many spa bathers in search of peace and quiet come to this site close to water.

Surroundings : 🏊 ⛺ ♨
Leisure activities : ♟ ✕ 🏛 🚣 🎿 ⛷
Facilities : ♿ ⚡ ☷ ♨ 🚿 ♈ launderette
Nearby : 🛶

⚠ Municipal Le Rayonnement

✆ 05 46 82 67 70. camping.municipal@ville-rochefort.fr

Address : 3 avenue de la Fosse aux Mâts (near the town centre)

Opening times : from beginning March to end Nov.

2 ha (138 pitches) flat, fine gravel, grassy

Tariff : 16.19€ ★★ ⇔ 🔲 🔌 (16A) – Extra per person 2.86€ – Reservation fee 30€

Rental rates : (from beginning March to end Nov.) ♿ (1 mobile home) – 19 🚐. Per week from 296 to 364 € – Reservation fee 30€

🚐 borne – 30 🔲

Surroundings : ⛺ ♨
Leisure activities : 🏛 🚣 🚴
Facilities : ♿ ⚡ ☷ ♨ 🚿 ♈ launderette

Longitude : -0.95835
Latitude : 45.93

LA ROCHE-POSAY

86270 – Michelin map **322** K4 – pop. 1 556 – alt. 112 – ♨
▶ Paris 325 – Le Blanc 29 – Châteauroux 76 – Châtellerault 23

⋀⋀ Club Airotel La Roche-Posay Vacances ♨♨

✆ 05 49 86 21 23. www.larocheposay-vacances.com

Address : route de Lésigny (located 1.5km north along the D 5, near the racecourse; beside the Creuse river)

Opening times : from mid April to end Sept.

5.5 ha (200 pitches)

Tariff : 35€ ★★ ⇔ 🔲 🔌 (10A) – Extra per person 4€

Rental rates : (from mid April to end Sept.) – 78 🚐. Per night from 44 to 134€ – Per week from 308 to 938€

🚐 borne 6€

Attractively marked out pitches around a partially covered water park.

Surroundings : 🏊 ⛺ ♨
Leisure activities : 🏛 🎣 🚴 🎿 ⛷ ⛵ boats to hire 🏇
Facilities : ♿ ⚡ ☷ ♨ 🚿 ♈ launderette
Nearby : 🐎

Longitude : 0.80963
Latitude : 46.7991

RONCE-LES-BAINS

17390 – Michelin map **324** D5
▶ Paris 505 – Marennes 9 – Rochefort 31 – La Rochelle 68

⋀⋀⋀ La Clairière ♨♨

✆ 05 46 36 36 63. www.camping-la-clairiere.com – limited spaces for one-night stay

Address : rue du Bois de la Pesse (3.6km south along the D 25, follow the signs for Arvert and take turning to the right)

12 ha/4 for camping (292 pitches) undulating, flat, grassy, sandy

Rentals : 25 🚐 – 8 🏠.

Located in a spacious and shaded setting, undulating and a little 'natural' in places.

Surroundings : 🏊 ♨
Leisure activities : ♟ ✕ 🏛 🎆 nighttime 🏃 🎣 🚴 🔲 🏊 ⛷ massages
Facilities : ♿ ⚡ ☷ – 10 private sanitary facilities (🛁 💧 wc) ♈ launderette 🚿
Nearby : 🐎

Longitude : -1.16844
Latitude : 45.77502

⋀⋀ Les Pins ♨♨

✆ 05 46 36 07 75. www.activ-loisirs.com – limited spaces for one-night stay

Address : 16 avenue Côte de Beauté (located 1km to the south)

Opening times : from beginning April to end Oct.

1.5 ha (89 pitches)

Tariff : 35.40€ ★★ ⇔ 🔲 🔌 (6A) – Extra per person 6.80€ – Reservation fee 20€

Rental rates : (from beginning April to end Nov.) – 32 🚐 – 23 🏠 – 14 canvas bungalows – 1 gîte. Per night from 50 to 132€ – Per week from 261 to 923€ – Reservation fee 20€

Various rental options at varying degrees of comfort and price.

Surroundings : ♨
Leisure activities : 🏛 🏃 🎣 🚴 🔲 (open air in season), entertainment room
Facilities : ♿ ⚡ ☷ ♈ launderette 🚿
Nearby : ✕

Longitude : -1.15862
Latitude : 45.78875

ROYAN

17200 – Michelin map **324** D6 – pop. 18 259 – alt. 20
▶ Paris 504 – Bordeaux 121 – Périgueux 183 – Rochefort 40

⋀⋀⋀ Le Royan

✆ 05 46 39 09 06. www.le-royan.com

Address : 10 rue des Bleuets

Opening times : from beginning April to mid Oct.

3.5 ha (194 pitches)

Tariff : (2014 Price) 28€ ★★ ⇔ 🔲 🔌 (10A) – Extra per person 6.50€ – Reservation fee 20€

Rental rates : (2014 Price) (from beginning April to mid Oct.) – 38 🚐 – 13 🏠. Per night from 48 to 100€ – Per week from 300 to 890€ – Reservation fee 20€

Various rental options and standards of comfort; pitches are well marked out, but choose those furthest away from the road.

Surroundings : ⛺ ♨
Leisure activities : ♟ ✕ 🏛 🎣 🔲 🏊 ⛷
Facilities : ♿ ⚡ ☷ 🚿 ♈ launderette 🚿

Longitude : -1.04207
Latitude : 45.64456

⛰ Le Chant des Oiseaux

🔗 05 46 39 47 47. www.camping-royan-chantdesoiseaux.com

Address : 19 rue des Sansonnets (2.3km to the northwest)

Opening times : from beginning May to end Sept.

2.5 ha (150 pitches)

Tariff : (2014 Price) 30€ ♦♦ ⇔ 🗐 🕅 (10A) – Extra per person 6.30€

Rental rates : (from beginning April to end Sept.) – 36 🚐. Per week from 155 to 930€ – Reservation fee 16€

🚐 borne – 5 🗐 19€

High-quality rental options, some offering accommodation on a hotel-style basis.

Surroundings : 🌿 ♀♀	G
Leisure activities : ✗ 🛋 ⊙ nighttime 🚣 🏊	P
Facilities : ♿ ⚬ 🔲 🖱 ⛺ launderette 🚿.	**Longitude : -1.02872**
	S **Latitude : 45.6466**

ST-AUGUSTIN-SUR-MER

17570 – Michelin map **324** D5 – pop. 1 219 – alt. 10
▶ Paris 512 – Marennes 23 – Rochefort 44 – La Rochelle 81

⛰ Le Logis du Breuil

🔗 05 46 23 23 45. www.logis-du-breuil.com

Address : 36 rue du Centre (located to the southeast along the D 145, follow the signs for Royan)

Opening times : from beginning May to end Sept.

30 ha/8.5 for camping (390 pitches) undulating, flat, grassy, wood

Tariff : 32.80€ ♦♦ ⇔ 🗐 🕅 (10A) – Extra per person 8.20€ – Reservation fee 10€

Rental rates : (from end April to end Sept.) – 7 🚐 – 1 🏠 – 9 gîtes. Per week from 295 to 770€ – Reservation fee 20€

🚐 borne

On the edge of the Forêt de St-Augustin (forest), with vast green spaces and meadows; this site is ideal for both relaxation and ball games.

Surroundings : 🌿 ♀♀	G
Leisure activities : ⬤✗ 🛋 🚣 🚲 ✂ 🏊 multi-sports ground	P
Facilities : ♿ ⚬ 🖱 – 4 private sanitary facilities (🔲 ⚬ WC) ⛺ launderette 🚿 🚿	**Longitude : -1.09612**
	S **Latitude : 45.67445**

ST-CYR

86130 – Michelin map **322** I4 – pop. 1 024 – alt. 62
▶ Paris 321 – Poitiers 18 – Tours 85 – Joué 82

⛰ Flower Lac de St-Cyr

🔗 05 49 62 57 22. www.campinglacdesaintcyr.com

Address : in St-Cyr park (located 1.5km northeast along the D 4, D 82, follow the signs for Bonneuil-Matours and take road to the left, near a lake – from the N10, access via La Tricherie)

Opening times : from beginning April to end Sept.

5.4 ha (198 pitches) flat, grassy

Tariff : 18€ ♦♦ ⇔ 🗐 🕅 (10A) – Extra per person 3€

Rental rates : (from beginning April to end Sept.) – 30 🚐 – 4 yurts – 3 canvas bungalows. Per night from 32 to 125€ – Per week from 160 to 875€ – Reservation fee 15€

Surroundings : ⬤ 🛶 ♀♀ 📐	G
Leisure activities : ✗ 🛋 🚣🏄 🛶 🚣 🚲 ✂	P
Facilities : ♿ ⚬ 🚿 ⛺ launderette 🚿 🚿	**Longitude : 0.44782**
Nearby : 🍴 🐎 🦆 pedalos	S **Latitude : 46.72056**

ST-GEORGES-DE-DIDONNE

17110 – Michelin map **324** D6 – pop. 5 055 – alt. 7
▶ Paris 505 – Blaye 84 – Bordeaux 117 – Jonzac 56

⛰ Bois-Soleil ♦♦

Bois-Soleil

🔗 05 46 05 05 94. www.bois-soleil.com
🏊 (from beginning July to end Sept.)

Address : 2 avenue de Suzac (situated to the south along the D 25, follow the signs for Meschers-sur-Gironde)

Opening times : from beginning April to beginning Oct.

10 ha (453 pitches) undulating, terraced, flat, grassy

Tariff : (2014 Price) 47€ ♦♦ ⇔ 🗐 🕅 (10A) – Extra per person 8€ – Reservation fee 15€

Rental rates : (2014 Price) Permanent 🏊 – 88 🚐 – 8 🏠 – 7 studios. Per week from 180 to 1,350€ – Reservation fee 30€

🚐 borne 7€

The site is in 3 sections: one section with 200 owner-occupier mobile homes; one with good shade and some pitches near the road; and a quiet section with rentals on terraces with a panoramic view of the sea.

Surroundings : 🛶 ♀♀ 📐	G
Leisure activities : 🍴✗ 🛋 ⊙ 🚣 📐 hammam 🚣 🚲 ✂ 🏊 multi-sports ground	P
Facilities : ♿ ⚬ 🔲 🖱 🖱 – 6 private sanitary facilities (🔲 ⚬ WC) 🚿 ⛺ launderette 🚿 🚿	**Longitude : -0.98629**
Nearby : 🐎	S **Latitude : 45.58371**

The Michelin classification (⛰⛰⛰ ... ⛰) is totally independent of the official star classification system awarded by the local prefecture or other official organisation.

ST-GEORGES-LÈS-BAILLARGEAUX

86130 – Michelin map **322** I4 – pop. 3 888 – alt. 100
▶ Paris 329 – Poitiers 12 – Joué 89 – Châtellerault 23

⛰ Kawan Village Le Futuriste

🔗 05 49 52 47 52. www.camping-le-futuriste.fr

Address : rue du Château (south of the town, access via the D 20)

Opening times : Permanent

2 ha (112 pitches) small lake

Tariff : 30.90€ ♦♦ ⇔ 🗐 🕅 (6A) – Extra per person 3.70€ – Reservation fee 15€

Rental rates : Permanent 🏊 – 4 🚐 – 6 🏠. Per night from 80 to 130€ – Per week from 452 to 900€

🚐 borne 6€

Surroundings : ⬤ Futuroscope 🛶 ♀♀	G
Leisure activities : 🍴✗ 🛋 🚣 📺 🏊 🛶 multi-sports ground	P
Facilities : ♿ ⚬ 🔲 🖱 🚿 ⛺ launderette 🚿	**Longitude : 0.39543**
	S **Latitude : 46.66468**

ST-HILAIRE-LA-PALUD

79210 – Michelin map **322** B7 – pop. 1 603 – alt. 15
▶ Paris 436 – Poitiers 104 – Niort 24 – La Rochelle 41

🏕 Le Lidon

📞 05 49 35 33 64. www.le-lidon.com

Address : Lidon (3km west along the D 3 follow the signs for Courçon and take road to the left, at the canoeing centre)

Opening times : from mid April to mid Sept.

3 ha (140 pitches) flat, grassy

Tariff : 28€ ★★ 🚐 🔋 🔌 (10A) – Extra per person 6.50€ – Reservation fee 13.50€

Rental rates : (from mid April to mid Sept.) – 1 caravan – 3 🏠 – 4 canvas bungalows – 9 tent lodges. Per night from 44 to 100€ – Per week from 220 to 700€ – Reservation fee 13.50€

🚐 borne 4€

Surroundings : 🏊 ♨♨
Leisure activities : ▼ ✕ 🏠 🚲 🎣 ⛵ boats for hire ⚓
Facilities : ♿ ⚡ 🅲🅲🄸 ♨ ♻ 🍴 launderette 🧺

There are several different types of sani-station ('borne' in French) – sanitation points providing fresh water and disposal points for grey water. See page 12 for further details.

GPS	Longitude : -0.74324
	Latitude : 46.28379

ST-JEAN-D'ANGÉLY

17400 – Michelin map **324** G4 – pop. 7 581 – alt. 25
▶ Paris 444 – Angoulême 70 – Cognac 35 – Niort 48

🏕 Val de Boutonne

📞 05 46 32 26 16. www.campingcharentemartime17.com

Address : 56 quai de Bernouet (take the northwestern exit, follow the signs for La Rochelle, then take left turning onto Av. du Port (D 18)

Opening times : from beginning April to end Sept.

1.8 ha (99 pitches) flat, grassy

Tariff : 18.50€ ★★ 🚐 🔋 🔌 (10A) – Extra per person 4€ – Reservation fee 5€

Rental rates : (from beginning April to end Sept.) – 7 🛖 – 5 🏠. Per week from 210 to 599€ – Reservation fee 10€

🚐 borne – 🚐 11€

A pleasant, simple site; only basic sanitary facilities, but not far from a good boating centre.

Surroundings : 🏊 ♨♨
Leisure activities : 🏠 🚣 🚲 🛶
Facilities : ♿ ⚡ ♨ ♻ 🍴 launderette
Nearby : ▼ ✕ 🏇 🏊 ⛵ watersports centre

GPS	Longitude : -0.53638
	Latitude : 45.94877

Michelin classification:

🏔🏔🏔🏔 *Extremely comfortable, equipped to a very high standard*

🏔🏔🏔 *Very comfortable, equipped to a high standard*

🏔🏔🏔 *Comfortable and well equipped*

🏔🏔 *Reasonably comfortable*

🏔 *Satisfactory*

ST-JUST-LUZAC

17320 – Michelin map **324** D5 – pop. 1 838 – alt. 5
▶ Paris 502 – Rochefort 23 – La Rochelle 59 – Royan 26

🏕 Les Castels Séquoia Parc 👥

Les Castels Séquoia Parc

📞 05 46 85 55 55. www.sequoiaparc.com

Address : at La Josephtrie (2.7km northwest along the D 728, follow the signs for Marennes and take the road to the right)

Opening times : from mid May to beginning Sept.

45 ha/28 for camping (460 pitches) flat, grassy

Tariff : 63€ ★★ 🚐 🔋 🔌 (10A) – Extra per person 11€ – Reservation fee 30€

Rental rates : (from mid May to beginning Sept.) ♿ (1 mobile home) 🚣 – 338 🛖 – 42 🏠 – 2 tent lodges. Per night from 45 to 248€ – Per week from 315 to 1,736€

🚐 borne

There's a pretty swimming area near the outbuildings of a château in a park featuring a variety of trees and flowers.

Surroundings : 🏊 🏕 ♨♨
Leisure activities : ▼ ✕ 🏠 🎣 🏇 🚴 🚲 ✂ 🛶 ♨ wildlife park, tourist information multi-sports ground
Facilities : ♿ ⚡ ♨ ♻ 🍴 launderette 🧺🧺

GPS	Longitude : -1.06046
	Latitude : 45.81173

ST-LAURENT-DE-LA-PRÉE

17450 – Michelin map **324** D4 – pop. 1 814 – alt. 7
▶ Paris 483 – Rochefort 10 – La Rochelle 31

🏕 Domaine des Charmilles 👥

📞 05 46 84 00 05. www.domainedescharmilles.com

Address : at Fouras, 1541 route de l'Océan (2.2km northwest along the D 214e 1, follow the signs for Fouras and turn right onto D 937, follow the signs for La Rochelle)

5 ha (270 pitches) flat, grassy
Rentals : 75 🛖 – 18 🏠.

There are also pitches for tents or caravans.

Surroundings : 🏕 ♨♨
Leisure activities : ▼ 🏠 🎆 nighttime 🏇 🚣 🚲 🛶 ♨ multi-sports ground
Facilities : ♿ ⚡ ♨ ♻ 🍴 launderette 🚿🧺

GPS	Longitude : -1.05034
	Latitude : 45.99052

🏕 Le Pré Vert 👥

📞 05 46 84 89 40. www.camping-prevert.com

Address : rue du Petit Loir (2.3km northeast along the D 214, follow the signs for la Rochelle; at St-Pierre – take the expressway, Fouras exit)

3 ha (168 pitches) terraced, flat, grassy
Rentals : 50 🛖.

Plenty of mobile homes and a few pitches for tents and caravans, set around a naturally filtered pool.

Surroundings : 🏕 ♨♨
Leisure activities : ✕ 🏠 🏇 🚣 ⛱ (pool)
Facilities : ♿ ⚡ ♨ ♻ 🍴 launderette 🧺

GPS	Longitude : -1.01917
	Latitude : 45.99046

ST-NAZAIRE-SUR-CHARENTE

17780 – Michelin map **324** D4 – pop. 1 124 – alt. 14
▶ Paris 491 – Fouras 27 – Rochefort 13 – La Rochelle 49

L'Abri-Cotier

℘ 05 46 84 81 65. www.camping-la-rochelle.net

Address : 26 La Bernardière (located 1km southwest along the D 125e1)

Opening times : from beginning April to end Sept.

1.8 ha (100 pitches)

Tariff : (2014 Price) 26.50€ ★ ★ ⇔ 🗉 🔌 (6A) – Extra per person 5.50€ Reservation fee 20€

Rental rates : (2014 Price) (from beginning April to end Sept.) ⅙ (1 mobile home) – 39 🛆 – 5 🛖. Per night from 58 to 114€ – Per week from 265 to 795€ – Reservation fee 20€
🚐 borne 5€ – 🚐 8€

Good shade, marked-out pitches and both new and slightly older rental accommodation.

Surroundings : ⛱ 🏖 🍷🍷
Leisure activities : 🍷 🍴 🛶 🛥 🖼 (open air in season)
Facilities : ⅙ ⚡ 🚿 🛁 🍵 launderette 🧺 refrigerators

G P S Longitude : -1.05856
Latitude : 45.93349

ST-PALAIS-SUR-MER

17420 – Michelin map **324** D6 – pop. 3 926 – alt. 5
▶ Paris 512 – La Rochelle 82 – Royan 6

Côte de Beauté

℘ 05 46 23 20 59. www.camping-cote-de-beaute.com

Address : 157 avenue de la Grande Côte (2.5km to the northwest, 50m from the sea)

Opening times : from mid April to end Sept.

1.7 ha (115 pitches) flat, grassy

Tariff : 33.50€ ★ ★ ⇔ 🗉 🔌 (10A) – Extra per person 5.30€ – Reservation fee 25€

Rental rates : (from mid April to end Sept.) – 13 🛆 – 2 canvas bungalows. Per night from 30 to 85€ – Per week from 250 to 690€ Reservation fee 25€

Some pitches above the road have a panoramic view of the ocean.

Surroundings : ⛱ 🍷
Leisure activities : 🖼 🛥
Facilities : ⅙ ⚡ 🚿 🛁 🍵 🖼
Nearby : 🏊 🍷 🍴 🧺

G P S Longitude : -1.1191
Latitude : 45.64973

ST-PIERRE-DE-MAILLÉ

86260 – Michelin map **322** L4 – pop. 925 – alt. 79
▶ Paris 333 – Le Blanc 22 – Châtellerault 32 – Chauvigny 21

Le Grand Pré

℘ 05 49 48 64 11. www.camping-saintpierredemaille.com

Address : 16 route de Vicq (take northwestern exit along the D 11; beside the Gartempe river)

3 ha (93 pitches)

Rentals : 4 canvas bungalows – 5 tent lodges.

Sports groups and children's minicamps are welcome.

Surroundings : 🏞 🍷🍷
Leisure activities : 🚲🏊 🛶 guided walks 🚶
Facilities : launderette

G P S Longitude : 0.83897
Latitude : 46.68463

ST-SAVINIEN

17350 – Michelin map **324** F4 – pop. 2 413 – alt. 18
▶ Paris 457 – Rochefort 28 – La Rochelle 62 – St-Jean-d'Angély 15

L'Île aux Loisirs

℘ 05 46 90 35 11. www.ilesauxloirs.com

Address : 102 rue de St-Savinien (500m west along the D 18, follow the signs for Pont-l'Abbé-d'Arnoult; between the Charente river and the canal, 200m from a small lake)

1.8 ha (82 pitches) flat, grassy
Rentals : 17 🛆.

Surroundings : ⛱ 🍷🍷
Leisure activities : 🍷 🍴 🛶 🚲 🚶
Facilities : ⅙ 🚿 🛁 🍵 launderette 🧺
Nearby : ✂ 🏊 🛥 🛶 ⚓ sports trail

G P S Longitude : -0.68427
Latitude : 45.87786

ST-SORNIN

17600 – Michelin map **324** E5 – pop. 303 – alt. 16
▶ Paris 495 – Marennes 13 – Rochefort 24 – La Rochelle 60

Le Valerick

℘ 05 46 85 15 95. www.camping-le-valerick.fr

Address : 1 La Mauvinière (1.3km northeast along the D 118, follow the signs for Pont-l'Abbé)

Opening times : from beginning April to end Sept.

1.5 ha (50 pitches) relatively flat, flat, grassy, wood

Tariff : 20.90€ ★ ★ ⇔ 🗉 🔌 (6A) – Extra per person 4.50€

Rental rates : (from beginning April to end Sept.) 🚶 – 2 🛆. Per week from 450 to 650€

An undulating site, very well maintained with basic sanitary facilities.

Surroundings : 🍷
Leisure activities : 🍴 🛥
Facilities : ⅙ ⚡ 🚿 🍵 🖼

G P S Longitude : -0.96521
Latitude : 45.77446

ST-YRIEIX-SUR-CHARENTE

16710 – Michelin map **324** K5 – pop. 7 025 – alt. 53
▶ Paris 451 – Poitiers 114 – Angoulême 7 – La Rochelle 142

du Plan d'Eau

camping du Plan d'Eau

℘ 05 45 92 14 64. www.camping-angouleme.fr

Address : 1 rue du Camping

Opening times : from beginning April to end Oct.

6 ha (148 pitches) flat, grassy, stony

Tariff : (2014 Price) 19.85€ ★ ★ ⇔ 🗉 🔌 (10A) – Extra per person 4.70€

Rental rates : (2014 Price) (from beginning April to end Oct.) ⅙ (1 mobile home) – 15 🛆. Per night from 37 to 84 € – Per week from 204 to 531€
🚐 borne 2.50€ – 14 🗉 7.20€ – 🚐 7.20€

Located near Angoulême town centre with a bus stop for trips to town.

Surroundings : 🏞 ⛱
Leisure activities : 🖼 🛥 🚲 🛶 multi-sports ground
Facilities : ⅙ 🏛 🍵 launderette
Nearby : 🛁 hammam, jacuzzi 🖼 🛥 (beach) 🛶 🚶 💧 watersports centre

G P S Longitude : 0.13808
Latitude : 45.67652

SAUJON

17600 – Michelin map **324** E5 – pop. 6 636 – alt. 7
▶ Paris 499 – Poitiers 165 – La Rochelle 71 – Saintes 28

⚲ Lac de Saujon ♣♣

Lac de Saujon

✆ 05 46 06 82 99. www.campingsaujon.com

Address : voie des Tourterelles

Opening times : from beginning April to mid Oct.

3.7 ha (150 pitches) flat, grassy

Tariff : (2014 Price) 26€ ♣♣ 🚗 🔳 ⚡ (10A) – Extra per person 5.50€ – Reservation fee 19€

Rental rates : (2014 Price) (from beginning March to beginning Nov.) 🚿 – 36 🚐 – 4 🏠 – 4 canvas bungalows. Per week from 200 to 710€ – Reservation fee 19€

🚐 borne 5€ – 13 🔳 15€

A pleasant site beside a large lake; a high standard of rental accommodation.

Surroundings : 🐾
Leisure activities : 🍴 🗙 🏛 🏃 ⚡ 🚲
Facilities : ♿ ⚲ 🧺 🧺 ⚡ 🍴 launderette 🚮 🚿
Nearby : 🎣 🛶 🏊 ⛵ 🎿 🐎 fitness trail

G P S Longitude : -0.93848 Latitude : 45.68282

SECONDIGNY

79130 – Michelin map **322** D5 – pop. 1 773 – alt. 177
▶ Paris 391 – Bressuire 27 – Champdeniers 15 – Coulonges-sur-l'Autize 22

⚲ Le Moulin des Effres

✆ 05 49 95 61 97. www.campinglemoulindeseffres.fr

Address : take the southern exit along the D 748, follow the signs for Niort and take road to the left, near a lake

Opening times : from mid Apr. to mid Sept.

2 ha (90 pitches)

Tariff : (2014 Price) 21€ ♣♣ 🚗 🔳 ⚡ (6A) – Extra per person 4.50€ Reservation fee 10€

Rental rates : (2014 Price) (from mid April to end Sept.) – 17 🚐 – 3 tipis – 2 tent lodges. Per night from 43 to 85€ – Per week from 189 to 679€ – Reservation fee 10€

🚐 borne 5€

Surroundings : 🐾 🗺 ⚡
Leisure activities : 🏛 🚲 🎿 🏊
Facilities : ♿ ⚲ (June–Aug) 🧺 🍴 🔳
Nearby : 🍴 🗙 🏃 🎱 🎿 pedalos

G P S Longitude : -0.41418 Latitude : 46.60421

SEMUSSAC

17120 – Michelin map **324** E6 – pop. 1 998 – alt. 36
▶ Paris 520 – Poitiers 187 – La Rochelle 85 – Angoulême 111

⚲ Le 2 B

✆ 05 46 05 95 16. www.camping-2b.com

Address : 9 chemin des Bardonneries (3.8km east along the D 730, follow the signs for St-Georges-de-Didonne)

Opening times : from beginning April to end Sept.

1.8 ha (93 pitches)

Tariff : 25€ ♣♣ 🚗 🔳 ⚡ (10A) – Extra per person 5€ – Reservation fee 14€

Rental rates : (from beginning April to end Sept.) – 20 🚐 – 10 tent lodges. Per night from 37 to 98€ – Per week from 217 to 680€ – Reservation fee 14€

Choose the pitches away from the road if possible.

Surroundings : ⚡⚡
Leisure activities : 🍴 🗙 🏛 🏃 🎿 🏊
Facilities : ♿ ⚲ 🧺 🍴 launderette

G P S Longitude : -0.94793 Latitude : 45.6041

SIREUIL

16440 – Michelin map **324** K6 – pop. 1 189 – alt. 26
▶ Paris 460 – Angoulême 16 – Barbezieux 24 – Cognac 35

⚲ Nizour

✆ 05 45 90 56 27. www.campingdunizour.com

Address : 2 route de la Charente (located 1.5km southeast along the D 7, follow the signs for Blanzac, turn left before the bridge; 120m from the Charente (direct access)

Opening times : from mid April to end Sept.

1.6 ha (56 pitches) flat, grassy

Tariff : 21.75€ ♣♣ 🚗 🔳 ⚡ (6A) – Extra per person 5.15€ – Reservation fee 8€

Rental rates : (from mid May to mid Sept.) 🚿 – 5 🚐 – 1 🏠. Per night from 65 to 78€ – Per week from 453 to 545€ – Reservation fee 8€

🚐 borne 5€ – 1 🔳 12€

Choose the pitches further away from the road in preference.

Surroundings : 🗺 ⚡⚡
Leisure activities : 🍴 🏛 🏃 🚲 🎿 🏊
Facilities : ♿ ⚲ 🧺 launderette
Nearby : ⚓ ⚓

G P S Longitude : 0.02418 Latitude : 45.60688

Some information or pricing may have changed since the guide went to press. We recommend you check the price list online in advance or at the entrance to the campsite and enquire about possible restrictions.

VAUX-SUR-MER

17640 – Michelin map **324** D6 – pop. 3 835 – alt. 12
▶ Paris 514 – Poitiers 181 – La Rochelle 75 – Rochefort 44

⚲ Le Nauzan-Plage

✆ 05 46 38 29 13. www.campinglenauzanplage.com

Address : 39 avenue de Nauzan-Plage (500m from the beach)

Opening times : from beginning May to end Sept.

3.9 ha (239 pitches) flat, grassy

Tariff : 46€ ♣♣ 🚗 🔳 ⚡ (10A) – Extra per person 10.23€ – Reservation fee 20€

Rental rates : (from beginning May to end Sept.) – 40 🚐. Per night from 51 to 96€ – Per week from 233 to 1,130€ – Reservation fee 20€

🚐 borne 8€ – 2 🔳 8€ – 🚐 8€

The site is beside a pretty park, crossed by a stream.

Surroundings : 🗺 ⚡
Leisure activities : 🍴 🗙 🏛 ☀daytime 🏃 🎿 🏊
Facilities : ♿ ⚲ 🧺 🍴 launderette 🚮 🚿
Nearby : 🎯 🎱 🚣

G P S Longitude : -1.07196 Latitude : 45.64295

⚲ Le Val-Vert

℘ 05 46 38 25 51. www.val-vert.com

Address : 108 avenue Fréderic Garnier (to the southwest of the town)

Opening times : from mid April to end Sept.

3 ha (181 pitches) terraced, flat, grassy, stony

Tariff : 39.20€ ✶✶ ⇔ ▣ ⏚ (10A) – Extra per person 6€ – Reservation fee 16€

Rental rates : (from mid April to end Sept.) – 36 ⟦⋯⟧ – 35 ⌂. Per week from 250 to 799€ – Reservation fee 16€

⛽ borne

Beside a pretty park, lake and stream.

Surroundings : ⌑ ❤❤
Leisure activities : ✗ 🏄 ⛵ ⚲ 🚲 ⟱
Facilities : ♿ ⚿ ⟦cc⟧ ⛊ ⚐ launderette ⚲
Nearby : ⚔ 🗺 ⟱

GPS	Longitude : -1.06299
	Latitude : 45.64357

86190 – Michelin map **322** G5 – pop. 3 498 – alt. 118
▶ Paris 345 – Châtellerault 46 – Parthenay 34 – Poitiers 18

⚲ Municipal

℘ 05 49 51 90 10. www.vouille86.fr

Address : chemin de la Piscine (in the town; beside the Auxance)

Opening times : from beginning June to end Aug.

0.5 ha (48 pitches) flat, grassy

Tariff : (2014 Price) ✶ 3.80€ ⇔ 5€ ▣ 5€ – ⏚ (10A) 5€

Surroundings : 🌊 ❤❤
Leisure activities : ⚲ ⟱ ⟱
Facilities : ♿ ⚐ ⟦⚑⟧ ▤
Nearby : ✗

GPS	Longitude : 0.16417
	Latitude : 46.64016

PROVENCE-ALPES-CÔTE D'AZUR

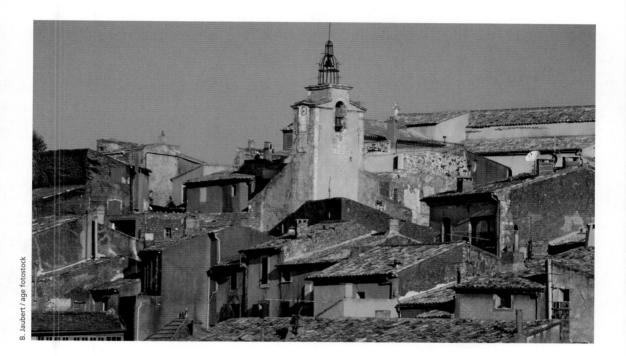

A new day dawns in sun-drenched Provence. As the fishmongers tell jokes, chat and sell their freshly-caught fish under clear blue skies, you cannot help but fall in love with the relaxed, happy-go-lucky spirit of Marseilles. In the countryside beyond, the sun casts its first amber rays across the ochre walls of a hilltop village and over the glorious fields of lavender in the valley below. The steady chirping of the cicadas is interrupted only by the gentle sound of sheep bells ringing in the hills. Slow down to the gentle pace of the villagers and join them as they gather within the refreshingly cool walls of a local café. However, by 2pm you may begin to wonder where everyone has gone. On hot afternoons, most people exercise their traditional right to a siesta, even those who frequent the chic beaches of St Tropez and in the seaside cabins of the Camargue. Fear not, it will soon be time to wake up and prepare for a serious game of *pétanque* and a chilled glass of pastis.

Legend:

- ● Locality with campsite
- ■ Locality with campsite and rental option
- Vannes Locality with campsite and campervan area
- Moyaux Locality with at least one pleasant campsite
- 🚐 Motorway service area for campervans

la Toussuire
Bramans
A 32
le Bourg-d'Oisans
la Grave
Névache
le Bourg-d'Arud
D 1091
N 94
St-Laurent-en-Beaumont
St-Christophe-en-Oisans
Briançon
Villar-Loubière
l'Argentière-la-Bessée
HAUTES- ALPES
ITALIA
la Roche-de-Rame
A 6
Pont-du-Fossé
Ceillac
Guillestre
St-Apollinaire
St-Clément-s-Durance
la Roche-des-Arnaud
Ancelle
N 94
Embrun
Gap
Chorges
Baratier
Veynes
Espinasses
Prunières
Larche
le Sauzé-du-Lac
A 51
Curbans
Col St-Jean
St-Pons
Ubaye
Clamensane
Seyne
Méolans-Revel
Les Thuiles
ALPES - DE - HAUTE -
St-Étienne-de-Tinée
le Vernet
Isola
Sisteron
PROVENCE
Villars-Colmars
St-Martin-d'Entraunes
St-Martin-Vésubie
Volonne
Digne-les-Bains
D 6204
N 85
Var
Tinée
St-André-les-Alpes
ALPES - MARITIMES
Niozelles
Puimichel
N 202
Sospel
Volx
Riez
Moustiers-Ste-Marie
Castellane
Contes
A 10
Gréoux-les-Bains
Ste-Croix-de-Verdon
D 6202
A 8
Montpezat
Verdon
la Colle-s-Loup
Vence
Monaco
les Salles-s-Verdon
le Bar-s-Loup
NICE
Esparron-de-Verdon
St-Laurent-du-Verdon
D 6085
Grasse
Cagnes-s-Mer
Régusse
Callas
Cros-de-Cagnes
Villecroze
St-Paul-en-Forêt
Auribeau-s-S.
Villeneuve-Loubet-Plage
Salernes
Draguignan
Le Cannet
le Muy
les Adrets-de-l'Esterel
CANNES
Argens
Taradeau
A 8
Mandelieu-la-Napoule
Brignoles
Agay
Nans-les-Pins
Roquebrune-s-Argens
St-Raphaël
VAR
Grimaud
Puget-s-A.
Fréjus
A 57
D 559
St-Aygulf
Bormes-les-Mimosas
Ramatuelle
D 98
la Croix-Valmer
La Londe-les-Maures
Cavalaire-s-Mer
A 570
le Lavandou
A 50
TOULON
Hyères
St-Mandrier-s-Mer
Sanary-s-M.
Giens
Îles d'Hyères

LES ADRETS-DE-L'ESTEREL

83600 – Michelin map **340** P4 – pop. 2 063 – alt. 295
▶ Paris 881 – Cannes 26 – Draguignan 44 – Fréjus 17

⚞ Les Philippons

✆ 04 94 40 90 67. www.lesphilippons.com

Address : 378 route de l'Argentière (head 3km east along the D 237)

Opening times : from mid April to beginning Oct.

5 ha (120 pitches) very uneven, terraced, flat, grassy, stony

Tariff : (2014 Price) 33.60€ ✶✶ ⇖ 🗉 ⚡ (10A)

Extra per person 6.50€ – Reservation fee 20€

Rental rates : (2014 Price) (from mid April to beginning Oct.) –
14 🏠. Per night from 45 to 132€ – Per week from 315 to 924€
Reservation fee 30€

The site is in two sections in a Mediterranean setting, in the shade of olive trees, eucalyptus, cork oaks and mimosas.

Surroundings : ⅏ ⬱ ⬅ 🗂 ⅏
Leisure activities : 🍴 ✗ ⚴⬱ ⌇
Facilities : ⊶ 🖻 🛉 ⫶ launderette ⟿
refrigerators

| | GPS | Longitude : 6.84002 |
| | | Latitude : 43.52876 |

*The classification (1 to 5 tents, **black** or red) that we award to selected sites in this guide is our own system. It should not be confused with the classification (1 to 5 stars) of official organisations.*

AGAY

83530 – Michelin map **340** Q5 – alt. 20
▶ Paris 880 – Cannes 34 – Draguignan 43 – Fréjus 12

⚞⚞ Esterel Caravaning ♟♟

Esterel Caravaning

✆ 04 94 82 03 28. www.esterel-caravaning.fr

Address : avenue des Golfs (situated 4km to the northwest)

Opening times : from end March to end Sept.

15 ha (495 pitches) terraced, relatively flat, flat, grassy, stony

Tariff : 55€ ✶✶ ⇖ 🗉 ⚡ (16A) –
Extra per person 11€ – Reservation fee 40€

Rental rates : (from end March to end Sept.) – 331 🏠. Per night from 24 to 420€ – Per week from 168 to 2,940€ – Reservation fee 35€

🔲 borne 10€

There's a nursery and an indoor swimming pool for children; some luxury pitches have private sanitary facilities and a jacuzzi and kitchenette.

Surroundings : ⅏ 🗂 ⅏
Leisure activities : 🍴 ✗ 🖾 ⅏ ⚴⬱ ⌰ ⬱
hammam ⚴⬱ ⚲ ⚞ ⌰ ⌇ ⚘ disco, squash, multi-sports ground, spa centre, skate park
Facilities : ⬧ ⊶ 🖾 🖻 ⚘ – 18 individual sanitary facilities (⚲ ⚲ wc) ⟿ ⫶ ⫶ launderette ⟿ ⟿

| | GPS | Longitude : 6.83256 |
| | | Latitude : 43.45419 |

⚞⚞⚞ Campéole Le Dramont ♟♟

✆ 04 94 82 07 68. www.camping-mer.com

Address : 986 boulevard de la 36ème Division du Texas

Opening times : from beginning April to beginning Oct.

6.5 ha (374 pitches) undulating, flat, sandy, stony

Tariff : (2014 Price) 47.20€ ✶✶ ⇖ 🗉 ⚡ (10A) –
Extra per person 10.30€ – Reservation fee 25€

Rental rates : (2014 Price) (from beginning April to end Sept.) –
47 🏠 – 21 🏠 – 65 canvas bungalows. Per night from 29 to 168€ –
Per week from 203 to 1,176€ – Reservation fee 25€

🔲 borne 7.50€

In a pleasant wood of pine trees, with pitches near the sea and rental options of various standards.

Surroundings : ⅏ ⅏ ⚠
Leisure activities : 🍴 ✗ 🖾 ⅏ ⚴⬱ ⚴⬱ ⌰
scuba diving, multi-sports ground
Facilities : ⬧ ⊶ 🖻 ⚘ ⫶ launderette ⟿ ⟿

| | GPS | Longitude : 6.84835 |
| | | Latitude : 43.41782 |

⚞ Village Vacances Vallée du Paradis ♟♟

(rental of mobile homes only)

✆ 04 94 82 16 00. www.camping-vallee-du-paradis.fr

Address : avenue du Gratadis (located 1km to the northwest; beside the Agay)

Opening times : from mid March to mid Oct.

3 ha flat

Rental rates : ⚞ – 197 🏠. Per night from 45 to 218€ – Per week from 315 to 1,526 € – Reservation fee 20€

A mobile home village beside the Agay river, bordered by a pontoon walkway.

Surroundings : ⬅ 🗂 ⚲
Leisure activities : 🍴 ✗ 🖾 ⅏ ⚴⬱ ⌰ ⟿
⚴⬱ ⚲ ⌰
Facilities : ⬧ ⊶ 🖻 ⚘ ⫶ launderette ⟿ ⟿
Nearby : ⚓

| | GPS | Longitude : 6.85285 |
| | | Latitude : 43.43546 |

⚞ Les Rives de l'Agay

✆ 04 94 82 02 74. www.lesrivesdelagay.com

Address : 575 avenue du Gratadis (700m to the northwest; beside the Agay and 500m from the beach)

Opening times : from mid March to beginning Nov.

2 ha (171 pitches)

Tariff : (2014 Price) 48.60€ ✶✶ ⇖ 🗉 ⚡ (6A) – Extra per person 7€
Reservation fee 20€

Rental rates : (2014 Price) (from beginning March to beginning Nov.) – 43 🏠. Per night from 39 to 53€ – Per week from 347 to 1,006€ – Reservation fee 20€

The site is bordered by the Agay river, with a pontoon walkway.

Surroundings : 🗂 ⅏
Leisure activities : ✗ 🖾 ⌰ ⌇ scuba diving
Facilities : ⬧ ⊶ 🖻 ⚘ ⟿ ⫶ launderette ⟿ ⟿
Nearby : ⚓

| | GPS | Longitude : 6.85263 |
| | | Latitude : 43.43408 |

We have selected the best campsites in France with our usual care, listing those with the best facilities in the most pleasant surroundings.

⚠ Agay-Soleil

☎ 0494820079. www.agay-soleil.com ⚜ (from beginning July to beginning Sept)

Address : 1152 boulevard de la Plage (700m east on the D 559, follow the signs for Cannes)

Opening times : from end March to beginning Nov.

0.7 ha (53 pitches) terraced, relatively flat, flat, sandy

Tariff : (2014 Price) 35.50€ ♣♣ ⇔ ▣ (4) (6A) – Extra per person 6.50€ Reservation fee 20€

Rental rates : (2014 Price) (from end March to beginning Nov.) ⚜ – 5 🚐 – 2 🏠 – 1 apartment. Per night from 80 to 120€ – Per week from 320 to 775€

🚏 borne 10€

Surroundings : ≤ 🏕 🎭 ⚠
Leisure activities : 🍸 ✗ 🏛
Facilities : 🚿 ⚬━ ✉ 🏧 🖼 🚻 🖼 🛁
Nearby : ⚜ watersports centre

G P S Longitude : 6.86822
Latitude : 43.43333

⚠ Royal-Camping

☎ 0494820020. www.royalcamping.net

Address : rue Louise Robinson (located 1.5km west along the D 559, follow the signs for St Raphael and take turning to the left)

Opening times : from mid Feb. to beginning Nov.

0.6 ha (45 pitches)

Tariff : 33€ ♣♣ ⇔ ▣ (4) (6A) – Extra per person 7€ – Reservation fee 20€

Rental rates : (from end Feb. to beginning Nov.) – 9 🚐. Per night from 50 to 112€ – Per week from 320 to 790€ – Reservation fee 20€

Surroundings : 🎭 ⚠
Leisure activities : 🏛
Facilities : ⚬━ 🖼 🚻
Nearby : 🖼 🛶 🍸 ✗ 🛁

G P S Longitude : 6.85707
Latitude : 43.42027

AIX-EN-PROVENCE

13100 – Michelin map **340** H4 – pop. 141 895 – alt. 206
▶ Paris 752 – Aubagne 39 – Avignon 82 – Manosque 57

� Chantecler ♣♣

☎ 0442261298. www.campingchantecler.com

Address : 41 avenue du Val-Saint-André (2.5km southeast, access via Cours Gambetta – from the A8, take exit 31 for Aix - Val-St-André)

Opening times : Permanent

8 ha (240 pitches) undulating, terraced, flat, grassy, stony

Tariff : (2014 Price) ♣ 7.50€ ⇔ ▣ 8.40€ – (4) (10A) 4.70€

Rental rates : (2014 Price) Permanent ⚜ – 42 🚐 – 10 🏠. Per night from 134 to 240€ – Per week from 434 to 807€

🚏 borne 5€

There's a view of Mont Ste-Victoire from some pitches.

Surroundings : 🏕 🎶
Leisure activities : 🍸 ✗ 🏛 🏃 🛶 🛶
Facilities : 🚿 ⚬━ 🏧 🚻 launderette 🛁

G P S Longitude : 5.47416
Latitude : 43.51522

This guide is not intended as a list of all the camping sites in France; its aim is to provide a selection of the best sites in each category.

ANCELLE

05260 – Michelin map **334** F5 – pop. 854 – alt. 1 340 – Winter sports : 1 350/1 807 m
▶ Paris 665 – Gap 17 – Grenoble 103 – Orcières 18

⚠ Les Auches

☎ 0492508028. www.lesauches.com

Address : Les Auches (take the northern exit following signs for Pont du Fossé and take turning to the right.)

Opening times : from beginning April to end Oct.

2 ha (67 pitches) terraced, relatively flat, grassy

Tariff : 24.60€ ♣♣ ⇔ ▣ (4) (6A) – Extra per person 4.80€

Rental rates : Permanent ⚜ – 12 🚐 – 11 🏠 – 2 studios – 1 apartment – 2 canvas bungalows. Per week from 245 to 690€ Reservation fee 15€

Surroundings : 🐟 ≤ 🎭
Leisure activities : ✗ 🏛 🏃 jacuzzi 🛶 🛶
Facilities : 🚿 ⚬━ 🏧 🚻 launderette

G P S Longitude : 6.21075
Latitude : 44.62435

Using the traditional Michelin classification method, the guide provides you with an easy, speedy reference for assessing the category of each site: 1 to 5 tents (see page 10).

APT

84400 – Michelin map **332** F10 – pop. 11 405 – alt. 250
▶ Paris 728 – Aix-en-Provence 56 – Avignon 54 – Carpentras 49

⚠ Le Lubéron

☎ 0490048540. www.campingleluberon.com

Address : avenue de Saignon (situated 2km southeast along the D 48)

Opening times : from beginning April to end Sept.

5 ha (110 pitches) terraced, flat and relatively flat, grassy, fine gravel

Tariff : (2014 Price) 27.20€ ♣♣ ⇔ ▣ (4) (6A) – Extra per person 31.20€ – Reservation fee 18€

Rental rates : (2014 Price) Permanent – 29 🚐 – 29 🏠 – 6 canvas bungalows. Per night from 81 to 131€ – Per week from 570 to 920€ – Reservation fee 18€

🚏 borne 5€ – 🔋 26.50€

Surroundings : 🐟 ≤ 🎭
Leisure activities : 🍸 ✗ 🛶 🛶
Facilities : 🚿 ⚬━ 🏧 🚻 launderette

G P S Longitude : 5.41327
Latitude : 43.86632

⚠ Les Cèdres

☎ 0490741461. www.camping-les-cedres.fr

Address : take northwestern exit along the D 22, follow the signs for Rustrel

Opening times : from mid Feb. to mid Nov.

1.8 ha (75 pitches)

Tariff : (2014 Price) ♣ 2.80€ ⇔ 2€ ▣ 3.90€ – (4) (10A) 3.50€

Rental rates : (2014 Price) – 4 canvas bungalows. Per night from 35 to 39€ – Per week from 240 to 270€

🚏 borne 4€

Surroundings : 🎭
Leisure activities : 🏛 🛶 climbing wall
Facilities : 🚿 ⚬━ 🏧 🚻 🖼 refrigerators
Nearby : 🛶

G P S Longitude : 5.4013
Latitude : 43.87765

L'ARGENTIÈRE-LA-BESSÉE

05120 – Michelin map **334** H4 – pop. 2 328 – alt. 1 024
▶ Paris 696 – Briançon 17 – Embrun 33 – Gap 74

⚠ Municipal Les Écrins

📞 04 92 23 03 38. www.camping-les-ecrins.com

Address : avenue Pierre Sainte (head 2.3km south along the N 94, follow the signs for Gap, and take D 104 to the right)

Opening times : from mid April to mid Sept.

3 ha (71 pitches)

Tariff : 13.80€ ♥♥ ⇌ 🔲 🔌 (10A) – Extra per person 5.20€ – Reservation fee 2.50€
Rental rates : (from mid May to end Aug.) – 4 canvas bungalows. Per night from 40 to 65€ – Per week from 220 to 445€
🚐 borne 2€
A young and sporty crowd comes here for the numerous whitewater activities.

Surroundings : ≼ 🛒 ♀	**G P S**
Leisure activities : 🎪 ⛵ 🎿 🎣	Longitude : 6.55823
Facilities : ♿ 🚿 ▥ ⚹ 🗑 🚿	Latitude : 44.77687
Nearby : 🛶 🎿 🛥 (river) rafting and canyoning	

ARLES

13200 – Michelin map **340** C3 – pop. 52 979 – alt. 13
▶ Paris 719 – Aix-en-Provence 77 – Avignon 37 – Cavaillon 44
Ouest : 14 km via N 572 rte de St-Gilles and D 37 on the left

⚠ Crin Blanc 👥

📞 04 66 87 48 78. www.camping-crin-blanc.com

Address : in the hamlet of Saliers (located to the southwest of Saliers along the D 37)

Opening times : from beginning April to end Sept.

4.5 ha (170 pitches)

Tariff : (2014 Price) 19€ ♥♥ ⇌ 🔲 🔌 (10A) – Extra per person 5.50€ Reservation fee 10€
Rental rates : (2014 Price) (from beginning April to end Sept.) – 100 🚐. Per night from 60 to 85€ – Per week from 150 to 920€
Reservation fee 19€ 🚐 borne 19€

Surroundings : 🛒	**G P S**
Leisure activities : 🍴 🍽 🎪 🎠 🎯 ⛵ 🎿	Longitude : 4.47392
Facilities : ♿ 🚿 ⚹ 🗑 🚿 ⛺ launderette 🏊 🚣	Latitude : 43.66149
Nearby : 🐎	

AUBIGNAN

84810 – Michelin map **332** D9 – pop. 4 861 – alt. 65
▶ Paris 675 – Avignon 31 – Carpentras 7 – Orange 21

⚠ Le Brégoux

📞 04 90 62 62 50. www.camping-lebregoux.fr

Address : 410 chemin du Vas (800m southeast along the D 55, follow the signs for Caromb and take the road to the right.)

Opening times : from beginning March to end Oct.

3.5 ha (170 pitches) flat, grassy

Tariff : ♥ 3.85€ ⇌ 🔲 3.75€ – 🔌 (10A) 3.80€
Rental rates : (from mid March to end Oct.) – 5 🚐. Per week from 315 to 535€

Surroundings : ♀♀	**G P S**
Leisure activities : 🎪 🎿 🎯	Longitude : 5.03609
Facilities : 🚿 ▥ ⚹ ⛺ launderette	Latitude : 44.09808

AURIBEAU-SUR-SIAGNE

06810 – Michelin map **341** C6 – pop. 2 945 – alt. 85
▶ Paris 900 – Cannes 15 – Draguignan 62 – Grasse 9

⚠ Le Parc des Monges

📞 04 93 60 91 71. www.parcdesmonges.com

Address : 635 chemin du Gabre (head 1.4km northwest along the D 509, follow the signs for Tanneron)

Opening times : from end April to end Sept.

1.3 ha (55 pitches) terraced

Tariff : 38.50€ ♥♥ ⇌ 🔲 🔌 (10A) – Extra per person 6.10€
Rental rates : (from end April to end Sept.) 🚲 – 7 🚐 – 8 🏠. Per week from 365 to 930€
🚐 borne 7€
Beside the Siagne river, with pitches marked out by oleanders.

Surroundings : 🐟 🛒 ♀♀	**G P S**
Leisure activities : jacuzzi 🎿	Longitude : 6.90252
Facilities : ♿ 🚿 ⚹ 🗑 🚿 ⛺	Latitude : 43.60659
Nearby : 🍴 🍽 🚣 🛥 🎣	

Some information or pricing may have changed since the guide went to press. We recommend you check the price list online in advance or at the entrance to the campsite and enquire about possible restrictions.

AVIGNON

84000 – Michelin map **332** B10 – pop. 89 592 – alt. 21
▶ Paris 682 – Aix-en-Provence 82 – Arles 37 – Marseille 98

⚠ Aquadis Loisirs Le Pont d'Avignon

📞 04 90 80 63 50. www.aquadis-loisirs.com

Address : 10 chemin de la Barthelasse (take northwestern exit, follow the signs for Villeneuve-lès-Avignon across the Édouard-Daladier bridge and take a right turn, on the Île-de-la-Barthelasse)

Opening times : from beginning March to end Nov.

8 ha (300 pitches)

Tariff : 30.80€ ♥♥ ⇌ 🔲 🔌 (10A) – Extra per person 5.70€ – Reservation fee 9.90€
Rental rates : (from beginning March to end Nov.) – 14 canvas bungalows. Per night from 49€ – Per week from 200 to 629€
Reservation fee 19.90€
🚐 borne 5€ – 40 🔲 18.99€

Surroundings : 🛒 ♀♀	**G P S**
Leisure activities : 🍴 🍽 🎪 ⛵ 🎿 🎿	Longitude : 4.7971
Facilities : ♿ 🚿 🅿 ⛺ launderette 🏊 🚣	Latitude : 43.95331

BARATIER

05200 – Michelin map **334** G4 – pop. 511 – alt. 855
▶ Paris 704 – Marseille 214 – Gap 39 – Digne 90

⚠ Les Airelles

📞 04 92 43 11 57. www.lesairelles.com

Address : route des Orres (1.2km southeast along the D 40, follow the signs for Les Orres and take turning to the right)

Opening times : from beginning June to mid Sept.

5 ha/4 for camping (130 pitches) terraced, flat and relatively flat, grassy, stony

Tariff : (2014 Price) ♥ 7€ ⇌ 🔲 8€ – 🔌 (10A) 5€

Rental rates : (2014 Price) (from beginning June to mid Sept.) – 8 caravans – 16 🚐 – 32 🏠 – 4 canvas bungalows. Per week from 320 to 850€

Surroundings : 🐟 ≤ ♤♤
Leisure activities : ▼ ✗ 🏖 daytime 🛶
🏊 multi-sports ground
Facilities : 🚿 ⚡ 🍴 launderette

GPS Longitude : 6.50164
Latitude : 44.5291

⛰ Le Verger

🕿 06 81 93 06 15. www.campingleverger.fr – limited spaces for one-night stay

Address : chemin de Jouglar (take the western exit; recommended route for caravans is via the village)

Opening times : Permanent

4.3 ha/2.5 for camping (110 pitches) terraced, relatively flat, flat, grassy, stony

Tariff : (2014 Price) 18€ ★★ 🚗 ▣ ⚡ (10A) – Extra per person 5.50€
Reservation fee 14€

Rental rates : (2014 Price) Permanent – 14 🏠 – 14 gîtes.
Per night from 65 to 107€ – Per week from 440 to 750€

Surroundings : 🐟 �︎ ♤♤
Leisure activities : ▼ ✗ 🏖 🏊
Facilities : ⚡ 🍴 🛢
Nearby : 🎿 🐟

GPS Longitude : 6.49143
Latitude : 44.5374

⛰ Les Deux Bois

🕿 04 92 43 54 14. www.camping-les2bois.com

Address : route de Pra Fouran (access to the town along the D 204)

Opening times : from end May to mid Sept.

2.5 ha (100 pitches) terraced, sloping, flat, grassy, stony

Tariff : (2014 Price) 22.70€ ★★ 🚗 ▣ ⚡ (10A) –
Extra per person 5.60€ – Reservation fee 15€

Rental rates : (2014 Price) Permanent Ⓟ – 4 🚐. Per night from 78 to 132€ – Per week from 390 to 1,050€

High-quality mobile home accommodation; open all year.

Surroundings : 🐟 ♤♤
Leisure activities : ▼ ✗ 🛶 🏊
Facilities : 🚿 ⚡ 🍴 🏖 🛢 🚿
Nearby : 🎿 🐟

GPS Longitude : 6.49207
Latitude : 44.53837

⛺ Les Grillons

🕿 04 92 43 32 75. www.lesgrillons.com

Address : route de la Madeleine (located 1km north along the D 40, D 340 and take road to the left)

Opening times : from mid May to mid Sept.

1.5 ha (95 pitches) relatively flat, grassy, stony

Tariff : (2014 Price) 23€ ★★ 🚗 ▣ ⚡ (16A) – Extra per person 5.70€
Reservation fee 10€

Rental rates : (2014 Price) (from mid May to mid Sept.) – 16 🚐 – 2 tent lodges. Per night from 59 to 88€ – Per week from 250 to 709€ – Reservation fee 13€

Surroundings : 🐟 ♨♨
Leisure activities : 🎿 🏊
Facilities : 🚿 ⚡ 🍴 launderette

GPS Longitude : 6.49755
Latitude : 44.54689

Do not confuse:
⛺ *to* ⛰⛰ *: MICHELIN classification with*
★ *to* ★★★★★ *: official classification*

BARRET-SUR-MÉOUGE

05300 – Michelin map **334** C7 – pop. 220 – alt. 640
▶ Paris 700 – Laragne-Montéglin 14 – Sault 46 – Séderon 21

⛰ Les Gorges de la Méouge

🕿 04 92 65 08 47. www.camping-meouge.com

Address : Le Serre (take the eastern exit along the D 942, follow the signs for Laragne-Montéglin and take the road to the right, near the Méouge river)

Opening times : from beginning May to end Sept.

3 ha (115 pitches) flat, grassy

Tariff : 19.50€ ★★ 🚗 ▣ ⚡ (10A) – Extra per person 5.90€
Rental rates : (from beginning April to mid Sept.) – 13 🚐.
Per night from 64 to 89€ – Per week from 448 to 623€
🚐 borne 2€ – 🔌 10€

Surroundings : 🐟 ♤♤
Leisure activities : 🚲 🏊
Facilities : 🚿 ⚡ 🏖 🛶 🍴 🛢

GPS Longitude : 5.73822
Latitude : 44.26078

The pitches of many campsites are marked out with low hedges of attractive bushes and shrubs.

LE BAR-SUR-LOUP

06620 – Michelin map **341** C5 – pop. 2 805 – alt. 320
▶ Paris 916 – Cannes 22 – Grasse 10 – Nice 31

⛰ Les Gorges du Loup

🕿 04 93 42 45 06. www.lesgorgesduloup.com

Address : 965 chemin des Vergers (1km northeast along the D 2210)

Opening times : from beginning April to end Sept.

1.6 ha (70 pitches) very uneven, terraced, flat, grassy, stony

Tariff : (2014 Price) 30.80€ ★★ 🚗 ▣ ⚡ (10A) – Extra per person 6€
Reservation fee 15€

Rental rates : (from beginning April to end Sept.) – 5 🚐 – 10 🏠 – 1 apartment. Per week from 330 to 750€ – Reservation fee 15€

Small terraces, many shaded by centuries-old olive trees, with some pitches enjoying a view of the Gorges du Loup.

Surroundings : 🐟 ≤ 🚐 ♤♤
Leisure activities : 🏖 🛶 🏊
Facilities : 🚿 ⚡ Ⓟ 🏖 🍴 🛢 🚿

GPS Longitude : 6.99527
Latitude : 43.70183

BEAUMES-DE-VENISE

84190 – Michelin map **332** D9 – pop. 2 283 – alt. 100
▶ Paris 666 – Avignon 34 – Nyons 39 – Orange 23

⛺ Municipal de Roquefiguier

🕿 04 90 62 95 07. www.mairie-de-beaumes-de-venise – 🏪

Address : route de Lafare (take the northern exit along the D 90, follow the signs for Malaucène and take a right turn; beside the Salette river)

Opening times : from beginning March to end Oct.

1.5 ha (63 pitches) terraced, relatively flat, grassy, stony

Tariff : (2014 Price) ★ 2.85€ 🚗 1.95€ ▣ 3.40€ – ⚡ (16A) 3.30€

Surroundings : ≤ 🚐 ♀
Leisure activities : 🛶 🏊
Facilities : 🚿 ⚡ 🏖 🍴 🛢 refrigerators
Nearby : 🎿

GPS Longitude : 5.03448
Latitude : 44.12244

BEAUMONT-DU-VENTOUX

84340 – Michelin map **332** E8 – pop. 317 – alt. 360
▶ Paris 676 – Avignon 48 – Carpentras 21 – Nyons 28

⚠ Mont-Serein

✆ 04 90 60 49 16. www.camping-ventoux.com – alt. 1 400

Address : at the Mont-Serein ski resort (20km east along the D 974 and take the D 164a, r. du Mont-Ventoux via Malaucène)

Opening times : Permanent

1.2 ha (60 pitches)

Tariff : ♣ 6€ ⇌ ▣ 9€ – ⚡ (10A) 4€

Rental rates : Permanent – 8 🏠. Per night from 75 to 145€ – Per week from 450 to 650€

🚏 borne – 30 ▣ 9€

In an attractive elevated location.

Surroundings : ⚲ ≼ Mont Ventoux and the Alps ⚲	**GPS**	Longitude : 5.25898
Leisure activities : ⌂ 🎿		Latitude : 44.1811
Facilities : ⟲🛏 ⚲ ⵜ ▣ 🚿		

BÉDOIN

84410 – Michelin map **332** E9 – pop. 3 132 – alt. 295
▶ Paris 692 – Avignon 43 – Carpentras 16 – Vaison-la-Romaine 21

⚠ Municipal la Pinède

✆ 04 90 65 61 03. camping.municipal@bedoin.fr

Address : chemin des Sablières (take the western exit following signs for Crillon-le-Brave and take the road to the right, next to the municipal swimming pool)

Opening times : from mid March to end Oct.

6 ha (121 pitches)

Tariff : (2014 Price) 15€ ♣♣ ⇌ ▣ ⚡ (16A) – Extra per person 3.40€
Rental rates : (2014 Price) (from mid March to end Oct.) – 3 📷. Per week from 290 to 470€

Surroundings : ⚲⚲	**GPS**	Longitude : 5.17261
Facilities : ♿ ⟲🛏 ⚲ ⵜ ▣		Latitude : 44.12486
Nearby : ✗ ⛴		

BOLLÈNE

84500 – Michelin map **332** B8 – pop. 13 885 – alt. 40
▶ Paris 634 – Avignon 53 – Montélimar 34 – Nyons 35

⚠ La Simioune

✆ 04 90 63 17 91. www.la-simioune.fr

Address : De Guffiage district (5km northeast following signs for Lambisque (access on the D 8 along the old road to Suze-la-Rousse following the Lez) and take road to the left)

Opening times : Permanent

2 ha (80 pitches) terraced, flat, sandy

Tariff : 22.50€ ♣♣ ⇌ ▣ ⚡ (10A) – Extra per person 4.50€
Rental rates : Permanent – 3 📷 – 3 🏠. Per night from 60 to 100€ – Per week from 180 to 550€

🚏 borne – 🔌⚡ 8€

Equipped with wooden, ranch-style buildings.

Surroundings : ⚲ ⚲⚲	**GPS**	Longitude : 4.74848
Leisure activities : ♟ 🎱 🐎		Latitude : 44.28203
Facilities : ♿ ⟲🛏 ⚲ ⵜ ▣ ⇲		

BONNIEUX

84480 – Michelin map **332** E11 – pop. 1 424 – alt. 400
▶ Paris 721 – Aix-en-Provence 49 – Apt 12 – Cavaillon 27

⚠ Le Vallon

✆ 04 90 75 86 14. www.campinglevallon.com

Address : route de Ménerbes (take the southern exit along the D 3 and turn off left)

Opening times : from mid March to mid Oct.

1.3 ha (80 pitches) terraced, flat, grassy, stony, wood

Tariff : (2014 Price) 22.80€ ♣♣ ⇌ ▣ ⚡ (10A) – Extra per person 4.50€ – Reservation fee 10€
Rental rates : (2014 Price) (from mid March to mid Oct.) ⚄ – 1 📷 – 3 yurts – 5 canvas bungalows. Per night from 50 to 70€ – Per week from 55 to 390€

🚏 40 ▣ 19€

Surroundings : ⚲ ≼ 🏕 ♨	**GPS**	Longitude : 5.22838
Facilities : ⟲🛏 ⚲ ⵜ ⵜ ▣		Latitude : 43.81881
Nearby : 🏊 ✗		

BORMES-LES-MIMOSAS

83230 – Michelin map **340** N7 – pop. 7 321 – alt. 180
▶ Paris 871 – Fréjus 57 – Hyères 21 – Le Lavandou 4

⛰ Le Camp du Domaine

Le Camp du Domaine

✆ 04 94 71 03 12. www.campdudomaine.com

Address : at La Favière, 2581 route de Bénat (situated 2km to the south, near the port)

Opening times : from end March to end Oct.

38 ha (1300 pitches) very uneven, terraced, flat, stony, rocks

Tariff : (2014 Price) 50€ ♣♣ ⇌ ▣ ⚡ (16A) – Extra per person 11€ – Reservation fee 27€
Rental rates : (2014 Price) (from end March to end Oct.) ⚄ – 50 📷 – 120 🏠. Per night from 140€ – Per week from 450 to 1,270€ – Reservation fee 27€

🚏 borne – 100 ▣ 35€

An exclusive site on an undulating, wooded peninsula close to the beach. Excursions organised out of season

Surroundings : ⚲ 🏕 ⚲⚲ ♨		
Leisure activities : ♟ ✗ ⌂ 🎱 🕺 🏊 ✗ ⛴ multi-sports ground	**GPS**	Longitude : 6.35129
Facilities : ♿ ⟲🛏 ⚄ 🍴 ⚲ ⵜ ▦ launderette 🍴 ⇲ refrigerated food storage facilities		Latitude : 43.11788
Nearby : ⚓ ⚓ pedalos, water skiing		

⛰ Manjastre

✆ 04 94 71 03 28. www.campingmanjastre.com

Address : 150 chemin des Girolles (5km northwest sur N 98, follow the signs for Cogolin)

Opening times : Permanent

3.5 ha (120 pitches) terraced, flat and relatively flat, stony

Tariff : (2014 Price) 29.60€ ♣♣ ⇌ ▣ ⚡ (10A) – Extra per person 6.60€ – Reservation fee 15.50€

borne 6€

An attractive arrangement of terraces among mimosas and cork oaks.

Surroundings :
Leisure activities :
Facilities : launderette

GPS Longitude : 6.32153
Latitude : 43.16258

BRIANÇON

05100 – Michelin map **334** H2 – pop. 11 574 – alt. 1 321 – Winter sports : 1 200/2 800 m
▶ Paris 681 – Digne-les-Bains 145 – Embrun 48 – Grenoble 89

Les 5 Vallées

℘ 04 92 21 06 27. www.camping5vallees.com

Address : St-Blaise (situated 2km south along the N 94)

Opening times : from beginning May to end Sept.

5 ha (180 pitches)

Tariff : (2014 Price) 29.90€ ✶✶ ⬅ 🅔 (10A) – Extra per person 7.80€

Rental rates : (2014 Price) (from beginning May to end Sept.) – 30 . Per night from 60 to 85€ – Per week from 422 to 599€

borne 5€

Surroundings :
Leisure activities :
Facilities : launderette
Nearby :

GPS Longitude : 6.69323
Latitude : 45.11898

CADENET

84160 – Michelin map **332** F11 – pop. 4 061 – alt. 170
▶ Paris 734 – Aix-en-Provence 33 – Apt 23 – Avignon 63

Homair Vacances Val de Durance

℘ 04 90 68 37 75. www.homair.com

Address : 570 avenue du Club Hippique (2.7km southwest along the D 943, follow the signs for Aix, turn right onto the D 59 and take road to the left)

Opening times : from mid April to end Sept.

10 ha/2.4 for camping (232 pitches)

Tariff : 34€ ✶✶ ⬅ 🅔 (8A) – Extra per person 7€ – Reservation fee 49€

Rental rates : (from mid April to end Sept.) – 220 . Per night from 15 to 165€ – Per week from 705 to 1,155€ – Reservation fee 49€

Located beside a lake and 300m from the Durance river.

Surroundings :
Leisure activities : daytime multi-sports ground
Facilities :

GPS Longitude : 5.35515
Latitude : 43.71957

Key to rentals symbols:

12		*Number of mobile homes*
20		*Number of chalets*
6		*Number of rooms to rent*
Per night 30–50€		*Minimum/maximum rate per night*
Per week 300–1,000€		*Minimum/maximum rate per week*

CAGNES-SUR-MER

06800 – Michelin map **341** D6 – pop. 48 024 – alt. 20
▶ Paris 915 – Antibes 11 – Cannes 21 – Grasse 25

La Rivière

℘ 04 93 20 62 27. www.campinglariviere06.fr

Address : 168 chemin des Salles (3.5km to the north; beside the Cagne river)

Opening times : from beginning April to end Sept.

1.2 ha (90 pitches)

Tariff : (2014 Price) 25€ ✶✶ ⬅ 🅔 (6A) – Extra per person 4€

Rental rates : (from beginning April to end Sept.) – 4 . Per week from 240 to 430€

The campsite has few mobile homes.

Surroundings :
Leisure activities :
Facilities :

GPS Longitude : 7.14283
Latitude : 43.69581

Le Colombier

℘ 04 93 73 12 77. www.campinglecolombier.com

Address : 35 chemin Sainte Colombe (head 2km north towards the hills by the road to Vence)

0.5 ha (33 pitches) flat and relatively flat, grassy, gravelled

Rentals : – 2 – 1 studio.

The sanitary faciliies are rather old and basic. The swimming pool is across the road.

Surroundings :
Leisure activities : (small swimming pool)
Facilities : launderette, refrigerators

GPS Longitude : 7.13893
Latitude : 43.67107

*For more information on visiting particular towns or regions, consult the relevant regional **MICHELIN Green Guide**. We also recommend you use the appropriate Michelin regional map to locate your selected campsite, to calculate distances and to work out the best route.*

CALLAS

83830 – Michelin map **340** O4 – pop. 1 813 – alt. 398
▶ Paris 872 – Castellane 51 – Draguignan 14 – Toulon 94

Les Blimouses

℘ 04 94 47 83 41. www.campinglesblimouses.com

Address : 3km south along the D 25 and take the D 225, follow the signs for Draguignan

Opening times : from beginning March to mid Nov.

6 ha (170 pitches) terraced, flat and relatively flat, grassy, stony

Tariff : 31€ ✶✶ ⬅ 🅔 (10A) – Extra per person 4€ – Reservation fee 20€

Rental rates : (from mid March to mid Nov.) – 42 – 7 . Per night from 55 to 75€ – Per week from 250 to 790€ – Reservation fee 20€

borne 8€

Shaded pitches with many owner-occupiers.

Surroundings :
Leisure activities :
Facilities :

GPS Longitude : 6.53242
Latitude : 43.57456

CANNES

06400 – Michelin map **341** D6 – pop. 73 372 – alt. 2
▶ Paris 898 – Aix-en-Provence 149 – Marseille 160 – Nice 33

▲▲ Le Parc Bellevue

✆ 04 93 47 28 97. www.parcbellevue.com

Address : at La Bocca, 67 avenue Maurice Chevalier (to the north, behind the municipal stadium)

Opening times : from beginning April to end Sept.

5 ha (250 pitches) very uneven, terraced, flat, grassy, gravelled

Tariff : 30€ ♣♣ ⟵ ▣ ⌷ (6A) – Extra per person 4€
Rental rates : (from beginning April to end Sept.) – 50 ⌷⌷⌷.
Per night from 35 to 45€ – Per week from 251 to 762€

⟐ borne – 20 ▣ 26€
In a shaded setting, but choose the pitches away from the road in preference.

Surroundings : ⊏⊐ ⊙⊙
Leisure activities : ✗ ⟞⟞ ⟵⟶ ⟋
Facilities : ⅙ ⟞ ▣ⅽⅽ ⅜⟝ ▣ ⅛

G P S	Longitude : 6.96042 Latitude : 43.55617

The guide covers all 22 regions of France – see the map and list of regions on pages 4–5.

LE CANNET

06110 – Michelin map **341** C6 – pop. 41 725 – alt. 80
▶ Paris 909 – Marseille 180 – Nice 39 – Monaco 54

▲▲ Le Ranch

✆ 04 93 46 00 11. www.leranchcamping.fr

Address : at Aubarède, chemin St. Joseph (located 1.5km northwest along the D 9, then take bd. de l'Esterel to the right)

Opening times : from mid April to mid Oct.

2 ha (128 pitches) terraced, relatively flat, flat, grassy, stony

Tariff : (2014 Price) ♣ 7€ ⟵ 3€ ▣ 21€ ⌷ (6A) – Reservation fee 15€
Rental rates : (2014 Price) (from mid April to mid Oct.) – 17 ⌷⌷⌷ –
5 ⟐ – 2 ⊨⊨ – 1 studio. Per week from 390 to 695€ – Reservation fee 15€

⟐ borne 5€
In a residential area, choose the pitches away from the road in preference.

Surroundings : ⊏⊐ ⊙⊙
Leisure activities : ⟞⟞ ⟵⟶ ⟋ (open air in season)
Facilities : ⅙ ⟞ ⅢⅢ ⅜⟝ launderette ⅛

G P S	Longitude : 6.97698 Latitude : 43.56508

CARPENTRAS

84200 – Michelin map **332** D9 – pop. 29 271 – alt. 102
▶ Paris 679 – Avignon 30 – Cavaillon 28 – Orange 24

▲▲ Flower Lou Comtadou

✆ 04 90 67 03 16. www.campingloucomtadou.com

Address : 881 avenue Pierre de Coubertin (located 1.5km southeast along the D 4, follow the signs for St-Didier and take turning to the right, near the sports centre)

Opening times : from beginning March to end Oct.

1 ha (99 pitches) small lake

Tariff : 17.50€ ♣♣ ⟵ ▣ ⌷ (6A) – Extra per person 4.50€ –
Reservation fee 10€

Rental rates : (from beginning March to end Oct.) – 21 ⌷⌷⌷ –
2 canvas bungalows – 3 tent lodges. Per night from 33 to 80€ –
Per week from 231 to 560€ – Reservation fee 20€

⟐ borne
Surroundings : ⊏⊐ ⊙⊙
Leisure activities : ⟞⟞ ⟵⟶
Facilities : ⅙ ⟞ ⅜ ⟋ ⅜⟝ ▣
Nearby : ✗ ⟋ ⟋

G P S	Longitude : 5.05429 Latitude : 44.04417

CARRO

13500 – Michelin map **340** F6
▶ Paris 787 – Marseille 44 – Aix-en-Provence 51 – Martigues 13

▲▲ Yelloh! Village Les Chalets de la Mer

(rental of chalets only)

✆ 04 42 80 73 46. www.semovim-martigues.com

Address : rue de la Tramontane

Opening times : mid April to end Sept.

3 ha flat

Rentals : ⅙ (8 chalets) – 78 ⟐.

Around 20 of the chalets offer accommodation on a hotel-style basis, with half board available.

Surroundings : ⅏ ⊏⊐ ⊙⊙
Leisure activities : ❡ ✗ ⟞⟞ ⓦ nighttime ⟶
⟋⊚ ⟸⟸ ⟋
Facilities : ⟞ ⟝ launderette ⅛

G P S	Longitude : 5.04117 Latitude : 43.33291

Michelin classification:

▲▲▲▲ *Extremely comfortable, equipped to a very high standard*
▲▲▲ *Very comfortable, equipped to a high standard*
▲▲ *Comfortable and well equipped*
▲▲ *Reasonably comfortable*
▲ *Satisfactory*

CASTELLANE

04120 – Michelin map **334** H9 – pop. 1 553 – alt. 730
▶ Paris 797 – Digne-les-Bains 54 – Draguignan 59 – Grasse 64

▲▲▲ Les Castels Le Domaine du Verdon ♣♣

✆ 04 92 83 61 29. www.camp-du-verdon.com

Address : Domaine de la Salaou (2km southwest along the D 952, follow signs for Moustier-Ste-Marie)

Opening times : from mid May to mid Sept.

9 ha (500 pitches) flat, grassy

Tariff : 48€ ♣♣ ⟵ ▣ ⌷ (16A) – Extra per person 14€ – Reservation fee 20€

Rental rates : (from mid May to mid Sept.) ⅙ (1 mobile home) –
260 ⌷⌷⌷. Per night from 52 to 147€ – Per week from 374 to 1,106€
Reservation fee 20€

⟐ borne
The rental options are good, but the sanitary facilities for tents and caravans are basic or even delapidated.

Surroundings : ⊏⊐ ⊙⊙
Leisure activities : ❡ ✗ ⟞⟞ ⓦ ⟶ ⟵⟶ ⟋⟋ ⟋
⟆⟆ ⟋ ⟍ entertainment room
Facilities : ⅙ ⟞ ⅜⟝ launderette ⟞ ⅛
refrigerated food storage facilities
Nearby : rafting and canyoning

G P S	Longitude : 6.49402 Latitude : 43.83895

⛰ RCN Les Collines de Castellane ♣♨

📞 04 92 83 68 96. www.rcn.fr/collinesdecastellane – pitches accessed via steep slope, help moving caravans onto and off pitches avilable on request – alt. 1 000

Address : route de Grasse (7km southeast along the N 85; at La Garde)

Opening times : from end April to end Sept.

7 ha (200 pitches) terraced, relatively flat, stony, flat, grassy, wood

Tariff : 50€ ♣♣ ⟷ 🅴 🄷 (12A) – Extra per person 6.75€ – Reservation fee 19.95€

Rental rates : (from end April to end Sept.) – 36 🛏 – 4 🏠 – 4 tent lodges. Per night from 40 to 277€ – Per week from 280 to 1,337€ Reservation fee 19.95€

Surroundings : ⅗ ≼ ⊏ ♀♀
Leisure activities : 🍷 ✕ 🎱 ⚽ 🚣 ✂ 🏊
🎿 forest trail
Facilities : ♿ ⌬ 🚿 🗑 🚰 🍴 launderette 🧺 🧊 refrigerators

G P S Longitude : 6.56994
Latitude : 43.8244

⛰ Calme et Nature La Colle

📞 04 92 83 61 57. www.camping-lacolle.com

Address : 2.5km southwest along the D 952, follow the signs for Moustiers-Ste-Marie and take a right turn (GR 4)

Opening times : from beginning April to end Sept.

3 ha/1.5 (41 pitches) very uneven, terraced, flat and relatively flat, grassy, stony

Tariff : (2014 Price) 23€ ♣♣ ⟷ 🅴 🄷 (10A) – Extra per person 5.80€

Rental rates : (2014 Price) (from beginning April to end Sept.) ✂ – 12 🛏 – 2 🏠. Per night from 36 to 88€ – Per week from 252 to 610€

The campsite is laid out on terraces and is crossed by a small stream.

Surroundings : ⅗ ⊏ ♀♀
Leisure activities : 🍷 ✕ 🚲 small petting zoo
Facilities : ♿ ⌬ 🚿 🚰 🍴 🗑

G P S Longitude : 6.49312
Latitude : 43.83864

⛰ Notre-Dame

📞 04 92 83 63 02. www.camping-notredame.com

Address : route des Gorges du Verdon (500m southwest along the D 952, follow the signs for Moustiers-Ste-Marie; beside a stream)

Opening times : from beginning April to mid Oct.

0.6 ha (44 pitches) flat, grassy

Tariff : (2014 Price) 24.50€ ♣♣ ⟷ 🅴 🄷 (6A) – Extra per person 6.10€ Reservation fee 9€

Rental rates : (2014 Price) (from beginning April to mid Oct.) ✂ – 11 🛏. Per night from 51 to 99 € – Per week from 330 to 630€ Reservation fee 9€

🚐 borne 6€ – 🚿 🄷14.50€

Located at the entrance to the village, near the road.

Surroundings : ♀♀
Leisure activities : 🚣
Facilities : ♿ ⌬ 🍴 launderette
Nearby : adventure park

G P S Longitude : 6.50425
Latitude : 43.84545

There are several different types of sani-station ('borne' in French) – sanitation points providing fresh water and disposal points for grey water. See page 12 for further details.

See page 12 for further details.

CAVALAIRE-SUR-MER

83240 – Michelin map **340** O6 – pop. 6 731 – alt. 2
▶ Paris 880 – Draguignan 55 – Fréjus 41 – Le Lavandou 21

⛰ Cros de Mouton

📞 04 94 64 10 87. www.crosdemouton.com – pitches accessed via steep slope, help moving caravans onto and off pitches avilable on request

Address : chemin du Cros de Mouton (located 1.5km to the northwest)

Opening times : from end March to end Oct.

5 ha (199 pitches) very uneven, terraced, flat, stony

Tariff : (2014 Price) ♣ 9.50€ ⟷ 🅴 9.50€ – 🄷 (10A) 5.20€ – Reservation fee 20€

Rental rates : (2014 Price) (from end March to end Oct.) – 65 🛏 – 9 🏠. Per night from 57 to 150€ – Per week from 395 to 1,030€ Reservation fee 20€

Situated on a hill with a panoramic view of the sea from some pitches and from the restaurant terrace.

Surroundings : ⅗ ≼ Baie de Cavalaire ⊏ ♀♀
Leisure activities : 🍷 ✕ 🎱 jacuzzi ⚽ 🏊
Facilities : ♿ ⌬ 🚿 🚰 🍴 🖼 🗑 ♨

G P S Longitude : 6.51662
Latitude : 43.18243

CEILLAC

05600 – Michelin map **334** I4 – pop. 307 – alt. 1 640 – Winter sports : 1 700/2 500 m
▶ Paris 729 – Briançon 50 – Gap 75 – Guillestre 14

⛰ Les Mélèzes

📞 04 92 45 21 93. www.campingdeceillac.com

Address : La Rua des Reynauds (1.8km southeast)

Opening times : from beginning June to beginning Sept.

3 ha (100 pitches) very uneven, terraced, relatively flat, stony, grassy

Tariff : ♣ 6.80€ ⟷ 🅴 7.20€ – 🄷 (10A) 10€

A pleasant campsite and location, beside the Mélezet river.

Surroundings : ⅗ ≼ ♀
Leisure activities : ⚽
Facilities : ⌬ ⎁ 🚿 🚰 🗑

G P S Longitude : 6.78843
Latitude : 44.65389

CHÂTEAUNEUF-DE-GADAGNE

84470 – Michelin map **332** C10 – pop. 3 249 – alt. 90
▶ Paris 701 – Marseille 95 – Avignon 14 – Nîmes 58

⛰ Le Fontisson

📞 04 90 22 59 77. www.campingfontisson.com

Address : 1125 route d'Avignon (near the exit from town along the follow the signs for Avignon and take road to the right)

Opening times : from beginning April to mid Oct.

2 ha (55 pitches)

Tariff : (2014 Price) 30.60€ ♣♣ ⟷ 🅴 🄷 (10A) – Extra per person 7.20€ – Reservation fee 10€

Rental rates : (2014 Price) (from beginning April to mid Oct.) – 19 🛏 – 4 canvas bungalows. Per night from 105 to 250€ – Per week from 255 to 860€ – Reservation fee 15€

🚐 borne

Surroundings : ⅗ ⊏ ♀♀
Leisure activities : 🎱 ⚽ ✂ 🎣 🏊 multi-sports ground
Facilities : ♿ ⌬ 🚿 🍴 🖼

G P S Longitude : 4.93297
Latitude : 43.92846

CHÂTEAURENARD

13160 – Michelin map **340** E2 – pop. 14 971 – alt. 37
▶ Paris 692 – Avignon 10 – Carpentras 37 – Cavaillon 23

⚠ La Roquette

✆ 04 90 94 46 81. www.camping-la-roquette.com

Address : 745 avenue Jean-Mermoz (located 1.5km east along the D 28, follow the signs for Noves and take a right turn, near the swimming pool - from A 7 take exit Avignon-Sud)

Opening times : from beginning April to end Oct.

2 ha (74 pitches) flat, grassy

Tariff : 25€ ♣♣ ⇦ 🅴 🔌 (10A) – Extra per person 7€ – Reservation fee 12€

Rental rates : (from beginning April to end Oct.) – 14 🛏. Per night from 39 to 114€ – Per week from 267 to 915€ – Reservation fee 12€

Surroundings : 🖵 ⚲
Leisure activities : 🍷 ✕ ⛵ 🎿
Facilities : 🚿 ⚍ 🛁 🚾 🔲

GPS Longitude : 4.87017
Latitude : 43.88328

The Michelin classification (⚠⚠⚠... ⚠) is totally independent of the official star classification system awarded by the local prefecture or other official organisation.

CHORGES

05230 – Michelin map **334** F5 – pop. 2 567 – alt. 864
▶ Paris 676 – Embrun 23 – Gap 18 – Savines-le-Lac 12

⚠ Municipal

✆ 04 92 50 67 72. www.baiestmichel.com

Address : Baie St-Michel (4.5km southeast along the N 94, follow the signs for Briançon, 200m from the lake at Serre-Ponçon)

Opening times : from mid May to mid Sept.

2 ha (110 pitches) terraced, flat, grassy, stony

Tariff : (2014 Price) 19.20€ ♣♣ ⇦ 🅴 🔌 (16A) – Extra per person 5€
Rental rates : (2014 Price) (from end April to end Oct.) ♿ (1 chalet) – 10 🛏. Per night from 57 to 100€ – Per week from 320 to 625€

🛏 borne

Surroundings : 🌳 ⛰ ⚲
Leisure activities : 🖼 ⛵ 🏊 (lake)
Facilities : 🚿 ⚍ 🚾
Nearby : 🍷 ✕ 🎣 ⚓ 🚣 pedalos

GPS Longitude : 6.32379
Latitude : 44.5283

CLAMENSANE

04250 – Michelin map **334** E7 – pop. 166 – alt. 694
▶ Paris 720 – Avignon 180 – Grenoble 158 – Marseille 152

⚠ Le Clot du Jay en Provence ♣♣

✆ 04 92 68 35 32. www.clotdujay.com

Address : route de Bayons (located 1km east along the D 1, follow the signs for Bayons, near the Sasse river)

Opening times : from mid April to end Sept.

6 ha/3 for camping (50 pitches) very uneven, terraced, flat, grassy, stony

Tariff : (2014 Price) 25.50€ ♣♣ ⇦ 🅴 🔌 (10A) – Extra per person 4€
Reservation fee 9€

Rental rates : (from mid April to end Sept.) – 8 🛏 – 12 🏠 – 1 tent lodge. Per night from 50 to 80€ – Per week from 250 to 800€ – Reservation fee 9€

Choose the pitches at the edge of the Forêt Domaniale du Grand Vallon (forest), furthest away from the road.

Surroundings : 🖵 ⚲⚲
Leisure activities : 🍷 ✕ 🚣 ⛵ 🎿 ⚲
Facilities : ♿ ⚍ 🛁 🚾 🔲 ⚙

GPS Longitude : 6.0845
Latitude : 44.3226

LA COLLE-SUR-LOUP

06480 – Michelin map **341** D5 – pop. 7 640 – alt. 90
▶ Paris 919 – Antibes 15 – Cagnes-sur-Mer 7 – Cannes 26

⚠ Sites et Paysages Les Pinèdes ♣♣

✆ 04 93 32 98 94. www.lespinedes.com

Address : route du Pont de Pierre (located 1.5km west along the D 6, follow the signs for Grasse, 50m from the Loup river)

Opening times : from end March to end Sept.

3.8 ha (149 pitches) very uneven, terraced, flat, grassy, fine gravel

Tariff : 43.70€ ♣♣ ⇦ 🅴 🔌 (10A) – Extra per person 6.20€ – Reservation fee 20€

Rental rates : (from end March to end Sept.) – 32 🛏 – 9 🏠. Per night from 55 to 165€ – Per week from 350 to 1,230€ – Reservation fee 20€

🛏 borne 6€ – 🚐 🔌14€

The campsite is laid out across shaded terraces, with good-quality rental options.

Surroundings : 🖵 ⚲⚲
Leisure activities : 🍷 ✕ 🏠 🚣 ⛵ 🎿
multi-sports ground
Facilities : ⚍ ▥ 🛁 🚾 ⚙ 🚾 launderette ⚙
refrigerated food storage facilities
Nearby : 🏊 🐴 leisure park

GPS Longitude : 7.08337
Latitude : 43.68177

⚠ Flower Le Vallon Rouge

✆ 04 93 32 86 12. www.auvallonrouge.com – limited spaces for one-night stay

Address : route de Gréolières (3.5km west along the D 6, follow signs for Grasse)

Opening times : from end April to mid Sept.

3 ha (103 pitches) terraced, flat, grassy, sandy, fine gravel

Tariff : (2014 Price) 18€ ♣♣ ⇦ 🅴 🔌 (10A) – Extra per person 6€ – Reservation fee 20€

Rental rates : Permanent – 45 🛏 – 19 🏠 – 7 canvas bungalows. Per night from 60 to 110€ – Per week from 60 to 100€ – Reservation fee 20€

🛏 borne 4€
Choose the pitches beside the Loup river, furthest away from the road.

Surroundings : 🌳 🖵 ⚲⚲
Leisure activities : ✕ 🏠 🚣 🎿 🏊
multi-sports ground
Facilities : ♿ ⚍ 🛁 🚾 ⚙ launderette ⚙

GPS Longitude : 7.07324
Latitude : 43.68452

Routes nationales are main roads and their identifying numbers begin with N or RN. Routes départementales are generally quieter roads and begin with D or DN.

COL-ST-JEAN

04340 – Michelin map **334** G6 – alt. 1 333 – Winter sports : 1 300/2 500 m
▶ Paris 709 – Barcelonnette 34 – Savines-le-Lac 31 – Seyne 10

ᴀᴡᴀ Yelloh! Village L'Étoile des Neiges ▲▮

✆ 04 92 35 01 29. www.etoile-des-neiges.com – alt. 1 300

Address : at the Col St-Jean ski resort (800m south along the D 207 and turn right onto D 307)

Opening times : from mid May to beginning Sept.

3 ha (150 pitches) terraced, flat, grassy, stony

Tariff : 38€ ✸✸ ⇦ 🄴 🄷 (6A) – Extra per person 8€
Rental rates : (from mid May to beginning Sept. and from end May to beginning Sept) ⇗ 🄿 – 65 ⏢ – 25 ⌂ – 1 ⊨ – 1 studio.
Per night from 39 to 175€ – Per week from 273 to 1,225€
⊞ borne 8€
Various rental options, including some high-quality chalets.

Surroundings : ⥤ ⟨ ☐ 🗘🗘
Leisure activities : 🍴✗ ☐ 🎯✲ 🏊 ⥤ hammam, jacuzzi ⚓ ✄ 🎱 multi-sports ground, spa centre
Facilities : 🚿 ⊶ 🗄 🗖 🝐 ✄ ⚑ launderette ⚘
Nearby : ⚓ 🚴 adventure park

Longitude : 6.348
Latitude : 44.40927

To visit a town or region, use the MICHELIN Green Guides.

CONTES

06390 – Michelin map **341** E5 – pop. 7 095 – alt. 250
▶ Paris 954 – Marseille 208 – Monaco 30 – Nice 19

ᴀᴀ La Ferme Riola

✆ 04 93 79 03 02. www.campinglafermeriola.com

Opening times : from beginning April to end Sept.

3 ha (25 pitches) terraced, flat, grassy, stony

Tariff : 23€ ✸✸ ⇦ 🄴 🄷 (6A) – Extra per person 10€
Rental rates : Permanent ⇗ – 6 ⌂ – 2 studios – 4 gîtes.
Per week from 250 to 600€
⊞ 4 🄴 10€
There is a small museum of agricultural tools and local olive oil is for sale.

Surroundings : ⥤ 🗘🗘
Leisure activities : ☐ ⚓ 🎱
Facilities : 🚿 ⊶ ✄ ⚑

Longitude : 7.34379
Latitude : 43.8152

LA COURONNE

13500 – Michelin map **340** F5
▶ Paris 786 – Marseille 42 – Aix-en-Provence 49 – Martigues 11

ᴀᴡᴀ Le Mas ▲▮

✆ 04 42 80 70 34. www.camping-le-mas.com – limited spaces for one-night stay ⇗

Address : chemin de Sainte Croix (4km southeast along the D 49, follow the signs for Sausset-les-Pins and take a right turn; near the beach at Ste-Croix)

Opening times : from mid March to beginning Nov.

5.5 ha (300 pitches) terraced, flat, grassy, stony

Tariff : 31€ ✸✸ ⇦ 🄴 🄷 (10A) – Extra per person 8€ – Reservation fee 20€

Rental rates : (2014 Price) (from mid March to beginning Nov.) ⇗ – 151 ⏢ – 45 ⌂. Per week from 224 to 1,421€ – Reservation fee 20€
⊞ borne
Some pitches have a sea view.

Surroundings : ⥤ 🗘🗘
Leisure activities : 🍴✗ ☐ 🎯✲ ⚓ ✄ 🎱 multi-sports ground
Facilities : 🚿 ⊶ 🝐 ⚑ launderette ⚘
Nearby : ⚓

Longitude : 5.07349
Latitude : 43.33168

ᴀᴀ Yelloh! Village La Côte Bleue

✆ 04 42 42 81 00. www.semovim-martigues.com

Address : chemin de la Batterie

Opening times : from mid April to end Sept.

6 ha (200 pitches) terraced, flat, stony, sandy

Tariff : 47€ ✸✸ ⇦ 🄴 🄷 (10A) – Extra per person 8€
Rental rates : (from mid April to end Sept.) 🚿 (1 mobile home) – 80 ⏢. Per night from 39 to 241€ – Per week from 273 to 1,687€
⊞ borne

Surroundings : ⥤ 🗘🗘
Leisure activities : ✗ ☐ 🎯✲ ⚓ ✄ 🎱
Facilities : 🚿 ⊶ ⚑ launderette ⚓ ⚘

Longitude : 5.05639
Latitude : 43.33067

ᴀᴀ Flower Le Marius

✆ 04 42 80 70 29. www.camping-marius.com

Address : Plage de la Saulce (beach) (3km southeast along the D 49)

Opening times : from beginning April to mid Oct.

2 ha (113 pitches)

Tariff : 36€ ✸✸ ⇦ 🄴 🄷 (6A) – Extra per person 9€ – Reservation fee 10.50€
Rental rates : (from mid June to end Aug.) 🚿 (2 chalets) – 37 ⌂ – 2 tent lodges – 15 canvas bungalows (with/without sanitary facilities). Per week from 266 to 1,512€

Surroundings : ⥤ ☐ 🗘🗘
Leisure activities : 🍴✗ ⥤ hammam, jacuzzi ⚓ 🚴🎱
Facilities : 🚿 ✄ launderette ⚘

Longitude : 5.06744
Latitude : 43.33512

⚠ Les Mouettes

✆ 04 42 80 70 01. www.campinglesmouettes.fr – limited spaces for one-night stay

Address : 16 chemin de la Quiétude (4km southeast along the D 49, follow the signs for Sausset, along the r. du Tamaris, near the beach at Ste-Croix)

Opening times : from beginning April to end Sept.

2 ha (131 pitches) terrace, flat, stony

Tariff : 31€ ✸✸ ⇦ 🄴 🄷 (6A) – Extra per person 8€ – Reservation fee 8€
Rental rates : Permanent – 30 ⏢ – 20 ⌂. Per night from 48 to 69€ – Per week from 190 to 880€ – Reservation fee 8€
Some pitches with a sea view.

Surroundings : ⥤ 🗘🗘
Leisure activities : 🍴✗
Facilities : 🚿 ⊶ ✄ ⚑ launderette
Nearby : ⚓

Longitude : 5.07618
Latitude : 43.33024

LA CROIX-VALMER

83420 – Michelin map **340** O6 – pop. 3 351 – alt. 120
▶ Paris 873 – Brignoles 70 – Draguignan 48 – Fréjus 35

⚞⚞⚞ Sélection Camping ♣♣

✆ 04 94 55 10 30. www.selectioncamping.com ✖ (from mid March to end June)

Address : 12 boulevard de la Mer (2.5km southwest along the D 559, follow the signs for Cavalaire and take road to the right at the roundabout)

Opening times : from mid March to mid Oct.

4 ha (185 pitches) terraced, flat, grassy, stony

Tariff : 45€ ♣♣ ⚘ 🔲 🔌 (10A) – Reservation fee 32€

Rental rates : (from mid March to mid Oct.) ✖ – 53 🔲 – 15 🔲 – 15 gîtes. Per night from 54 to 185€ – Per week from 375 to 1,290€ Reservation fee 32€

On shaded terraces under eucalyptus, mimosa and other Mediterranean trees.

Surroundings : 🔲 ◯◯		
Leisure activities : ▼ ✖ daytime ♦ ⚓ 🛥 multi-sports ground, entertainment room	**G P S**	Longitude : 6.55501 Latitude : 43.19439
Facilities : ♿ ⚭ ▥ ♨ launderette		

Some information or pricing may have changed since the guide went to press. We recommend you check the price list online in advance or at the entrance to the campsite and enquire about possible restrictions.

CROS-DE-CAGNES

06800 – Michelin map **341** D6
▶ Paris 923 – Marseille 194 – Nice 12 – Antibes 11

⚞⚞⚞ Homair Vacances Green Park ♣♣

✆ 04 93 07 09 96. www.homair.com – limited spaces for one-night stay

Address : 159 bis chemin du Vallon des Vaux (3.8km to the north)

Opening times : from mid April to end Sept.

5 ha (156 pitches) very uneven, terraced, flat, grassy, fine gravel

Tariff : 33€ ♣♣ ⚘ 🔲 🔌 (6A) – Extra per person 8€ – Reservation fee 49€

Rental rates : (from mid April to end Sept.) ♿ (2 chalets) – 63 🔲 – 55 🔲. Per night from 24 to 191€ – Per week from 168 to 1,337€ Reservation fee 49€

A free shuttle to the beaches. Chalets and mobile homes.

Surroundings : 🔲 ◯		
Leisure activities : ▼ ✖ 🏠 ♦ ⚓ 🚲 🛥 multi-sports ground	**G P S**	Longitude : 7.1569 Latitude : 43.68904
Facilities : ♿ ⚭ 🔲 ♨ launderette		
Nearby : ✖ golf practice		

⚞ Le Val Fleuri

✆ 04 93 31 21 74. www.campingvalfleuri.fr

Address : 139 chemin du Vallon des Vaux (3.5km to the north)

Opening times : from beginning April to end Sept.

1.5 ha (87 pitches) very uneven, terraced, flat, grassy, stony

Tariff : (2014 Price) 31.50€ ♣♣ ⚘ 🔲 🔌 (10A) – Extra per person 4€

Rental rates : (2014 Price) (from beginning April to end Sept.) – 11 🔲 – 1 studio – 1 apartment. Per week from 280 to 600€

The site is in two sections. There's a bus to the beach.

Surroundings : 🔲 ◯◯		
Leisure activities : ▼ ⚓ 🛥	**G P S**	Longitude : 7.15577 Latitude : 43.68745
Facilities : ♿ ⚭ ▥ ♨ 🔲		
Nearby : ✖ golf practice		

⚞⚞⚞ Homair Vacances Le Todos

(rental of mobile homes and chalets only)

✆ 04 93 07 09 96. www.homair.com – limited spaces for one-night stay

Address : 159bis chemin du Vallon des Vaux (3.8km to the north)

1.6 ha (63 pitches) terraced, flat, grassy, stony

Rentals : 44 🔲 – 9 🔲.

All the services and leisure facilities are at the Homair Vacances Green Park campsite opposite. There's a bus to the beach.

Surroundings : 🔲)))		
Leisure activities : 🛥	**G P S**	Longitude : 7.1569 Latitude : 43.68904
Facilities : ⚭ ♨ launderette		
Nearby : 🔲 ▼ ✖ 🏠 🔲 ♦ 🚲 ✖ m golf practice		

CUCURON

84160 – Michelin map **332** F11 – pop. 1 844 – alt. 350
▶ Paris 739 – Aix-en-Provence 34 – Apt 25 – Cadenet 9

⚞ Le Moulin à Vent

✆ 04 90 77 25 77. www.le-moulin-a-vent.com

Address : chemin de Gastoule (located 1.5km south along the D 182; follow the signs for Villelaure then continue 800m along the turning to the left)

Opening times : from beginning April to beginning Oct.

2.2 ha (80 pitches) terraced, relatively flat, flat, stony

Tariff : 19.60€ ♣♣ ⚘ 🔲 🔌 (10A) – Extra per person 5.10€

Rental rates : (from beginning April to beginning Oct.) ✖ – 1 🔲 – 4 🔲. Per night from 67 to 72€ – Per week from 425 to 557€ 🔲 borne 5€

This campsite is surrounded by vineyards.

Surroundings : 🔲 ◯◯		
Leisure activities : 🏠 ⚓	**G P S**	Longitude : 5.44484 Latitude : 43.75641
Facilities : ♿ ⚭ ♨ 🔲 refrigerators		

Some campsites benefit from proximity to a municipal leisure centre.

CURBANS

05110 – Michelin map **334** E6 – pop. 418 – alt. 650
▶ Paris 717 – Marseille 171 – Digne-les-Bains 78 – Gap 20

⚞⚞⚞ Le Lac

✆ 04 92 54 23 10. www.au-camping-du-lac.com – limited spaces for one-night stay

Address : at Le Fangeas

Opening times : from beginning April to end Oct.

5.2 ha (140 pitches)

Tariff : (2014 Price) 28.20€ ♣♣ ⚘ 🔲 🔌 (10A) – Extra per person 6€ Reservation fee 14€

Rental rates : (2014 Price) Permanent – 39 ⛺. Per night from 31 to 127€ – Per week from 217 to 890€ – Reservation fee 14€

This site has an Hautes-Alpes post code (05), but is actually located in the Alpes-de-Haute-Provence (04).

Surroundings : ≤ ♀
Leisure activities : ♉ ✗ 🕯nighttime ✂ ⛵ ⛷ 🪁 multi-sports ground
Facilities : ⊶ ♈ launderette ⚲

GPS Longitude : 6.0299
Latitude : 44.42452

DIGNE-LES-BAINS

04000 – Michelin map **334** F8 – pop. 17 172 – alt. 608 – ⚒
▶ Paris 744 – Aix-en-Provence 109 – Antibes 140 – Avignon 167

🏔 Les Eaux Chaudes

🅟 04 92 32 31 04. www.campingleseauxchaudes.com

Address : 32 avenue des Thermes (located 1.5km southeast along the D 20; beside a stream)

Opening times : from mid April to mid Oct.

3.7 ha (90 pitches)

Tariff : 25.50€ ✦✦ ⛟ 🅔 ⚡ (10A) – Extra per person 6.50€ – Reservation fee 15€

Rental rates : (from beginning April to end Oct.) – 55 ⛺ – 4 🏠. Per night from 49 to 133€ – Per week from 343 to 931€ Reservation fee 18€

🛒 borne 5€

Situated beside a stream, with both new and older rental options, equipped to varying standards.

Surroundings : ♀♀
Leisure activities : 🏓 ⛷ ⛷
Facilities : ♿ ⊶ 🎱 ⚲ ⛏ ♈ launderette

GPS Longitude : 6.2507
Latitude : 44.08656

EMBRUN

05200 – Michelin map **334** G5 – pop. 6 188 – alt. 871
▶ Paris 706 – Barcelonnette 55 – Briançon 48 – Digne-les-Bains 97

🏔 Municipal de la Clapière

🅟 04 92 43 01 83. www.camping-embrun-clapiere.com

Address : avenue du Lac (2.5km southwest along the N 94, follow the signs for Gap and take a right turn; at the leisure and activity park)

Opening times : from end April to end Sept.

6.5 ha (291 pitches) terraced, flat, grassy, fine gravel

Tariff : (2014 Price) 23.64€ ✦✦ ⛟ 🅔 ⚡ (16A) – Extra per person 6.32€ –

Rental rates : (2014 Price) Permanent – 6 ⛺ – 14 🏠. Per night from 90 to 100€ – Per week from 340 to 775€

🛒 borne

There's a pleasant leisure and activity centre with direct access in season.

Surroundings : ♀♀
Leisure activities : 🏓 🕯nighttime ⛷
Facilities : ♿ ⊶ ⛏ ♈ launderette
Nearby : 🍵 ♉ ✗ ⚲ ✂ 🎿 🖥 (lake) ⛷ 🪁 ⛵ pedalos

GPS Longitude : 6.47875
Latitude : 44.55075

We value your opinion and welcome your feedback. Do email us at campingfrance@tp.michelin.com

ESPARRON-DU-VERDON

04800 – Michelin map **334** D10 – pop. 433 – alt. 397
▶ Paris 795 – Barjols 31 – Digne-les-Bains 58 – Gréoux-les-Bains 13

🏔 Le Soleil

Le Soleil

🅟 04 92 77 13 78. www.camping-le-soleil.com 🪁

Address : 1,000 av. du Lac (2.km southwest along the N94, follow the signs for Gap and take a right turn; at the leisure and activity park)

Opening times : from mid April to mid Oct.

2 ha (100 pitches) very uneven, terraced, stony, fine gravel

Tariff : (2014 Price) 28.20€ ✦✦ ⛟ 🅔 ⚡ (6A) – Extra per person 7.25€ – Reservation fee 15€

Rental rates : (2014 Price) (from mid April to mid Oct.) 🪁 – 12 ⛺ – 2 canvas bungalows. Per night from 30 to 88€ – Per week from 120 to 640€ – Reservation fee 20€

🛒 borne 5€ – 🚐 ⚡28.20€

In a pleasant setting beside a lake.

Surroundings : ⛷ 🏕 ♀♀ ⛰
Leisure activities : ♉ ✗ 🛶 ⛵ 🪁
Facilities : ♿ ⊶ 🅟 ⛏ ♈ 🖥 ♨ ⚲
Nearby : ⛵ pedalos

GPS Longitude : 5.97062
Latitude : 43.73439

We have selected the best campsites in France with our usual care, listing those with the best facilities in the most pleasant surroundings.

ESPINASSES

05190 – Michelin map **334** F6 – pop. 665 – alt. 630
▶ Paris 689 – Chorges 19 – Gap 25 – Le Lauzet-Ubaye 23

🏔 La Viste

🅟 04 92 54 43 39. www.laviste.fr – alt. 900

Address : Belvédère de Serre-Ponçon (head 5.5km northeast along the D 900b, take the D 3 following signs for Chorges and turn left onto D 103)

Opening times : from mid May to mid Sept.

4.5 ha/2.5 for camping (170 pitches) terraced, undulating, flat, grassy, stony

Tariff : (2014 Price) ✦ 7.40€ ⛟ 🅔 7.40€ – ⚡ (5A) 3.90€ – Reservation fee 15€

Rental rates : (2014 Price) (from mid May to mid Sept.) – 10 ⛺ – 35 🏠. Per night from 50 to 136€ – Per week from 345 to 950€ – Reservation fee 15€

🛒 borne

In an attractive location overlooking the Lac de Serre-Ponçon.

Surroundings : ⛷ ≤ mountains, lake and Barrage de Serre-Ponçon (dam) ♀♀
Leisure activities : ♉ ✗ 🕯daytime ⛷ ⛷
Facilities : ♿ ⊶ ♈ launderette ♨ ⚲
Nearby : 🖥 (lake) 🪁 water skiing

GPS Longitude : 6.26832
Latitude : 44.47613

FAUCON

84110 – Michelin map **332** D8 – pop. 414 – alt. 350
▶ Paris 677 – Marseille 152 – Avignon 59 – Montélimar 68

⚠ L'Ayguette

✆ 0490464035. www.ayguette.com

Address : take the eastern exit along the D 938, follow the signs for Nyons and continue 4.1 km to the right along the D 71, follow the signs for St-Romains-Viennois then take the D 86

Opening times : from beginning April to end Sept.

2.8 ha (100 pitches) undulating, flat, grassy, stony

Tariff : 31€ ★★ ⬅ 🅴 (10A) – Extra per person 5.50€

Rental rates : (from beginning April to end Sept.) – 24 🚐.
Per night from 34 to 99€ – Per week from 238 to 693€
🚐 borne
In a natural setting.

Surroundings : 🐟 ⌂ 🌳🌳		
Leisure activities : ✗ 🏊 ⚓	**G**	Longitude : 5.12933
Facilities : ⛫ ⚲ 🚻♟🏠🚿	**P**	Latitude : 44.26215
	S	

FORCALQUIER

04300 – Michelin map **334** C9 – pop. 4 640 – alt. 550
▶ Paris 747 – Aix-en-Provence 80 – Apt 42 – Digne-les-Bains 50

🏔 Indigo Forcalquier

A©Campingindigo

✆ 04 92 75 27 94. www.camping-indigo.com

Address : route de Sigonce (take the eastern exit on D 16)

Opening times : from end April to end Sept.

2.9 ha (130 pitches) terraced, relatively flat, flat, grassy, stony

Tariff : (2014 Price) 29€ ★★ ⬅ 🅴 (10A) – Extra per person 6.40€ –
Reservation fee 22€

Rental rates : (2014 Price) (from end April to end Sept.) 🅿 – 25 🚐 – 4 🏠 – 25 tent lodges. Per night from 48 to 117€ – Per week from 235 to 819€ – Reservation fee 22€
🚐 borne 7€ – 40 🅴 23.70€
There are numerous and varied rental options.

Surroundings : ⌂ 🌳🌳		
Leisure activities : ✗ 🏠 🌳🌳 ⚓ 🚲 ⚓	**G**	Longitude : 5.78723
Facilities : ⛫ ⚲ ⚓🚿♟🏠🚿	**P**	Latitude : 43.96218
Nearby : ✗	**S**	

FRÉJUS

83600 – Michelin map **340** P5 – pop. 52 203 – alt. 20
▶ Paris 868 – Brignoles 64 – Cannes 40 – Draguignan 31

🏔🏔🏔 La Baume - La Palmeraie 👥

✆ 04 94 19 88 88. www.labaume-lapalmeraie.com – limited spaces for one-night stay

Address : 3775 rue des Combattants d'Afrique du Nord (4.5km north along the D 4; follow the signs for Bagnols-en-Forêt)

Opening times : from end March to end Sept.

26 ha/20 for camping (780 pitches) relatively flat, flat, stony, sandy

Tariff : 54€ ★★ ⬅ 🅴 (6A) – Extra per person 15€ – Reservation fee 33€

Rental rates : (from end March to end Sept.) ⛫ (11 gîtes) – 180 🚐 – 182 🏠. Per night from 38 to 290€ – Per week from 266 to 2,030€ – Reservation fee 33€
There are two swimming areas, one partially covered, and a variety of rental options. Choose the pitches furthest from the road.

Surroundings : ⌂ 🌳🌳		
Leisure activities : 🍴 ✗ 🏠 ⑤(open-air theatre) 🌳🌳 🏊 hammam, jacuzzi ⚓🚲 ✗🔲⚓disco, skate park	**G**	Longitude : 6.72319
Facilities : ⛫ ⚲ 🚻♟⚓🚿🍴 launderette ⚓⚓	**P**	Latitude : 43.46655
	S	

🏔🏔🏔 Yelloh! Village Domaine du Colombier 👥

✆ 04 94 51 56 01. www.domaine-du-colombier.com – limited spaces for one-night stay

Address : 1052 rue des Combattants en Afrique du Nord (situated 2km north along the D 4; follow the signs for Bagnols-en-Forêt)

Opening times : from beginning April to mid Oct.

10 ha (400 pitches) very uneven, terraced, undulating, flat, grassy

Tariff : 64€ ★★ ⬅ 🅴 (16A) – Extra per person 9€

Rental rates : (from beginning April to mid Oct.) – 344 🚐 – 39 🏠. Per night from 39 to 160€ – Per week from 273 to 1,120€
🚐 borne
A themed mobile home village, some of which are high quality, with a partially covered spa area. Choose the pitches furthest from the road.

Surroundings : 🐟 ⬅ ⌂		
Leisure activities : 🍴 ✗ 🏠 ⑤🌳🌳 🏊 hammam, jacuzzi ⚓🚲⚓🔲disco, spa centre, entertainment room	**G**	Longitude : 6.72688
Facilities : ⛫ ⚲ 🚻♟⚓🚿🍴 launderette ⚓⚓	**P**	Latitude : 43.44588
	S	

🏔🏔🏔 Sunêlia Holiday Green

✆ 04 94 19 88 30. www.holidaygreen.com – limited spaces for one-night stay

Address : rue des Anciens Combattants d'Afrique du Nord (towards Bagnols-en-Forêt)

Opening times : from beginning April to end Sept.

15 ha (640 pitches) very uneven, terraced, flat, grassy, stony

Tariff : 62€ ★★ ⬅ 🅴 (16A) – Extra per person 10€ – Reservation fee 40€

Rental rates : (from beginning April to end Sept.) ⛫ (1 mobile home) 🐟 – 300 🚐. Per night from 57 to 368€ – Per week from 399 to 2,576€ – Reservation fee 40€
There's an attractive, partially-covered swimming area. Choose the pitches furthest from the road.

Surroundings : 🐟 ⌂ 🌳🌳		
Leisure activities : 🍴 ✗ 🏠 ⑤🌳🌳 hammam, jacuzzi 🚲🔲⚓disco, multi-sports ground, spa centre	**G**	Longitude : 6.71683
Facilities : ⛫ ⚲ ♟🍴 launderette ⚓⚓	**P**	Latitude : 43.48481
	S	

This guide is not intended as a list of all the camping sites in France; its aim is to provide a selection of the best sites in each category.

⚲ La Pierre Verte ⚲⚲

✆ 04 94 40 88 30. www.campinglapierreverte.com

Address : rue des Anciens Combattants d'Afrique du Nord (6.5km north, follow the signes for Bagnols-en-Forêt and take a right turn)

Opening times : from beginning April to end Sept.

28 ha/15 for camping (450 pitches) very uneven, terraced, flat, grassy, stony, rocks

Tariff : 42 € ♦♦ ⇔ 回 ⑭ (10A) – Extra per person 10 € – Reservation fee 25 €

Rental rates : (from beginning April to end Sept.) – 150 ⟨⟩. Per night from 50 to 100 € – Per week from 280 to 1,295 € – Reservation fee 25 €

Situated in a wooded environment, with plenty of space and quiet, peaceful pitches.

Surroundings : ⚲ ⟨⟩ 🌿🌿
Leisure activities : ⛴ ✕ 🏠 ⚐ ⚶⚶ ⚶ ✂ 🛷 multi-sports ground
Facilities : ⚹ ⚞ ⚲ ⚲ ⚲ ⚲ launderette ⚲ ⚲

Longitude : 6.72054
Latitude : 43.48382

⚲ La Plage d'Argens

✆ 04 94 51 14 97. www.laplagedargens.fr

Address : 541 road RD 559 (3km south along the N 98, direct access to the beach)

Opening times : from beginning April to end Oct.

7 ha (436 pitches) flat, grassy, sandy

Rental rates : (2014 Price) (from beginning April to mid Oct.) – 91 ⟨⟩ – 8 tent lodges. Per night from 41 to 180 € – Per week from 287 to 1,260 € – Reservation fee 30 €

⟨⟩ borne

Situated beside the Argens river, with direct access to the beach. Choose the pitches away from the road.

Surroundings : 🌿🌿
Leisure activities : ⛴ ✕ 🏠 ⚶⚶ 🚲 🛷 scuba diving, multi-sports ground
Facilities : ⚹ ⚞ ⚲ ⚲ launderette ⚲ ⚲ refrigerators

Longitude : 6.72489
Latitude : 43.4087

⚲ Les Pins Parasols

✆ 04 94 40 88 43. www.lespinsparasols.com

Address : 3360 rue des Combattants d'Afrique du Nord (4km north along the D 4, follow the signs for Bagnols-en-Forêt)

Opening times : from beginning April to end Sept.

4.5 ha (200 pitches) terraced, undulating, flat, grassy, stony

Tariff : 31.10 € ♦♦ ⇔ 回 ⑭ (6A) – Extra per person 6.80 €

Rental rates : (from beginning April to end Sept.) ✄ – 13 ⟨⟩. Per week from 199 to 769 €

Some pitches have private sanitary facilities; a spacious site among shady pine trees.

Surroundings : ⟨⟩ 🌿🌿
Leisure activities : ✕ 🏠 ⚶⚶ 🛷 ⛷
Facilities : ⚹ ⚞ ⚲ ⚲ – 48 individual sanitary facilities (⚲ ⚲ ⚲ wc) ⚲ ⚲ ⚲ ⚲

Longitude : 6.7253
Latitude : 43.464

Do not confuse:
⚲ to ⚲⚲⚲ : MICHELIN classification with
★ to ★★★★★ : official classification

GAP

05000 – Michelin map **334** E5 – pop. 39 243 – alt. 735
▶ Paris 665 – Avignon 209 – Grenoble 103 – Sisteron 52

⚲ Alpes-Dauphiné

✆ 04 92 51 29 95. www.alpesdauphine.com – alt. 850

Address : route Napoléon (3km north along the N 85, follow the signs for Grenoble)

Opening times : from mid April to mid Oct.

10 ha/6 for camping (185 pitches)

Tariff : 26.20 € ♦♦ ⇔ 回 ⑭ (6A) – Extra per person 7 € – Reservation fee 20 €

Rental rates : (from mid April to mid Oct.) – 47 ⟨⟩ – 14 🏠 – 3 gîtes. Per night from 55 to 80 € – Per week from 310 to 730 € Reservation fee 20 €

⟨⟩ borne

Surroundings : 🌿🌿
Leisure activities : ⛴ ✕ 🏠 jacuzzi ⚶⚶ 🛷
Facilities : ⚹ ⚞ ⚲ ⚲ ⚲ ⚲ launderette ⚲

Longitude : 6.08255
Latitude : 44.58022

GIENS

83400 – Michelin map **340** L7
▶ Paris 869 – Marseille 93 – Toulon 29 – La Seyne-sur-Mer 37

⚲ La Presqu'île de Giens ⚲⚲

✆ 04 94 58 22 86. www.vacances-giens.com

Address : 153 route de la Madrague

Opening times : from end March to beginning Oct.

7 ha (427 pitches) very uneven, terraced, flat, grassy, stony

Tariff : (2014 Price) 35.62 € ♦♦ ⇔ 回 ⑭ (16A) – Extra per person 9.22 € –

Rental rates : (2014 Price) (from end March to beginning Oct.) – 80 ⟨⟩ – 30 🏠. Per night from 52 to 174 € – Per week from 217 to 1,218 € – Reservation fee 18 €

⟨⟩ borne

Numerous small terraces and good-quality sanitary facilities.

Surroundings : ⟨⟩ 🌿🌿
Leisure activities : ⛴ ✕ 🏠 ⚐ daytime ⚶⚶ ⚶⚶
Facilities : ⚞ ⚲ ⚲ ⚲ ⚲ launderette ⚲ ⚲

Longitude : 6.14332
Latitude : 43.04084

⚲ La Tour Fondue

✆ 04 94 58 22 86. www.vacances-giens.com – ⚲

Address : avenue des Arbanais

Opening times : from end March to beginning Nov.

2 ha (146 pitches) terraced, relatively flat, flat, grassy

Tariff : (2014 Price) 32.84 € ♦♦ ⇔ 回 ⑭ (16A) – Extra per person 8.82 €

Rental rates : (2014 Price) (from end March to beginning Nov.) – 21 ⟨⟩. Per night from 75 to 11 7 € – Per week from 371 to 819 € Reservation fee 18 €

⟨⟩ borne

Situated at the southern end of the Giens Peninsula, opposite the Île de Porquerolles.

Surroundings : ⚲ ⟨⟩ 🌿🌿 ⚲
Leisure activities : ⛴ ✕
Facilities : ⚞ ⚲ ⚲ launderette ⚲ ⚲
Nearby : scuba diving

Longitude : 6.15569
Latitude : 43.02971

⚠ Olbia

📞 0494582286. www.camping-olbia.com

Address : near La Madrague harbour

Opening times : from mid April to beginning Oct.

1.5 ha (100 pitches) terraced, relatively flat, flat, stony, fine gravel

Tariff : (2014 Price) 32€ ✚✚ 🚐 📧 💧 (6A) – Extra per person 6.90€

Pitches beneath the shade of eucalyptus, maritime pines and palm trees.

Surroundings : 🏖 🗟 ♨♨
Leisure activities : ♈ ✕ ⚓
Facilities : ♿ ⊶ 🚿 ♊ 🍴 🖼 ♨ 🛒

G P S Longitude : 6.10325
Latitude : 43.03966

LA GRAVE

05320 – Michelin map **334** F2 – pop. 493 – alt. 1 526 – Winter sports : 1 450/3 250 m
▶ Paris 642 – Briançon 38 – Gap 126 – Grenoble 80

⚠ La Meije

© B.Boone

📞 0608543084. www.camping-delameije.com

Address : head east towards Briançon along the D 1091; beside the Romanche river

Opening times : from mid May to mid Sept.

2.5 ha (50 pitches) terrace, flat and relatively flat, grassy

Tariff : 19.60€ ✚✚ 🚐 📧 💧 (6A) – Extra per person 3€

The site has a magnificent view of the La Grave glacier

Surroundings : 🏖 ≤ ♨♨
Leisure activities : ✂ 🎿 🎣 ⟋
Facilities : ♿ ⊶ 🚿 ♊ 🍴 🖼
Nearby : ⚓ rafting and canyoning

G P S Longitude : 6.30911
Latitude : 45.04526

⚠ Le Gravelotte

📞 0476799314. www.camping-le-gravelotte.com

Address : 1.2km west along the D 1091, follow the signs for Grenoble and take road to the left; beside the Meije river

Opening times : from mid June to end Sept.

4 ha (75 pitches) flat, grassy

Tariff : 14.50€ ✚✚ 🚐 📧 💧 (10A) – Extra per person 3.70€

In an attractive location at the foot of the mountains and beside the Romanche river.

Surroundings : ≤ ♨
Leisure activities : ♈ 🎣 ⟋
Facilities : ♿ ⊶ 🍴 🖼

G P S Longitude : 6.29697
Latitude : 45.04328

Key to rentals symbols:

12 🚐	*Number of mobile homes*	
20 🏠	*Number of chalets*	
6 🛏	*Number of rooms to rent*	
Per night 30–50€	*Minimum/maximum rate per night*	
Per week 300–1,000€	*Minimum/maximum rate per week*	

GRAVESON

13690 – Michelin map **340** D2 – pop. 3 875 – alt. 14
▶ Paris 696 – Arles 25 – Avignon 14 – Cavaillon 30

⚠ Les Micocouliers

📞 0490958149. www.lesmicocouliers.fr

Address : 445 route de Cassoulen (1.2km southeast along the D 28, follow the signs for Châteaurenard and turn right onto D 5, follow the signs for Maillane)

Opening times : from mid March to mid Oct.

3.5 ha (118 pitches) flat, grassy

Tariff : (2014 Price) 30€ ✚✚ 🚐 📧 💧 (6A) – Extra per person 8€ – Reservation fee 10€

Rental rates : (2014 Price) (from mid March to mid Oct.) – 6 🚐. Per night from 60 to 105€ – Per week from 410 to 730€ – Reservation fee 20€

🚉 borne 6€

Surroundings : 🗟 ♨
Leisure activities : ⚓ 🎿
Facilities : ♿ ⊶ ♊ 🖼

G P S Longitude : 4.78111
Latitude : 43.84389

The prices listed were supplied by the campsite owners in 2014 (if prices were not available, those from the previous year are given). The fees should be regarded as basic charges and may fluctuate with inflation.

GRÉOUX-LES-BAINS

04800 – Michelin map **334** D10 – pop. 2 510 – alt. 386 – ⚕
▶ Paris 783 – Aix-en-Provence 55 – Brignoles 52 – Digne-les-Bains 69

⛰ Yelloh! Village le Verdon Parc ♣

📞 0492780808. www.campingverdonparc.fr

Address : Domaine de la Paludette (600m south along the D 8, follow the signs for St-Pierre and take the turning to the left after the bridge; beside the Verdon river)

Opening times : from beginning April to end Oct.

8 ha (324 pitches) terraced, flat, grassy, stony, gravelled

Tariff : 41€ ✚✚ 🚐 📧 💧 (16A) – Extra per person 7€

Rental rates : (from beginning April to end Oct.) ♿ (2 mobile homes) 🚐 – 180 🚐 – 8 🏠 – 8 tent lodges. Per night from 29 to 186€ – Per week from 203 to 1,302€

🚉 borne

The site is set beside the Verdon river and a small beach with activities.

Surroundings : 🏖 🗟 ♨♨
Leisure activities : ♈ ✕ 🎱 🎰 ⚓ 🚴 ✂ 🎿 🎣 multi-sports ground
Facilities : ♿ ⊶ 🏛 🚿 🍴 launderette 🖼 🛒 refrigerators

G P S Longitude : 5.89407
Latitude : 43.75188

⛰ La Pinède

📞 0492780547. www.camping-lapinede-04.com

Address : route de Saint-Pierre (located 1.5km south along the D 8, 200m from the Verdon river)

Opening times : from beginning March to end Nov.

3 ha (166 pitches) terraced, flat and relatively flat, stony, fine gravel

Tariff : 25.70€ ✚✚ 🚐 📧 💧 (10A) – Extra per person 5.40€

Rental rates : (from beginning March to end Nov.) – 56 🚐. Per night from 34 to 107€ – Per week from 242 to 750€

🚉 borne 4€

Attractive, shaded terraces and good sanitary facilities.

Surroundings : 🦢 ≤ 🏠 ♀♀
Leisure activities : 🍴 ✕ 🏠 ⚡ 🏊 multi-sports ground
Facilities : 👤 ⛬ cc ▥ 🍴 launderette
Nearby : 🦢

GPS Longitude : 5.88294 / Latitude : 43.74848

🏔 Verseau

📞 04 92 77 67 10. www.camping-le-verseau.com

Address : 113 chemin Gaspard de Besse (1.2km south along the D 8, follow the signs for St-Pierre and take the road to the right, near the Verdon river)

2.5 ha (120 pitches) flat and relatively flat, grassy, stony
Rentals : 👤 (1 chalet) – 47 🚐 – 13 🏠.

Situated close to the Verdon river and one of the river's five dams.

Surroundings : 🦢 ≤ 🏠 ♀♀
Leisure activities : 🍴 🏠 ⚡ 🏊 entertainment room
Facilities : 👤 ⛬ ▥ ♨ 🚿 🍴 ▦ refrigerators
Nearby : 🏊 🦢

GPS Longitude : 5.88199 / Latitude : 43.75152

The information in the guide may have changed since going to press.

GRIMAUD

83310 – Michelin map **340** O6 – pop. 4 309 – alt. 105
▶ Paris 861 – Brignoles 58 – Fréjus 32 – Le Lavandou 32

🏔 Les Prairies de la Mer 👥

📞 04 94 79 09 09. www.riviera-villages.com

Address : at Saint-Pons-les-Mûres (RN 98)

Opening times : beginning April to mid Oct.

30 ha (1400 pitches) open site
Rentals : 🅿 – 150 🚐 – 150 🏠.
🚐 borne

A vast complex divided into several villages: tents and caravanes, owner-occupiers, classic mobile homes, luxury rental options (some opposite the beach).

Surroundings : 🦢 ≤ St Tropez and the gulf 🏠 ♀♀ ⛰
Leisure activities : 🍴 ✕ 🏠 ☺ 🧑 🎣 ⚓ hammam, jacuzzi ⚡ 🦢 🏊 💿 disco, concierge services, scuba diving, multi-sports ground, spa centre
Facilities : 👤 ⛬ ▥ ♨ 🚿 🍴 launderette 🐕 🚿

GPS Longitude : 6.58241 / Latitude : 43.28086

🏔 Domaine des Naïades 👥

📞 04 94 55 67 80. www.lesnaiades.com – limited spaces for one-night stay

Address : at Saint-Pons-les-Mûres (RN 98 and take a left turn)

Opening times : from mid April to beginning Oct.

27 ha/14 for camping (470 pitches) very uneven, terraced, flat, grassy, sandy

Tariff : (2014 Price) 60€ 🧍🧍 🚗 🔲 🔌 (10A) – Extra per person 8.50€
Rental rates : (2014 Price) (from mid April to beginning Oct.) – 225 🚐. Per night from 49 to 259€ – Per week from 343 to 1,813€
🚐 borne 2.50€

A long site, part of which is very quiet and peaceful and with luxury rentals.

Surroundings : 🦢 ≤ 🏠 ♀♀
Leisure activities : 🍴 ✕ ☺ 🧑 ⚡ 🚲 🏊 🦢
Facilities : 👤 ⛬ ▥ ♨ 🍴 launderette 🐕 🚿

GPS Longitude : 6.57937 / Latitude : 43.28517

GUILLESTRE

05600 – Michelin map **334** H5 – pop. 2 308 – alt. 1 000
▶ Paris 715 – Barcelonnette 51 – Briançon 36 – Digne-les-Bains 114

🏔 Parc Le Villard

📞 04 92 45 06 54. www.camping-levillard.com

Address : route des campings, Le Villard (situated 2km west along the D 902a, follow the signs for Gap; beside the Chagne river)

Opening times : from beginning Jan. to mid Nov.

3.2 ha (120 pitches) flat and relatively flat, grassy, stony

Tariff : (2014 Price) 🧍 6€ 🚗 2€ 🔲 22€ – 🔌 (10A) 4.50€ – Reservation fee 8€

Rental rates : Permanent – 17 🚐 – 6 🏠 – 4 canvas bungalows. Per night from 50 to 60€ – Per week from 300 to 800€ – Reservation fee 8€

The site occupies both sides of a small road.

Surroundings : ≤ ♀
Leisure activities : ✕ 🏠 ⚡ 🦢 🧗 🏊 🦢
Facilities : 👤 ⛬ 🚿 🍴 launderette 🐕 refrigerators

GPS Longitude : 6.62687 / Latitude : 44.65895

🏔 St-James-les-Pins

📞 04 92 45 08 24. www.lesaintjames.com

Address : route des Campings (head 1.5km west following signs for Risoul and take turning to the right)

Opening times : from beginning Jan. to end Oct.

2.5 ha (100 pitches)

Tariff : 19.70€ 🧍🧍 🚗 🔲 🔌 (10A) – Extra per person 3.60€
Rental rates : Permanent – 10 🚐 – 13 🏠. Per night from 54 to 80€ – Per week from 320 to 660€
🚐 borne 4.60€ – 5 🔲 15€

The Chagne river runs beside and through part of the campsite.

Surroundings : ❄ ♀♀
Leisure activities : 🏠 ⚡ 🦢 multi-sports ground
Facilities : 👤 ⛬ ▥ 🚿 🍴 launderette
Nearby : 🏊 🏊

GPS Longitude : 6.63293 / Latitude : 44.65685

🏔 La Rochette

📞 04 92 45 02 15. www.campingguillestre.com

Address : route des Campings (head 1km west following signs for Risoul and take turning to the right)

Opening times : from mid May to end Sept.

4 ha (190 pitches) flat and relatively flat, stony, grassy

Tariff : (2014 Price) 15.60€ 🧍🧍 🚗 🔲 🔌 (10A) – Extra per person 4€
Reservation fee 9€
🚐 borne

Surroundings : ≤ ♀♀
Leisure activities : 🏠 ⚡ 🦢
Facilities : 👤 ⛬ cc 🚿 🍴 launderette 🏊
Nearby : ✕ 🚿 🦢 🏊

GPS Longitude : 6.63845 / Latitude : 44.65895

HYÈRES

83400 – Michelin map **340** L7 – pop. 54 686 – alt. 40
▶ Paris 851 – Aix-en-Provence 102 – Cannes 123 – Draguignan 78

Les Palmiers (rental of mobile homes only)

04 94 66 39 66. www.camping-les-palmiers.fr

Address : rue du Ceinturon, L'Ayguade

Opening times : from mid March to mid Oct.

5.5 ha

Rental rates : 348. Per night from 48 to 117€ – Per week from 665 to 1,610€ – Reservation fee 20€

Numerous mobile homes are positioned around a water park.

Surroundings :
Leisure activities : nighttime hammam
Facilities : launderette

G P S Longitude : 6.16725
Latitude : 43.10344

Le Ceinturon 3

04 94 66 32 65. www.ceinturon3.fr

Address : 2 rue des Saraniers (5km southeast, 100m from the sea)

2.5 ha (200 pitches)

Rentals : (1 mobile home) – 1 – 40.

There are pitches in the shade and good-quality sanitary facilities.

Surroundings :
Leisure activities : multi-sports ground
Facilities : launderette
Nearby :

G P S Longitude : 6.16962
Latitude : 43.10109

L'ISLE-SUR-LA-SORGUE

84800 – Michelin map **332** D10 – pop. 18 936 – alt. 57
▶ Paris 693 – Apt 34 – Avignon 23 – Carpentras 18

Club Airotel La Sorguette

04 90 38 05 71. www.camping-sorguette.com

Address : 871 route d'Apt (located 1.5km southeast along the N 100; near the Sorgue)

Opening times : from mid March to mid Oct.

2.5 ha (164 pitches)

Tariff : 28.60€ (10A) – Extra per person 8.20€ – Reservation fee 20€

Rental rates : (from mid March to mid Oct.) (1 mobile home) – 30 – 3 yurts – 1 tipi – 1 canvas bungalow – 3 tent lodges. Per night from 46 to 94€ – Per week from 287 to 658€ – Reservation fee 20€

borne 7€ – 3 16.40€ – 11€

Surroundings :
Leisure activities :
Facilities : launderette refrigerated food storage facilities

G P S Longitude : 5.07192
Latitude : 43.9146

*The classification (1 to 5 tents, **black** or red) that we award to selected sites in this guide is our own system. It should not be confused with the classification (1 to 5 stars) of official organisations.*

ISOLA

06420 – Michelin map **341** D2 – pop. 748 – alt. 873
▶ Paris 897 – Marseille 246 – Nice 76 – Cuneo 79

Le Lac des Neiges

04 93 02 18 16. www.princiland.fr – alt. 875

Address : route de St-Etienne-de-Tinée (located 1km north of the village along the D 2205)

Opening times : Permanent

3 ha (98 pitches)

Tariff : (2014 Price) 23€ (6A) – Extra per person 5€

Rental rates : (2014 Price) Permanent – 13 – 5 – 2 gîtes. Per night from 60 to 120€ – Per week from 400 to 500€

In two sections, situated a little apart from one another.

Surroundings :
Leisure activities :
Facilities :
Nearby :

G P S Longitude : 7.03912
Latitude : 44.18898

This guide is updated regularly, so buy your new copy every year!

LARCHE

04530 – Michelin map **334** J6 – pop. 74 – alt. 1 691
▶ Paris 760 – Barcelonnette 28 – Briançon 81 – Cuneo 70

Domaine des Marmottes

04 92 84 33 64. www.camping-marmottes.fr

Address : Malboisset (800m southeast down a turning to the right; beside the Ubayette river)

Opening times : from beginning June to end Sept.

2 ha (52 pitches)

Tariff : 8€ – (10A) 3.50€

Rental rates : (from beginning June to end Sept.) – 2. Per night from 60 to 80€ – Per week from 300 to 400€

borne 3€

Near a pretty waterfall; the site is well equipped for walkers.

Surroundings :
Leisure activities :
Facilities : launderette
Nearby :

G P S Longitude : 6.85257
Latitude : 44.44615

LE LAVANDOU

83980 – Michelin map **340** N7 – pop. 5 747 – alt. 1
▶ Paris 873 – Cannes 102 – Draguignan 75 – Fréjus 61

Beau Séjour

04 94 71 25 30. www.campingbeausejourvar.com

Address : la Grande Bastide (located 1.5km to the southwest)

1.5 ha (135 pitches)

Attractive and shaded marked-out pitches. Choose those furthest from the road.

Surroundings :
Leisure activities :
Facilities :
Nearby :

G P S Longitude : 6.35165
Latitude : 43.13497

LA LONDE-LES-MAURES

83250 – Michelin map **340** M7 – pop. 9 910 – alt. 24
▶ Paris 861 – Bormes-les-Mimosas 11 – Cuers 31 – Hyères 10

⚠ Les Moulières

✆ 04 94 01 53 21. www.campinglesmoulieres.com

Address : 15 chemin de la Garenne, Le Puits de Magne (situated 2.5km southeast; follow the signs for Port-de-Miramar and take turning to the right)

Opening times : from beginning May to mid Sept.

3 ha (250 pitches) flat, grassy

Tariff : (2014 Price) 37.60€ ✫✫ ⇌ 🅴 (½) (6A) – Extra per person 8.30€ Reservation fee 10€

🚐 borne 3.50€

Surroundings : ⚲ ⚲
Leisure activities : 🍴 ✗ 🛶 ⚙
Facilities : ᪣ ⚬⊐ 🌡 🍴 🖭 ⚗

Longitude : 6.23526
Latitude : 43.12236

LOURMARIN

84160 – Michelin map **332** F11 – pop. 1 000 – alt. 224
▶ Paris 732 – Aix-en-Provence 37 – Apt 19 – Cavaillon 73

⚠ Les Hautes Prairies

✆ 04 90 68 02 89. www.campinghautesprairies.com

Address : route de Vaugines (700m east along the D 56)

Opening times : from mid April to end Sept.

3.6 ha (158 pitches) flat and relatively flat, grassy, stony

Tariff : 30€ ✫✫ ⇌ 🅴 (½) (10A) – Extra per person 6€ – Reservation fee 20€

Rental rates : (from mid April to end Sept.) – 20 🚐 – 16 🏠 – 6 🛏. Per night from 50 to 165€ – Per week from 195 to 950€ Reservation fee 20€

🚐 borne 4€

Surroundings : ⊐ ⚲
Leisure activities : 🍴 ✗ 🛶 ⚙
Facilities : ᪣ ⚬⊐ ⚗ ⚗ 🍴 🖭 ⚗

Longitude : 5.37291
Latitude : 43.76784

MALEMORT-DU-COMTAT

84570 – Michelin map **332** D9 – pop. 1 461 – alt. 208
▶ Paris 688 – Avignon 33 – Carpentras 11 – Malaucène 22

⚠ Font Neuve

✆ 04 90 69 90 00. www.campingfontneuve.com

Address : Font-Neuve district (1.6km southeast along the D 5, follow the signs for Méthanis and take road to the left)

Opening times : from beginning April to end Sept.

1.5 ha (54 pitches) terraced, relatively flat, flat, grassy, stony

Tariff : (2014 Price) 22.80€ ✫✫ ⇌ 🅴 (½) (6A) – Extra per person 5€ Reservation fee 10€

Rental rates : (2014 Price) (from beginning April to end Sept.) – 5 🏠. Per night from 75€ – Per week from 300 to 480€ – Reservation fee 10€

Surroundings : ⚲ ⋖ ⊐ ⚲
Leisure activities : ✗ 🛶 ⚙ ⚙
Facilities : ᪣ ⚬⊐ ⚗ ⚗ ⚗ 🍴 🖭 ⚗

Longitude : 5.17098
Latitude : 44.0142

To visit a town or region, use the MICHELIN Green Guides.

MALLEMORT

13370 – Michelin map **340** G3 – pop. 5 925 – alt. 120
▶ Paris 716 – Aix-en-Provence 34 – Apt 38 – Cavaillon 20

🏔 Durance Luberon

✆ 04 90 59 13 36. www.campingduranceluberon.com – for caravans, access via town centre not advised, acces via N 7 and D 561, follow signs for Charleval

Address : at the Domaine du Vergon (2.8km southeast along the D 23, 200m from the canal, towards the power station – from the A 7 take exits 26 and 7)

Opening times : from beginning April to end Sept.

4 ha (110 pitches) flat, grassy

Tariff : (2014 Price) 28.80€ ✫✫ ⇌ 🅴 (½) (10A) – Extra per person 6.30€ – Reservation fee 15€

Rental rates : (2014 Price) (from beginning April to end Sept.) – 8 🚐. Per night from 56 to 74€ – Per week from 390 to 720€ Reservation fee 15€

🚐 borne 5€

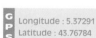

Surroundings : ⚲ ⊐ ⚲⚲
Leisure activities : ✗ 🛶 ⚙
Facilities : ᪣ ⚬⊐ 🌡 ⚗ ⚗ ⚗ 🍴 🖭 ⚗
Nearby : 🐎

Longitude : 5.20492
Latitude : 43.72091

MANDELIEU-LA-NAPOULE

06210 – Michelin map **341** C6 – pop. 21 764 – alt. 4
▶ Paris 890 – Brignoles 86 – Cannes 9 – Draguignan 53

⚠ Les Pruniers - Les Bungalows du Golfe

✆ 04 93 49 99 23. www.bungalow-camping.com

Address : 118 rue de la Pinéa (via the av. de la Mer)

Opening times : from beginning March to end Nov.

0.8 ha (64 pitches)

Tariff : (2014 Price) ✫ 5.20€ ⇌ 4€ 🅴 18€ – (½) (10A) 4€

Rental rates : (2014 Price) (from beginning March to end Nov.) – 36 🏠. Per night from 40 to 98€ – Per week from 285 to 685€
The site has a swimming pool beside the Siagne river.

Surroundings : ⚲ ⚲⚲
Leisure activities : 🚣 🛶 ⚙
Facilities : ⚬⊐ 🍴 🖭 ⚗
Nearby : 🍴 ✗ 🎣 ⚓

Longitude : 6.94349
Latitude : 43.53503

⚠ Les Cigales

✆ 04 93 49 23 53. www.lescigales.com

Address : 505 avenue de la Mer (at Mandelieu)

Opening times : Permanent

1 ha (62 pitches)

Tariff : (2014 Price) 58.20€ ✫✫ ⇌ 🅴 (½) (6A) – Extra per person 8.60€ Reservation fee 25€

Rental rates : (2014 Price) (from beginning March to beginning Nov.) – 29 🚐 – 8 studios. Per night from 67 to 175€ – Per week from 405 to 1,050€ – Reservation fee 25€

🚐 borne

A green 'oasis' in the town; beside the Siagne river, equipped with a small decking area.

Surroundings : ⚲ ⊐ ⚲⚲
Leisure activities : 🛶 ⚙
Facilities : ᪣ ⚬⊐ ⚗ ⚗ 🍴 launderette
Nearby : 🍴 ✗ 🚲 🚴 ⚓

Longitude : 6.9424
Latitude : 43.53883

MAUBEC

84660 – Michelin map **332** D10 – pop. 1 877 – alt. 120
▶ Paris 706 – Aix-en-Provence 68 – Apt 25 – Avignon 32

⚠ Municipal Les Royères du Prieuré

☏ 04 90 76 50 34. www.campingmaubec-luberon.com

Address : 52 chemin de la Combe St-Pierre (south of the town)

Opening times : from beginning April to mid Oct.

1 ha (93 pitches) terraced, flat, grassy, stony

Tariff : (2014 Price) ♛ 3.50€ ⇔ 2.30€ 🔲 2.30€ – 🔌 (10A) 4€ –
Reservation fee 10€
Rental rates : (2014 Price) (from beginning April to mid Oct.) ⌘ –
3 🛖 – 1 gîte. Per week from 375 to 520€ – Reservation fee 10€
Lovely terraces with plenty of shade.

Surroundings : ⌂ ≤ 𝟿𝟿
Facilities : ⊶ 🔧 📺

Longitude : 5.1326
Latitude : 43.84032

MAUSSANE-LES-ALPILLES

13520 – Michelin map **340** D3 – pop. 2 076 – alt. 32
▶ Paris 712 – Arles 20 – Avignon 30 – Marseille 81

⚠ Municipal les Romarins

☏ 04 90 54 33 60. www.maussane.com

Address : avenue des Alpilles (take the northern exit along the D 5,
follow the signs for St-Rémy)

3 ha (145 pitches)

*Note that the reception is at the tourist office (Maison du Tou-
risme).*

Surroundings : ⌒ 𝟿𝟿
Leisure activities : 🎮 🚣 ✂
Facilities : ♿ ⊶ 🚿 🔥 ☔ 🍴 launderette
Nearby : 🏊

Longitude : 4.8093
Latitude : 43.72104

MAZAN

84380 – Michelin map **332** D9 – pop. 5 641 – alt. 100
▶ Paris 684 – Avignon 35 – Carpentras 9 – Cavaillon 30

🏔 Le Ventoux

☏ 04 90 69 70 94. www.camping-le-ventoux.com

Address : 1348 chemin de la Combe (3km north along the D 70,
follow the signs for Caromb then take the road to the left, follow the
signs for Carpentras, recommended route via D 974)

0.7 ha (49 pitches)
Rentals : 16 🛖.

Surroundings : ⌂ ≤ Mont Ventoux 𝟿𝟿
Leisure activities : 🍴 ✗ 🚣 🏊
Facilities : ♿ ⊶ 🚿 🔥 🍴 launderette �

Longitude : 5.11378
Latitude : 44.0805

*For more information on visiting particular towns or
regions, consult the relevant regional MICHELIN Green
Guide. We also recommend you use the appropriate
Michelin regional map to locate your selected campsite,
to calculate distances and to work out the best route.*

MÉOLANS-REVEL

04340 – Michelin map **334** H6 – pop. 333 – alt. 1 080
▶ Paris 787 – Marseille 216 – Digne-les-Bains 74 – Gap 64

🏔 Le Rioclar ♁

☏ 04 92 81 10 32. www.rioclar.com – alt. 1 073

Address : D 900 (located 1.5km east, follow the signs for
Barcelonnette, near the Ubaye et a small lake)

Opening times : from mid May to mid Sept.

8 ha (200 pitches) terraced, flat, grassy, stony

Tariff : 28.50€ ♛♛ ⇔ 🔲 🔌 (10A) – Extra per person 6€ – Reservation
fee 18€
Rental rates : (from mid May to mid Sept.) – 26 🛖 – 3 🏠.
Per night from 60 to 98€ – Per week from 420 to 690 € –
Reservation fee 18€
*The owners go to great lengths to ensure the setting remains
'natural'; mobile homes with large verandah/patio areas.*

Surroundings : ⌂ ⌒ 𝟿𝟿
Leisure activities : 🍴 ✗ 🚣 🎣 ⛩ 🚣 🚴
🧗 🏊 rafting and canyoning 🌿 multi-sports
ground
Facilities : ♿ ⊶ 🔥 🍴 launderette 🚿 �
Nearby : 🛶 (lake)

Longitude : 6.53172
Latitude : 44.39928

🏔 Domaine Loisirs de l'Ubaye

☏ 04 92 81 01 96. www.loisirsubaye.com – alt. 1 073

Address : D 900 (3km east, follow the signs for Barcelonnette, beside
the Ubaye river)

Opening times : from mid May to mid Oct.

9.5 ha (267 pitches)

Tariff : 28.50€ ♛♛ ⇔ 🔲 🔌 (6A) – Extra per person 6.50€ –
Reservation fee 15€
Rental rates : (from mid Jan. to mid Oct.) – 17 🛖 – 19 🏠 –
5 🛏. Per week from 310 to 810€ – Reservation fee 15€
🚐 borne
*Choose those pitches that look out over the river, or are near
it, in preference.*

Surroundings : ⌂ ⌒ 𝟿𝟿
Leisure activities : ✗ 🚣 ⛩ daytime 🚣
🎣 ✂ 🏊
Facilities : ♿ ⊶ 🚿 🔥 ☔ 🍴 launderette
🚿 �
Nearby : rafting and canyoning

Longitude : 6.54638
Latitude : 44.39645

*A chambre d'hôte is a guesthouse or B & B-style
accommodation.*

MONTPEZAT

04500 – Michelin map **334** E10
▶ Paris 806 – Digne-les-Bains 54 – Gréoux-les-Bains 23
Manosque 37

🏔 Tohapi Côteau de la Marine ♁

☏ 08 25 00 20 30. www.campings.village-center.fr

Address : at Vauvert, route de Baudinard (situated 2km southeast)

Opening times : from mid April to mid Sept.

12 ha (251 pitches) very uneven

Tariff : 42€ ♛♛ ⇔ 🔲 🔌 (6A) – Extra per person 7€ – Reservation
fee 10€

Rental rates : (from mid April to mid Sept.) – 177 – 46 tent lodges. Per night from 45 to 177€ – Per week from 315 to 1,239€ Reservation fee 10€

Some pitches enjoy a view of the Verdon river.

Surroundings : ⌂ ≤ ⊑ ΩΩ
Leisure activities : ▼ ✕ ☺ ⚡ ⚡ ✖ ☷ ⛵ pedalos, electric boats ⚤
Facilities : ♿ ⛟ ⛺ ॥ launderette ⚌ ⚞

GPS Longitude : 6.09818
Latitude : 43.74765

MOUSTIERS-STE-MARIE

04360 – Michelin map **334** F9 – pop. 718 – alt. 631
▶ Paris 783 – Aix-en-Provence 90 – Castellane 45 – Digne-les-Bains 47

⛰ St-Jean

☏ 04 92 74 66 85. www.camping-st-jean.fr

Address : Saint Jean district (located 1km southwest along the D 952, follow the signs for Riez; beside the Maïre river)

Opening times : from beginning April to mid Oct.

1.6 ha (125 pitches)

Tariff : (2014 Price) 22.80€ ✳✳ ⚤ ▣ ⚡ (6A) – Extra per person 6.30€ Reservation fee 10€

Rental rates : (2014 Price) (from beginning April to mid Oct.) – 14 – 2 canvas bungalows. Per night from 40 to 55€ – Per week from 260 to 630€ – Reservation fee 10€

⛽ borne 4€

Situated beside a river and boasting high-quality sanitary facilities.

Surroundings : ⌂ ΩΩ
Leisure activities : ▼ ⚡ ॥
Facilities : ♿ ⛟ ⛺ ⚌ ⚞ ॥ refrigerated food storage facilities

GPS Longitude : 6.21496
Latitude : 43.84366

⛰ Le Vieux Colombier

☏ 04 92 74 61 89. www.lvcm.fr

Address : St Michel district (800m to the south)

Opening times : from mid April to mid Sept.

2.7 ha (70 pitches) very uneven, terraced, relatively flat, grassy, stony

Tariff : (2014 Price) 22.80€ ✳✳ ⚤ ▣ ⚡ (6A) – Extra per person 6€ Reservation fee 9€

Rental rates : (2014 Price) (from mid April to mid Sept.) – 16 . Per night from 44 to 58€ – Per week from 320 to 630€ – Reservation fee 9€

⛽ borne 7€

Situated on quiet, peaceful terraces, with some well marked-out pitches.

Surroundings : ⌂ ≤ ⊑ ΩΩ
Leisure activities : ⟱
Facilities : ♿ ⛟ ॥ launderette ⚞
Nearby : ✕ ⚒

These symbols are used for a campsite that is exceptional in its category:

⛰⛰⛰....⛰ *Particularly pleasant setting, quality and range of services available*

⌂⌂ *Tranquil, isolated site – quiet site, particularly at night*

≤ ≤ *Exceptional view – interesting or panoramic view*

⛺ Manaysse

☏ 04 92 74 66 71. www.camping-manaysse.com

Address : Manaysse district (900m southwest along the D 952, follow the signs for Riez)

Opening times : from beginning April to end Oct.

1.6 ha (97 pitches) terraced, sloping, flat, grassy, gravelled

Tariff : (2014 Price) 15.20€ ✳✳ ⚤ ▣ ⚡ (10A) – Extra per person 3.90€

⛽ borne – 70 ▣ 11.50€

Some pitches overlook the village.

Surroundings : ⌂
Leisure activities : ⟱ ⚘
Facilities : ♿ ⛟ ⚌ ⛺ ॥ ⚞

GPS Longitude : 6.21494
Latitude : 43.84452

MURS

84220 – Michelin map **332** E10 – pop. 428 – alt. 510
▶ Paris 704 – Apt 17 – Avignon 48 – Carpentras 26

⛺ Municipal des Chalottes

☏ 04 90 72 63 08. www.communedemurs-vaucluse.fr

Address : take the southern exit along the D 4, follow the signs for Apt then continue 1.8km to the right, after the VVF holiday village

Opening times : from beginning April to mid Sept.

4 ha (50 pitches) very uneven, relatively flat to hilly, stony

Tariff : 14.94€ ✳✳ ⚤ ▣ ⚡ (6A) – Extra per person 3.50€

A wooded setting in a pleasant location.

Surroundings : ⌂ ≤ ⚘
Leisure activities : ⟱
Facilities : ♿ (July–Aug.) ⚌ ॥

GPS Longitude : 5.22749
Latitude : 43.93864

We have selected the best campsites in France with our usual care, listing those with the best facilities in the most pleasant surroundings.

LE MUY

83490 – Michelin map **340** O5 – pop. 8 983 – alt. 27
▶ Paris 853 – Les Arcs 9 – Draguignan 14 – Fréjus 17

⛰ Les Cigales ⚐

☏ 04 94 45 12 08. www.camping-les-cigales-sud.fr

Address : 4 chemin de Jas de la Paro (3km southwest, access via the junction with the A 8 and take the road to the right before the toll road)

Opening times : from mid March to mid Oct.

22 ha (437 pitches) very uneven, terraced, flat, grassy, stony, rocks

Tariff : 47€ ✳✳ ⚤ ▣ ⚡ (16A) – Extra per person 11.20€ – Reservation fee 20€

Rental rates : (from mid March to mid Oct.) – 224 – 47 ⌂. Per night from 43 to 110€ – Per week from 301 to 1,442€ – Reservation fee 29€

In an undulating setting with pitches in both sun and shade.

Surroundings : ⊑ ΩΩ
Leisure activities : ▼ ✕ ☺ ⚡ jacuzzi ⟱ ⚒ ☷ forest trail, multi-sports ground
Facilities : ♿ ⛟ ⛺ ॥ launderette ⚌ ⚞ refrigerators

GPS Longitude : 6.54355
Latitude : 43.46225

🏕 RCN Le Domaine de la Noguière 👥

📞 0494451378. www.rcn.fr

Address : 1617 route de Fréjus

Opening times : from mid March to end Oct.

11 ha (350 pitches) undulating, flat, stony, grassy

Tariff : 19.50€ ♥♥ ⏚ 🔲 ⚡ (6A) – Extra per person 3.75€ – Reservation fee 19.95€

Rental rates : (from mid March to end Oct.) ⚡ – 35 🚐 – 26 canvas bungalows – 4 tent lodges. Per night from 36 to 190€ – Per week from 252 to 1,330€ – Reservation fee 19.95€

Pitches in both sun and shade, with good-quality rental options and a small lake for relaxing.

Surroundings : ≼ 🖵 ♤♤
Leisure activities : ♚ ✕ 🖵 🖥 🏃 ⚓ ✗ 🛶 🏊 multi-sports ground
Facilities : ♿ ⛺ 🆑 🚮 ⛾ launderette 🔧 🚿
Longitude : 6.59222
Latitude : 43.46828

NANS-LES-PINS

83860 – Michelin map **340** J5 – pop. 4 123 – alt. 380
▶ Paris 794 – Aix-en-Provence 44 – Brignoles 26 – Marseille 42

🏕 Domaine de La Sainte Baume 👥

📞 0494789268. www.saintebaume.com – limited spaces for one-night stay

Address : Delvieux Sud district (900m north along the D 80 and take a right turn, from the A 8: take exit St-Maximin-la-Ste-Baume)

Opening times : from beginning April to end Sept.

8 ha (250 pitches) relatively flat, flat, grassy, stony

Tariff : 39€ ♥♥ ⏚ 🔲 ⚡ (10A) – Extra per person 11€ – Reservation fee 22€

Rental rates : Permanent – 160 🚐. Per night from 39 to 183€ – Per week from 225 to 1,295 € – Reservation fee 22€

🚐 borne

The pitches are well shaded and laid out around a water park.

Surroundings : 🌄 🖵 ♤♤
Leisure activities : ♚ ✕ 🖵 🖥 🏃 jacuzzi 🏊 🚴 🛶 🏊 multi-sports ground, entertainment room
Facilities : ♿ ⛺ 🆑 🚮 ⛾ launderette 🔧 🚿
Nearby : 🐎
Longitude : 5.78808
Latitude : 43.37664

NÉVACHE

05100 – Michelin map **334** H2 – pop. 339 – alt. 1 640 – Winter sports : 1 400/2 000 m
▶ Paris 693 – Bardonècchia 18 – Briançon 21

⛰ Fontcouverte

📞 0492213821. www.camping-fontcouverte-névache-alpes – access difficult for caravans – alt. 1 860 – 🏔

Address : 1 lot. de l'Aiguille Rouge (6.2km northwest along the D 301t, Vallée de la Clarée)

Opening times : from end May to end Sept.

2 ha (100 pitches) terraced, relatively flat, flat, grassy, stony

Tariff : 🚶 2.90€ ⏚ 1.70€ 🔲 3.50€

In a pleasant location at the end of the valley and beside a mountain stream.

Surroundings : 🌄 ≼ 🖵 ♤♤
Leisure activities : 🛶
Facilities : ♿ ⛺ 🚮 🔧
Nearby : ✕
Longitude : 6.69323
Latitude : 45.11898

NIOZELLES

04300 – Michelin map **334** D9 – pop. 237 – alt. 450
▶ Paris 745 – Digne-les-Bains 49 – Forcalquier 7 – Gréoux-les-Bains 33

🏕 Sites et Paysages Moulin de Ventre 👥

📞 0492786331. www.moulin-de-ventre.com

Address : 2.5km east along the N 100, follow the signs for La Brillanne

28 ha/3 for camping (124 pitches) terraced, flat and relatively flat, grassy

Rentals : 12 🚐 – 5 🏠 – 2 apartments – 2 tent lodges.

Situated beside the Lauzon river and a small lake.

Surroundings : 🌄 🖵 ♤♤
Leisure activities : ♚ ✕ 🖵 🖥 daytime (July-Aug.) 🏃 🛶 🏊 pedalos
Facilities : ♿ ⛺ 🏛 🚮 ⛾ launderette 🔧
Longitude : 5.86798
Latitude : 43.9333

ORGON

13660 – Michelin map **340** F3 – pop. 3 055 – alt. 90
▶ Paris 709 – Marseille 72 – Avignon 29 – Nîmes 98

🏕 La Vallée Heureuse

📞 0490441713. www.valleeheureuse.com

Address : Lavau district (situated 2km to the south, follow the signs for Sénas then take left turning along the D 73D)

Opening times : from beginning April to end Oct.

8 ha (80 pitches)

Tariff : (2014 Price) 24€ ♥♥ ⏚ 🔲 ⚡ (16A) – Extra per person 6.50€ Reservation fee 20€

Rental rates : (2014 Price) (from beginning April to end Oct.) – 8 🚐 – 2 gîtes. Per night from 62 to 90€ – Per week from 284 to 810€ – Reservation fee 20€

🚐 borne – 🔋 11€

In a beautiful, natural setting.

Surroundings : 🌄 ≼ 🖵 ♤♤
Leisure activities : 🖵 🛶 🏊
Facilities : ♿ ⛺ 🚮 ⛾ launderette, refrigerated food storage facilities
Nearby : ✕ 🏊 🛶
Longitude : 5.03956
Latitude : 43.7817

This guide is updated regularly, so buy your new copy every year!

ORPIERRE

05700 – Michelin map **334** C7 – pop. 326 – alt. 682
▶ Paris 689 – Château-Arnoux 47 – Digne-les-Bains 72 – Gap 55

🏕 Les Princes d'Orange

📞 0492662253. www.campingorpierre.com

Address : Le Flonsaine (300m south of the town, 150m from the Céans river)

Opening times : from beginning April to end Oct.

20 ha/4 for camping (120 pitches) very uneven, terraced, flat, grassy, stony

Tariff : (2014 Price) 39€ ♥♥ ⏚ 🔲 ⚡ (10A) – Extra per person 10.20€ Reservation fee 10€

Rental rates : (2014 Price) (from beginning April to end Oct.) – 35 ⌷⌷ – 2 tent lodges. Per night from 68 to 116€ – Per week from 336 to 854€ – Reservation fee 12€

borne 4€ – 13.50€

Surroundings : ⩗ ≼ Orpierre and the mountains ♀♀
Leisure activities : ♀ ✗ ▱ ⛴ ⅃ ⚲
Facilities : 👤 ⌐ 🚇 ☒ ▥ launderette
Nearby : ⚘

| | GPS | Longitude : 5.69652 |
| | | Latitude : 44.31077 |

To visit a town or region, use the MICHELIN Green Guides.

PERNES-LES-FONTAINES

84210 – Michelin map **332** D10 – pop. 10 454 – alt. 75
▶ Paris 685 – Apt 43 – Avignon 23 – Carpentras 6

⚠ Municipal de la Coucourelle

✆ 04 90 66 45 55. www.campingfontaines.com

Address : 391 avenue René Char (located 1km east along the D 28, follow the signs for St-Didier, at the sports centre)

1 ha (40 pitches) flat, grassy
In a leafy, green setting with bushes and shrubs.

Surroundings : ⩗ ▱ ♀
Leisure activities : ♒
Facilities : 👤 ⌐ ☒ ▥ 🏢
Nearby : ✗ ⅃

| | GPS | Longitude : 5.0677 |
| | | Latitude : 43.99967 |

PERTUIS

84120 – Michelin map **332** G11 – pop. 18 706 – alt. 246
▶ Paris 747 – Aix-en-Provence 23 – Apt 36 – Avignon 76

⚠⚠ Franceloc Domaine les Pinèdes du Luberon 👥⇆

✆ 04 90 79 10 98. www.campings-franceloc.fr/accueil-camping-les_pinedes_du_luberon

Address : avenue Pierre Augier (situated 2km east along the D 973)

5 ha (220 pitches) terraced, flat, grassy, stony
Rentals : 👤 (1 mobile home) – 141 ⌷⌷ – 6 🏠 – 8 tent lodges.

Surroundings : ▱ ♀♀
Leisure activities : ♀ ✗ ▱ 🎮 🤸 ⛴ ⅃ ♒ 🛶
Facilities : 👤 ⌐ ▥ ☒ ▥ launderette
Nearby : ✗

| | GPS | Longitude : 5.5253 |
| | | Latitude : 43.68979 |

PONT-DU-FOSSÉ

05260 – Michelin map **334** F4 – pop. 980
▶ Paris 673 – Marseille 204 – Gap 24 – Grenoble 102

⚠ Le Diamant

✆ 04 92 55 91 25. www.campingdiamant.com

Address : at Pont du Fossé (800m southwest along the D 944, follow the signs for Gap)

Opening times : from beginning May to end Sept.

4 ha (100 pitches) flat, grassy

Tariff : 23.70€ ✚✚ ⛺ ▤ [⚡] (20A) – Extra per person 4.80€
Rental rates : (from beginning May to end Sept.) – 15 ⌷⌷.
Per night from 60 to 78€ – Per week from 210 to 550€

borne 19.70€ – 10 ▤ 19.70€

Situated beside the Drac river.

Surroundings : ♀♀
Leisure activities : ▱ 🤸 ⅃ 🎣 climbing wall
Facilities : 👤 ⌐ ☒ ▥ 🏢 launderette ⚲

| | GPS | Longitude : 6.2197 |
| | | Latitude : 44.66535 |

LE PONTET

84130 – Michelin map **332** C10 – pop. 16 891 – alt. 40
▶ Paris 688 – Marseille 100 – Avignon 5 – Aix 83

⚠ Le Grand Bois

✆ 04 90 31 37 44. www.campinglegrandbois.webeasysite.fr

Address : 1340 chemin du Grand Bois (3km northeast along the D 62, follow the signs for Vedène and take turning to the left, at a place called La Tapy, from the A 7 take the Avignon-Nord exit)

Opening times : from mid May to mid Sept.

1.5 ha (100 pitches) flat, grassy

Tariff : 25€ ✚✚ ⛺ ▤ [⚡] (5A) – Extra per person 6€
borne 4€
This is a pleasant wooded campsite.

Surroundings : ▱ ♀♀
Leisure activities : ▱ ⅃
Facilities : 👤 ⌐ ☒ ▥ 🏢 ▥

| | GPS | Longitude : 4.8836 |
| | | Latitude : 43.97455 |

We value your opinion and welcome your feedback.
Do email us at campingfrance@tp.michelin.com

PRUNIÈRES

05230 – Michelin map **334** F5 – pop. 287 – alt. 1 018
▶ Paris 681 – Briançon 68 – Gap 23 – Grenoble 119

⚠⚠ Le Roustou

✆ 04 92 50 62 63. www.campingleroustou.com

Address : 4km south along the N 94

Opening times : from mid May to end Sept.

11 ha/6 for camping (180 pitches) terraced, undulating, relatively flat, flat, grassy, fine gravel

Tariff : (2014 Price) ✚ 7.40€ ⛺ ▤ 7.80€ – [⚡] (6A) 4€
Rental rates : (from mid May to end Sept.) – 26 🏠 – 1 gîte. Per night from 52 to 149€ – Per week from 312 to 1,049€ – Reservation fee 12€

Surroundings : ⩗ ≼ ▱ ♀♀ ⛰
Leisure activities : ♀ ✗ ▱ 🤸 ✗ ⅃ ♒
Facilities : 👤 ⌐ ☒ 🏢 ▥ ⚲
Nearby : ⚓

| | GPS | Longitude : 6.34111 |
| | | Latitude : 44.5225 |

Michelin classification:

⚠⚠⚠⚠ *Extremely comfortable, equipped to a very high standard*
⚠⚠⚠ *Very comfortable, equipped to a high standard*
⚠⚠⚠ *Comfortable and well equipped*
⚠⚠ *Reasonably comfortable*
⚠ *Satisfactory*

PUGET-SUR-ARGENS

83480 – Michelin map **340** P5 – pop. 6 722 – alt. 17
▶ Paris 863 – Les Arcs 21 – Cannes 41 – Draguignan 26

▲▲▲ La Bastiane ▲▲

✆ 04 94 55 55 94. www.labastiane.com

Address : 1056 chemin de Suvière (2.50km to the north)

Opening times : from mid April to mid Oct.

4 ha (180 pitches) terraced, flat, grassy, stony

Tariff : 47€ ✸✸ ⇌ 🔲 (10A) – Extra per person 9€ – Reservation fee 20€

Rental rates : (from mid April to mid Oct.) – 80 🚐 – 6 🏠 – 18 canvas bungalows. Per night from 27 to 205€ – Per week from 189 to 1,435€ – Reservation fee 30€

The site is pleasantly shaded by pine trees.

Surroundings : 🌲 🗻🗻
Leisure activities : ▼ ✕ 🎦 🏃 🏄 🚲 ✕
🏊 disco, multi-sports ground
Facilities : ♿ ⚬━ 🏛 🏕 launderette 🧺
Nearby : 🏇 🏊 | **G P S** | Longitude : 6.67837
Latitude : 43.46975

PUIMICHEL

04700 – Michelin map **334** E9 – pop. 253 – alt. 723
▶ Paris 737 – Avignon 140 – Grenoble 175 – Marseille 112

△ Les Matherons

✆ 04 92 79 60 10. www.campinglesmatherons.com

Address : 3km southwest along the D 12, follow the signs for Oraison and take the gravel road to the right

Opening times : from end April to end Sept.

70 ha/4 for camping (27 pitches) terraced, relatively flat, flat, grassy, stony

Tariff : (2014 Price) ✸ 5.25€ ⇌ 🔲 9€ – 🔌 (3A) 3.25€

Rental rates : (2014 Price) Permanent – 2 🚐. Per week from 290 to 550€

In an unspoilt, natural setting among woods and chirping cicadas; a car-free site.

Surroundings : 🌲 🗻🗻
Leisure activities : 🏄🏄
Facilities : ⚬━ Ⓟ 🚿 🏕 🍳 | **G P S** | Longitude : 6.00763
Latitude : 43.96035

PUYLOUBIER

13114 – Michelin map **340** J4 – pop. 1 798 – alt. 380
▶ Paris 775 – Aix-en-Provence 26 – Rians 38 – St-Maximin-la-Ste-Baume 19

△ Municipal Cézanne

✆ 04 42 66 36 33. www.le-cezanne.com

Address : chemin Philippe Noclercq (take the eastern exit along the D 57, by the stadium)

Opening times : from mid March to mid Nov.

1 ha (50 pitches) terraced, relatively flat, flat, grassy, stony

Tariff : ✸ 6.10€ ⇌ 2.70€ 🔲 3.10€ – 🔌 (6A) 3.50€

Rental rates : (from mid March to mid Nov.) – 3 🚐 – 3 gîtes. Per night from 40 to 90€ – Per week from 300 to 480€ – Reservation fee 20€

🚐 borne 3€ – 4 🔲 15€

Situated at the foot of Mont Ste-Victoire.

Surroundings : 🌲 🏛
Leisure activities : ✕
Facilities : ⚬━ 🏕 📷 | **G P S** | Longitude : 5.68227
Latitude : 43.527

RAMATUELLE

83350 – Michelin map **340** O6 – pop. 2 240 – alt. 136
▶ Paris 873 – Fréjus 35 – Hyères 52 – Le Lavandou 34

▲▲▲▲ Yelloh! Village les Tournels ▲▲

Yelloh! Village les Tournels

✆ 04 94 55 90 90. www.tournels.com

Address : route de Camarat

Opening times : from mid March to beginning Nov.

20 ha (890 pitches) very uneven, terraced, flat, grassy, stony

Tariff : 65€ ✸✸ ⇌ 🔲 (10A) – Extra per person 8€

Rental rates : (from mid March to beginning Nov.) ♿ (2 mobile homes) – 300 🚐 – 60 🏠. Per night from 39 to 319€ – Per week from 273 to 2,233€

🚐 borne 5€

On a shaded hillside with a lovely water complex; some pitches have a panoramic view of Pampelonne beach.

Surroundings : 🌲 ⬅🏕 🗻🗻
Leisure activities : ▼ ✕ 🎦 ⓐ (amphitheatre)
🏃 🛝 🏊 hammam, jacuzzi 🏄 🚲 ✕ 🏊
🏊 disco, multi-sports ground, spa centre
Facilities : ♿ ⚬━ 🏛 🏕 🍳 🏕 launderette
🧺 refrigerated food storage facilities | **G P S** | Longitude : 6.65112
Latitude : 43.20537

▲▲▲ Village Vacances La Toison d'Or ▲▲

(rental of mobile homes only)

✆ 04 94 79 83 54. www.riviera-villages.com

Address : route des Tamaris (Plage de Pampelonne (beach)

Opening times : from mid March to beginning Oct.

5 ha (500 pitches) open site

Rental rates : (2014 Price) – 220 🚐. Per night from 44 to 310€ – Per week from 490 to 2,170€

Several mobile home villages with themed decoration, a very popular campsite.

Surroundings : 🌲 🗻🗻 ⛰
Leisure activities : ▼ ✕ 🎦 ⓐ 🏃 🛝 🏊
hammam, jacuzzi 🏄 🏊 concierge services, spa centre
Facilities : ⚬━ 🍳 🏕 launderette 🧺 🧺
Nearby : 🎣 | **G P S** | Longitude : 6.66007
Latitude : 43.23884

The Michelin classification (▲▲▲ ... △) is totally independent of the official star classification system awarded by the local prefecture or other official organisation.

🏕 Campéole la Croix du Sud ▲▲

📞 0494555123. www.campeole.com – limited spaces for one-night stay

Address : route des Plages

Opening times : from end March to beginning Oct.

3 ha (120 pitches) terraced, flat, grassy, stony, sandy

Tariff : (2014 Price) 48.40€ ⚥⚥ 🚗 🔲 (10A) –
Extra per person 10.30€ – Reservation fee 15€

Rental rates : (2014 Price) (from end March to beginning Oct.) –
17 🏠 – 11 🏠 – 30 canvas bungalows. Per night from 29 to 165€ –
Per week from 203 to 1,155€ – Reservation fee 25€

In the heart of wine country, with pitches in the shade of pine trees.

Surroundings : 🌳 ♤♤
Leisure activities : 🍷 ⛩ ⚡ 🚴 🏊
Facilities : 🚿 ☎ 🔧🍴 🖼

Longitude : 6.64104
Latitude : 43.21426

RÉGUSSE

83630 – Michelin map **340** L4 – pop. 2 067 – alt. 545
▶ Paris 838 – Marseille 113 – Toulon 94 – Digne-les-Bains 75

🏕 Homair Vacances Les Lacs du Verdon

📞 0494701795. www.homair.com

Address : Domaine de Roquelande

Opening times : from mid April to end Sept.

17 ha (444 pitches) fine gravel

Tariff : 29€ ⚥⚥ 🚗 🔲 (8A) – Extra per person 6€ – Reservation fee 49€

Rental rates : (from mid April to end Aug.) – 361 🏠 – 10 tent lodges. Per night from 15 to 168€ – Per week from 105 to 1,176€ Reservation fee 49€

The site is in two sections, lying on either side of a small road.

Surroundings : 🌳 🏠 ♤♤
Leisure activities : 🍷 🍴 🏠 ⛩ ⚡ 🚴
🔧 🏓 🏊 multi-sports area
Facilities : 🚿 ☎ 🖼🍴 launderette 🔧 🔧
Nearby : 🐎

Longitude : 6.15073
Latitude : 43.66041

RIEZ

04500 – Michelin map **334** E10 – pop. 1 783 – alt. 520
▶ Paris 792 – Marseille 105 – Digne-les-Bains 41 – Draguignan 64

🏕 Rose de Provence

📞 0492777545. www.rose-de-provence.com

Address : rue Edouard Dauphin

Opening times : from mid April to beginning Oct.

1 ha (81 pitches) terrace, flat, grassy, gravelled

Tariff : (2014 Price) 21€ ⚥⚥ 🚗 🔲 (6A) – Extra per person 6€ – Reservation fee 15€

Rental rates : (2014 Price) (from mid April to beginning Oct.) –
7 🏠 – 2 🏠 – 2 canvas bungalows – 1 gîte. Per night from 38 to 58€ – Per week from 210 to 609€ – Reservation fee 15€

A variety of good-quality rental accommodation.

Surroundings : 🌳 🏠 ♤♤
Leisure activities : ⚡
Facilities : 🚿 ☎ 🔧🍴 🖼 refrigerated food storage facilities
Nearby : 🛒 🍴

Longitude : 6.09922
Latitude : 43.81307

LA ROCHE-DE-RAME

05310 – Michelin map **334** H4 – pop. 830 – alt. 1 000
▶ Paris 701 – Briançon 22 – Embrun 27 – Gap 68

🏕 Le Verger

📞 0492209223. www.campingleverger.com

Address : at Les Gillis, north of La Roche-de-Rame (head 1.2km northwest along the N 94, follow the signs for Briançon)

Opening times : Permanent

1.6 ha (50 pitches) terraced, relatively flat, grassy

Tariff : (2014 Price) 20€ ⚥⚥ 🚗 🔲 (10A) – Extra per person 5.50€ Reservation fee 30€

Rental rates : (2014 Price) (from beginning May to mid Nov.) –
6 🏠 – 1 🏠 – 1 gîte. Per night from 50 to 70€ – Per week from 350 to 490€ – Reservation fee 10€

🚐 borne 3.50€

Pitches in the shade of cherry and apricot trees.

Surroundings : 🌳 ≼ 💧
Leisure activities : 🏠 ⚡
Facilities : 🚿 ☎ 🔧 ⊘ 🔧 🍴 launderette

Longitude : 6.57951
Latitude : 44.7581

🏕 Municipal du Lac

📞 0682047071. www.campingdulac05.fr

Address : on the N 94 (take the southern exit, i.e. south of La Roche-de-Rame)

Opening times : from beginning May to end Sept.

1 ha (81 pitches)

Tariff : (2014 Price) ⚥ 4.80€ 🚗 🔲 5.50€ – 🔲 (10A) 4.50€

Rental rates : (2014 Price) – 2 canvas bungalows – 1 tent lodge. Per week from 350 to 380€

Surroundings : ≼ 💧
Leisure activities : ⚡
Facilities : 🚿 ☎ 🔧 ⊘ 🍴 🖼
Nearby : 🍴 🔧 🏊 (lake) 🚣 pedalos

Longitude : 6.58145
Latitude : 44.74673

For more information on visiting particular towns or regions, consult the relevant regional MICHELIN Green Guide. We also recommend you use the appropriate Michelin regional map to locate your selected campsite, to calculate distances and to work out the best route.

LA ROCHE DES ARNAUDS

05400 – Michelin map **334** D5 – pop. 1 372 – alt. 945
▶ Paris 672 – Corps 49 – Gap 15 – St-Étienne-en-Dévoluy 33

🏕 Au Blanc Manteau

📞 0492578256. www.campingaublancmanteau.fr – alt. 900 – ⛽

Address : route de Ceuze (1.3km southwest along the D 18; beside some rapids)

Opening times : Permanent

4 ha (40 pitches)

Tariff : 22.50€ ⚥⚥ 🚗 🔲 🔲 (10A) – Extra per person 4.50€

Surroundings : ❄ 🌳 ≼ 💧💧
Leisure activities : 🍷 🏠 ⚡ 🚴 🔧 🏊
Facilities : 🚿 ☎ 🔧🍴 🔧 🖼 🔧

Longitude : 5.95085
Latitude : 44.54962

ROQUEBRUNE-SUR-ARGENS

83520 – Michelin map **340** O5 – pop. 12 708 – alt. 13
▶ Paris 862 – Les Arcs 18 – Cannes 49 – Draguignan 23

ᴧᴧᴧ Domaine de la Bergerie 👥

📞 04 98 11 45 45. www.domainelabergerie.com

Address : Vallée du Fournel – route du Col de Bougnon (head 8km southeast along the D 7, follow the signs for St-Aygulf and turn right onto D 8; beside some lakes)

Opening times : from end April to end Sept.

60 ha (700 pitches) very uneven, terraced, flat, grassy, stony

Tariff : 57€ ♦♦ ⇌ 🔲 ⚡ (10A) – Extra per person 12.10€ – Reservation fee 25€

Rental rates : (from beginning March to mid Nov.) – 380 🚐. Per night from 66 to 303€ – Per week from 462 to 2,121€

Attractive pitches, partly on a wooded hill.

Surroundings : 🐟 ⛱ ♨♨
Leisure activities : 🍸 ✗ 🎬 🎮(open-air theatre) 🏃 🎣 ⛵ hammam, jacuzzi 🏄
🚴 ⛳ ✗ ⚽ 🏊 disco, paintballing, farm or petting farm, ponies, multi-sports ground, spa centre, entertainment room
Facilities : ⚿ ⛟ 🧺 🚿 🍴 launderette 🍽 🚲

Longitude : 6.67535
Latitude : 43.39879

ᴧᴧᴧ Les Pêcheurs 👥

📞 04 94 45 71 25. www.camping-les-pecheurs.com

Address : 700m northwest along the D 7, northwest of Roquebrunes

Opening times : from beginning April to end Sept.

3.3 ha (195 pitches) flat, grassy

Tariff : (2014 Price) 49.50€ ♦♦ ⇌ 🔲 ⚡ (10A) – Extra per person 9.45€ – Reservation fee 25€

Rental rates : (2014 Price) (from beginning April to end Sept.) – 47 🚐 – 20 🏠. Per night from 49 to 185€ – Per week from 294 to 1,295€ – Reservation fee 25€

🚐 borne

An open spa area with access via a tunnel to a small boating centre on the other side of the road.

Surroundings : 🐟 ⛱ ♨♨
Leisure activities : 🍸 ✗ 🎬 🎮daytime 🏃
♨ hammam, jacuzzi 🎣 ♒ 🏊 ✈ multi-sports ground
Facilities : ⚿ ⛟ 🧺 🚿 🍴 launderette 🍽 🚲
Nearby : 🚣 watersports centre, pedalos

Longitude : 6.63354
Latitude : 43.45094

ᴧᴧᴧ Lei Suves

📞 04 94 45 43 95. www.lei-suves.com – limited spaces for one-night stay

Address : Le Blavet district (head 4km north along the D 7 and take underpass under A 8)

Opening times : from beginning April to mid Oct.

7 ha (309 pitches) terraced, flat, grassy, stony

Tariff : 51.20€ ♦♦ ⇌ 🔲 ⚡ (6A) – Extra per person 11€ – Reservation fee 25€

Rental rates : (from beginning April to mid Oct.) 🎿 – 40 🚐. Per week from 385 to 1,050€ – Reservation fee 25€

🚐 borne

In a pleasant wooded setting, with pines and cork oaks.

Surroundings : 🐟 ⛱ ♨♨
Leisure activities : 🍸 ✗ 🎮(open-air theatre)
🏃 🎣 ✗ 🏊 multi-sports ground 🚴 🚲
Facilities : ⚿ ⛟ 🧺 🚿 🍴 launderette 🍽 🚲

Longitude : 6.63882
Latitude : 43.47821

⛺ Moulin des Iscles

📞 04 94 45 70 74. www.campingdesiscles.com

Address : chemin du Moulin des Iscles (head 1.8km east along the D 7, follow the signs for St-Aygulf and take road to the left)

Opening times : from beginning April to end Sept.

1.5 ha (90 pitches) flat, grassy

Tariff : 23.40€ ♦♦ ⇌ 🔲 ⚡ (6A) – Extra per person 3.50€ – Reservation fee 15€

Rental rates : (from beginning April to end Sept.) ⚿ (1 mobile home) – 5 🚐 – 5 apartments. Per night from 68 to 120 € – Per week from 480 to 780€ – Reservation fee 15€
🚐 2 🔲 23.40€

A peaceful site beside the Argens river.

Surroundings : 🐟 ♨♨
Leisure activities : ✗ 🎬 🚴 ♒ 🎣 🚲
Facilities : ⚿ ⛟ 🧻 🚿 🍴 🧺 launderette 🍽 🚲

Longitude : 6.65784
Latitude : 43.44497

LA ROQUE-D'ANTHÉRON

13640 – Michelin map **340** G3 – pop. 5 143 – alt. 183
▶ Paris 726 – Aix-en-Provence 29 – Cavaillon 34 – Manosque 60

ᴧᴧᴧ Tohapi Les Iscles (rental of mobile homes only)

📞 08 25 00 20 30. www.village-center.com

Address : la Durance (head 3km south along the D 23)

Opening times : from mid April to mid Sept.

10 ha (269 pitches)

Rental rates : 267 🚐. Per night from 28 to 142€ – Per week from 196 to 994€ – Reservation fee 10€

Surroundings : 🐟 ♨♨
Leisure activities : 🍸 ✗ 🎮 🏃 🎣 ⚽ 🏊 (river) 🎿 🚲 🚲
Facilities : ⛟ 🍴 launderette 🍽 🚲

Longitude : 5.32099
Latitude : 43.72819

This guide is not intended as a list of all the camping sites in France; its aim is to provide a selection of the best sites in each category.

ST-ANDRÉ-LES-ALPES

04170 – Michelin map **334** H9 – pop. 930 – alt. 914
▶ Paris 786 – Castellane 20 – Colmars 28 – Digne-les-Bains 43

⛺ Municipal les Iscles

📞 04 92 89 02 29. www.camping-les-iscles.com – alt. 894

Address : chemin des Iscles (located 1km south along the N 202, follow the signs for Annot and take the turning to the left, 300m from the Verdon river)

Opening times : from beginning April to mid Oct.

2.5 ha (200 pitches)

Tariff : (2014 Price) ♦ 4.30€ ⇌ 1.50€ – ⚡ (10A) 3€

Rental rates : (2014 Price) (from beginning April to end Oct.)
⬧ (1 mobile home) ⚞ – 16 ⬚. Per night from 30 to 90€ –
Per week from 210 to 630€ – Reservation fee 10€

Situated in a pleasant pine wood.

Surroundings : ⛰ ♨♨
Leisure activities : 🛶 🏊
Facilities : ⬧ ⚷ 🏕 launderette
Nearby : 🍴 🌳 sports trail

Longitude : 6.50844
Latitude : 43.9612

ST-APOLLINAIRE

05160 – Michelin map **334** G5 – pop. 117 – alt. 1 285
▶ Paris 684 – Embrun 19 – Gap 27 – Mont-Dauphin 37

⚠ Campéole Le Clos du Lac

☎ 04 92 44 27 43. www.camping-closdulac.com – access difficult for
caravans and campervans – alt. 1 450

Address : route des Lacs (2.3km northwest along the D 509; 50m
from the small lake at St-Apollinaire)

2 ha (68 pitches)
Rentals : 18 ⬚.

In an attractive, elevated location.

Surroundings : ⛰ ≤ Lac de Serre-Ponçon
and mountains ♨
Leisure activities : ☷ jacuzzi 🏊
Facilities : ⚷ 🏕
Nearby : 🍴 🍽 🌳 ⛵ (lake) 🎣

Longitude : 6.34642
Latitude : 44.56127

ST-AYGULF

83370 – Michelin map **340** P5
▶ Paris 872 – Brignoles 69 – Draguignan 35 – Fréjus 6

🏔 L'Étoile d'Argens 👥

☎ 04 94 81 01 41. www.etoiledargens.com

Address : chemin des Étangs (5km northwest along the D 7, follow
the signs for Roquebrune-sur-Argens and turn right onto the D 8;
beside the Argens river)

Opening times : from beginning April to end Sept.

11 ha (493 pitches) flat, grassy

Tariff : 67€ ✦✦ ⛌ 🅴 ⚡ (10A) – Extra per person 11€ – Reservation
fee 35€

Rental rates : (from beginning April to end Sept.) ⚞ – 103 ⬚.
Per night from 150 to 230€ – Per week from 1,050 to 1,610€ –
Reservation fee 35€

⬚ 180 🅴 67€

*Pretty, spacious pitches with shade. A river shuttle service to
the beaches (duration: 30 min).*

Surroundings : ⛰ 🌊 ♨♨
Leisure activities : 🍴 🍽 🏹 jacuzzi 🏊
🚴 🎯 🌳 🏓 disco, multi-sports ground
Facilities : ⬧ ⚷ ▥ 🏕 launderette
🏊🛒
Nearby : ⚓ scuba diving

Longitude : 6.70562
Latitude : 43.41596

*Routes nationales are main roads and their identifying
numbers begin with N or RN. Routes départementales are
generally quieter roads and begin with D or DN.*

🏔 Sandaya Résidence du Campeur

☎ 04 94 81 01 59. www.sandaya.fr

Address : 189 Les Grands Châteaux-de-Villepey (3km northwest along
the D 7, follow the signs for Roquebrune-sur-Argens)

Opening times : from beginning April to mid Oct.

10 ha (451 pitches) stony

Tariff : (2014 Price) 67€ ✦✦ ⛌ 🅴 ⚡ (10A) – Extra per person 7.50€
Reservation fee 32€

Rental rates : (2014 Price) (from beginning April to mid Oct.) –
265 ⬚ – 20 tent lodges – (on stilts). Per night from 48 to 87€ –
Per week from 336 to 1,670€ – Reservation fee 32€

*There's a variety of good-quality rental options, with private
sanitary facilities for each pitch.*

Surroundings : ⛰ 🌊 ♨♨
Leisure activities : 🍴 🍽 🛶 🏹 🏊 🚴 🏐
🌳 🏊 🎿 multi-sports ground
Facilities : ⚷ – 451 individual sanitary
facilities (🚿 🧺 🚽 wc) 🏊 🛒 🏕 launderette
🏊🛒

Longitude : 6.70875
Latitude : 43.40867

🏔 Au Paradis des Campeurs

☎ 04 94 96 93 55. www.paradis-des-campeurs.com

Address : La Gaillarde-Plage (2.5km south along the N 98, follow the
signs for Ste-Maxime)

Opening times : from beginning April to beginning Oct.

6 ha/3.5 for camping (180 pitches)

Tariff : (2014 Price) 31€ ✦✦ ⛌ 🅴 ⚡ (6A) – Extra per person 6€
Rental rates : (from beginning April to beginning Oct.) ⬧
(1 mobile home) – 17 ⬚. Per week from 280 to 740€
⬚ borne

*Some pitches have a sea view and direct access to the beach via
a tunnel. Choose those pitches furthest away from the road.*

Surroundings : 🌊 ♨♨
Leisure activities : 🍴 🍽 🛶 🏊
Facilities : ⬧ ⚷ ▣ 🏕 🏊 🏓 launderette
🏊🛒
Nearby : disco

Longitude : 6.71235
Latitude : 43.366

ST-CLÉMENT-SUR-DURANCE

05600 – Michelin map **334** H5 – pop. 285 – alt. 872
▶ Paris 715 – L'Argentière-la-Bessée 21 – Embrun 13 – Gap 54

⚠ Les Mille Vents

☎ 04 92 45 10 90. www.camping-les-mille-vents.com

Address : located 1km east along the N 94, follow the signs for
Briançon and take D 994d to the right after the bridge and the white
water sports centre

Opening times : from mid June to beginning Sept.

3.5 ha (100 pitches) terrace, flat, grassy

Tariff : (2014 Price) 16€ ✦✦ ⛌ 🅴 ⚡ (5A) – Extra per person 3€
Rental rates : (2014 Price) (from mid June to beginning Sept.) –
3 ⬚. Per week from 350 to 450€

Situated beside the river.

Surroundings : ≤ ♨
Leisure activities : 🏊 🎿
Facilities : ⬧ ⚷ 🚿 ▣ 🏊 🏓 🖼
Nearby : 🍴 rafting and canyoning

Longitude : 6.6618
Latitude : 44.66362

ST-CYR-SUR-MER

83270 – Michelin map **340** J6 – pop. 11 865 – alt. 10
▶ Paris 810 – Bandol 8 – Brignoles 70 – La Ciotat 10

▲▲▲ Le Clos Ste-Thérèse

℘ 04 94 32 12 21. www.clos-therese.com – pitches accessed via steep slope, help moving caravans onto and off pitches avilable on request (limited spaces for one-night stay)

Address : 3.5km southeast along the D 559 (route de Bandol), south of St-Cyr-sur-Mer

Opening times : from beginning April to end Sept.

4 ha (123 pitches) very uneven, terraced, flat, grassy, stony

Tariff : 34.50€ ✹✹ ⇌ 🔲 🔌 (10A) – Extra per person 6.80€ – Reservation fee 23€

Rental rates : (2014 Price) (from beginning April to end Sept.) – 6 🛖 – 24 🛖 – 5 canvas bungalows. Per night from 44 to 157€ – Per week from 252 to 1,208€ – Reservation fee 23€
🛢 borne – 🔋11€

Choose those pitches furthest away from the road.

Surroundings : 🔲 ⏸⏸	**G**	Longitude : 5.72951
Leisure activities : 🍸 🏊 🚣 🚤	**P**	Latitude : 43.15955
Facilities : ⅊ 🔑 🗏 🖽 🍴 📺 🍽	**S**	

ST-ÉTIENNE-DE-TINÉE

06660 – Michelin map **341** C2 – pop. 1 311 – alt. 1 147
▶ Paris 788 – Grenoble 226 – Marseille 262 – Nice 90

▲ Municipal du Plan d'Eau

℘ 04 93 02 41 57. www.campingduplandeau.com

Address : route du col de la Bonette (500m north of the town)

Opening times : from beginning June to end Sept.

0.5 ha (23 pitches)

Tariff : (2014 Price) ✹ 3€ ⇌ 🚗 🔲 10€ – 🔌 (13A) 2.50€
🛢 borne 3€ – 5 🔲

Situated beside the Tinée river, overlooking a small, pretty lake. Reserved for tents. Electricity hook-ups for campervans only.

Surroundings : 🏞 ⛰ 🔲	**G**	Longitude : 6.92299
Leisure activities : 🏖 🏊 (beach) 🎣 🛶	**P**	Latitude : 44.25858
Facilities : 🔑 Ⓟ 🍽	**S**	
Nearby : fitness trail		

ST-ÉTIENNE-DU-GRÈS

13103 – Michelin map **340** D3 – pop. 2 202 – alt. 7
▶ Paris 706 – Arles 16 – Avignon 24 – Les Baux-de-Provence 15

▲ Municipal du Grès

℘ 04 90 49 00 03. www.campingalpilles.com

Address : avenue du Dr-Barberin (take the northwestern exit along the D 99, follow the signs for Tarascon; near the stadium, 50m from the Vigueira)

Opening times : Permanent

0.6 ha (40 pitches)

Tariff : (2014 Price) 16€ ✹✹ ⇌ 🔲 🔌 (16A) – Extra per person 3.50€
🛢 borne – 6 🔲 12€

Surroundings : 🔲 ⏸⏸	**G**	Longitude : 4.71772
Facilities : ⅊ 🗏 🚿 🍴 🍽 launderette	**P**	Latitude : 43.78628
	S	

ST-LAURENT-DU-VERDON

04500 – Michelin map **334** E10 – pop. 92 – alt. 468
▶ Paris 797 – Marseille 118 – Digne-les-Bains 59 – Avignon 166

▲▲▲ La Farigoulette 👫

℘ 04 92 74 41 62. www.camping-la-farigoulette.com

Address : lake St Laurent (located 1km north follow signs along the C 1 for Montpezat)

Opening times : from mid May to mid Sept.

14 ha (219 pitches)

Tariff : (2014 Price) 33.50€ ✹✹ ⇌ 🔲 🔌 (5A) – Extra per person 5.50€ Reservation fee 15€

Rental rates : (2014 Price) (from mid May to mid Sept.) – 24 🛖. Per night from 32 to 160€ – Per week from 224 to 1,120€ – Reservation fee 20€
🛢 borne

The site nestles in a pretty pine forest that stretches down to the banks of the lake.

Surroundings : 🏊 🔲 ⏸⏸	**G**	Longitude : 6.0777
Leisure activities : ✗ 🎯daytime 🏃 🚣 🚤 🏊 pedalos, electric boats 🛴 multi-sports ground	**P**	Latitude : 43.73407
Facilities : 🔑 🍴 🍽 launderette 🎱 🍽	**S**	

ST-MANDRIER-SUR-MER

83430 – Michelin map **340** K7 – pop. 5 773 – alt. 1
▶ Paris 836 – Bandol 20 – Le Beausset 22 – Hyères 30

▲▲▲ Homair Vacances La Presqu'île

(rental of mobile homes only)

℘ 04 94 30 74 70. www.homair.com

Address : Port Pin Rolland district (2.5km west, the D 18, and follow the signs for La Pointe de Marégau (headland), near the marina)

Opening times : from mid April to beginning Oct.

Rental rates : 125 🛖. Per night from 24 to 195€ – Per week from 168 to 1,365€ – Reservation fee 49€

Choose the pitches in the shade of eucalyptus trees and furthest away from the road.

Surroundings : 🌊	**G**	Longitude : 5.90577
Leisure activities : 🍸 ✗ 🎯 🏃 🚣 🚲 🏊	**P**	Latitude : 43.07655
Facilities : ⅊ 🔑 🆒 🍽 🖽 🍽	**S**	
Nearby : 🎾		

ST-MARTIN-D'ENTRAUNES

06470 – Michelin map **341** B3 – pop. 83 – alt. 1 050
▶ Paris 778 – Annot 39 – Barcelonnette 50 – Puget-Théniers 44

▲▲▲ Le Prieuré

℘ 04 93 05 54 99. www.le-prieure.com – alt. 1 070 🍽

Address : route des Blancs (located 1km east along the D 2202, follow the signs for Guillaumes then continue 1.8km along the road to the left, after the bridge over the Var)

Opening times : from beginning May to end Sept.

12 ha/1.5 (35 pitches) terraced, relatively flat, flat, grassy

Tariff : (2014 Price) ✹ 5€ ⇌ 🔲 10€ – 🔌 (6A) 3.50€ – Reservation fee 10€

Rental rates : (2014 Price) 🚿 – 8 🏠 – 4 canvas bungalows – 1 tent lodge – 9 gîtes. Per night from 50 to 90€ – Per week from 300 to 660€ – Reservation fee 10€

Situated in a mountain location, with simple but varied rental accommodation.

Surroundings : 🌳 ⬅ 🛶 🎣
Leisure activities : ✗ 🏕 ⛵ 🛝 (small swimming pool)
Facilities : 🚰 🎿 🍴 🖼 🛁

GPS Longitude : 6.76283
Latitude : 44.14895

Some information or pricing may have changed since the guide went to press. We recommend you check the price list online in advance or at the entrance to the campsite and enquire about possible restrictions.

ST-MARTIN-VESUBIE

06450 – Michelin map **341** E3 – pop. 1 325 – alt. 1 000
▶ Paris 899 – Marseille 235 – Nice 65 – Cuneo 140

🏕 À la Ferme St-Joseph

📞 06 70 51 90 14. www.camping-alafermestjoseph.com

Address : to the southeast of the town along the D 2565, follow the signs for Roquebillière, near Saint-Martin-Vésubie

Opening times : from end April to end Sept.

0.6 ha (50 pitches)

Tariff : ⭑ 4.90€ ⬅ 3.50€ 🔲 7€ – (6A) 4.90€ – Reservation fee 10€
Rental rates : (from end April to end Sept.) 🚿 – 3 🛏. Per night from 54 to 86€ – Per week from 370 to 594€
🚐 borne

The site has shaded terraces, often beneath pear trees.

Surroundings : 🌳 ⬅ 🏊
Facilities : 🚰 (July-Aug.) 🎿 🍴 🖼
Nearby : 🍴 🛝

GPS Longitude : 7.25711
Latitude : 44.06469

ST-PAUL-EN-FORÊT

83440 – Michelin map **340** P4 – pop. 1 616 – alt. 310
▶ Paris 884 – Cannes 46 – Draguignan 27 – Fayence 10

🏔 Le Parc 👤👤

Le Parc

📞 04 94 76 15 35. www.campingleparc.com

Address : 408 Trestaure district (3km north along the D 4, follow the signs for Fayence then take the road to the right)

Opening times : from beginning April to end Sept.

3 ha (110 pitches) terraced, flat, grassy, stony

Tariff : 44€ ⭑⭑ ⬅ 🔲 (10A) – Extra per person 7.20€ – Reservation fee 25€
Rental rates : (from beginning April to end Sept.) – 12 🚐 – 4 🏠 – 1 🛏 – 1 apartment – 2 tent lodges. Per night from 42 to 140€ – Per week from 200 to 980€ – Reservation fee 25€

Pitches that are well shaded and peaceful.

Surroundings : 🌳 🌲
Leisure activities : ✗ 🏕 🏇 ⛵ 🎣 🛝
Facilities : 🚿 🚰 🎿 🛁 🍴 launderette 🚲

GPS Longitude : 6.68979
Latitude : 43.58445

ST-PONS

04400 – Michelin map **334** H6 – pop. 742 – alt. 1 157
▶ Paris 797 – Marseille 227 – Digne-les-Bains 84 – Gap 74

🏔 Village Vacances Le Loup Blanc du Riou

(rental of chalets only)

📞 04 92 81 44 97. www.leloupblanc.com

Address : located 1km southwest, behind Ubaye aerodrome

Opening times : Permanent

2 ha

Rental rates : ♿ (1 chalet) – 10 🏠. Per night from 90 to 120€ – Per week from 295 to 780€

A chalet village in a pinewood, with some owner-occupiers but also chalets to rent.

Surroundings : 🌳 ⬅ 🏊
Leisure activities : 🏕 ⛵ 🛝
Facilities : 🚰 🅿 🍴 launderette
Nearby : ✗ 🏇 🚶 adventure park

GPS Longitude : 6.6122
Latitude : 44.39107

The Michelin classification (△△△… △) is totally independent of the official star classification system awarded by the local prefecture or other official organisation.

ST-RAPHAËL

83700 – Michelin map **340** P5 – pop. 34 269
▶ Paris 870 – Aix-en-Provence 121 – Cannes 42 – Fréjus 4

🏔 Les Castels Douce Quiétude 👤👤

📞 04 94 44 30 00. www.douce-quietude.com – limited spaces for one-night stay

Address : 3435 boulevard Jacques Baudino (take northeastern exit towards Valescure then continue 3km – from A8, take exit 38)

Opening times : from mid April to mid Oct.

10 ha (440 pitches) terraced, undulating, flat, grassy, stony

Tariff : 62€ ⭑⭑ ⬅ 🔲 (16A) – Extra per person 11.30€ – Reservation fee 30€
Rental rates : (from mid April to mid Oct.) – 258 🚐. Per night from 35 to 269€ – Per week from 245 to 1,883€ – Reservation fee 30€

Some pitches and high-quality rental options. Shuttle buses for the beaches.

Surroundings : 🌳 🛶 🏊
Leisure activities : 🍴 ✗ 🏕 🏇 🎣 🏊 hammam, jacuzzi ⛵ 🚴 ✗ 🚶 🛝 disco, covered paddling pool, multi-sports ground
Facilities : ♿ 🚰 🎿 🛁 🚲 🍴 launderette 🚲 🛁

GPS Longitude : 6.80587
Latitude : 43.44734

Key to rentals symbols:

12 🚐	*Number of mobile homes*
20 🏠	*Number of chalets*
6 🛏	*Number of rooms to rent*
Per night 30–50€	*Minimum/maximum rate per night*
Per week 300–1,000€	*Minimum/maximum rate per week*

ST-RÉMY-DE-PROVENCE

13210 – Michelin map **340** D3 – pop. 10 458 – alt. 59
▶ Paris 702 – Arles 25 – Avignon 20 – Marseille 89

⩕ Monplaisir

𝒫 04 90 92 22 70. www.camping-monplaisir.fr

Address : chemin de Monplaisir (800m northwest along the D 5, follow the signs for Maillane and take road to the left)

Opening times : from beginning March to beginning Nov.

2.8 ha (140 pitches)

Tariff : 30€ ⋆⋆ ⇌ 🔲 ⚡ (10A) – Extra per person 7€ – Reservation fee 19€

Rentals : Permanent ⅀⅀ – 12 🛏. Per week from 800€

A pleasant site with flowers, set around a Provençal mas (traditional house).

Surroundings : ⅀ ⊏⊐ ♉♉		
Leisure activities : ⛉ ✕ ⟐ ⤳ ⅄	**G**	Longitude : 4.8729
Facilities : ⅍ ⊶ ▥ ⅃ ⅌ launderette ⅍ ⅍	**P** **S**	Latitude : 43.78417
Nearby : ⅄		

⩕ Pégomas

𝒫 04 90 92 01 21. www.campingpegomas.com

Address : 3 avenue Jean Moulin (take the eastern exit along the D 99a, follow the signs for Cavaillon and take the turning to the left, at intersection of the Chemin de Pégomas and avenue Jean-Moulin (towards D 30, follow the signs for Noves)

Opening times : from mid March to end Oct.

2 ha (105 pitches) flat, grassy

Tariff : 31.30€ ⋆⋆ ⇌ 🔲 ⚡ (6A) – Extra per person 8€ – Reservation fee 17€

Rental rates : (from mid April to mid Oct.) ⅀⅀ – 6 🛏. Per week from 360 to 500€

🛏 borne

Surroundings : ⊏⊐ ♉♉		
Leisure activities : ⛉ ⤳ ⅄	**G**	Longitude : 4.84099
Facilities : ⅍ ⊶ ▥ ⅃ ⅌ launderette, refrigerated food storage facilities	**P** **S**	Latitude : 43.78838
Nearby : ✕		

STE-CROIX-DU-VERDON

04500 – Michelin map **334** E10 – pop. 124 – alt. 530
▶ Paris 780 – Brignoles 59 – Castellane 59 – Digne-les-Bains 51

⩕ Municipal les Roches

𝒫 04 92 77 78 99. www.blog4ever.com

Address : route du Lac (located 1km northeast of the village, 50m from the lake at Ste-Croix – caravans are not permitted through village)

Opening times : from beginning April to end Sept.

6 ha (199 pitches) terraced, undulating, flat, grassy, fine gravel

Tariff : (2014 Price) 19.40€ ⋆⋆ ⇌ 🔲 ⚡ (10A) – Extra per person 4€ Reservation fee 30€

🛏 borne

The pitches enjoy the shade of olive and almond trees and some have a view of the lake or the village.

Surroundings : ⅀ ≤ ♉♉		
Facilities : ⅍ ⊶ ⅃ launderette, refrigerated food storage facilities	**G** **P** **S**	Longitude : 6.15381 Latitude : 43.76043
Nearby : ✕ ⚓ ♦ pedalos		

STES-MARIES-DE-LA-MER

13460 – Michelin map **340** B5 – pop. 2 308 – alt. 1
▶ Paris 761 – Aigues-Mortes 31 – Arles 40 – Marseille 131

⩕⩕⩕ Sunêlia Le Clos du Rhône

Le Clos du RhÃ´ne

𝒫 04 90 97 85 99. www.camping-leclos.fr

Address : route d'Aigues-Mortes (head 2km west along the D 38 and take the turning to the left)

Opening times : from beginning April to beginning Nov.

7 ha (376 pitches)

Tariff : 32€ ⋆⋆ ⇌ 🔲 ⚡ (16A) – Extra per person 9€ – Reservation fee 23€

Rental rates : (from beginning April to beginning Nov.) ⅍ (1 mobile home) – 98 🛏 – 14 tent lodges. Per night from 39 to 108€ – Per week from 273 to 1,220€ – Reservation fee 23€

🛏 borne

Situated near the Petit Rhône river and the beach.

Surroundings : ♀ ⛰		
Leisure activities : ✕ ⟐ ⫲ ⅄ ⤳	**G**	Longitude : 4.40231
Facilities : ⅍ ⊶ ▥ ⅃ ⅄ ⅌ launderette ⅍ ⅍ refrigerated food storage facilities	**P** **S**	Latitude : 43.44996
Nearby : ⅍ boat trips on the Rhône		

Michelin classification:

⩕⩕⩕⩕	*Extremely comfortable, equipped to a very high standard*
⩕⩕⩕	*Very comfortable, equipped to a high standard*
⩕⩕	*Comfortable and well equipped*
⩕	*Reasonably comfortable*
⩕	*Satisfactory*

SALERNES

83690 – Michelin map **340** M4 – pop. 3 574 – alt. 209
▶ Paris 830 – Aix-en-Provence 81 – Brignoles 33 – Draguignan 23

⩕ Municipal les Arnauds

𝒫 04 94 67 51 95. www.village-vacances-lesarnauds.com

Address : Les Arnauds district (take the northwestern exit along the D 560, follow the signs for Sillans-la-Cascade and take the turning to the left)

Opening times : from beginning May to end Sept.

2 ha (52 pitches) flat, grassy

Tariff : (2014 Price) ⋆ 7.50€ ⇌ 🔲 11.50€ ⚡ (10A)

Rental rates : (2014 Price) Permanent – 6 studios – 13 apartments. Per week from 136 to 715€

Access to the village by a footpath along the Bresque river.

Surroundings : ⅀ ⊏⊐ ♉♉		
Leisure activities : ⟐ ⤳ ⅍ ⅌ (river)	**G**	Longitude : 6.2257
Facilities : ⅍ ⊶ ⅃ ⅄ ⅌ launderette, refrigerated food storage facilities	**P** **S**	Latitude : 43.56623

LES SALLES-SUR-VERDON

83630 – Michelin map **340** M3 – pop. 231 – alt. 440
▶ Paris 790 – Brignoles 57 – Digne-les-Bains 60 – Draguignan 49

⚠ Les Pins

℘ 04 98 10 23 80. www.campinglespins.com

Address : take the southern exit along the D 71 then continue 1.2km along the road to the right; 100m from the Lac de Ste-Croix

Opening times : from beginning April to mid Oct.

3 ha/2 for camping (104 pitches) terraced, very uneven, flat, grassy, stony

Tariff : (2014 Price) ♀ 6.10€ ⇔ ▣ 12.60€ ⚡ (6A) – Reservation fee 25€

🚐 borne

In an attractive, shaded setting, adjoining a small pine wood, with direct access to the village.

Surroundings : 🏔 ⌂ ΩΩ
Leisure activities : 🎣 ⚓
Facilities : ♿ ⚲ 🚿 🛁 ♨ ♈ launderette, refrigerated food storage facilities
Nearby : ⛵ 🎣 ♨ fitness trail

GPS	Longitude : 6.2084
	Latitude : 43.77603

⚠ La Source

℘ 04 94 70 20 40. www.camping-la-source.eu

Address : southern exit along the D 71, then 1km along the road to the right, 100 m from Lac de Ste-Croix, direct access for pedestrians from the town centre

Opening times : from end April to mid Oct.

2 ha (89 pitches) terraced, very uneven, relatively flat, flat, stony, fine gravel

Tariff : (2014 Price) 24.80€ ♀♀ ⇔ ▣ ⚡ (10A) –
Extra per person 6.70€

🚐 borne

The site is close to the Lac de Sainte-Croix and the village.

Surroundings : 🏔 ⌂ ΩΩ
Leisure activities : ✗ 🎣 ⚓
Facilities : ♿ ⚲ 🚿 🛁 ♈ launderette 🔧
Nearby : ⛵ 🎣 ♨ fitness trail

GPS	Longitude : 6.20737
	Latitude : 43.77547

We have selected the best campsites in France with our usual care, listing those with the best facilities in the most pleasant surroundings.

SALON-DE-PROVENCE

13300 – Michelin map **340** F4 – pop. 42 440 – alt. 80
▶ Paris 720 – Aix-en-Provence 37 – Arles 46 – Avignon 50

⚠ Nostradamus

℘ 04 90 56 08 36. www.camping-nostradamus.com

Address : route d'Eyguières (5.8km northwest along the D 17 and turn left onto D 72D)

2.7 ha (83 pitches) flat, grassy
Rentals : 18 🚐.

Situated beside a canal.

Surroundings : 🏔 ⌂ ♒♒
Leisure activities : 🎣 ⚓ 🏊
Facilities : ♿ ⚲ ▥ 🛁 ♈ launderette

GPS	Longitude : 5.06229
	Latitude : 43.68401

SANARY-SUR-MER

83110 – Michelin map **340** J7 – pop. 16 806 – alt. 1
▶ Paris 824 – Aix-en-Provence 75 – La Ciotat 23 – Marseille 55

⚠⚠⚠ Campasun Parc Mogador ♣♀

℘ 04 94 74 53 16. www.campasun.eu

Address : 167 chemin de Beaucours

Opening times : from end March to beginning Nov.

3 ha (160 pitches) terraced, flat, grassy, stony

Tariff : (2014 Price) 48.50€ ♀♀ ⇔ ▣ ⚡ (10A) –
Extra per person 9.50€ – Reservation fee 25€

Rental rates : (2014 Price) (from end March to beginning Nov.) – 65 🚐 – 5 🏠. Per night from 44 to 190€ – Per week from 220 to 1,140€ – Reservation fee 25€

🚐 borne 5€

In a peaceful residential area, with some rental options and good quality sanitary facilities.

Surroundings : 🏔 ⌂ ♒♒
Leisure activities : ♈ ✗ 🎣 ⚓ 🏊 🔧 bowling
Facilities : ♿ ⚲ 🚿 🛁 ♈ launderette 🔧

GPS	Longitude : 5.78777
	Latitude : 43.12367

These symbols are used for a campsite that is exceptional in its category:

⚠⚠⚠...⚠ *Particularly pleasant setting, quality and range of services available*

🏔🏔 *Tranquil, isolated site – quiet site, particularly at night*

≪ ≪ *Exceptional view – interesting or panoramic view*

⚠⚠⚠ Campasun Mas de Pierredon ♣♀

℘ 04 94 74 25 02. www.campasun.eu

Address : 652 chemin Raoul Coletta (3km to the north, follow the signs for Ollioules and take the turning to the left after the motorway bridge)

Opening times : from mid April to end Sept.

6 ha/2.5 for camping (120 pitches) very uneven, terraced, flat, grassy, stony

Tariff : (2014 Price) 48.50€ ♀♀ ⇔ ▣ ⚡ (10A) –
Extra per person 9.50€ – Reservation fee 25€

Rental rates : (2014 Price) (from mid April to end Sept.) – 45 🚐 – 10 🏠. Per night from 43 to 190€ – Per week from 217 to 1,140€ Reservation fee 25€

🚐 borne 5€

The pitches at the top of the site are more impacted by the noise of the motorway.

Surroundings : ⌂ ♒♒
Leisure activities : ♈ ✗ 🎣 ⚓ 🏊 ♘ 🎯 🏊 🏊
Facilities : ♿ ⚲ 🛁 – 12 individual sanitary facilities (▥ 🚽 WC) 🛁 ♈ ♈ ▣ 🔧

GPS	Longitude : 5.81452
	Latitude : 43.13159

The guide covers all 22 regions of France – see the map and list of regions on pages 4–5.

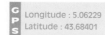

LE SAUZÉ-DU-LAC

05160 – Michelin map **334** F6 – pop. 129 – alt. 1 052
▶ Paris 697 – Barcelonette 35 – Digne-les-Bains 74 – Gap 40

⚠ La Palatrière

✆ 04 92 44 20 98. www.lapalatriere.com

Address : site des Demoiselles Coiffées (4.6km south along the D 954, follow the signs for Savines-Lac)

Opening times : from beginning May to end Sept.

3 ha (30 pitches) terraced, flat, grassy, stony

Tariff : (2014 Price) 24.50€ ✦✦ ⬌ 🔲 🔌 (12A) – Extra per person 7€
Rental rates : (2014 Price) (from beginning April to beginning Oct.) – 6 🏠 – 10 🏠. Per night from 49 to 100€ – Per week from 250 to 760€

🚻 2 🔲 24.50€

In an attractive location overlooking the Lac de Serre-Ponçon.

Surroundings : 🏞 ≤ Lac de Serre-Ponçon and the mountains ♀♀
Leisure activities : 🍴 ✗ 🎮 jacuzzi ⛵ 🛶
Facilities : 🔌 ⚲ 🚰 🔲

| G P S | Longitude : 6.34543 |
| | Latitude : 44.49909 |

*To visit a town or region, use the **MICHELIN Green Guides**.*

SERRES

05700 – Michelin map **334** C6 – pop. 1 308 – alt. 670
▶ Paris 670 – Die 68 – Gap 41 – Manosque 89

⚠ Domaine des Deux Soleils 🏕

✆ 04 92 67 01 33. www.domaine-2soleils.com – alt. 800

Address : avenue Des Pins - La Flamenche (800m southeast along the N 75, follow the signs for Sisteron then continue 1km along the turning to the left; at Super-Serres)

Opening times : from mid April to mid Oct.

26 ha/12 for camping (72 pitches) terraced, flat, grassy, stony

Tariff : 25€ ✦✦ ⬌ 🔲 🔌 (6A) – Extra per person 4.50€ – Reservation fee 15€
Rental rates : (from mid April to mid Oct.) – 7 🏠 – 18 🏠. Per night from 38 to 62€ – Per week from 295 to 720€ – Reservation fee 15€

Many pitches are set among trees and bushes in a natural and unspoilt setting.

Surroundings : 🏞 🚰 ♀
Leisure activities : ✗ 🎯 ⛵ 🛶 multi-sports ground
Facilities : 🔌 ⚲ 🚰 🚰 🔲 🛠

| G P S | Longitude : 5.72767 |
| | Latitude : 44.4203 |

SEYNE

04140 – Michelin map **334** G6 – pop. 1 434 – alt. 1 200
▶ Paris 719 – Barcelonnette 43 – Digne-les-Bains 43 – Gap 54

⚠ Les Prairies

✆ 04 92 35 10 21. www.campinglesprairies.com

Address : at Haute Gréyère, chemin Charcherie (located 1km south along the D 7, follow the signs for Auzet and take road to the left; beside the Blanche river)

Opening times : from beginning May to mid Sept.

3.6 ha (100 pitches) open site, flat, grassy, stony

Tariff : (2014 Price) 28.50€ ✦✦ ⬌ 🔲 🔌 (10A) – Extra per person 5.70€ – Reservation fee 16€

Rental rates : (2014 Price) (from beginning May to mid Sept.) – 8 🏠 – 8 🏠. Per week from 265 to 685€ – Reservation fee 16€

In a pleasant setting, partially wooded, beside a stream.

Surroundings : 🏞 ≤ 🚰 ♀♀
Leisure activities : 🍴 ✗ 🎮 ⛵ 🛶
Facilities : 🔌 ⚲ 🚰 launderette 🛠
Nearby : ✗ 🔲

SISTERON

04200 – Michelin map **334** D7 – pop. 7 427 – alt. 490
▶ Paris 704 – Barcelonnette 100 – Digne-les-Bains 40 – Gap 52

⚠ Municipal des Prés-Hauts

✆ 04 92 61 19 69. www.sisteron.fr

Address : 44 chemin des Prés Hauts (3km north following signs for Gap and take D 951 to the right, follow the signs for La Motte-du-Caire, near the Durance river)

Opening times : from beginning April to end Sept.

4 ha (145 pitches)Tariff : 26.50€ ✦✦ ⬌ 🔲 🔌 (10A) – Extra per person 4€ – Reservation fee 10€
Rental rates : (from beginning May to end Sept.) – 10 🏠. Per week from 290 to 545€

🚻 18 🔲 14.50€

There's a shuttle bus for the town centre.

Surroundings : 🏞 ≤ 🚰 ♀
Leisure activities : 🎮 ⛵ 🛶
Facilities : 🔌 ⚲ 🚰 🔲 🚰 🛠 🛠

| G P S | Longitude : 5.93645 |
| | Latitude : 44.21432 |

Key to rentals symbols:

12 🏠	*Number of mobile homes*
20 🏠	*Number of chalets*
6 🛏	*Number of rooms to rent*
Per night 30–50€	*Minimum/maximum rate per night*
Per week 300–1,000€	*Minimum/maximum rate per week*

SOSPEL

06380 – Michelin map **341** F4 – pop. 3 523 – alt. 360
▶ Paris 967 – Breil-sur-Roya 21 – L'Escarène 22 – Lantosque 42

⚠ Domaine Ste-Madeleine

✆ 04 93 04 10 48. www.camping-sainte-madeleine.com

Address : route de Moulinet (4.5km northwest along the D 2566, follow the signs for Le Col de Turini)

Opening times : from end March to beginning Oct.

3 ha (90 pitches) very uneven

Tariff : 25.50€ ✦✦ ⬌ 🔲 🔌 (10A) – Extra per person 5€
Rental rates : (from end March to beginning Oct.) 🏠 – 3 🏠 – 10 🏠 – 1 apartment. Per night from 55 to 100€ – Per week from 320 to 620€

🚻 borne 3€

The pitches are on shaded terrances beneath olive trees, but the rental and sanitary facilities are old.

Surroundings : 🏞 ≤ ♀♀
Leisure activities : 🛶
Facilities : 🔌 ⚲ 🚰 🛠

| G P S | Longitude : 7.41575 |
| | Latitude : 43.8967 |

TARADEAU

83460 – Michelin map **340** N5 – pop. 1 694 – alt. 74
▶ Paris 853 – Marseille 107 – Toulon 66 – Monaco 111

⋀⋀ La Vallée de Taradeau

La Vallée de Taradeau

📞 04 94 73 09 14. www.
campingdetaradeau.com

Address : towards Vidauban, just off
the D 73, south of Taradeau

Opening times : Permanent

1.5 ha (80 pitches) flat, stony, gravelled

Tariff : (2014 Price) 31.45€ ♠♠ ⇐ 🗉
🖑 (6A) – Extra per person 10€ –
Reservation fee 16.50€

Rental rates : (2014 Price) Permanent – 8 ⟦ ⟧ – 11 🏠 – 3 tent
lodges – 3 canvas bungalows (with sanitary facilities). Per night
from 52 to 150€ – Per week from 319 to 1,080 € – Reservation
fee 16.50€

🖭 borne 5€

*There's a variety of rental accommodation, including some
good-quality. options.*

Surroundings : 🐟 ⊡ 〰	**G**	Longitude : 6.42755
Leisure activities : ♛ ✗ ⛵ jacuzzi ⤙ ⤙	**P**	Latitude : 43.44118
Facilities : ⊶ launderette ⤙	**S**	

LE THOR

84250 – Michelin map **332** C10 – pop. 8 099 – alt. 50
▶ Paris 688 – Avignon 18 – Carpentras 16 – Cavaillon 14

⋀⋀ FranceLoc Domaine Le Jantou

📞 04 90 33 90 07. www.campings-franceloc.fr

Address : 535 chemin des Coudelières (head 1.2km west via the
northern exit towards Bédarrides; direct access to the Sorgue,
recommended route via the D 1 (bypass)

Opening times : from beginning April to end Sept.

6 ha/4 for camping (195 pitches) flat, grassy

Tariff : (2014 Price) 34€ ♠♠ ⇐ 🗉 🖑 (10A) – Extra per person 7€
Rental rates : (2014 Price) (from beginning April to end Sept.) –
8 caravans – 146 ⟦ ⟧ – 6 🏠 – 6 tent lodges. Per night
from 33 to 166€ – Per week from 133 to 1,162€

Surroundings : 🐟 〰	**G**	Longitude : 4.98282
Leisure activities : ⛵ ⤙⤙ 🏊 ⛷ ⟲	**P**	Latitude : 43.92969
Facilities : ♿ ⊶ ▥ ♨ ⤙ ⅋ launderette	**S**	
⤙ refrigerators		
Nearby : 🛒		

LES THUILES

04400 – Michelin map **334** H6 – pop. 374 – alt. 1 130
▶ Paris 752 – Marseille 221 – Digne-les-Bains 82 – Gap 62

⋀⋀ Le Fontarache

📞 04 92 81 90 42. www.camping-fontarache.fr – alt. 1 108

Address : Les Thuiles Basses (take the eastern exit out of the town,
D 900, follow the signs for Barcelonnette)

Opening times : from beginning June to mid Sept.

6 ha (150 pitches) open site, grassy

Tariff : (2014 Price) 24.20€ ♠♠ ⇐ 🗉 🖑 (6A) – Extra per person 5€ –
Reservation fee 12€

Rental rates : (2014 Price) (from beginning June to mid Sept.) –
16 ⟦ ⟧ – 2 🏠. Per week from 250 to 670€ – Reservation fee 12€
🖭 borne 5€ – 🔋 11€

Choose the pitches furthest away from the river in preference.

Surroundings : ⋞ ⊡ 〰	**G**	Longitude : 6.57537
Leisure activities : ♛ ✗ 🏊 multi-sports	**P**	Latitude : 44.3924
ground	**S**	
Facilities : ♿ ⊶ ⊟ ♨ ⅋ launderette		
Nearby : 🏊 ✗ ⤙ ⛵ (river) rafting and		
canyoning		

*Some campsites benefit from proximity to a municipal
leisure centre.*

VAISON-LA-ROMAINE

84110 – Michelin map **332** D8 – pop. 6 153 – alt. 193
▶ Paris 664 – Avignon 51 – Carpentras 27 – Montélimar 64

⋀⋀ FranceLoc Le Carpe Diem ⛾⛾

📞 04 90 36 02 02. www.camping-carpe-diem.com

Address : route de St-Marcellin (situated 2km southeast at the
intersection of the D 938 (rte de Malaucène) and the D 151)

Opening times : from mid April to beginning Nov.

10 ha/6.5 for camping (232 pitches) terraced, relatively flat, flat,
grassy

Tariff : (2014 Price) 40€ ♠♠ ⇐ 🗉 🖑 (10A) – Extra per person 7€ –
Reservation fee 27€

Rental rates : (2014 Price) (from mid April to beginning Nov.) –
202 ⟦ ⟧ – 14 🏠 – 1 cabin in the trees – 3 canvas bungalows –
6 tent lodges. Per night from 37 to 150€ – Per week
from 147 to 1,050€ – Reservation fee 27€

🖭 borne

*There's an unusual reconstruction of an amphitheatre beside
the swimming pool.*

Surroundings : 🐟 ⊡ 〰	**G**	Longitude : 5.08945
Leisure activities : ♛ ✗ ⛵ ☗ ⤙⤙ ⤙⤙	**P**	Latitude : 44.23424
🏊 ⛷ ⟲	**S**	
Facilities : ♿ ⊶ ♨ ▣ 🏊 ⤙ refrigerated		
food storage facilities		

⋀⋀ Le Soleil de Provence

📞 04 90 46 46 00. www.camping-soleil-de-provence.fr

Address : Trameiller district (3.5km northeast along the D 938, follow
the signs for Nyons)

4 ha (153 pitches) terraced, relatively flat, flat, grassy, stony
Rentals : 26 ⟦ ⟧.

Surroundings : ⋞ Ventoux and mountains of	**G**	Longitude : 5.10616
Nyons ⊡ ♀	**P**	Latitude : 44.26838
Leisure activities : ⛵ ⤙⤙ 🏊 ⛷	**S**	
Facilities : ♿ ⊶ ▥ ♨ ⅋ ▣		

Michelin classification:

⋀⋀⋀⋀ *Extremely comfortable, equipped to a very high
standard*

⋀⋀⋀ *Very comfortable, equipped to a high standard*

⋀⋀⋀ *Comfortable and well equipped*

⋀⋀ *Reasonably comfortable*

⋀ *Satisfactory*

⚫ Théâtre Romain

Théâtre Romain

📞 04 90 28 78 66. www.camping-theatre.com

Address : Les Arts district – Chemin du Brusquet (to the northeast of the town, recommended route via the bypass (rocade)

Opening times : from mid March to beginning Nov.

1.2 ha (75 pitches) flat, grassy, fine gravel

Tariff : (2014 Price) 29.90€ ★★ ⚌ 🄴 ⚡ (10A) – Extra per person 8€ Reservation fee 11€

Rental rates : (from mid March to beginning Nov.) – 9 🛖. Per night from 35 to 95€ – Per week from 220 to 660€ – Reservation fee 11€

🚐 borne 5€ – 🔋14€

Surroundings : 🏕 ♨️
Leisure activities : 🏖 🚣 🏊 (small swimming pool)
Facilities : ♿ ⚊ 🍽 🏕 🚿 🛗 🔲
Nearby : 🍴

GPS Longitude : 5.07843
Latitude : 44.24505

VENCE

06140 – Michelin map **341** D5 – pop. 19 183 – alt. 325
▶ Paris 923 – Antibes 20 – Cannes 30 – Grasse 24

⚫ Domaine de la Bergerie

Domaine de la Bergerie

📞 04 93 58 09 36. www.camping-domainedelabergerie.com

Address : 1330 chemin de la Sine (4km west along the D 2210, follow the signs for Grasse and take road to the left)

Opening times : from end March to mid Oct.

30 ha/13 for camping (450 pitches) terraced, flat, grassy, stony

Tariff : (2014 Price) 33€ ★★ ⚌ 🄴 ⚡ (5A) – Extra per person 5.30€ – Reservation fee 15€

Rental rates : (2014 Price) Permanent 🏠 – 6 cabins and 2 chalets (without sanitary facilities). Per night from 30.40 to 41.40€ – Per week from 250 to 460€ – Reservation fee 15€

🚐 borne 5€

A very pleasant natural setting in an old, attractively restored sheep farm.

Surroundings : 🏔 🏕 ♨️
Leisure activities : 🍴 🍽 🚣 🎿 🏊
Facilities : ♿ ⚊ 🔲 🏕 🚿 🛗 launderette 🍴🚿
Nearby : sports trail

GPS Longitude : 7.08981
Latitude : 43.71253

LE VERNET

04140 – Michelin map **334** G7 – pop. 123 – alt. 1 200
▶ Paris 729 – Digne-les-Bains 32 – La Javie 16 – Gap 68

⚫ Lou Passavous

📞 04 92 35 14 67. www.loupassavous.com

Address : route Roussimal (800m north following signs for Roussimat; beside the Bès river)

Opening times : from beginning May to mid Sept.

1.5 ha (60 pitches) open site, relatively flat, flat, grassy, stony

Tariff : (2014 Price) 16€ ★★ ⚌ 🄴 ⚡ (6A) – Extra per person 5.25€ Reservation fee 13.50€

Rental rates : (2014 Price) (from beginning May to mid Sept.) 🏠 – 2 🛖 – 2 tent lodges. Per night from 75€ – Per week from 540 to 640€ – Reservation fee 13.50€

In a green setting, crossed by a small stream.

Surroundings : 🏔 ♨️
Leisure activities : 🍴 🚣
Facilities : ♿ ⚊ 🔲 🏕 🚿 🍴 🔲 🚿
Nearby : 🍴 🏊 🎣

GPS Longitude : 6.39139
Latitude : 44.28194

VEYNES

05400 – Michelin map **334** C5 – pop. 3 166 – alt. 827
▶ Paris 660 – Aspres-sur-Buëch 9 – Gap 25 – Sisteron 51

⚫ Les Prés

📞 04 92 57 26 22. www.camping-les-pres.com – alt. 960

Address : Le Petit Vaux (3.4km northeast along the D 994 follow the signs for Gap, then continue 5.5km along the D 937 following signs for Superdevoluy and take road to the left via the bridge over the Béoux)

Opening times : from mid April to mid Oct.

0.35 ha (22 pitches)

Tariff : (2014 Price) 14.50€ ★★ ⚌ 🄴 ⚡ (10A) – Extra per person 4€

Rental rates : (2014 Price) Permanent 🏠 – 4 🛖 – 3 canvas bungalows. Per night from 45 to 120€ – Per week from 120 to 490€

🚐 borne – 🔋8€

Surroundings : 🏔 ♨️
Facilities : ♿ ⚊ 🍴 🔲

GPS Longitude : 5.84995
Latitude : 44.58842

VILLAR-LOUBIÈRE

05800 – Michelin map **334** E4 – pop. 48 – alt. 1 026
▶ Paris 648 – La Chapelle-en-Valgaudémar 5 – Corps 22 – Gap 43

⚫ Municipal Les Gravières

📞 04 92 55 35 35. http://www.sudrafting.fr/camping-villar-loubiere.html

Address : 700m east following signs for La Chapelle-en-Valgaudémar and take the road to the right

Opening times : from mid May to end Aug.

2 ha (50 pitches) flat, grassy, stony, wood

Tariff : (2014 Price) 17.40€ ★★ ⚌ 🄴 ⚡ (2A) – Extra per person 3.70€

An ideal destination for whitewater sports fans.

Surroundings : 🏔 ♨️
Leisure activities : 🏖 🎣 🛶 rafting and canyoning
Facilities : ♿ ⚊ (July–Aug.) 🍴 🔲

GPS Longitude : 6.1464
Latitude : 44.82373

VILLARS-COLMARS

04370 – Michelin map **334** H7 – pop. 246 – alt. 1 225
▶ Paris 774 – Annot 37 – Barcelonnette 46 – Colmars 3

🏔 Le Haut-Verdon

🖉 04 92 83 40 09. www.lehautverdon.com – access via Col d'Allos strictly not advised

Address : 0.6km south along the D 908, follow the signs for Castellane

Opening times : Permanent

3.5 ha (109 pitches) open site

Tariff : 28€ ✹✹ 🚐 🔲 (10A) (10A) – Extra per person 5€ – Reservation fee 15€

Rental rates : Permanent – 6 🚲 – 4 🏠. Per night from 45 to 75€ – Per week from 250 to 700€ – Reservation fee 15€

🚰 borne 4€
Choose the pitches near the Verdon river in preference.

Surroundings : ≼ 🏕 🎠
Leisure activities : 🍷✗ 🏠 🏋 🎣 🏊 🛶
Facilities : ❍🛒 🏛 🍴 🔲 🗑

GPS Longitude : 6.60573
Latitude : 44.1604

A 'quartier' is a district or area of a town or village.

VILLECROZE

83690 – Michelin map **340** M4 – pop. 1 128 – alt. 300
▶ Paris 835 – Aups 8 – Brignoles 38 – Draguignan 21

🏔 Le Ruou 👥

🖉 04 94 70 67 70. www.leruou.com – limited spaces for one-night stay

Address : 309 road RD 560 (5.4km southeast along the D 251, follow the signs for Barbebelle and take D 560, follow the signs for Flayosc, recommended route via the D 560)

Opening times : from mid April to mid Oct.

4.3 ha (134 pitches) very uneven, terraced, flat, grassy

Tariff : (2014 Price) 40€ ✹✹ 🚐 🔲 (10A) – Extra per person 7.20€ Reservation fee 25€

Rental rates : (2014 Price) (from mid April to mid Oct.) – 39 🚲 – 19 🏠 – 12 canvas bungalows. Per night from 33 to 147€ – Per week from 231 to 1,029€ – Reservation fee 25€

🚰 borne 5€ – 10 🔲 18.50€ – 🚐 🚰18.50€
The pitches are arranged on terraces under pine trees, with a view from some over the water park.

Surroundings : 🎠
Leisure activities : 🍷✗ 🏠 🎪 🏋 🏊 🔍
Facilities : ❤ ❍🛒 🍴 launderette 🗑

GPS Longitude : 6.29795
Latitude : 43.55542

VILLENEUVE-LOUBET-PLAGE

06270 – Michelin map **341**
▶ Paris 919 – Marseille 191 – Nice 24 – Monaco 38

🏔 La Vieille Ferme

🖉 04 93 33 41 44. www.vieilleferme.com

Address : 296 boulevard des Groules (2.8km south along the N 7, follow the signs for Antibes and take a right turn)

Opening times : Permanent

2.9 ha (153 pitches) terraced, flat, grassy, fine gravel

Tariff : 43€ ✹✹ 🚐 🔲 (10A) – Extra per person 6€ – Reservation fee 28€

Rental rates : Permanent – 32 🏠. Per night from 55 to 80€ – Per week from 365 to 960€ – Reservation fee 2€

🚰 borne

Surroundings : 🏕 🎠
Leisure activities : 🏠 ⛲daytime jacuzzi 🏋 🔍 (open air in season)
Facilities : ❤ ❍🛒 🏛 🎪 🗑 🍴 launderette 🧊 refrigerated food storage facilities

GPS Longitude : 7.12579
Latitude : 43.61967

🏔 Parc des Maurettes

🖉 04 93 20 91 91. www.parcdesmaurettes.com

Address : 730 avenue du Dr Lefèbvre (along the N 7)

Opening times : from beginning Jan. to mid Nov.

2 ha (108 pitches) terraced, flat, grassy, gravelled, stony

Tariff : (2014 Price) 38€ ✹✹ 🚐 🔲 (10A) – Extra per person 6€ – Reservation fee 25€

Rental rates : (2014 Price) (from beginning Jan. to mid Nov.) – 14 🏠 – 2 🏚 – 3 studios. Per night from 63 to 77€ – Per week from 685 to 799€ – Reservation fee 25€

🚰 borne 6€ – 5 🔲 16.70€
Situated in an urban zone, with plenty of shade and a pleasant spa and relaxation area

Surroundings : 🏕 🎠
Leisure activities : 🏠 ⛲s jacuzzi 🏋
Facilities : ❤ ❍🛒 🅿 🏛 🗑 🍴 launderette
Nearby : 🛒

GPS Longitude : 7.12964
Latitude : 43.63111

🏔 L'Hippodrome

🖉 04 93 20 02 00. www.camping-hippodrome.com

Address : 5 avenue des Rives (400m from the beach, behind the Géant Casino commercial centre)

Opening times : Permanent

0.8 ha (57 pitches) flat, grassy, fine gravel

Tariff : 35.50€ ✹✹ 🚐 🔲 (10A) – Extra per person 5.50€ – Reservation fee 20€

Rental rates : Permanent 🏚 – 15 studios. Per night from 40 to 65.90€ – Per week from 280 to 462€ – Reservation fee 20€

🚰 borne – 57 🔲 35€
Situated in an urban area, the site is in two sections.

Surroundings : 🏕 🎠
Leisure activities : 🏠 🏋 🔍 (open air in season)
Facilities : ❤ ❍🛒 🎪 🗑 🍴 launderette refrigerators
Nearby : 🛒 ✗

GPS Longitude : 7.13771
Latitude : 43.64199

These symbols are used for a campsite that is exceptional in its category:

🏔🏔...🏔   *Particularly pleasant setting, quality and range of services available*

🐚🐚   *Tranquil, isolated site – quiet site, particularly at night*

≼≼   *Exceptional view – interesting or panoramic view*

VILLES-SUR-AUZON

84570 – Michelin map **332** E9 – pop. 1 296 – alt. 255
▶ Paris 694 – Avignon 45 – Carpentras 19 – Malaucène 24

🏔 Les Verguettes

🕾 04 90 61 88 18. www.provence-camping.com
Address : route de Carpentras (take the western exit along the D 942)
2 ha (88 pitches) terraced, relatively flat, flat, grassy, stony
Rentals : 8 🚐.

Surroundings : 🏞 ≤ Mont Ventoux 🖵 ♀♀ Leisure activities : 🏠 ✂ 🏓 🏊 Facilities : ♿ ⚡ ▥ 🏕 ☂ 🚰 🍴 🔲 🛒 refrigerators	**GPS** Longitude : 5.22834 Latitude : 44.05686

VIOLÈS

84150 – Michelin map **332** C9 – pop. 1 546 – alt. 94
▶ Paris 659 – Avignon 34 – Carpentras 21 – Nyons 33

🏕 Les Favards

🕾 04 90 70 90 93. www.favards.com
Address : route d'Orange (1.2km west along the D 67)
20 ha/1.5 (49 pitches) flat, grassy
Situated in the grounds of a vineyard.

Surroundings : 🏞 ≤ 🖵 ♀ Leisure activities : 🍷 🏊 Facilities : ♿ ⚡ 🍴 🔲 refrigerated food storage facilities	**GPS** Longitude : 4.93528 Latitude : 44.16229

VISAN

84820 – Michelin map **332** C8 – pop. 1 956 – alt. 218
▶ Paris 652 – Avignon 57 – Bollène 19 – Nyons 20

🏕 L'Hérein

🕾 04 90 41 95 99. www.campingvisan.com
Address : route de Bouchet (located 1km west along the D 161,
follow the signs for Bouchet; near a stream)
Opening times : from mid March to mid Oct.
3.3 ha (75 pitches)
Tariff : 16.50€ ✹✹ 🚗 🔲 🎆 (10A) – Extra per person 4.70€ –
Reservation fee 10€
Rental rates : (from mid March to mid Oct.) – 5 🚐. Per night
from 45 to 75€ – Per week from 285 to 380€ – Reservation fee 10€
🚽 borne – 8 🔲 11.50€

Surroundings : 🏞 🖵 ♀♀ Leisure activities : ✗ 🏠 🏄 🏓 🏊 Facilities : ♿ ⚡ ▥ ☂ 🚰 🍴 🔲 🛒	**GPS** Longitude : 4.93601 Latitude : 44.31236

VOLONNE

04290 – Michelin map **334** E8 – pop. 1 658 – alt. 450
▶ Paris 718 – Château-Arnoux-St-Aubin 4 – Digne-les-Bains 29 –
Forcalquier 33

🏔 Sunêlia L'Hippocampe ♟♙

🕾 04 92 33 50 00. www.l-hippocampe.com
Address : route Napoléon (500m southeast along the D 4)
Opening times : from end April to end Sept.
8 ha (447 pitches) flat, grassy, fruit trees
Tariff : 36€ ✹✹ 🚗 🔲 🎆 (10A) – Extra per person 8€ – Reservation
fee 30€
Rental rates : (from end April to end Sept.) – 185 🚐 – 30 🏠 –
16 canvas bungalows. Per night from 35 to 214€ – Per week
from 245 to 1,498€ – Reservation fee 30€
🚽 borne 5€ – 9 🔲 11€ – 🚐8€
*Situated beside the Durance river; various rental options and
some luxury mobile homes and chalets.*

Surroundings : 🏞 ≤ 🖵 ♀♀ Leisure activities : 🍷 ✗ 🏠 🖼 🏃 🏄 🚴 🏓 🏊 🎣 disco, pedalos 🚣 multi-sports ground, entertainment room Facilities : ♿ ⚡ ▥ ☂ 🚰 🍴 launderette 🔲 🛒	**GPS** Longitude : 6.0173 Latitude : 44.1054

*This guide is not intended as a list of all the camping
sites in France; its aim is to provide a selection of the
best sites in each category.*

VOLX

04130 – Michelin map **334** D9 – pop. 2 953 – alt. 350
▶ Paris 748 – Digne-les-Bains 51 – Forcalquier 15 – Gréoux-les-
Bains 22

🏕 La Vandelle

🕾 04 86 56 67 83. www.camping-lavandelle.com
Address : avenue de la Vandelle (1.3km southwest of the town)
Opening times : from beginning May to end Sept.
2 ha (50 pitches) terrace
Tariff : (2014 Price) 20€ ✹✹ 🚗 🔲 🎆 (10A) – Extra per person 4€
🚽 borne 5€
*Part of the site is situated among trees, very quiet and
peaceful.*

Surroundings : 🏞 ♀♀ Leisure activities : 🏊 Facilities : ♿ ⚡ 🚽 🚰 🍴 🔲	**GPS** Longitude : 5.83162 Latitude : 43.869

RHÔNE-ALPES

G. Labriet / Photononstop

Rhône-Alpes is a region of contrasts and a cultural crossroads. Its lofty peaks are a snow-covered paradise for skiers, climbers and hikers, drawn by the beauty of its shimmering glaciers and tranquil lakes; stylish Chamonix and Courchevel set the tone and the pace in cool Alpine chic. Descend from the roof of Europe, past herds of cattle on the mountain pastures and into the bustle of the Rhône valley. From Roman roads to speedy TGVs, playing host to the main arteries between north and south has forged the region's reputation for economic drive. Holidaymakers may rush through Rhône-Alpes in summer but those in the know linger to enjoy its culinary specialities. The region boasts a host of Michelin-starred restaurants: three-starred trendsetters and the legendary neighbourhood *bouchons* (small, family-run bistros) of Lyon, capital of this gastronomic paradise, make it a compulsory stop. Enjoy a Bresse chicken, cheese and sausages from Lyon and a glass of Côtes du Rhône.

RHÔNE-ALPES

LES ABRETS

38490 – Michelin map **333** G4 – pop. 3 186 – alt. 398
▶ Paris 514 – Aix-les-Bains 45 – Belley 31 – Chambéry 38

⛰ Kawan Village Le Coin Tranquille 👥

✆ 04 76 32 13 48, www.coin-tranquille.com

Address : 6 chemin des Vignes (head 2.3km east along the N 6, follow the signs for Le Pont-de-Beauvoisin and take turning to the left)

Opening times : from beginning April to end Oct.

4 ha (196 pitches)

Tariff : 37 € 👬 🚐 🗐 ⚡ (10A) – Extra per person 8 € – Reservation fee 16 €

Rental rates : (from beginning April to end Oct.) 🅿 – 14 🏠. Per night from 84 to 108 € – Per week from 385 to 861 € – Reservation fee 31 €

🚐 borne

Some lovely, well marked-out pitches, on a site decorated with flowers.

Surroundings : 🏊 ≼ 🏞 ♨♨
Leisure activities : 🍷 ✗ 🛶 🎣 🏊 🚴 multi-sports ground
Facilities : 🚻 🔌 🆑🏭 🚿 ⛲ launderette 🧺 🚮

Longitude : 5.6084
Latitude : 45.54139

To visit a town or region, use the MICHELIN Green Guides.

AIGUEBLANCHE

73260 – Michelin map **333** M4 – pop. 3 129 – alt. 461
▶ Paris 641 – Lyon 174 – Chambéry 74 – Albertville 25

⛰ Marie-France

✆ 06 09 47 32 30. www.campingresidencesmariefrance.fr

Address : 453 avenue de Savoie

Opening times : Permanent

0.5 ha (30 pitches)

Tariff : 14.20 € 👬 🚐 🗐 ⚡ (10A) – Extra per person 2.90 €
Rental rates : Permanent – 20 studios – 10 apartments. Per night from 45 to 120 € – Per week from 200 to 360 €
🚐 borne – 10 🗐 4 € – 🚰 11.60 €

The pitches have plenty of shade and there's a good choice of rentals.

Surroundings : ≼ 🏞 ♨♨
Leisure activities : 🛶 🎿
Facilities : 🚻 🔌 ⛲ 🔲
At the leisure/activities centre : 🍷 ✗ 🚡 🛶 ⛷ ⛳ 🎳 🏊 ♨ 🚣 sports trail

Longitude : 6.489
Latitude : 45.50717

AIX-LES-BAINS

73100 – Michelin map **333** I3 – pop. 26 819 – alt. 200 – ♨
▶ Paris 539 – Annecy 34 – Bourg-en-Bresse 115 – Chambéry 18

⛰ International du Sierroz

✆ 04 79 61 89 89, www.camping-sierroz.com

Address : boulevard Robert Barrier (2.5km to the northwest)

Opening times : from mid March to mid Nov.

5 ha (255 pitches)

Tariff : 25.80 € 👬 🚐 🗐 ⚡ (10A) – Extra per person 5.40 € – Reservation fee 3.50 €

Rental rates : (from mid March to mid Nov.) ♿ (1 mobile home) – 34 🏠. Per week from 289 to 689 € – Reservation fee 12 €
🚐 borne 5 €

In two sections with an annexe at 500m, close to the Lac du Bourget.

Surroundings : 🏞 ♨♨
Leisure activities : 🍷 ✗ 🛶 🎣
Facilities : 🚻 🔌 🏭 🚿 🛁 ⛲ launderette 🧺
Nearby : 🏊 🎣 🚣

Longitude : 5.88628
Latitude : 45.70104

ALEX

74290 – Michelin map **328** K5 – pop. 980 – alt. 589
▶ Paris 545 – Albertville 42 – Annecy 12 – La Clusaz 20

⛰ La Ferme des Ferrières

✆ 04 50 02 87 09, www.camping-des-ferrieres.com

Address : located 1.5km west along the D 909, follow the signs for Annecy and take the road to the right

Opening times : from beginning June to end Sept.

5 ha (200 pitches) relatively flat, flat, grassy

Tariff : (2014 Price) 16.50 € 👬 🚐 🗐 ⚡ (5A) – Extra per person 2.80 €

The campsite is on an attractive, shaded field, at a working farm.

Surroundings : 🏊 ≼ ♨♨
Leisure activities : 🍷 🛶 🎣
Facilities : 🚻 🔌 🚿 🛁 🔲

Longitude : 6.22346
Latitude : 45.89015

ALLEVARD

38580 – Michelin map **333** J5 – pop. 3 768 – alt. 470 – ♨
▶ Paris 593 – Albertville 50 – Chambéry 33 – Grenoble 40

⛰ Clair Matin

✆ 04 76 97 55 19, www.camping-clair-matin.com

Address : 20 rue des Pommiers (take the southwestern exit along the D 525, follow the signs for Grenoble)

Opening times : from beginning May to mid Oct.

5.5 ha (200 pitches) terraced, relatively flat, flat, grassy

Tariff : (2014 Price) 🚶 3.70 € 🚐 🗐 13.85 € – ⚡ (10A) 5.75 € – Reservation fee 8 €
Rental rates : (2014 Price) (from beginning May to mid Oct.) – 29 🏠. Per night from 29 to 78 € – Per week from 204 to 597 € Reservation fee 13 €
🚐 borne – 4 🗐 11 € – 🚰 ⚡ 8 €

Surroundings : 🏊 ≼ ♨♨
Leisure activities : ✗ 🛶 🏊
Facilities : 🚻 🔌 🚿 🛁 ⛲ launderette

Longitude : 6.06591
Latitude : 45.38869

ANNECY

74000 – Michelin map **328** J5 – pop. 51 012 – alt. 448
▶ Paris 544 – Chambéry 51 – Genève 42 – Lyon 138

⛰ Municipal Le Belvédère

✆ 04 50 45 48 30. www.annecy.fr

Address : to the south along the D 41

Opening times : from end March to mid Oct.

3 ha (102 pitches) terraced, flat, grassy, gravelled

Tariff : (2014 Price) 26 € 👬 🚐 🗐 ⚡ (16A) – Extra per person 6.20 €

Rental rates : (2014 Price) (from end March to mid Oct.) ♿ (10 chalets) – 12 🏠. Per week from 390 to 690€

🚐 borne

A pretty little chalet village adjacent to a forest.

Surroundings : 🌲 ⚲⚲
Leisure activities : 🍸 🏛 ⚡ 🛶 ⛷
Facilities : ♿ ⚬➡ 🏬 ⚱ ➡ launderette

| | Longitude : 6.13237 |
|**GPS**| Latitude : 45.89025 |

ANSE

69480 – Michelin map **327** H4 – pop. 5 604 – alt. 170
▶ Paris 436 – L'Arbresle 17 – Bourg-en-Bresse 57 – Lyon 27

⛰ **Les Portes du Beaujolais**

🕾 04 74 67 12 87, www.camping-beaujolais.com

Address : 495 avenue Jean Vacher (take the southeastern exit, follow the signs for Lyon and 600m along the road turn left before the bridge)

Opening times : from beginning March to end Oct.

7.5 ha (198 pitches) flat, grassy

Tariff : 29.50€ ⚝⚝ ⚗ 🔲 ⚡ (16A) – Extra per person 5.20€
Rental rates : Permanent – 35 🏕 – 30 🏠. Per week from 299 to 1,189€ – Reservation fee 5€

🚐 borne

Situated at the point where the Azergues and Saône rivers meet.

Surroundings : ▱ ⚲
Leisure activities : 🍸 ✕ 🏛 🏊 hammam, jacuzzi ⚡ 🌊 spa centre
Facilities : ♿ ⚬➡ CC 🏬 ⚱ ➡ ⚘ ⚌ ⚑
Nearby : 🎣

| | Longitude : 4.72616 |
|**GPS**| Latitude : 45.94106 |

ARGENTIÈRE

74400 – Michelin map **328** O5 – alt. 1 252
▶ Paris 619 – Annecy 106 – Chamonix-Mont-Blanc 10 – Vallorcine 10

⛰ **Le Glacier d'Argentière**

🕾 04 50 54 17 36. www.campingchamonix.com – 🏶

Address : 161 chemin des Chosalets (located 1km south following signs for Chamonix, 200m from the Arve river)

Opening times : from mid May to end Sept.

1 ha (80 pitches)

Tariff : 21.80€ ⚝⚝ ⚗ 🔲 ⚡ (10A) – Extra per person 5.60€
Rental rates : (from mid May to end April) – 1 apartment – 1 canvas bungalow – 1 tent lodge. Per night from 30 to 50€ – Per week from 210 to 350€

🚐 borne 10€ – 25 🔲 17.30€

Surroundings : ⚟ ⚲
Leisure activities : ✕ 🏛
Facilities : ♿ ⚬➡ (July–Aug.) ➡ ⚘
launderette

| | Longitude : 6.92363 |
|**GPS**| Latitude : 45.9747 |

Key to rentals symbols:

12 🏕	*Number of mobile homes*
20 🏠	*Number of chalets*
6 🛏	*Number of rooms to rent*
Per night 30–50€	*Minimum/maximum rate per night*
Per week 300–1,000€	*Minimum/maximum rate per week*

ARTEMARE

01510 – Michelin map **328** H5 – pop. 1 112 – alt. 245
▶ Paris 506 – Aix-les-Bains 33 – Ambérieu-en-Bugey 47 – Belley 18

⛰ Sites et Paysages **Le Vaugrais**

🕾 04 79 87 37 34. www.camping-le-vaugrais.fr

Address : at Cerveyrieu, 2 chemin le Vaugrais (700m west along the D 69d, follow the signs for Belmont, beside the Séran river)

1 ha (33 pitches) flat, grassy

Surroundings : ⚟ ▱ ⚲
Leisure activities : 🍸 🏛 ⚡ 🚲 🌊 🎣
Facilities : ♿ ⚬➡ 🏬 ⚱ ⚘ ⚌ ⚑

| | Longitude : 5.68383 |
|**GPS**| Latitude : 45.87465 |

*The classification (1 to 5 tents, **black** or red) that we award to selected sites in this guide is our own system. It should not be confused with the classification (1 to 5 stars) of official organisations.*

AUSSOIS

73500 – Michelin map **333** N6 – pop. 677 – alt. 1 489
▶ Paris 670 – Albertville 97 – Chambéry 110 – Lanslebourg-Mont-Cenis 17

⛰ **Municipal la Buidonnière**

🕾 04 79 20 35 58, www.camping-aussois.com

Address : route de Cottériat (take the southern exit along the D 215, follow the signs for Modane and take road to the left)

Opening times : Permanent

4 ha (160 pitches) terraced, relatively flat, grassy, stony

Tariff : ⚝ ⚗ 🔲 6.90€ – ⚡ (10A) 6€
🚐 borne 2€ – 40 🔲 6.90€

Panoramic views and numerous owner-occupier caravans.

Surroundings : ❄ 🌲 ⚟ Parc de la Vanoise ▱ ⚲
Leisure activities : 🏛 ⚡ 🎿 ⛷ 🌊 (pool) sports trail
Facilities : ♿ ⚬➡ 🏬 ⚑ launderette

| | Longitude : 6.74586 |
|**GPS**| Latitude : 45.22432 |

AUTRANS

38880 – Michelin map **333** G6 – pop. 1 676 – alt. 1 050 – Winter sports : 1 050/1 650 m
▶ Paris 586 – Grenoble 36 – Romans-sur-Isère 58 – St-Marcellin 47

⛰ Yelloh! Village **au Joyeux Réveil** ⚏

🕾 04 76 95 33 44. www.camping-au-joyeux-reveil.fr

Address : Le Château (take the northeastern exit following signs for Montaud and take a right turn)

Opening times : from beginning May to end Sept.

1.5 ha (100 pitches) flat, grassy

Tariff : (2014 Price) 18€ ⚝⚝ ⚗ 🔲 ⚡ (6A) – Extra per person 6€
Rental rates : (2014 Price) (from beginning May to end Sept.) – 30 🏕. Per night from 39 to 109€ – Per week from 273 to 763€

Some luxury rental accommodation is available.

Surroundings : ⚟
Leisure activities : ✕ 🏛 ⚡ 🏊 hammam, jacuzzi ⚡ 🌊 🌊 spa centre
Facilities : ♿ ⚬➡ 🏬 ⚑ ⚌ ⚘

| | Longitude : 5.54844 |
|**GPS**| Latitude : 45.17555 |

BALBIGNY

42510 – Michelin map **327** E5 – pop. 2 809 – alt. 331
▶ Paris 423 – Feurs 10 – Noirétable 44 – Roanne 29

⚒ La Route Bleue

✆ 04 77 27 24 97, http://camping-de-la-route-bleue.fr

Address : Pralery (2.8km northwest along the N 82 and turn left onto D 56, follow the signs for St-Georges-de-Baroille)

Opening times : from mid March to end Oct.

2 ha (100 pitches) relatively flat, flat, grassy

Tariff : 18.30€ ✶✶ ⇌ 🅴 (10A) – Extra per person 3.50€

Rental rates : (from beginning May to end Sept.) – 2 🚐. Per night from 50 to 80€ – Per week from 270 to 540€

In a pleasant location beside the Loire river.

Surroundings : 🏕 ♀	**G**	Longitude : 4.15725
Leisure activities : ⛲✕ 🏛 🎳 🎣	**P**	Latitude : 45.82719
Facilities : 🚿 ⚡ 🚽 launderette	**S**	

LA BALME-DE-SILLINGY

74330 – Michelin map **328** J5 – pop. 4 891 – alt. 480
▶ Paris 524 – Dijon 250 – Grenoble 111 – Lons-le-Saunier 136

⚒ La Caille

✆ 04 50 68 85 21. www.domainedelacaille.com

Address : 18 chemin de la Caille (4km north on N 508 towards Frangy and take the road to the right)

4 ha/1 for camping (50 pitches) relatively flat, flat, grassy

Rentals : 🅿 – 8 🚐 – 12 🏠 – 2 gîtes.
🚐 borne

Gîtes, wooden chalets, mobile homes and camping around the Auberg de la Caille hostel and restaurant.

Surroundings : 🏕 🚐 ♀	**G**	Longitude : 6.03609
Leisure activities : ⛲✕ 🏛 🚣 🎣	**P**	Latitude : 45.97828
Facilities : 🚿 ⚡ 🚽 launderette 🔧	**S**	

BARBIÈRES

26300 – Michelin map **332** D4 – pop. 771 – alt. 426
▶ Paris 586 – Lyon 124 – Valence 23 – Grenoble 79

⚒ Le Gallo-Romain

✆ 04 75 47 44 07, www.legalloromain.net

Address : route du Col de Tourniol (1.2km southeast along the D 101; beside the Barberolle river)

Opening times : from mid April to end Sept.

3 ha (62 pitches) terrace, flat and relatively flat, grassy, stony

Tariff : (2014 Price) 36.50€ ✶✶ ⇌ 🅴 (6A) – Extra per person 6€
Reservation fee 15€

Rental rates : (2014 Price) (from mid April to end Sept.) – 14 🚐. Per night from 51 to 119€ – Per week from 196 to 833€ – Reservation fee 15€

Surroundings : 🏕 ♀ 🚐 ♀♀	**G**	Longitude : 5.15092
Leisure activities : ⛲✕ 🏛 🎳 🎣	**P**	Latitude : 44.94456
Facilities : 🚿 ⚡ 🏧 🍴 launderette 🔧 refrigerators	**S**	

This guide is updated regularly, so buy your new copy every year!

BEAUFORT

73270 – Michelin map **333** M3 – pop. 2 206 – alt. 750
▶ Paris 601 – Albertville 21 – Chambéry 72 – Megève 37

⚑ Municipal Domelin

✆ 04 79 38 33 88, www.mairie-beaufort73.com

Address : in the town (RD 925)

Opening times : from beginning June to end Sept.

2 ha (100 pitches) relatively flat, flat, grassy

Tariff : (2014 Price) ✶ 3.60€ ⇌ 2.35€ 🅴 3.15€ – (2A) 3.20€

This pretty, grassy site is in partial shade, but one of the sanitary blocks is not of a high standard.

Surroundings : 🏕 ≤ ♀	**G**	Longitude : 6.56403
Facilities : 🚿 ⚡ (July–Aug.) 🚽 launderette	**P**	Latitude : 45.7218
	S	

The pitches of many campsites are marked out with low hedges of attractive bushes and shrubs.

BELMONT-DE-LA-LOIRE

42670 – Michelin map **327** F3 – pop. 1 515 – alt. 525
▶ Paris 405 – Chauffailles 6 – Roanne 35 – St-Étienne 108

⚑ Municipal les Écureuils

✆ 04 77 63 72 25. www.belmontdelaloire.fr

Address : Le Plan d'Eau leisure centre (1.4km west along the D 4, follow the signs for Charlieu and take road to the left, 300m from a lake)

Opening times : from beginning May to end Sept.

0.6 ha (28 pitches) terraced, relatively flat to hilly, grassy, gravelled

Tariff : (2014 Price) ✶ 2.35€ ⇌ 1.20€ 🅴 1.45€ – (5A) 2.45€

Rental rates : (2014 Price) Permanent – 9 🏠 – 9 gîtes. Per night from 44 to 77 € – Per week from 255 to 457€
🚐 borne

Situated beside a leisure and activity park.

Surroundings : 🏕 🚐	**G**	Longitude : 4.33819
Leisure activities : 🚣	**P**	Latitude : 46.1662
Facilities : 🚿 🍴 🎳	**S**	
Nearby : 🍴 🎣		

BENIVAY-OLLON

26170 – Michelin map **332** E8 – pop. 66 – alt. 450
▶ Paris 689 – Lyon 227 – Valence 126 – Avignon 71

⚒ Domaine de l'Écluse

✆ 04 75 28 07 32. www.campecluse.com

Address : Barastrage (1km south on the D 347)

Opening times : from end April to mid Sept.

4 ha (75 pitches) undulating, terraced, flat, grassy, stony, fine gravel

Tariff : 28.50€ ✶✶ ⇌ 🅴 (6A) – Extra per person 7€ – Reservation fee 20€

Rental rates : (from mid April to mid Sept.) 🚿 🏊 (from mid July to end Aug.) – 12 🚐 – 12 🏠 – 2 gîtes. Per night from 43 to 150€ – Per week from 301 to 812€ – Reservation fee 20€

Shaded by cherry trees, surrounded by vineyards and beside a stream.

Surroundings : 🏕 ≤ 🚐 ♀♀	**G**	Longitude : 5.18545
Leisure activities : ⛲✕ 🏛 🚣 🎳 🏊 🎣	**P**	Latitude : 44.30298
Facilities : 🚿 ⚡ 🚽 🍴 🏧	**S**	

BERRIAS-ET-CASTELJAU

07460 – Michelin map **331** H7 – pop. 643 – alt. 126
▶ Paris 668 – Aubenas 40 – Largentière 29 – St-Ambroix 18

⛰ Les Cigales

📞 04 75 39 30 33. www.camping-cigales-ardeche.com

Address : La Rouvière (1km to the northeast, follow the signs for Casteljau)

Opening times : Permanent

3 ha (110 pitches) terraced, relatively flat, flat, grassy

Tariff : 30€ ♀♀ ⛺ 🗐 ⚡ (10A) – Extra per person 5.50€

Rental rates : Permanent ⚑ (from beginning April to end Sept.) – 23 🛖 – 7 🏠 – 2 gîtes. Per night from 60 to 90€ – Per week from 250 to 610€

Shaded pitches, on terraces with a pleasant swimming pool.

Surroundings : 🏞 ♤♤
Leisure activities : ♀ 🏠 ⛷ ☆ 🎿
Facilities : ♿ ⛲ 🚾 ♨ 🍴 🗐 🛒

GPS Longitude : 4.21133
Latitude : 44.37829

⛰ La Source ♟

📞 04 75 39 39 13. www.camping-source-ardeche.com

Address : La Rouvière (situated 1.5km northeast, follow the signs for Casteljau)

2.5 ha (93 pitches)

Rentals : 24 🛖 – 4 🏠 – 2 tent lodges – (on stilts).

Various rental options with chalets of a good standard, a pleasant swimming pool area on a site bordered by a stream called Le Gravierou.

Surroundings : 🏞 ⛺ ♤♤
Leisure activities : ☆ 🏠 ⛷ ☆ 🎿
Facilities : ♿ ⛲ ♨ 🍴 🗐 🛒

GPS Longitude : 4.20646
Latitude : 44.37725

BILIEU

38850 – Michelin map **333** G5 – pop. 1 232 – alt. 580
▶ Paris 526 – Belley 44 – Chambéry 47 – Grenoble 38

⛺ Municipal Bord du Lac

📞 04 76 06 67 00. http://campingleborddulac.fr – limited spaces for one-night stay

Address : Le Petit Bilieu (1.9km west, follow the signs for Charavines, recommended route via the D 50d and D 90)

1.3 ha (81 pitches) terraced, flat, grassy, fine gravel

Surroundings : 🏞 ♤♤ ⛰
Leisure activities : 🎣
Facilities : ♿ ⛲ 🚾 🍴 🗐
Nearby : ⚓

GPS Longitude : 5.5312
Latitude : 45.44615

Michelin classification:

⛰⛰⛰⛰ *Extremely comfortable, equipped to a very high standard*
⛰⛰⛰ *Very comfortable, equipped to a high standard*
⛰⛰ *Comfortable and well equipped*
⛰ *Reasonably comfortable*
⛺ *Satisfactory*

BOURDEAUX

26460 – Michelin map **332** D6 – pop. 621 – alt. 426
▶ Paris 608 – Crest 24 – Montélimar 42 – Nyons 40

⛰ Yelloh! Village Les Bois du Châtelas

📞 04 75 00 60 80. www.chatelas.com

Address : route de Dieulefit (1.4km southwest along the D 538)

Opening times : from mid April to beginning Sept.

17 ha/7 for camping (80 pitches) terraced, relatively flat, stony, grassy

Tariff : 48€ ♀♀ ⛺ 🗐 ⚡ (10A) – Extra per person 8€

Rental rates : (from mid April to mid Sept.) – 56 🛖 – 26 🏠 – 3 tipis – 8 tent lodges – 1 gîte. Per night from 35 to 196€ – Per week from 111 to 1,372€

🚐 borne 1€ – 20 🗐 27€ – 🔌 ⚡24€

The campsite boasts a panoramic view from the chalets and restaurant.

Surroundings : 🏞 ⛰ 🏠
Leisure activities : ♀ ☆ 🏠 🛁 hammam, jacuzzi ⛷ 🎡 🎿 multi-sports ground, spa centre
Facilities : ♿ ⛲ 🚾 ♨ ☆ 🍴 🗐 🛒 ♤
Nearby : ☆ ♞

GPS Longitude : 5.12783
Latitude : 44.57832

*For more information on visiting particular towns or regions, consult the relevant regional **MICHELIN Green Guide**. We also recommend you use the appropriate Michelin regional map to locate your selected campsite, to calculate distances and to work out the best route.*

LE BOURG-D'ARUD

38520 – Michelin map **333** J8
▶ Paris 628 – L'Alpe-d'Huez 25 – Le Bourg-d'Oisans 15 – Les Deux-Alpes 29

⛰ Le Champ du Moulin

📞 04 76 80 07 38. www.champ-du-moulin.com

Address : take the western exit along the D 530

Opening times : from beginning June to mid Sept. and from mid Dec. to end April

1.5 ha (80 pitches) open site, flat, grassy, stony

Tariff : 29.20€ ♀♀ ⛺ 🗐 ⚡ (10A) – Extra per person 6.30€ – Reservation fee 17€

Rental rates : (from beginning June to mid Sept. and from mid Dec. to end April) – 4 🛖 – 10 🏠 – 4 apartments – 2 canvas bungalows. Per night from 43 to 102€ – Per week from 301 to 714€ Reservation fee 17€

🚐 borne – 30 🗐 23.30€ – 🔌 ⚡11€

The site is surrounded by the Oisans mountains and beside the Vénéon river.

Surroundings : ❄ 🏞 ♟
Leisure activities : ♀ ☆ 🏠 🛁
Facilities : ♿ ⛲ 🚾 ♨ 🍴 🗐 🛒
At the leisure/activities centre : ⛷ ☆ 🎿 ⛵ rafting and canyoning

GPS Longitude : 6.11986
Latitude : 44.98596

LE BOURG-D'OISANS

38520 – Michelin map **333** J7 – pop. 3 381 – alt. 720
▶ Paris 614 – Briançon 66 – Gap 95 – Grenoble 52

🏔 Les Castels Le Château de Rochetaillée 👥

🖉 0476110440. www.camping-le-chateau.fr

Address : at Rochetaillée, chemin de Bouthéon

Opening times : from mid May to mid Sept.

2.6 ha (135 pitches) flat, grassy

Tariff : 43.40€ ★★ ⏚ 🔲 ⚡ (10A) – Extra per person 9.60€ –
Reservation fee 10€

Rental rates : (from mid May to mid Sept.) – 50 ⛺ – 3 🛏.
Per night from 66 to 124€ – Per week from 290 to 870€ –
Reservation fee 10€

⛽ borne 5€ – 5 🔲 38€ – 🚐 ⚡16€

| Surroundings : ≤ ⏚ ♨♨ |
| Leisure activities : 🍽 🍴 🏊 🎮 🏃 🏄 hammam, jacuzzi 🏄 🧗 climbing wall |
| Facilities : ♿ 🔑 🏕 🚿 ♨ 🍽 launderette 🔌 🌿 |

Longitude : 6.00512
Latitude : 45.11543

🏔 Sites et Paysages À la Rencontre du Soleil

🖉 0476791222. www.alarencontredusoleil.com

Address : route de l'Alpe d'Huez (1.7km to the northeast)

Opening times : from beginning May to end Sept.

1.6 ha (73 pitches) flat, grassy

Tariff : 35€ ★★ ⏚ 🔲 ⚡ (10A) – Extra per person 8.45€ – Reservation
fee 20€

Rental rates : Permanent 🅿 – 4 caravans – 12 ⛺ – 11 🏠.
Per night from 67 to 124€ – Per week from 340 to 865€ –
Reservation fee 20€

⛽ 2 🔲 22€ – 🚐 ⚡18€

| Surroundings : ≤ ⏚ ♨♨ |
| Leisure activities : 🍴 🍽 🏊 (open air in season) multi-sports ground |
| Facilities : 🔑 🏕 ♨ launderette 🌿 |
| Nearby : 🛒 |

Longitude : 6.03716
Latitude : 45.06296

🏔 RCN Belledonne

🖉 0476800718, www.rcn-belledonne.fr

Address : at Rochetaillée

3.5 ha (180 pitches) flat, grassy

Rentals : 24 ⛺.

The whole site is very green with plenty of flowers.

| Surroundings : ≤ ♨♨ |
| Leisure activities : 🍴 🍽 🏊 🎮 🏊 hammam 🏄 🚲 🎯 🏊 sports trail |
| Facilities : ♿ 🔑 🏕 ♨ 🍽 launderette 🔌 🌿 |

Longitude : 6.01095
Latitude : 45.11331

🏔 Le Colporteur 👥

🖉 0476791144. www.camping-colporteur.com

Address : Le Mas du Plan (south of the town, access via r. de la
Piscine)

3.3 ha (135 pitches) flat, grassy

Rentals : 4 caravans – 4 ⛺ – 30 🏠.

Located beside a small river.

| Surroundings : 🏞 ≤ ⏚ ♨♨ |
| Leisure activities : 🍴 🍽 🍽 🏃 🏄 |
| Facilities : ♿ 🔑 ♨ 🍽 🌿 |
| Nearby : 🛒 🛷 |

Longitude : 6.03546
Latitude : 45.0527

🏔 La Cascade

🖉 0476800242. www.lacascadesarenne.com

Address : located 1.5km to the northeast, follow the signs for L'Alpe-
d'Huez, near the Sarennes river

2.4 ha (140 pitches)

Rentals : 18 🏠.

| Surroundings : ❄ ≤ ⏚ ♨♨ |
| Leisure activities : 🍴 🏄 🏊 |
| Facilities : 🔑 🏕 🏕 ♨ 🍽 🍽 |
| Nearby : 🛒 |

Longitude : 6.03988
Latitude : 45.06446

BOURG-EN-BRESSE

01000 – Michelin map **328** E3 – pop. 39 586 – alt. 251
▶ Paris 424 – Annecy 113 – Besançon 152 – Chambéry 120

🏔 Municipal de Challes

🖉 0474453721. www.bourgenbresse.fr – 🅵🆁

Address : 5 allée du Centre Nautique (take northeastern exit
following signs for Lons-le-Saunier; by the swimming pool)

Opening times : from beginning April to mid Oct.

1.3 ha (120 pitches)

Tariff : (2014 Price) 17,80€ ★★ ⏚ 🔲 ⚡ (16A) –
Extra per person 4.44€

⛽ borne – 18 🔲 17.80€ – 🚐 ⚡15.20€

The pitches have the benefit of some pleasant shade.

| Surroundings : ♨♨ |
| Leisure activities : 🍽 |
| Facilities : 🔑 🏕 🏕 ♨ 🍽 🔲 |
| Nearby : 🏊 |

Longitude : 5.2403
Latitude : 46.20905

*Some information or pricing may have changed since
the guide went to press. We recommend you check the
price list online in advance or at the entrance to the
campsite and enquire about possible restrictions.*

BOURGET-DU-LAC

73370 – Michelin map **333** I4 – pop. 4 277 – alt. 240
▶ Paris 531 – Aix-les-Bains 10 – Annecy 44 – Chambéry 13

🏔 International l'Île aux Cygnes

🖉 0479250176. www.campingileauxcygnes.fr

Address : 501 boulevard E.Coudurier (located 1km to the north;
beside the lake)

Opening times : from mid April to beginning Oct.

2.5 ha (267 pitches)

Tariff : (2014 Price) 23.58€ ★★ ⏚ 🔲 ⚡ (6A) – Extra per person 5.21€
Reservation fee 10€

Rental rates : (2014 Price) (from mid April to beginning Oct.) ♿
(1 mobile home) – 6 ⛺ – 4 🏠. Per night from 72 to 154 € –
Per week from 275 to 794€ – Reservation fee 10€

⛽ borne 2.06€ – 29 🔲 12.33€ – 🚐 ⚡12.51€

The campervan pitches are at the entrance to the campsite.

| Surroundings : 🏞 ≤ ♨♨ ⛰ |
| Leisure activities : 🍴 🍽 🎮 daytime 🏄 🚲 🛥 (beach) 🏊 |
| Facilities : 🔑 🏕 🏕 🚿 ♨ 🍽 launderette 🌿 |
| Nearby : 🎿 🎣 🚣 ⚓ |

Longitude : 5.86308
Latitude : 45.65307

BOURG-ST-MAURICE

73700 – Michelin map **333** N4 – pop. 7 650 – alt. 850 – Winter sports : at Les Arcs : 1 600/3 226 m
▶ Paris 635 – Albertville 54 – Aosta 79 – Chambéry 103

⛰ Le Versoyen

✆ 0479070345. www.leversoyen.com

Address : route des Arcs road RD 119 (take the northeastern exit along the N 90, follow the signs for Séez then continue 500m along the turning to the right, near some rapids)

3.5 ha (153 pitches) surfaced road

Rentals : 2 caravans – 11 🚐.

There's a free shuttle service to the funicular railway.

Surroundings : ❄ ⅏ ‹ ⚲⚲	
Leisure activities : 🎦 ⚄	**G**
Facilities : ⚡ 🔟 ⛺ launderette	**P** Longitude : 6.78373
At the leisure/activities park : ✂ 🎿ₘ 🖼 ⛷	**S** Latitude : 45.6221
🐎 sports trail	

We value your opinion and welcome your feedback. Do email us at campingfrance@tp.michelin.com

BRAMANS

73500 – Michelin map **333** N6 – pop. 388 – alt. 1 200
▶ Paris 673 – Albertville 100 – Briançon 71 – Chambéry 113

⛰ Le Val d'Ambin

✆ 0479050305. www.camping-bramansvanoise.com

Address : 602 route de l'église (700m northeast - access is recommended via Le Verney, on the N6)

Opening times : from mid April to end Oct. and winter holidays

6 ha (166 pitches) open site, undulating, terraced, flat, grassy, pond

Tariff : 🚶 3.40€ 🚗 1.90€ – 🔌 (6A) 4€

Rental rates : Permanent ⚡ (1 chalet) – 1 caravan – 10 🏠 – 5 tent lodges. Per night from 29 to 139€ – Per week from 175 to 675€
🚐 borne 2€

In a lovely situation not far from an old church; good-quality rental accommodation.

Surroundings : ⅏ ‹ ⚲	
Leisure activities : 🎦 ⚄ ✂ 🐟	**G**
Facilities : ⚡ ⌁ (season) 🔟 ⛺ ⛽	**P** Longitude : 6.78144
launderette	**S** Latitude : 45.22787
Nearby : ⚲ ✂	

BRIDES-LES-BAINS

73570 – Michelin map **333** M5 – pop. 560 – alt. 580
▶ Paris 612 – Albertville 32 – Annecy 77 – Chambéry 81

⛺ La Piat

✆ 0479552274. www.camping-brideslesbains.com

Address : avenue du Comte Greyfié de Bellecombe

Opening times : from mid April to mid Oct.

2 ha (80 pitches)

Tariff : 16€ 🚶🚶 🚗 🔲 🔌 (10A) – Extra per person 3.50€

Rental rates : (from beginning April to mid Oct.) – 2 caravans – 5 🚐. Per night from 38 to 78€ – Per week from 232 to 472€
🚐 borne 3.50€

The site is laid out on terraces with little shade, near the town centre.

Surroundings : ⅏ ⚲	
Facilities : ⚡ ⌁ 🔟 ⛺ ⛽ launderette	**G** Longitude : 6.56172
	P Latitude : 45.453
	S

BUIS-LES-BARONNIES

26170 – Michelin map **332** E8 – pop. 2 291 – alt. 365
▶ Paris 685 – Carpentras 39 – Nyons 29 – Orange 50

⛰ La Fontaine d'Annibal

✆ 0475280312. www.vacances-baronnies.com

Address : route de Séderon (located 1km to the north, road to the left just after the bridge over the Ouvèze)

Opening times : from beginning April to mid Oct.

(50 pitches)

Tariff : 19€ 🚶🚶 🚗 🔲 🔌 (10A) – Extra per person 5€

Rental rates : (from beginning April to mid Oct.) ⚡ – 2 🚐 – 8 🏠 – 36 🛏 – 8 apartments – 4 canvas bungalows. Per night from 50 to 113€ – Per week from 290 to 785€

Surroundings : 🖼 ⚲	
Leisure activities : 🎦 ⛷	**G**
Facilities : ⚡ ⌁ 🔟 ⛺ ⛷ ⛽ launderette	**P** Longitude : 5.28187
Nearby : 🍴 ⚲	**S** Latitude : 44.28438

⛺ La Via Natura Les Éphélides

✆ 0475281015. www.ephelides.com

Address : Tuves district (1.4km southwest along av. de Rieuchaud)

Opening times : from mid May to mid Sept.

2 ha (40 pitches)

Tariff : (2014 Price) 25.40€ 🚶🚶 🚗 🔲 🔌 (16A) – Extra per person 4.90€ – Reservation fee 12€

Rental rates : (2014 Price) (from mid April to mid Oct.) – 1 caravan – 6 🚐 – 5 🏠. Per night from 36 to 85€ – Per week from 300 to 575€ – Reservation fee 12€

The site is shaded by cherry trees, near the Ouvèze river, and welcomes horses and their riders.

Surroundings : ⅏ ‹ ⚲	
Leisure activities : ✗ ⚄ ⛷	**G**
Facilities : ⚡ ⌁ ⛺ 🖼	**P** Longitude : 5.26793
Nearby : ✂ 🐎 skateboarding	**S** Latitude : 44.21875

⛺ Domaine de la Gautière

✆ 0475280268. www.camping-lagautiere.com

Address : La Gautière (5km southwest along the D 5, then take a right turn)

Opening times : from beginning April to end Oct.

6 ha/3 for camping (40 pitches) terraced, relatively flat, grassy, stony

Tariff : 🚶 6.30€ 🚗 🔲 7€ – 🔌 (10A) 5€ – Reservation fee 10€

Rental rates : (from beginning April to mid Nov.) – 8 🚐 – 4 🏠. Per night from 140 to 250€ – Per week from 280 to 750€ – Reservation fee 15€
🚐 borne 4€ – 🚐 11€

The site is largely shaded by olive trees.

Surroundings : ⅏ ‹ ⚲	
Leisure activities : 🎦 ⚄ ⛷	**G**
Facilities : ⚡ ⌁ ⛺ ⛽ 🖼	**P** Longitude : 5.24258
	S Latitude : 44.2517

CASTELJAU

07460 – Michelin map **331** H7
▶ Paris 665 – Aubenas 38 – Largentière 28 – Privas 69

La Rouveyrolle

✆ 0475390067, www.campingrouveyrolle.fr – limited spaces for one-night stay

Address : La Rouveyrolle hamlet (to the east of the village)

3 ha (100 pitches)

Rentals : 64 ☷.

A spacious site in a natural setting beside the river, a range of large and luxury mobile homes, but also some rather old sanitary facilities.

Surroundings : ⌇ ⊏ ♋♋
Leisure activities : ▼ ✕ ⌂ ⅍ ⅃♨ jacuzzi ⥲ ⤣ ≋ ⤳
Facilities : ⅋ ⊶ ⋔ launderette ⤳ ⤸

Longitude : 4.22222
Latitude : 44.39583

Bel Air (rental of mobile homes only)

✆ 0475393639, www.camping-belair-ardeche.com

Address : at Les Tournaires (500m to the north, follow the signs for Chaulet-Plage)

Opening times : from beginning April to end Oct.

1.5 ha (60 pitches)

Rental rates : – 43 ☷. Per night from 40 to 85€ – Per week from 240 to 990€ – Reservation fee 30€

A mobile home park, some very well equipped and some owner-occupiers, sometimes a little too close together.

Surroundings : ⌇ ♋♋
Leisure activities : ▼ ✕ ⌂ ⅍⤣ ≋
Facilities : ⅋ ⊶ ⋔ ▣ ⤸
Nearby : ≋ ⤳

Longitude : 4.21574
Latitude : 44.4006

Chaulet Plage

✆ 0475393027, www.chaulet-plage.com

Address : Terres du Moulin (600m to the north, follow the signs for Chaulet-Plage)

1.5 ha (62 pitches)

Rentals : 6 ⌂ – 6 apartments – military tents.

Pitches on terraces that descend to the snackbar beside the Chassezac river.

Surroundings : ⌇ ♋♋
Leisure activities : ▼ ✕ ≋ ⤳ ⤳
Facilities : ⅋ ⊶ ⌂ ⋔ launderette ⤳ ⤸

Longitude : 4.21528
Latitude : 44.40453

Le Pousadou

✆ 0475390405. www.pousadou.fr

Address : Domaine de Cassagnole, Les Tournaires

Opening times : from beginning May to end Sept.

23 ha/1.7 (52 pitches) flat, grassy

Tariff : (2014 Price) 24.50€ ✦✦ ⬡ ▣ ⌗ (10A) – Extra per person 4.10€

In the heart of the Domaine de Cassagnole vineyards, near the river; the reception is in the vineyard's wine cellar.

Surroundings : ⌇ ⋖ ♋♋
Leisure activities : ≋ ⤳
Facilities : ⅋ ⊶ – 52 private sanitary facilities (⊡ ⥲ ⊡ wc) ⋔

Longitude : 4.21788
Latitude : 44.40158

CHABEUIL

26120 – Michelin map **332** D4 – pop. 6 568 – alt. 212
▶ Paris 569 – Crest 21 – Die 59 – Romans-sur-Isère 18

FranceLoc Le Grand Lierne

✆ 0475598314. www.grandlierne.com ⤴ (from beginning July to end Aug.)

Address : 5km northeast along the D 68, follow the signs for Peyrus, turn left onto D 125 and turn right onto D 143 – from A 7, Valence-Sud exit towards Grenoble

Opening times : from end April to mid Sept.

3.6 ha (216 pitches)

Tariff : (2014 Price) 40€ ✦✦ ⬡ ▣ ⌗ (10A) – Extra per person 7€ – Reservation fee 27€
Rental rates : (2014 Price) (from end April to mid Sept.) ⤴ – 183 ☷ – 6 ⌂ – 13 tent lodges. Per night from 37 to 123€ – Per week from 147 to 1,281€ – Reservation fee 27€
☷ borne

Numerous rental options and pitches for tents and caravans in a wooded setting, with facilities suitable for families.

Surroundings : ⌇ ⊏ ♋♋
Leisure activities : ▼ ✕ ⌂ ⅍ ⥲⤣ ⅍⤳
⥥ ⅃ ⤸
Facilities : ⅋ ⊶ ⌂ ⋔ launderette ⤳ ⤸ refrigerated food storage facilities

Longitude : 5.065
Latitude : 44.91572

CHALLES-LES-EAUX

73190 – Michelin map **333** I4 – pop. 5 073 – alt. 310 – ♨
▶ Paris 566 – Albertville 48 – Chambéry 6 – Grenoble 52

Municipal le Savoy

✆ 0479729731. www.camping-challesleseaux.com

Address : avenue du Parc (take the r. Denarié, 100m from the N 6)

Opening times : from beginning April to mid Oct.

2.8 ha (88 pitches)

Tariff : (2014 Price) 12.70€ ✦✦ ⬡ ▣ ⌗ (10A) – Extra per person 4.10€ – Reservation fee 10€
Rental rates : (from beginning April to mid Oct.) – 4 ☷ – 6 ⌂ – 2 canvas bungalows. Per night from 38 to 84€ – Per week from 215 to 550€ – Reservation fee 10€
☷ borne 14€ – 22 ▣ 14€

Pretty pitches lined with hedges, near a small lake.

Surroundings : ⌇ ⋖ ⊏ ♀
Leisure activities : ⌂ ⅍⤣ ⅍⤳
Facilities : ⅋ ⊶ ▥ ⌂ ⤳ ⋔ launderette
Nearby : ⅏ ≋ (beach) ⤳

Longitude : 5.98418
Latitude : 45.55152

CHAMONIX-MONT-BLANC

74400 – Michelin map **328** O5 – pop. 9 054 – alt. 1 040
▶ Paris 610 – Albertville 65 – Annecy 97 – Aosta 57

L'Île des Barrats

✆ 0450535144. www.campingdesbarrats.com – ⅋

Address : 185 chemin de l'Île des Barrats (to the southwest of the town, opposite the main hospital.)

Opening times : from beginning June to mid Sept.

0.8 ha (52 pitches)

Tariff : (2014 Price) 29.50€ ✦✦ ⬡ ▣ ⌗ (10A) – Extra per person 6.50€

Rental rates : (2014 Price) (from beginning June to end Sept.) 🐾 – 4 🏠. Per week from 750 to 1,050€

In a green setting opposite the Bossons glacier, but choose the pitches furthest from the road.

Surroundings : 🏔 ≤ Mont Blanc mountain range and glaciers ⌁ 🌳
Leisure activities : 🏊
Facilities : 🚿 ⚷ 🛒 🚐 🔥 launderette

GPS Longitude : 6.86135
Latitude : 45.91463

⚠ La Mer de Glace

📞 04 50 53 44 03. www.chamonix-camping.com – 🈵

Address : 200 chemin de la Bagna (at Les Bois, 80m from the Arveyron (direct access)

Opening times : from end April to beginning Oct.

2 ha (150 pitches) sandy, gravelled

Tariff : 🚶 8.60€ 🚐 🅿 9.50€ – 🔌 (10A) 4€

In a wooded setting, with clearly marked-out or more natural pitches.

Surroundings : 🏔 ≤ Mont Blanc mountain range ⌁ 🌳🌳
Leisure activities : 🏊 ⚓
Facilities : 🚿 ⚷ 🛒 🏢 🔥 launderette

GPS Longitude : 6.89142
Latitude : 45.93846

A 'quartier' is a district or area of a town or village.

CHAMPDOR

01110 – Michelin map **328** G4 – pop. 462 – alt. 833
▶ Paris 486 – Ambérieu-en-Bugey 38 – Bourg-en-Bresse 51 – Hauteville-Lompnes 6

⚠ Municipal le Vieux Moulin

📞 06 50 54 28 98, www.champdor.jimdo.com

Address : route de Corcelles (800m northwest along the D 57a)

Opening times : Permanent

1.6 ha (62 pitches) flat, grassy

Tariff : (2014 Price) 14.30€ 🚶🚶 🚐 🅿 🔌 (10A) – Extra per person 3.30€
Rental rates : (2014 Price) Permanent ♿ (2 chalets) 🐾 – 2 yurts – 3 cabins. Per week 380€
🈳 1 🅿 6.30€

In the Le Bugey hills close to two natural lakes – one for swimming, one for fishing.

Surroundings : 🏔 ≤
Leisure activities : 🏊 ⚓
Facilities : ♿ (July–Aug.) 🛒 🏢 🔥 📶
Nearby : 🍴 🏖 (pool) 🎣

GPS Longitude : 5.59138
Latitude : 46.023

CHANCIA

01590 – Michelin map **321** D8 – pop. 237 – alt. 320
▶ Paris 452 – Bourg-en-Bresse 48 – Lons-le-Saunier 46 – Nantua 30

⚠ Municipal les Cyclamens

📞 04 74 75 82 14. www.camping-chancia.com – limited spaces for one-night stay

Address : La Presqu'île (located 1.5km southwest along the D 60e and take road to the left, where the Ain and the Bienne rivers meet)

2 ha (155 pitches) flat, grassy

On a tiny peninsula in the Lac de Coiselet; a rural site surrounded by beautiful cliffs.

Surroundings : 🏔 ≤ 🌳
Leisure activities : 🏊 ⚓
Facilities : ♿ 🛒 🚐 🔥 launderette
Nearby : 🏖 🎣 🚣

GPS Longitude : 5.6311
Latitude : 46.34203

CHARAVINES

38850 – Michelin map **333** G5 – pop. 1 758 – alt. 500
▶ Paris 534 – Belley 47 – Chambéry 49 – Grenoble 40

⚠ Les Platanes

📞 04 76 06 64 70. www.camping-lesplatanes.com

Address : 85 rue du Camping (take the northern exit along the D 50d, 150m from the lake)

Opening times : from beginning April to end Sept.

1 ha (67 pitches) flat, grassy

Tariff : (2014 Price) 18.50€ 🚶🚶 🚐 🅿 🔌 (10A) – Extra per person 5€ Reservation fee 15€

Rental rates : (2014 Price) (from beginning April to end Sept.) 🐾 – 7 🏠 – 2 🏠. Per night from 50 to 108€ – Per week from 350 to 590€ – Reservation fee 15€
🈳 borne 2€ – 8 🅿 13€

Surroundings : 🌳🌳
Leisure activities : ✕ 🏊
Facilities : ♿ ⚷ 🏢 🔥 📶
Nearby : 🍴 🍷 🍴 🏖 (beach) 🎣 🚣 pedalos

GPS Longitude : 5.51545
Latitude : 45.43096

The Michelin classification (⚠⚠⚠⚠ ... ⚠) is totally independent of the official star classification system awarded by the local prefecture or other official organisation.

CHASSAGNES

07140 – Michelin map **331** H7
▶ Paris 644 – Lyon 209 – Privas 67 – Nîmes 85

⚠⚠⚠⚠ Domaine des Chênes

📞 04 75 37 34 35. www.domaine-des-chenes.fr – limited spaces for one-night stay

Address : at Chassagnes Haut

Opening times : from beginning April to end Sept.

2.5 ha (122 pitches) flat, grassy, stony

Tariff : (2014 Price) 32€ 🚶🚶 🚐 🅿 🔌 (10A) – Extra per person 4€ – Reservation fee 25€

Rental rates : (2014 Price) (from beginning April to end Sept.) – 39 🏠 – 4 tent lodges. Per night from 37 to 180€ – Per week from 259 to 1,260€ – Reservation fee 25€
🈳 borne 19€ – 4 🅿 19€

Varied rental options, including some high-quality mobile homes, owner-occupiers, and pitches for tents and caravans.

Surroundings : 🏔 ≤ ⌁ 🌳🌳
Leisure activities : 🍷 ✕ 🏊 💆 🏊
hammam, jacuzzi 🏊
Facilities : ♿ ⚷ 🔥 📶
Nearby : 🏖 🎣

GPS Longitude : 4.13218
Latitude : 44.39899

CHASSIERS

07110 – Michelin map **331** H6 – pop. 1 008 – alt. 340
▶ Paris 643 – Aubenas 16 – Largentière 4 – Privas 48

⏶⏶⏶ Sunêlia Domaine Les Ranchisses ▲⁑

☎ 04 75 88 31 97, www.lesranchisses.fr

Address : route de Rocher (1.6km to the northwest, access via the D 5, follow the signs for Valgorge)

Opening times : from mid April to end Sept.

6 ha (226 pitches) terraced, relatively flat, flat, grassy

Tariff : 50€ ★★ ⇔ 🔲 🔋 (10A) – Extra per person 11€ – Reservation fee 15€

Rental rates : (from end April to end Sept.) – 101 ⟦⎗⟧ – 3 gîtes. Per night from 39 to 198€ – Per week from 245 to 1,386€ – Reservation fee 30€

🚐 borne

In 2 separate sections on either side of the road, linked by a tunnel. Choose the more peaceful pitches near the river with better shade. A well-equipped spa area.

Surroundings : ⛺ ♀♀ ⚠
Leisure activities : ♟ ✗ 🏠 ⑤ ⛏ ⅃⁶ ⩵ᵴ hammam, jacuzzi ✦✦ ✗ 🎿 ⅃ 〰 ⅃ multi-sports ground, spa centre, skate park
Facilities : 🚿 ⟶ ⟦cc⟧ ⊟ ♒ ♻ ⟍⟍⤥ launderette ⟍⟍⤥

Longitude : 4.28536
Latitude : 44.56137

The information in the guide may have changed since going to press.

CHÂTEAUNEUF-DE-GALAURE

26330 – Michelin map **332** C2 – pop. 1 557 – alt. 253
▶ Paris 531 – Annonay 29 – Beaurepaire 19 – Romans-sur-Isère 27

⏶⏶⏶ Iris Parc Le Château de Galaure

☎ 04 75 68 65 22. www.chateaudegalaure.com

Address : route de St-Vallier (800m southwest along the D 51)

12 ha (400 pitches) flat, grassy

Rentals : 148 ⟦⎗⟧ – 105 canvas bungalows.

In a pleasant, green setting with good shade.

Surroundings : ♀♀
Leisure activities : ♟ ✗ 🏠 ⑤ ✦✦ ⅃ 〰 skateboarding
Facilities : 🚿 ⟶ ⊟ ⟍⟍⤥ 🔲 ♒ ♻
Nearby : ✗ 🏠 🌳 fitness trail

Longitude : 4.95644
Latitude : 45.23029

CHÂTEAUNEUF-SUR-ISÈRE

26300 – Michelin map **332** C3 – pop. 3 707 – alt. 118
▶ Paris 561 – Lyon 98 – Valence 13 – Privas 55

⏶⏶⏶ Sunêlia Le Soleil Fruité ▲⁑

☎ 04 75 84 19 70. www.lesoleilfruite.com

Address : Les Pêches (4km, take exit 14 Valence Nord towards Châteauneuf sur Isère, continue along the D 877; near the 'Les Folies du Lac' cabaret)

Opening times : from end April to mid Sept.

4 ha (138 pitches) flat, grassy

Tariff : 35.30€ ★★ ⇔ 🔲 🔋 (10A) – Extra per person 7.95€ – Reservation fee 16€

Rental rates : (from end April to mid Sept.) – 34 ⟦⎗⟧. Per week from 29 to 899€ – Reservation fee 16€

🚐 borne 3.10€

Surroundings : ⛳ ⟦⎘ ♀
Leisure activities : ♟ ✗ 🏠 ⑤ ⛏ ⅃⁶ ✦✦ ⅃ 〰
Facilities : ⟶ ⊟ ⟍⟍⤥ launderette ⟍⟍⤥♻

Longitude : 4.89372
Latitude : 44.99707

CHÂTEL

74390 – Michelin map **328** O3 – pop. 1 213 – alt. 1 180 – Winter sports : 1 200/2 100 m
▶ Paris 578 – Annecy 113 – Évian-les-Bains 34 – Morzine 38

⏶⏶⏶ L'Oustalet ▲⁑

☎ 04 50 73 21 97, www.oustalet.com – alt. 1 110

Address : 1428 route des Freinets (head 2km southwest following the signs for Le Col de Bassachaux; beside the Dranse river)

Opening times : from mid June to mid Sept. and from mid Dec to mid Apr

3 ha (100 pitches)

Tariff : 34.70€ ★★ ⇔ 🔲 🔋 (6A) – Extra per person 7€ – Reservation fee 10€

Rental rates : (from mid June to mid Sept. and from mid Dec to mid Apr) ⟍⟍ (from mid June to mid Sept.) – 16 ⟦⎗⟧ – 1 apartment. Per week from 380 to 840€ – Reservation fee 10€

🚐 borne 6€ – 14 🔲 6€

In two sections on either side of the small road, with a pretty view of the Vallée de l'Abondance.

Surroundings : ❄ ☸ ⩽♀
Leisure activities : 🏠 ⑤ daytime ⛏ ⩵ᵴ ✦✦ ✗ ⅃
Facilities : 🚿 ⟶ 🔲 ♒ ⟍⟍⤥ launderette
Nearby : ♟ ✗ 🌳 🚴 ⅃

Longitude : 6.82981
Latitude : 46.25755

The Michelin classification (⏶⏶⏶... ⏶) is totally independent of the official star classification system awarded by the local prefecture or other official organisation.

LE CHÂTELARD

73630 – Michelin map **333** J3 – pop. 645 – alt. 750
▶ Paris 562 – Aix-les-Bains 30 – Annecy 30 – Chambéry 35

⏶ Les Cyclamens

☎ 04 79 54 80 19, www.camping-cyclamens.com

Address : head towards the northwestern exit and take road to the left, follow the signs for Le Champet

Opening times : from beginning May to beginning Oct.

0.7 ha (34 pitches) flat, grassy

Tariff : 16.40€ ★★ ⇔ 🔲 🔋 (10A) – Extra per person 4.10€ – Reservation fee 4€

Rental rates : Permanent – 1 studio – 1 cabin in the trees. Per night from 78 to 98 € – Per week 525€

🚐 borne 4€ – 4 🔲 13.20€

The pitches are partly in shade, partly in sun.

Surroundings : ☸ ♀♀
Leisure activities : 🏠 ✦✦
Facilities : 🚿 ⟶ ⟌ ⊟ ⟍⟍⤥ 🔲

Longitude : 6.13263
Latitude : 45.68782

CHÂTILLON-SUR-CHALARONNE

01400 – Michelin map **328** C4 – pop. 4 899 – alt. 177
▶ Paris 418 – Bourg-en-Bresse 28 – Lyon 55 – Mâcon 28

⚠ **Municipal du Vieux Moulin**

📞 04 74 55 04 79, www.camping-vieuxmoulin.com – limited spaces for one-night stay

Address : rue Jean Jaurès (take southeastern exit along the D 7, follow the signs for Chalamont; beside the Chalaronne, 150m from a lake – direct access)

Opening times : from end April to beginning Oct.

3 ha (140 pitches) flat, grassy

Tariff : (2014 Price) 🧍 5€ 🚗 5€ ▣ 5€ – ⚡ (10A) 5€ – Reservation fee 11€

Rental rates : (2014 Price) (from end April to end Oct.) – 5 🏠. Per week from 323 to 441€ – Reservation fee 11€

🚐 borne 6€ – 20 ▣ 20€

In a shaded green setting beside a river.

Surroundings : 🌿 ♤♤ Leisure activities : 🛶 🎣 🚣 multi-sports ground Facilities : 👤 ⚡ 🚻 📷 Nearby : 🍴🍷✕✂ 🛶 ⛵	**GPS** Longitude : 4.96228 Latitude : 46.11654

CHAUZON

07120 – Michelin map **331** I7 – pop. 341 – alt. 128
▶ Paris 649 – Aubenas 20 – Largentière 14 – Privas 51

⚠⚠ **La Digue**

📞 04 75 39 63 57, www.camping-la-digue.fr – access difficult for caravans

Address : Les Aires (located 1km east of the town, 100m from the Ardèche river (direct access)

7 ha/3 for camping (141 pitches) terraced, flat, grassy

Rentals : 37 🚐 – 8 🏠.

There are shaded pitches with some good-quality mobile home rentals.

Surroundings : 🌿 ♤♤ Leisure activities : 🍷✕ 🎣 ✂ 🛶 ⛵ 🚣 Facilities : 👤 ⚡ 🚻 🚿 🍴 📷 🛶	**GPS** Longitude : 4.37337 Latitude : 44.48437

LE CHEYLARD

07160 – Michelin map **331** I4 – pop. 3 289 – alt. 450
▶ Paris 598 – Aubenas 50 – Lamastre 21 – Privas 47

⚠ **Municipal Le Cheylard**

📞 04 75 29 09 53, www.camping-le-cheylard.com

Address : Le Vialon

Opening times : from beginning April to end Sept.

1.5 ha (61 pitches) relatively flat, flat, grassy

Tariff : 17€ 🧍🧍 🚗 ▣ ⚡ (6A) – Extra per person 6€

Rental rates : (from beginning April to end Sept.) 🏖 – 4 🚐 – 4 canvas bungalows – 1 gîte. Per night from 40 to 85€ – Per week from 175 to 550€

Surroundings : 🌿 ♤♤ Facilities : 👤 ⚡ 🍴 📷 🚿	**GPS** Longitude : 4.42011 Latitude : 44.9155

CHORANCHE

38680 – Michelin map **333** F7 – pop. 132 – alt. 280
▶ Paris 588 – La Chapelle-en-Vercors 24 – Grenoble 52 – Romans-sur-Isère 32

⚠ **Le Gouffre de la Croix**

📞 04 76 36 07 13. www.camping-choranche.com

Address : Combe Bernard (to the southeast of the town, follow the signs for Chatelas; beside the Bourne river)

Opening times : from mid April to mid Sept.

2.5 ha (52 pitches) open site, terraced, flat, grassy

Tariff : (2014 Price) 24.80€ 🧍🧍 🚗 ▣ ⚡ (6A) – Extra per person 4.80€ Reservation fee 13€

Rental rates : (from mid April to mid Sept.) 🏖 – 2 🚐. Per night from 50 to 65€ – Per week from 290 to 520€ – Reservation fee 13€

In a natural wooded setting at the bottom of the valley.

Surroundings : 🌿 ≤ ♤♤ Leisure activities : 🍷 🎣 🚣 🚣 Facilities : 👤 ⚡ 🚿 🍴 🛶	**GPS** Longitude : 5.39447 Latitude : 45.06452

These symbols are used for a campsite that is exceptional in its category:

⚠⚠⚠ ... ⚠ *Particularly pleasant setting, quality and range of services available*

🌿🌿 *Tranquil, isolated site – quiet site, particularly at night*

≤≤ *Exceptional view – interesting or panoramic view*

LA CLUSAZ

74220 – Michelin map **328** L5 – pop. 1 876 – alt. 1 040 – Winter sports : 1 100/2 600 m
▶ Paris 564 – Albertville 40 – Annecy 32 – Bonneville 26

⚠ **FranceLoc Le Plan du Fernuy**

📞 04 50 02 44 75. www.franceloc.fr

Address : 1800 route des Confins (located 1.5km to the east)

Opening times : from mid Dec. to end April and from mid June to mid Sept

1.3 ha (80 pitches) terraced, relatively flat, flat, grassy, gravelled

Tariff : 41.30€ 🧍🧍 🚗 ▣ ⚡ (13A) – Extra per person 6.30€ – Reservation fee 27€

Rental rates : (from mid Dec. to end April and from mid June to mid Sept) 🏖 – 21 🚐 – 12 🏠 – 1 studio – 3 apartments. Per night from 33 to 159€ – Per week from 231 to 1,113€ – Reservation fee 27€

🚐 borne 10€

There are good-quality rental options in both summer and winter, based around an indoor swimming pool.

Surroundings : ❄ 🌿 ≤ Aravis range ⌂ ⛰ Leisure activities : 🍷 🛶 🎣 🏊 Facilities : 👤 ⚡ 🚻 🚿 🛶 🍴 launderette	**GPS** Longitude : 6.45174 Latitude : 45.90948

The prices listed were supplied by the campsite owners in 2014 (if prices were not available, those from the previous year are given). The fees should be regarded as basic charges and may fluctuate with inflation.

CORDELLE

42123 – Michelin map **327** D4 – pop. 896 – alt. 450
▶ Paris 409 – Feurs 35 – Roanne 14 – St-Just-en-Chevalet 27

⚲ De Mars

✆ 0477649442. www.camping-de-mars.com

Address : Presqu'île de Mars (a bend in the river) (4.5km south along the D 56 and take the road to the right)

Opening times : from beginning April to mid Oct.

1.2 ha (63 pitches) terraced, relatively flat, flat, grassy

Tariff : (2014 Price) 29.50€ ✲ ✲ ⮕ 国 (၅) (10A)

Extra per person 7.80€ – Reservation fee 14€
Rental rates : (2014 Price) (from beginning April to mid Oct.) ⭐ (1 mobile home) – 11 ⟮🛏⟯ – 2 ⟮🏠⟯ – 2 canvas bungalows. Per night from 45 to 125€ – Per week from 315 to 875€ – Reservation fee 14€

In an attractive location overlooking the Loire river gorges.

Surroundings : ⧖ ⪦ ⌂ ⚲
Leisure activities : ⵏ ✕ ⟮🎬⟯ ⛵ ⬚ 🚲 ⯑ 🛝 ⟋
Facilities : ⭐ ⊶ 国 ⛲ ⛐ ⚥ ⵀ ⵜ launderette ⛲
Nearby : ⟋

Longitude : 4.06101
Latitude : 45.91668

CORMORANCHE-SUR-SAÔNE

01290 – Michelin map **328** B3 – pop. 1 051 – alt. 172
▶ Paris 399 – Bourg-en-Bresse 44 – Châtillon-sur-Chalaronne 23 – Mâcon 10

⚲ Le Lac

✆ 0385239710. www.lac-cormoranche.com

Address : Les Luizants (take the western exit along the D 51a and continue 1.2km along the turning to the right; at the leisure and activity park)

Opening times : from beginning May to end Sept.

48 ha/4.5 for camping (117 pitches) flat, grassy, sandy, wood

Tariff : (2014 Price) 21.55€ ✲ ✲ ⮕ 国 (၅) (10A) –
Extra per person 5.55€ – Reservation fee 7€
Rental rates : (2014 Price) (from beginning May to end Sept.) ⬭ –
9 ⟮🛏⟯ – 12 ⟮🏠⟯ – 4 tipis. Per night from 44 to 120€ – Per week from 163 to 582€ – Reservation fee 7€

⟮🛏⟯ borne

Trees and shrubs surround the pitches, near a small but pretty lake.

Surroundings : ⌂ ⚲
Leisure activities : ⵏ ✕ ⛵ 🚲 ⛐ ⯑ (beach) ⟋ ♨ entertainment room
Facilities : ⭐ ⊶ ⛐ ⚥ ⵀ ⵜ launderette ⟋

Longitude : 4.82573
Latitude : 46.25105

CREST

26400 – Michelin map **332** D5 – pop. 7 857 – alt. 196
▶ Paris 585 – Die 37 – Gap 129 – Grenoble 114

⚲ Les Clorinthes ⚼⚹

✆ 0475250528. www.lesclorinthes.com

Address : quai Soubeyran (take the southern exit along the D 538 then take the road to the left after the bridge, near the Drôme river and the sports centre)

Opening times : from end April to mid Sept.

4 ha (160 pitches)

Tariff : (2014 Price) 30.90€ ✲ ✲ ⮕ 国 (၅) (6A) – Extra per person 7.20€
Reservation fee 21€

Rental rates : (2014 Price) (from end April to mid Sept.) – 14 ⟮🛏⟯ –
2 canvas bungalows. Per week from 336 to 686€ – Reservation fee 21€

Surroundings : ⪦ ⚲
Leisure activities : ⵏ ✕ ⟮🏊⟯ ⦿daytime ⯑ ⛐ 🚲 ⬚
Facilities : ⭐ ⊶ ⛐ ⵜ launderette
Nearby : ⟋ ⯑

Longitude : 5.0277
Latitude : 44.724

CUBLIZE

69550 – Michelin map **327** F3 – pop. 1 242 – alt. 452
▶ Paris 422 – Amplepuis 7 – Chauffailles 29 – Roanne 30

⚲ Campéole le Lac des Sapins

✆ 0474895283. www.campinglacdessapins.com – limited spaces for one-night stay

Address : rue du Lac (800m to the south; beside the Reins stream and 300m from the lake (direct access)

Opening times : from beginning April to end Sept.

4 ha (182 pitches) flat, grassy

Tariff : (2014 Price) 22.80€ ✲ ✲ ⮕ 国 (၅) (6A)
Rental rates : (2014 Price) (from beginning April to end Sept.) –
24 ⟮🛏⟯ – 26 ⟮🏠⟯ – 6 tent lodges. Per night from 55 to 140 € –
Per week from 399 to 896€

⟮🛏⟯ borne

Surroundings : ⧖ ⪦ ⌂
Leisure activities : ⛵ 🚲 ⯑ multi-sports ground
Facilities : ⭐ ⊶ ⛐ ⵜ ⵀ launderette
At the leisure/activities centre : ⛐ ⬚ ⛵ ⟋

Longitude : 4.37849
Latitude : 46.0132

CULOZ

01350 – Michelin map **328** H5 – pop. 2 920 – alt. 248
▶ Paris 512 – Aix-les-Bains 24 – Annecy 55 – Bourg-en-Bresse 88

⚲ Le Colombier

✆ 0479871900. http://camping.colombier.free.fr

Address : Ile de Verbaou (1.3km east, at Junction of D 904 and D 992; beside a stream)

1.5 ha (81 pitches)

Rentals : 5 ⟮🛏⟯.

Near a leisure centre.

Surroundings : ⪦ ⌂ ⚲
Leisure activities : ⵏ ⛵ 🚲
Facilities : ⭐ ⊶ ⛐ ⚥ ⵀ ⵜ launderette ⟋
Nearby : ⯑ ⟮🏊⟯ ⛐ ⟋

Longitude : 5.79346
Latitude : 45.85158

DARBRES

07170 – Michelin map **331** J6 – pop. 252 – alt. 450
▶ Paris 618 – Aubenas 18 – Montélimar 34 – Privas 21

⚲ Les Lavandes

✆ 0475942065. www.les-lavandes-darbres.com

Address : in the town

Opening times : from mid April to mid Sept.

1.5 ha (70 pitches) terraced, flat, grassy, stony

Tariff : 29.40€ ✲ ✲ ⮕ 国 (၅) (6A) – Extra per person 4.50€ –
Reservation fee 15€

Rental rates : (from mid April to mid Sept.) – 12 🏠. Per night from 53 to 59€ – Per week from 270 to 670€ – Reservation fee 15€

Near the centre of the village, with an attractive vew of the bar's terrace, swimming pool; some elevated pitches.

Surroundings : 🌊 ♀♀
Leisure activities : 🍴✕ 🏖 ⛵
Facilities : ⚡ 🖥️ 🍽️ launderette 🏢

G P S Longitude : 4.50402
Latitude : 44.64701

There are several different types of sani-station ('borne' in French) – sanitation points providing fresh water and disposal points for grey water. See page 12 for further details.

DARDILLY

69570 – Michelin map **327** H5 – pop. 8 384 – alt. 338
▶ Paris 457 – Lyon 13 – Villeurbanne 21 – Vénissieux 26

⚠ Indigo International Lyon

Campingindigo ©R. Etienne

🅿 04 78 35 64 55. www.camping-indigo.com

Address : Poroute de Lyon (10km northwest along the N 6, follow the signs for Mâcon – from the A 6, take the Limonest exit)

Opening times : Permanent

6 ha (150 pitches) flat, grassy

Tariff : (2014 Price) 27€ ✶✶ 🚗 🔲 🔌 (10A) – Extra per person 5.10€ –

Reservation fee 22€

Rental rates : (2014 Price) Permanent – 6 caravans – 41 🚐 – 7 tent lodges. Per night from 41 to 112€ – Per week from 201 to 627€ – Reservation fee 22€

🚽 borne 7€ – 30 🔲 21.20€

Surroundings : ♀♀
Leisure activities : 🍴✕ 🏖 ⛸⛵
Facilities : ♿ ⚡ 🖥️ 🛖 🏢 🍽️ launderette

G P S Longitude : 4.76125
Latitude : 45.81817

DIE

26150 – Michelin map **332** F5 – pop. 4 357 – alt. 415
▶ Paris 623 – Gap 92 – Grenoble 110 – Montélimar 73

⚠ Le Glandasse

🅿 04 75 22 02 50. www.camping-glandasse.com

Address : De la Maldrerie district (1km southeast along the D 93, follow the signs for Gap then take the road to the right, beside the Drôme river)

Opening times : from mid April to end Sept.

3.5 ha (120 pitches) relatively flat, flat, grassy, stony

Tariff : 26€ ✶✶ 🚗 🔲 🔌 (10A) – Extra per person 6€ – Reservation fee 10€

Rental rates : (from mid April to end Sept.) – 2 🚐 – 15 🏠. Per night from 40 to 82€ – Per week from 280 to 574 €
Reservation fee 10€

Note for access: maximum height 2.80m.

Surroundings : 🌊 ⛰ 🛏 ♀♀
Leisure activities : ✕ 🏖 🛁jacuzzi ⛸
🚴 ⛵ 🎯 multi-sports ground
Facilities : ♿ ⚡ 🍽️ launderette 🏢

G P S Longitude : 5.38403
Latitude : 44.73993

⚠ Le Riou Merle

🅿 04 75 22 21 31. www.camping-lerioumerle.com

Address : route de Romeyer (head north along the D 742)

Opening times : from beginning April to mid Oct.

2.5 ha (97 pitches) flat, grassy

Tariff : (2014 Price) 26€ ✶✶ 🚗 🔲 🔌 (10A) – Extra per person 6.50€

Rental rates : (2014 Price) (from beginning April to mid Oct.) – 12 🚐 – 3 🏠. Per week from 252 to 630€

🚽 borne

Surroundings : 🛏 ♀
Leisure activities : 🍴✕ 🏖 ⛵
Facilities : ⚡ 🖥️ 🍽️ launderette 🏢

G P S Longitude : 5.37776
Latitude : 44.75441

DIEULEFIT

26220 – Michelin map **332** D6 – pop. 3 028 – alt. 366
▶ Paris 614 – Crest 30 – Montélimar 29 – Nyons 30

⚠ Huttopia Dieulefit

© Huttopia R. Etienne

🅿 04 75 54 63 94. www.huttopia.com

Address : Espeluche district (3km north along the D 540 follow the signs for Bourdeaux then take the road to the left)

Opening times : from beginning April to beginning Oct.

17 ha (140 pitches) undulating, flat, grassy

Tariff : (2014 Price) 46.80€ ✶✶ 🚗 🔲 🔌 (10A) – Extra per person 7.80€ – Reservation fee 22€

Rental rates : (2014 Price) (from beginning April to beginning Oct.) – 20 🚐 – 54 tent lodges. Per night from 49 to 177€ – Per week from 258 to 1,239€ – Reservation fee 22€

🚽 borne 7€ – 20 🔲 41€

Surroundings : 🌊
Leisure activities : ✕ 🏖 ⛸⛵
Facilities : ⚡ 🖥️ launderette 🏢

G P S Longitude : 5.05826
Latitude : 44.53987

⚠ Le Domaine des Grands Prés

🅿 04 75 49 94 36. www.lesgrandspres-dromeprovencale.com

Address : Les Grands Prés district (take the western exit along the D 540, follow the signs for Montélimar, near the Jabron - direct access to the town along the pedestrian path)

1.8 ha (91 pitches) flat, grassy

Rentals : 9 caravans – 5 🏠 – 6 yurts – 1 cabin in the trees – 2 tipis – 3 canvas bungalows – 4 tent lodges – 1 gîte – 2 cabin lodges on stilts.

🚽 borne

Surroundings : 🌊 ♀♀
Leisure activities : 🏖 ⛵ ⛲
Facilities : ♿ ⚡ 🛖 🍽️ launderette
Nearby : 🛒 ✗

G P S Longitude : 5.06149
Latitude : 44.52141

The Michelin classification (⚠⚠⚠ ... ⚠) is totally independent of the official star classification system awarded by the local prefecture or other official organisation.

DIVONNE-LES-BAINS

01220 – Michelin map **328** J2 – pop. 7 926 – alt. 486 – ⚕
▶ Paris 488 – Bourg-en-Bresse 129 – Genève 18 – Gex 9

⛰ Indigo Divonne - Le Fleutron

📞 04 50 20 01 95. www.camping-indigo.
com

Address : 2465 Vie de L'Etraz (3km to
the north, after Villard)

Opening times : from end April to
end Oct.

8 ha (253 pitches) terraced, flat and
relatively flat, stony, grassy

Tariff : (2014 Price) 29.90 € ♦♦ ⛟ 🅴
🔌 (10A) – Extra per person 6.10 € –
Reservation fee 22 €

Rental rates : (2014 Price) (from end April to end Oct.) – 8 caravans –
20 🛖 – 8 🏠 – 16 tent lodges. Per night from 45 to 102 € –
Per week from 221 to 714 € – Reservation fee 22 €
🚐 borne 7 € – 40 🅴 25.20 €
In a wooded setting looking out on a nearby mountain.

Surroundings : 🌲 ♤♤ Leisure activities : 🍴✗ 🎯 🎿 ⛵ 🚲 ✂ ⛵ Facilities : 🚿 ⛲ 🏛 🛒 🧺 launderette 🏖 ⛴	**G P S** Longitude : 6.1178 Latitude : 46.37137

*To visit a town or region, use the **MICHELIN Green Guides.***

DOUSSARD

74210 – Michelin map **328** K6 – pop. 3 473 – alt. 456
▶ Paris 555 – Albertville 27 – Annecy 20 – La Clusaz 36

⛰ International du Lac Bleu 👫

📞 04 50 44 30 18. www.camping-lac-bleu.com

Address : route de la Plage (follow the signs for Albertville)

Opening times : from beginning April to end Sept.

3.3 ha (221 pitches)

Tariff : (2014 Price) 18.50 € ♦♦ ⛟ 🅴 🔌 (10A) – Extra per person 6 €
Reservation fee 25 €

Rental rates : (2014 Price) (from beginning March to end Oct.) –
47 🛖 – 2 🏠 – 12 studios – 10 apartments. Per night
from 64 to 140 € – Per week from 350 to 1,100 € – Reservation
fee 25 €
🚐 borne
*In two sections, with a water and activity park and a small lake-
side beach.*

Surroundings : 🌲 < 🌳 ♤♤ 🏔 Leisure activities : 🍴✗ 🎯 🎡 jacuzzi ⛵ 🚲 🏊 multi-sports ground Facilities : 🚿 ⛲ (season) 🧺 launderette Nearby : 🐴 ✂ 🎣 🚣 🎣 ⚓ paragliding, marina	**G P S** Longitude : 6.21648 Latitude : 45.79103

⛰ Campéole la Nublière 👫

📞 04 50 44 33 44. www.campeole.com

Address : 30 allée de la Nublière (located 1.8km to the north)

Opening times : from beginning May to mid Sept.

9.2 ha (467 pitches)

Tariff : (2014 Price) 30.20 € ♦♦ ⛟ 🅴 🔌 (6A) – Extra per person 7.90 €
Reservation fee 25 €

Rental rates : (2014 Price) (from beginning May to mid Sept.) –
56 🛖 – 10 🏠 – 40 canvas bungalows. Per night from 33 to
145 € – Per week from 231 to 1,015 € – Reservation fee 25 €
🚐 borne
*In a pleasant setting beside the lake (beach), with a variety of
rental options.*

Surroundings : ♨♨ 🏔 Leisure activities : 🎯 🎿 🏊 🎣 ⛵ multi- sports ground, entertainment room Facilities : 🚿 ⛲ 🏛 🧺 launderette Nearby : 🐴 🍴✗ 🎣 🎡 ✂ 🎣 🔥 🚣 ⚓ paragliding	**G P S** Longitude : 6.21763 Latitude : 45.79014

⛰ La Ferme de Serraz

📞 04 50 44 33 068, www.campinglaserraz.com

Address : rue de la Poste (in the town, take the eastern exit near the
post office)

Opening times : from beginning May to mid Sept.

3.5 ha (197 pitches) relatively flat, flat, grassy

Tariff : (2014 Price) 35 € ♦♦ ⛟ 🅴 🔌 (16A) – Extra per person 7.50 €
Reservation fee 25 €

Rental rates : (2014 Price) (from beginning May to mid Sept.) –
41 🛖. Per night from 50 to 180 € – Per week from 290 to 1,235 € –
Reservation fee 25 €
🚐 borne 4.50 €
A well-shaded campsite with many tour operator pitches.

Surroundings : ♨♨ Leisure activities : 🍴✗ 🎯 ⛵ 🚲 🏊 Facilities : 🚿 ⛲ 🏛 🛒 🧺 launderette	**G P S** Longitude : 6.22588 Latitude : 45.77508

DUINGT

74410 – Michelin map **328** K6 – pop. 891 – alt. 450
▶ Paris 548 – Albertville 34 – Annecy 12 – Megève 48

⛰ Municipal les Champs Fleuris

📞 04 50 68 57 31. www.camping-duingt.com

Address : 631 voie Romaine - Les Perris (located 1km west)

1.3 ha (112 pitches) terraced, relatively flat, flat, grassy

Rentals : 6 🛖 – 2 tent lodges.
Pitches on terraces, some with shade, various types of rentals.

Surroundings : 🌲 < ♨♨ Leisure activities : ⛵ Facilities : 🚿 ⛲ launderette	**G P S** Longitude : 6.18882 Latitude : 45.82658

ÉCLASSAN

07370 – Michelin map **331** K3 – pop. 910 – alt. 420
▶ Paris 534 – Annonay 21 – Beaurepaire 46 – Condrieu 42

⛰ La Via Natura L'Oasis

📞 04 75 34 56 23. www.oasisardeche.com – pitches accessed via steep
slope, help moving caravans onto and off pitches avilable on request

Address : Le Petit Chaléat (4.5km northwest, follow the signs for
Fourany and take road to the left)

Opening times : from beginning May to beginning Sept.

4 ha (63 pitches) terraced, flat, grassy, stony

Tariff : 28.30 € ♦♦ ⛟ 🅴 🔌 (6A) – Extra per person 5 € – Reservation
fee 8 €

Rental rates : (from beginning May to beginning Sept.) – 4 🚐 – 10 🏠 – 10 tent lodges. Per night from 72 to 131€ – Per week from 518 to 735€ – Reservation fee 8€

Pitches on natural-style terraces, some beside the Ay river.

Surroundings : 🐟 ≤ 🏕 ⚲
Leisure activities : 🍸 ✕ 🏛 🏊 🎣 🛶 ⛵
Facilities : 👤 ⚬➤ 🚿 🚮 ✈ 🌳 🔲 🖈

GPS Longitude : 4.73944
Latitude : 45.17889

EXCENEVEX

74140 – Michelin map **328** L2 – pop. 988 – alt. 375
▶ Paris 564 – Annecy 71 – Bonneville 42 – Douvaine 9

🔺🔺🔺 Campéole La Pinède

🖋 04 50 72 85 05. www.camping-lac-leman.info – limited spaces for one-night stay

Address : 10 avenue de la Plage (located 1km southeast along the D 25)

Opening times : from mid April to mid Sept.

12 ha (525 pitches) undulating, sandy

Tariff : (2014 Price) 25.60€ 🚶🚶 🚗 🔲 ⚡ (16A) – Extra per person 7.90€ – Reservation fee 25€

Rental rates : (2014 Price) (from mid April to mid Sept.) 👤 (2 mobile homes) – 84 🚐 – 20 🏠 – 57 canvas bungalows. Per night from 21 to 145€ – Per week from 147 to 1,015€ – Reservation fee 25€

🚐 borne

In a pleasant wooded site close to a beach on Lac Léman, but choose those pitches furthest away from the road.

Surroundings : 🏕 ⚲⚲
Leisure activities : 🏛 🎬 🏃 ⛱ jacuzzi 🏊 🚴 🛶 🎿 multi-sports ground, entertainment room
Facilities : 👤 ⚬➤ 🚿 ✈ launderette 🚮
Nearby : 🍸 ✕ 🍴 🏸 🥄 🎣 ⚓ pedalos

GPS Longitude : 6.35799
Latitude : 46.34543

FARAMANS

38260 – Michelin map **333** D5 – pop. 906 – alt. 375
▶ Paris 518 – Beaurepaire 12 – Bourgoin-Jallieu 35 – Grenoble 60

🔺 Municipal des Eydoches

🖋 04 74 54 21 78, mairie.faramans@wanadoo.fr – limited spaces for one-night stay

Address : 515 avenue des Marais (take the eastern exit along the D 37, follow the signs for La Côte-St-André)

Opening times : Permanent

1 ha (60 pitches) flat, grassy

Tariff : (2014 Price) 🚶 4.10€ 🚗 🔲 5.90€ – ⚡ (5A) 3.50€

Rental rates : (2014 Price) Permanent – 2 🏠. Per night from 62 to 70€ – Per week from 227 to 300€

🚐 borne 6.80€ – 2 🔲 12.50€

Surroundings : ⚲
Facilities : 👤 🚮 ✈ 🚿 🖈
Nearby : 🏸 🎣

GPS Longitude : 5.17563
Latitude : 45.39348

Using the traditional Michelin classification method, the guide provides you with an easy, speedy reference for assessing the category of each site: 1 to 5 tents (see page 10).

FÉLINES

07340 – Michelin map **331** K2 – pop. 1 475 – alt. 380
▶ Paris 520 – Annonay 13 – Beaurepaire 31 – Condrieu 24

🔺🔺🔺 Bas-Larin

🖋 04 75 34 87 93. www.camping-bas-larin.com

Address : 88 route de Larin-le-Bas (situated 2km southeast, along the N 82, follow the signs for Serrières and take the road to the right)

Opening times : from beginning April to end Sept.

1.5 ha (67 pitches) terraced, relatively flat to hilly, grassy

Tariff : 21.90€ 🚶🚶 🚗 🔲 ⚡ (10A) – Extra per person 3.50€

Rental rates : (from beginning April to end Sept.) – 12 🚐 – 3 canvas bungalows. Per night from 40 to 85€ – Per week from 220 to 499€ – Reservation fee 12€

🚐 20 🔲 18€

The pitches on terraces are well shaded, but choose those furthest away from the road (a former national highway).

Surroundings : 🏕 ⚲⚲
Leisure activities : 🍸 ✕ 🏛 🏊 🎣 🛶
Facilities : 👤 ⚬➤ 🚿 🚮 ✈ 🌳 🔲 🖈

GPS Longitude : 4.74665
Latitude : 45.3086

LA FERRIÈRE

38580 – Michelin map **333** J6 – pop. 226 – alt. 926
▶ Paris 613 – Lyon 146 – Grenoble 52 – Chambéry 47

🔺🔺🔺 Neige et Nature

🖋 04 76 45 19 84. www.neige-nature.fr – alt. 900

Address : chemin de Montarmand (to the west of the village; beside the Bréda river)

Opening times : from mid May to mid Sept.

1.2 ha (45 pitches) terraced, relatively flat, flat, grassy

Tariff : 22.70€ 🚶🚶 🚗 🔲 ⚡ (10A) – Extra per person 5.90€

Rental rates : Permanent – 2 🚐 – 2 🏠. Per night from 65 to 85€ – Per week from 325 to 650€

🚐 20 🔲 18.30€

In a green, well-kept setting.

Surroundings : 🐟 ≤ 🏕 ⚲
Leisure activities : 🏛
Facilities : 👤 ⚬➤ 🚮 🚿 ✈ 🔲 🖈
Nearby : 🏊 (pool)

GPS Longitude : 6.08331
Latitude : 45.3184

FEURS

42110 – Michelin map **327** E5 – pop. 7 741 – alt. 343
▶ Paris 433 – Lyon 69 – Montbrison 24 – Roanne 38

🔺🔺🔺 Municipal du Palais

🖋 04 77 26 43 41. mairie.camping@feurs.fr

Address : route de Civens (take the northern exit along the N 82, follow the signs for Roanne and take a right turn)

Opening times : from beginning April to end Oct.

5 ha (385 pitches)

Tariff : (2014 Price) 🚶 3.20€ 🚗 2.70€ 🔲 3.20€ – ⚡ (16A) 3.60€

🚐 30 🔲 16.50€

In a peaceful area, close to the town centre.

Surroundings : ⚲⚲
Leisure activities : 🏊
Facilities : 👤 ⚬➤ 🚮 🚿 🌳 🔲
Nearby : 🏸 🎣

GPS Longitude : 4.22572
Latitude : 45.75429

FLEURIE

69820 – Michelin map **327** H2 – pop. 1 250 – alt. 320
▶ Paris 410 – Bourg-en-Bresse 46 – Chauffailles 44 – Lyon 58

⚠ VivaCamp la Grappe Fleurie

✆ 0474698007, www.beaujolais-camping.com

Address : rue de la Grappe Fleurie (600m south of the town along the D 119e and take a right turn.)

Opening times : from mid April to mid Oct.

2.5 ha (85 pitches) flat, grassy

Tariff : (2014 Price) 26€ ♣♣ ⬅ 🔲 – Extra per person 6.50€ Reservation fee 15€

Rental rates : (2014 Price) (from mid April to mid Oct.) – 20 🚐 – 4 🏠 – 3 canvas bungalows – 2 'barrel' rooms (without sanitary facilities). Per night from 30 to 110€ – Per week from 158 to 770€ – Reservation fee 25€

In the heart of a vineyard; some rental options have a local flavour (barrel-shaped).

Surroundings : 🌄 ⟨ 🏘 ♨	
Leisure activities : 🏊 ⚔ 🛶 Finnish sauna	
Facilities : 🚿 🔧 🍽 🔥 🚽 launderette	
Nearby : 🎣 ✕	

Longitude : 4.7001
Latitude : 46.18854

This guide is updated regularly, so buy your new copy every year!

LES GETS

74260 – Michelin map **328** N4 – pop. 1 254 – alt. 1 170 – Winter sports : 1 170/2 000 m
▶ Paris 579 – Annecy 77 – Bonneville 33 – Chamonix-Mont-Blanc 60

⚠ Le Frêne

✆ 0450758060. www.alpensport-hotel.com – alt. 1 315 – 🅿

Address : Les Cornus (take the southwestern exit along the D 902 then continue 2.3km, following signs for Les Platons to the right)

Opening times : from end June to beginning Sept.

0.3 ha (40 pitches) very uneven, open site, terraced, flat, grassy

Tariff : (2014 Price) 26€ ♣♣ ⬅ 🔲 🌶 (4A) – Extra per person 7.50€

A small and quiet road crosses the campsite.

Surroundings : 🌄 ⟨ Aiguille du Midi,	
Mt Blanc mountain range 🏘 ♨	
Leisure activities : 🏘 ⚔ 🛶	
Facilities : 🚿 🔧 🔥 🚽 🍽	

Longitude : 6.64296
Latitude : 46.15065

GEX

01170 – Michelin map **328** J3 – pop. 9 882 – alt. 626
▶ Paris 490 – Genève 19 – Lons-le-Saunier 93 – Pontarlier 110

⚠ Municipal les Genêts

✆ 0450428457, www.pays-de-gex.org

Address : route de Divonne-les-Bains (located 1km east along the D 984 and take the road to the right)

Opening times : from beginning May to end Sept.

3.3 ha (140 pitches)

Tariff : (2014 Price) ♣ 4.20€ ⬅ 🔲 6.30€ – 🌶 (16A) 3.40€

Rental rates : (2014 Price) (from beginning May to end Sept.) – 4 🚐. Per night from 60 to 80€ – Per week from 295 to 533€

🚽 borne 3€ – 1 🔲

Pretty situation between Lake Geneva and the Jura mountains.

Surroundings : ⟨ 🏞	
Leisure activities : ✕ 🏘 🛶 🚴	
Facilities : 🚿 🔧 🍽 🔥 🚽 launderette	
Nearby : 🎿 🛶	

Longitude : 6.06841
Latitude : 46.33564

LE GRAND-BORNAND

74450 – Michelin map **328** L5 – pop. 2 195 – alt. 934 – Winter sports : 1 000/2 100 m
▶ Paris 564 – Albertville 47 – Annecy 31 – Bonneville 23

⚠ L'Escale

✆ 0450022069, www.campinglescale.com

Address : route de la Patinoire (east of the town, near the church, near the Borne river)

Opening times : from mid Dec. to end Sept.

2.8 ha (149 pitches) terraced, relatively flat, flat, grassy, stony

Tariff : (2014 Price) 25.70€ ♣♣ ⬅ 🔲 🌶 (10A) – Extra per person 6.70€ – Reservation fee 12€

Rental rates : (2014 Price) Permanent – 26 🚐 – 26 🏠 – 2 🛏 – 6 studios – 20 apartments – 3 tent lodges. Per night from 45 to 95€ – Per week from 300 to 700€ – Reservation fee 12€

🚽 borne 25.70€

Numerous rental options based around a small, partly covered water park.

Surroundings : ❄ ⟨ ♨	
Leisure activities : ♣ ✕ 🏘 🛶 🎿 🎱 🛶	
Facilities : 🚿 🔧 🔲 🍽 🔥 🚽 🍽 launderette 🚲	
Nearby : 🚵 🎿 sports trail	

Longitude : 6.42817
Latitude : 45.94044

⚠ Le Clos du Pin

✆ 0450022761. www.le-clos-du-pin.com – alt. 1 015 – limited spaces for one-night stay

Address : 1.3km east along the follow the signs for Le Bouchet; beside the Borne river

Opening times : from beginning Dec. to mid May from mid June to mid Sept.

1.3 ha (61 pitches)

Tariff : 23.10€ ♣♣ ⬅ 🔲 🌶 (10A) – Extra per person 4.80€ – Reservation fee 8€

Rental rates : (2014 Price) (from beginning Dec. to mid May and from mid June to mid Sept.) – 2 🚐 – 1 apartment. Per night from 50 to 90€ – Per week from 270 to 600 €

🚽 borne

There are numerous owner-occupier mobile homes. Choose the pitches the furthest away from the road.

Surroundings : ❄ 🌄 ⟨ Chaîne des Aravis	
mountains ♨	
Leisure activities : 🏘	
Facilities : 🚿 🔧 🍽 🔥 🚽 🍽 launderette	

Longitude : 6.44281
Latitude : 45.93971

GRANE

26400 – Michelin map **332** C5 – pop. 1 730 – alt. 175
▶ Paris 583 – Crest 10 – Montélimar 34 – Privas 29

⚠ Flower Les Quatre Saisons

✆ 0475626417, www.camping-4saisons.com

Address : take the southeastern exit, 900m along the D 113, follow the signs for la Roche-sur-Grâne

Opening times : from beginning April to end Sept.

2 ha (80 pitches) terraced, relatively flat, flat, grassy, sandy

Tariff : (2014 Price) 31.50€ ♣♣ ⬅ 🔲 🌶 (6A) – Extra per person 6€

Rental rates : (2014 Price) – 4 🛏 – 11 🏠 – 4 tent lodges. Per night from 42 to 117€ – Per week from 294 to 819€

🚐 borne

Surroundings : 🏊 ⩽ 🛶 🎣
Leisure activities : 🍸 🏇 🏄
Facilities : 👤 🚿 🅒🅒 🎬 🛁 🎾 🛒 🍴 launderette 👶
Nearby : 🎿

	GPS
Longitude : 4.92671	
Latitude : 44.72684	

GRAVIÈRES

07140 – Michelin map **331** G7 – pop. 391 – alt. 220
▶ Paris 636 – Lyon 213 – Privas 71 – Nîmes 92

⚠ Le Mas du Serre

🔗 0475373384. www.campinglemasduserre.com

Address : Le Serre (1.3km southeast along the D 113 and take the road to the left, 300m from the Chassezac)

Opening times : from beginning April to end Oct.

1.5 ha (75 pitches) terraced, relatively flat, flat, grassy

Tariff : 26.50€ 👫 🚗 🔲 ⚡ (6A) – Extra per person 7€
Rental rates : (from beginning April to end Sept.) – 6 🛏 – 1 gîte. Per night from 55 to 95€ – Per week from 390 to 670€

🚐 borne 5€

An attractive site set around an old mas (house).

Surroundings : 🏊 ⩽ 🎣
Leisure activities : 🏇 🏄
Facilities : 👤 🚿 🎾 🍴
Nearby : 🏊

	GPS
Longitude : 4.1016	
Latitude : 44.41475	

*The classification (1 to 5 tents, **black** or red) that we award to selected sites in this guide is our own system. It should not be confused with the classification (1 to 5 stars) of official organisations.*

GRESSE-EN-VERCORS

38650 – Michelin map **333** G8 – pop. 394 – alt. 1 205 – Winter sports : 1 300/1 700 m
▶ Paris 610 – Clelles 22 – Grenoble 48 – Monestier-de-Clermont 14

⚠ Les 4 Saisons

🔗 0476343027, www.camping-les4saisons.com

Address : 1.3km southwest, at La Ville

Opening times : from beginning May to mid Oct. and from Christmas to end March

2.2 ha (90 pitches) terraced, flat, grassy, fine gravel, stony

Tariff : (2014 Price) 25€ 👫 🚗 🔲 ⚡ (10A) – Extra per person 5.20€ Reservation fee 6€
Rental rates : (2014 Price) (from beginning May to mid Oct. and from Christmas to end March) – 9 🛏 – 3 🏠. Per night from 90 to 110€ – Per week from 402 to 704€ – Reservation fee 16€

🚐 borne 5.70€

In a pleasant location at the foot of the Massif du Vercors plateau and mountains

Surroundings : ❄ 🏊 ⩽ Massif du Vercors mountains
Leisure activities : 🍸 🍴 🏠 🏇 🏄
Facilities : 👤 🚿 🎾 🍴 launderette
Nearby : 🚵 🍴

	GPS
Longitude : 5.55559	
Latitude : 44.8965	

GRIGNAN

26230 – Michelin map **332** C7 – pop. 1 564 – alt. 198
▶ Paris 629 – Crest 46 – Montélimar 25 – Nyons 25

⛰ Les Truffières

🔗 0475469362. www.lestruffieres.com 🏊

Address : 1100 chemin Belle-Vue-d'Air, Nachony district (situated 2km southwest along the D 541, follow the signs for Donzère and take the D 71, follow the signs for Chamaret)

Opening times : from mid April to end Sept.

1 ha (85 pitches) flat, grassy, stony, wood

Tariff : (2014 Price) 👤 5€ 🚗 🔲 22€ – ⚡ (10A) 4.20€ – Reservation fee 15€
Rental rates : (2014 Price) (from end April to end Sept.) 🏊 – 12 🛏. Per night from 60 to 95€ – Per week from 230 to 760€ – Reservation fee 15€

In a wooded setting.

Surroundings : 🏊 🛶 🎣
Leisure activities : ❌ 🏠 🏇 🏄
Facilities : 👤 🚿 🎾 🅒🅒 🍴

	GPS
Longitude : 4.89121	
Latitude : 44.41163	

GROISY

74570 – Michelin map **328** K4 – pop. 2 976 – alt. 690
▶ Paris 534 – Dijon 228 – Grenoble 120 – Lons-le-Saunier 146

⚠ Le Moulin Dollay

🔗 0450680031. www.moulindollay.fr

Address : 206 rue du Moulin Dollay (situated 2km southeast, Junction of D 2 and N 203; beside a stream, at Le Plot)

Opening times : from beginning April to beginning Oct.

3 ha (30 pitches)

Tariff : 23€ 👫 🚗 🔲 ⚡ (6A) – Extra per person 5€
🚐 borne 5€ – 6 🔲 17€ – 🚐 ⚡17€

Surroundings : 🛶 🎣
Leisure activities : 🏠
Facilities : 👤 🚿 🎬 🅒🅒 🛁 🎾 🛒 🍴 launderette

	GPS
Longitude : 6.19076	
Latitude : 46.00224	

HAUTECOURT

01250 – Michelin map **328** F4 – pop. 760 – alt. 370
▶ Paris 442 – Bourg-en-Bresse 20 – Nantua 24 – Oyonnax 33

⚠ L'Île de Chambod

🔗 0474372541. www.campingilechambod.com

Address : 3232 route du Port (4.5km southeast along the D 59, follow the signs for Poncin then take the turning to the left, 300m from the Ain (small lake)

2.4 ha (110 pitches) flat, grassy

Rentals : 7 🛏 – 4 canvas bungalows.

Surroundings : ⩽ 🛶 🎣
Leisure activities : 🍸 ❌ 🎣 🏄
Facilities : 👤 🚿 🛁 🍴 🎬
Nearby : 🏊 🚵 sports trail

	GPS
Longitude : 5.42819	
Latitude : 46.12761	

This guide is not intended as a list of all the camping sites in France; its aim is to provide a selection of the best sites in each category.

ISSARLÈS

07470 – Michelin map **331** G4 – pop. 165 – alt. 946
▶ Paris 574 – Coucouron 16 – Langogne 36 – Le Monastier-sur-Gazeille 18

⚠ La Plaine de la Loire

𝒫 06 24 49 22 79, www.campinglaplainedelaloire.fr – alt. 900

Address : Le Moulin du Lac - Pont de Laborie (3km west along the D 16, follow the signs for Coucouron and take the road to the left before the bridge, beside the Loire river)

Opening times : from beginning May to end Sept.

1 ha (50 pitches) flat, grassy

Tariff : (2014 Price) 16.10€ ★ ★ ⇌ 🔲 🔌 (10A) – Extra per person 3.80€

Perfect for those in search of peace, nature and fishing.

Surroundings : 🐟 ⬳ 𝟬𝟬
Leisure activities : ✗ 🛶 ⚓ 🎣 🐎
Facilities : ⊶ 🚿 ⛺

GPS Longitude : 4.05207
Latitude : 44.818

JAUJAC

07380 – Michelin map **331** H6 – pop. 1 212 – alt. 450
▶ Paris 612 – Privas 44 – Le Puy-en-Velay 81

⚠ Bonneval

𝒫 04 75 93 27 09, www.campingbonneval.com ✉ 07380 Fabras

Address : Les Plots district of Fabras (situated 2km northeast along the D 19 and take D 5, follow the signs for Pont-de-Labeaume, 100m from the Lignon and basalt columns)

Opening times : from beginning April to end Sept.

3 ha (60 pitches) terraced, relatively flat, flat, grassy

Tariff : (2014 Price) 28.30€ ★ ★ ⇌ 🔲 🔌 (10A) – Extra per person 6.20€

Rental rates : (2014 Price) (from beginning April to end Oct.) – 4 🚐 – 4 🏠 – 1 tent lodge. Per week from 275 to 680€ – Reservation fee 15€

Pitches in both sun and shade; various rental options and a good standard of sanitary facilities suitable for families.

Surroundings : 🐟 ⬳ Chaîne du Tanargue mountains 𝟬
Leisure activities : 🍹 🛶 🚡 🛶
Facilities : ♿ ⊶ (season) 🚿 ▥ ⛺ 🍴 🔲
Nearby : ⚓

JEANSAGNIÈRE

42920 – Michelin map **327** C5 – pop. 84 – alt. 1 050
▶ Paris 440 – Lyon 111 – St-Étienne 84 – Clermont-Ferrand 88

⚠ Village de la Droséra   (rental of chalets only)

𝒫 04 77 24 81 44, www.ladrosera.fr

Address : La Droséra

16 ha

Rentals : 7 🏠.

Pretty wooden chalets in a mountain park.

Surroundings : 🐟 ⬳ of the Monts du Forez 𝟬𝟬
Leisure activities : 🏠 🛶 ▥ walking trails
Facilities : ⊶

GPS Longitude : 3.83592
Latitude : 45.73828

JOANNAS

07110 – Michelin map **331** H6 – pop. 342 – alt. 430
▶ Paris 650 – Aubenas 23 – Largentière 8 – Privas 55

⚠⚠ La Marette

𝒫 04 75 88 38 88, www.lamarette.com

Address : route de Valgorge (2.4km west along the D 24, after La Prade)

4 ha (97 pitches)

Rentals : 2 caravans – 24 🚐 – 19 🏠.

The site is laid out across numerous small, individual terraces, in a natural setting with good shade.

Surroundings : 🐟 ⌂ 𝟬𝟬
Leisure activities : 🍹 ✗ 🏠 🛶 🛶 🏊
Facilities : ♿ ⊶ 🚿 ⛺ 🔲 🛁

GPS Longitude : 4.22913
Latitude : 44.56662

⚠⚠ Le Roubreau

𝒫 04 75 88 32 07, www.leroubreau.com

Address : route de Valgorge (1.4km west along the D 24 and take road to the left)

Opening times : from mid April to mid Sept.

3 ha (100 pitches) relatively flat, flat, grassy, stony

Tariff : 30€ ★ ★ ⇌ 🔲 🔌 (6A) – Extra per person 7€ – Reservation fee 7.50€

Rental rates : (from mid March to mid Sept.) – 14 🚐 – 16 🏠 – 2 canvas bungalows. Per night from 29 to 110€ – Per week from 200 to 770€ – Reservation fee 7.50€

🚐 borne 5€

Well-shaded pitches and rental options beside the Roubreau river, with good sanitary facilities.

Surroundings : 🐟 ⌂ 𝟬𝟬
Leisure activities : 🍹 ✗ 🏠 🛶 🎣 🛶 🐎
Facilities : ♿ ⊶ 🚿 ⛺ 🔲 🛁

GPS Longitude : 4.23865
Latitude : 44.55964

> *Do not confuse:*
> ⚠ to ⚠⚠⚠ : *MICHELIN classification with*
> ★ to ★★★★★ : *official classification*

JOYEUSE

07260 – Michelin map **331** H7 – pop. 1 640 – alt. 180
▶ Paris 650 – Alès 54 – Mende 97 – Privas 55

⚠⚠ La Nouzarède

𝒫 04 75 39 92 01, www.camping-nouzarede.fr

Address : north of the town along the rte du Stade, 150m from the Beaume (direct access)

Opening times : from mid April to mid Sept.

2 ha (103 pitches)

Tariff : 30.50€ ★ ★ ⇌ 🔲 🔌 (10A) – Extra per person 6.70€ – Reservation fee 14.50€

Rental rates : (from mid April to mid Sept.) – 27 🚐 – 1 🏠. Per night from 55 to 65€ – Per week from 280 to 820€ – Reservation fee 14.50€

Opposite a well-equipped horse and pony centre; good sanitary facilities.

Surroundings : ⌂ 𝟬𝟬
Leisure activities : 🍹 ✗ 🏠 🛶 🛶 🐎
Facilities : ♿ ⊶ 🔲 ▥ ⛺ 🚿 🍴 🔲 🛁
Nearby : ✗ ⚓ 🛶

GPS Longitude : 4.23526
Latitude : 44.48368

LAGORCE

07150 – Michelin map **331** I7 – pop. 700 – alt. 120
▶ Paris 648 – Aubenas 23 – Bourg-St-Andéol 34 – Privas 54

⚠ Les Castels Domaine de Sévenier

Domaine de Sévenier

(rental of chalets only)

✆ 04 75 88 29 44. www.sevenier.net

Address : Sévenier district (1.6km south along the D 1, follow signs for Vallon-Pont-d'Arc)

Opening times : from beginning April to mid Nov.

4 ha undulating

Rental rates : ♿ (3 chalets) – 56 🏠. Per night from 57 to 328€ – Per week from 399 to 2,296€ – Reservation fee 20€

An attractive chalet site, some equipped for very young children or large families, some on a hotel-style basis.

Surroundings : 🏞
Leisure activities : ▼ ✕ ⚓ 🏊
Facilities : ⚐ ▥ ♒ ⚑ 🍴

G P S Longitude : 4.41153
Latitude : 44.4338

LALLEY

38930 – Michelin map **333** H9 – pop. 205 – alt. 850
▶ Paris 626 – Grenoble 63 – La Mure 30 – Sisteron 80

⚠ Sites et Paysages Belle Roche

✆ 04 76 34 75 33. www.camping-belleroche.com – alt. 860

Address : chemin de Combe Morée (head south of the town following signs for Mens and take the road to the right)

2.4 ha (60 pitches) terrace, flat, grassy, stony

Rentals : 6 🚐 – 1 cabin.

In a pleasant location opposite the village.

Surroundings : 🏞 ≼ ⌂ ♀
Leisure activities : ▼ ✕ 🏓 ⚓ 🏊 multi-sports ground
Facilities : ♿ ⚐ ▥ ⚑ launderette 🍴
Nearby : ✕

G P S Longitude : 5.67889
Latitude : 44.75472

LALOUVESC

07520 – Michelin map **331** J3 – pop. 496 – alt. 1 050
▶ Paris 553 – Annonay 24 – Lamastre 25 – Privas 80

⚠ Municipal le Pré du Moulin

✆ 04 75 67 84 86. www.lalouvesc.com

Address : chemin de l'Hermuzière (north of the village)

Opening times : from beginning May to end Sept.

2.5 ha (70 pitches) terraced, relatively flat, grassy

Tariff : (2014 Price) ♟ 2.60€ – ⚘ 1.80€ 🔲 2.80€ – (10A) 3.30€

Rental rates : (2014 Price) (from beginning May to end Sept.) – 5 🚐 – 5 tree houses and 10 huts (without sanitary facilities). Per night from 28 to 110€ – Per week from 150 to 343€

🚰 borne 2€

Various rental options, some with rather old, basic facilities.

Surroundings : 🏞 ♀
Leisure activities : 🏓 ⚓ ✕
Facilities : ♿ ⚐ ⚘ ⚑ ♒ ⚑ ▥ 🍴

G P S Longitude : 4.53392
Latitude : 45.12388

LAMASTRE

07270 – Michelin map **331** J4 – pop. 2 501 – alt. 375
▶ Paris 577 – Privas 55 – Le Puy-en-Velay 72 – Valence 38

⚠ Le Retourtour

✆ 04 75 06 40 71. www.campingderetourtour.com

Address : 1 rue de Retourtour

Opening times : from mid April to end Sept.

2.9 ha (130 pitches)

Tariff : (2014 Price) 23.96€ ♟♟ ⚘ 🔲 (4) (13A) – Extra per person 4.98€ – Reservation fee 10€

Rental rates : (2014 Price) (from mid April to end Sept.) – 16 🚐 – 3 🏠 – 3 canvas bungalows – 2 gîtes. Per night from 59 to 109€ – Per week from 238 to 599€ – Reservation fee 10€

🚰 borne – 50 🔲 18.96€

Well-shaded pitches, near a small lake.

Surroundings : 🏞 ♀♀
Leisure activities : ▼ ✕ ⚓ 🏓 ⚓ 🏊
Facilities : ♿ ⚐ ♒ ⚑ ▥ ♒ 🍴
Nearby : ▥ (beach)

G P S Longitude : 4.56483
Latitude : 44.99164

These symbols are used for a campsite that is exceptional in its category :

⚠⚠⚠...⚠ *Particularly pleasant setting, quality and range of services available*

🏞🏞 *Tranquil, isolated site – quiet site, particularly at night*

≼≼ *Exceptional view – interesting or panoramic view*

LANSLEVILLARD

73480 – Michelin map **333** O6 – pop. 457 – alt. 1 500 – Winter sports : 1 400/2 800 m
▶ Paris 689 – Albertville 116 – Briançon 87 – Chambéry 129

⚠ Caravaneige de Val Cenis

✆ 04 79 05 90 52. www.camping-valcenis.com

Address : rue sous l'Église (southwestern exit, follow the signs for Lanslebourg ; beside rapids)

Opening times : from mid Dec. to end April from beginning June to mid Sept.

3 ha (100 pitches)

Tariff : 23.10€ ♟♟ ⚘ 🔲 (4) (10A) – Extra per person 7.10€ – Reservation fee 6€

🚰 borne 4.15€

The site boasts excellent sanitary facilities.

Surroundings : ❄ ≼ ♀
Leisure activities : ▼ ✕ ⚓ ⚓ 🏊
Facilities : ♿ ⚐ ▥ ⚑ launderette 🍴
Nearby : ✕ 🏓

G P S Longitude : 6.90928
Latitude : 45.29057

For more information on visiting particular towns or regions, consult the relevant regional MICHELIN Green Guide. We also recommend you use the appropriate Michelin regional map to locate your selected campsite, to calculate distances and to work out the best route.

LARNAS

07220 – Michelin map **331** J7 – pop. 97 – alt. 300
▶ Paris 631 – Aubenas 41 – Bourg-St-Andéol 12 – Montélimar 24

FranceLoc Le Domaine d'Imbours 👥👤

0475543950. www.domaine-imbours.com

Address : 2.5km southwest along the D 262 - for caravans, from Bourg-St-Andéol, go via St-Remèze and Mas du Gras (D 4, D 362 and D 262)

Opening times : from beginning April to end Sept.

270 ha/10 for camping (694 pitches) relatively flat, flat, grassy, stony

Tariff : (2014 Price) 38€ 👫 🚐 🔲 🔌 (6A) – Extra per person 7€ Reservation fee 27€

Rental rates : (2014 Price) (from beginning April to end Sept.) – 6 caravans – 387 🛖 – 64 🏠 – 32 tent lodges – 100 gîtes – hotel (96 rooms). Per night from 32 to 191€ – Per week from 126 to 1,337€ – Reservation fee 27€

Surroundings : 🌊 ♨️ Leisure activities : 🍴 ✕ 🏠 🎣 🏃 🏊 🚴 🎯 🎿 🔲 🏄 multi-sports ground Facilities : 🚿 ☕ 🛁 🏧 🍴 🛥️ 🚤 Nearby : 🐎	**GPS** Longitude : 4.5764 Latitude : 44.4368

LATHUILE

74210 – Michelin map **328** K6 – pop. 960 – alt. 510
▶ Paris 554 – Albertville 30 – Annecy 18 – La Clusaz 38

L'Idéal

0450443297, www.campingideal.com

Address : 715 route de Chaparon (located 1.5km to the north)

3.2 ha (300 pitches) gravelled

Rental rates : ♿ (1 mobile home) – 80 🛖 – 1 studio – 7 apartments.

The site has plenty of space and a variety of rentals, based around an extensive water park.

Surroundings : 🌊 < ♨️ Leisure activities : 🍴 ✕ 🏠 🎣 jacuzzi 🏄 ✕ 🏊 🔲 (open air in season) 🎿 🏄 multi-sports ground Facilities : 🚿 ☕ 🛁 🍴 launderette 🚤 🛥️	**GPS** Longitude : 6.20582 Latitude : 45.79537

Les Fontaines 👥👤

0450443122. www.campinglesfontaines.com

Address : 1295 route de Chaparon (situated 2km to the north at Chaparon)

Opening times : from beginning May to mid Sept.

3 ha (170 pitches) terraced, sloping, flat, grassy

Tariff : (2014 Price) 35.40€ 👫 🚐 🔲 🔌 (6A) – Extra per person 8€ Reservation fee 16€

Rental rates : (2014 Price) (from mid April to mid Sept.) – 57 🛖 – 3 🏠 – 8 tipis. Per night from 55 to 99€ – Per week from 260 to 977€ – Reservation fee 16€

The site boasts some different and rather unusual rental options.

Surroundings : 🌊 < ♨️ Leisure activities : 🍴 ✕ 🏠 🎣 🏃 🏄 🔲 (open air in season) 🎿 🏄 multi-sports ground Facilities : 🚿 ☕ 🎰 🍴 launderette 🚤 🛥️	**GPS** Longitude : 6.20444 Latitude : 45.80037

La Ravoire

0450443780. www.camping-la-ravoire.fr

Address : route de la Ravoire (2.5km to the north)

Opening times : from mid May to mid Sept.

2 ha (124 pitches) flat, grassy

Tariff : 31.50€ 👫 🚐 🔲 🔌 (5A) – Extra per person 8€ – Reservation fee 16€

Rental rates : 🏄 – 22 🛖 – 4 🏠. Per night from 63 to 99€ – Per week from 260 to 922€ – Reservation fee 16€

Located in a pleasant, green setting near the lake.

Surroundings : 🌊 < 🎣 ♨️ Leisure activities : 🍴 ✕ 🏠 🏄 🎿 🏄 multi-sports ground Facilities : 🚿 ☕ 🆔 🛁 🏧 🛥️ 🍴 launderette Nearby : 🎣	**GPS** Longitude : 6.20975 Latitude : 45.80244

Le Taillefer

0450443030. www.campingletaillefer.com

Address : 1530 route de Chaparon (situated 2km to the north, at Chaparon)

Opening times : from beginning May to end Sept.

1 ha (32 pitches) open site, terraced, sloping, flat, grassy

Tariff : 23.50€ 👫 🚐 🔲 🔌 (6A) – Extra per person 6€

This grassy site has some shade and clean if somewhat old sanitary facilities.

Surroundings : 🌊 ♨️ Leisure activities : 🍴 🏠 🏄 🚴 Facilities : 🚿 ☕ 🏧 🍴 🔲	**GPS** Longitude : 6.20565 Latitude : 45.80231

LAURAC-EN-VIVARAIS

07110 – Michelin map **331** H6 – pop. 885 – alt. 182
▶ Paris 646 – Alès 60 – Mende 102 – Privas 50

Les Châtaigniers

0475368626. www.chataigniers-laurac.com

Address : Prends-toi Garde (to the southeast of the town, recommended route via the D 104)

Opening times : from beginning April to end Sept.

1.2 ha (71 pitches)

Tariff : (2014 Price) 23€ 👫 🚐 🔲 🔌 (10A) – Extra per person 4€

Rental rates : (2014 Price) (from beginning April to end Sept.) 🏄 (from beginning June to end Aug.) – 12 🛖. Per night from 50 to 65€ – Per week from 290 to 650€

🚐 borne – 6 🔲

The upper part of the site has the most shade, the lower part has marked-out pitches.

Surroundings : ♨️ Leisure activities : 🏠 🏄 🎿 Facilities : 🚿 ☕ 🏧 🍴 🔲	**GPS** Longitude : 4.29497 Latitude : 44.50429

Some information or pricing may have changed since the guide went to press. We recommend you check the price list online in advance or at the entrance to the campsite and enquire about possible restrictions.

LÉPIN-LE-LAC

73610 – Michelin map **333** H4 – pop. 407 – alt. 400
▶ Paris 555 – Belley 36 – Chambéry 24 – Les Échelles 17

⚠ Le Curtelet

𝒞 0479441122. www.camping-le-curtelet.com

Address : 1.4km to the northwest

Opening times : from mid May to mid Sept.

1.3 ha (91 pitches) relatively flat, flat, grassy

Tariff : 23.70€ ♜♜ ⇌ 🔲 (∦) (10A) – Extra per person 5.20€ –
Reservation fee 10€

Surroundings : 🏊 ⚶ ♨♨ 🏖 (beach) 🐟	
Leisure activities : 🍸 🏖🏄 (beach) 🐟	
Facilities : 🚿 ⚎ (Jul–Sept) 🧺 🏕🍴	**GPS** Longitude : 5.77916
launderette	Latitude : 45.54002
Nearby : 🍴 🎿	

LESCHERAINES

73340 – Michelin map **333** J3 – pop. 731 – alt. 649
▶ Paris 557 – Aix-les-Bains 26 – Annecy 26 – Chambéry 29

⚠ Municipal l'Île

𝒞 0479638000. www.savoie-camping.com

Address : leisure centre, Les Îles du Chéran (2.5km southeast along
the D 912, follow the signs for Annecy and take the turning to the
right, 200m from the Chéran)

Opening times : from end April to end Sept.

7.5 ha (215 pitches) open site, terraced, relatively flat, flat, grassy

Tariff : 20.50€ ♜♜ ⇌ 🔲 (∦) (10A) – Extra per person 4.55€ –
Reservation fee 10€

Rental rates : (from end April to end Sept.) – 13 🛖 – 5 🏠 –
3 gîtes. Per night from 37 to 86€ – Per week from 260 to 600€
🚐 borne 1.50€ – 8 🔲 4€

Situated beside a small lake and bordered by river and forest.

Surroundings : 🏊 ⚶ ♨ ⛰	
Leisure activities : 🏛	
Facilities : 🚿 ⚎ 🏕🧺🍴 launderette	**GPS** Longitude : 6.11207
At the leisure/activities centre : 🍸 🍴 🍴	Latitude : 45.70352
🏖🏄 🎿 🏖 🌲 forest trail	

LUGRIN

74500 – Michelin map **328** N2 – pop. 2 260 – alt. 413
▶ Paris 584 – Annecy 91 – Évian-les-Bains 8 – St-Gingolph 12

⚠ Vieille Église

𝒞 0450760195. www.campingvieilleeglise.fr

Address : 53 route des Préparraux (situated 2km west, at Vieille-
Église)

Opening times : from mid April to end Oct.

1.6 ha (97 pitches) terraced, relatively flat, flat, grassy

Tariff : 27€ ♜♜ ⇌ 🔲 (∦) (10A) – Extra per person 7.40€ – Reservation
fee 5€

Rental rates : (from mid April to end Oct.) – 27 🛖 – 1 🏕 –
1 studio – 1 apartment. Per week from 295 to 795€ – Reservation
fee 5€

🚐 borne 7€ – 🚐 (∦)21.50€

Some pitches have a view over Lac Léman.

Surroundings : ⚶ 🏕 ♨♨	
Leisure activities : 🏛 🏖🏄 🎿 🎿	
Facilities : 🚿 ⚎ 🏕🍴 launderette 🐟	**GPS** Longitude : 6.64655
	Latitude : 46.40052

LUS-LA-CROIX-HAUTE

26620 – Michelin map **332** H6 – pop. 507 – alt. 1 050
▶ Paris 638 – Alès 207 – Die 45 – Gap 49

⚠ Champ la Chèvre

𝒞 0492585014. www.campingchamplachevre.com

Address : to the southeast of the town, near the swimming pool

Opening times : Permanent

3.6 ha (100 pitches) terraced, relatively flat, flat, grassy

Tariff : 29.10€ ♜♜ ⇌ 🔲 (∦) (6A) – Extra per person 7.50€

Rental rates : Permanent – 8 🛖 – 8 🏠 – 3 tent lodges. Per night
from 46 to 90€ – Per week from 309 to 830€ – Reservation fee 15€

Surroundings : 🏊 ⚶ ♨	
Leisure activities : 🏛 🔲 (open air	
in season)	**GPS** Longitude : 5.70998
Facilities : 🚿 ⚎ ▣🍴 🏖	Latitude : 44.6629
Nearby : 🐎	

To visit a town or region, use the MICHELIN Green Guides.

LES MARCHES

73800 – Michelin map **333** I5 – pop. 2 453 – alt. 328
▶ Paris 572 – Albertville 43 – Chambéry 12 – Grenoble 44

⚠ La Ferme du Lac

𝒞 0479281348, www.campinglafermedulac.fr

Address : located 1km southwest along the N 90, follow the signs for
Pontcharra and take the D 12 to the right

Opening times : from beginning April to beginning Sept.

2.6 ha (100 pitches) flat, grassy

Tariff : ♜ 4.80€ ⇌ 🔲 5.70€ – (∦) (10A) 10€

Rental rates : (2014 Price) Permanent 🚫 – 9 🛖 – 1 🏠.
Per night from 60€ – Per week from 265 to 415€
🚐 borne 4€ – 8 🔲 11€ – 🚐 (∦)14.90€

Choose the pitches furthest away from the road.

Surroundings : 🚐 ♨♨	
Leisure activities : 🏛 🎿	
Facilities : 🚿 ⚎ 🏕🍴 🏖	**GPS** Longitude : 5.99327
	Latitude : 45.49595

MARS

07320 – Michelin map **331** H3 – pop. 279 – alt. 1 060
▶ Paris 579 – Annonay 49 – Le Puy-en-Velay 44 – Privas 71

⚠ La Prairie

𝒞 0475302447, www.camping-laprairie.com

Address : Laillier (to the northeast of the town along the D 15, follow
the signs for St-Agrève and take road to the left)

Opening times : from mid May to mid Sept.

0.6 ha (30 pitches)

Tariff : (2014 Price) ♜ 3.50€ ⇌ 1.60€ 🔲 3€ – (∦) (6A) 3.30€

Rental rates : (2014 Price) (from mid May to mid Sept.) – 1 🏠.
Per week from 500 to 1,000€

🚐 borne 4€

Well-kept pitches, in a peaceful, green site.

Surroundings : 🏊 ⚶	
Leisure activities : 🍴 🏖🏄 🚲	
Facilities : 🚿 ⚎ 🧺 ▣	**GPS** Longitude : 4.32632
Nearby : 🍴 18-hole golf course	Latitude : 45.02393

MASSIGNIEU-DE-RIVES

01300 – Michelin map **328** H6 – pop. 591 – alt. 295
▶ Paris 516 – Aix-les-Bains 26 – Belley 10 – Morestel 37

⛰ VivaCamp le Lac du Lit du Roi

☎ 04 79 42 12 03. www.camping-savoie.com

Address : La Tuillère (2.5km north following signs for Belley and take the road to the right)

Opening times : from end April to end Sept.

4 ha (120 pitches)

Tariff : (2014 Price) 27€ ★★ ⇔ 🖹 🔌 (10A) – Extra per person 6.50€ Reservation fee 15€

Rental rates : (2014 Price) (from end April to end Sept.) – 20 🚐 – 5 🏠 – 2 tipis – 3 canvas bungalows. Per night from 30 to 85€ – Per week from 157 to 805€ – Reservation fee 25€

In a pleasant location beside a lake formed by the Rhône river.

Surroundings : 🐟 ⩽ lake and hills 🏞 ⚲ ⚠
Leisure activities : ▼ ✕ 🚣 🚴 ✗ 🏊 🎣 pedalos 🛶
Facilities : ♿ ⚿ 🚮 🚿 🍴 📷

GPS Longitude : 5.77001 Latitude : 45.76861

MATAFELON-GRANGES

01580 – Michelin map **328** G3 – pop. 653 – alt. 453
▶ Paris 460 – Bourg-en-Bresse 37 – Lons-le-Saunier 56 – Mâcon 75

⛰ Les Gorges de l'Oignin

☎ 04 74 76 80 97, www.gorges-de-loignin.com

Address : rue du Lac (900m south of the village, near the Oignin river)

Opening times : from mid April to end Sept.

2.6 ha (128 pitches) terraced, flat, grassy, gravelled

Tariff : 28.90€ ★★ ⇔ 🖹 🔌 (10A) – Extra per person 7.10€ – Reservation fee 16€

Rental rates : (from mid April to end Sept.) ✗ (from beginning July to end Aug.) – 2 🚐 – 10 🏠. Per night from 32 to 95€ – Per week from 224 to 660€ – Reservation fee 16€

🚐 20 🖹 25.90€

Situated near a lake.

Surroundings : ⩽
Leisure activities : ▼ ✕ 🚣 🏊
Facilities : ♿ ⚿ 🏛 🚮 🚿 🍴 📷
Nearby : 🏊 🎣

LES MAZES

07150 – Michelin map **331** I7
▶ Paris 669 – Lyon 207 – Privas 58 – Nîmes 83

⛰ La Plage Fleurie ▲▲

☎ 04 75 88 01 15. www.laplagefleurie.com

Address : 3.5km west

Opening times : from end April to beginning Sept.

12 ha/6 for camping (300 pitches) terraced, flat and relatively flat, grassy

Tariff : 48€ ★★ ⇔ 🖹 🔌 (10A) – Extra per person 8.60€ – Reservation fee 20€

Rental rates : (from end April to beginning Sept.) – 32 canvas bungalows. Per night from 54 to 105€ – Per week from 378 to 740€ – Reservation fee 25€

🚐 borne

Located beside the Ardèche river, with a sandy beach and an area of grass and several luxurious mobile homes.

Surroundings : 🐟 ⩽ ⚲⚲
Leisure activities : ▼ ✕ 🏠 🎱 🚣 🚙 🏊 🎣 (beach)
Facilities : ♿ ⚿ 🚮 🍴 📷 🚿 🛁

GPS Longitude : 4.3546 Latitude : 44.40837

⛰ Beau Rivage

☎ 04 75 88 03 54. www.beaurivage-camping.com

Address : take the D 579

Opening times : from end April to mid Sept.

2 ha (100 pitches)

Tariff : 36€ ★★ ⇔ 🖹 🔌 (10A) – Extra per person 6.20€ – Reservation fee 16€

Rental rates : (from beginning April to mid Sept.) ✗ – 14 🚐. Per night from 42 to 117€ – Per week from 299 to 895€ – Reservation fee 23€

Located among the vineyards on the banks of the Ardèche river, the perfect place for some peace and quiet.

Surroundings : 🐟 🏞 ⚲⚲
Leisure activities : ✕ 🏠 🚣 🏊 🎣 🛶
Facilities : ♿ ⚿ 🚮 🍴 📷 🛁

GPS Longitude : 4.3649 Latitude : 44.4103

⛰ Arc-en-Ciel ▲▲

☎ 04 75 88 04 65. www.arcenciel-camping.com

Address : take the D 579

Opening times : from mid April to mid Sept.

5 ha (218 pitches)

Tariff : (2014 Price) 37.50€ ★★ ⇔ 🖹 🔌 (10A) – Extra per person 7.70€ – Reservation fee 20€

Rental rates : (2014 Price) (from mid April to mid Sept.) – 66 🚐 – 14 canvas bungalows – 2 gîtes. Per week from 270 to 920€ – Reservation fee 20€

Beside the Ardèche river with a sandy beach and grassy area. A wide range of local rental options of differing standards.

Surroundings : 🐟 ⚲⚲
Leisure activities : ▼ ✕ 🏠 🎱 🚣 🏊 (beach) 🎣 🛶
Facilities : ♿ ⚿ 🚮 🍴 📷 🛁 🛁

GPS Longitude : 4.3512 Latitude : 44.41177

MÉAUDRE

38112 – Michelin map **333** G7 – pop. 1 321 – alt. 1 012 – Winter sports : 1 000/1 600 m
▶ Paris 588 – Grenoble 38 – Pont-en-Royans 26 – Tullins 53

⛰ Les Buissonnets

☎ 04 76 95 21 04. www.camping-les-buissonnets.com – limited spaces for one-night stay

Address : Les Grangeons (500m northeast along the D 106 and take turning to the right, 200m from the Méaudret river)

Opening times : from beginning Dec. to end Oct.

2.8 ha (100 pitches)

Tariff : 21.70€ ★★ ⇔ 🖹 🔌 (10A) – Extra per person 5€

Rental rates : (from mid Dec. to end Oct.) 🅿 – 10 🚐 – 3 🏠. Per week from 304 to 489€

🚐 borne 5€ – 40 🖹 16.10€ – 🚐 14.50€

Surroundings : ❄ 🐟 ⩽ ⚲
Leisure activities : 🎱 🚣
Facilities : ♿ ⚿ 🏛 🚮 🚿 🍴 📷
Nearby : ✗ 🏊

GPS Longitude : 5.53243 Latitude : 45.12955

⚠ Les Eymes

℘ 0476952485. www.camping-les-eymes.com

Address : 3.8km north along the D 106c, follow the signs for Autrans and take turning to the left

Opening times : Permanent

1.3 ha (40 pitches)

Tariff : 23€ ★★ ⚌ 🅴 (⚡) (10A) – Extra per person 7€ – Reservation fee 2€

Rental rates : (2014 Price) Permanent – 7 [🚐] – 4 🏠. Per night from 53 to 106€ – Per week from 318 to 636€ – Reservation fee 10€

[🚐] borne 5€ – 6 🅴 19€ – 🚐11€

Surroundings : 🌿 ⋖
Leisure activities : ✗ 🏊
Facilities : ♿ ⚬� [cc] 🏢 🏕 ✽ 🍴 🖼 🏊 🏖

G P S
Longitude : 5.51574
Latitude : 45.14468

MEGÈVE

74120 – Michelin map **328** M5 – pop. 3 907 – alt. 1 113 – Winter sports : 1 113/2 350 m
▶ Paris 598 – Albertville 32 – Annecy 60 – Chamonix-Mont-Blanc 33

⚠ Bornand

℘ 0450930086. www.camping-megeve.com – alt. 1 060

Address : 57 route du Grand Bois - Demi quartier (3km northeast along the N 212, follow the signs for Sallanches and the Rte de la télécabine (cable car) to the right)

Opening times : from mid June to end Aug.

1.5 ha (55 pitches) open site, terraced, sloping, flat, grassy

Tariff : (2014 Price) ★ 4.10€ ⚌ 🅴 4.70€ – (⚡) (6A) 4€

Rental rates : Permanent 🏕 – 4 🏠. Per week from 330 to 595€

[🚐] borne 3€

A collection of genuine wooden Savoyard chalets!

Surroundings : 🌿 ⋖ 🌳
Leisure activities : 🏊
Facilities : ♿ ⚬ 🏕 ✽ 🍴 launderette

G P S
Longitude : 6.64161
Latitude : 45.87909

MENGLON

26410 – Michelin map **332** F6 – pop. 406 – alt. 550
▶ Paris 645 – Lyon 183 – Valence 80 – Grenoble 90

⚠ L'Hirondelle 👥

℘ 0475218208, www.campinghirondelle.com

Address : bois de Saint Ferréol (2.8km northwest along the D 214 and D 140, follow the signs for Die, near the D 539 (recommended route)

7.5 ha (180 pitches) undulating, flat, grassy

Rentals : 20 [🚐] – 24 🏠 – 4 canvas bungalows – 9 tent lodges (on stilts).

A pleasant site and setting beside the Bez river.

Surroundings : 🌿 ⋖ 🏕 〰
Leisure activities : 🍴 ✗ 🏊 🌙nighttime 🏃
🏊 🏖 ≋ (river) ⚽ multi-sports ground
Facilities : ♿ ⚬ 🏕 🍴 launderette 🏊 🏖

G P S
Longitude : 5.44746
Latitude : 44.68143

*The classification (1 to 5 tents, **black** or red) that we award to selected sites in this guide is our own system. It should not be confused with the classification (1 to 5 stars) of official organisations.*

MENTHON-ST-BERNARD

74290 – Michelin map **328** K5 – pop. 1 876 – alt. 482
▶ Paris 552 – Lyon 148 – Annecy 9 – Genève 51

⚠ Le Clos Don Jean

℘ 0450601866. www.campingclosdonjean.com

Address : 435 route du Clos-Don-Jean

Opening times : from beginning June to beginning Sept.

1 ha (64 pitches)

Tariff : (2014 Price) 20€ ★★ ⚌ 🅴 (⚡) (6A) – Extra per person 4.70€

Rental rates : (2014 Price) (from end May to beginning Sept.) – 9 [🚐]. Per night from 58 to 79€ – Per week from 278 to 530€

The site has a view over the imposing Château de Menthon.

Surroundings : 🌿 ⋖ 🌳
Leisure activities : 🏊
Facilities : ♿ ⚬ 🏕 🖼

G P S
Longitude : 6.19699
Latitude : 45.86298

The Michelin classification (△△△ ... △) is totally independent of the official star classification system awarded by the local prefecture or other official organisation.

MEYRAS

07380 – Michelin map **331** H5 – pop. 842 – alt. 450
▶ Paris 609 – Aubenas 17 – Le Cheylard 54 – Langogne 49

△△△ Sites et Paysages Domaine de La Plage

℘ 0475364059, www.lecampingdelaplage.com – limited spaces for one-night stay

Address : Neyrac-les-Bains (3km southwest along the N 102, follow the signs for Le Puy-en-Velay)

0.8 ha (45 pitches)

Rentals : 27 [🚐] – 12 🏠 – 7 gîtes.

Below the road; choose those pitches beside the Ardèche river.

Surroundings : ⋖ 🏕 🌳🌳
Leisure activities : 🍴 ✗ 🏊 🚴 🏊 ≋ 🎣
multi-sports ground, entertainment room
Facilities : ♿ ⚬ 🏢 🏊 🏕 ✽ 🍴 launderette 🏖

G P S
Longitude : 4.26067
Latitude : 44.67315

△△ Le Ventadour

℘ 0475941815. www.leventadour.com

Address : at the Pont de Rolandy (3.5km southeast, along the N 102, follow the signs for Aubenas; beside the Ardèche river)

Opening times : from mid April to beginning Oct.

3 ha (115 pitches)

Tariff : 29.40€ ★★ ⚌ 🅴 (⚡) (10A) – Extra per person 6€ – Reservation fee 15€

Rental rates : (from mid April to beginning Oct.) – 17 [🚐]. Per week from 179 to 790€ – Reservation fee 15€

[🚐] borne 2€

Choose pitches beside the river, furthest away from the road.

Surroundings : 🏕 🌳
Leisure activities : 🍴 ✗ 🏊 🚴 ≋
(beach) 🎣
Facilities : ♿ ⚬ 🏢 🏕 🍴 launderette 🏖

G P S
Longitude : 4.28291
Latitude : 44.66757

MEYRIEU-LES-ÉTANGS

38440 – Michelin map **333** E4 – pop. 839 – alt. 430
▶ Paris 515 – Beaurepaire 31 – Bourgoin-Jallieu 14 – Grenoble 78

⛰ Base de Loisirs du Moulin

✆ 0474593034. www.camping-meyrieu.com

Address : route de Saint-Anne (800m southeast along the D 56b, follow the signs for Châtonnoy and turn left towards Ste-Anne; near a small lake)

1 ha (58 pitches)

Rentals : 🅿 – 3 🚐 – 11 🏠.

The pitches are arranged on terraces looking out over the lake.

Surroundings : 🏞 🗺 ♨	**G**	Longitude : 5.20175
Leisure activities : 🏖 🎯 🎣	**P**	Latitude : 45.5152
Facilities : ♿ ⛽ 🚿 🚾 🖼	**S**	
Nearby : 🍷 🍴 🏄 🚣 🚴 🏊 pedalos		

MIRABEL-ET-BLACONS

26400 – Michelin map **332** D5 – pop. 904 – alt. 225
▶ Paris 595 – Crest 7 – Die 30 – Dieulefit 33

⛰ Gervanne

✆ 0475400020. www.gervanne-camping.com

Address : Bellevue district (situated where the Drôme and the Gervanne rivers meet, at Blacons)

Opening times : from beginning April to end Sept.

3.7 ha (150 pitches) Tariff : 31.30€ ♦♦ 🚗 🗐 ⚡ (6A) – Extra per person 7.40€ – Reservation fee 15€

Rental rates : (from beginning April to end Sept.) ♿ (1 chalet) 🍽 – 3 caravans – 3 🚐 – 18 🏠. Per night from 66 to 90€ – Per week from 308 to 878€ – Reservation fee 15€

🚐 borne 4.50€

A green setting beside the Gervanne and Drôme rivers.

Surroundings : 🏞 ♨ 🏔	**G**	Longitude : 5.08917
Leisure activities : 🏖 🍷 🍴 🏄 🚴 🎣 🎣	**P**	Latitude : 44.71083
Facilities : ♿ ⛽ 🏧 🚾 🍴 launderette 🖼 🏖	**S**	
Nearby : fitness trail		

MONTCHAVIN

73210 – Michelin map **333** N4 – alt. 1 206
▶ Paris 672 – Lyon 206 – Chambéry 106 – Albertville 57

⛰ Caravaneige de Montchavin

✆ 0479078323. www.montchavin-lescoches.com – alt. 1 250

Address : Montchavin

Opening times : Permanent

1.33 ha (90 pitches)

Tariff : 16.50€ ♦♦ 🚗 🗐 ⚡ (10A) – Extra per person 5.50€

Rental rates : Permanent – 2 🚐. Per night from 98€ – Per week from 294 to 686€

🚐 borne 10€ – 5 🗐 16.50€

A superb location and view.

Surroundings : ❄ 🏞 ≼ Tarentaise valley, Bourg-St-Maurice and Mont Blanc ♨♨	**G**	Longitude : 6.73933
Leisure activities : 🏖	**P**	Latitude : 45.56058
Facilities : ♿ ⛽ 🏧 🍴 launderette	**S**	
Nearby : 🍷 🍷 🍴 🎣 🖼 🏖		

MONTREVEL-EN-BRESSE

01340 – Michelin map **328** D2 – pop. 2 363 – alt. 215
▶ Paris 395 – Bourg-en-Bresse 18 – Mâcon 25 – Pont-de-Vaux 22

⛰ La Plaine Tonique 👥

✆ 0474308052. www.laplainetonique.com

Address : leisure centre (500m east along the D 28; at the leisure park)

Opening times : from mid April to mid Sept.

27 ha/15 for camping (548 pitches)

Tariff : (2014 Price) ♦ 7.30€ 🚗 🗐 16.10€ ⚡ (16A) – Reservation fee 10€

Rental rates : (2014 Price) (from mid April to mid Sept.) 🍽 – 21 🚐 – 57 🏠 – 14 🏡 – 8 tipis – 10 canvas bungalows – 1 gîte. Per night from 136 to 150€ – Per week from 400 to 844€ Reservation fee 10€

🚐 borne 2€ – 12 🗐 16.10€

Beside a lake and with an attractive swimming area.

Surroundings : 🗺 ♨ 🏔	**G**	Longitude : 5.136
Leisure activities : 🍷 🍴 🏖 🎣 🎯 🏊 🎿	**P**	Latitude : 46.33902
🏄 🎣 🗐 🏊 🛶 🎣 🚣 sports trail	**S**	
Facilities : ♿ ⛽ 🏧 🚿 🚾 🍴 🖼 🏖 🏖		

MONTRIGAUD

26350 – Michelin map **332** D2 – pop. 496 – alt. 462
▶ Paris 560 – Lyon 97 – Valence 51 – Grenoble 75

⛰ La Grivelière

✆ 0475717071. www.lagriveliere.com

Address : route de Roybon

Opening times : from beginning April to end Sept.

2.6 ha (59 pitches) flat, grassy

Tariff : 25.50€ ♦♦ 🚗 🗐 ⚡ (6A) – Extra per person 5€ – Reservation fee 10€

Rental rates : (from beginning April to end Sept.) – 2 caravans – 4 🚐 – 1 🏠 – 2 canvas bungalows. Per night from 42 to 107€ – Per week from 299 to 749€ – Reservation fee 10€

Surroundings : 🏞 🗺 ♨	**G**	Longitude : 5.16711
Leisure activities : 🍷 🍴 🏖 🏄 🎣	**P**	Latitude : 45.22176
Facilities : ⛽ 🏧 🍴 launderette 🏖	**S**	

MORNANT

69440 – Michelin map **327** H6 – pop. 5 438 – alt. 380
▶ Paris 478 – Givors 12 – Lyon 26 – Rive-de-Gier 13

⛰ Municipal de la Trillonière

✆ 0478441647. www.ville-mornant.fr

Address : boulevard Général de Gaulle (southern exit, Junction of D 30 and D 34, near a stream)

Opening times : from beginning May to end Sept.

1.5 ha (60 pitches) relatively flat, flat, grassy

Tariff : (2014 Price) 16.80€ ♦♦ 🚗 🗐 ⚡ (10A) – Extra per person 4.20€

🚐 borne – 30 🗐 16.80€ – ⚡ 15.98€

At the foot of the medieval old town; a bus stop for Lyon.

Facilities : ♿ 🚮 🍴 🖼	**G**	Longitude : 4.67073
Nearby : 🎿 🏊	**P**	Latitude : 45.61532
	S	

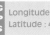

MORZINE

74110 – Michelin map **328** N3 – pop. 2 930 – alt. 960 – Winter sports : 1 000/2 100 m

▶ Paris 586 – Annecy 84 – Chamonix-Mont-Blanc 67 – Cluses 26

⚠ Les Marmottes

🖉 04 50 75 74 44. www.campinglesmarmottes.com – alt. 938

Address : Essert-Romand (3.7km northwest along the D 902, follow the signs for Thonon-les-Bains and take D 329 to the left)

Opening times : from end June to beginning Sept. and from mid Dec to end Mar

0.5 ha (26 pitches)

Tariff : (2014 Price) 26€ ✚✚ ⇔ 🗉 (4) (6A) – Extra per person 8€

Rental rates : (2014 Price) (from mid June to mid Sept. and from mid Dec to end Mar) 🏕 – 2 ⛺ – 1 🛏 – 1 studio. Per week from 370 to 598€ – Reservation fee 10€

Choose the pitches furthest from the road, which is very busy during the day. There's a bus into Morzine.

Surroundings : ❄ ⩽ 🌳		
Leisure activities : 🏠	G P S	Longitude : 6.67725
Facilities : ♿ ⚡ 🚿 🏛 🔥 🍴 launderette		Latitude : 46.19487

The pitches of many campsites are marked out with low hedges of attractive bushes and shrubs.

MURS-ET-GELIGNIEUX

01300 – Michelin map **328** G7 – pop. 236 – alt. 232

▶ Paris 509 – Aix-les-Bains 37 – Belley 17 – Chambéry 42

⚠ Île de la Comtesse

🖉 04 79 87 23 33. www.ile-de-la-comtesse.com

Address : located 1km southwest on the D 992

Opening times : from beginning May to mid Sept.

3 ha (100 pitches)

Tariff : (2014 Price) 25.80€ ✚✚ ⇔ 🗉 (4) (6A) – Extra per person 7.50€ Reservation fee 14€

Rental rates : (2014 Price) (from end April to beginning Jan.) – 30 ⛺ – 10 🏠 – 6 canvas bungalows – 2 tent lodges. Per night from 70 to 110€ – Per week from 350 to 889€ – Reservation fee 28€

🚰 borne 5€ – 8 🗉 33€

Near the Rhône river (small lake).

Surroundings : ⩽		
Leisure activities : 🍴✗ 🏠 🔥 🚲 🏊 🎣	G P S	Longitude : 5.64876
Facilities : ♿ ⚡ 🔥 🍴 launderette 🏠 🚿		Latitude : 45.63993
Nearby : 🏊		

NEYDENS

74160 – Michelin map **328** J4 – pop. 1 486 – alt. 560

▶ Paris 525 – Annecy 36 – Bellegarde-sur-Valserine 33 – Bonneville 34

⚠ Sites et Paysages La Colombière

🖉 04 50 35 13 14. www.camping-la-colombiere.com

Address : 166 chemin Neuf (east of the town)

Opening times : from beginning April to end Oct.

2.5 ha (156 pitches) relatively flat, flat, grassy, gravelled

Tariff : 39€ ✚✚ ⇔ 🗉 (4) (10A) – Extra per person 6€ – Reservation fee 12€

Rental rates : Permanent – 31 ⛺ – 8 🏠. Per night from 75 to 140€ – Reservation fee 12€

🚰 borne 5€ – 3 🗉 14€ – 🚐 14€

The pitches are clearly marked out and authentic wooden chalets are available to rent.

Surroundings : 🌄 ⩽ 🏕 🌳		
Leisure activities : 🍴✗ 🏠 🎮 daytime 🚿 hammam 🔥 🚲 🏊 🛝	G P S	Longitude : 6.10578
Facilities : ♿ ⚡ 🏛 🏠 🚿 🍴 launderette 🚿		Latitude : 46.11997

NOVALAISE-LAC

73470 – Michelin map **328** H4 – pop. 1 712 – alt. 427

▶ Paris 524 – Belley 24 – Chambéry 21 – Les Échelles 24

⚠ Le Grand Verney

🖉 04 79 36 02 54. www.camping-legrandverney.info – limited spaces for one-night stay

Address : Le Neyret (1.2km southwest along the C 6)

Opening times : from beginning April to end Oct.

2.5 ha (116 pitches) terraced, relatively flat, flat, grassy

Tariff : 20€ ✚✚ ⇔ 🗉 (4) (10A) – Extra per person 4.75€

Rental rates : (from beginning April to end Oct.) ♿ (2 mobile homes) – 20 ⛺. Per night from 75 to 80€ – Per week from 325 to 640€

There's a lot of owner-occupier accommodation, but also some pitches for tents and caravans.

Surroundings : 🌄 ⩽ 🏕 🌳🌳		
Leisure activities : 🏊	G P S	Longitude : 5.78371
Facilities : ♿ ⚡ 🚿 🍴 🍴 🖥		Latitude : 45.5683

NYONS

26110 – Michelin map **332** D7 – pop. 7 104 – alt. 271

▶ Paris 653 – Alès 109 – Gap 106 – Orange 43

⚠ L'Or Vert

🖉 04 75 26 24 85. www.camping-or-vert.com 🏕 (from beginning April to end June)

Address : at Aubres, quai de la Charité (3km northeast along the D 94, follow the signs for Serres; beside the Eygues)

Opening times : from beginning April to end Sept.

1 ha (79 pitches) small orchard

Tariff : 25.90€ ✚✚ ⇔ 🗉 (4) (6A) – Extra per person 6.50€

Rental rates : (2014 Price) (from beginning April to end Sept.) 🏕 – 7 🏠. Per night from 45 to 85€ – Per week from 260 to 790€

Surroundings : ⩽ 🏕 🌳🌳		
Leisure activities : ✗ 🏠 🔥 🎣 🎣	G P S	Longitude : 5.16272
Facilities : ⚡ 🚿 🍴 🖥 refrigerators		Latitude : 44.37273

Key to rentals symbols:

12 ⛺	*Number of mobile homes*
20 🏠	*Number of chalets*
6 🛏	*Number of rooms to rent*
Per night 30–50€	*Minimum/maximum rate per night*
Per week 300–1,000€	*Minimum/maximum rate per week*

⚴ Les Terrasses Provençales

✆ 04 75 27 92 36. www.lesterrassesprovencales.com

Address : Les Barroux - Novezan (7km northwest along the D 538, then take the D 232 to the right.)

Opening times : from beginning April to end Sept.

2.5 ha (70 pitches)

Tariff : (2014 Price) 17.50 € ♦♦ ⇦ 🖳 ⑫ (10A) – Extra per person 4.90 € – Reservation fee 8 €

Rental rates : (2014 Price) (from beginning April to end Sept.) ⌇ – 9 🛏. Per night from 45 to 65 € – Per week from 285 to 700 € – Reservation fee 12 €

🚐 borne 4 € – 6 🖳 7 € – 🚌 7 €

Surroundings : 🏊 ⟨ ⌇
Leisure activities : ♈ ✕ 🏊 🚴 ⛵
Facilities : ♿ ⚲ 🛁 ♨ launderette

GPS Longitude : 5.08047
Latitude : 44.40949

LES OLLIÈRES-SUR-EYRIEUX

07360 – Michelin map **331** J5 – pop. 927 – alt. 200
▶ Paris 593 – Le Cheylard 28 – Lamastre 33 – Montélimar 53

⚴ FranceLoc Domaine des Plantas ♠♠

✆ 04 75 66 21 53. http://campingplantas.franceloc.fr/fr/accueil.htm

Address : 3km east of the town via narrow road, access near the bridge; beside the Eyrieux river

Opening times : from end April to mid Sept.

27 ha/7 for camping (172 pitches)

Tariff : (2014 Price) 33 € ♦♦ ⇦ 🖳 ⑫ (8A) – Extra per person 7 € – Reservation fee 11 €

Rental rates : (2014 Price) (from end April to mid Sept.) – 2 caravans – 86 🛏 – 21 🏚 – 4 tent lodges. Per night from 40 to 111 € – Per week from 161 to 1,057 € – Reservation fee 27 €

Various hostel-style rental options and facilities.

Surroundings : 🏊 ⟨ ⌇ ⌇
Leisure activities : ♈ ✕ 🛶 🎣 🏊 ⛷ ⛵
Facilities : ♿ ⚲ 🛁 ♨ launderette ⚒ ⚬
Nearby : 🐎

GPS Longitude : 4.63565
Latitude : 44.8087

⚴ VivaCamp le Mas de Champel ♠♠

✆ 04 75 66 23 23. www.masdechampel.com

Address : at the Domaine de Champel (north of the town along the D 120, follow the signs for la Voulte-sur-Rhône and take the road to the left, near L'Eyrieux)

Opening times : from end April to mid Sept.

4 ha (95 pitches)

Tariff : 29.80 € ♦♦ ⇦ 🖳 ⑫ (6A) – Extra per person 6 € – Reservation fee 15 €

Rental rates : (from end April to mid Sept.) – 30 🛏 – 1 tipi – 10 canvas bungalows. Per night from 40 to 130 € – Per week from 168 to 910 € – Reservation fee 25 €

Various rental options of varying standards; there's a pleasant small beach beside the Eyrieux river.

Surroundings : 🏊 ⟨ ⌇
Leisure activities : ♈ ✕ 🛶 ☺ nighttime 🏃 🏊 jacuzzi 🎣 🚴 ⛷ ⛵ 🐾
Facilities : ♿ ⚲ 🏚 🛁 ♨ launderette ⚬

GPS Longitude : 4.6146
Latitude : 44.80603

⚴ Eyrieux-Camping ♠♠

✆ 04 75 66 30 08, www.eyrieuxcamping.com

Address : La Feyrère (take the eastern exit along the D 120, follow the signs for La Voulte-sur-Rhône and take the road to the right; 100m from the Eyrieux river (direct access)

Opening times : from beginning April to mid Nov.

3 ha (94 pitches)

Tariff : 32.30 € ♦♦ ⇦ 🖳 ⑫ (10A) – Extra per person 6.90 € – Reservation fee 15 €

Rental rates : (from beginning April to mid Nov.) ♿ (1 mobile home) – 25 🛏 – 25 🏚 – 11 chalets (without sanitary facilities). Per night from 33.80 to 142.60 € – Per week from 118.30 to 998.20 € – Reservation fee 15 €

Various rental options, ranging from basic to more luxurious.

Surroundings : 🏊 ⟨ ⌇ ⌇
Leisure activities : ♈ ✕ 🏃 🎿 🚣 🚴 ⛷ ⛵ multi-sports ground
Facilities : ♿ ⚲ 🛁 ♨ launderette ⚬ refrigerators

GPS Longitude : 4.63072
Latitude : 44.80764

LA PACAUDIÈRE

42310 – Michelin map **327** C2 – pop. 1 078 – alt. 363
▶ Paris 370 – Lapalisse 24 – Marcigny 21 – Roanne 25

⚴ Municipal Beausoleil

✆ 04 77 64 11 50. lapacaudiere@wanadoo.fr

Address : Beausoleil (700m east along the D 35, follow the signs for Vivans and take a right turn, near the sports field and the college)

Opening times : from beginning May to end Sept.

1 ha (35 pitches)

Tariff : ♦ 3.80 € ⇦ 1.75 € 🖳 2 € – ⑫ (6A) 3.10 €

Rental rates : (from beginning May to end Sept.) – 5 🏚 – 1 apartment. Per night from 56 to 73 € – Per week from 260 to 352 €

🚐 borne 12.75 € – 30 🖳 12.75 €

On the outskirts of the village, a beautiful swimming pool and a pretty chalet village.

Surroundings : ⌇
Leisure activities : 🛶 🚣 ⚽ 🎣 ⛷
Facilities : ♿ ⚲ 🛁 ♨ ⚒ ♨

GPS Longitude : 3.87236
Latitude : 46.17562

A 'quartier' is a district or area of a town or village.

PALADRU

38850 – Michelin map **333** G5 – pop. 1 044 – alt. 503
▶ Paris 523 – Annecy 84 – Chambéry 47 – Grenoble 43

⚴ Le Calatrin

✆ 04 76 32 37 48, www.camping-paladru.fr

Address : 799 rue de la Morgerie (near the exit from town, towards Charavines)

2 ha (60 pitches)

Rentals : 2 canvas bungalows.

Surroundings : 🏊 ⟨
Leisure activities : 🛶 ⛷
Facilities : ♿ ⚲ 🏚 ♨ 🖳
Nearby : ♈ ✕ 🚣 (beach)

GPS Longitude : 5.54673
Latitude : 45.47077

PETICHET

38119 – Michelin map **333** H7
▶ Paris 592 – Le Bourg-d'Oisans 41 – Grenoble 30 – La Mure 11

⛰ Ser-Sirant

☏ 04 76 83 91 97, www.campingsersirant.fr

Address : at Lac Laffrey Petichet (take the eastern exit and take road to the left)

Opening times : from end April to beginning Oct.

2 ha (100 pitches) terraced, flat, grassy, stony, wood

Tariff : 26.30€ ✶✶ ⇌ 🔲 ⚡ (10A) – Extra per person 5.90€ – Reservation fee 9€

Rental rates : (from end April to beginning Oct.) – 7 🚐 – 6 🏠. Per night from 80 to 95€ – Per week from 285 to 665€ – Reservation fee 16€

🚱 borne 3€ – 3 🔲 9€ – 🚤12€

Surroundings : 🌲 🏞 ⛰
Leisure activities : 🍸 🏛 🚣 🎣 boats for hire
Facilities : ⚲ 🍴 launderette
Nearby : 🎣

GPS Longitude : 5.77759
Latitude : 45.00038

LE POËT-CÉLARD

26460 – Michelin map **332** D6 – pop. 133 – alt. 590
▶ Paris 618 – Lyon 156 – Valence 53 – Avignon 114

⛰ Club Airotel Le Couspeau

☏ 04 75 53 30 14. www.couspeau.com – alt. 600

Address : Bellevue district (1.3km southeast along the D 328A)

Opening times : from mid April to mid Sept.

6 ha (133 pitches) terraced, relatively flat, flat, grassy

Tariff : 38.60€ ✶✶ ⇌ 🔲 ⚡ (6A) – Extra per person 8€ – Reservation fee 16€

Rental rates : (from mid April to mid Sept.) – 14 🚐 – 31 🏠 – 6 tent lodges. Per week from 275 to 1,027€ – Reservation fee 16€

🚱 borne

In an elevated location with panoramic views.

Surroundings : 🌲 ⬅ 🏞 ⚲
Leisure activities : 🍸 🍴 🚣 🚴 🎿 🍽 🔳 (small swimming pool) 🏊 ⛳ multi-sports ground, water park
Facilities : ♿ ⚲ 🏢 🍴 🌳 launderette

GPS Longitude : 5.11152
Latitude : 44.59641

LE POËT-LAVAL

26160 – Michelin map **332** D6 – pop. 922 – alt. 311
▶ Paris 619 – Crest 35 – Montélimar 25 – Nyons 35

⛰ Municipal Lorette

☏ 04 75 91 00 62. www.campinglorette.fr

Address : Lorette district (located 1km east along the D 540, follow the signs for Dieulefit)

Opening times : from beginning May to end Sept.

2 ha (60 pitches)

Tariff : 15.50€ ✶✶ ⇌ 🔲 ⚡ (6A) – Extra per person 3.50€

🚱 borne

Situated beside the Jabron river.

Surroundings : ⬅ ⚲
Leisure activities : 🚣 🏊 🎣
Facilities : ♿ 🌳 🍴 📷
Nearby : 🍽

GPS Longitude : 5.02277
Latitude : 44.52922

PONCIN

01450 – Michelin map **328** F4 – pop. 1 618 – alt. 255
▶ Paris 456 – Ambérieu-en-Bugey 20 – Bourg-en-Bresse 28 – Nantua 25

⛰ Vallée de l'Ain

☏ 04 74 35 72 11. www.campingvalleedelain.com – limited spaces for one-night stay

Address : route d'Allement (500m northwest along the D 91 and D 81, follow the signs for Meyriat, near the Ain river)

Opening times : from beginning April to mid Sept.

1.5 ha (89 pitches) flat, grassy

Tariff : (2014 Price) 19.50€ ✶✶ ⇌ 🔲 ⚡ (16A) – Extra per person 4€

Rental rates : (2014 Price) (from beginning April to end Sept.) – 4 🚐 – 3 🏠. Per night from 35 to 50€ – Per week from 238 to 620€ – Reservation fee 12€

🚱 borne 5€ – 10 🔲 12€

Surroundings : ⚲
Leisure activities : 🍸 🍴 🚣 🚴
Facilities : ⚲ 🍴
Nearby : 🍽 🛥 🎣

GPS Longitude : 5.40407
Latitude : 46.08996

PONCINS

42110 – Michelin map **327** D5 – pop. 869 – alt. 339
▶ Paris 446 – Lyon 77 – St-Étienne 50 – Clermont-Ferrand 109

⛺ Village Vacances Le Nid Douillet (rental of chalets only)

☏ 04 77 27 80 36. www.le-nid-douillet.com

Address : Les-Baraques-des-Rotis, route de Montbrison-es-Baraques-des-Rotis

2 ha flat, grassy

Rentals : 6 🏠.

The chalets are set in a lush green landscape.

Surroundings : 🌲
Leisure activities : 🍴 🏛 🚣
Facilities : ⚲ 🍴
Nearby : 🏇

GPS Longitude : 4.1615
Latitude : 45.7123

The guide covers all 22 regions of France – see the map and list of regions on pages 4–5.

PONT-DE-VAUX

01190 – Michelin map **328** C2 – pop. 2 187 – alt. 177
▶ Paris 380 – Bourg-en-Bresse 40 – Lons-le-Saunier 69 – Mâcon 24

⛰ Champ d'Été

☏ 03 85 23 96 10. www.camping-champ-dete.com

Address : 800m northwest along the D 933, towards Mâcon and take the road to the right, near a small lake

Opening times : from beginning April to mid Oct.

3.5 ha (150 pitches) flat, grassy

Tariff : ✶ 5€ ⇌ 🔲 9€ – ⚡ (10A) 4€

Rental rates : (from beginning March to end Nov.) – 2 🚐 – 30 🏠 – 2 tent lodges – 1 gîte. Per week from 235 to 900€

🚱 borne 3€ – 4 🔲 23€

Leisure activities : 🏛 🚣 🔳 🏊 🎿
Facilities : ♿ ⚲ 🌳 🍴 📷
Nearby : 🎣

GPS Longitude : 4.93301
Latitude : 46.42966

⛰ Aux Rives du Soleil ♣♦

📞 03 85 30 33 65. www.rivesdusoleil.com

Address : Le Port

Opening times : from mid April to mid Oct.

8 ha (160 pitches) flat, grassy

Tariff : 27 € ♣♣ ⇔ 回 ♨ (6A) – Extra per person 6.50 € – Reservation fee 15 €

Rental rates : (from mid April to end Sept.) – 1 caravan – 11 🚐 – 8 canvas bungalows. Per night from 26 to 94 € – Per week from 182 to 658 € – Reservation fee 15 €

On a peninsula at the confluence of the Saône and Reyssouze rivers.

Surroundings : ♀ ⛺ Leisure activities : ♈ ✗ 🎦 ☺ ⚱ 🚣 🚴 🛶 ⚓ 🐟 🐎 Facilities : ♿ ⛽ 🕯 🍴 launderette ⚘	**GPS** Longitude : 4.89892 Latitude : 46.44701

⛺ Les Ripettes

📞 03 85 30 66 58, www.camping-les-ripettes.com

Address : Les Tourtes

Opening times : from beginning April to end Sept.

2.5 ha (54 pitches) flat, grassy

Tariff : (2014 Price) 21 € ♣♣ ⇔ 回 ♨ (10A) – Extra per person 4 €

Rental rates : (2014 Price) (from mid April to end Sept.) ✗ – 1 tent lodge. Per night from 40 to 60 € – Per week from 280 to 420 € 🚐 4 回 21 €

A very well-kept camping area with lots of green space.

Surroundings : 🏞 ♀ Leisure activities : 🏊 Facilities : ♿ ⛽ ☺ 🍴 launderette	**GPS** Longitude : 4.98073 Latitude : 46.44449

POUILLY-SOUS-CHARLIEU

42720 – Michelin map **327** D3 – pop. 2 582 – alt. 264

▶ Paris 393 – Charlieu 5 – Digoin 43 – Roanne 15

⛺ Municipal les Ilots

📞 04 77 60 80 67, www.pouillysouscharlieu.fr

Address : route de Marcigny (take the northern exit along the D 482, follow the signs for Digoin and take right turn; beside the Sornin river)

1 ha (50 pitches) flat, grassy

The site is on the edge of town and has a family atmosphere.

Surroundings : 🏞 ♀ Leisure activities : 🎦 🚴 Facilities : ♿ ⛽ 🗄 🍴 🖲 Nearby : ✗ 🐟	**GPS** Longitude : 4.11135 Latitude : 46.15101

Key to rentals symbols:

12 🚐	*Number of mobile homes*
20 🏠	*Number of chalets*
6 🛏	*Number of rooms to rent*
Per night 30–50 €	*Minimum/maximum rate per night*
Per week 300–1,000 €	*Minimum/maximum rate per week*

POULE-LES-ÉCHARMEAUX

69870 – Michelin map **327** F3 – pop. 1 045 – alt. 570

▶ Paris 446 – Chauffailles 17 – La Clayette 25 – Roanne 47

⛺ Municipal les Écharmeaux

📞 06 79 30 46 62. www.poulelesecharmeaux.eu

Address : to the west of the village

Opening times : from beginning May to end Sept.

0.5 ha (24 pitches) terraced, flat, grassy

Tariff : (2014 Price) ♣ 3.90 € ⇔ 回 3 € ♨ (10A)

The pitches are arranged on individual terraces overlooking a lake.

Surroundings : 🏊 ⛰ 🏞 Leisure activities : ✂ Facilities : ⛽ 🗄 ☑ 🖲 Nearby : 🐟	**GPS** Longitude : 4.4598 Latitude : 46.14871

This guide is not intended as a list of all the camping sites in France; its aim is to provide a selection of the best sites in each category.

PRADONS

07120 – Michelin map **331** I7 – pop. 421 – alt. 124

▶ Paris 647 – Aubenas 20 – Largentière 16 – Privas 52

⛰ Les Coudoulets ♣♦

📞 04 75 93 94 95. www.coudoulets.com

Address : chemin de l'Ardèche (to the northwest of the town)

Opening times : from mid April to mid Sept.

3.5 ha/2.5 for camping (123 pitches)

Tariff : 36.50 € ♣♣ ⇔ 回 ♨ (16A) – Extra per person 7.50 € – Reservation fee 10 €

Rental rates : (from mid April to mid Sept.) – 34 🚐 – 4 gîtes. Per night from 43 to 120 € – Per week from 300 to 840 € – Reservation fee 10 €

🚐 borne

Well shaded near the river, with good sanitary facilities; entertainment for the family.

Surroundings : 🏊 🏞 ♀♀ Leisure activities : ♈ ✗ ☺ daytime 🏹 ⚱ 🏊 ⚓ 🐎 Facilities : ♿ ⛽ ☺ 🍴 launderette	**GPS** Longitude : 4.3572 Latitude : 44.47729

⛰ Le Pont

📞 04 75 93 93 98, www.campingdupontardeche.com

Address : chemin du Cirque de Gens (300m west along the D 308, follow the signs for Chauzon)

Opening times : from end March to end Sept.

2 ha (80 pitches)

Tariff : 35.30 € ♣♣ ⇔ 回 ♨ (10A) – Extra per person 7.20 € – Reservation fee 10 €

Rental rates : (from end March to end Sept.) – 16 🚐 – 3 🏠. Per night from 50 to 70 € – Per week from 294 to 889 € – Reservation fee 10 €

Choose the pitches near the steps down to the Ardèche river, further from the road.

Surroundings : 🏞 ♀♀ Leisure activities : ♈ ✗ 🎦 ⚱ 🏊 ⚓ 🐟 Facilities : ♿ ⛽ 🍴 🖲	**GPS** Longitude : 4.35337 Latitude : 44.47392

⛰ Laborie ♟♟

📞 0475397226. www.campingdelaborie.com

Address : route de Ruoms (1.8km northeast along the follow the signs for Aubenas)

Opening times : from mid April to mid Sept.

3 ha (100 pitches) flat, grassy

Tariff : 32€ ♟♟ ⟷ 🔲 (10A) – Extra per person 6.50€ – Reservation fee 10€

Rental rates : (from mid April to mid Sept.) – 13 🚐. Per night from 31 to 103€ – Per week from 220 to 723€ – Reservation fee 10€

Choose pitches near the river, furthest away from the road.

Surroundings : ♨
Leisure activities : 🍴 🏕 🏃 ⛵ 🎣 🏊 🚣
Facilities : ♿ ⛟ 🚿 🍴 🚻

Longitude : 4.3783
Latitude : 44.48161

PRALOGNAN-LA-VANOISE

73710 – Michelin map **333** N5 – pop. 754 – alt. 1 425 – Winter sports : 1 410/2 360 m

▶ Paris 634 – Albertville 53 – Chambéry 103 – Moûtiers 28

⛰ Alpes Lodges - Le Parc Isertan

📞 0479087524. www.alpes-lodges.com

Address : Isertan district (south of the town)

Opening times : from mid Dec. to mid April from end May to end Sept.

4.5 ha (152 pitches) open site, terraced, flat, grassy, stony

Tariff : 15€ ♟♟ ⟷ 🔲 (20A) – Extra per person 5€ – Reservation fee 5€

Rental rates : (from mid Dec. to mid April and from end May to end Sept.) –3 🚐 –3 🏠 –6 🛏 –9 tent lodges –1 gîte. Per night from 35 to 110€ – Per week from 190 to 1,110€ – Reservation fee 15€

🚐 borne 3€ – 8 🔲 14€ – 🚐16€

In a pleasant location beside a mountain stream.

Surroundings : ❄ ♨ ⟨
Leisure activities : 🍴 ✕ 🏕 🏊
Facilities : ♿ ⛟ 🏪 🚿 🍴 🚿
Nearby : ⛵ 🎿 🎣 🏊 🏂 climbing, skating rink

Longitude : 6.72883
Latitude : 45.37189

There are several different types of sani-station ('borne' in French) – sanitation points providing fresh water and disposal points for grey water. See page 12 for further details.

PRIVAS

07000 – Michelin map **331** J5 – pop. 8 461 – alt. 300

▶ Paris 596 – Alès 107 – Mende 140 – Montélimar 34

⛰ Kawan Village Ardèche Camping ♟♟

📞 0475640580. www.ardechecamping.fr

Address : boulevard de Paste (located 1.5km south along the D 2, follow the signs for Montélimar; beside the Ouvèze river)

Opening times : from mid April to end Sept.

5 ha (170 pitches)

Tariff : 33€ ♟♟ ⟷ 🔲 (10A) – Extra per person 9€ – Reservation fee 20€

Rental rates : (from mid April to end Sept.) – 2 caravans – 32 🚐 – 18 🏠 – 4 canvas bungalows – 4 tent lodges. Per night from 32 to 135€ – Per week from 224 to 945€ – Reservation fee 20€

Situated near the town centre with facilities suitable for families with young children.

Surroundings : ♨ ⟨ ♀
Leisure activities : 🍴 ✕ 🏃 🏕 ⛵ 🔳 🎣 🏊 🚣 multi-sports ground
Facilities : ♿ ⛟ 🔲 🚿 🍴 🚿 🚿
Nearby : 🛒

Longitude : 4.59698
Latitude : 44.72597

RECOUBEAU-JANSAC

26310 – Michelin map **332** F6 – pop. 240 – alt. 500

▶ Paris 637 – La Chapelle-en-Vercors 55 – Crest 51 – Die 14

⛰ Le Couriou

📞 0475213323. www.lecouriou.fr

Address : Combe Lambert (head 700m northwest along the D 93, follow the signs for Dié)

7 ha/4.5 for camping (138 pitches) terraced, relatively flat, flat, grassy, gravelled, stony, wood

Rentals : 22 🚐 – 15 🏠.

The site has a large water park with chutes and swimming pools and a small but pretty chalet village.

Surroundings : ⟨ 🚐 ♀
Leisure activities : 🍴 ✕ 🏕 🏊 🚣 jacuzzi ⛵ 🏊 🏂 multi-sports ground, spa centre
Facilities : ♿ ⛟ 🚿 🍴 launderette 🚿

Longitude : 5.41098
Latitude : 44.65689

To make the best possible use of this guide, please read pages 2–15 carefully.

RIBES

07260 – Michelin map **331** H7 – pop. 266 – alt. 380

▶ Paris 656 – Aubenas 30 – Largentière 19 – Privas 61

⛰ Les Cruses

📞 0475395469, www.campinglescruses.com

Address : Le Champcros (located 1km southeast of the town, along the D 450)

Opening times : from mid April to mid Sept.

0.7 ha (47 pitches)

Tariff : 30€ ♟♟ ⟷ 🔲 (6A) – Extra per person 7€ – Reservation fee 16.50€

Rental rates : (2014 Price) (from mid April to mid Sept.) – 2 caravans – 8 🚐 – 17 🏠 – 2 gîtes. Per night from 45 to 114€ – Per week from 317 to 852€ – Reservation fee 16.50€

🚐 borne 2€ – 2 🔲 17€ – 🚐 17€

In 2 distinct sections on either side of a small path; pitches that look out over the Ardeche vineyards.

Surroundings : 🚐 ♨
Leisure activities : ✕ 🏕 jacuzzi ⛵ 🏊
Facilities : ⛟ (July–Aug.) 🚿 🚿 🍴 🚿

Longitude : 4.20757
Latitude : 44.4927

Some campsites benefit from proximity to a municipal leisure centre.

LA ROSIÈRE 1850

73700 – Michelin map **333** O4 – alt. 1 850 – Winter sports : 1 100/2 600 m
▶ Paris 657 – Albertville 76 – Bourg-St-Maurice 22 – Chambéry 125

⚠ La Forêt

✆ 0479068621. www.camping-larosiere.com – alt. 1 730

Address : situated 2km south along the N 90, follow the signs for Bourg-St-Maurice - direct access to the village

1.5 ha (67 pitches) open site, terraced, relatively flat, flat, grassy, stony
Rentals : 3 🛏 – 1 🏠 – 3 huts.

In an attractive location among pine trees, with a panoramic view.

Surroundings : ❄ 🌲 ⩽ Mont Pourri, Aiguille Rouge, Arc 2000 ♤♤
Leisure activities : 🍷 ✕ 🚣 (small swimming pool)
Facilities : 🚻 ⊶ ▥ 🚰 launderette
Nearby : 🍴

GPS Longitude : 6.85425
Latitude : 45.6234

ROSIÈRES

07260 – Michelin map **331** H7 – pop. 1 121 – alt. 175
▶ Paris 649 – Aubenas 22 – Largentière 12 – Privas 54

🏔 Arleblanc

✆ 0475395311. www.arleblanc.com

Address : take the northeastern exit, follow the signs for Aubenas and proceed 2.8km along the road to the right, beside the Intermarché commercial centre

Opening times : from end March to beginning Nov.

10 ha/6 for camping (167 pitches) flat, grassy

Tariff : 32.50€ ✚✚ 🚗 🔌 (6A) – Extra per person 7€ – Reservation fee 15€
Rental rates : (from end March to beginning Nov.) – 34 🛏 – 6 🏠 – 4 gîtes. Per night from 54 to 59€ – Per week from 370 to 745€ Reservation fee 16€

An extensive site set around a 12th-century priory and beside the Beaume river. Ideal for swimming and fishing.

Surroundings : 🌲 ♤♤
Leisure activities : 🍷 ✕ 🚣 ✶ 🎣 🏊 ⚓ 🏹
Facilities : 🚻 ⊶ ▥ 🚿 🚰 🚽 ▦ launderette 🛁 🚲
Nearby : 🐎

GPS Longitude : 4.27221
Latitude : 44.46552

🏔 La Plaine

✆ 0475395135. www.campinglaplaine.com

Address : Les Plaines (700m northeast along the D 104)

Opening times : from beginning April to mid Sept.

4.5 ha/3.5 for camping (128 pitches)

Tariff : 34€ ✚✚ 🚗 🔌 (10A) – Extra per person 6.50€ – Reservation fee 20€
Rental rates : (from beginning April to mid Sept.) – 52 🛏 – 2 🏠. Per week from 210 to 790€ – Reservation fee 20€

A good amount of shade for the pitches and a small pool for anglers.

Surroundings : 🏠 ♤♤
Leisure activities : 🍷 🏡 🚣 ✶ 🎣 🏊 🏹
Facilities : 🚻 ⊶ 🚿 ▦
Nearby : 🛒

GPS Longitude : 4.26677
Latitude : 44.48608

🏔 Les Platanes

✆ 0475395231. www.campinglesplatanesardeche.com

Address : La Charve (take the northeastern exit, follow the signs for Aubenas and proceed 3.7km along the road to the right, beside the Intermarché commercial centre)

Opening times : from beginning April to end Sept.

2 ha (90 pitches) flat, grassy

Tariff : 30.20€ ✚✚ 🚗 🔌 (16A) – Extra per person 5.40€
Rental rates : (from beginning April to end Sept.) 🏐 (from beginning July to end Aug.) – 27 🛏. Per night from 49 to 55€ – Per week from 265 to 795€
🚐 borne

Pitches for tents and caravans beside the river, beneath hackberry trees; the mobile homes are across a small road.

Surroundings : 🌲 ⩽ ♤♤
Leisure activities : 🍷 ✕ 🏡 🚣 ✶ 🏊 ⚓ 🏹
Facilities : 🚻 ⊶ ▥ 🚿 ▦ 🛁 🚲

GPS Longitude : 4.27766
Latitude : 44.45702

⚠ Les Hortensias

✆ 0475399138. www.leshortensias.com

Address : Ribeyre-Bouchet district (1.8km northwest along the D 104, follow the signs for Joyeuse, D 303, follow the signs for Vernon to the right, and take road to the left)

Opening times : from end May to mid Sept.

1 ha (43 pitches)

Tariff : ✚ 4.60€ 🚗 🔌 24€ – 🔌 (10A) 3.50€
Rental rates : (from end May to mid Sept.) – 20 🛏 – 2 canvas bungalows – 1 gîte. Per night from 65€ – Per week from 240 to 740€

Surrounded by vineyards, a peaceful site, various rental options, but few pitches for tents and caravans

Surroundings : 🌲 🏠 ♤♤
Leisure activities : 🏊
Facilities : 🚻 ⊶ ▦ 🛁
Nearby : 🏊 (river) 🏹

GPS Longitude : 4.23976
Latitude : 44.48755

RUFFIEUX

73310 – Michelin map **333** I2 – pop. 800 – alt. 282
▶ Paris 517 – Aix-les-Bains 20 – Ambérieu-en-Bugey 58 – Annecy 51

🏔 Saumont

✆ 0479542626. www.campingsaumont.com

Address : Saumont (1.2km west, access on the D 991, near the carr. du Saumont (junction with D904/D55), towards Aix-les-Bains)

Opening times : from beginning April to mid Oct.

1.6 ha (66 pitches) open site, flat, grassy, gravelled

Tariff : 22.20€ ✚✚ 🚗 🔌 (10A) – Extra per person 4.70€ – Reservation fee 12€
Rental rates : (2014 Price) (from beginning April to mid Oct.) – 18 🛏 – 1 🏠. Per night from 28 to 108€ – Per week from 190 to 750€ – Reservation fee 12€

Some pitches are among trees and shrubs, by a small stream.

Surroundings : 🏠 ♤♤
Leisure activities : 🍷 🚣 🚲 ✶ 🏊 🚲
Facilities : 🚻 ⊶ ▥ 🛁 🚿 ▦ launderette

GPS Longitude : 5.83663
Latitude : 45.8486

RUMILLY

74150 – Michelin map **328** I5 – pop. 13 197 – alt. 334
▶ Paris 530 – Aix-les-Bains 21 – Annecy 19 – Bellegarde-sur-Valserine 37

Le Madrid

℘ 04 50 01 12 57, www.camping-le-madrid.com

Address : route de Saint-Félix (3km southeast along the D 910, follow the signs for Aix-les-Bains then turn left onto D 3 and take D 53 to the right; 500m from a small lake)

3.2 ha (107 pitches)

Rentals : 4 🚐 – 23 🏠.

Choose those pitches furthest away from the road.

Surroundings : 🖵 ♤♤
Leisure activities : 🍷 ✕ 🎞 ♤ 🏊
Facilities : ⅙ ☛ ▥ 🛁 🚿 🚽 ♈ launderette
🍴 refrigerated food storage facilities
Nearby : 🏊 🚣

GPS Longitude : 5.96239
Latitude : 45.84084

RUOMS

07120 – Michelin map **331** I7 – pop. 2 249 – alt. 121
▶ Paris 651 – Alès 54 – Aubenas 24 – Pont-St-Esprit 49

Sunêlia Aluna Vacances ♨♨

Aluna Vacances

℘ 04 75 93 93 15. www.alunavacances.fr

Address : route de Lagorce (2km east along the D 559)

Opening times : from mid April to mid Sept.

10 ha (430 pitches) terraced, relatively flat, flat, grassy, stony

Tariff : 53€ ♤♤ 🚐 🔌 🔋 (10A) – Extra per person 11.60€ – Reservation fee 30€

Rental rates : (from mid April to mid Sept.) ⅙ (2 mobile homes) – 230 🚐 – 2 tent lodges. Per night from 40 to 253€ – Per week from 280 to 1,771€ – Reservation fee 30€

The Aluna music festival is held every year in mid June, with 4 to 7 concerts every evening; it attracts crowds of up to 35,000 over the 3 days.

Surroundings : 🗻 ♤♤
Leisure activities : 🍷 ✕ 🎞 ♤ 🏊 hammam, jacuzzi 🚴 🎾 ♤ 🏊 ♤ multi-sports ground, spa centre
Facilities : ☛ 🛁 🚽 ♈ launderette 🚮 🍴
Nearby : 🐎

GPS Longitude : 4.3526
Latitude : 44.44962

Yelloh! Village La Plaine ♨♨

℘ 04 75 39 65 83. www.yellohvillage-la-plaine.com

Address : La Grand Terre district (3.5km to the south)

Opening times : from mid April to mid Sept.

4.5 ha (212 pitches) relatively flat, flat, grassy, sandy

Tariff : 48€ ♤♤ 🚐 🔌 🔋 (8A) – Extra per person 8€

Rental rates : (from mid April to mid Sept.) ⅙ 🅿 – 87 🚐. Per night from 39 to 249€ – Per week from 273 to 1,743€
🚐 borne

Located near vineyards and the Ardèche river, with well-shaded pitches and some high-quality rentals.

Surroundings : 🗻 ≤ ♨♨
Leisure activities : 🍷 ✕ 🎞 ♤ 🏊 ♤ 🏊 🚴 🛴 🚣 ♤ 🏊 ♤ multi-sports ground
Facilities : ⅙ ☛ 🛁 🚿 🚽 ♈ launderette 🚮

GPS Longitude : 4.33596
Latitude : 44.42666

Domaine de Chaussy ♨♨

(rental of mobile homes, gîtes, hotel only)

℘ 04 75 93 99 66. www.domainedechaussy.com

Address : Le Petit Chaussy district (2.3km east along the D 559, follow the signs for Lagorce)

Opening times : from beginning April to mid Sept.

18 ha/5.5 for camping (250 pitches) undulating

Rental rates : – 150 🚐 – 40 🛏 – 17 gîtes. Per night from 42 to 160€ – Per week from 294 to 1,120€ – Reservation fee 20€

Numerous sporting activities for the family.

Surroundings : 🗻 ♤♤
Leisure activities : 🍷 ✕ 🎞 ♤ 🏊 🏊 hammam, jacuzzi 🚴 🚴 ♤ 🏊 fitness trail, mountain biking trail
Facilities : ⅙ ☛ 🛁 ♈ launderette 🚮 🍴

GPS Longitude : 4.36913
Latitude : 44.4472

RCN La Bastide en Ardèche ♨♨

℘ 04 75 39 64 72. www.rcn.fr

Address : route d'Alès - D111, at the bridge (4km southwest, at Labastide)

7 ha (300 pitches)

Rentals : 40 🚐.

In an attractive location beside the Ardèche river, with a sandy beach, but choose the pitches further away from the road.

Surroundings : ≤ ♤♤
Leisure activities : 🍷 ✕ 🎞 ♤ 🏊 🚣 (beach) 🐎
Facilities : ⅙ ☛ 🛁 🚿 🚽 ♈ launderette 🚮 🍴

GPS Longitude : 4.32524
Latitude : 44.42326

La Grand'Terre ♨♨

℘ 04 75 39 64 94. www.camping-lagrandterre.com

Address : 3.5km to the south

Opening times : from mid April to mid Sept.

10 ha (296 pitches)

Tariff : 40€ ♤♤ 🚐 🔌 🔋 (10A) – Extra per person 9.20€

Rental rates : (from mid April to mid Sept.) ⅙ – 66 🚐. Per night from 43 to 149€ – Per week from 301 to 1,043€
🚐 borne 2€ – 6 🔌 17€

Most of the pitches are in a wooded setting, with the added bonus of a beautiful sandy beach beside the Ardèche river.

Surroundings : 🗻 ♤♤
Leisure activities : 🍷 ✕ 🎞 ♤ 🏊 🚴 🎾 🏊 🚣 (beach) 🐎 multi-sports ground
Facilities : ⅙ ☛ 🛁 ♈ launderette 🚮 🍴

GPS Longitude : 4.33192
Latitude : 44.42522

In order for the guide to remain wholly objective, the selection of campsites is made on an entirely independent basis.

⛰ La Chapoulière 🏕

📞 0475396498, www.lachapouliere.com

Address : 3.5km to the south

Opening times : from end March to mid Oct.

2.5 ha (164 pitches)

Tariff : (2014 Price) 34€ ♣♣ ⬛ 🔌 (6A) – Extra per person 9.30€

Rental rates : (2014 Price) (from end March to mid Oct.) ➤ – 20 🚐. Per night from 44 to 113€ – Per week from 311 to 793€
🚐 borne

A lovely grassy area beside the Ardèche river, with some pitches overlooking the water.

Surroundings : 🌳 ♀♀	**G**	Longitude : 4.32972
Leisure activities : ♀ ✗ 🏠 🎮 🏃 🏇 🏊	**P**	Latitude : 44.43139
🎣 🚵 multi-sports ground	**S**	
Facilities : 🚻 🔑 🍳 🍴 🖥 🛁 🔧		

⛰ Sites et Paysages Le Petit Bois 🏕

📞 0475396072. www.campinglepetitbois.fr

Address : 87 rue du Petit Bois (800m north of the town, 80m from the Ardèche river)

Opening times : from beginning April to end Sept.

2.5 ha (110 pitches) terraced, flat and relatively flat, grassy, stony, rocks

Tariff : 37€ ♣♣ ⬛ 🔌 (10A) – Extra per person 8.50€ –Reservation fee 15€

Rental rates : (from beginning April to mid Sept.) ➤ – 2 caravans – 19 🚐 – 17 🏠 – 3 tent lodges – 1 gîte. Per night from 40 to 190€ – Per week from 278 to 1,300€ – Reservation fee 15€
🚐 borne 16€ – 5 🖥 16€ – 🔧 🔌12€

Some rentals (including some high-quality accommodation) have a panoramic view over the Ardèche river and the gorge, with access to the river via a very steep path.

Surroundings : 🌳 🏞 ♀♀	**G**	Longitude : 4.33789
Leisure activities : ♀ ✗ 🏠 🏃 🎣	**P**	Latitude : 44.45882
hammam 🏇 🏊 (open air in season) 🏊 🏄	**S**	
🎣 🚵 multi-sports ground		
Facilities : 🚻 🔑 🍳 🍴 launderette		

⛰ Les Paillotes en Ardèche

📞 0475396205. www.campinglespaillotes.com – limited spaces for one-night stay

Address : chemin de l'Espédès (600m north along the D 579, follow the signs for Pradons and take road to the left)

Opening times : Permanent

1 ha (45 pitches) flat, grassy

Tariff : 39€ ♣♣ ⬛ 🔌 (10A) – Extra per person 9€ – Reservation fee 10€

Rental rates : Permanent – 30 🚐 – 5 canvas bungalows – 2 gîtes. Per night from 42 to 105€ – Per week from 180 to 970€ Reservation fee 10€

Well marked-out pitches but little space for tents and caravans, based around a large canoeing centre.

Surroundings : 🏞 ♀♀	**G**	Longitude : 4.34184
Leisure activities : ♀ ✗ 🏇 🏊 🏄	**P**	Latitude : 44.45938
Facilities : 🚻 🔑 🚮 🖥 🛁 🔧 🚰 🍴	**S**	

*We value your opinion and welcome your feedback.
Do email us at campingfrance@tp.michelin.com*

⛰ Le Carpenty

📞 0475397429, www.camping-ruoms-ardeche.com

Address : 3.6km south along the D 111

Opening times : from end April to beginning Sept.

0.7 ha (45 pitches)

Tariff : 27.50€ ♣♣ ⬛ 🔌 (16A) – Extra per person 6€

Rental rates : (from beginning April to end Sept.) – 28 🚐. Per night from 32 to 60€ – Per week from 210 to 707€

A lovely green site beside the Ardèche river, but choose pitches away from the road and the bridge.

Surroundings : 🏞 ♀♀	**G**	Longitude : 4.32842
Leisure activities : ♀ ✗ 🏇 🏊 🏄	**P**	Latitude : 44.42695
Facilities : 🚻 🔑 🍴 🖥 🔧	**S**	

SABLIÈRES

07260 – Michelin map **331** G6 – pop. 144 – alt. 450
▶ Paris 629 – Aubenas 48 – Langogne 58 – Largentière 38

⛰ La Drobie

📞 0475369522. www.ladrobie.com

Address : Le Chambon (3km west along the D 220 and take turning to the right; beside the river, for caravans recommended route is via Lablachère along the D 4)

Opening times : from mid April to end Oct.

1.5 ha (80 pitches) terraced, relatively flat, stony, grassy

Tariff : (2014 Price) 20€ ♣♣ ⬛ 🔌 (12A) – Extra per person 6.50€ Reservation fee 5€

Rental rates : (2014 Price) (from beginning April to end Oct.) – 3 🚐 – 10 🏠 – 1 gîte. Per night from 45 to 60€ – Per week from 384 to 600€ – Reservation fee 5€

Surroundings : 🌳 ≤	**G**	Longitude : 4.04863
Leisure activities : ♀ ✗ 🏇 🎮 🏊 🏄 🎣	**P**	Latitude : 44.54368
Facilities : 🚻 🔑 🍳 🍴 🖥 🛁 🔧	**S**	

The Michelin classification (⛰⛰⛰... ⛰) is totally independent of the official star classification system awarded by the local prefecture or other official organisation.

SAHUNE

26510 – Michelin map **332** E7 – pop. 322 – alt. 330
▶ Paris 647 – Buis-les-Baronnies 27 – La Motte-Chalancon 22 – Nyons 16

⛰ Vallée Bleue

📞 0475274442. www.lavalleebleue.com

Address : take the southwestern exit along the D 94, follow the signs for Nyons; beside the Eygues

Opening times : from beginning April to end Sept.

3 ha (45 pitches)

Tariff : ♣ 6.50€ ⬛ 🔌 11€ – 🔌 (6A) 3.50€

Rental rates : (from beginning April to end Sept.) ➤ – 2 🏠. Per night from 60 to 850€ – Per week from 400 to 850€

Surroundings : ≤ ♀	**G**	Longitude : 5.26139
Leisure activities : ✗ 🏇 🎣 🏊	**P**	Latitude : 44.41148
Facilities : 🚻 🔑 🚮 🖥 🔧 🍴 🖥	**S**	

ST-AGRÈVE

07320 – Michelin map **331** I3 – pop. 2 522 – alt. 1 050
▶ Paris 582 – Aubenas 68 – Lamastre 21 – Privas 64

🏔 Le Riou la Selle

📞 0475302928, www.camping-riou.com

Address : 2.8km southeast along the D 120, follow the signs for Cheylard, take the D 21, follow the signs for Nonières to the left and take the Chemin de la Roche to the right

Opening times : from mid April to mid Oct.

1 ha (29 pitches) terraced, relatively flat, flat, grassy

Tariff : (2014 Price) 22.50€ ♯♯ ⇔ 📵 🔌 (16A) – Extra per person 6€

Rental rates : Permanent – 2 🚐 – 2 🏠. Per night from 85 to 130 € – Per week from 300 to 590€

A peaceful, pleasant wooded site, with rental options of a fairly basic standard.

Surroundings : 🔊 ⌂ 🞬🞬
Leisure activities : 🍴 ✗ 🛶 🎣
Facilities : ৬ ⛟ (July–Aug.) 🎻 👤 🗜 👕 📷 ♨

GPS Longitude : 4.40462
Latitude : 44.98892

Michelin classification:

🔺🔺🔺🔺 *Extremely comfortable, equipped to a very high standard*

🔺🔺🔺 *Very comfortable, equipped to a high standard*

🔺🔺🔺 *Comfortable and well equipped*

🔺🔺 *Reasonably comfortable*

🔺 *Satisfactory*

ST-ALBAN-AURIOLLES

07120 – Michelin map **331** H7 – pop. 994 – alt. 108
▶ Paris 656 – Alès 49 – Aubenas 28 – Pont-St-Esprit 55

🔺🔺🔺🔺 Sunêlia Le Ranc Davaine ♣♣

Le Ranc Davaine

📞 0475396055. www.camping-ranc-davaine.fr

Address : route de Chandolas (2.3km southwest along the D 208)

Opening times : from mid April to mid Sept.

13 ha (435 pitches)

Tariff : 52€ ♯♯ ⇔ 📵 🔌 (10A) – Extra per person 12.30€ – Reservation fee 30€

Rental rates : (from mid April to mid Sept.) ৬ (1 mobile home) 🚾 – 280 🚐 – 2 tent lodges. Per night from 43 to 224€ – Per week from 301 to 1,568€ – Reservation fee 30€

A good amount of shade is provided by oak trees, around a partially covered water and play park, with direct access to the river.

Surroundings : 🔊 ⌂ 🞬🞬
Leisure activities : 🍴 ✗ 🛶 🎣 ⚽🞬 🏌 🛶 hammam, jacuzzi 🛶 ✂ 🗜 🎣 ♨ disco 🞯 spa centre
Facilities : ৬ ⛟ 🎻 👤 🗜 👕 launderette ♨ ♨

GPS Longitude : 4.26868
Latitude : 44.40014

🏔 Le Mas du Sartre

📞 0475397174. www.camping-mas-du-sartre-07.com

Address : at Auriolles, 5 chemin de la Vignasse (1.8km northwest along the D 208)

1.6 ha (49 pitches) terraced, flat and relatively flat, grassy, stony
Rentals : 10 🚐 – 4 🏠.

Choose the pitches surrounded by shrubs and bushes, furthest away from the road.

Surroundings : ⌂ 🞬🞬
Leisure activities : 🍴 ✗ 🛶 🛶 🎣 multi-sports ground
Facilities : ৬ ⛟ 👤 📷 ♨ refrigerators

GPS Longitude : 4.31477
Latitude : 44.43418

ST-ALBAN-DE-MONTBEL

73610 – Michelin map **333** H4 – pop. 605 – alt. 400
▶ Paris 551 – Belley 32 – Chambery 21 – Grenoble 74

🏔 Le Sougey ♣♣

📞 0479360144. www.camping-sougey.com

Address : Le Sougey (1.2km to the northeast, 300m from the lake)

4 ha (159 pitches) terrace, relatively flat, flat, grassy, fine gravel
Rentals : ৬ (1 chalet) – 7 🚐 – 8 🏠.

A small and pretty chalet village and pitches that are well marked out.

Surroundings : 🔊 ⌂ 🞬🞬
Leisure activities : 🛶 🏌 🛶 🚲
Facilities : ৬ ⛟ 🗜 👕 launderette ♨
Nearby : 🏊 🍴 ✗ 🛶 🎣 pedalos

GPS Longitude : 5.79069
Latitude : 45.55562

ST-AVIT

26330 – Michelin map **332** C2 – pop. 326 – alt. 348
▶ Paris 536 – Annonay 33 – Lyon 81 – Romans-sur-Isère 22

🏔 Domaine la Garenne

📞 0475686226. www.domaine-la-garenne.com

Address : 156 chemin de Chablezin

Opening times : from mid April to end Sept.

14 ha/6 for camping (112 pitches) terraced, relatively flat to hilly, flat, grassy

Tariff : (2014 Price) 31€ ♯♯ ⇔ 📵 🔌 (6A) – Extra per person 6.90€

Rental rates : (2014 Price) (from mid April to end Sept.) 🚾 – 42 🚐 – 6 🏠. Per night from 60 to 90€ – Per week from 350 to 750€ – Reservation fee 10€
🚐 borne

Surroundings : 🔊 ≤ 🞬🞬
Leisure activities : ✗ 🛶 🛶 🎣
Facilities : ৬ ⛟ 🗜 👕 📷
Nearby : 🛶

GPS Longitude : 4.9549
Latitude : 45.20176

*For more information on visiting particular towns or regions, consult the relevant regional **MICHELIN** Green Guide. We also recommend you use the appropriate Michelin regional map to locate your selected campsite, to calculate distances and to work out the best route.*

ST-CHRISTOPHE-EN-OISANS

38520 – Michelin map **333** K8 – pop. 123 – alt. 1 470
▶ Paris 635 – L'Alpe-d'Huez 31 – La Bérarde 12 – Le Bourg-d'Oisans 21

⚠ Municipal la Bérarde

℘ 04 76 79 20 45 – access narrow, sometimes only possible using passing places – alt. 1 738

Address : La Bérarde (10.5km southeast along the D 530; difficult access for caravans (steep slope)

Opening times : from end May to end Sept.

2 ha (165 pitches) open site, terraced, relatively flat, flat, grassy, stony, rocks

Tariff : (2014 Price) ⚹ 5€ ⇌ 2€ 🔲 – ⚡ (6A) 2.50€

A very pleasant rural site beside the Vénéon river.

Surroundings : ⅏ ≼ Parc National des Écrins ⚲
Leisure activities : ⌂ ⚓
Facilities : ⚭ ⫶⫶⫶ ⬚
Nearby : ⌁ ⵋ ✕

GPS	Longitude : 6.29205 Latitude : 44.93309

ST-CIRGUES-EN-MONTAGNE

07510 – Michelin map **331** G5 – pop. 248 – alt. 1 044
▶ Paris 586 – Aubenas 40 – Langogne 31 – Privas 68

⚠ Les Airelles

℘ 04 75 38 92 49, www.camping-les-airelles.fr

Address : route de Lapalisse (take the northern exit along the D 160, follow the signs for the Lac-d'Issarlès, right bank of the Vernason river)

0.7 ha (50 pitches) terraced, relatively flat, grassy, stony

Rentals : 10 ⌂⌂ – 9 ⊨.

Surroundings : ⅏ ≼ ⚲⚲
Leisure activities : ⵋ ✕ ⌂ ⪥ ⚓
Facilities : ⚭ ⫶⫶⫶ launderette
Nearby : ⌁ ⵋⵋ

GPS	Longitude : 4.0949 Latitude : 44.75648

ST-CLAIR-DU-RHÔNE

38370 – Michelin map **333** B5 – pop. 3 886 – alt. 160
▶ Paris 501 – Annonay 35 – Givors 26 – Le Péage-de-Roussillon 10

⛰ Le Daxia

℘ 04 74 56 39 20. www.campingledaxia.com

Address : route du Péage - avenue du Plateau des Frères (2.7km south along the D 4 and take road to the left, recommended route via the N 7 and D 37)

Opening times : from beginning April to end Sept.

7.5 ha (120 pitches) flat, grassy

Tariff : (2014 Price) 22.75€ ⚹⚹ ⇌ 🔲 ⚡ (6A) – Extra per person 4.70€
Reservation fee 15€

Rental rates : (2014 Price) (from beginning April to end Sept.) – 6 ⌂⌂. Per night from 60 to 90€ – Per week from 270 to 595€
Reservation fee 20€

🚐 borne 18.75€

Pretty, marked out pitches; beside the Varèze river.

Surroundings : ⅏ ⌑ ⚲⚲
Leisure activities : ⵋ✕ ⌂ ⌁ ⊿ ⚓
Facilities : ⚭ ⚭ ⬚⫶ 🔲 ⚬

GPS	Longitude : 4.78129 Latitude : 45.42128

ST-DONAT-SUR-L'HERBASSE

26260 – Michelin map **332** C3 – pop. 3 825 – alt. 202
▶ Paris 545 – Grenoble 92 – Hauterives 20 – Romans-sur-Isère 13

⛰⛰ Domaine du Lac de Champos

℘ 04 75 45 17 81. www.lacdechampos.com

Address : situated 2km northeast along the D 67

Opening times : from mid April to mid Sept.

43 ha/6 for camping (60 pitches)

Tariff : 15€ ⚹⚹ ⇌ 🔲 ⚡ (10A) – Extra per person 3€

Rental rates : (from beginning April to beginning Nov.) – 21 ⌂ – 4 tent lodges. Per night from 89 to 139€ – Per week from 199 to 565€ – Reservation fee 15€

🚐 borne – 5 🔲 11€ – ⛟ 11€

In a pleasant setting beside the Lac de Champos.

Surroundings : ⚲ ⚠
Leisure activities : ⵋ ✕ ⌂ ⌁ ⵋ ⌁ ⚓ pedal go-carts ⚓
Facilities : ⚭ ⬚ ⫶ launderette

GPS	Longitude : 5.00543 Latitude : 45.13615

⛰⛰ Domaine des Ulèzes

℘ 04 75 47 83 20. www.camping-des-ulezes.fr

Address : route de Romans (take southeastern exit along the D 53 and take the road to the right; near the Herbasse)

Opening times : from beginning April to end Oct.

2.5 ha (85 pitches) flat, grassy

Tariff : (2014 Price) 24.80€ ⚹⚹ ⇌ 🔲 ⚡ (10A) – Extra per person 4.80€

Rental rates : (2014 Price) (from beginning April to end Oct.) – 8 ⌂⌂ – 3 canvas bungalows. Per night from 60 to 130€ – Per week from 295 to 680€

🚐 borne

Surroundings : ⅏ ⌑ ⚲
Leisure activities : ✕ ⌂ ⌁ ⌁ ⚓
Facilities : ⚭ ⚭ ⬚ ⚬ ⫶ 🔲
Nearby : ⵋ ⵋ

GPS	Longitude : 4.99285 Latitude : 45.11914

We have selected the best campsites in France with our usual care, listing those with the best facilities in the most pleasant surroundings.

ST-FERRÉOL-TRENTE-PAS

26110 – Michelin map **332** E7 – pop. 228 – alt. 417
▶ Paris 634 – Buis-les-Baronnies 30 – La Motte-Chalancon 34 Nyons 14

⛰ La Via Natura Le Pilat

℘ 04 75 27 72 09, www.campinglepilat.com

Address : route de Bourdeau (located 1km north along the D 70; beside a stream)

Opening times : from beginning April to end Sept.

1 ha (90 pitches)

Tariff : ⚹ 7€ ⇌ 🔲 10.50€ – ⚡ (6A) 4€

Rental rates : (from beginning March to end Sept.) ⵋ – 21 ⌂⌂ – 2 gîtes. Per night from 50 to 95€ – Per week from 250 to 820€

🚐 borne – 4 🔲 18€

Surroundings : ⅏ ≼ ⌑ ⚲
Leisure activities : ✕ ⌂ ⌁ ⊿ ⪥ ⚓
Facilities : ⚭ ⚭ ⬚ ⫶ 🔲 ⌁

GPS	Longitude : 5.21195 Latitude : 44.43406

ST-GALMIER

42330 – Michelin map **327** E6 – pop. 5 596 – alt. 400

▶ Paris 457 – Lyon 82 – Montbrison 25 – Montrond-les-Bains 11

⛰ Campéole Val de Coise ♁♁

𝒫 0477541482. www.camping-valdecoise.com – limited spaces for one-night stay

Address : route de la Thiery (situated 2km to the east along the D 6 and take the road to the left)

Opening times : from beginning April to end Sept.

3.5 ha (92 pitches) terraced, relatively flat, flat, grassy

Tariff : (2014 Price) 15.70€ ♛♛ ⇔ 🔲 ⚡ (16A) – Extra per person 4.20€

Rental rates : (from beginning April to end Sept.) – 11 🚐 – 5 🛖 – 4 canvas bungalows. Per night from 26 to 96€ – Per week from 182 to 672€

🚰 borne 1€

Not far from the source of Badoit mineral water and the Coise river.

Surroundings : ♀		
Leisure activities : 🏛 ☺ 🏃 ⛷ ↲ ☃	**G**	Longitude : 4.33552
Facilities : ⚒ ⚬ 🍴 ♨ 🍸 launderette	**P**	Latitude : 45.59308
Nearby : 🐟	**S**	

ST-GENEST-MALIFAUX

42660 – Michelin map **327** F7 – pop. 2 916 – alt. 980

▶ Paris 528 – Annonay 33 – St-Étienne 16 – Yssingeaux 46

⚠ Municipal de la Croix de Garry

𝒫 0685409538, www.st-genest-malifaux.fr – alt. 928 – limited spaces for one-night stay

Address : La Croix de Garry (Take the southern exit along the D 501, follow the signs for Montfaucon-en-Velay; near a lake and 150m from the Semène river)

Opening times : Permanent

2 ha (85 pitches) terraced, relatively flat, flat, grassy

Tariff : (2014 Price) 16€ ♛♛ ⇔ 🔲 ⚡ (6A) – Extra per person 2.10€

Rental rates : (2014 Price) Permanent ⚒ (1 chalet) – 8 🛖 – 4 🛏 – 1 gîte. Per night from 100€ – Per week from 280 to 400€

A little way out of town; beside a small lake that is ideal for fishing.

Surroundings : ≼		
Leisure activities : 🏃⛷	**G**	Longitude : 4.42258
Facilities : ⚒ ⚬ 🍴 🍸 ▣	**P**	Latitude : 45.33357
Nearby : ✂ 🐟	**S**	

ST-GERVAIS-LES-BAINS

74170 – Michelin map **328** N5 – pop. 5 673 – alt. 820 – ⚜ – Winter sports : 1 400/2 000 m

▶ Paris 597 – Annecy 84 – Bonneville 42 – Chamonix-Mont-Blanc 25

⚠ Les Dômes de Miage

𝒫 0450934596. http://www.natureandlodge.fr – alt. 890

Address : 197 route des Contamines (situated 2km south along the D 902, at Les Bernards)

Opening times : from mid May to mid Sept.

3 ha (150 pitches) flat, grassy

Tariff : 31.20€ ♛♛ ⇔ 🔲 ⚡ (10A) – Extra per person 6.20€ – Reservation fee 10€

Rental rates : Permanent – 1 🛖. Per night from 220 to 260€ – Per week from 630 to 2,030€

🚰 borne – 10 ▣ 31.20€

In a lush green setting, on a field crossed by a small stream. One original Savoyard chalet, equipped to a high standard.

Surroundings : ≼ ♀		
Leisure activities : 🏃⛷	**G**	Longitude : 6.72022
Facilities : ⚒ ⚬ 🍴 ♨ 🍸 launderette 🚿	**P**	Latitude : 45.87355
Nearby : 🍸 ✕ 🐟	**S**	

ST-JEAN-DE-MAURIENNE

73300 – Michelin map **333** L6 – pop. 8 374 – alt. 556

▶ Paris 641 – Lyon 174 – Chambéry 75 – St-Martin-d'Hères 105

⚠ Municipal les Grands Cols

𝒫 0479642802. www.campingdesgrandscols.com

Address : 422 avenue du Mont Cenis

Opening times : from mid May to end Sept.

2.5 ha (80 pitches)

Tariff : (2014 Price) 20€ ♛♛ ⇔ 🔲 ⚡ (16A) – Extra per person 6€ – Reservation fee 8€

Rental rates : (from mid May to mid Sept.) ⚒ (1 mobile home) – 7 🚐. Per night from 45 to 95€ – Per week from 270 to 540€ Reservation fee 8€

In a green setting, with mobile homes on well-situated terraces.

Surroundings : 🏔 ≼ mountains 🚲 ♀♀		
Leisure activities : ✕ 🏛 multi-sports ground	**G**	Longitude : 6.3515
Facilities : ⚒ ⚬ 🚿 ↬ 🍸 launderette	**P**	Latitude : 45.2716
Nearby : 🚲	**S**	

These symbols are used for a campsite that is exceptional in its category:

🏔 ...🏔   *Particularly pleasant setting, quality and range of services available*

🐟   *Tranquil, isolated site – quiet site, particularly at night*

≼≼   *Exceptional view – interesting or panoramic view*

ST-JEAN-DE-MUZOLS

07300 – Michelin map **331** K3 – pop. 2 444 – alt. 123

▶ Paris 541 – Annonay 34 – Beaurepaire 53 – Privas 62

⛰ Le Castelet

𝒫 0475080948, www.camping-lecastelet.com

Address : 113 route du Grand Pont (2.8km southwest along the D 238, follow the signs for Lamastre; beside the Doux river and near the Tournon - St-Jean-de-Muzols railway station)

3 ha (66 pitches) terraced, flat, grassy, stony

Rentals : 3 🚐 – 4 🛖.

Pitches on terraces extending down to the river, below vineyards and the road.

Surroundings : 🏔 ≼ 🚲 ♀♀		
Leisure activities : 🍸 🏛 ⛷ ↬ 🏊 🐟	**G**	Longitude : 4.78564
Facilities : ⚒ ⚬ ♨ 🍸 ▣	**P**	Latitude : 45.0681
	S	

ST-JEAN-LE-CENTENIER

07580 – Michelin map **331** J6 – pop. 668 – alt. 350
▶ Paris 623 – Alès 83 – Aubenas 20 – Privas 24

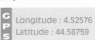 Les Arches

📞 0475367519, www.camping-les-arches.com

Address : Le Cluzel (1.2km west along the D 458a and take D 258, follow the signs for Mirabel then take the road to the right)

Opening times : from end April to end Sept.

10 ha/5 for camping (177 pitches) terraced, relatively flat, flat, grassy

Tariff : (2014 Price) 25.50€ ✴✴ ⟷ 🔲 ⚡ (10A) – Extra per person 6€

Rental rates : (2014 Price) Permanent – 30 ⟐ – 13 tent lodges – 2 gîtes. Per week from 250 to 765€ – Reservation fee 10€
🛏 borne
Pitches and rental options in both sun and shade, situated with a view of or beside a small natural pool, near a waterfall.

Surroundings : 🌄 ⌂ ♡		G
Leisure activities : ♟ ✗ ⚓ 🚲 ⛷ ≋		P
Facilities : ♿ ⛽ ♨ 🍴 🖥 🚿		S

Longitude : 4.52576
Latitude : 44.58759

ST-JORIOZ

74410 – Michelin map **328** J5 – pop. 5 716 – alt. 452
▶ Paris 545 – Albertville 37 – Annecy 9 – Megève 51

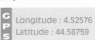 Europa ♟♟

📞 0450685101. www.camping-europa.com

Address : 1444 route d'Albertville (1.4km southeast)

Opening times : from end April to mid Sept.

3 ha (190 pitches)

Tariff : (2014 Price) 39.80€ ✴✴ ⟷ 🔲 ⚡ (6A) – Extra per person 8.30€ Reservation fee 25€

Rental rates : (from end April to mid Sept.) ⛷ – 55 ⟐ – 4 ⟐. Per week from 400 to 1,300€ – Reservation fee 25€

There's an attractive swimming area; rental of good-quality mobile homes.

Surroundings : ≤ ♡ ♡		G
Leisure activities : ♟ ✗ 🎲 ♣ ⚓ 🚲 ⛷ ⛵ multi-sports ground		P
Facilities : ♿ ⛽ ♨ 🚿 🍴 launderette		S

Longitude : 6.18185
Latitude : 45.83

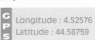 International du Lac d'Annecy

📞 0450686793. www.camping-lac-annecy.com

Address : 1184 route d'Albertville (located 1km southeast)

Opening times : from end April to end Sept.

2.5 ha (163 pitches) flat, grassy

Tariff : 40€ ✴✴ ⟷ 🔲 ⚡ (10A) – Extra per person 8€ – Reservation fee 22€

Rental rates : (from end April to end Sept.) ♿ (1 mobile home) ⛷ – 25 ⟐ – 3 ⟐ – 4 tent lodges. Per night from 37 to 142€ – Per week from 259 to 994€ – Reservation fee 22€
🛏 10 🔲 41€
The campsite is in 2 distinct sections on either side of the Voie Verte (cycle path).

Surroundings : ♡ ♡		G
Leisure activities : ♟ ✗ ⊟ ⚓ 🚲 ⛷ ⛵ multi-sports ground		P
Facilities : ♿ ⛽ ♨ 🚿 🍴 launderette		S

Longitude : 6.17845
Latitude : 45.83078

Le Solitaire du Lac

📞 0450685930. www.campinglesolitaire.com – access difficult

Address : 615 route de Sales (located 1km to the north)

Opening times : from beginning April to mid Sept.

3.5 ha (185 pitches) flat, grassy

Tariff : (2014 Price) 28€ ✴✴ ⟷ 🔲 ⚡ (6A) – Extra per person 6€ – Reservation fee 8€

Rental rates : (2014 Price) (from beginning April to mid Sept.) ⛷ (from beginning April to end June) – 14 ⟐ – 1 ⟐. Per night from 61 to 83€ – Per week from 308 to 686 € – Reservation fee 8€
🛏 borne
Set on a pleasant, green field stretching down to the lake.

Surroundings : 🌄 ♡ ♡		G
Leisure activities : ⊟ ⚓ 🚲 ⛵		P
Facilities : ♿ ⛽ ♨ 🍴 launderette 🚿		S

Longitude : 6.14875
Latitude : 45.84177

ST-JULIEN-EN-ST-ALBAN

07000 – Michelin map **331** K5 – pop. 1 311 – alt. 131
▶ Paris 587 – Aubenas 41 – Crest 29 – Montélimar 35

L'Albanou

📞 0475660097, www.camping-albanou.com

Address : chemin de Pampelonne (head 1.4km east along the N 304, follow the signs for Pouzin and take the Celliers road to the right; near the Ouvèze)

Opening times : from end April to end Sept.

1.5 ha (87 pitches) flat, grassy

Tariff : 26.50€ ✴✴ ⟷ 🔲 ⚡ (10A) – Extra per person 6€ – Reservation fee 3€

Rental rates : (from end April to end Sept.) – 3 ⟐. Per week from 320 to 655€ – Reservation fee 5€
🛏 borne – 6 🔲 22.50€
Attractive neatly marked-out pitches.

Surroundings : 🌄 ⌂ ♡		G
Leisure activities : jacuzzi ⚓ ⛷		P
Facilities : ♿ ⛽ 🍴 🖥 🚿		S

Longitude : 4.71369
Latitude : 44.75651

Routes nationales are main roads and their identifying numbers begin with N or RN. Routes départementales are generally quieter roads and begin with D or DN.

ST-LAURENT-DU-PONT

38380 – Michelin map **333** H5 – pop. 4 496 – alt. 410
▶ Paris 560 – Chambéry 29 – Grenoble 34 – La Tour-du-Pin 42

Municipal les Berges du Guiers

📞 0476552063. www.camping-chartreuse.com

Address : avenue de la gare (take the northern exit along the D 520, follow the signs for Chambéry and take the turning to the left; beside the Guiers Mort – pedestrian walkway to village)

Opening times : from mid June to mid Sept.

1 ha (45 pitches) flat, grassy

Tariff : (2014 Price) 17.50€ ✴✴ ⟷ 🔲 ⚡ (5A) – Extra per person 5€ – Reservation fee 10€

Surroundings : ≤ ♡		G
Facilities : ♿ ⛽ ♨ 🍴 🖥		P
Nearby : ⚓ ✗ ⛷		S

Longitude : 5.73615
Latitude : 45.39068

ST-LAURENT-EN-BEAUMONT

38350 – Michelin map **333** I8 – pop. 436 – alt. 900
▶ Paris 613 – Le Bourg-d'Oisans 43 – Corps 16 – Grenoble 51

⚠ Belvédère de l'Obiou

✆ 0476304080. www.camping-obiou.com

Address : Les Égats (1.3km southwest along the N 85)

Opening times : from mid April to mid Oct.

1 ha (45 pitches) terraced, relatively flat, flat, grassy

Tariff : (2014 Price) 21.50€ ✶✶ ⇔ 🔲 ⚡ (10A) –
Extra per person 5.90€ – Reservation fee 15€

Rental rates : (2014 Price) (from beginning May to end Sept.) –
5 🚐 – 2 🛏. Per week from €294 to 672 – Reservation fee 15€

🚐 borne 5€ – 3 🔲

Surroundings : 🦢 ⚲ ♀
Leisure activities : ✗ 🏛 🚣 🖼
Facilities : 🚻 ⛲ cc 🛎 🔥 ⛲ 🔲 🚿
Nearby : 🍸

Longitude : 5.83779
Latitude : 44.87597

ST-LAURENT-LES-BAINS

07590 – Michelin map **331** F6 – pop. 156 – alt. 840
▶ Paris 603 – Aubenas 64 – Langogne 30 – Largentière 52

⚠ Le Ceytrou

✆ 0466460203. www.campingleceytrou.free.fr

Address : situated 2.1km to the southeast along the D 4

Opening times : from beginning April to mid Nov.

2.5 ha (60 pitches) terraced, flat and relatively flat, grassy, stony

Tariff : 17.90€ ✶✶ ⇔ 🔲 ⚡ (10A) – Extra per person 4.30€

Rental rates : (from beginning April to mid Nov.) – 12 🏠.
Per night from 40 to 50€ – Per week from 150 to 388€

In a charming location in the heart of the Vivarais Cévenol mountains.

Surroundings : 🦢 ⚲ ♀
Leisure activities : 🏛 ✗ 🎣 🖼 🚣
Facilities : 🚻 ⛲ 🚿 🔥 🔲

Longitude : 3.97962
Latitude : 44.59922

ST-MARTIN-D'ARDÈCHE

07700 – Michelin map **331** I6 – pop. 886 – alt. 46
▶ Paris 641 – Bagnols-sur-Cèze 21 – Barjac 27 – Bourg-St-Andéol 13

⚠ Le Pontet 👥

✆ 0475046307, www.campinglepontet.com

Address : Le Pontet (located 1.5km east along the D 290, follow the signs for St-Just and take road to the left)

Opening times : from beginning April to end Sept.

1.8 ha (97 pitches)

Tariff : (2014 Price) 25.40€ ✶✶ ⇔ 🔲 ⚡ (10A) –
Extra per person 5.70€ – Reservation fee 10€

Rental rates : (2014 Price) (from beginning April to end Sept.) –
17 🚐. Per night from 40 to 80€ – Per week from 240 to 710€
Reservation fee 26€

🚐 borne 3€ – 4 🔲 8€ – 🚐 8€

The site is surrounded by vineyards, with plenty of shade; the swimming pool is on the other side of the small road.

Surroundings : 🦢 ♀♀
Leisure activities : 🍸 ✗ 🏛 🚶 🚣 🚴 🖼
Facilities : 🚻 ⛲ 🛎 🔥 🔲 🚿

Longitude : 4.58453
Latitude : 44.30409

⚠ Les Gorges

✆ 0475046109, www.camping-des-gorges.com

Address : chemin de Sauze (located 1.5km to the northwest)

Opening times : from end April to mid Sept.

3 ha (145 pitches) terraced, flat, grassy, stony

Tariff : (2014 Price) 38€ ✶✶ ⇔ 🔲 ⚡ (10A) – Extra per person 8.60€ –
Reservation fee 30€

Rental rates : (2014 Price) (from end April to mid Sept.) – 24 🚐 –
1 gîte. Per night from 39 to 160€ – Per week from 273 to 1,120€ –
Reservation fee 30€

🚐 borne

A well-shaded site with access to the banks of the Ardèche river.

Surroundings : 🏞 ♀♀
Leisure activities : 🍸 ✗ 🏛 🚣 🚣 🖼 🎣
🌿 multi-sports ground
Facilities : 🚻 ⛲ 🛎 🔥 🔲 🚿

Longitude : 4.55547
Latitude : 44.31155

⚠ Indigo le Moulin

Camping Indigo ©R. Etienne

✆ 0475046620. www.camping-indigo.
com

Address : take southeastern exit along
the D 290, follow the signs for St-Just
and take a right turn (D 200); beside the
Ardèche river

Opening times : from end April to
end Sept.

6.5 ha (200 pitches) relatively flat, flat,
grassy, sandy

Tariff : (2014 Price) 33.30€ ✶✶ ⇔ 🔲 ⚡ (10A) –
Extra per person 6.90€ – Reservation fee 22€

Rental rates : (2014 Price) (from end April to end Sept.) –
16 caravans – 8 🚐 – 50 tent lodges. Per night from 68 to 121€ –
Per week from 334 to 847€ – Reservation fee 22€

🚐 borne 7€ – 40 🔲 28€

Surroundings : ♀
Leisure activities : ✗ 🏛 🚣 🚣 🖼 🎣
Facilities : 🚻 ⛲ 🔥 🔲 🚿

Longitude : 4.57122
Latitude : 44.30035

ST-MARTIN-DE-CLELLES

38930 – Michelin map **333** G8 – pop. 157 – alt. 750
▶ Paris 616 – Lyon 149 – Grenoble 48 – St-Martin-d'Hères 49

⚠ La Chabannerie

✆ 0476340038, www.camping-isere.net

Address : Lotissement La Chabannerie

2.5 ha (49 pitches) terraced, flat and relatively flat, grassy, stony

Surroundings : 🦢 ⚲ 🏞 ♀♀
Leisure activities : 🏛 🚣
Facilities : ⛲ 🔥 🔥 🔲 🚿

Longitude : 5.61624
Latitude : 44.82574

ST-MARTIN-EN-VERCORS

26420 – Michelin map **332** F3 – pop. 378 – alt. 780
▶ Paris 601 – La Chapelle-en-Vercors 9 – Grenoble 51 – Romans-sur-Isère 46

� La Porte St-Martin

℘ 04 75 45 51 10. www.camping-laportestmartin.com

Address : take the northern exit along the D 103

Opening times : from mid April to end Sept.

1.5 ha (66 pitches) terraced, sloping, flat, grassy, stony, gravelled

Tariff : (2014 Price) 18.90€ ✶✶ ⇔ ▣ ⚡ (10A) – Extra per person 7€

Rental rates : (2014 Price) Permanent ⚲ – 3 ⌂ – 1 gîte. Per week from 230 to 650€

⛽ borne 9€

Surroundings : ≤ ♀
Leisure activities : 🏡 ⚲ 🏊 (small swimming pool)
Facilities : ⚅ ⊶ 🚿 🗑
Longitude : 5.44336
Latitude : 45.02456

ST-MAURICE-D'ARDÈCHE

07200 – Michelin map **331** I6 – pop. 312 – alt. 140
▶ Paris 639 – Aubenas 12 – Largentière 16 – Privas 44

⚲ Le Chamadou ♣♣

℘ 08 20 36 61 97, www.camping-le-chamadou.com ✉ 07120 Balazuc

Address : Mas de Chaussy (500m from a lake)

Opening times : from beginning April to end Oct.

1 ha (86 pitches)

Tariff : 31.50€ ✶✶ ⇔ ▣ ⚡ (10A) – Extra per person 7€ – Reservation fee 15€

Rental rates : (from beginning April to end Oct.) ⚲ – 24 ⌂. Per night from 40 to 140€ – Per week from 220 to 1,200€ – Reservation fee 15€

In the heart of the Ardèche wine-growing area, with a pretty traditional stone farmhouse.

Surroundings : 🌄 ⌂ ♀
Leisure activities : 🍷 ✗ 🏡 🏃 🛝 🛶 🏊 multi-sports ground
Facilities : ⚅ ⊶ 🚿 🗑
Nearby : 🏊
Longitude : 4.40384
Latitude : 44.50826

ST-NAZAIRE-EN-ROYANS

26190 – Michelin map **332** E3 – pop. 716 – alt. 172
▶ Paris 576 – Grenoble 69 – Pont-en-Royans 9 – Romans-sur-Isère 19

⚲ Municipal du Lac

℘ 04 75 48 41 18, www.saint-nazaire-en-royans.com

Address : 100B rue des Condamines (700m southeast, follow the signs for St-Jean-en-Royans)

Opening times : from mid May to mid Sept.

1.5 ha (75 pitches)

Tariff : (2014 Price) 15€ ✶✶ ⇔ ▣ ⚡ (6A) – Extra per person 4.30€
Rentals : 2 tent lodges.

⛽ borne

Situated beside the Bourne river, where it widens into a small lake.

Surroundings : ⌂ ♀♀
Leisure activities : 🏡 🏊
Facilities : ⚅ ⊶ 🚿 🗑
Longitude : 5.25368
Latitude : 45.05912

ST-PAUL-DE-VÉZELIN

42590 – Michelin map **327** D4 – pop. 303 – alt. 431
▶ Paris 415 – Boën 19 – Feurs 30 – Roanne 26

⚲ Arpheuilles

℘ 04 77 63 43 43. www.camping-arpheuilles.com – access difficult for caravans

Address : 4km to the north, at Port Piset, near the river (and lake)

Opening times : from mid April to end Sept.

3.5 ha (80 pitches) terraced, relatively flat, grassy

Tariff : 26.50€ ✶✶ ⇔ ▣ ⚡ (10A) – Extra per person 3€

Rental rates : (from mid April to end Sept.) – 4 ⌂ – 7 ⌂. Per week from 70 to 135€ – Per week from 210 to 695€

In an attractive setting in the steep valley of the Loire river, on a secluded and unspoilt site.

Surroundings : 🌄 ≤ ♀♀ ⚓
Leisure activities : 🍷 ✗ 🏡 🏃 🛶 🏊 💧 ⚲
Facilities : ⚅ ⊶ 🚿 🗑 🍽 launderette 🧺
Nearby : 🏊
Longitude : 4.06314
Latitude : 45.91178

ST-PIERRE-D'ALBIGNY

73250 – Michelin map **333** J4 – pop. 3 269 – alt. 410
▶ Paris 587 – Aix-les-Bains 43 – Albertville 27 – Annecy 52

⚲ Lac de Carouge

℘ 04 79 28 58 16. www.campinglacdecarouge.fr

Address : 2.8km south along the D 911 and take a left turn, 300m from the N 6

Opening times : from end April to beginning Sept.

1.9 ha (81 pitches) flat, grassy

Tariff : 26.50€ ✶✶ ⇔ ▣ ⚡ (10A) – Extra per person 4.50€ – Reservation fee 20€

Rental rates : (from end April to beginning Sept.) – 15 ⌂ – 4 canvas bungalows. Per night from 50 to 78€ – Per week from 280 to 749€ – Reservation fee 20€

⛽ borne

A pleasant and shaded site near a boating centre.

Surroundings : ⌂ ♀♀
Leisure activities : 🍷
Facilities : ⚅ ⊶ 🚿 🍽 launderette
Nearby : 🏃 🏊 (beach) 🛶 pedalos, cable wakeboarding, pedalos
Longitude : 6.17092
Latitude : 45.56057

ST-PIERRE-DE-CHARTREUSE

38380 – Michelin map **333** H5 – pop. 999 – alt. 885 – Winter sports : 900/1 800 m
▶ Paris 571 – Belley 62 – Chambéry 39 – Grenoble 28

⚲ Sites et Paysages De Martinière

℘ 04 76 88 60 36. www.campingdemartiniere.com

Address : route du Col de Porte (3km southwest along the D 512, follow the signs for Grenoble)

Opening times : from beginning May to mid Sept.

1.5 ha (100 pitches) open site, relatively flat, flat, grassy

Tariff : 27.90€ ✶✶ ⇔ ▣ ⚡ (10A) – Extra per person 6.40€ – Reservation fee 8€

Rental rates : (from mid May to mid Sept.) ⚲ – 4 ⌂ – 3 ⌂. Per night from 100 to 250€ – Per week from 300 to 750€ – Reservation fee 8€

⛽ borne – 2 ▣ 21.90€ – 🚐 11€

In a pleasant location situated in the heart of the Chartreuse National Park.

Surroundings : ⩽ ⚲
Leisure activities : 🏠 ⛵ ⤢
Facilities : ⚬━ 🏛 ♨ 🚻 ▨
Nearby : ✕

GPS Longitude : 5.79717
Latitude : 45.32583

ST-PRIVAT

07200 – Michelin map **331** I6 – pop. 1 588 – alt. 304
▶ Paris 631 – Lyon 169 – Privas 26 – Valence 65

🏕 Le Plan d'Eau

✆ 04 75 35 44 98, www.campingleplandeau.fr

Address : route de Lussas (situated 2km southeast along the D 259)

Opening times : from end April to end Sept.

3 ha (100 pitches)

Tariff : 31€ ✝✝ ⇌ ▣ [½] (8A) – Extra per person 7.50€ – Reservation fee 20€

Rental rates : (2014 Price) (from end April to end Sept.) – 25 🏠. Per night from 36 to 126€ – Per week from 250 to 885€ – Reservation fee 20€

Good shade cover; pitches near the Ardèche river.

Surroundings : ⧖ ⊏ ⚲⚲
Leisure activities : ♈✕ ⛵ 🏊 ⤢ ⤹
multi-sports ground
Facilities : ⚒ ⚬━ ♨ 🚻 launderette

GPS Longitude : 4.43296
Latitude : 44.61872

ST-REMÈZE

07700 – Michelin map **331** J7 – pop. 863 – alt. 365
▶ Paris 645 – Barjac 30 – Bourg-St-Andéol 16 – Pont-St-Esprit 27

🏕 Domaine de Briange

✆ 04 75 04 14 43. www.campingdebriange.com

Address : route de Gras (situated 2km north along the D 362)

Opening times : from beginning May to mid Sept.

4 ha (80 pitches) relatively flat, flat, grassy, stony, sandy

Tariff : 38.50€ ✝✝ ⇌ ▣ [½] (6A) – Extra per person 9€

Rental rates : (from beginning March to mid Nov.) ⚒ (1 chalet) – 1 caravan – 24 🏠 – 1 cabin in the trees – 6 canvas bungalows – 6 gîtes. Per night from 52 to 172€

Many different rental options are available, including some good-quality accommodation that is well spaced out.

Surroundings : ⧖ ⚲
Leisure activities : ✕ ⛵ ✂ 🏊
Facilities : ⚒ ⚬━ 🚻 ▨

GPS Longitude : 4.5139
Latitude : 44.40615

⛰ La Résidence d'Été

✆ 04 75 04 26 87, www.campinglaresidence.com

Address : rue de la Bateuse

1.6 ha (60 pitches) terraced, relatively flat to hilly, grassy, stony, fruit trees

Rentals : 19 🚐.

Situated very close to the centre of the village; a lovely natural area beneath the shade of cherry trees.

Surroundings : ⩽ ⚲⚲
Leisure activities : ✕ ⛵ 🏊
Facilities : ⚒ ⚬━ 🚻 ▨ ⤹

GPS Longitude : 4.50437
Latitude : 44.39105

ST-SAUVEUR-DE-CRUZIÈRES

07460 – Michelin map **331** H8 – pop. 535 – alt. 150
▶ Paris 674 – Alès 28 – Barjac 9 – Privas 81

🏕 La Claysse

✆ 04 75 35 40 65. www.campingdelaclaysse.com – For caravans and campervans, access via the top of the village.

Address : La Digue (to the northwest of the town; beside the river)

5 ha/1 for camping (60 pitches)

Rentals : 13 🚐.

Below the road, with some pitches beside the river. The production and sale of olive oil on site.

Surroundings : ⊏ ⚲⚲
Leisure activities : ✕ 🏠 ⛵ 🚲 🏊 ⤢ ⤹
Facilities : ⚒ ⚬━ 🚻 ▨
Nearby : climbing

GPS Longitude : 4.25085
Latitude : 44.29984

The guide covers all 22 regions of France – see the map and list of regions on pages 4–5.

ST-SAUVEUR-DE-MONTAGUT

07190 – Michelin map **331** J5 – pop. 1 144 – alt. 218
▶ Paris 597 – Le Cheylard 24 – Lamastre 29 – Privas 24

🏕 L'Ardéchois

✆ 04 75 66 61 87, www.ardechois-camping.fr

Address : situated 8.5km west along the D 102, follow the signs for Albon

Opening times : from beginning May to end Sept.

37 ha/5 for camping (107 pitches)

Tariff : 34.40€ ✝✝ ⇌ ▣ [½] (16A) – Extra per person 7.15€ – Reservation fee 23€

Rental rates : (from beginning May to end Sept.) – 18 🚐 – 9 🏠. Per night from 100 to 200€ – Per week from 380 to 905€ – Reservation fee 23€

 borne

In 2 separate sections on either side of the road, with pitches beside the Glueyre river.

Surroundings : ⧖ ⩽ ⚲⚲
Leisure activities : ♈✕ 🏠 ⛵ 🚲 🏊 ⤢ ⤹
Facilities : ⚒ ⚬━ [cc] 🚻 launderette ⤹

GPS Longitude : 4.52294
Latitude : 44.82893

ST-SYMPHORIEN-SUR-COISE

69590 – Michelin map **327** F6 – pop. 3 438 – alt. 558
▶ Paris 489 – Andrézieux-Bouthéon 26 – L'Arbresle 36 – Feurs 30

🏕 Hurongues

✆ 04 78 48 44 29, www.camping-hurongues.com

Address : 3.5km west along the D 2, follow the signs for Chazelles-sur-Lyon, 400m from a small lake

3.6 ha (114 pitches) terraced, flat, grassy

In a pleasant wooded setting, based beside a leisure park.

Surroundings : ⧖ ⊏ ⚲⚲
Leisure activities : 🏠 ⛵
Facilities : ⚬━ 🏛 ♨ ▨
Nearby : ✂ 🗾 ⤹

GPS Longitude : 4.4282
Latitude : 45.63481

ST-THÉOFFREY

38119 – Michelin map **333** H8 – pop. 444 – alt. 936
▶ Paris 595 – Le Bourg-d'Oisans 44 – Grenoble 33 – La Mure 10

⛰ Au Pré du Lac

📞 04 76 83 91 34. www.aupredulac.eu

Address : Pétichet hamlet

Opening times : from beginning March to end Oct.

3 ha (96 pitches) flat, grassy

Tariff : 25 € ★ ★ 🚗 🅴 🔌 (10A) – Extra per person 5 € – Reservation fee 8 €

Rental rates : Permanent – 4 🏠 – 3 🏠. Per week from 260 to 790 € – Reservation fee 12.50 €

Surroundings : 💧⛰		
Leisure activities : 🍴✕🏓⚽🎣🏊🐎🛶		G P S
Facilities : ♿ ☕ 🏧 🛖 🚿 launderette 🧹		Longitude : 5.77224
Nearby : ⚓⛵		Latitude : 45.00454

ST-VALLIER

26240 – Michelin map **332** B2 – pop. 4 000 – alt. 135
▶ Paris 526 – Annonay 21 – St-Étienne 61 – Tournon-sur-Rhône 16

⛰ Municipal les Îsles de Silon

📞 04 75 23 22 17, www.saintvallier.com

Address : Les Îles (situated to the north, near the Rhône river)

1.35 ha (92 pitches)

Rentals : 4 🏠.

Surroundings : ⟨ ☕ 💧💧		
Leisure activities : 🚣		G P S
Facilities : ☕ 🛖 🚿 🔲		Longitude : 4.81237
Nearby : ✕ 🏊		Latitude : 45.1879

STE-CATHERINE

69440 – Michelin map **327** G6 – pop. 911 – alt. 700
▶ Paris 488 – Andrézieux-Bouthéon 38 – L'Arbresle 37 – Feurs 43

⛰ Municipal du Châtelard

📞 04 78 81 80 60. http://mairie-saintecatherine.fr – alt. 800 – limited spaces for one-night stay

Address : Le Châtelard (situated 2km to the south)

Opening times : from beginning March to end Nov.

4 ha (61 pitches) terraced, flat, grassy

Tariff : (2014 Price) ★ 2.25 € 🚗 🅴 2.55 € – 🔌 (6A) 2.80 €

Surroundings : 🚣 ⟨ Mont Pilat and Monts du Lyonnais 🔲		
Leisure activities : 🏠		G P S
Facilities : 🚿 🚿 🔲		Longitude : 4.57344
		Latitude : 45.58817

Key to rentals symbols:

12 🏠	*Number of mobile homes*
20 🏠	*Number of chalets*
6 🛏	*Number of rooms to rent*
Per night 30–50 €	*Minimum/maximum rate per night*
Per week 300–1,000 €	*Minimum/maximum rate per week*

SALAVAS

07150 – Michelin map **331** I7 – pop. 530 – alt. 96
▶ Paris 668 – Lyon 206 – Privas 58 – Nîmes 77

⛰ Le Péquelet

📞 04 75 88 04 49, www.lepequelet.com

Address : Le Cros (take the southern exit along the D 579, follow the signs for Barjac and continue along the turning to the left for 2km)

Opening times : from beginning April to end Sept.

2 ha (60 pitches) flat, grassy

Tariff : 30.50 € ★ ★ 🚗 🅴 🔌 (10A) – Extra per person 8 € – Reservation fee 10 €

Rental rates : (from beginning April to end Sept.) – 8 🏠 – 5 🏠 – 2 apartments – 2 canvas bungalows. Per night from 40 to 100 € – Per week from 280 to 700 € – Reservation fee 10 €

🚐 borne – 🔌 🔌 25 €

Beside the Ardèche river and surrounded by vineyards.

Surroundings : 🚣 🔲 💧💧⛰		
Leisure activities : 🏠 🛝 🏊 🐎 🛶		G P S
Facilities : ♿ ☕ 🚿 🚿 🔲		Longitude : 4.39806
		Latitude : 44.39075

SALLANCHES

74700 – Michelin map **328** M5 – pop. 15 619 – alt. 550
▶ Paris 585 – Annecy 72 – Bonneville 29 – Chamonix-Mont-Blanc 28

⛰ Tohapi Les Îles

📞 08 25 00 53 18, http://campings.village-center.fr/rhones-alpes/camping-montagne-il

Address : 245 chemin de la Cavettaz (situated 2km to the southeast; beside a stream and 250m from a lake)

Opening times : from mid April to mid Sept.

4.6 ha (260 pitches)

Tariff : 17 € ★ ★ 🚗 🅴 🔌 (6A) – Extra per person 5 € – Reservation fee 10 €

Rental rates : (from mid April to mid Sept.) – 41 🏠 – 11 🏠. Per night from 28 to 123 € – Per week from 196 to 861 € – Reservation fee 10 €

A thickly wooded site, close to a large leisure complex.

Surroundings : 🔲 💧💧		
Leisure activities : 🍴✕🏠 🕐daytime 🏃🚴		G P S
Facilities : ♿ ☕ 🛖 🚿 🧹 🚿 🚿 launderette 🧹		Longitude : 6.65103
Nearby : 🏖 🏊 (beach) 🛶 ⚡ electric boats		Latitude : 45.92404

LA SALLE-EN-BEAUMONT

38350 – Michelin map **333** I8 – pop. 297 – alt. 756
▶ Paris 614 – Le Bourg-d'Oisans 44 – Gap 51 – Grenoble 52

⛰ Le Champ Long

📞 04 76 30 41 81. www.camping-champlong.com – help moving caravans onto and off pitches avilable on request

Address : Le Champ-Long (2.7km southwest along the N 85, follow the signs for la Mure and take road to the left)

Opening times : Permanent

5 ha (97 pitches) open site, very uneven, terraced, flat, grassy

Tariff : 21 € ★ ★ 🚗 🅴 🔌 (10A) – Extra per person 6 € – Reservation fee 15 €

Rental rates : Permanent – 4 ⊡ – 14 ⌂ – 3 ⊨ – 3 studios. Per night from 62 to 105€ – Per week from 310 to 670€ – Reservation fee 15€

⊡ borne 5€ – 3 ▣ 18€ – 🔋13€

Surroundings : ⊰ ⊰ Lac du Sautet and valley ⊏ ♀♀
Leisure activities : ▼ ✗ ⊞ ⊰⊱ ⅃
Facilities : & ⊶ ⓒ ⅋ launderette ⊰

GPS	Longitude : 5.84416
	Latitude : 44.85725

SAMOËNS

74340 – Michelin map **328** N4 – pop. 2 311 – alt. 710
▶ Paris 598 – Lyon 214 – Annecy 82 – Genève 63

⋀⋀ Club Airotel Le Giffre

Club Airotel Le Giffre

𝒫 04 50 34 41 92. www.camping-samoens.com

Address : La Glière

Opening times : Permanent

7 ha (212 pitches)

Tariff : 30.70€ ✦✦ ⇋ ▣ ⌘ (10A) –
Extra per person 4.35€ – Reservation fee 50€

Rental rates : Permanent ⅋ – 1 ⊡ –
6 ⌂ – 5 canvas bungalows.
Per night from 43 to 71€ – Per week from 190 to 635€

⊡ borne 6€ – 14 ▣ 20.35€ – 🔋11€

In a pleasant location, near a lake and a leisure park.

Surroundings : ⊰♀♀
Leisure activities : ⅂⊰
Facilities : & ⊶ ⊞ ⊞ ⊰ ⅋ launderette
Nearby : ▼✗ ⊰⊱ ⅋ ⅃ ⊱ ⋀ sports trail, golf practice

GPS	Longitude : 6.71917
	Latitude : 46.07695

Routes nationales are main roads and their identifying numbers begin with N or RN. Routes départementales are generally quieter roads and begin with D or DN.

SAMPZON

07120 – Michelin map **351** I7 – pop. 224 – alt. 120
▶ Paris 660 – Lyon 198 – Privas 56 – Nîmes 85

⋀⋀⋀ Yelloh! Village Soleil Vivarais ⋀⋀

𝒫 04 75 39 67 56. www.soleil-vivarais.com

Address : at the bridge (follow the signs for Vallon Pont d'Arc)

Opening times : from beginning April to mid Sept.

12 ha (350 pitches)

Tariff : 52€ ✦✦ ⇋ ▣ ⌘ (10A) – Extra per person 8€
Rental rates : (from beginning April to mid Sept.) – 249 ⊡.
Per night from 39 to 374€ – Per week from 273 to 2,618€

Near a lovely beach on the Ardèche river; mobile homes ranging from a good standard to luxurious.

Surroundings : ⊰ ⊰♀♀
Leisure activities : ▼✗ ⊡ ⊕ ⋔ ⊰⊱ ⅋
⅋ ⅃ ⊱ (beach) ⅋ ⅋
Facilities : & ⊶ ⊞ ⊰ ⅋ launderette ⊰ ⊰

GPS	Longitude : 4.35528
	Latitude : 44.42916

⋀ Le Mas de la Source

𝒫 04 75 39 67 98, www.campingmasdelasource.com

Address : La Tuillière

Opening times : from mid April to end Sept.

1.2 ha (30 pitches)

Tariff : ✦ 6.90€ ⇋ 6.30€ ▣ 28€ – ⌘ (6A) 6.90€ – Reservation fee 5€
Rental rates : (from mid April to end Sept.) ⅋ – 9 ⊡ –
2 canvas bungalows. Per night from 35 to 104€ – Per week from 150 to 730€ – Reservation fee 8€

On the Sampzon river peninsula; easy, shaded access to the Ardèche river.

Surroundings : ⊰ ⊏ ♀♀
Leisure activities : ⊰⊱ ⅃ ⊱ ⅋
Facilities : & ⊶ ⊰ ⅋ ▣

GPS	Longitude : 4.3466
	Latitude : 44.42242

⋀ Sun Camping

𝒫 04 75 39 76 12. www.suncamping.com

Address : 10 chemin des Piboux (200m from the Ardèche)

1.2 ha (70 pitches) terraced, flat, grassy

Rentals : 14 ⊡.

On the Presqu'île de Sampzon (river peninsula) with good-quality mobile home rentals.

Surroundings : ⊰ ♀♀
Leisure activities : ▼ ⊰⊱ ⅃
Facilities : & ⊶ ⊰ ⅋ launderette
Nearby : ⊰ ✗ ⊰ ⊱

GPS	Longitude : 4.35352
	Latitude : 44.42895

SATILLIEU

07290 – Michelin map **331** J3 – pop. 1 616 – alt. 485
▶ Paris 542 – Annonay 13 – Lamastre 36 – Privas 87

⋀ Municipal le Grangeon

𝒫 04 75 67 84 86. www.lalouvesc.com

Address : chemin de l'Hermuzière (head 1.1km southwest along the D 578a; follow the signs for Lalouvesc and take the turning to the left)

Opening times : from mid May to end Sept.

1 ha (52 pitches) terraced, flat, grassy

Tariff : (2014 Price) ✦ 2.60€ ⇋ 1.80€ ▣ 2.80€ – ⌘ (10A) 3.30€
Rental rates : (2014 Price) (from mid May to end Sept.) – 5 ⊡.
Per night from 40€ – Per week from 188 to 343€

Both the pitches and the chalets have good shade; beside the Ay river and an attractive lake.

Surroundings : ⊰ ⊏ ♀♀
Leisure activities : ⊡
Facilities : & ⊶ ⊰ ⅋ ▣
Nearby : ⊱ (fresh water)

GPS	Longitude : 4.60389
	Latitude : 45.14438

Michelin classification:

⋀⋀⋀⋀	*Extremely comfortable, equipped to a very high standard*
⋀⋀⋀	*Very comfortable, equipped to a high standard*
⋀⋀	*Comfortable and well equipped*
⋀⋀	*Reasonably comfortable*
⋀	*Satisfactory*

SCIEZ

74140 – Michelin map **328** L3 – pop. 5 269 – alt. 406
▶ Paris 561 – Abondance 37 – Annecy 69 – Annemasse 24

⚑ Le Chatelet

☏ 04 50 72 52 60. www.camping-chatelet.com – limited spaces for one-night stay

Address : 658 chemin des Hutins Vieux (3km northeast along the N 5, follow the signs for Thonon-les-Bains and turn left onto the rte du Port at Sciez-Plage, 300m from the beach)

2.5 ha (121 pitches)

Rentals : ♿ (1 chalet) – 12 🏠 – 2 tent lodges.

There are some pitches for tents and caravans, but a lot of owner-occupier mobile homes.

Surroundings : 🌿
Leisure activities : ♨ 🚴
Facilities : ♿ ⛟ ▥ 🍳 🍴 launderette
Nearby : ✗ 🛶 🚣 pedalos

G P S Longitude : 6.39705
Latitude : 46.34079

SÉEZ

73700 – Michelin map **333** N4 – pop. 2 332 – alt. 904
▶ Paris 638 – Albertville 57 – Bourg-St-Maurice 4 – Moûtiers 31

⚑ Le Reclus

☏ 04 79 41 01 05. www.campinglereclus.com

Address : route de Tignes (take northwestern exit along the N 90, follow the signs for Bourg-St-Maurice ; beside the Reclus river)

Opening times : Permanent

1.5 ha (108 pitches) terraced, relatively flat, grassy, stony

Tariff : 19.90€ ★★ � 🔲 💧 (10A) – Extra per person 5€ – Reservation fee 5€

Rental rates : Permanent – 1 caravan – 3 🚐 – 4 🏠 – 6 yurts – 1 apartment – 1 tipi. Per night from 50 to 85€ – Per week from 300 to 490€ – Reservation fee 10€

🚐 borne 5€ – 6 🔲 12.90€ – 🚐 11€

Choose the pitches furthest away from the road in preference.

Surroundings : ❄ 🎋
Leisure activities : 🎣 🚴
Facilities : ♿ ⛟ ▥ 🍴 launderette

G P S Longitude : 6.7927
Latitude : 45.62583

SERRIÈRES-DE-BRIORD

01470 – Michelin map **328** F6 – pop. 1 143 – alt. 218
▶ Paris 481 – Belley 29 – Bourg-en-Bresse 57 – Crémieu 24

⚑ Le Point Vert

☏ 04 74 36 13 45. www.camping-ain-bugey.com – limited spaces for one-night stay

Address : route du Point Vert (2.5km west, at the leisure and activity park)

Opening times : from beginning April to beginning Oct.

1.9 ha (137 pitches) flat, grassy

Tariff : 24€ ★★ 🚗 🔲 💧 (6A) – Extra per person 5€

Rental rates : (from beginning April to beginning Oct.) – 5 🚐. Per week from 400 to 1,450€

Situated beside a small lake near the Rhône river.

Surroundings : ≤ 🎋 🏔
Leisure activities : 🎣 🕐 daytime 🎿 🚴
🚲 🛶 🚣
Facilities : ♿ ⛟ ▦ 🍳 🍴 launderette 🔋
Nearby : ♨ ✗ 🛶 🚣 (beach) 🛶 pedalos

G P S Longitude : 5.42731
Latitude : 45.81633

SÉVRIER

74320 – Michelin map **328** J5 – pop. 3 835 – alt. 456
▶ Paris 541 – Albertville 41 – Annecy 6 – Megève 55

⚑⚑ Le Panoramic

☏ 04 50 52 43 09. www.camping-le-panoramic.com

Address : 22 chemin des Bernets (located 3.5km to the south)

Opening times : from end April to end Sept.

3 ha (189 pitches) flat, relatively flat, grassy

Tariff : 28.80€ ★★ 🚗 🔲 💧 (10A) – Extra per person 6€ – Reservation fee 10€

Rental rates : (2014 Price) (from end April to end Sept.) – 18 🚐 – 17 🏠 – 4 studios – 3 apartments. Per night from 50 to 90€ – Per week from 275 to 870€ – Reservation fee 10€

🚐 borne 8€

The site is in 2 separate sections, looking out over the lake.

Surroundings : ≤ 🎋
Leisure activities : ♨ ✗ 🎣 🕐 daytime
🎿 🛶
Facilities : ♿ ⛟ 🍳 🍴 launderette 🔋 🔋

G P S Longitude : 6.1417
Latitude : 45.84308

⚑ Au Coeur du Lac

☏ 04 50 52 46 45. www.campingaucoeurdulac.com ✄ (from end June to mid Aug.)

Address : 3233 route d'Albertville (located 1km to the south)

Opening times : from beginning April to end Sept.

1.7 ha (105 pitches) terraced, relatively flat, grassy, fine gravel

Tariff : 28.20€ ★★ 🔲 💧 (13A) – Extra per person 5.50€

Rental rates : (from mid April to end Sept.) ✄ – 10 🚐. Per week from 270 to 690€

🚐 borne

In an attractive location near the lake (direct access).

Surroundings : ≤ 🎋
Leisure activities : 🎣 🕐 daytime 🎿 🚴 🛶
Facilities : ♿ ⛟ ▥ 🍳 🍴 launderette
Nearby : 🍴 🚣

G P S Longitude : 6.14399
Latitude : 45.85487

To visit a town or region, use the MICHELIN Green Guides.

SEYSSEL

01420 – Michelin map **328** H5 – pop. 948 – alt. 258
▶ Paris 517 – Aix-les-Bains 33 – Annecy 41 – Genève 52

⚑ L' International

☏ 04 50 59 28 47. www.camp-inter.fr

Address : chemin de la Barotte (2.4km southwest along the D 992, follow the signs for Culoz and take the road to the right)

Opening times : from mid May to end Sept.

1.5 ha (45 pitches)

Tariff : 26€ ★★ 🚗 🔲 💧 (10A) – Extra per person 4.50€ – Reservation fee 10€

Rental rates : (from mid March to mid Oct.) – 15 🚐. Per night from 57 to 103€ – Per week from 240 to 700€ – Reservation fee 20€

🚐 3 🔲 26€

A peaceful setting in an elevated location.

Surroundings : 🌿 ≤ 🎋
Leisure activities : ✗ 🎣 🎿 🚴 🎿
Facilities : ⛟ 🍴 launderette 🔋

G P S Longitude : 5.82349
Latitude : 45.94957

SEYSSEL

74910 – Michelin map **328** I5 – pop. 2 262 – alt. 252
▶ Paris 517 – Aix-les-Bains 32 – Annecy 40

Le Nant-Matraz

℘ 04 50 48 56 40. www.camping-seyssel.com

Address : 15 route de Genève (take the northern exit along the D 992)

Opening times : from beginning April to end Sept.

1 ha (67 pitches)

Tariff : (2014 Price) 17.50€ ♥♥ ⊶ ▣ ⨷ (6A) – Extra per person 4€

Rental rates : (2014 Price) (from beginning April to end Sept.) – 1 ⌂ – 4 tipis – 1 tent lodge – 3 cabins. Per night from 35 to 80€ – Per week from 160 to 390€

Choose the pitches overlooking the Rhône river.

Surroundings : ⌂ ♧♧	G
Leisure activities : ♟ ✗ ⚓ (small swimming pool)	P
Facilities : ⊶ ♨ launderette	S
Nearby : ⚲	Longitude : 5.83574 Latitude : 45.96339

TANINGES

74440 – Michelin map **328** M4 – pop. 3 414 – alt. 640
▶ Paris 570 – Annecy 68 – Bonneville 24 – Chamonix-Mont-Blanc 51

Municipal des Thézières

℘ 04 50 34 25 59, www.prazdelys-sommand.com

Address : les Vernays-sous-la-Ville (take the southern exit, follow the signs for Cluses; beside the Foron river and 150m from the Giffre)

Opening times : Permanent

2 ha (113 pitches)

Tariff : (2014 Price) 10.10€ ♥♥ ⊶ ▣ ⨷ (10A) – Extra per person 2.90€

⊡ borne 4.90€ – 3 ▣ 10.10€

Situated in a pretty green park with shade, near a fast-flowing stream.

Surroundings : ⚶ ≼ ♧♧	G
Leisure activities : ⚲	P
Facilities : ⚿ ⊶ ▥ ⬚ launderette	S
Nearby : ⌂ ⚡ ✗	Longitude : 6.58837 Latitude : 46.09866

TERMIGNON

73500 – Michelin map **333** N6 – pop. 423 – alt. 1 290
▶ Paris 680 – Bessans 18 – Chambéry 120 – Lanslebourg-Mont-Cenis 6

Les Mélèzes

℘ 04 79 20 51 41. www.camping-termignon-lavanoise.com

Address : route du Doron (in the village; beside some rapids)

0.7 ha (66 pitches) flat, grassy

Rentals : ⚶ – 4 ⌂.

The shaded pitches lie beside the Arc river.

Surroundings : ⚶ ≼ ♧♧	G
Leisure activities : ⌂ ⚲	P
Facilities : ⚿ ⊶ ▥ ⬚ ⊡	S
	Longitude : 6.81535 Latitude : 45.27815

LA TOUSSUIRE

73300 – Michelin map **333** K6 – alt. 1 690
▶ Paris 651 – Albertville 78 – Chambéry 91 – St-Jean-de-Maurienne 16

Caravaneige du Col

℘ 04 79 83 00 80. www.camping-du-col.com – alt. 1 640

Address : 1 km east of La Toussuire, on rte de St-Jean-de-Maurienne

Opening times : from end Dec. to mid April from mid June to end Aug.

0.8 ha (40 pitches) flat, grassy

Tariff : 27.80€ ♥♥ ⊶ ▣ ⨷ (10A) – Extra per person 5.90€ – Reservation fee 10€

Rental rates : (from end Dec. to mid April and from mid June to end Aug.) – 7 ⌂ – 3 ⌂ – 2 apartments. Per night from 64 to 71€ – Per week from 220 to 820€ – Reservation fee 10€

⊡ borne 7€

There's a free shuttle service to the ski resort.

Surroundings : ❄ ≼ Les Aiguilles d'Arves (peaks) ♧	G
Leisure activities : ♟ ✗ ⚓ ⬚daytime ⛷ ⚡ ⚓	P
Facilities : ♿ ⊶ ▥ ⬚ ⬚ launderette	S
	Longitude : 6.2739 Latitude : 45.25727

These symbols are used for a campsite that is exceptional in its category:

▲▲▲…▲   *Particularly pleasant setting, quality and range of services available*

⚶ ⚶   *Tranquil, isolated site – quiet site, particularly at night*

≼ ≼   *Exceptional view – interesting or panoramic view*

TREPT

38460 – Michelin map **333** E3 – pop. 1 741 – alt. 275
▶ Paris 495 – Belley 41 – Bourgoin-Jallieu 13 – Lyon 52

Sites et Paysages Les 3 Lacs du Soleil

℘ 04 74 92 92 06. www.camping-les3lacsdusoleil.com

Address : La Plaine Serrière (2.7km east along the D 517, follow the signs for Morestel and take the road to the right, near two lakes)

Opening times : from end April to beginning Sept.

25 ha/3 for camping (160 pitches) flat, grassy

Tariff : 35.50€ ♥♥ ⊶ ▣ ⨷ (6A) – Extra per person 7€

Rental rates : (2014 Price) (from end April to mid Sept.) ⚶ – 30 ⌂ – 7 ⌂ – 20 canvas bungalows – 2 tent lodges. Per night from 44 to 126€ – Per week from 308 to 882€

Surroundings : ⚶ ♧ ⚇	G
Leisure activities : ♟ ✗ ⚓ ⬚daytime ⚡ ⚡ ✗ ≛ ⚓ ⚓(beach) ⚑ ⚲	P
Facilities : ♿ ⊶ ⬚ launderette	S
	Longitude : 5.33447 Latitude : 45.69039

The Michelin classification (▲▲▲…▲) is totally independent of the official star classification system awarded by the local prefecture or other official organisation.

TULETTE

26790 – Michelin map **332** C8 – pop. 1 915 – alt. 147
▶ Paris 648 – Avignon 53 – Bollène 15 – Nyons 20

⚠ Les Rives de l'Aygues

📞 04 75 98 37 50. www.lesrivesdelaygues.com

Address : route de Cairanne (head 3km south along the D 193 and take road to the left)

Opening times : from beginning May to end Sept.

3.6 ha (100 pitches)

Tariff : (2014 Price) 28.60€ ✦✦ ⬅ 🔲 🔌 (6A) – Extra per person 6.10€ Reservation fee 10€
Rental rates : (2014 Price) (from beginning May to end Sept.) ✂ – 2 🚐 – 6 🏠. Per night from 42 to 106€ – Per week from 293 to 742€ – Reservation fee 10€

In a natural setting among vineyards.

Surroundings : 🐟 🗂 ♤♤		Longitude : 4.933
Leisure activities : 🍸 ✗ 🏠 🛥 ⳩	G P S	Latitude : 44.2648
Facilities : 🕭 ⚬━ 🗲 🔌 🖼 🛒		

A 'quartier' is a district or area of a town or village.

UCEL

07200 – Michelin map **331** I6 – pop. 1 929 – alt. 270
▶ Paris 626 – Aubenas 6 – Montélimar 44 – Privas 31

⛰ Domaine de Gil ♠♠

📞 04 75 94 63 63. www.domaine-de-gil.com ✂ (from beginning July to end Aug.)

Address : route de Vals (take northwestern exit along the D 578b)

Opening times : from mid April to mid Sept.

4.8 ha/2 for camping (80 pitches)

Tariff : 40€ ✦✦ ⬅ 🔲 🔌 (10A) – Extra per person 7€ – Reservation fee 22€
Rental rates : (from mid April to mid Sept.) ✂ – 52 🚐. Per night from 49 to 135€ – Per week from 245 to 945€ – Reservation fee 22€

🚐 borne

Well-shaded pitches and mobile homes in a very pleasant natural setting beside the Ardèche river.

Surroundings : 🐟 ⟨ 🗂 ♤♤ ⛰		Longitude : 4.37959
Leisure activities : 🍸 ✗ 🏠 🌙 nighttime 🏃 jacuzzi 🛥 ⳩ ✂ 🏊 ⳩ multi-sports ground	G P S	Latitude : 44.64308
Facilities : 🕭 ⚬━ 🗲 🔌 🛒 launderette 🛒		

VAGNAS

07150 – Michelin map **331** I7 – pop. 521 – alt. 200
▶ Paris 670 – Aubenas 40 – Barjac 5 – St-Ambroix 20

⛰ La Rouvière-Les Pins

📞 04 75 38 61 41. www.rouviere07.com

Address : La Rouvière (take the southern exit following signs for Barjac then continue 1.5km along the road to the right)

Opening times : from beginning April to mid Sept.

2 ha (100 pitches) terraced, relatively flat, flat, grassy

Tariff : (2014 Price) 25€ ✦✦ ⬅ 🔲 🔌 (10A) – Extra per person 6.50€ Reservation fee 15€

Rental rates : (2014 Price) (from beginning April to end Sept.) – 2 🚐 – 2 apartments – 3 canvas bungalows. Per week from 250 to 730€ – Reservation fee 15€

🚐 borne

A spacious site in the heart of the vineyards.

Surroundings : 🐟 ♤♤		Longitude : 4.34194
Leisure activities : 🍸 🏠 🛥 ⳩	G P S	Latitude : 44.3419
Facilities : 🕭 ⚬━ 🗲 🔌 🛒 🖼 🛒		

VALLIÈRES

74150 – Michelin map **328** I5 – pop. 1 393 – alt. 347
▶ Paris 533 – Lyon 132 – Annecy 30 – Genève 59

⛰ Les Charmilles

📞 04 50 62 10 60. www.campinglescharmilles.com

Address : 625 route de Val de Fier

Opening times : from beginning April to end Oct.

3 ha (81 pitches) flat, grassy

Tariff : 15€ ✦✦ ⬅ 🔲 🔌 (8A) – Extra per person 4€ – Reservation fee 10€
Rental rates : (from beginning April to end Oct.) – 13 🚐 – 10 🏠. Per night from 60€ – Per week from 231 to 695€ – Reservation fee 10€

🚐 3 🔲 12€ – 🔌 12€

The site is surrounded by an apple orchard.

Surroundings : 🐟 🗂 ♤♤		Longitude : 5.9285
Leisure activities : 🍸 ✗ 🏠 🛥 ⳩	G P S	Latitude : 45.90286
Facilities : 🕭 ⚬━ 🗲 🔌 launderette		

There are several different types of sani-station ('borne' in French) – sanitation points providing fresh water and disposal points for grey water. See page 12 for further details.

VALLON-PONT-D'ARC

07150 – Michelin map **331** I7 – pop. 2 337 – alt. 117
▶ Paris 658 – Alès 47 – Aubenas 32 – Avignon 81

⛰ Les Castels Nature Parc l'Ardéchois ♠♠

📞 04 75 88 06 63. www.ardechois-camping.com

Address : route Touristique des Gorges de l'Ardèche (located 1.5km southeast along the D 290)

Opening times : from end March to end Sept.

5 ha (240 pitches) flat, grassy

Tariff : 56€ ✦✦ ⬅ 🔲 🔌 (6A) – Extra per person 10.90€ – Reservation fee 40€

Rental rates : (from end March to mid Sept.) – 25 🚐. Per night from 78 to 131€ – Per week from 546 to 1,150€ – Reservation fee 40€

🚐 borne

In a green setting with some very well-equipped pitches and an attractive terraced layout, above the Ardèche river.

Surroundings : 🐟 ⟨ 🗂 ♤♤ ⛰		Longitude : 4.39673
Leisure activities : 🍸 ✗ 🏠 🌙 🏃 🛥 ✂ 🏊 ⳩ ⳩ multi-sports ground	G P S	Latitude : 44.39672
Facilities : 🕭 ⚬━ 🔲 🖼 🗲 🔌 🛒 launderette 🗲 🛒		
Nearby : 🎣		

⚠ La Roubine ♣♣

📞 0475880456. www.camping-roubine.com

Address : route de Ruoms (located 1.5km west)

Opening times : from end April to mid Sept.

7 ha/4 for camping (135 pitches)

Tariff : (2014 Price) 51€ ♣♣ ⇦ 🖭 🗟 (10A) – Extra per person 10.10€ Reservation fee 30€

Rental rates : (2014 Price) (from end April to mid Sept.) 🖕 (1 mobile home) 🦟 – 38 🛏. Per night from 68 to 226€ – Per week from 476 to 1,582€ – Reservation fee 30€

🖭 borne

An attractive campsite beside the Ardèche river; some high-quality mobile homes and good sanitary facilities.

Surroundings : 🏊 ⊏ 🌳🌳 ⛰
Leisure activities : 🍴 🗙 🖻 🗟 🤸 🛶 jacuzzi 🏄 ♨ 🛌 🚣 multi-sports ground, spa centre
Facilities : 🖕 ⛇ 🎽 🗑 🍴 launderette 🖭 🍴

Longitude : 4.37835
Latitude : 44.40636

⚠ Mondial-Camping ♣♣

📞 0475880044. www.mondial-camping.com

Address : route des Gorges de l'Ardèche (located 1.5km southeast)

Opening times : from end March to end Sept.

4 ha (240 pitches) flat, grassy

Tariff : 46€ ♣♣ ⇦ 🖭 🗟 (10A) – Extra per person 9.50€ – Reservation fee 30€

Rental rates : (2014 Price) (from end March to end Sept.) 🦟 – 24 🛏 – 7 canvas bungalows. Per night from 55 to 80€ – Per week from 320 to 820€ – Reservation fee 30€

🖭 borne

A green site beside the Ardèche river, with some pitches well marked out.

Surroundings : ⊏ 🌳🌳 ⛰
Leisure activities : 🍴 🗙 🖻 🗟 🤸 🏄 🛌 🚣 🖕 multi-sports ground
Facilities : 🖕 ⛇ 🎽 🗟 🍴 launderette 🖭
Nearby : 🤸

Longitude : 4.40139
Latitude : 44.39695

⚠ International

📞 0475880099, www.internationalcamping07.com

Address : La Plaine Salavas (located 1km southwest)

2.7 ha (120 pitches) relatively flat, flat, grassy, sandy

Rentals : 14 🛏 – 2 🏠.

Choose the pitches away from the bridge and beside the Ardèche river.

Surroundings : ⊏ 🌳🌳 ⛰
Leisure activities : 🍴 🗙 🏄 🛌
Facilities : 🖕 ⛇ 🎽 🗟 🖭 🍴

Longitude : 4.38203
Latitude : 44.39925

⚠ L'Esquiras

📞 0475880416. www.camping-esquiras.com

Address : chemin du Fez (2.8km northwest along the D 579, follow the signs for Ruoms and take the road to the right after the Intermarché service station)

Opening times : from beginning April to end Sept.

2 ha (106 pitches) relatively flat, flat, grassy, stony

Tariff : (2014 Price) 34€ ♣♣ ⇦ 🖭 🗟 (10A) – Extra per person 7.50€ Reservation fee 16€

Rental rates : (2014 Price) (from beginning April to end Sept.) – 40 🛏. Per night from 44 to 155€ – Per week from 308 to 1,085€ Reservation fee 16€

🖭 borne 4€ – 6 🖭 10€

In a green setting with a plenty of room in which to unwind; mobile homes of a good standard.

Surroundings : 🏊 ⩽ 🌳🌳
Leisure activities : 🗙 🖻 🏄 🚣
Facilities : 🖕 ⛇ 🖭 🎽 🍴 🗟
Nearby : forest trail

Longitude : 4.37913
Latitude : 44.41536

⚠ La Rouvière ♣♣

📞 0475371007, www.campinglarouviere.com

Address : route des Gorges Chames (6.6km southeast along the D 290; at Chames)

3 ha (153 pitches) terraced, relatively flat, sandy

Rentals : 39 🛏 – 3 tent lodges.

Below the road, beside the Ardèche river, with well-organised canoeing activities.

Surroundings : 🌳🌳 ⛰
Leisure activities : 🗙 🤸 🏄 🚣 🖕 multi-sports ground
Facilities : ⛇ 🎽 🍴 🖭 🖭

Longitude : 4.42649
Latitude : 44.37796

⚠ Le Midi

📞 0475880678, www.camping-midi.com

Address : route des Gorges de l'Ardèche (6.5km southeast along the D 290; at Chames)

Opening times : from mid March to end Sept.

1.6 ha (52 pitches) terraced, relatively flat, sandy, grassy

Tariff : 31€ ♣♣ ⇦ 🖭 🗟 (16A) – Extra per person 9€ – Reservation fee 10€

Rental rates : (from mid March to end Sept.) – 6 🛏. Per night from 70 to 120€ – Per week from 360 to 840€ – Reservation fee 10€

Below the road, a spacious site near the Ardèche river, with well-organised canoeing activities. Groups are welcome.

Surroundings : 🏊 ⊏ 🌳🌳 ⛰
Leisure activities : 🏄 🚣 🖕
Facilities : 🖕 ⛇ 🎽 🍴 🖭 🖭
Nearby : 🗙

Longitude : 4.42093
Latitude : 44.37672

VALLORCINE

74660 – Michelin map **328** O4 – pop. 419 – alt. 1 260 – Winter sports : 1 260/1 400 m

▶ Paris 628 – Annecy 115 – Chamonix-Mont-Blanc 19 – Thonon-les-Bains 96

⚠ Les Montets

📞 0679021881. www.camping-montets.fr – alt. 1 300 – ℞

Address : 671 route du Treuil, Le Montet (2.8km southwest along the N 506, access via Chemin de la Gare, at Le Buet)

Opening times : from beginning June to mid Sept.

1.7 ha (75 pitches) open site, terraced, relatively flat, flat, grassy, stony

Tariff : (2014 Price) ♣ 4.50€ ⇦ 1.50€ 🖭 5.90€ – 🗟 (6A) 3.50€

In a pleasant setting near a stream and the small railway line connecting St-Gervais with Châtelart (Switzerland).

Surroundings : 🏊 ⩽ 🌲
Leisure activities : 🗙
Facilities : 🖕 ⛇ 🅿 🎽 🖭
Nearby : 🦟 🚣

Longitude : 6.92376
Latitude : 46.02344

LES VANS

07140 – Michelin map **331** G7 – pop. 2 805 – alt. 170
▶ Paris 663 – Alès 44 – Aubenas 37 – Pont-St-Esprit 66

⚠ Le Pradal

✆ 04 75 37 25 16. www.camping-lepradal.com

Address : 1.5km west along the D 901

Opening times : from beginning April to end Sept.

1 ha (36 pitches) terraced, relatively flat, stony, grassy

Tariff : (2014 Price) 22.80€ ✦ ✦ ⇔ 🔲 ⑭ (6A) – Extra per person 6.50€
Rental rates : (from beginning April to end Sept.) – 3 🛏 – 1 🏠.
Per night from 50 to 70€ – Per week from 200 to 630€

🚐 borne 5€ – 4 🔲 19€

Numerous pitches on small, individual terraces enclosed by hedges.

Surroundings : ♤♤ Leisure activities : 🍸 🏖 🛶 multi-sports ground Facilities : 🛁 ⚡ 📮 🚻	**G P S** Longitude : 4.11023 Latitude : 44.40809

VERCHAIX

74440 – Michelin map **328** N4 – pop. 661 – alt. 800
▶ Paris 580 – Annecy 74 – Chamonix-Mont-Blanc 59 – Genève 52

⚠ Municipal Lac et Montagne

✆ 04 50 90 10 12. www.mairie-verchaix.fr – alt. 660

Address : 1.8km south along the D 907; beside the Giffre river

2 ha (104 pitches) open site, flat, grassy, stony

Choose the pitches furthest away from the busy road.

Surroundings : ≼ ♤ Leisure activities : 🛶 🎿 🎣 Facilities : 🛁 ⚡ 📮 launderette Nearby : 🍸 ✕ 🚻	**G P S** Longitude : 6.67527 Latitude : 46.09001

VERNIOZ

38150 – Michelin map **333** C5 – pop. 1 182 – alt. 250
▶ Paris 500 – Annonay 38 – Givors 25 – Le Péage-de-Roussillon 12

⚠ Le Bontemps

✆ 04 74 57 83 52. www.camping-lebontemps.com

Address : 5 impasse du Bontemps (4.5km east along the D 37 and take the road to the right; beside the Varèze river, at St-Alban-de-Varèze)

Opening times : from beginning April to end Sept.

6 ha (175 pitches)

Tariff : 29€ ✦ ✦ ⇔ 🔲 ⑭ (10A) – Extra per person 7€
Rental rates : (from beginning April to end Sept.) 🎿 – 7 🛏 – 3 🏠. Per night from 50 to 115€ – Per week from 300 to 805€

Surroundings : 🍃 🔲 ♤♤ Leisure activities : 🍸 ✕ 🏖 ⑭ 🎣 🛶 🚴 🎿 🚻 🛶 🎣 entertainment room Facilities : 🛁 ⚡ 🔲 🚿 🚽 🚻 launderette 🚿	**G P S** Longitude : 4.92836 Latitude : 45.42798

VILLARD-DE-LANS

38250 – Michelin map **333** G7 – pop. 4 031 – alt. 1 040
▶ Paris 584 – Die 67 – Grenoble 34 – Lyon 123

🏔 FranceLoc Domaine de L'Oursière

✆ 04 76 95 14 77. www.camping-oursiere.fr

Address : avenue du Général de Gaulle (take the northern exit along the D 531, follow the signs for Grenoble; pedestrian path to village)

Opening times : from mid Dec. to end March and from mid May to end Sept

4 ha (189 pitches) relatively flat, flat, grassy, gravelled, stony

Tariff : 28€ ✦ ✦ ⇔ 🔲 ⑭ (10A) – Extra per person 5€ – Reservation fee 11€

Rental rates : (2014 Price) (from mid Dec. to end March and from mid May to end Sept) – 49 🛏 – 4 🏠. Per night from 44 to 82€ – Per week from 175 to 700€ – Reservation fee 27€

🚐 borne 5€ – 30 🔲 22€

Surroundings : ❄ ≼ Leisure activities : 🏖 🛶 🚶 🎿 🎿 spa facilities Facilities : 🛁 ⚡ 🏧 🚿 🚻 🔲 🚿 Nearby : 🎳 bowling	**G P S** Longitude : 5.55639 Latitude : 45.0775

VILLARS-LES-DOMBES

01330 – Michelin map **328** D4 – pop. 4 328 – alt. 281
▶ Paris 433 – Bourg-en-Bresse 29 – Lyon 37 – Villefranche-sur-Saône 29

🏔 Indigo Parc des Oiseaux 👥

✆ 04 74 98 00 21. www.lenidduparc – limited spaces for one-night stay

Address : 164 avenue des Nations (southwestern exit, RD 1083 following signs for Lyon and take a left turn; near the swimming pool)

Opening times : from mid April to end Oct.

5 ha (191 pitches)

Tariff : 26.90€ ✦ ✦ ⇔ 🔲 ⑭ (6A) – Extra per person 5.50€ – Reservation fee 10€

Rental rates : (from mid April to end Oct.) 🎿 – 4 caravans – 4 🛏 – 20 tent lodges. Per night from 65 to 110€ – Per week from 390 to 660€ – Reservation fee 10€

🚐 borne 5€ – 46 🔲 22.40€

In a pleasant setting in partial shade beside the Chalaronne river.

Surroundings : 🍃 🔲 ♤ Leisure activities : ✕ 🏖 🚶 🛶 🚴 🎣 Facilities : 🛁 ⚡ 🚿 🚻 launderette Nearby : 🎿 🎣 🛶 🎿	**G P S** Longitude : 5.03039 Latitude : 45.99749

Key to rentals symbols:

12 🛏	*Number of mobile homes*
20 🏠	*Number of chalets*
6 🛏	*Number of rooms to rent*
Per night 30–50€	*Minimum/maximum rate per night*
Per week 300–1,000€	*Minimum/maximum rate per week*

We have selected the best campsites in France with our usual care, listing those with the best facilities in the most pleasant surroundings.

VINSOBRES

26110 – Michelin map **332** D7 – pop. 1 109 – alt. 247
▶ Paris 662 – Bollène 29 – Grignan 24 – Nyons 9

▵▵▵ Franceloc Le Sagittaire ▵▵

✆ 04 75 27 00 00. www.campings-franceloc.fr

Address : le Pont de Mirabel (Junction of D 94 and D 4, near the Eygues (direct access)

Opening times : Permanent

14 ha/8 for camping (274 pitches)

Tariff : (2014 Price) 44€ ★★ ⛺ 🔲 🔌 (10A) – Extra per person 8€ – Reservation fee 27€

Rental rates : (2014 Price) Permanent – 6 caravans – 118 🚐 – 60 🏠 – 4 tipis – 2 gîtes. Per night from 34 to 116€ – Per week from 168 to 1,505€ – Reservation fee 27€

There's an attractive swimming and play area.

Surroundings : ≼ ⊏⊐ ᴖᴖ
Leisure activities : ⬤ ✗ 🛏 🎣 ⛹ ⎵ 🐎
✂ 🎿 🔲 ⎵ ⛄ (fresh water) ⛷ 🦢 multi-sports ground
Facilities : ♿ ⚬⊶ ⫿⫿⫿ ♨ ⚗ ⛱ 🅟 launderette
⚒ ⚗

G P S	Longitude : 5.08002
	Latitude : 44.22661

▵ Municipal

✆ 04 75 27 61 65. camping-municipal@club-internet.fr

Address : Champessier district (located south of the town along the D 190; by the stadium)

1.9 ha (70 pitches)

Rentals : 1 🚐.

Surroundings : ≼ ᴖᴖ
Leisure activities : 🛏
Facilities : ♿ ⚬⊶ 🅟 🔲 refrigerators

G P S	Longitude : 5.06594
	Latitude : 44.32912

These symbols are used for a campsite that is exceptional in its category:

▵▵▵...▵ *Particularly pleasant setting, quality and range of services available*

🦢🦢 *Tranquil, isolated site – quiet site, particularly at night*

≼≼ *Exceptional view – interesting or panoramic view*

VION

07610 – Michelin map **331** K3 – pop. 905 – alt. 128
▶ Paris 537 – Annonay 30 – Lamastre 34 – Tournon-sur-Rhône 7

▵▵ L'Iserand

✆ 04 75 08 01 73. www.iserandcampingardeche.com

Address : 1307 rue Royale (located 1km north along the N 86, follow the signs for Lyon)

1.3 ha (60 pitches)

Rentals : ⛺ – 8 🚐 – 8 🏠.

Choose those pitches furthest away from the road out of preference.

Surroundings : ≼ ᴖᴖ
Leisure activities : ✗ 🛏 🎣 ⎵
Facilities : ♿ ⚬⊶ 🅟 🔲 ⚗

G P S	Longitude : 4.80027
	Latitude : 45.12117

VIZILLE

38220 – Michelin map **333** H7 – pop. 7 592 – alt. 270
▶ Paris 582 – Le Bourg-d'Oisans 32 – Grenoble 20 – La Mure 22

▵ Le Bois de Cornage

✆ 06 83 18 17 87, www.campingvizille.com

Address : chemin du Camping (take the northern exit towards the N 85, follow the signs for Grenoble and turn right onto av. de Venaria)

Opening times : from beginning April to end Oct.

2.5 ha (128 pitches) terraced, relatively flat, grassy

Tariff : 21€ ★★ ⛺ 🔲 🔌 (16A) – Extra per person 5.30€ – Reservation fee 10€

Rental rates : Permanent – 22 🚐. Per night from 45 to 55€ – Per week from 260 to 485€ – Reservation fee 10€

🚰 borne 3.50€

Partially shaded by centuries-old trees.

Surroundings : 🦢 ≼ ᴖᴖ
Leisure activities : ✗ 🛏 ⎵
Facilities : ⚬⊶ ⫿⫿⫿ ⛱ 🔲 ⚗

G P S	Longitude : 5.76948
	Latitude : 45.08706

*For more information on visiting particular towns or regions, consult the relevant regional **MICHELIN Green Guide**. We also recommend you use the appropriate Michelin regional map to locate your selected campsite, to calculate distances and to work out the best route.*

VOGÜÉ

07200 – Michelin map **331** I6 – pop. 917 – alt. 150
▶ Paris 638 – Aubenas 9 – Largentière 16 – Privas 40

▵▵▵ Domaine du Cros d'Auzon ▵▵

✆ 04 75 37 75 86. www.domaine-cros-auzon.com

Address : 2.5km south along the D 579 and take the road to the right

Opening times : from beginning April to mid Sept.

18 ha/6 for camping (170 pitches)

Tariff : 20€ ★★ ⛺ 🔲 🔌 (6A) – Extra per person 4€ – Reservation fee 12€

Rental rates : (from beginning April to mid Sept.) ♿ (5 mobile homes) – 37 🚐 – 4 🏠 – 37 🏡. Per night from 31 to 148€ – Per week from 217 to 1,036€ – Reservation fee 12€

🚰 borne

The lower part of the site is near the river with shaded pitches, the upper part includes the services: water park, restaurant, hotel.

Surroundings : 🦢 ⊏⊐ ᴖᴖ
Leisure activities : ⬤ ✗ 🛏 🎣 ⛹ 🛏 ✂
🔲 ⎵ ⛄⛷
Facilities : ♿ ⚬⊶ ⚗ ⛱ ⛱ 🅟 launderette ⚗

G P S	Longitude : 4.40678
	Latitude : 44.53178

Michelin classification:

▵▵▵▵ *Extremely comfortable, equipped to a very high standard*

▵▵▵ *Very comfortable, equipped to a high standard*

▵▵▵ *Comfortable and well equipped*

▵▵ *Reasonably comfortable*

▵ *Satisfactory*

⚠ Les Roches

✆ 04 75 37 70 45. www.campinglesroches.fr

Address : Bausson district (located 1.5km south along the D 579; at Vogüé-Gare, 200m from the Auzon and the Ardèche rivers)

Opening times : from beginning May to end Aug.

2.5 ha (100 pitches)

Tariff : (2014 Price) 26€ ✦✦ ⇔ 🔲 ⚡ (10A) – Extra per person 6.50€
Rental rates : (2014 Price) (from beginning May to end Aug.) ⚡ – 8 🚐. Per week from 350 to 650€

🚰 borne 4€

Shaded pitches on small terraces, in a wild setting among rocks.

	Longitude : 4.41406
Surroundings : 🏞 ♤♤	Latitude : 44.542
Leisure activities : ⛾ 🖼 🏊 ⛷	
Facilities : ♿ ⊶ 🚻 🏕 launderette, refrigerators	
Nearby : 🏊	

⚠ Les Peupliers

✆ 04 75 37 71 47, www.campingpeupliers.com

Address : Gourgouran (head 2km south along the D 579 and take the road to the right; at Vogüé-Gare)

3 ha (100 pitches)

Rentals : 10 🚐 – 9 🏠.

Some pitches and rental accommodation beside the Ardèche river, some of the rental options are a bit old.

	Longitude : 4.411
Surroundings : 🏞 ♤♤	Latitude : 44.53765
Leisure activities : ⛾ ✕ 🏊 ⛷ 🏊 ⤵	
Facilities : ⊶ 🏕 launderette	

⚠ Les Chênes Verts

✆ 04 75 37 71 54. www.camping-chenesverts.com

Address : Champ Redon (1.7km southeast along the D 103)

Opening times : from mid May to mid Sept.

2.5 ha (37 pitches)

Tariff : (2014 Price) 26€ ✦✦ ⇔ 🔲 ⚡ (16A) – Extra per person 4€
Rental rates : (from beginning April to end Sept.) – 26 🏠. Per night from 57 to 120€ – Per week from 270 to 850€ – Reservation fee 25€

A well shaded site, laid out on terraces above the road, but few pitches for tents and caravans.

	Longitude : 4.42075
Surroundings : ♤♤	Latitude : 44.54425
Leisure activities : ✕ 🏊 ⛷	
Facilities : ♿ ⊶ 🏕 🖼 ⤵	

Michelin classification:

⚠⚠⚠⚠ *Extremely comfortable, equipped to a very high standard*

⚠⚠⚠ *Very comfortable, equipped to a high standard*

⚠⚠⚠ *Comfortable and well equipped*

⚠⚠ *Reasonably comfortable*

⚠ *Satisfactory*

CANILLO

AD100 – Michelin map **343** H9 – pop. 4 826 – alt. 1 531
▶ Andorra-la-Vella 13 – Barcelona 207 – Foix 88 – Perpignan 152

⛰ Santa-Creu

🖉 (00-376) 85 14 62, www.elsmeners.com

Address : in the town (beside the Valira-del-Orient (left bank)

Opening times : from mid June to mid Sept.

0,5 ha terraced, relatively flat, grassy

Tariff : 🧍 4.30€ 🚗 4.30€ 🔲 4.30€ 🔌 (3A)

In a green setting with plenty of shade, near the town centre.

Surroundings : ⇔ ♀
Leisure activities : 🍸
Facilities : ♿ ⚿ 🛒 🗑 ▾ 🔳

GPS Longitude : 1.59978
Latitude : 42.56579

⛰ Jan-Ramon

🖉 (00-376) 75 14 54, www.elsmeners.com

Address : carretera General (400m northeast following signs for Port d'Envalira; beside the Valira del Orient (left bank)

Opening times :

0.6 ha flat, grassy

Tariff : 🧍 4.30€ 🚗 4.30€ 🔲 4.30€ 🔌 (3A)

Rental rates : (2014 Price) Permanent – 5 🏠. Per night from 73 to 83€ – Per week from 511 to 581€

A pleasant and partially shaded site, but there is noise from the nearby road.

Surroundings : ⇔ ♀
Leisure activities : 🍸 ✕
Facilities : ⚿ 🗑 ▾ 🔳 🍽

GPS Longitude : 1.59975
Latitude : 42.56594

For more information on visiting particular towns or regions, consult the relevant regional MICHELIN Green Guide. We also recommend you use the appropriate Michelin regional map to locate your selected campsite, to calculate distances and to work out the best route.

LA MASSANA

AD400 – Michelin map **343** H9 – pop. 9 744 – alt. 1 241
▶ Andorra-la-Vella 6 – Barcelona 204 – Foix 101 – Perpignan 164

⛰ Xixerella

🖉 (00-376) 73 86 13, www.xixerellapark.com – alt. 1 450

Address : Xixerella (3.5km northeast along the CG 4 then continue to Erts, taking turning to the left)

Opening times : from beginning Dec. to end Sept.

5 ha terraced, relatively flat, stony, grassy

Tariff : (2014 Price) 🧍 6,60€ 🚗 6,60€ 🔲 13,20€ – 🔌 (6A) 6,60€

Rental rates : (2014 Price) (from beginning Dec. to end Oct.) – 13 🏠 – 28 apartments. Per week from 972 to 1,224€

A shady grass area for tents and caravans; a range of rental options of good quality.

Surroundings : ⇔ ♀♀
Leisure activities : 🍸 ✕ 🏠 🈺 hammam, jacuzzi 🏊 ▸ 🔳
Facilities : ♿ ⚿ 🗑 🕋 ▾ 🍽 launderette 🔲 🍽

GPS Longitude : 1.48882
Latitude : 42.55327

ORDINO

AD300 – Michelin map **343** H9 – pop. 4 322 – alt. 1 304
▶ Andorra-la-Vella 8 – Barcelona 207 – Foix 105 – Perpignan 168

⛰ Borda d'Ansalonga

🖉 (00-376) 85 03 74, www.campingansalonga.net

Address : carretera Général del Serrat (2.3km northwest along the CG-3, follow the signs for Le Circuit de Tristaina; beside the Valira del Nord river)

Opening times : from beginning June to mid Sept.

3 ha flat, grassy

Tariff : (2014 Price) 25€ 🧍🧍 🚗 🔲 🔌 (10A) – Extra per person 7€

A shady, grassy site, but choose the pitches near the stream and away from the road in preference.

Surroundings : ⇔ ♀♀
Leisure activities : 🍸 ✕ 🏠 🏊 🛶
Facilities : ♿ ⚿ 🗑 🕋 ▾ launderette 🍽

GPS Longitude : 1.52162
Latitude : 42.56855

Michelin Travel Partner

Société par actions simplifiées au capital de 11 288 880 EUR
27 cours de l'Ile Seguin – 92100 Boulogne Billancourt (France)
R.C.S. Nanterre 433 677 721

No part of this publication may be reproduced in any form
without the prior permission of the publisher.

© Michelin Travel Partner
ISBN 978-2-067202-61-0

Although the information in this guide was believed by the authors
and publisher to be accurate and current at the time of publication,
they cannot accept responsibility for any inconvenience, loss, or injury
sustained by any person relying on information or advice contained
in this guide. Things change over time and travellers should take
steps to verify and confirm information, especially time-sensitive
information related to prices, hours of operation, and availability.

Layout: Jean-Luc Carnet
Translation: JMS Books llp (www.jmswords.com)
Layout of English edition: Chris Bell, cbdesign
Printed: February 2015
Printed and bound in Italy
Printed on paper from sustainable forests